QPB BOOK OF

IRISH

LITERATURE

IRELAND

QPB BOOK OF

⚹

IRISH

LITERATURE

Quality Paperback Book Club
New York

Edited by Kathy Kiernan

Additional material selected by Virginia Clerkin

Book design, illustrations, and map of Ireland by Felicia Telsey-MacKinnon

Acknowledgment of permission to reprint copyright material can be found starting on page 945.

All best efforts have been made to contact the owners of copyrighted material reprinted here. The editor would be pleased to hear from copyright holders who could not be found so that proper acknowledgments might be made.

QPB Book of Irish Literature is a publication of Quality Paperback Book Club, 1271 Avenue of the Americas, New York, NY 10020.

Printed in the United States of America

CONTENTS

INTRODUCTION

⭣

THERE ARE NOT VERY MANY countries other than Ireland whose literature could command its own 960-page anthology. (And, indeed, this book easily could have been three times as long.) Four of Ireland's writers have been awarded the Nobel Prize for Literature: W. B. Yeats, George Bernard Shaw, Samuel Beckett, and Seamus Heaney. Also indicative of the Irish passion and genius for words: they turn to the pen rather than the brush; the great Irish painters can be counted on one hand. The Quality Paperback Book Club editorial team felt the world needed a book that would do justice to the centuries of great Irish writing, and being lovers of Irish literature ourselves, we felt up to the task.

With an abundance of Irish literary gems to choose from, it was painful to make selections here. We had to ask, how many plays can one anthology handle? How much poetry? Sometimes, we uncovered intriguing and unconventional pieces. The great playwright Sean O'Casey is represented here, for example, but with a short story; poet Louis MacNeice couldn't be forgotten either, but we've chosen to represent his critical skills with a piece that reviews two books about James Joyce. Lord Dunsany's greatest fame was as a playwright, but he also wrote wonderful short stories; we include "The Hashish Man."

Also somewhat surprising: many of the pieces here involve great Irish writers commenting on their fellow great Irish writers. Along with MacNeice on Joyce, we've got Beckett on Joyce, Flann O'Brien on Joyce, Shaw on Oscar Wilde, Austin Clarke on Jonathan Swift, and Thomas D'Arcy McGee on Thomas Moore. Even when individual selections are not specifically about an Irish writer, one or two are often mentioned within the pieces. (As is the complicated and bloody history of Ireland.) The Irish seem more self-referential than most.

We have tried to represent the full range of genres Irish writers have mastered. There are three jail memoirs spanning one hundred years: John Mitchel's *Jail Journal*, Oscar Wilde's *The Ballad of Reading Gaol*, and Brendan Behan's *Borstal Boy*. We've got science fiction and horror, too: respectively Fitz-James O'Brien's "The Diamond Lens" and Sheridan Le Fanu's "Carmilla," and the aforementioned story from Lord Dunsany, "The Hashish Man," which strikes us as just plain weird. We have Irish folktales (but not too many; since these are anthologized elsewhere) and fiction by some of the most recently published Irish writers: Emer Martin, Patrick McCabe, Colum McCann, and Niall Williams.

INTRODUCTION

With one notable exception, the selections are arranged chronologically. We found that there are at least three Irish literary dynasties: the Sheridans, the Wildes, and the O'Faolains, and have grouped the writings of each family together.

As much as American readers like the Irish, we don't keep their books in print. *Borstal Boy*, Ireland's sixth-bestselling book of all time, is no longer available in the United States; you'll find a sizable excerpt—almost half of it—here. Francis MacManus's *Fire in the Dust*, a truly brilliant novel, is also out of print, as is the work of Mary Lavin, a master of the short story; Brian Moore's early novels; James Joyce's poetry; Sean O'Faolain's collected stories; and Sean O'Casey's fiction. *Jail Journal*, considered to be one of the greatest accounts of prison life, could be found only in the vaults of the New York Public Library, which is also where we finally located a copy of Frances Sheridan's *Memoirs of Miss Sidney Bidulph*. Other great rediscoveries here are Liam O'Flaherty, Benedict Kiely, and Patrick Kavanagh, all of whom were new to us, each of whom is shockingly good.

And one more thing. The word "bog" appears in about half of the selections. What could be more Irish than that?

QPB BOOK OF

IRISH

LITERATURE

EDMUND SPENSER

FROM
COLIN CLOUTS
COME HOME AGAINE

In his December 27, 1591, letter dedicating "Colin Clouts Come Home Againe" to his friend and patron Sir Walter Raleigh, Edmund Spenser describes the poem as a simple pastoral, but his allusion to "the malice of evil mouthes" that he encountered during his recent visit to London is more fully developed in a poem that is not as simple as he pretends. While the poem contains a number of lovely lyric passages (often in the form of implied tributes to Queen Elizabeth I as the poet's exalted object of adoration) in its nearly thousand lines, it also features a stinging rebuke of courtly life, and a kind of validation of Spenser's relatively simpler mode of existence in Ireland. Two excerpts follow.

> "Ah far be it (quoth Colin Clout) fro me,
> That I of gentle Mayds should ill deserve!
> For that my selfe I do professe to be
> Vassall to one, whom all my dayes I serve;
> The beame of beautie sparkled from above,
> The floure of vertue and pure chastitie,
> The blossome of sweet joy and perfect love,
> The pearle of peerlesse grace and modestie:
> To her my thoughts I daily dedicate,
> To her my heart I nightly martyrize:
> To her my love I lowly do prostrate,
> To her my life I wholly sacrifice:
> My thought, my heart, my love, my life is shee,
> And I hers ever onely, ever one:
> One ever I all vowed hers to bee,
> One ever I, and others never none."

"Why Colin, since thou foundst such grace
With Cynthia and all her noble crew;
Why didst thou ever leave that happie place,
In which such wealth might unto thee accrew;
And back returnedst to this barrein soyle,
Where cold and care and penury do dwell,
Here to keep sheepe, with hunger and with toyle?
Most wretched he, that is and cannot tell."

 "Happie indeed (said Colin) I him hold,
That may that blessed presence still enjoy,
Of fortune and of envy uncomptrold,
Which still are wont most happie states t'annoy:
But I, by that which little while I prooved,
Some part of those enormities did see,
The which in Court continually hooved,
And followd those which happie seemd to bee.
Therefore I, silly man, whose former dayes
Had in rude fields bene altogether spent,
Durst not adventure such unknowen wayes,
Nor trust the guile of fortunes blandishment;
But rather chose back to my sheep to tourne,
Whose utmost hardnesse I before had tryde,
Then, having learnd repentance late, to mourne
Emongst those wretches which I there descryde."

 "Shepheard, (said Thestylis) it seems of spight
Thou speakest thus gainst their felicitie,
Which thou enviest, rather then of right
That ought in them blameworthie thou doest spie."

 "Cause have I none (quoth he) of cancred will
To quite them ill, that me demeand so well:
But selfe-regard of private good or ill
Moves me of each, so as I found, to tell
And eke to warne yong shepheards wandring wit,
Which, through report of that lives painted blisse,
Abandon quiet home to seeke for it,

And leave their lambes to losse, misled amisse.
For, sooth to say, it is no sort of life,
For shepheard fit to lead in that same place,
Where each one seeks with malice, and with strife,
To thrust downe other into foule disgrace,
Himselfe to raise: and he doth soonest rise
That best can handle his deceitfull wit
In subtil shifts, and finest sleights devise,
Either by slaundring his well-deemed name,
Through leasings lewd, and fained forgerie;
Or else by breeding him some blot of blame,
By creeping close into his secrecie;
To which him needs a guilefull hollow hart,
Masked with faire dissembling curtesie,
A filed toung, furnisht with tearmes of art,
No art of schoole, but Courtiers schoolery.
For arts of schoole have there small countenance,
Counted but toyes to busie ydle braines;
And there professours find small maintenance,
But to be instruments of others gaines.
Ne is there place for any gentle wit,
Unlesse to please it selfe it can applie;
But shouldred is, or out of doore quite shit,
As base, or blunt, unmeet for melodie.
For each mans worth is measured by his weed,*
As harts by hornes, or asses by their eares:
Yet asses been not all whose eares exceed,
Nor yet all harts that hornes the highest beares;
For highest lookes have not the highest mynd,
Nor haughtie words most full of highest thoughts:
But are like bladders blowen up with wynd,
That being prickt do vanish into noughts.
Even such is all their vaunted vanitie,
Nought else but smoke, and fumeth soone away.
Such is their glorie that in simple eie
Seeme greatest, when their garments are most gay.
So they themselves for praise of fooles do sell,
And all their wealth for painting on a wall;
With price whereof they buy a golden bell,

* Clothes

3

And purchace highest rowmes in bowre and hall:
Whiles single Truth and simple Honestie
Do wander up and downe despys'd of all,
Their plaine attire such glorious gallantry
Disdaines so much, that none them in doth call."

FROM
A VIEW OF THE
PRESENT STATE OF IRELAND

Although he is famous as a poet, Edmund Spenser served for years as a minor colonial official in Ireland. A View of the Present State of Ireland, *written in dialogue form, was written in 1596, at a time of persistent local revolts. The following excerpt, recommending harsh measures for suppressing rebellion, is especially notable for its evocation of the ravages of war among the general population.*

EUDOX: YOU SPEAK NOW, Irenius, of an infinite charge to Her Majesty to send over such an army as should tread down all that standeth before them on foot and lay on the ground all the stiff necked people of that land, for there is now but one outlaw of any great reckoning, to wit, the Earl of Tyrone, abroad in arms, against whom you see what huge charges she hath been at this last year in sending of men providing of victuals and making head against him, yet there is little or nothing at all done. But the Queen's treasure spent, her people wasted, the poor country troubled, and the enemy nevertheless brought into no more subjection than he was, or list outwardly to show which in effect is none, but rather a scorn of her power, and enboldening of a proud rebel, and an encouragement unto all like lewd disposed traitors that shall dare to lift up their heel against their sovereign Lady, therefore it were hard counsel to draw such an exceeding charge upon her, whose event should be so uncertain.

Iren: True, indeed, if the event should be uncertain, but the certainty of the effect hereof shall be so infallible as that no reason can gainsay it, neither shall the charge of all this army which I demand be much greater than so much as in this last two years' wars, hath vainly been expended, for I dare undertake that it hath cost the Queen above 200,000 pounds already, and for the present charge that she is now at there, amounteth to very near 12,000 pounds a month, whereof cast ye the count; yet nothing done. The which sum, had it been employed as it should be, would have effected all this that I now go about.

Eudox: How mean you to have it employed, but to be spent in the pay of soldiers and provision of victual?

Iren: Right so, but it is now not disbursed at once as it might be, but drawn out into a long length, by sending over now 20,000 pounds, and next half year 10,000, so as the soldier in the meantime is for want of due provision of victual and good payment of his sold, starved and consumed, that of 1,000 which came over lusty, able men in half a year, there are not left 500 and yet is the Queen's charge nevertheless, but what is not paid in present money is accounted in debt, which will not be long unpaid, for the captain, half of whose soldiers are dead, and the other quarter never mustered nor seen, comes shortly to demand payment here of his whole account, where by good means of some great ones and privy sharing with the officers and servants of other some, he receiveth his debt, much less perhaps than was due, yet much more indeed than he justly deserved.

Eudox: I take this sure to be no good husbandry, for what must needs be spent, as good spent at once where is enough, as to have it drawn out into long delays, seeing that thereby both the service is much hindered and yet nothing saved, but it may be that the Queen's treasure in so great occasions of huge disbursements as it is well known she hath been at lately, is not always so ready, nor so plentiful as it can spare so great a sum together, but being paid as it is, now some and then some, it is no great burden unto her, nor any great impoverishing to her coffers, seeing by such delay of time that it daily cometh in so fast as she poureth it out.

Iren: It may be as you said, but for the going through of so honourable a course, I doubt not but if the Queen's coffers be not so well stored (which we are not to look into) but that the whole realm, which now (as things are used) do feel a continual burden of that wretched realm hanging upon their backs, would for a final riddance of that trouble be once troubled for all and put to all their shoulders and helping hands and hearts also to the defraying of that charge most gladfully and willingly, and surely the charge in effect is nothing to the infinite great good which should come thereby both to the Queen and all this realm generally, as when time serveth shall be showed.

Eudox: How many men then would you require to the finishing of this which ye take in hand, and how long space would you have them entertained?

Iren: Verily, not about 10,000 footmen and 1,000 horse, and all those not above the space of one year and a half, for I would still, as the heat of the service abateth, abate the number in pay, and make other provision for them, as I will show.

Eudox: Surely, it seemeth not much that ye require, nor no long time, but how would you have them used? Would you lead forth your army against the enemy and seek him where he is to fight?

Iren: No, Eudoxius, that would not be, for it is well known that he is a flying enemy, hiding himself in woods and bogs, from whence he will not draw forth but into some strait passage or perilous ford where he knows the army must needs pass, there will he lie in wait, and if he find advantage fit, will dangerously hazard the troubled soldier, therefore to seek him out that still flyeth, and follow him that can hardly be found were vain and bootless, but I would divide my men in garrison upon his country, in such places as I should think might most annoy him.

Eudox: But how can that be, Irenius, with so few men? For the enemy as ye now see is not all in one country, but some in Ulster, some in Connaught, and others in Leinster, so as to plant strong garrisons in all these places should need many more men than you speak of, or to plant all in one and to leave the rest naked, should be but to leave them to the spoil.

Iren: I would wish the chief power of the army to be garrisoned in one country, that is strongest, and the other upon the rest that are weakest. As for example, the Earl of Tyrone is now counted the strongest. Upon him would I lay 8,000 men in garrison, 1,000 upon Feagh MacHugh and the Cavanaghs, and 1,000 upon some parts of Connaught to be at the direction of the Governor.

Eudox: I see now all your men bestowed, but in what places would you set their garrison that they might rise out most conveniently to service? And though perhaps I am ignorant of the places, yet I will take the map of Ireland before me and make my eyes in the meanwhile my schoolmasters to guide my understanding to judge of your plot.

Iren: These 8,000 of Ulster I would divide likewise into four parts, so as there should be 2,000 footmen in every garrison, the which I would thus place: upon the Black-Water in some convenient place, as high upon the river as might be, I would lay one garrison; another would I put at Castleliffer or Castlefynn or thereabouts, so as they should have all the passages upon the river to Loughfoyle; the third I would place about Fermanagh or Bondroise, so as they might lie between Connaught and Ulster, to serve upon both sides as occasion shall be offered, and this therefore would I have stronger than any of the rest, because it should be most enforced and most employed, and that they might put wards as Ballashanie, Belike and all those passages. The rest would I set about Monaghan, or Belterbert, so as it should front both upon the enemy that way, and also keep the county of Cavan and Meath in awe from passing of stragglers and outgadders from those parts whence they use to come forth and oftentimes work much mischief; and to every of these garrisons of 2,000 footmen I would have 200 horsemen added, for the one without the other can do but little service. The four garrisons thus being placed I would have to be victualled aforehand for half a year, which ye will say to be hard, considering the corruption and usual waste of victuals. But why should they not as well be victualled for so long time as the ships are, usually for a year, and sometimes two, seeing it is easier to keep them on land than on water? Their bread would I have in flour, so as it might be baked still to serve their necessary want, their drink also there brewed within them from time to time, and their beef before hand barrelled, the which may be used but as it is needed, for I make no doubt but fresh victual they will sometimes purvey themselves amongst the enemy's creet. Hereunto would I also have them a store of hose and shoes with such other necessaries as may be needful for soldiers, so as they should have no occasion to look for relief from abroad, or occasion such trouble for their continual supply, as I see and have often proved in Ireland to be cumbrous to the deputy, and more dangerous to them that relieve them than half the leading of an army, for the enemy, knowing the ordinary ways by which their relief must be brought them, useth commonly to draw himself into the strait passages thitherward, and oftentimes doth dangerously distress them. Besides the pay of such force as should be sent for their convoy, the charge of the carriages, the exactions of the country shall be spared. But only every half year, the supply brought by the deputy himself and his power, who shall then visit and overlook all those garrisons, to see what is needed, to change what is expedient, and to direct what he shall best advise. And these four garrisons, issuing forth at such convenient times as they shall have intelligence or espial upon the enemy, will so drive him from one stead to another, and tennis him amongst them, that he shall find nowhere safe to keep his creet nor hide himself, but flying from the fire shall fall into the water, and out of one danger into another, that in short time his creet, which is his most sustenance, shall be wasted with preying, or killed with driving, or starved for want of pasture in the woods, and he himself brought so low that he shall have no heart nor ability to endure his wretchedness; the which will surely come to pass in very short space, for one winter's well following of him will so pluck him on his knees that he will never be able to stand up again.

Eudox: Do you then think the wintertime fittest for the services of Ireland? How falls it then that our most employments be in summer, and the armies then led commonly forth?

Iren: It is surely misconceived, for it is not with Ireland as with other countries, where the wars flame most in summer, and the helmets glister brightest in the fair sunshine, but in Ireland the winter yieldeth best services, for then the trees are bare and naked, which use both to clothe and house the kerne, the ground is cold and wet which useth to be his bedding, the air is sharp and bitter which useth to blow through his naked sides and legs, the kine are barren and without milk, which useth to be his only food; neither if he kill them, then will they yield him flesh, nor if he keep them will they give him food, besides then being all in calf, for the most part they will through much chasing and driving, cast all their calves and lose all their milk which should relieve him the next summer after.

Eudox: I do well understand your reason, but by your leave I have heard it otherwise said of some that were outlaws, that in summer they kept themselves quiet, but in winter they would play their parts, and when the nights were longest, then burn and spoil most, so that they might safely return before day.

Iren: I have likewise heard and likewise seen proof thereof true, but that was of such outlaws as was either abiding in well inhabited countries, as in Munster or bordering to the English Pale, as Feagh MacHugh, the Cavanaghs, the Moores, the Dempseys, the Keetings, the Kellies, or such like. For for them indeed the winter is the fittest time for spoiling and robbing, because the nights are then as ye said longest and darkest, and also the countries all about are then fullest of corn and good provision to be everywhere gotten by them; but it is far otherwise with a strong peopled enemy, that possess a whole country, for the other being but a few are indeed privily lodged and kept in out villages and corners nigh the woods and mountains by some their privy friends to whom they bring their spoils and stealths, and of whom they continually receive secret relief; but the open enemy having all his country wasted, what by himself and what by the soldier, findeth then succour in no place, towns there are none of which he may get spoil, they are all burnt, country houses and farmers there are none, they be all fled, bread he hath none, he ploughed not in summer, flesh he hath, but if he kill it in winter he shall want milk in summer. Therefore, if they be well followed but one winter ye shall have little work with them in the next summer.

Eudox: I do now well perceive the difference, and do verily think that the winter time is their fittest for service, withal I perceive the manner of your handling the service by drawing sudden draughts upon the enemy when he looketh not for you, and to watch advantages upon him as he doth upon you, by which strait keeping of them in and not suffering them long at any time to rest, I must needs think that they will soon be brought low and driven to great extremities. All which when you have performed and brought them to the very last cast, suppose that either they will offer to come in unto you, and submit themselves, or that some of them will seek to withdraw themselves, what is your advice to do? Will you have them received?

Iren: No, but at the beginning of these wars, and when the garrisons are well planted and fortified, I would wish a proclamation were made generally to come to their knowledge that what persons soever would within twenty days absolutely submit themselves (excepting only the very principal and ringleaders), should find grace, I doubt not but upon the settling of these garrisons, such a terror and near consideration of their perilous estate will be stricken into most of them that they will covet to draw away from their leaders. And again I well know that the rebels themselves (as I saw by proof in the Desmonds' wars) will turn away all their rascal people whom they think unserviceable, as old men, women, children and hinds, which they call churls, which only waste their victuals and yield them no aid but their cattle, they will surely keep away. These therefore, though policy would turn them back again that they might the rather consume and afflict the other rebels, yet in a pitiful commiseration I would wish them to be received, the rather for that this base sort of people doth not for the most part rebel of himself, having no heart thereunto, but is of force drawn by the grand rebels into their action, and carried away with the violence of the stream, else he should be sure to lose all that he hath and perhaps his life also, the which now he carrieth unto them in hope to enjoy them there, but he is there by the strong rebels themselves soon turned out of all, so that the constraint hereof may in him deserve pardon. Likewise if any of their able men or gentlemen shall then offer to come away and to bring their creet with them, as some no doubt may steal them away privily, I wish them also to be received for the disabling of the enemy: but withal that good assurance may be taken for their true behaviour and absolute submission, and that they then be not suffered to remain any longer in those parts, no, nor about the garrison, but sent away into the inner parts of the realm and dispersed in such sort as they shall not come together, nor easily return if they would, for if they might be suffered to remain about the garrison and there inhabit as they will offer, to till the ground and yield a great part of the profit thereof and of their cattle to the Colonel, wherewith they have heretofore tempted many, they would (as I have by experience known) be ever after such a gall and inconvenience to them, as that their profit should not recompense their hurt, for they will privily relieve their friends that are forth, they will send the enemy secret advertisement of all their purposes and journeys which they mean to make upon them, they will also not stick to draw the enemy privily upon them, yea and to betray the fort itself, by discovery of all the defects and disadvantages if any be, to the cutting of all their throats. For avoiding whereof and many other inconveniences, I wish that they should be carried far from thence into some other parts, so that as I said they come in and submit themselves upon the first summons; but afterwards I would have none received, but left to their fortune and miserable end. My reason is, for that those which will afterwards remain without are stout and obstinate rebels, such as will never be made dutiful and obedient, nor brought to labour or civil conversation, having once tasted that licentious life, and being acquainted with spoil and outrages, will ever after be ready for the like occasions, so as there is no hope of their amendment or recovery, and therefore needful to be cut off.

Eudox: Surely of some desperate persons as wilfully follow the course of their own folly, there is no compassion to be had, and for the others ye have proposed a merciful means, much more than they have deserved. But what then shall be the conclusion of this war, for you have prefixed a short time of his continuance?

Iren: The end I assure me will be very short and much sooner than can be in so great a trouble (as it seemeth) hoped for. Although there should none of them fall by the sword, nor be slain by the soldier, yet thus being kept from manurance, and their cattle from running abroad by this hard restraint, they would quickly consume themselves and devour one another. The proof whereof I saw sufficiently ensampled in those late wars in Munster, for notwithstanding that the same was a most rich and plentiful country, full of corn and cattle, that you would have thought they would have been able to stand long, yet ere one year and a half they were brought to such wretchedness, as that any stony heart would have rued the same. Out of every corner of the woods and glens they came creeping forth upon their hands, for their legs could not bear them. They looked anatomies of death, they spake like ghosts crying out of their graves, they did eat of the dead carrions, happy were they could find them, yea and one another soon after in so much as the very carcasses they spared not to scrape out of their graves, and if they found a plot of water cress or shamrocks, there they flocked as to a feast for the time, yet not able long to continue therewithal, that in short space there were none almost left and a most populous and plentiful country suddenly left void of man or beast. Yet sure in all that war there perished not many by the sword, but all by the extremity of famine, which they themselves had wrought.

BRIGHTNESS MOST BRIGHT

This eighteenth-century vision poem (aisling) *is a political allegory in which Ireland under English domination is portrayed as a sorrowful enchanted beauty.*

The Brightness of Brightness I saw in a lonely path,
Crystal of crystal, her blue eyes tinged with green,
Melody of melody, her speech not morose with age,
The ruddy and white appeared in her glowing cheeks.

Plaiting of plaiting in every hair of her yellow locks,
That robbed the earth of its brilliancy by their full sweeping,
An ornament brighter than glass on her swelling breast,
Which was fashioned at her creation in the world above.

A tale of knowledge she told me, all lonely as she was,
News of the return of HIM to the place which is his by
    kingly descent,
News of the destruction of the bands who expelled him,
And other tidings which, through sheer fear, I will not
    put in my lays.

Oh, folly of follies for me to go up close to her!
By the captive I was bound fast a captive;
As I implored the Son of Mary to aid me, she bounded
    from me,
And the maiden went off in a flash to the fairy
    mansion of Luachair.

BRIGHTNESS MOST BRIGHT

I rush in mad race running with a bounding heart,
Through margins of a morass, through meads, through
    a barren moorland,
I reach the strong mansion—the way I came I know not—
That dwelling of dwellings, reared by wizard sorcery.

They burst into laughter, mockingly—a troop of wizards
And a band of maidens, trim, with plaited locks;
In the bondage of fetters they put me without much
    respite,
While to my maiden clung a clumsy, lubberly clown.

I told her then, in words the sincerest,
How it ill became her to be united to an awkward,
    sorry churl,
While the fairest thrice over of all the Scotic race
Was waiting to receive her as his beauteous bride.

As she hears my voice she weeps through wounded pride,
The streams run down plenteously from her glowing cheeks,
She sends me with a guide for my safe conduct from
    the mansion,
She is the Brightness of Brightness I saw upon a lonely path.

THE BINDING

O my sickness, my misfortune, my fall, my sorrow, my loss!
The bright, fond, kind, fair, soft-lipped, gentle maiden,
Held by a horned, malicious, croaking, yellow clown, with
    a black troop!
While no relief can reach her until the heroes come back
    across the main.

—Translated by Patrick S. Dinneen

JONATHAN SWIFT

THE FURNITURE
OF A WOMAN'S MIND

The most brilliant satirist of all time, who just happens to be Irish, takes on the gentler sex in this poem from 1727.

A set of Phrases learn't by Rote;
A Passion for a Scarlet-Coat;
When at a Play to laugh, or cry,
Yet cannot tell the Reason why:
Never to hold her Tongue a Minute;
While all she prates has nothing in it.
Whole Hours can with a Coxcomb sit,
And take his Nonsense all for Wit:
Her Learning mounts to read a Song,
But, half the Words pronouncing wrong;
Has ev'ry Repartee in Store,
She spoke ten Thousand Times before.
Can ready Compliments supply
On all Occasions, cut and dry.
Such Hatred to a Parson's Gown,
The Sight will put her in a Swown.
For Conversation well endu'd;
She calls it witty to be rude;
And, placing Raillery in Railing,
Will tell aloud your greatest Failing;
Nor makes a Scruple to expose
Your bandy Leg, or crooked Nose.
Can, at her Morning Tea, run o'er
The Scandal of the Day before.
Improving hourly in her Skill,
To cheat and wrangle at Quadrille.

THE FURNITURE OF A WOMAN'S MIND

In chusing Lace a Critick nice,
Knows to a Groat the lowest Price;
Can in her Female Clubs dispute
What Lining best the Silk will suit;
What Colours each Complexion match:
And where with Art to place a Patch.

If chance a Mouse creeps in her Sight,
Can finely counterfeit a Fright;
So, sweetly screams if it comes near her,
She ravishes all Hearts to hear her.
Can dext'rously her Husband teize,
By taking Fits whene'er she please:
By frequent Practice learns the Trick
At proper Seasons to be sick;
Thinks nothing gives one Airs so pretty;
At once creating Love and Pity.
If Molly happens to be careless,
And but neglects to warm her Hair-Lace,
She gets a Cold as sure as Death;
And vows she scarce can fetch her Breath.
Admires how modest Women can
Be so *robustious* like a Man.

In Party, furious to her Power;
A bitter Whig, or Tory sow'r;
Her Arguments directly tend
Against the Side she would defend:
Will prove herself a Troy plain,
From Principles the Whigs maintain;
And, to defend the Whiggish Cause,
Her Topicks from the Tories draws.

O yes! If any Man can find
More virtues in a Woman's Mind,
Let them be sent to Mrs. Harding;*
She'll pay the Charges to a Farthing:
Take Notice, she has my Commission
To add them in the next Edition;
They may out-sell a better Thing;
So, Holla Boys; God save the King.

* A printer

16

A MODEST PROPOSAL

FOR PREVENTING THE CHILDREN OF POOR PEOPLE IN IRELAND FROM BEING A BURDEN TO THEIR PARENTS OR COUNTRY, AND FOR MAKING THEM BENEFICIAL TO THE PUBLIC

Inspired by his anger at the English landlords whose greediness, he felt, was devouring the Irish people, Jonathan Swift put together a proposal in 1729 that to this day sets a standard to which all satirists aspire.

I T IS A MELANCHOLY OBJECT to those who walk through this great town or travel in the country, when they see the streets, the roads, and cabin doors, crowded with beggars of the female sex, followed by three, four, or six children, all in rags and importuning every passenger for an alms. These mothers, instead of being able to work for their honest livelihood, are forced to employ all their time in strolling to beg sustenance for their helpless infants, who, as they grow up, either turn thieves for want of work, or leave their dear native country to fight for the Pretender in Spain, or sell themselves to the Barbadoes.

I think it is agreed by all parties that this prodigious number of children in the arms, or on the backs, or at the heels of their mothers, and frequently of their fathers, is in the present deplorable state of the kingdom a very great additional grievance; and therefore whoever could find out a fair, cheap, and easy method of making these children sound, useful members of the commonwealth would deserve so well of the public as to have his statue set up for a preserver of the nation.

But my intention is very far from being confined to provide only for the children of professed beggars; it is of a much greater extent, and shall take in the whole number of infants at a certain age who are born of parents in effect as little able to support them as those who demand our charity in the streets.

As to my own part, having turned my thoughts for many years upon this important subject, and maturely weighed the several schemes of other projectors, I have always found them grossly mistaken in their computation. It is true, a child just dropped from its dam may be supported by her milk for a solar year, with little other nourishment; at most not above the value of two shillings, which the mother may certainly get, or the value in scraps, by her lawful occupation of begging; and it is exactly at one year old that I propose to provide for them in such a manner as instead of being a charge upon their parents or the parish, or wanting food and raiment for the rest of their lives, they shall on the contrary contribute to the feeding, and partly to the clothing, of many thousands.

There is likewise another great advantage in my scheme, that it will prevent those voluntary abortions, and that horrid practice of women murdering their bastard children, alas, too frequent among us, sacrificing the poor innocent babes, I doubt, more to avoid the expense than the shame, which would move tears and pity in the most savage and inhuman breast.

The number of souls in this kingdom being usually reckoned one million and a half, of these I calculate there may be about two hundred thousand couples whose wives are breeders; from which number I subtract thirty thousand couples who are able to maintain their own children, although I apprehend there cannot be so many under the present distresses of the kingdom; but this being granted, there will remain an hundred and seventy thousand breeders. I again subtract fifty thousand for those women who miscarry, or whose children die by accident or disease within the year. There only remain an hundred and twenty thousand children of poor parents annually born. The question therefore is, how this number shall be reared and provided for, which, as I have already said, under the present situation of affairs, is utterly impossible by all the methods hitherto proposed. For we can neither employ them in handicraft or agriculture; we neither build houses (I mean in the country) nor cultivate land. They can very seldom pick up a livelihood by stealing till they arrive at six years old, except where they are of towardly parts; although I confess they learn the rudiments much earlier, during which time they can however be looked upon only as probationers, as I have been informed by a principal gentleman in the county of Cavan, who protested to me that he never knew above one or two instances under the age of six, even in a part of the kingdom so renowned for the quickest proficiency in that art.

I am assured by our merchants that a boy or a girl before twelve years old is no salable commodity; and even when they come to this age they will not yield above three pounds, or three pounds and half a crown at most on the Exchange; which cannot turn to account either to the parents or the kingdom, the charge of nutriment and rags having been at least four times that value.

I shall now therefore humbly propose my own thoughts, which I hope will not be liable to the least objection.

I have been assured by a very knowing American of my acquaintance in London, that a young healthy child well nursed is at a year old a most delicious, nourishing, and wholesome food, whether stewed, roasted, baked, or boiled; and I make no doubt that it will equally serve in a fricassee or a ragout.

I do therefore humbly offer it to public consideration that of the hundred and twenty thousand children, already computed, twenty thousand may be reserved for breed, whereof only one fourth part to be males, which is more than we allow to sheep, black cattle, or swine; and my reason is that these children are seldom the fruits of marriage, a circumstance not much regarded by our savages, therefore one male will be sufficient to serve four females. That the remaining hundred thousand may at a year old be offered in sale to the persons of quality and fortune through the kingdom, always advising the mother to let them suck plentifully in the last month, so as to render them plump and fat for a good table. A child will make two dishes at an entertainment for friends; and when the family dines alone, the fore or hind quarter will make a reasonable dish, and seasoned with a little pepper or salt will be very good boiled on the fourth day, especially in winter.

I have reckoned upon a medium that a child just born will weigh twelve pounds, and in a solar year if tolerably nursed increaseth to twenty-eight pounds.

I grant this food will be somewhat dear, and therefore very proper for landlords, who, as they have already devoured most of the parents, seem to have the best title to the children.

Infant's flesh will be in season throughout the year, but more plentiful in March, and a little before and after. For we are told by a grave author, an eminent French physician, that fish being a prolific diet, there are more children born in Roman Catholic countries about nine months after Lent than at any other season; therefore, reckoning a year after Lent, the markets will be more glutted than usual, because the number of popish infants is at least three to one in this kingdom; and therefore it will have one other collateral advantage, by lessening the number of Papists among us.

I have already computed the charge of nursing a beggar's child (in which list I reckon all cottagers, laborers, and four fifths of the farmers) to be about two shillings per annum, rags included; and I believe no gentleman would repine to give ten shillings for the carcass of a good fat child, which, as I have said, will make four dishes of excellent nutritive meat, when he hath only some particular friend or his own family to dine with him. Thus the squire will learn to be a good landlord, and grow popular among the tenants; the mother will have eight shillings net profit, and be fit for work till she produces another child.

Those who are more thrifty (as I must confess the times require) may flay the carcass; the skin of which artificially dressed will make admirable gloves for ladies, and summer boots for fine gentlemen.

As to our city of Dublin, shambles may be appointed for this purpose in the most convenient parts of it, and butchers we may be assured will not be wanting; although I rather recommend buying the children alive, and dressing them hot from the knife as we do roasting pigs.

A very worthy person, a true lover of his country, and whose virtues I highly esteem, was lately pleased in discoursing on this matter to offer a refinement upon my scheme. He said that many gentlemen of this kingdom, having of late destroyed their deer, he conceived that the want of venison might be well supplied by the bodies of young lads and maidens, not exceeding fourteen years of age nor under twelve, so great a number of both sexes in every county being now ready to starve for want of work and service; and these to be disposed of by their parents, if alive, or otherwise by their nearest relations. But with due deference to so excellent a friend and so deserving a patriot, I cannot be altogether in his sentiments; for as to the males, my American acquaintance assured me from frequent experience that their flesh was generally tough and lean, like that of our schoolboys, by continual exercise, and their taste disagreeable; and to fatten them would not answer the charge. Then as to the females, it would, I think with humble submission, be a loss to the public, because they soon would become breeders themselves: and besides, it is not improbable that some scrupulous people might be apt to censure such a practice (although indeed very unjustly) as a little bordering upon cruelty; which, I confess, hath always been with me the strongest objection against any project, how well soever intended.

But in order to justify my friend, he confessed that this expedient was put into his head by the famous Psalmanazar, a native of the island Formosa, who came from thence to London above twenty years ago, and in conversation told my friend that in his country when any young person happened to be put to death, the executioner sold the carcass to persons of quality as a prime dainty; and that in his time the body of a plump girl of fifteen, who was crucified for an attempt to poison the emperor, was sold to his Imperial Majesty's prime minister of state, and other great mandarins of the court, in joints from the gibbet, at four hundred crowns. Neither indeed can I deny that if the same use were made of several plump young girls in this town, who without one single groat to their fortunes cannot stir abroad without a chair, and appear at the playhouse and assemblies in foreign fineries which they never will pay for, the kingdom would not be the worse.

Some persons of a desponding spirit are in great concern about that vast number of poor people who are aged, diseased, or maimed, and I have been desired to employ my thoughts what course may be taken to ease the nation of so grievous an encumbrance. But I am not in the least pain upon that matter, because it is very well known that they are every day dying and rotting by cold and famine, and filth and vermin, as fast as can be reasonably expected. And as to the younger laborers, they are now in almost as hopeful a condition. They cannot get work, and consequently pine away for want of nourishment to a degree that if at any time they are accidentally hired to common labor, they have not strength to perform it; and thus the country and themselves are happily delivered from the evils to come.

I have too long digressed, and therefore shall return to my subject. I think the advantages by the proposal which I have made are obvious and many, as well as of the highest importance.

For first, as I have already observed, it would greatly lessen the number of Papists, with whom we are yearly overrun, being the principal breeders of the nation as well as our most dangerous enemies; and who stay at home on purpose to deliver the kingdom to the Pretender, hoping to take their advantage by the absence of so many good Protestants, who have chosen rather to leave their country than stay at home and pay tithes against their conscience to an Episcopal curate.

Secondly, the poorer tenants will have something valuable of their own, which by law may be made liable to distress, and help to pay their landlord's rent, their corn and cattle being already seized and money a thing unknown.

Thirdly, whereas the maintenance of an hundred thousand children, from two years old and upwards, cannot be computed at less than ten shillings a piece per annum, the nation's stock will be thereby increased fifty thousand pounds per annum, besides the profit of a new dish introduced to the tables of all gentlemen of fortune in the kingdom who have any refinement in taste. And the money will circulate among ourselves, the goods being entirely of our own growth and manufacture.

Fourthly, the constant breeders, besides the gain of eight shillings sterling per annum by the sale of their children, will be rid of the charge of maintaining them after the first year.

Fifthly, this food would likewise bring great custom to taverns, where the vintners will certainly be so prudent as to procure the best receipts for dressing it to perfection, and consequently have their houses frequented by all the fine gentlemen, who justly value themselves upon their knowledge in good eating; and a skillful cook, who understands how to oblige his guests, will contrive to make it as expensive as they please.

Sixthly, this would be a great inducement to marriage, which all wise nations have either encouraged by rewards or enforced by laws and penalties. It would increase the care and tenderness of mothers toward their children, when they were sure of a settlement for life to the poor babes, provided in some sort by the public, to their annual profit instead of expense. We should see an honest emulation among the married women, which of them could bring the fattest child to the market. Men would become as fond of their wives during the time of their pregnancy as they are now of their mares in foal, their cows in calf, or sows when they are ready to farrow; nor offer to beat or kick them (as is too frequent a practice) for fear of a miscarriage.

Many other advantages might be enumerated. For instance, the addition of some thousand carcasses in our exportation of barreled beef, the propagation of swine's flesh, and improvement in the art of making good bacon, so much wanted among us by the great destruction of pigs, too frequent at our tables, which are no way comparable in taste or magnificence to a well-grown, fat, yearling child, which roasted whole will make a considerable figure at a lord mayor's feast or any other public entertainment. But this and many others I omit, being studious of brevity.

Supposing that one thousand families in this city would be constant customers for infants' flesh, besides others who might have it at merry meetings, particularly weddings and christenings, I compute that Dublin would take off annually about twenty thousand carcasses, and the rest of the kingdom (where probably they will be sold somewhat cheaper) the remaining eighty thousand.

I can think of no one objection that will possibly be raised against this proposal, unless it should be urged that the number of people will be thereby much lessened in the kingdom. This I freely own, and it was indeed one principal design in offering it to the world. I desire the reader will observe, that I calculate my remedy for this one individual kingdom of Ireland and for no other that ever was, is, or I think ever can be upon earth. Therefore let no man talk to me of other expedients: of taxing our absentees at five shillings a pound: of using neither clothes nor household furniture except what is of our own growth and manufacture: of utterly rejecting the materials and instruments that promote foreign luxury: of curing the expensiveness of pride, vanity, idleness, and gaming in our women: of introducing a vein of parsimony, prudence, and temperance: of learning to love our country, in the want of which we differ even from Laplanders and the inhabitants of Topinamboo: of quitting our animosities and factions, nor acting any longer like the Jews, who were murdering one another at the very moment their city was taken: of being a little cautious not to sell our country and conscience for nothing: of teaching landlords to have at least one degree of mercy toward their tenants: lastly, of putting a spirit of honesty, industry, and skill into our shopkeepers; who, if a resolution could now be taken to buy only our native goods, would immediately unite to cheat and exact upon us in the price, the measure, and the goodness, nor could ever yet be brought to make one fair proposal of just dealing, though often and earnestly invited to it.

Therefore I repeat, let no man talk to me of these and the like expedients, till he hath at least some glimpse of hope that there will ever be some hearty and sincere attempt to put them in practice.

But as to myself, having been wearied out for many years with offering vain, idle, visionary thoughts, and at length utterly despairing of success, I fortunately fell upon this proposal, which, as it is wholly new, so it hath something solid and real, of no expense and little trouble, full in our own power, and whereby we can incur no danger in disobliging England. For this kind of commodity will not bear exportation, the flesh being of too tender a consistence to admit a long continuance in salt, although perhaps I could name a country which would be glad to eat up our whole nation without it.

After all, I am not so violently bent upon my own opinion as to reject any offer proposed by wise men, which shall be found equally innocent, cheap, easy, and effectual. But before something of that kind shall be advanced in contradiction to my scheme, and offering a better, I desire the author or authors will be pleased maturely to consider two points. First, as things now stand, how they will be able to find food and raiment for an hundred thousand useless mouths and backs. And secondly, there being a round million of creatures in human figure throughout this kingdom, whose sole subsistence put into a common stock would leave them in debt two millions of pounds sterling, adding those who are beggars by profession to the bulk of farmers, cottagers, and laborers, with their wives and children who are beggars in effect; I desire those politicians who dislike my overture, and may perhaps be so bold to attempt an answer, that they will first ask the parents of these mortals whether they would not at this day think it a great happiness to have been sold for food at a year old in the manner I prescribe, and thereby have avoided such a perpetual scene of misfortunes as they have since gone through by the oppression of landlords, the impossibility of paying rent without money or trade, the want of common sustenance, with neither house nor clothes to cover them from the inclemencies of the weather, and the most inevitable prospect of entailing the like or greater miseries upon their breed forever.

I profess, in the sincerity of my heart, that I have not the least personal interest in endeavoring to promote this necessary work, having no other motive than the public good of my country, by advancing our trade, providing for infants, relieving the poor, and giving some pleasure to the rich. I have no children by which I can propose to get a single penny; the youngest being nine years old, and my wife past childbearing.

FINNEGAN'S WAKE

This lilting lyric of a whiskey-borne resurrection, in which Tim Finnegan wakes at his own wake, may have provided James Joyce with the title of his own pun-filled masterpiece.

Tim Finnegan liv'd in Walkin Street
    a gentleman Irish mighty odd.
He had a tongue both rich and sweet,
    an' to rise in the world he carried a hod.
Now Tim had a sort of a tipplin' way,
    with the love of the liquor he was born,
An' to help him on with his work each day
    he'd a drop of the craythur ev'ry morn.

Chorus: Whack fol the dah,
        dance to your partner
      Welt the flure yer trotters shake
        Wasn't it the truth I told you,
         Lot's of fun at Finnegan's wake.

One morning Tim was rather full,
    His head felt heavy which made him shake,
He fell from the ladder and broke his skull,
    So they carried him home his corpse to wake,
They rolled him up in a nice clean sheet
And laid him out upon the bed,
With a gallon of whiskey at his feet,
    And a barrel of porter at his head.

His friends assembled at the wake,
    And Mrs. Finnegan called for lunch,
First they brought in tay and cake,
    The pipes, tobacco, and whiskey punch.
Miss Biddy O'Brien began to cry,
    "Such a neat clean corpse, did you ever see,
Arrah, Tim avourneen, why did you die?"
    "Ah, hould your gab," said Paddy McGee.

Then Biddy O'Connor took up the job,
    "Biddy," says she, "you're wrong, I'm sure,"
But Biddy gave her a belt in the gob,
    And left her sprawling on the floor;
Oh, then the war did soon enrage;
    'Twas woman to woman and man to man,
Shillelagh law did all engage,
    And a row and a ruction soon began.

Then Micky Maloney raised his head,
    When a noggin of whiskey flew at him,
It missed and falling on the bed,
    The liquor scattered over Tim;
Bedad he revives, see how he rises,
    And Timothy rising from the bed,
Says, "Whirl your liquor round like blazes,
    Thanam o'n dhoul, do ye think I'm dead?"

THE WEARIN' O' THE GREEN

This traditional Irish patriotic song, presented here in a translation by the popular nineteenth-century playwright Dion Boucicault, was inspired by government attempts to suppress the use of the shamrock as a symbol of Irish resistance to English rule.

Oh, Paddy dear! an' did ye hear the news that's goin' round?
The shamrock is by law forbid to grow on Irish ground.
No more St. Patrick's Day we'll keep, his color can't be seen,
For there's a cruel law agin the wearin' o' the green!

I met wid Napper Tandy, and he took me by the hand.
And he said, "How's poor Ould Ireland, and how does she stand?"
She's the most disthressful country that iver yet was seen,
For they're hangin' men and women there for wearin' o' the green.

An' if the color we must wear is England's cruel red,
Let it remind us of the blood that Ireland has shed;
Then pull the shamrock from your hat, and throw it on the sod,—
And never fear, 'twill take root there, tho' under foot 'tis trod!

When law can stop the blades of grass from growin' as they grow,
And when the leaves in summer-time their color dare not show,
Then I will change the color, too, I wear in my caubeen,
But till that day, plaze God, I'll stick to wearin' o' the green.

THE
SHERIDANS

ↆ

GENERATIONS OF SHERIDANS have formed a loosely knit literary dynasty for over two centuries. The founder of this tradition was Frances Chamberlaine Sheridan, the wife of Thomas Sheridan, an actor and theater manager. Frances, who was both a popular novelist and playwright, was the mother of the most illustrious (and notorious) member of this clan, the playwright, theater owner, and politician Richard Brinsley Sheridan. Born in Dublin like his mother, Richard was sent off to boarding school in England at the age of eleven and never returned to Ireland. Known primarily for his brilliant early dramatic work, filled with sparkling repartee and satire, Richard's fortunes declined throughout his life, but though he died in debt, his early achievements were never forgotten, and he lies buried in the Poets' Corner of Westminster Abbey. Shortly before his death, a niece of Sheridan gave birth (also in Dublin) to Joseph Sheridan Le Fanu, who became famous for his supernatural tales and novels of psychological suspense, quite a departure from the comic masterpieces of his distinguished forebears. A century later, Lady Caroline Blackwood was born at the family estate in County Down, a nobleman's daughter (whose mother was a Guinness) and the direct descendant of Richard Brinsley Sheridan (her great-great-grandmother, Sheridan's granddaughter, was rumored to have had a child by Benjamin Disraeli, thus enriching the Anglo-Irish mixture with a Jewish component). Lady Caroline, besides being an accomplished author, was married both to the artist Lucian Freud (Sigmund's grandson) and to the American poet Robert Lowell, with whom she had a son named Sheridan, thus extending the saga to yet another generation.

FROM
MEMOIRS OF
MISS SIDNEY BIDULPH

In the style of her friend Samuel Richardson's Pamela, *Mrs. Frances Sheridan published her popular first novel,* Memoirs of Miss Sidney Bidulph, *in 1761. Although* Pamela *continues to be read, Mrs. Sheridan's book does not, perhaps because of the melodramatic surplus of troubles piled upon her undeserving heroine. Here are the opening pages, in which Sidney's brother teases her with the possibility of a new suitor, "the prettiest fellow in England."*

MISS CATHARINE SIDNEY BIDULPH was the daughter of Sir Robert Bidulph of Wiltshire. Her father died when she was very young; and of ten children none survived him but this lady, and his eldest son, afterwards Sir George Bidulph. The family estate was not very considerable; and Miss Bidulph's portion was but four thousand pounds; a fortune however at that time not quite contemptible: it was in the beginning of Queen Anne's reign.

Lady Bidulph was a woman of plain sense, but exemplary piety; the strictness of her notions (highly commendable in themselves) now and then gave a tincture of severity to her actions, though she was ever esteemed a truly good woman.

She had educated her daughter, who was one of the greatest beauties of her time, in the strictest principles of virtue; from which she never deviated, through the course of an innocent though unhappy life.

Sir George Bidulph was nine or ten years older than his sister. He was a man of good understanding, moral as to his general conduct, but void of any of those refined sentiments, which constitute what is called delicacy. Pride is sometimes accounted laudable; that which Sir George possessed (for he had pride) was not of this kind.

He was of a weakly constitution, and he had been ordered by the physicians to Spa for the recovery of a lingering disorder, which he had laboured under for some time. It was just on his return to England that the busy scene of his sister's life opened. An intimate friend of hers, of her own sex, to whom she revealed all the secrets of her heart, happened at this juncture to go abroad, and it was for her perusal only the following journal was intended. That friend has carefully preserved it, as she thinks it may serve for an example, to prove that neither prudence, foresight, nor even the best disposition that the human heart is capable of, are of themselves sufficient to defend us against the inevitable ills that sometimes are allotted, even to the best. "The race is not to the swift, nor the battle to the strong."

THE JOURNAL

April 2, 1703. My dear and ever-beloved Cecilia is now on her way to Harwich. How insipid will this talk of recording all the little incidents of the day now appear to me, when you, my sister, friend of my heart, are no longer near me? How many tedious months will it be before I again embrace you? How many days of impatience must I suffer before I can even hear from you, or communicate to you the actions, the words, the thoughts of your Sidney?—But let me not grow plaintive, the style my friend hates. I should be ungrateful (if I indulged it) to the best of mothers, who, to gratify and amuse me on this first occasion of sorrow which I ever experienced, has been induced to quit her beloved retirement, and come on purpose to London, to rouse up my spirits, and, as she expresses herself, to keep me from the sin of murmuring.

Avaunt then complainings! Let me rest assured that my Cecilia is happy in her pursuits, and let me resolve on making myself so in mine.

April 3. We have had a letter from my brother George; he is landed, and we expect him hourly in town. As our house is large enough, I hope he will consent to take up his abode with us while we stay in London. My mother intends to request it of him: she says it will be for the *reputation* of a gay young man to live in a *sober* family. I know not how Sir George may relish the proposal, as our hours are not likely to correspond with those which I suppose he has been used to since he has been absent from us. But perhaps he may not refuse the compliment; Sir George is not averse to economy. —How kind, how indulgent, is this worthy parent of mine! She will not suffer me to stay at home with her, nay scarce allows me time for my journal. "Sidney, I won't have you stay within; I won't have you write; I won't have you think—I will make a rake of you; you shall go to the play tonight, and I am almost tempted to go with you myself, though I have not been at one since your father's death." These were her kind expressions to me just now. I am indeed indebted to her tenderness, when she relaxes so much of her usual strictness, as even to *think* of such a thing.

April 5. My brother returned to us this day, thank God! in perfect health. Never was there such an alteration seen in a man; he is grown fat, and looks quite robust. He dropped in upon us just as we sat down to dinner: what a clutter has his arrival made! My mother was *so* rejoiced, and *so* thankful, and *so* full of praises, and asked *so* many questions, that George could hardly find words enough to answer the over-flowings of her kind inquisitiveness, which lasted all the time of dinner.

When the cloth was removed, my mother proposed his taking up his abode with us: "You see," said she, "your sister and I have got here into a large house; there is full room enough in it for you and your servants; and as I think in such a town as this, it will be a reputable place for you to live in, I shall be glad of your company; provided you do not encroach upon my rules by unseasonable hours, or receiving visits from such as I may not approve of the acquaintance of your sister." I was afraid Sir George would disrelish the terms, as perhaps some of his acquaintance (though far from faulty ones) might fall within my mother's predicament: but I was mistaken, he accepted of the invitation, after making some slight apologies about the inconvenience of having so many servants: this however was soon got over.

To say the truth, I am very glad that my brother has consented to be our guest, as I hope by his means our circle of acquaintance will be a good deal enlarged. There is no pleasure in society, without a proper mixture of well-bred sensible people of both sexes, and I have hitherto been chiefly confined to those of my own.

I asked Sir George jocosely, what he had brought me home? He answered— "Perhaps a good husband." My mother catched up the word, "What do you mean, son?" —"I mean, Madam, that there is come over with me a gentleman, with whom I became acquainted in Germany, and whom of all the men I ever knew, I should wish to have for a brother. If Sidney should fortunately be born under the influence of *uncommonly* good stars, it may happen to be brought about. I can tell you," applying himself to me, "he is prepossessed in your favour already; I have shewn him some of your letters, and he thinks you a good sensible girl. I told him you were very well in your person, and that you have had an excellent education." —"I hope so," said my mother, looking pleased; "and what have you to tell us of this wonderful man that so much surpasses every body?" —"Why, Madam, for *your* part of his character, he is the best *behaved* young man I ever saw. I never knew any body equal to him for sobriety, nor so entirely free from all the other vices of youth: as I lived in the same house with him for some months I had frequent opportunities of making my observations. I have known him to *avoid* many irregularities, but never saw him guilty of *one*."

"An admirable character indeed," said my mother. So thought I too; but I wanted to know a little more of him. "Now, Sidney, for your share in the description; I must tell you he is most exquisitely handsome, and extremely sensible."

"Good sense to be sure is requisite," said my mother, "but as for beauty, it is but a fading flower at best, and in a man not at all necessary." —"A man is not the worst for it, however," cried my brother. "No," my mother answered, "provided it does not make him vain, and too fond of the admiration of giddy girls." —"That I will be sworn is not the case of my friend," answered Sir George; "I believe nobody with such a person as his (if there *can* be such another) would be so little vain of it; nay, I have heard him declare, that even in a woman he would give the preference to sense and virtue."

"Good young man!" cried my mother, "I should like to be acquainted with him." —"So should I," whispered I to my own heart.

"Well, brother," said I, "you have drawn a good picture; but to make it complete, you must throw in generosity, valour, sweetness of temper, and a great deal of money." —"Fie, my dear," said my good *literal* parent, "a *great deal* is not necessary; a very moderate fortune with *such* a man is sufficient."

"The good qualities you require in the finishing of my piece," answered my brother, "he possesses in an eminent degree—will that satisfy you? As for his fortune—*there* perhaps a difficulty may step in. What estate, Madam," to my mother, "do you think my sister's fortune may intitle her to?"

"Dear brother," I cried, "pray do not speak in that *bargaining* way."

My mother answered him very gravely, "Your father you know left her but four thousand pounds; it is in my power to add a *little* to it, if she marries to please me. Great matters we have no right to expect; but a *very* good girl, as my daughter is, I think, deserves something more than a bare equivalent." —"The equality," said my brother, with a demure look, "I fear is out of all proportion here, for the gentleman I speak of has but—six thousand pounds a year."

He burst out a laughing; it was not good-natured, and I was vexed at his joke. My poor mother dropped her countenance; I looked silly, as if I had been disappointed, but I said nothing.

"Then he is above our reach, Sidney," answered my mother.

I made no reply. "Have a good heart, Sid," cried my brother, "if my nonpareil likes you, when he sees you," I felt myself hurt, and grew red, "and without a compliment, sister," seeing me look mortified, "I think he will, fortune will be no objection. I have already told him the utmost extent of your expectations; he would hardly let me mention the subject; he has a mind for *my* sister, and if he finds personal accomplishments answer a brother's (perhaps partial) description, it will be your own fault if you have not the prettiest fellow in England for your husband."

My mother reassumed her pleased countenance. "Where is he? Let us see him." I forced a smile, though I did not feel myself quite satisfied. "We parted on the road," my brother answered; "he is gone to Bath for a few weeks; he has sent his servants and his baggage to town before him, and has commissioned me to take a house for him in St. James's Square or some of the adjacent streets; to that we shall have him in our neighbourhood."

My mother enquired on what account he went to Bath. Sir George said, he complained of a weakness in one of his wrists, which was the consequence of a fever that had seized him on his journey in their return to England. It seems he had finished his travels, on which he had been absent near five years, when my brother and he met in Germany. The liking he took to Sir George protracted his stay, and he resolved not to quit him while his health obliged him to continue abroad; they took a trip to Paris together, and returned home by Holland.

The name of this piece of perfection is Faulkland—Orlando Faulkland. What a pretty name Orlando is! My mother says it is romantic, and wonders how *sober* people can give their children such names.

Now am I dying with curiosity to see this man. A few weeks at Bath—what business he had to go to Bath till he had first settled his household at London? His wrist might have grown well without the pump. I am afraid he has gone to Bath only to shew himself, and that he will be snapped up before he comes to town. I wish Sir George had kept the account of him to himself, till he returned to London again.

THE
CRITIC

Richard Brinsley Sheridan's uproarious last play, The Critic, *or a* Tragedy Rehearsed, *was produced in 1779, after which he turned to politics. It mocks the theatre conventions and clichés of the period as critics Sneer and Dangle watch a rehearsal of* The Spanish Armada, *a shockingly bad new tragedy, which is penned by a public relations man called Puff, and features among its cast a man playing the river Thames.*

PROLOGUE

By the Honorable RICHARD FITZPATRICK

The Sister Muses, whom these realms obey,
Who o'er the Drama hold divided sway,
Sometimes, by evil counsellors, 'tis said
Like earth-born potentates have been misled:
In those gay days of wickedness and wit,
When Villiers criticiz'd what Dryden writ,
The Tragick Queen, to please a tasteless crowd,
Had learn'd to bellow, rant, and roar so loud,
That frighten'd Nature, her best friend before,
The blust'ring beldam's company forswore.
Her comic Sister, who had wit 'tis true,
With all her merits, had her failings too;
And would sometimes in mirthful moments use
A style too flippant for a well-bred Muse.
Then female modesty abash'd began

To seek the friendly refuge of the fan,
Awhile behind that slight entrenchment stood,
'Till driv'n from thence, she left the stage for good.
In our more pious, and far chaster times!
These sure no longer are the Muse's crimes!
But some complain that, former faults to shun,
The reformation to extremes has run.
The frantick hero's wild delirium past,
Now insipidity succeeds bombast;
So slow Melpomene's cold numbers creep,
Here dullness seems her drowsy court to keep,
And we, are scarce awake, whilst you are fast asleep.
Thalia, once so ill behav'd and rude,
Reform'd; is now become an arrant prude,
Retailing nightly to the yawning pit,
The purest morals, undefil'd by wit!
Our Author offers in these motley scenes,
A slight remonstrance to the Drama's queens,
Nor let the goddesses by over nice;
Free spoken subjects give the best advice.
Although not quite a novice in his trade,
His cause to night requires no common aid.
To this, a friendly, just, and pow'rful court,
I come Ambassador to beg support.
Can he undaunted, brave the critick's rage?
In civil broils, with brother bards engage?
Hold forth their errors to the publick eye,
Nay more, e'en News-papers themselves defy?
Say, must his single arm encounter all?
By numbers vanquish'd, e'en the brave may fall;
And though no leader should success distrust,
Whose troops are willing, and whose cause is just;
To bid such hosts of angry foes defiance,
His chief dependance must be, YOUR ALLIANCE.

ACT I

SCENE I

MR. *and* MRS. DANGLE *at Breakfast, and reading Newspapers.*

DANGLE. [*reading*] "Brutus to Lord North."—"Letter the second on the State of the Army"—Pshaw! "To the first L— dash D of the A— dash Y." "Genuine Extract of a Letter from St. Kitt's."—"Coxheath Intelligence"—"It is now confidently asserted that Sir Charles Hardy."—Pshaw!—Nothing but about the fleet, and the nation!—and I hate all politics but theatrical politics.—Where's the Morning Chronicle?

MRS. DANGLE. Yes, that's your gazette.

DANGLE. So, here we have it.—"*Theatrical intelligence extraordinary,*"——"We hear there is a new tragedy in rehearsal at Drury-lane Theatre, call'd the Spanish Armada, said to be written by Mr. Puff, a gentleman well known in the theatrical world; if we may allow ourselves to give credit to the report of the performers, who, truth to say, are in general but indifferent judges, this piece abounds with the most striking and received beauties of modern composition"—So! I am very glad my friend Puff's tragedy is in such forwardness.—Mrs. Dangle, my dear, you will be very glad to hear that Puff's tragedy——

MRS. DANGLE. Lord, Mr. Dangle, why will you plague me about such nonsense?—Now the plays are begun I shall have no peace.—Isn't it sufficient to make yourself ridiculous by your passion for the theatre, without continually teazing me to join you? Why can't you ride your hobby-horse without desiring to place me on a pillion behind you, Mr. Dangle?

DANGLE. Nay, my dear, I was only going to read——

MRS. DANGLE. No, no; you will never read any thing that's worth listening to:—you hate to hear about your country; there are letters every day with Roman signatures, demonstrating the certainty of an invasion, and proving that the nation is utterly undone.—But you never will read any thing to entertain one.

DANGLE. What has a woman to do with politics, Mrs. Dangle?

MRS. DANGLE. And what have you to do with the theatre, Mr. Dangle? Why should you affect the character of a Critic? I have no patience with you!—haven't you made yourself the jest of all your acquaintance by your interference in matters where you have no business? Are not you call'd a theatrical Quidnunc, and a mock Maecenas to second-hand authors?

DANGLE. True; my power with the Managers is pretty notorious; but is it no credit to have applications from all quarters for my interest?—From lords to recommend fidlers, from ladies to get boxes, from authors to get answers, and from actors to get engagements.

MRS. DANGLE. Yes, truly; you have contrived to get a share in all the plague and trouble of theatrical property, without the profit, or even the credit of the abuse that attends it.

DANGLE. I am sure, Mrs. Dangle, you are no loser by it, however; YOU have all the advantages of it:—mightn't you, last winter, have had the reading of the new Pantomime a fortnight previous to its performance? And doesn't Mr. Fosbrook let you take places for a play before it is advertis'd, and set you down for a Box for every new piece through the season? And didn't my friend, Mr. Smatter, dedicate his last Farce to you at my particular request, Mrs. Dangle?

MRS. DANGLE. Yes; but wasn't the Farce damn'd, Mr. Dangle? And to be sure it is extremely pleasant to have one's house made the motley rendezvous of all the lackeys of literature!—The very high change of trading authors and job-bing critics!—Yes, my drawing room is an absolute register-office for candi-date actors, and poets without character; then to be continually alarmed with Misses and Ma'ams piping histeric changes on Juliets and Dorindas, Pollys and Ophelias; and the very furniture trembling at the probationary starts and unprovok'd rants of would-be Richards and Hamlets!—And what is worse than all, now that the Manager has monopoliz'd the Opera-House, haven't we the Signors and Signoras calling here, sliding their smooth semibreves, and gargling glib divisions in their outlandish throats—with foreign emissaries and French spies, for ought I know, disguised like fidlers and figure dancers!

DANGLE. Mercy! Mrs. Dangle!

MRS. DANGLE. And to employ yourself so idly at such an alarming crisis as this too—when, if you had the least spirit, you would have been at the head of one of the Westminster associations—or trailing a volunteer pike in the Artillery Ground?—But you—o' my conscience, I believe if the French were landed to-morrow your first enquiry would be, whether they had brought a theatri-cal troop with them.

DANGLE. Mrs. Dangle, it does not signify—I say the stage is "the Mirror of Nature," and the actors are "the Abstract, and brief Chronicles of the Time":—and pray what can a man of sense study better?—Besides, you will not easily persuade me that there is no credit or importance in being at the head of a band of critics, who take upon them to decide for the whole town, whose opin-ion and patronage all writers solicit, and whose recommendation no manager dares refuse!

MRS. DANGLE. Ridiculous!—Both managers and authors of the least merit, laugh at your pretensions.—The Public is their Critic—without whose fair approbation they know no play can rest on the stage, and with whose applause they welcome such attacks as yours, and laugh at the malice of them, where they can't at the wit.

DANGLE. Very well, Madam—very well.

Enter SERVANT

SERVANT. Mr. Sneer, Sir, to wait on you.

DANGLE. O, shew Mr. Sneer up. [*Exit* SERVANT.] Plague on't, now we must appear loving and affectionate, or Sneer will hitch us into a story.

MRS. DANGLE. With all my heart; you can't be more ridiculous than you are.

DANGLE. You are enough to provoke——

Enter MR. SNEER.

—Hah! my dear Sneer, I am vastly glad to see you. My dear, here's Mr. Sneer.

MRS. DANGLE. Good morning to you, Sir.

DANGLE. Mrs. Dangle and I have been diverting ourselves with the papers.— Pray, Sneer, won't you go to Drury-lane theatre the first night of Puff's tragedy?

SNEER. Yes; but I suppose one shan't be able to get in, for on the first night of a new piece they always fill the house with orders to support it. But here, Dangle, I have brought you two pieces, one of which you must exert yourself to make the managers accept, I can tell you that, for 'tis written by a person of consequence.

DANGLE. So! Now my plagues are beginning!

SNEER. Aye, I am glad of it, for now you'll be happy. Why, my dear Dangle, it is a pleasure to see how you enjoy your volunteer fatigue, and your solicited solicitations.

DANGLE. It's a great trouble—yet, egad, it's pleasant too.—Why, sometimes of a morning, I have a dozen people call on me at breakfast time, whose faces I never saw before, nor ever desire to see again.

SNEER. That must be very pleasant indeed!

DANGLE. And not a week but I receive fifty letters, and not a line in them about any business of my own.

SNEER. An amusing correspondence!

DANGLE. [*reading*] "Bursts into tears, and exit." What, is this a tragedy!

SNEER. No, that's a genteel comedy, not a translation—only *taken from the French*; it is written in a stile which they have lately tried to run down; the true sentimental, and nothing ridiculous in it from the beginning to the end.

MRS. DANGLE. Well, if they had kept to that, I should not have been such an enemy to the stage, there was some edification to be got from those pieces, Mr. Sneer!

SNEER. I am quite of your opinion, Mrs. Dangle; the theatre in proper hands, might certainly be made the school of morality; but now, I am sorry to say it, people seem to go there principally for their entertainment!

MRS. DANGLE. It would have been more to the credit of the Managers to have kept it in the other line.

SNEER. Undoubtedly, Madam, and hereafter perhaps to have had it recorded, that in the midst of a luxurious and dissipated age, they preserv'd *two* houses in the capital, where the conversation was always moral at least, if not entertaining!

DANGLE. Now, egad, I think the worst alteration is in the nicety of the audience.—No double entendre, no smart innuendo, admitted; even Vanburgh and Congreve obliged to undergo a bungling reformation!

SNEER. Yes, and our prudery in this respect is just on a par with the artificial bashfulness of a courtezan, who encreases the blush upon her cheek in an exact proportion to the diminution of her modesty.

DANGLE. Sneer can't even give the Public a good word!—But what have we here?—This seems a very odd——

SNEER. O, that's a comedy, on a very new plan; replete with wit and mirth, yet of a most serious moral! You see it is call'd "The Reformed Housebreaker"; where, by the mere force of humour, Housebreaking is put into so ridiculous a light, that if the piece has its proper run, I have no doubt but that bolts and bars will be entirely useless by the end of the season.

DANGLE. Egad, this is new indeed!

SNEER. Yes; it is written by a particular friend of mine, who has discovered that the follies and foibles of society, are subjects unworthy the notice of the Comic Muse, who should be taught to stoop only at the greater vices and blacker crimes of humanity—gibbeting capital offences in five acts, and pillorying petty larcenies in two.—In short, his idea is to dramatize the penal laws, and make the Stage a court of ease to the Old Bailey.

DANGLE. It is truly moral.

Enter SERVANT.

Sir Fretful Plagiary, Sir.

DANGLE. Beg him to walk up.—[*Exit* SERVANT.] Now, Mrs. Dangle, Sir Fretful Plagiary is an author to your own taste.

MRS. DANGLE. I confess he is a favourite of mine, because every body else abuses him.

SNEER. —Very much to the credit of your charity, Madam, if not of your judgment.

DANGLE. But, egad, he allows no merit to any author but himself, that's the truth on't—tho' he's my friend.

SNEER. Never.—He is as envious as an old maid verging on the desperation of six-and-thirty: and then the insiduous humility with which he seduces you to give a free opinion on any of his works, can be exceeded only by the petulant arrogance with which he is sure to reject your observations.

DANGLE. Very true, egad—tho' he's my friend.

SNEER. Then his affected contempt of all newspaper strictures; tho', at the same time, he is the sorest man alive, and shrinks like scorch'd parchment from the fiery ordeal of true criticism: yet is he so covetous of popularity, that he had rather be abused than not mentioned at all.

DANGLE. There's no denying it—tho' he is my friend.

SNEER. You have read the tragedy he has just finished, haven't you?

DANGLE. O yes; he sent it to me yesterday.

SNEER. Well, and you think it execrable, don't you?

DANGLE. Why between ourselves, egad I must own—tho' he's my friend—that it is one of the most—He's here [*Aside*]—finished and most admirable perform—

[SIR FRETFUL *without*.] Mr. Sneer with him, did you say?

Enter SIR FRETFUL.

Ah, my dear friend!—Egad, we were just speaking of your Tragedy.—Admirable, Sir Fretful, admirable!

SNEER. You never did any thing beyond it, Sir Fretful—never in your life.

SIR FRETFUL. You make me extremely happy;—for without a compliment, my dear Sneer, there isn't a man in the world whose judgment I value as I do yours.—And Mr. Dangle's.

MRS. DANGLE. They are only laughing at you, Sir Fretful; for it was but just now that—

DANGLE. Mrs. Dangle! Ah, Sir Fretful, you know Mrs. Dangle.—My friend Sneer was rallying just now—He knows how she admires you, and—

SIR FRETFUL. O Lord—I am sure Mr. Sneer has more taste and sincerity than to——A damn'd double-faced fellow! [*Aside*.]

DANGLE. Yes, yes,—Sneer will jest—but a better humour'd——

SIR FRETFUL. O, I know——

DANGLE. He has a ready turn for ridicule—his wit costs him nothing.—

SIR FRETFUL. No, egad,—or I should wonder how he came by it. [*Aside*.]

MRS. DANGLE. Because his jest is always at the expence of his friend.

DANGLE. But, Sir Fretful, have you sent your play to the managers yet?—or can I be of any service to you?

SIR FRETFUL. No, no, I thank you; I believe the piece had sufficient recommendation with it.—I thank you tho'.—I sent it to the manager of Covent-garden theatre this morning.

SNEER. I should have thought now, that it might have been cast (as the actors call it) better at Drury-lane.

SIR FRETFUL. O lud! no—never sent a play there while I live— harkee! [*Whispers* SNEER.]

SNEER. *Writes himself!*—I know he does—

SIR FRETFUL. I say nothing—I take away from no man's merit—am hurt at

43

no man's good fortune—I say nothing—But this I will say—through all my knowledge of life, I have observed—that there is not a passion so strongly rooted in the human heart as envy!

SNEER. I believe you have reason for what you say, indeed.

SIR FRETFUL. Besides—I can tell you it is not always so safe to leave a play in the hands of those who write themselves.

SNEER. What, they may steal from them, hey, my dear Plagiary?

SIR FRETFUL. Steal!—to be sure they may; and, egad, serve your best thoughts as gypsies do stolen children, disfigure them to make 'em pass for their own.

SNEER. But your present work is a sacrifice to Melpomene, and HE, you know, never——

SIR FRETFUL. That's no security.—A dext'rous plagiarist may do any thing.— Why, Sir, for ought I know, he might take out some of the best things in my tragedy, and put them into his own comedy.

SNEER. That might be done, I dare be sworn.

SIR FRETFUL. And then, if such a person gives you the least hint or assistance, he is devilish apt to take the merit of the whole.—

DANGLE. If it succeeds.

SIR FRETFUL. Aye,—but with regard to this piece, I think I can hit that gentleman, for I can safely swear he never read it.

SNEER. I'll tell you how you may hurt him more—

SIR FRETFUL. How?—

SNEER. Swear he wrote it.

SIR FRETFUL. Plague on't now, Sneer, I shall take it ill.—I believe you want to take away my character as an author!

SNEER. Then I am sure you ought to be very much oblig'd to me.

SIR FRETFUL. Hey!—Sir!—

DANGLE. O you know, he never means what he says.

SIR FRETFUL. Sincerely then—you do like the piece?

SNEER. Wonderfully!

SIR FRETFUL. But come now, there must be something that you think might be mended, hey?—Mr. Dangle, has nothing struck you?

DANGLE. Why faith, it is but an ungracious thing for the most part to—

SIR FRETFUL.—With most authors it is just so indeed; they are in general strangely tenacious!—But, for my part, I am never so well pleased as when a judicious critic points out any defect to me; for what is the purpose of shewing a work to a friend, if you don't mean to profit by his opinion?

SNEER. Very true.—Why then, tho' I seriously admire the piece upon the whole, yet there is one small objection; which, if you'll give me leave, I'll mention.

SIR FRETFUL. SIR,—you can't oblige me more.

SNEER. I think it wants incident.

SIR FRETFUL. Good God!—you surprize me!—wants incidents—

SNEER. Yes; I own I think the incidents are too few.

SIR FRETFUL. Good God!—Believe me, Mr. Sneer, there is no person for whose judgment I have a more implicit deference.—But I protest to you, Mr. Sneer, I am only apprehensive that the incidents are too crowded.—My dear Dangle, how does it strike you?

DANGLE. Really I can't agree with my friend Sneer.—I think the plot quite sufficient; and the four first acts by many degrees the best I ever read or saw in my life. If I might venture to suggest any thing, it is that the interest rather falls off in the fifth.—

SIR FRETFUL. —Rises; I believe you mean, Sir.

DANGLE. No; I don't upon my word.

SIR FRETFUL. Yes, yes, you do upon my soul—it certainly don't fall off, I assure you—No, no, it don't fall off.

DANGLE. Now, Mrs. Dangle, didn't you say it struck you in the same light?

MRS. DANGLE. No, indeed, I did not—I did not see a fault in any part of the play from the beginning to the end.

SIR FRETFUL. Upon my soul the women are the best judges after all!

MRS. DANGLE. Or if I made any objection, I am sure it was to nothing in the piece; but that I was afraid it was, on the whole, a little too long.

SIR FRETFUL. Pray, Madame, do you speak as to duration of time; or do you mean that the story is tediously spun out?

MRS. DANGLE. O Lud! no.—I speak only with reference to the usual length of acting plays.

SIR FRETFUL. Then I am very happy—very happy indeed,—because the play is a short play, a remarkably short play:—I should not venture to differ with a lady on a point of taste; but, on these occasions, the watch, you know, is the critic.

MRS. DANGLE. Then, I suppose, it must have been Mr. Dangle's drawling manner of reading it to me.

SIR FRETFUL. O, if Mr. Dangle read it! that's quite another affair!—But I assure you, Mrs. Dangle, the first evening you can spare me three hours and an half, I'll undertake to read you the whole from beginning to end, with the Prologue and Epilogue, and allow time for the music between the acts.

MRS. DANGLE. I hope to see it on the stage next.

DANGLE. Well, Sir Fretful, I wish you may be able to get rid as easily of the news-paper criticisms as you do of ours.—

SIR FRETFUL. The News-papers!—Sir, they are the most villainous—licentious—abominable—infernal—Not that I ever read them—No—I make it a rule never to look into a news-paper.

DANGLE. You are quite right—for it certainly must hurt an author of delicate feelings to see the liberties they take.

SIR FRETFUL. No!—quite the contrary;—their abuse is, in fact, the best pane-gyric—I like it of all things.—An author's reputation is only in danger from their support.

SNEER. Why that's true—and that attack now on you the other day—

SIR FRETFUL. ——What? where?

DANGLE. Aye, you mean in a paper of Thursday; it was compleatly ill-natur'd to be sure.

SIR FRETFUL. O, so much the better.—Ha! ha! ha!—I wou'dn't have it otherwise.

DANGLE. Certainly it is only to be laugh'd at; for—

SIR FRETFUL. —You don't happen to recollect what the fellow said, do you?

SNEER. Pray, Dangle—Sir Fretful seems a little anxious—

SIR FRETFUL.—O lud, no!—anxious,—not I,—not the least.—I—But one may as well hear you know.

DANGLE. Sneer, do *you* recollect?—Make out something. [*Aside.*]

SNEER. I will, [*to* DANGLE.]—Yes, yes, I remember perfectly.

SIR FRETFUL. Well, and pray now—Not that it signifies—what might the gentleman say?

SNEER. Why, he roundly asserts that you have not the slightest invention, or original genius whatever; tho' you are the greatest traducer of all other authors living.

SIR FRETFUL. Ha! ha! ha!—very good.

SNEER. That as to Comedy, you have not one idea of your own, he believes, even in your common place-book—where stray jokes, and pilfered witticisms are kept with as much method as the ledger of the Lost-and-Stolen Office.

SIR FRETFUL. —Ha! ha! ha!—very pleasant!

SNEER. Nay, that you are so unlucky as not to have the skill even to *steal* with taste.—But that you gleen from the refuse of obscure volumes, where more judicious plagiarists have been before you; so that the body of your work is a composition of dregs and sediments—like a bad tavern's worst wine.

SIR FRETFUL. Ha! ha!

SNEER. In your more serious efforts, he says, your bombast would be less intol-erable, if the thoughts were ever suited to the expression; but the homeliness of the sentiment stares thro' the fantastic encumbrance of its fine language, like a clown in one of the new uniforms!

SIR FRETFUL. Ha! ha!

SNEER. That your occasional tropes and flowers suit the general coarseness of your stile, as tambour sprigs would a ground of linsey-wolsey; while your imi-tations of Shakespeare resemble the mimicry of Falstaff's Page, and are about as near the standard of the original.

SIR FRETFUL. Ha!—

SNEER. —In short, that even the finest passages you steal are of no service to you; for the poverty of your own language prevents their assimilating; so that they lie on the surface like lumps of marl on a barren moor, encumbering what it is not in their power to fertilize!—

SIR FRETFUL. [*after great agitation.*]——Now another person would be vex'd at this.

SNEER. Oh! but I wouldn't have told you, only to divert you.

SIR FRETFUL. I know it— I *am* diverted,—Ha! ha! ha!—not the least invention!— Ha! ha! ha!—very good!—very good!

SNEER. Yes—no genius! Ha! ha! ha!

DANGLE. A severe rogue! Ha! ha! ha! But you are quite right, Sir Fretful, never to read such nonsense.

SIR FRETFUL. To be sure—for if there is any thing to one's praise, it is a foolish vanity to be gratified at it, and if it is abuse,—why one is always sure to hear of it from one damn'd good natur'd friend or another!

Enter SERVANT.

Sir, there is an Italian gentleman, with a French Interpreter, and three young ladies, and a dozen musicians, who say they are sent by Lady Rondeau and Mrs. Fuge.

DANGLE. Gadso! they come by appointment. Dear Mrs. Dangle do let them know I'll see them directly.

MRS. DANGLE. You know, Mr. Dangle, I shan't understand a word they say.

DANGLE. But you hear there's an interpreter.

MRS. DANGLE. Well, I'll try to endure their complaisance till you come.

[*Exit.*]

SERVANT. And Mr. Puff, Sir, has sent word that the last rehearsal is to be this morning, and that he'll call on you presently.

DANGLE. That's true—I shall certainly be at home. [*Exit* SERVANT.]

Now, Sir Fretful, if you have a mind to have justice done you in the way of answer—Egad, Mr. Puff's your man.

SIR FRETFUL. Pshaw! Sir, why should I wish to have it answered, when I tell you I am pleased at it?

DANGLE. True, I had forgot that.—But I hope you are not fretted at what Mr. Sneer——

SIR FRETFUL. —Zounds! no, Mr. Dangle, don't I tell you these things never fret me in the least.

SNEER. Nay, I only thought——

SIR FRETFUL. —And let me tell you, Mr. Dangle, 'tis damn'd affronting in you to suppose that I am hurt, when I tell you I am not.

SNEER. But why so warm, Sir Fretful?

SIR FRETFUL. Gadslife! Mr. Sneer, you are as absurd as Dangle; how often must I repeat it to you, that nothing can vex me but your supposing it possible for me to mind the damn'd nonsense you have been repeating to me!—and let me tell you, if you continue to believe this, you must mean to insult me, gentlemen—and then your disrespect will affect me no more than the news-paper criticisms—and I shall treat it—with exactly the same calm indifference and philosophic contempt—and so your servant. [*Exit.*]

SNEER. Ha! ha! ha! Poor Sir Fretful! Now will he go and vent his philosophy in anonymous abuse of all modern critics and authors—But Dangle, you must get your friend Puff to take me to the rehearsal of his tragedy.

DANGLE. I'll answer for't, he'll thank you for desiring it. But come and help me to judge of this musical family; they are recommended by people of consequence, I assure you.

SNEER. I am at your disposal the whole morning—but I thought you had been a decided critic in musick, as well as in literature?

DANGLE. So I am—but I have a bad ear.—Efaith, Sneer, tho', I am afraid we were a little too severe on Sir Fretful—tho' he is my friend.

SNEER. Why, 'tis certain, that unnecessarily to mortify the vanity of any writer, is a cruelty which mere dulness never can deserve; but where a base and personal malignity usurps the place of literary emulation, the aggressor deserves neither quarter nor pity.

DANGLE. That's true—egad!—tho' he's my friend.

SCENE II

A Drawing Room, Harpsichord, &c. Italian Family, French Interpreter,
MRS. DANGLE *and* SERVANTS *discovered.*

INTERPRETER. Je dis madame, j'ai l'honneur to *introduce* & de vous demander votre protection pour le Signor Pasticcio Retornello & pour sa charmante famille.

SIGNOR PASTICCIO. Ah! Vosignoria noi vi preghiamo di favoritevi colla vostra protezione.

1ST DAUGHTER. Vosignoria fatevi questi grazzie.

2D DAUGHTER. Si Signora.

INTERPRETER. Madame—*me interpret.*—C'est à dire—in English—qu'ils vous prient de leur faire l'honneur—

MRS. DANGLE. —I say again, gentlemen, I don't understand a word you say.

SIGNOR PASTICCIO. Questo Signore spiegheró.

INTERPRETER. Oui—*me interpret.*—nous avons les lettres de recommendation pour Monsieur Dangle de——

MRS. DANGLE. —Upon my word, Sir, I don't understand you.

SIGNOR PASTICCIO. La Contessa Rondeau e nostra padrona.

3D DAUGHTER. Si, padre, & mi Ladi Fuge.

INTERPRETER. O!—*me interpret.*—Madame, ils disent—*in* English—Qu'ils ont l'honneur d'etre protegés de ces Dames.—*You understand?*

MRS. DANGLE. No, Sir,——no understand!

Enter DANGLE *and* SNEER.

INTERPRETER. Ah voici Monsieur Dangle!

ALL ITALIANS. A! Signor Dangle!

MRS. DANGLE. Mr. Dangle, here are two very civil gentlemen trying to make themselves understood, and I don't know which is the interpreter.

DANGLE. Ebien!

[Speaking together.]

INTERPRETER. Monsieur Dangle—le grand bruit de vos talents pour la critique & de votre interest avec Messieurs les Directeurs a tous les Theatres.

SIGNOR PASTICCIO. Vosignoria siete si famoso par la vostra conoscensa e vostra interessa colla le Direttore da—

DANGLE. Egad I think the Interpreter is the hardest to be understood of the two!

SNEER. Why I thought, Dangle, you had been an admirable linguist!

DANGLE. So I am, if they would not talk so damn'd fast.

SNEER. Well I'll explain that—the less time we lose in hearing them the better,—for that I suppose is what they are brought here for.

[SNEER speaks to SIG. PAST.—They sing trios, &c. DANGLE beating out of time. SERVANT enters and whispers DANGLE.]

DANGLE. Shew him up. *[Exit SERVANT.]* Bravo! admirable! bravissimo! admirablissimo!—Ah! Sneer! where will you find such as these voices in England!

SNEER. Not easily.

DANGLE. But Puff is coming.—Signor and little Signora's—obligatissimo! — Sposa Signora Danglena—Mrs. Dangle, shall I beg you to offer them some refreshments, and take their address in the next room.

[Exit MRS. DANGLE *with the* ITALIANS *and* INTERPRETER *ceremoniously.]*

Re-enter SERVANT.

Mr. Puff, Sir.

DANGLE. My dear Puff!

Enter PUFF.

My dear Dangle, how is it with you?

DANGLE. Mr. Sneer, give me leave to introduce Mr. Puff to you.

PUFF. Mr. Sneer is this? Sir, he is a gentleman whom I have long panted for the honour of knowing—a gentleman whose critical talents and transcendant judgment——

SNEER. —Dear Sir——

DANGLE. Nay, don't be modest, Sneer, my friend Puff only talks to you in the stile of his profession.

SNEER. His profession!

PUFF. Yes, Sir; I make no secret of the trade I follow—among friends and brother authors, Dangle knows I love to be frank on the subject, and to advertise myself *vivâ voce*.—I am, Sir, a Practitioner in Panegyric, or to speak more plainly—a Professor of the Art of Puffing, at your service—or any body else's.

SNEER. Sir, you are very obliging!—I believe, Mr. Puff, I have often admired your talents in the daily prints.

PUFF. Yes, Sir, I flatter myself I do as much business in that way as any six of the fraternity in town—Devilish hard work all the summer—Friend Dangle? never work'd harder!—But harkee,—the Winter Managers were a little sore I believe.

DANGLE. No—I believe they took it all in good part.

PUFF. Aye!—Then that must have been affectation in them, for egad, there were some of the attacks which there was no laughing at!

SNEER. Aye, the humorous ones.—But I should think Mr. Puff, that Authors would in general be able to do this sort of work for themselves.

PUFF. Why yes—but in a clumsy way.—Besides, we look on that as an encroachment, and so take the opposite side.—I dare say now you conceive half the very civil paragraphs and advertisements you see, to be written by the parties concerned, or their friends?—No such thing—Nine out of ten, manufactured by me in the way of business.

SNEER. Indeed!—

PUFF. Even the Auctioneers now,—the Auctioneers I say, tho' the rogues have lately got some credit for their language—not an article of the merit their's!—take them out of their Pulpits, and they are as dull as Catalogues.—— No, sir;—'twas I first enrich'd their style—'twas I first taught them to crowd their advertisements with panegyrical superlatives, each epithet rising above the other—like the Bidders in their own Auction-rooms! From ME they learn'd to enlay their phraseology with variegated chips of exotic metaphor: by ME too their inventive faculties were called forth.—Yes Sir, by ME they were instructed

50

to clothe ideal walls with gratuitous fruits—to insinuate obsequious rivulets into visionary groves—to teach courteous shrubs to nod their approbation of the grateful soil! or on emergencies to raise upstart oaks, where there never had been an acorn; to create a delightful vicinage without the assistance of a neighbour; or fix the temple of Hygeia in the fens of Lincolnshire!

DANGLE. I am sure, you have done them infinite service; for now, when a gentleman is ruined, he parts with his house with some credit.

SNEER. Service! if they had any gratitude, they would erect a statue to him, they would figure him as a presiding Mercury, the god of traffic and fiction, with a hammer in his hand instead of a caduceus.—But pray, Mr. Puff, what first put you on exercising your talents in this way?

PUFF. Egad, sir,—sheer necessity—the proper parent of an art so nearly allied to invention: you must know Mr. Sneer, that from the first time I tried my hand at an advertisement, my success was such, that for sometime after, I led a most extraordinary life indeed!

SNEER. How, pray?

PUFF. Sir, I supported myself two years entirely by my misfortunes.

SNEER. By your misfortunes!

PUFF. Yes Sir, assisted by long sickness, and other occasional disorders; and a very comfortable living I had of it.

SNEER. From sickness and misfortunes!—You practised as a Doctor, and an Attorney at once?

PUFF. No egad, both maladies and miseries were my own.

SNEER. Hey!—what the plague!

DANGLE. 'Tis true, efaith.

PUFF. Harkee!—By advertisements—"To the charitable and humane!" and "to those whom Providence hath blessed with affluence!"

SNEER. Oh,—I understand you.

PUFF. And in truth, I deserved what I got, for I suppose never man went thro' such a series of calamities in the same space of time!—Sir, I was five times made a bankrupt, and reduced from a state of affluence, by a train of unavoidable misfortunes! then Sir, tho' a very industrious tradesman, I was twice burnt out, and lost my little all, both times!—I lived upon those fires a month.—I soon after was confined by a most excruciating disorder, and lost the use of my limbs!—That told very well, for I had the case strongly attested, and went about to collect the subscriptions myself.

DANGLE. Egad, I believe that was when you first called on me.—

PUFF. —In November last?—O no!—I was at that time, a close prisoner in the Marshalsea, for a debt benevolently contracted to serve a friend!—I was afterwards, twice tapped for a dropsy, which declined into a very profitable consumption!—I was then reduced to—O no—then, I became a widow with six

51

helpless children,—after having had eleven husbands pressed, and being left every time eight months gone with child, and without money to get me into a hospital!

SNEER. And you bore all with patience, I make no doubt?

PUFF. Why, yes,—tho' I made some occasional attempts at felo de se; but as I did not find those *rash actions* answer, I left off killing myself very soon.—Well, Sir,—at last, what with bankruptcies, fires, gouts, dropsies, imprisonments, and other valuable calamities, having got together a pretty handsome sum, I determined to quit a business which had always gone rather against my conscience, and in a more liberal way still to indulge my talents for fiction and embellishment, thro' my favourite channels of diurnal communication—and so, Sir, you have my history.

SNEER. Most obligingly communicative indeed; and your confession if published, might certainly serve the cause of true charity, by rescuing the most useful channels of appeal to benevolence from the cant of imposition.—But surely, Mr. Puff, there is no great *mystery* in your present profession?

PUFF. Mystery? Sir, I will take upon me to say the matter was never scientifically treated, nor reduced to rule before.

SNEER. Reduced to rule?

PUFF. O lud, Sir! you are very ignorant, I am afraid.—Yes Sir,—Puffing is of various sorts—the principal are, The Puff Direct—the Puff Preliminary—the Puff Collateral—the Puff Collusive, and the Puff Oblique, or Puff by Implication.—These all assume, as circumstances require, the various forms of Letter to the Editor—Occasional Anecdote—Impartial Critique— Observation from Correspondent,—or Advertisement from the Party.

SNEER. The puff direct, I can conceive—

PUFF. O yes, that's simple enough,—for instance—A new Comedy or Farce is to be produced at one of the Theatres (though by the bye they don't bring out half what they ought to do). The author, suppose Mr. Smatter, or Mr. Dapper—or any particular friend of mine—very well; the day before it is to be performed, I write an account of the manner in which it was received—I have the plot from the author,—and only add—Characters strongly drawn—highly coloured—hand of a master—fund of genuine humor—mine of invention— neat dialogue—attic salt! Then for the performance—Mr. Dodd was astonishingly great in the character of Sir Harry! That universal and judicious actor Mr. Palmer, perhaps never appeared to more advantage than in the Colonel,— but it is not in the power of language to do justice to Mr. King!—Indeed he more than merited those repeated bursts of applause which he drew from a most brilliant and judicious audience! As to the scenery—The miraculous power of Mr. De Loutherbourg's pencil are universally acknowledged!—In short, we are at a loss which to admire most,—the unrivalled genius of the author, the great attention and liberality of the managers—the wonderful abilities of the painter, or the incredible exertions of all the performers!—

SNEER. That's pretty well indeed, Sir.

PUFF. O cool—quite cool—to what I sometimes do.

SNEER. And do you think there are any who are influenced by this.

PUFF. O, lud! yes, Sir;—the number of those who go thro' the fatigue of judging for themselves is very small indeed!

SNEER. Well, Sir,—the Puff Preliminary?

PUFF. O that, Sir, does well in the form of a *Caution*.—In a matter of gallantry now—Sir Flimsy Gossimer, wishes to be well with Lady Fanny Fete—He applies to me——I open trenches for him with a paragraph in the Morning Post.——It is recommended to the beautiful and accomplished Lady F four stars F dash E to be on her guard against that dangerous character, Sir F dash G; who, however pleasing and insinuating his manners may be, is certainly not remarkable for the *constancy of his attachments!*—in Italics.—Here you see, Sir Flimsy Gossimer is introduced to the particular notice of Lady Fanny—who, perhaps never thought of him before—she finds herself publickly cautioned to avoid him which naturally makes her desirous of seeing him;—the observation of their acquaintance causes a pretty kind of mutual embarrassment, this produces a sort of sympathy of interest—which, if Sir Flimsy is unable to improve effectually, he at least gains the credit of having their names mentioned together, by a particular set, and in a particular way,—which nine times out of ten is the full accomplishment of modern gallantry!

DANGLE. Egad, Sneer, you will be quite an adept in the business.

PUFF. Now, Sir, the Puff Collateral is much used as an appendage to advertisements, and may take the form of anecdote.—Yesterday as the celebrated George Bon-Mot was sauntering down St. James's-street, he met the lively Lady Mary Myrtle, coming out of the Park,—"Good God, Lady Mary, I'm surprised to meet you in a white jacket,—for I expected never to have seen you, but in a full-trimmed uniform, and a light-horseman's cap!"—"Heavens, George, where could you have learned that?"—"Why, replied the wit, I just saw a print of you, in a new publication called The Camp Magazine, which, by the bye, is a devilish clever thing,—and is sold at No. 3, on the right hand of the way, two doors from the printing-office, the corner of Ivy-lane, Paternoster-row, price only one shilling!"

SNEER. Very ingenious indeed!

PUFF. But the Puff Collusive is the newest of any; for it acts in the disguise of determined hostility.—It is much used by bold booksellers and enterprising poets.—An indignant correspondent observes—that the new poem called Beelzebub's Cotillion, or Proserpine's Fete Champetre, is one of the most unjustifiable performances he ever read! The severity with which certain characters are handled is quite shocking! And as there are many descriptions in it too warmly coloured for female delicacy, the shameful avidity with which this piece is bought by all people of fashion, is a reproach on the taste of the times, and a disgrace to the delicacy of the age!—Here you see the two strongest inducements are held forth;—First, that nobody ought to read it;—and secondly, that every body buys it; on the strength of which, the publisher boldly prints the tenth edition, before he had sold ten of the first; and then establishes it by threatening himself with the pillory, or absolutely indicting himself for Scan. Mag!

DANGLE. Ha! ha! ha!—'gad I know it is so.

PUFF. As to the Puff Oblique, or Puff by Implication, it is too various and extensive to be illustrated by an instance;—it attracts in titles, and presumes in patents; it lurks in the *limitation* of a subscription, and invites in the assurance of croud and incommodation at public places; it delights to draw forth concealed merit, with a most disinterested assiduity; and sometimes wears a countenance of smiling censure and tender reproach.—It has a wonderful memory for Parliamentary Debates, and will often give the whole speech of a favoured member, with the most flattering accuracy. But, above all, it is a great dealer in reports and suppositions.—It has the earliest intelligence of intended preferments that will reflect *honor* on the *patrons*; and embryo promotions of modest gentlemen—who know nothing of the matter themselves. It can hint a ribband for implied services, in the air of a common report; and with the carelessness of a casual paragraph, suggest officers into commands—to which they have no pretension but their wishes. This, Sir, is the last principal class in the Art of Puffing—An art which I hope you will now agree with me, is of the highest dignity—yielding a tablature of benevolence and public spirit; befriending equally trade, gallantry, criticism, and politics: the applause of genius! the register of charity! the triumph of heroism! the self defence of contractors! the fame of orators!—and the gazette of ministers!

SNEER. Sir, I am compleatly a convert both to the importance and ingenuity of your profession; and now, Sir, there is but one thing which can possibly encrease my respect for you, and that is, your permitting me to be present at the rehearsal of your new trage——

PUFF. —Hush, for heaven's sakes.—*My* tragedy!—Egad, Dangle, I take this very ill—you know how apprehensive I am of being known to be the author.

DANGLE. 'Efaith I would not have told—but it's in the papers, and your name at length—in the Morning Chronicle.

PUFF. Ah! those damn'd editors never can keep a secret!—Well, Mr. Sneer—no doubt you will do me great honour—I shall be infinitely happy—highly flattered——

DANGLE. I believe it must be near the time—shall we go together.

PUFF. No; It will not be yet this hour, for they are always late at that theatre: besides, I must meet you there, for I have some little matters here to send to the papers, and a few paragraphs to scribble before I go.

[*Looking at memorandums.*]

—Here is "a Conscientious Baker, on the Subject of the Army Bread;" and "a Detester of Visible Brick-Work, in favor of the new invented Stucco"; both in the style of Junius, and promised for to-morrow.—The Thames navigation too is at a stand.—Misomud or Anti-shoal must go to work again directly.— Here too are some political memorandums I see; aye—To take Paul Jones, and get the Indiamen out of the Shannon—reinforce Byron—compel the Dutch to—so!— I must do that in the evening papers, or reserve it for the Morning Herald, for I know that I have undertaken to-morrow, besides, to establish the unanimity of the fleet in the Public Advertiser, and to shoot Charles Fox in the Morning Post.—So, egad, I ha'n't a moment to lose!

DANGLE. Well!—we'll meet in the Green Room.   [*Exeunt severally.*]

ACT II

SCENE I

The THEATRE

Enter DANGLE, PUFF, *and* SNEER, *as before the Curtain.*

PUFF. No, no, Sir; what Shakespeare says of Actors may be better applied to the purpose of Plays; *they* ought to be "the abstract and brief Chronicles of the times." Therefore when history, and particularly the history of our own country, furnishes any thing like a case in point, to the time in which an author writes, if he knows his own interest, he will take advantage of it; so, Sir, I call my tragedy The Spanish Armada; and have laid the scene before Tilbury Fort.

SNEER. A most happy thought certainly!

DANGLE. Egad it was—I told you so.—But pray now I don't understand how you have contrived to introduce any love into it.

PUFF. Love!—Oh nothing so easy; for it is a received point among poets, that where history gives you a good heroic out-line for a play, you may fill up with a little love at your own discretion; in doing which, nine times out of ten, you only make up a deficiency in the private history of the times.—Now I rather think I have done this with some success.

SNEER. No scandal about Queen Elizabeth, I hope?

PUFF. O Lud! no, no.—I only suppose the Governor of Tilbury Fort's daughter to be in love with the son of the Spanish Admiral.

SNEER. Oh, is that all?

DANGLE. Excellent, Efaith!—I see it at once.—But won't this appear rather improbable?

PUFF. To be sure it will—but what the plague! a play is not to shew occurrences that happen every day, but things just so strange, that tho' they never *did*, they *might* happen.

SNEER. Certainly nothing is unnatural, that is not physically impossible.

PUFF. Very true—and for that matter Don Ferolo Whiskerandos—for that's the lover's name, might have been over here in the train of the Spanish Ambassador; or Tilburina, for that is the lady's name, might have been in love with him, from having heard his character, or seen his picture; or from knowing that he was the last man in the world she ought to be in love with—or for any other good female reason.—However, Sir, the fact is, that tho' she is but a Knight's daughter, egad! she is in love like any Princess!

DANGLE. Poor young lady! I feel for her already! for I can conceive how great the conflict must be between her passion and her duty; her love for her country, and her love for Don Ferolo Whiskerandos!

PUFF. O amazing!—her poor susceptible heart is swayed to and fro, by contending passions like—

Enter UNDER PROMPTER.

UNDER PROMPTER. Sir, the scene is set, and every thing is ready to begin if you please.—

PUFF. 'Egad; then we'll lose no time.

UNDER PROMPTER. Tho' I believe, Sir, you will find it very short, for all the performers have profited by the kind permission you granted them.

PUFF. Hey! what!

UNDER PROMPTER. You know, Sir, you gave them leave to cut out or omit whatever they found heavy or unnecessary to the plot, and I must own they have taken very liberal advantage of your indulgence.

PUFF. Well, well.—They are in general very good judges; and I know I am luxuriant.—Now, Mr. Hopkins, as soon as you please.

UNDER PROMPTER *to the Musick.* Gentlemen, will you play a few bars of something, just to—

PUFF. Aye, that's right,—for as we have the scenes, and dresses, egad, we'll go to't, as if it was the first night's performance;—but you need not mind stopping between the acts. [*Exit* UNDER PROMPTER.]

[*Orchestra play. Then the Bell rings.*]

Soh! stand clear gentlemen.—Now you know there will be a cry of down!—
down!—hats off! silence!—Then up curtain,—and let us see what our
painters have done for us.

SCENE II

The Curtain rises and discovers TILBURY FORT

Two Centinels asleep.

DANGLE. Tilbury Fort!—very fine indeed!

PUFF. Now, what do you think I open with?

SNEER. Faith, I can't guess—

PUFF. A clock.—Hark!—[*clock strikes.*] I open with a clock striking, to beget an
aweful attention in the audience—it also marks the time, which is four o'clock
in the morning, and saves a description of the rising sun, and a great deal about
gilding the eastern hemisphere.

DANGLE. But pray, are the centinels to be asleep?

PUFF. Fast as watchmen.

SNEER. Isn't that odd tho' at such an alarming crisis?

PUFF. To be sure it is,—but smaller things must give way to a striking scene at
the opening; that's a rule.—And the case is, that two great men are coming to
this very spot to begin the piece; now, it is not to be supposed they would open
their lips, if these fellows were watching them, so, egad, I must either have sent
them off their posts, or set them asleep.

SNEER. O that accounts for it!—But tell us, who are these coming?—

PUFF. These are they—Sir Walter Raleigh, and Sir Christopher Hatton.—You'll
know Sir Christopher, by his turning out his toes—famous you know for his
dancing. I like to preserve all the little traits of character.—Now attend.

Enter SIR WALTER RALEIGH *and* SIR CHRISTOPHER HATTON.

SIR CHRISTOPHER.
True, gallant Raleigh!—

DANGLE. What, they had been talking before?

PUFF. O, yes; all the way as they came along.—I beg pardon gentlemen [*to the
Actors*] but these are particular friends of mine, whose remarks may be of great
service to us.—Don't mind interrupting them whenever any thing strikes you.
[*To* SNEER *and* DANGLE.]

> SIR CHRISTOPHER.
>> True, gallant Raleigh!
>> But O, thou champion of thy country's fame,
>> There *is* a question which I yet must ask;
>> A question, which I never ask'd before—
>> What mean these mighty armaments?
>> This general muster? and this throng of chiefs?

SNEER. Pray, Mr. Puff, how came Sir Christopher Hatton never to ask that question before?

PUFF. What, before the Play began? how the plague could he?

DANGLE. That's true efaith!

PUFF. But you will hear what he thinks of the matter.

> SIR CHRISTOPHER.
>> Alas, my noble friend, when I behold
>> Yon tented plains in martial symmetry
>> Array'd.——When I count o'er yon glittering lines
>> Of crested warriors, where the proud steeds neigh,
>> And valor-breathing trumpet's shrill appeal,
>> Responsive vibrate on my listning ear;
>> When virgin majesty herself I view,
>> Like her protecting Pallas veil'd in steel,
>> With graceful confidence exhort to arms!
>> When briefly all I hear or see bears stamp
>> Of marital vigilance, and stern defence,
>> I cannot but surmise.——Forgive, my friend,
>> If the conjecture's rash——I cannot but
>> Surmise.——The state some danger apprehends!

SNEER. A very cautious conjecture that.

PUFF. Yes, that's his character; not to give an opinion, but on secure grounds—now then.

> SIR WALTER.
>> O, most accomplished Christopher.—

PUFF. He calls him by his Christian name, to shew that they are on the most familiar terms.

SIR WALTER.

O, most accomplished Christopher, I find
Thy staunch sagacity still tracks the future,
In the fresh print of the o'ertaken past.

PUFF. Figurative!

SIR WALTER.

Thy fears are just.

SIR CHRISTOPHER.

But where? whence? when? and what
The danger is——Methinks I fain would learn.

SIR WALTER.

You know, my friend, scarce two revolving suns,
And three revolving moons, have closed their course,
Since haughty Philip, in despight of peace,
With hostile hand hath struck at England's trade.

SIR CHRISTOPHER.

I know it well.

SIR WALTER.

Philip you know is proud, Iberia's king!

SIR CHRISTOPHER.

He is.

SIR WALTER.

——His subjects in base bigotry
And Catholic oppression held,——while we
You know, the protestant persuasion hold.

SIR CHRISTOPHER.

We do.

SIR WALTER.

You know beside,——his boasted armament.
The fam'd Armada,——by the Pope baptized,
With purpose to invade these realms——

SIR CHRISTOPHER.

——Is sailed,
Our last advices so report.

SIR WALTER.

While the Iberian Admiral's chief hope,
His darling son——

SIR CHRISTOPHER.
——Ferolo Whiskerandos hight——
SIR WALTER.
The same—by chance a pris'ner hath been ta'en,
And in this fort of Tilbury——
SIR CHRISTOPHER.
——Is now
Confin'd—'tis true, and oft from yon tall turrets top
I've marked the youthful Spaniard's haughty mien
Unconquer'd, tho' in chains!
SIR WALTER.
You also know——

DANGLE.—Mr. Puff, as he *knows* all this, why does Sir Walter go on telling him?

PUFF. But the audience are not supposed to know any thing of the matter, are they?

SNEER. True, but I think you manage ill: for there certainly appears no reason why Sir Walter should be so communicative.

PUFF. Fore Gad now, that is one of the most ungrateful observations I ever heard—for the less inducement he has to tell all this, the more I think, you ought to be oblig'd to him; for I am sure you'd know nothing of the matter without it.

DANGLE. That's very true, upon my word.

PUFF. But you will find he was *not* going on.

SIR CHRISTOPHER.
Enough, enough,—'tis plain—and I no more
Am in amazement lost!——

PUFF. Here, now you see, Sir Christopher did not in fact ask any one question for his own information.

SNEER. No indeed:—his has been a most disinterested curiosity!

DANGLE. Really, I find, we are very much oblig'd to them both.

PUFF. To be sure you are. Now then for the Commander in Chief, the Earl of Leicester! who, you know, was no favourite but of the Queen's.—We left off—"in amazement lost!"—

SIR CHRISTOPHER.
Am in amazement lost.——
But, see where noble Leicester comes! supreme
In honours and command.

SIR WALTER.
>And yet methinks,
>At such a time, so perilous, so fear'd
>That staff might well become an abler grasp.

SIR CHRISTOPHER.
>And so by heav'n! think I; but soft, he's here!

PUFF. Aye, they envy him.

SNEER. But who are these with him?

PUFF. O! very valiant knights; one is the Governor of the fort, the other the master of the horse.—And now, I think you shall hear some better language: I was obliged to be plain and intelligible in the first scene, because there was so much matter of fact in it: but now, efaith, you have trope, figure, and metaphor, as plenty as noun-substantives.

>*Enter* EARL OF LEICESTER, THE GOVERNOR, *and others.*

LEICESTER.
>How's this my friends! is't thus your new fledg'd zeal
>And plumed valor moults in roosted sloth?
>Why dimly glimmers that heroic flame,
>Whose red'ning blaze by patriot spirit fed,
>Should be the beacon of a kindling realm?
>Can the quick current of a patriot heart,
>Thus stagnate in a cold and weedy converse,
>Or freeze in tideless inactivity?
>No! rather let the fountain of your valor
>Spring thro' each stream of enterprize,
>Each petty channel of conducive daring,
>Till the full torrent of your foaming wrath
>O'erwhelm the flats of sunk hostility!

PUFF. There it is,—follow'd up!

SIR WALTER.
>No more! the fresh'ning breath of thy rebuke
>Hath fill'd the swelling canvass of our souls!
>And thus, tho' fate should cut the cable of [*All take hands.*]
>Our topmost hopes, in friendship's closing line
>We'll grapple with despair, and if we fall,
>We'll fall in Glory's wake!

EARL OF LEICESTER.
>   There spoke Old England's genius!
>   Then, are we all resolv'd?
ALL
>   We are——all resolv'd.
EARL OF LEICESTER.
>   To conquer——or be free?
ALL
>   To conquer, or be free.
EARL OF LEICESTER.
>   All?
ALL.
>   All.

DANGLE. *Nem. con.* egad!
PUFF. O yes, where they *do* agree on the stage, their unanimity is wonderful!

EARL OF LEICESTER.
>   Then, let's embrace——and now——

SNEER. What the plague, is he going to pray?
PUFF. Yes, hush!—in great emergencies, there is nothing like a prayer!

EARL OF LEICESTER.
>   O mighty Mars!

DANGLE. But why should he pray to *Mars?*
PUFF. Hush!

EARL OF LEICESTER.
>   If in thy homage bred,
>   Each point of discipline I've still observ'd;
>   Nor but by due promotion, and the right
>   Of service, to the rank of Major-General
>   Have ris'n; assist thy votary now!
GOVERNOR.
>   Yet do not rise,——hear me!
MASTER OF HORSE.
>   And me!
KNIGHT.
>   And me!

SIR WALTER.
    And me!
SIR CHRISTOPHER.
    And me!

PUFF. Now, pray all together.

ALL.
    Behold thy votaries submissive beg,
    That thou will deign to grant them all they ask;
    Assist them to accomplish all their ends,
    And sanctify whatever means they use
    To gain them!

SNEER. A very orthodox quintetto!
PUFF. Vastly well, gentlemen.—Is that well managed or not? Have you such a
    prayer as that on the stage?
SNEER. Not exactly.

    [EARL OF LEICESTER to PUFF]
    But, Sir, you hav'nt settled how we are to get off here.

PUFF. You could not go off kneeling, could you?

    [SIR WALTER to PUFF.]
    O no, Sir! impossible!

PUFF. It would have a good effect efaith, if you could! exeunt praying!—Yes,
    and would vary the established mode of springing off with a glance at the pit.
SNEER. O never mind, so as you get them off, I'll answer for it the audience
    won't care how.
PUFF. Well then, repeat the last line standing, and go off the old way.

ALL.
    And sanctify whatever means we use to gain them.   *[Exeunt.]*

DANGLE. Bravo! a fine exit.
SNEER. Well, really Mr. Puff.——
PUFF. Stay a moment.——

THE CENTINELS *get up.*

1ST CENTINEL.
    All this shall to Lord Burleigh's ear.

2D CENTINEL.
    'Tis meet it should.   [*Exeunt* CENTINELS.]

DANGLE. Hey!—why, I thought those fellows had been asleep?

PUFF. Only a pretence, there's the art of it; they were spies of Lord Burleigh's.

SNEER.—But isn't it odd, they were never taken notice of, not even by the commander in chief.

PUFF. O lud, Sir, if people who want to listen, or overhear, were not always conniv'd at in a Tragedy, there would be no carrying on any plot in the world.

DANGLE. That's certain!

PUFF. But take care, my dear Dangle, the morning gun is going to fire.

                                             [*Cannon fires.*]

DANGLE. Well, that will have a fine effect.

PUFF. I think so, and helps to realize the scene.—   [*Cannon twice.*]
    What the plague!—*three* morning guns!—there never is but one!—aye, this is always the way at the Theatre—give these fellows a good thing, and they never know when to have done with it. You have no more cannon to fire?

PROMPTER *from within*. No Sir.

PUFF. Now then, for soft musick.

SNEER. Pray what's that for?

PUFF. It shews that Tilburina is coming; nothing introduces you a heroine like soft musick.—Here she comes.

DANGLE. And her confidant, I suppose?

PUFF. To be sure: here they are—inconsolable to the minuet in Ariadne!
(*Soft musick.*)

Enter TILBURINA *and* CONFIDANT.

TILBURINA.
    Now has the whispering breath of gentle morn,
    Bad Nature's voice, and Nature's beauty rise;
    While orient Phoebus with unborrow'd hues,
    Cloaths the wak'd loveliness which all night slept
    In heav'nly drapery! Darkness is fled.
    Now flowers unfold their beauties to the sun,
    And blushing, kiss the beam he sends to wake them,
    The strip'd carnation, and the guarded rose,

> The vulgar wall flow'r, and smart gillyflower,
> The polyanthus mean—the dapper daizy,
> Sweet William, and sweet marjorum,——and all
> The tribe of single and of double pinks!
> Now too, the feather'd warblers tune their notes
> Around, and charm the listning grove.—The lark!
> The linnet! chafinch! bullfinch! goldfinch! greenfinch!
> ——But O to me, no joy can they afford!
> Nor rose, nor wall flow'r, nor smart gillyflower,
> Nor polyanthus mean, nor dapper daizy,
> Nor William sweet, no marjoram——nor lark,
> Linnet, nor all the finches of the grove!

PUFF. Your white handkerchief madam——
TILBURINA. I thought, Sir, I wasn't to use that 'till, "heart rending woe."
PUFF. O yes madam—at "the finches of the grove," if you please.

> TILBURINA.
> Nor lark,
> Linnet, nor all the finches of the grove!   [*Weeps.*]

PUFF. Vastly well madam!
DANGLE. Vastly well indeed!

> TILBURINA.
> For, O too sure, heart rending woe is now
> The lot of wretched Tilburina!

DANGLE. O!—'tis too much.
SNEER. Oh!—it is indeed

> CONFIDANT.
> Be comforted sweet lady—for who knows,
> But Heav'n has yet some milk-white day in store.

> TILBURINA.
> Alas, my gentle Nora,
> Thy tender youth, as yet hath never mourn'd
> Love's fatal dart.—Else wouldst thou know, that when
> The soul is sunk in comfortless despair,
> It cannot taste of merryment!

DANGLE. That's certain.

CONFIDANT.
   But see where your stern father comes;
   It is not meet that he should find you thus.

PUFF. Hey, what the plague!—what a cut is here!—why, what is become of the
   description of her first meeting with Don Whiskerandos? his gallant behav-
   iour in the sea fight, and the simile of the canary bird?
TILBURINA. Indeed, Sir, you'll find they will not be miss'd.
PUFF. Very well.—Very well!
TILBURINA. The cue ma'am if you please.

CONFIDANT.
   It is not meet that he should find you thus.
TILBURINA.
   Thou counsel'st right, but 'tis no easy task
   For barefaced grief to wear a mask of joy
Enter GOVERNOR.
   How's this—in tears?——O Tilburina, shame!
   Is this a time for maudling tenderness.
   And Cupid's baby woes?——hast thou not heard
   That haughty Spain's Pope-consecrated fleet
   Advances to our shores, while England's fate,
   Like a clipp'd guinea, trembles in the scale!
TILBURINA.
   Then, is the crisis of *my* fate at hand!
   I see the fleets approach——I see——

PUFF. Now, pray gentlemen mind.—This is one of the most useful figures we
   tragedy writers have, by which a hero or heroine, in consideration of their
   being often obliged to overlook things that *are* on the stage, is allow'd to hear
   and see a number of things that are not.
SNEER. Yes—a kind of poetical second-sight!
PUFF. Yes—now then madam.

TILBURINA.
   I see their decks
   Are clear'd——I see the signal made!
   The line is form'd!——a cable's length asunder!

> I see the frigates station'd in the rear;
> And now, I hear the thunder of the guns!
> I hear the victor's shouts——I also hear
> The vanquish'd groan!——and now 'tis smoke——and now
> I see the loose sails shiver in the wind!
> I see——I see——what soon you'll see——

GOVERNOR.

> Hold daughter! peace! this love hath turn'd thy brain:
> The Spanish fleet thou *canst* not see—because
> ——It is not yet in sight!

DANGLE. Egad tho', the governor seems to make no allowance for this poetical figure you talk of.

PUFF. No, a plain matter-of-fact man—that's his character.

TILBURINA.

> But will you then refuse his offer?

GOVERNOR.

> I must—I will—I can—I ought—I do.

TILBURINA.

> Think what a noble price.

GOVERNOR.

> No more——you urge in vain.

TILBURINA.

> His liberty is all he asks.

SNEER. All *who* asks Mr. Puff? Who is—

PUFF. Egad Sir, I can't tell.—Here has been such cutting and slashing, I don't know where they have got to myself.

TILBURINA. Indeed, Sir, you will find it will connect very well.

> ——And your reward secure.

PUFF. O,—if they had'nt been so devilish free with their cutting here, you would have found that Don Whiskerandos has been tampering for his liberty, and has persuaded Tilburina to make this proposal to her father—and now pray observe the conciseness with which the argument is conducted. Egad, the *pro & con* goes as smart as hits in a fencing match. It is indeed a sort of small-sword logic, which we have borrowed from the French.

TILBURINA.

> A retreat in Spain!

GOVERNOR.
　Outlawry here!
TILBURINA.
　Your daughter's prayer!
GOVERNOR.
　Your father's oath!
TILBURINA.
　My lover!
GOVERNOR.
　My country!
TILBURINA.
　Tilburina!
GOVERNOR.
　England!
TILBURINA.
　A title!
GOVERNOR.
　Honor!
TILBURINA.
　A pension!
GOVERNOR.
　Conscience!
TILBURINA.
　A thousand pounds!
GOVERNOR.
　Hah! thou hast touch'd me nearly!

PUFF. There you see—she threw in *Tilburina*, Quick, parry cart with *England!*—Hah! thrust in tierce a title!—parried by honor.—Hah! a pension over the arm!—put by by conscience.—Then flankonade with a thousand pounds—and a palpable hit egad!

TILBURINA.
　Canst thou——
　Reject the *suppliant*, and the *daughter* too?
GOVERNOR.
　No more, I wou'd not hear thee plead in vain,
　The *father* softens—but the *governor*
　Is fix'd!
　　　　　　　　　　　　　　　　　　　　　　　　［*Exit.*］

DANGLE. Aye, that antithesis of persons—is a most establish'd figure.

TILBURINA.
   'Tis well,——hence then fond hopes,——fond passion hence;
   Duty, behold I am all over thine——
WHISKERANDOS *without*.
   Where is my love——my——
TILBURINA.
   Ha!
WHISKERANDOS *entering*.
   My beauteous enemy——

PUFF. O dear ma'am, you must start a great deal more than that; consider you
   had just determined in favour of duty—when in a moment the sound of his
   voice revives your passion,—overthrows your resolution, destroys your obedience.—If you don't express all that in your start—you do nothing at all.
TILBURINA. Well, we'll try again!
DANGLE. Speaking from within, has always a fine effect.
SNEER. Very.

WHISKERANDOS.
   My conquering Tilburina! How! is't thus
   We meet? why are thy looks averse! what means
   That falling tear——that frown of boding woe?
   Hah! now indeed I am a prisoner!
   Yes, now I feel the galling weight of these
   Disgraceful chains——which, cruel Tilburina!
   Thy doating captive gloried in before.——
   But thou art false, and Whiskerandos is undone.
TILBURINA.
   O no; how little dost thou know thy Tilburina!
WHISKERANDOS.
   Art thou then true? Begone cares, doubts and fears,
   I make you all a present to the winds;
   And if the winds reject you——try the waves.

PUFF. The wind you know, is the established receiver of all stolen sighs, and cast
   off griefs and apprehensions.

TILBURINA.
   Yet must we part?——stern duty seals our doom:
   Though here I call yon conscious clouds to witness,

Could I pursue the bias of my soul,
All friends, all right of parents I'd disclaim
And thou, my Whiskerandos, should'st be father
And mother, brother, cousin, uncle, aunt,
And friend to me!
WHISKERANDOS.
O matchless excellence!——and must we part?
Well, if——we must——we must——and in that case,
The less is said the better.

PUFF. Hey day! here's a cut!—What, are all the mutual protestations out?
TILBURINA. Now, pray Sir, don't interrupt us just here, you ruin our feelings.
PUFF. *Your* feelings!—but zounds, *my* feelings, ma'am!
SNEER. No; pray don't interrupt them.

WHISKERANDOS.
One last embrace.——
TILBURINA.
Now,——farewell, for ever.
WHISKERANDOS.
For ever!
TILBURINA.
Aye, for ever.   [*Going.*]

PUFF. S'death and fury!—Gadslife! Sir! Madam! if you go out without the part-
   ing look, you might as well dance out—Here, here!
CONFIDANT. But pray Sir, how am *I* to get off here?
PUFF. *You,* pshaw! what the devil signifies how *you* get off! edge away at the top,
   or where you will—[*Pushes the confidant off.*] Now ma'am you see—
TILBURINA. We understand you Sir.

Aye for ever.
BOTH.
Ohh!——   [*Turning back and exeunt.*]
                                                    [*Scene closes.*]

DANGLE. O charming!
PUFF. Hey!—'tis pretty well I believe—you see I don't attempt to strike out any
   thing new—but I take it I improve on the established modes.
SNEER. You do indeed.—But pray is not Queen Elizabeth to appear?
PUFF. No not once—but she is to be talked of for ever; so that egad you'll think
   a hundred times that she is on the point of coming in.

SNEER. Hang it, I think its a pity to keep *her* in the green room all the night.

PUFF. O no, that always has a fine effect—it keeps up expectation.

DANGLE. But are we not to have a battle?

PUFF. Yes, yes, you will have a battle at last, but, egad, it's not to be by land—but by sea—and that is the only quite new thing in the piece.

DANGLE. What, Drake at the Armada, hey?

PUFF. Yes, efaith—fire ships and all—then we shall end with the procession.— Hey! that will do I think.

SNEER. No doubt on't.

PUFF. Come we must not lose time—so now for the Under Plot.

SNEER. What the plague, have you another plot?

PUFF. O lord, yes—ever while you live, have two plots to your tragedy.—The grand point in managing them, is only to let your under plot have as little connection with your main plot as possible.—I flatter myself nothing can be more distinct than mine, for as in my chief plot, the characters are all great people— I have laid my under plot in low life—and as the former is to end in deep distress, I make the other end as happy as a farce.—Now Mr. Hopkins, as soon as you please.

Enter UNDER PROMPTER.

UNDER PROMPTER. Sir, the carpenter says it is impossible you can go to the Park scene yet.

PUFF. The Park scene! No— I mean the description scene here, in the wood.

UNDER PROMPTER. Sir, the performers have cut it out.

PUFF. Cut it out!

UNDER PROMPTER. Yes Sir.

PUFF. What! the whole account of Queen Elizabeth?

UNDER PROMPTER. Yes Sir.

PUFF. And the description of her horse and the side-saddle?

UNDER PROMPTER. Yes Sir.

PUFF. So, so, this is very fine indeed! Mr. Hopkins, how the plague could you suffer this?

HOPKINS, *from within*. Sir, indeed the pruning knife—

PUFF. The pruning knife—zounds the axe! why, here has been such lopping and topping, I shan't have the bare trunk of my play left presently.—Very well, Sir—the performers must do as they please, but upon my soul, I'll print it every word.

SNEER. That I would indeed.

PUFF. Very well—Sir—then we must go on —zounds! I would not have parted with the description of the horse!—Well, Sir, go on—Sir, it was one of the finest and most laboured things—Very well, Sir, let them go on—there you

had him and his accoutrements from the bit to the crupper—very well, Sir, we
must go to the Park scene.

UNDER PROMPTER. Sir, there is the point, the carpenters say, that unless
there is some business put in here before the drop, they shan't have time to
clear away the fort, or sink Gravesend and the river.

PUFF. So! this is a pretty dilemma truly!—Gentlemen—you must excuse me,
these fellows will never be ready, unless I go and look after them myself.

SNEER. O dear Sir—these little things will happen—

PUFF. To cut out this scene!—but I'll print it—egad, I'll print it every word!

[*Exeunt.*]

ACT III

SCENE I

Before the Curtain.

Enter PUFF, SNEER, *and* DANGLE.

PUFF. Well, we are ready—now then for the justices.

[*Curtain rises; Justice, Constables, & c. discovered.*]

SNEER. This, I suppose, is a sort of senate scene.

PUFF. To be sure—there has not been one yet.

DANGLE. It is the under plot, isn't it?

PUFF. Yes. What, gentlemen, do you mean to go at once to the discovery scene?

JUSTICE. If you please, Sir.

PUFF. O very well—harkee, I don't chuse to say any thing more, but efaith, they
have mangled my play in a most shocking manner!

DANGLE. It's a great pity!

PUFF. Now then, Mr. Justice, if you please.

JUSTICE.
  Are all the volunteers without?
CONSTABLE.
  They are.
  Some ten in fetters, and some twenty drunk.
JUSTICE.
  Attends the youth, whose most opprobrious fame
  And clear convicted crimes have stampt him soldier?
CONSTABLE.
  He waits your pleasure; eager to repay
  The blest reprieve that sends him to the fields

> Of glory, there to raise his branded hand
> In honour's cause.

JUSTICE

> 'Tis well——'tis Justice arms him!
> O! may he now defend his country's laws
> With half the spirit he has broke them all!
> If 'tis your worship's pleasure, bid him enter.

CONSTABLE

> I fly, the herald of your will.   [*Exit* CONSTABLE.]

PUFF. Quick, Sir!——

SNEER. But, Mr. Puff, I think not only the Justice, but the clown seems to talk in as high a style as the first hero among them.

PUFF. Heaven forbid they should not in a free country!—Sir, I am not for making slavish distinctions, and giving all the fine language to the upper sort of people.

DANGLE. That's very noble in you indeed.

Enter JUSTICE'S LADY.

PUFF. Now pray mark this scene.

LADY.

> Forgive this interruption, good my love;
> But as I just now past, a pris'ner youth
> Whom rude hands hither lead, strange bodings seiz'd
> My fluttering heart, and to myself I said,
> An if our Tom had liv'd, he'd surely been
> This stripling's height!

JUSTICE.

> Ha! sure some powerful sympathy directs
> Us both——

Enter SON *and* CONSTABLE.

JUSTICE.

> What is thy name!

SON.

> My name's Tom Jenkins—*alias*, have I none—
> Tho' orphan'd, and without a friend!

JUSTICE.

> Thy parents?

SON.
>   My father dwelt in Rochester——and was,
>   As I have heard——a fishmonger——no more.

PUFF. What, Sir, do you leave out the account of your birth, parentage and education?

SON. They have settled it so, Sir, here.

PUFF. Oh! oh!

LADY.
>   How loudly nature whispers to my heart!
>   Had he no other name?

SON.
>   I've seen a bill
>   Of his, sign'd *Tomkins*, creditor.

JUSTICE.
>   This does indeed confirm each circumstance
>   The gypsey told!——Prepare!

SON.
>   I do.

JUSTICE.
>   No orphan, nor without a friend art thou—
>   *I* am thy father, *here's* thy mother, *there*
>   Thy uncle——this thy first cousin, and those
>   Are all your near relations!

MOTHER.
>   O ecstasy of bliss!

SON.
>   O most unlook'd for happiness!

JUSTICE.
>   O wonderful event!

>   [*They faint alternately in each others arms.*]

PUFF. There, you see relationship, like murder, will out.

JUSTICE.
>   Now let's revive——else were this joy too much!
>   But come——and we'll unfold the rest within,
>   And thou my boy must needs want rest and food.
>   Hence may each orphan hope, as chance directs,
>   To find a father—where he least expects!   [*Exeunt.*]

PUFF. What do you think of that?

DANGLE. One of the finest discovery-scenes I ever saw.—Why, this under-plot would have made a tragedy itself.

SNEER. Aye, or a comedy either.

PUFF. And keeps quite clear you see of the other.

Enter SCENEMEN, *taking away the Seats.*

PUFF. The scene remains, does it?

SCENEMAN. Yes, Sir.

PUFF. You are to leave one chair you know—But it is always awkward in a tragedy, to have you fellows coming in in your playhouse liveries to remove things—I wish that could be managed better.—So now for my mysterious yeoman.

Enter A BEEFEATER.

BEEFEATER.
    Perdition catch my soul but *I* do love thee.

SNEER. Haven't I heard that line before?

PUFF. No, I fancy not—Where pray?

DANGLE. Yes, I think there is something like it in Othello.

PUFF. Gad! now you put me in mind on't, I believe there is—but that's of no consequence—all that can be said is, that two people happened to hit on the same thought—And Shakespeare made use of it first, that's all.

SNEER. Very true.

PUFF. Now, Sir, your soliloquy—but speak more to the pit, if you please—the soliloquy always to the pit—that's a rule.

BEEFEATER.
    Tho, hopeless love finds comfort in despair,
    It never can endure a rival's bliss!
    But soft——I am observ'd.   [*Exit* BEEFEATER.]

DANGLE. That's a very short soliloquy.

PUFF. Yes—but it would have been a great deal longer if he had not been observed.

SNEER. A most sentimental Beefeater that, Mr. Puff.

PUFF. Hark'ee—I would not have you be too sure that he *is* a Beefeater.

SNEER. What! a hero in disguise?

PUFF. No matter—I only give you a hint—But now for my principal character—Here he comes—Lord Burleigh in person! Pray, gentlemen, step this
way—softly—I only hope the Lord High Treasurer is perfect—if he is but
perfect!

Enter BURLEIGH, *goes slowly to a chair and sits.*

SNEER. Mr. Puff!

PUFF. Hush!—vastly well, Sir! vastly well! a most interesting gravity!

DANGLE. What, isn't he to speak at all?

PUFF. Egad, I thought you'd ask me that—yes it is a very likely thing—that a
Minister in his situation, with the whole affairs of the nation on his head,
should have time to talk!—but hush! or you'll put him out.

SNEER. Put him out! how the plague can that be, if he's not going to say any
thing?

PUFF. There's a reason!—why, his part is to *think*, and how the plague! do you
imagine he can *think* if you keep talking?

DANGLE. That's very true upon my word!

[BURLEIGH *comes forward, shakes his head and exit.*]

SNEER. He is very perfect indeed—Now, pray what did he mean by that?

PUFF. You don't take it?

SNEER. No; I don't upon my soul.

PUFF. Why, by that shake of the head, he gave you to understand that even tho'
they had more justice in their cause and wisdom in their measures—yet, if
there was not a greater spirit shown on the part of the people—the country
would at last fall a sacrifice to the hostile ambition of the Spanish monarchy.

SNEER. The devil!—did he mean all that by shaking his head?

PUFF. Every word of it—If he shook his head as I taught him.

DANGLE. Ah! there certainly is a vast deal to be done on the stage by dumb
shew, and expression of face, and a judicious author knows how much he may
trust to it.

SNEER. O, here are some of our old acquaintance.

Enter HATTON *and* RALEIGH.

SIR CHRISTOPHER.

My niece, and *your* niece too!

By heav'n! there's witchcraft in't——He could not else

Have gain'd their hearts——But see where they approach;

Some horrid purpose low'ring on their brows!

SIR WALTER.

Let us withdraw and mark them.   [*They withdraw.*]

SNEER. What is all this?

PUFF. Ah! here has been more pruning!—but the fact is, these two young ladies are also in love with Don Whiskerandos.—Now, gentlemen, this scene goes entirely for what we call Situation and Stage Effect, by which the greatest applause may be obtained, without the assistance of language, sentiment or character: pray mark!

Enter the TWO NIECES.

1ST NIECE.
    Ellena here!
    She is his scorn as much as I—that is
    Some comfort still.

PUFF. O dear madam, you are not to say that to her face!—*aside*, ma'am, *aside.*— The whole scene is to be *aside*.

1ST NIECE.
    She is his scorn as much as I—that is
    Some comfort still!   [*Aside.*]
2D NIECE.
    I know he prizes not Pollina's love,
    But Tilburina lords it o'er his heart.   [*Aside.*]
1ST NIECE.
    But see the proud destroyer of my peace.
    Revenge is all the good I've left.   [*Aside.*]
2D NIECE.
    He comes, the false disturber of my quiet.
    Now vengeance do thy worst——   [*Aside.*]

Enter WHISKERANDOS.

    O hateful liberty—if thus in vain
    I seek my Tilburina!
BOTH NIECES.
    And ever shalt!

SIR CHRISTOPHER AND SIR WALTER *come forward.*
    Hold! we will avenge you.
WHISKERANDOS.
    Hold *you*—or see your nieces bleed!

[*The two nieces draw their two daggers to strike* Whiskerandos, *the two Uncles at the instant with their two swords drawn, catch their two nieces' arms, and turn the points of their swords to* Whiskerandos, *who immediately draws two daggers, and holds them to the two nieces' bosoms.*]

PUFF. There's situation for you!—there's an heroic group!—You see the ladies can't stab Whiskerandos—he durst not strike them for fear of their uncles—the uncles durst not kill him, because of their nieces—I have them all at a dead lock!—for every one of them is afraid to let go first.

SNEER. Why, then they must stand there for ever.

PUFF. So they would, if I hadn't a very fine contrivance for't—Now mind——

Enter BEEFEATER *with his Halberd.*

In the Queen's name I charge you all to drop
Your swords and daggers!   [*They drop their swords and daggers.*]

SNEER. That is a contrivance indeed.

PURR. Aye—in the queen's name.

SIR CHRISTOPHER.
Come niece!
SIR WALTER.
Come niece!   [*Exeunt with the two nieces.*]

WHISKERANDOS.
What's he, who bids us thus renounce our guard?
BEEFEATER.
Thou must do more, renounce thy love!
WHISKERANDOS.
Thou liest—base Beefeater!
BEEFEATER.
Ha! Hell! the lie!
By heav'n thou'st rous'd the lion in my heart!
Off yeomans' habit!—base disguise!—off! off!
                              [*Discovers himself, by throwing off his upper dress,
                                  and appearing in a very fine waistcoat.*]
Am I a Beefeater now!
Or beams my crest as terrible as when
In Biscay's Bay I took thy captive sloop.

PUFF. There, egad! he comes out to be the very Captain of the privateer who had
    taken Whiskerandos prisoner—and was himself an old lover of Tilburina's.
DANGLE. Admirably managed indeed.
PUFF. Now, stand out of their way.

> WHISKERANDOS.
>   I thank thee fortune! that has thus bestow'd
>   A weapon to chastise this insolent.   [*Takes up one of the swords.*]
> BEEFEATER.
>   I take thy challenge, Spaniard, and I thank
>   Thee Fortune too!—   [*Takes up the other sword.*]

DANGLE. That's excellently contrived!—it seems as if the two uncles had left
    their swords on purpose for them.
PUFF. No, egad, they could not help leaving them.

> WHISKERANDOS.
>   Vengeance and Tilburina!
> BEEFEATER.
>   Exactly so——   [*They fight—and after the usual number
>   of wounds given,* Whiskerandos *falls.*]
> WHISKERANDOS.
>   O cursed parry!——that last thrust in tierce
>   Was fatal——Captain, thou hast fenced well!
>   And Whiskerandos quits this bustling scene
>   For all eter——
> BEEFEATER.
>   —nity—He would have added, but stern death
>   Cut short his being, and the noun at once!

PUFF. O, my dear Sir, you are too slow, now mind me.—Sir, shall I trouble you
    to die again?

> WHISKERANDOS.
>   And Whiskerandos quits this bustling scene
>   For all eter——
> BEEFEATER.
>   ——nity—He would have added——

PUFF. No, Sir—that's not it—once more if you please—
WHISKERANDOS. I wish, Sir—that you would practise this without me—I

can't stay dying here all night.

PUFF. Very well, we'll go over it by and bye——I must humour these gentlemen!

[*Exit* WHISKERANDOS.]

BEEFEATER.
    Farewell,——brave Spaniard! and when next——

PUFF. Dear Sir, you needn't speak that speech as the body has walked off.

BEEFEATER. That's true, Sir—then I'll join the fleet.

PUFF. If you please.   [*Exit* BEEFEATER.]

    Now, who comes on?

Enter GOVERNOR, *with his hair properly disordered.*

GOVERNOR.
    A hemisphere of evil planets reign!
    And every planet sheds contagious phrensy!
    My Spanish prisoner is slain! my daughter,
    Meeting the dead corse borne along—has gone.
    Distract!   [*A loud flourish of trumpets.*]
    But hark! I am summon'd to the fort.
    Perhaps the fleets have met! amazing crisis!
    O Tilburina! from thy aged father's beard
    Thou'st pluck'd the few brown hairs which time had left!

[*Exit* GOVERNOR.]

SNEER. Poor gentleman!

PUFF. Yes—and no one to blame but his daughter!

DANGLE. And the planets——

PUFF. True.—Now enter Tilburina!—

SNEER. Egad, the business comes on quick here.

PUFF. Yes, Sir—now she comes in stark mad in white satin.

SNEER. Why in white satin?

PUFF. O Lord, Sir—when a heroine goes mad, she always goes into white satin—don't she, Dangle?

DANGLE. Always—it's a rule.

PUFF. Yes—here it is—[*looking at the book.*] "Enter Tilburina stark mad in white satin, and her confidant stark mad in white linen."

Enter TILBURINA *and* CONFIDANT *mad, according to custom.*

SNEER. But what the deuce, is the confidant to be mad too?

PUFF. To be sure she is, the confidant is always to do whatever her mistress does;

80

weep when she weeps, smile when she smiles, go mad when she goes mad.
——Now madam confidant—but—keep your madness in the back ground, if
you please.

TILBURINA.
    The wind whistles——the moon rises——see
    They have kill'd my squirrel in his cage!
    Is this a grasshopper!——Ha! no, it is my
    Whiskerandos——you shall not keep him——
    I know you have him in your pocket——
    An oyster may be cross'd in love!——Who says
    A whale's a bird?—Ha! did you call, my love?
    ——He's here! He's there!——He's every where!
    Ah me! He's no where!   [*Exit* TILBURINA.]

PUFF. There, do you ever desire to see any body madder than that?

SNEER. Never while I live!

PUFF. You observed how she mangled the metre?

DANGLE. Yes—egad, it was the first thing made me suspect she was out of her
    senses.

SNEER. And pray what becomes of her?

PUFF. She is gone to throw herself into the sea to be sure—and that brings us at
    once to the scene of action, and so to my catastrophe—my sea-fight, I mean.

SNEER. What, you bring that in at last?

PUFF. Yes—yes—you know my play is *called* the *Spanish Armada*, otherwise,
    egad, I have no occasion for the battle at all.—Now then for my magnifi-
    cence!—my battle!—my noise!—and my procession!—You are all ready?

PROMPTER *within*. Yes, Sir.

PUFF. Is the Thames drest?

Enter THAMES *with two Attendants.*

THAMES. Here I am, Sir.

PUFF. Very well indeed—See, gentlemen, there's a river for you!—This is blend-
    ing a little of the masque with my tragedy—a new fancy you know—and very
    useful in my case; for as there *must be* a *procession*, I suppose Thames and all
    his tributary rivers to compliment Britannia with a fete in honor of the victory.

SNEER. But pray, who are these gentlemen in green with him.

PUFF. Those?—those are his banks.

SNEER. His banks?

PUFF. Yes, one crown'd with alders and the other with a villa!—you take the
    allusions?—but hey! what the plague! you have got both your banks on one

side—Here Sir, come round—Ever while you live, Thames, go between your banks. (*Bell rings.*)—There, soh! now for't!—Stand aside my dear friends!—away Thames! [*Exit* THAMES *between his banks.*]

[*Flourish of drums——trumpets——cannon, &c. &c. Scene changes to the sea——the fleets engage——the musick plays "Britons strike home."—Spanish fleet destroyed by fire-ships, &c.—English fleet advances—musick plays "Rule Britannia."—The procession of all the English rivers and their tributaries with their emblems, &c. begins with Handel's water musick—ends with a chorus, to the march in Judas Maccabœus.—During this scene, Puff directs and applauds every thing—then*]

PUFF. Well, pretty well—but not quite perfect—so ladies and gentlemen, if you please, we'll rehearse this piece again to-morrow.

CURTAIN DROPS

END

CARMILLA

"Carmilla," Sheridan Le Fanu's tale of an exceedingly languorous female vampire, appeared in 1872, predating Dracula *by twenty-five years. Le Fanu set the supernatural activity in a region of Austria far from Dublin, where, after the death of his wife in 1858, he became a recluse and wrote a prodigious amount of spooky stories.*

I

AN EARLY FRIGHT

IN STYRIA, WE, THOUGH BY NO means magnificent people, inhabit a castle, or schloss. A small income, in that part of the world, goes a great way. Eight or nine hundred a year does wonders. Scantily enough ours would have answered among wealthy people at home. My father is English, and I bear an English name, although I never saw England. But here, in this lonely and primitive place, where everything is so marvellously cheap, I really don't see how ever so much more money would at all materially add to our comforts, or even luxuries.

My father was in the Austrian service, and retired upon a pension and his patrimony, and purchased this feudal residence, and the small estate on which it stands, a bargain.

Nothing can be more picturesque or solitary. It stands on a slight eminence in a forest. The road, very old and narrow, passes in front of its drawbridge, never raised in my time, and its moat, stocked with perch, and sailed over by many swans, and floating on its surface white fleets of water-lilies.

Over all this the schloss shows its many-windowed front; its towers, and its Gothic chapel.

The forest opens in an irregular and very picturesque glade before its gate, and at the right a steep Gothic bridge carries the road over a stream that winds in deep shadow through the wood.

I have said this is a very lonely place. Judge whether I say truth. Looking from the hall door towards the road, the forest in which our castle stands extends fifteen miles to the right, and twelve to the left. The nearest inhabited village is about seven of your English miles to the left. The nearest inhabited schloss of any historic associations, is that of old General Spielsdorf, nearly twenty miles away to the right.

I have said "the nearest *inhabited* village," because there is, only three miles westward, that is to say in the direction of General Spielsdorf's schloss, a ruined village, with its quaint little church, now roofless, in the aisle of which are the mouldering tombs of the proud family of Karnstein, now extinct, who once owned the equally desolate château which, in the thick of the forest, overlooks the silent ruins of the town.

Respecting the cause of the desertion of this striking and melancholy spot, there is a legend which I shall relate to you another time.

I must tell you now, how very small is the party who constitute the inhabitants of our castle. I don't include servants, or those dependents who occupy rooms in the buildings attached to the schloss. Listen, and wonder! My father, who is the kindest man on earth, but growing old; and I, at the date of my story, only nineteen. Eight years have passed since then. I and my father constituted the family at the schloss. My mother, a Styrian lady, died in my infancy, but I had a good-natured governess, who had been with me from, I might almost say, my infancy. I could not remember the time when her fat, benignant face was not a familiar picture in my memory. This was Madame Perrodon, a native of Berne, whose care and good nature in part supplied to me the loss of my mother, whom I do not even remember, so early I lost her. She made a third at our little dinner party. There was a fourth, Mademoiselle De Lafontaine, a lady such as you term, I believe, a "finishing governess." She spoke French and German, Madame Perrodon French and broken English, to which my father and I added English, which, partly to prevent its becoming a lost language among us, and partly from patriotic motives, we spoke every day. The consequence was a Babel, at which strangers used to laugh, and which I shall make no attempt to reproduce in this narrative. And there were two or three young lady friends besides, pretty nearly of my own age, who were occasional visitors, for longer or shorter terms; and these visits I sometimes returned.

These were our regular social resources; but of course there were chance visits from "neighbours" of only five or six leagues distance. My life was, notwithstanding, rather a solitary one, I can assure you.

My gouvernantes had just so much control over me as you might conjecture such sage persons would have in the case of a rather spoiled girl, whose only parent allowed her pretty nearly her own way in everything.

The first occurrence in my existence, which produced a terrible impression upon my mind, which, in fact, never has been effaced, was one of the very earliest incidents of my life which I can recollect. Some people will think it so trifling that it should not be recorded here. You will see, however, by-and-by, why I mention it. The nursery, as it was called, though I had it all to myself, was a large room in the upper story of the castle, with a steep oak roof. I can't have been more than six years old, when one night I awoke, and looking round the room from my bed, failed to see the nursery-maid. Neither was my nurse there; and I thought myself alone. I was not frightened, for I was one of those happy children who are studiously kept in ignorance of ghost stories, of fairy tales, and of all such lore as makes us cover up our heads when the door creaks suddenly, or the flicker of an expiring candle makes the shadow of a bed-post dance upon the wall, nearer to our faces. I was vexed and insulted at finding myself, as I conceived, neglected, and I began to whimper, preparatory to a hearty bout of roaring; when to my surprise, I saw a solemn, but very pretty face looking at me from the side of the bed. It was that of a young lady who was kneeling, with her hands under the coverlet. I looked at her with a kind of pleased wonder, and ceased whimpering. She caressed me with her hands, and lay down beside me on the bed, and drew me towards her, smiling; I felt immediately delightfully soothed, and fell asleep again. I was wakened by a sensation as if two needles ran into my breast very deep at the same moment, and I cried loudly. The lady started back, with her eyes fixed on me, and then slipped down upon the floor, and, as I thought, hid herself under the bed.

I was now for the first time frightened, and I yelled with all my might and main. Nurse, nursery-maid, housekeeper, all came running in, and hearing my story, they made light of it, soothing me all they could meanwhile. But, child as I was, I could perceive that their faces were pale with an unwonted look of anxiety, and I saw them look under the bed, and about the room, and peep under tables and pluck open cupboards; and the housekeeper whispered to the nurse: "Lay your hand along that hollow in the bed; some one *did* lie there, so sure as you did not; the place is still warm."

I remember the nursery-maid petting me, and all three examining my chest, where I told them I felt the puncture, and pronouncing that there was no sign visible that any such thing had happened to me.

The housekeeper and the two servants who were in charge of the nursery, remained sitting up all night; and from that time a servant always sat up in the nursery until I was about fourteen.

I was very nervous for a long time after this. A doctor was called in, he was pallid and elderly. How well I remember his long saturnine face, slightly pitted with smallpox, and his chestnut wig. For a good while, every second day, he came and gave me medicine, which of course I hated.

The morning after I saw this apparition I was in a state of terror, and could not bear to be left alone, daylight though it was, for a moment.

I remember my father coming up and standing at the bedside, and talking cheerfully, and asking the nurse a number of questions, and laughing very heartily at one of the answers; and patting me on the shoulder, and kissing me, and telling me not to be frightened, that it was nothing but a dream and could not hurt me.

But I was not comforted, for I knew the visit of the strange woman was *not* a dream; and I was *awfully* frightened.

I was a little consoled by the nursery-maid's assuring me that it was she who had come and looked at me, and lain down beside me in the bed, and that I must have been half-dreaming not to have known her face. But this, though supported by the nurse, did not quite satisfy me.

I remembered, in the course of that day, a venerable old man, in a black cassock, coming into the room with the nurse and housekeeper, and talking a little to them, and very kindly to me; his face was very sweet and gentle, and he told me they were going to pray, and joined my hands together, and desired me to say, softly, while they were praying, "Lord hear all good prayers for us, for Jesus' sake." I think these were the very words, for I often repeated them to myself, and my nurse used for years to make me say them in my prayers.

I remembered so well the thoughtful sweet face of that white-haired old man, in his black cassock, as he stood in that rude, lofty, brown room, with the clumsy furniture of a fashion three hundred years old, about him, and the scanty light entering its shadowy atmosphere through the small lattice. He kneeled, and the three women with him, and he prayed aloud with an earnest quavering voice for, what appeared to me, a long time. I forget all my life preceding that event, and for some time after it is all obscure also, but the scenes I have just described stand out vivid as the isolated pictures of the phantasmagoria surrounded by darkness.

II

A GUEST

I am now going to tell you something so strange that it will require all your faith in my veracity to believe my story. It is not only true, nevertheless, but truth of which I have been an eye-witness.

It was a sweet summer evening, and my father asked me, as he sometimes did, to take a little ramble with him along that beautiful forest vista which I have mentioned as lying in front of the schloss.

"General Spielsdorf cannot come to us so soon as I had hoped," said my father, as we pursued our walk.

He was to have paid us a visit of some weeks, and we had expected his arrival next day. He was to have brought with him a young lady, his niece and ward, Mademoiselle Rheinfeldt, whom I had never seen, but whom I had heard described as a very charming girl, and in whose society I had promised myself many happy days. I was more disappointed than a young lady living in a town, or a bustling neighbourhood can possibly imagine. This visit, and the new acquaintance it promised, had furnished my day dream for many weeks.

"And how soon does he come?" I asked.

"Not till autumn. Not for two months, I dare say," he answered. "And I am very glad now, dear, that you never knew Mademoiselle Rheinfeldt."

"And why?" I asked, both mortified and curious.

"Because the poor young lady is dead," he replied. "I quite forgot I had not told you, but you were not in the room when I received the General's letter this evening."

I was very much shocked. General Spielsdorf had mentioned in his first letter, six or seven weeks before, that she was not so well as he would wish her, but there was nothing to suggest the remotest suspicion of danger.

"Here is the General's letter," he said, handing it to me. "I am afraid he is in great affliction; the letter appears to me to have been written very nearly in distraction."

We sat down on a rude bench, under a group of magnificent lime-trees. The sun was setting with all its melancholy splendour behind the sylvan horizon, and the stream that flows beside our home, and passes under the steep old bridge I have mentioned, wound through many a group of noble trees, almost at our feet, reflecting in its current the fading crimson of the sky. General Spielsdorf's letter was so extraordinary, so vehement, and in some places so self-contradictory, that I read it twice over—the second time aloud to my father—and was still unable to account for it, except by supposing that grief had unsettled his mind.

It said "I have lost my darling daughter, for as such I loved her. During the last days of dear Bertha's illness I was not able to write to you. Before then I had no idea of her danger. I have lost her, and now learn *all*, too late. She died in the peace of innocence, and in the glorious hope of a blessed futurity. The fiend who betrayed our infatuated hospitality has done it all. I thought I was receiving into my house innocence, gaiety, a charming companion for my lost Bertha. Heavens! What a fool have I been! I thank God my child died without a suspicion of the cause of her sufferings. She is gone without so much as conjecturing the nature of her illness, and the accursed passion of the agent of all this misery. I devote my remaining days to tracking and extinguishing a monster. I am told I may hope to accomplish my righteous and merciful purpose. At present there is scarcely a gleam of light to guide me. I curse my conceited incredulity, my despicable affectation of superiority, my blindness, my obstinacy—all—too late. I cannot write or talk collectedly now. I am distracted. So soon as I shall have a little recovered, I mean to devote myself for a time to enquiry, which may possibly lead me as far as Vienna. Some time in the autumn, two months hence, or earlier if I live, I will see you—that is, if you permit me; I will then tell you all that I scarce dare put upon paper now. Farewell. Pray for me, dear friend."

In these terms ended this strange letter. Though I had never seen Bertha Rheinfeldt my eyes filled with tears at the sudden intelligence; I was startled, as well as profoundly disappointed.

The sun had now set, and it was twilight by the time I had returned the General's letter to my father.

It was a clear soft evening, and we loitered, speculating upon the possible meanings of the violent and incoherent sentences which I had just been reading. We had nearly a mile to walk before reaching the road that passes the schloss in front, and by that time the moon was shining brilliantly. At the drawbridge we met Madame Perrodon and Mademoiselle De Lafontaine, who had come out, without their bonnets, to enjoy the exquisite moonlight.

We heard their voices gabbling in animated dialogue as we approached. We joined them at the drawbridge, and turned about to admire with them the beautiful scene.

The glade through which we had just walked lay before us. At our left the narrow road wound away under clumps of lordly trees, and was lost to sight amid the thickening forest. At the right the same road crosses the steep and picturesque bridge, near which stands a ruined tower which once guarded that pass; and beyond the bridge an abrupt eminence rises, covered with trees, and showering in the shadows some grey ivy-clustered rocks.

Over the sward and low grounds a thin film of mist was stealing, like smoke, marking the distances with a transparent veil; and here and there we could see the river faintly flashing in the moonlight.

No softer, sweeter scene could be imagined. The news I had just heard made it melancholy; but nothing could disturb its character of profound serenity, and the enchanted glory and vagueness of the prospect.

My father, who enjoyed the picturesque, and I, stood looking in silence over the expanse beneath us. The two good governesses, standing a little way behind us, discoursed upon the scene, and were eloquent upon the moon.

Madame Perrodon was fat, middle-aged, and romantic, and talked and sighed poetically. Mademoiselle De Lafontaine—in right of her father, who was a German, assumed to be psychological, metaphysical, and something of a mystic—now declared that when the moon shone with a light so intense it was well known that it indicated a special spiritual activity. The effect of the full moon in such a state of brilliancy was manifold. It acted on dreams; it acted on lunacy, it acted on nervous people; it had marvellous physical influences connected with life. Mademoiselle related that her cousin, who was mate of a merchant ship, having taken a nap on deck on such a night, lying on his back, with his face full in the light of the moon, had wakened, after a dream of an old woman clawing him by the cheek, with his features horribly drawn to one side; and his countenance had never quite recovered its equilibrium.

"The moon, this night," she said, "is full of idyllic and magnetic influence—and see, when you look behind you at the front of the schloss how all its windows flash and twinkle with that silvery splendour, as if unseen hands had lighted up the rooms to receive fairy guests."

There are indolent states of the spirits in which, indisposed to talk ourselves, the talk of others is pleasant to our listless ears; and I gazed on, pleased with the tinkle of the ladies' conversation.

"I have got into one of my moping moods to-night," said my father, after a silence, and quoting Shakespeare, whom, by way of keeping up our English, he used to read aloud, he said:

In truth I know not why I am so sad:
It wearies me; you say it wearies you;
But how I got it—came by it.

"I forget the rest. But I feel as if some great misfortune were hanging over us. I suppose the poor General's afflicted letter has had something to do with it."

At this moment the unwonted sound of carriage wheels and many hoofs upon the road, arrested our attention.

They seemed to be approaching from the high ground overlooking the bridge, and very soon the equipage emerged from that point. Two horsemen first crossed the bridge, then came a carriage drawn by four horses, and two men rode behind.

It seemed to be the travelling carriage of a person of rank; and we were all immediately absorbed in watching that very unusual spectacle. It became, in a few moments, greatly more interesting, for just as the carriage had passed the summit of the steep bridge, one of the leaders, taking fright, communicated his panic to the rest, and after a plunge or two, the whole team broke into a wild gallop together, and dashing between the horsemen who rode in front, came thundering along the road towards us with the speed of a hurricane.

The excitement of the scene was made more painful by the clear, long-drawn screams of a female voice from the carriage window.

We all advanced in curiosity and horror; my father in silence, the rest with various ejaculations of terror.

Our suspense did not last long. Just before you reach the castle drawbridge, on the route they were coming, there stands by the roadside a magnificent lime-tree, on the other stands an ancient stone cross, at sight of which the horses, now going at a pace that was perfectly frightful, swerved so as to bring the wheel over the projecting roots of the tree.

I knew what was coming. I covered my eyes, unable to see it out, and turned my head away; at the same moment I heard a cry from my lady-friends, who had gone on a little.

Curiosity opened my eyes, and I saw a scene of utter confusion. Two of the horses were on the ground, the carriage lay upon its side with two wheels in the air; the men were busy removing the traces, and a lady, with a commanding air and figure had got out, and stood with clasped hands, raising the handkerchief that was in them every now and then to her eyes. Through the carriage door was now lifted a young lady, who appeared to be lifeless. My dear old father was already beside the elder lady, with his hat in his hand, evidently tendering his aid and the resources of his schloss. The lady did not appear to hear him, or to have eyes for anything but the slender girl who was being placed against the slope of the bank.

I approached; the young lady was apparently stunned, but she was certainly not dead. My father, who piqued himself on being something of a physician, had just had his fingers on her wrist and assured the lady, who declared herself her mother, that her pulse, though faint and irregular, was undoubtedly still distinguishable. The lady clasped her hands and looked upward, as if in a momentary transport of gratitude; but immediately she broke out again in that theatrical way which is, I believe, natural to some people.

She was what is called a fine looking woman for her time of life, and must have been handsome; she was tall, but not thin, and dressed in black velvet, and looked rather pale, but with a proud and commanding countenance, though now agitated strangely.

"Was ever being so born to calamity?" I heard her say, with clasped hands, as I came up. "Here am I, on a journey of life and death, in prosecuting which to lose an hour is possibly to lose all. My child will not have recovered sufficiently to resume her route for who can say how long. I must leave her; I cannot, dare not, delay. How far on, sir, can you tell, is the nearest village? I must leave her there; and shall not see my darling, or even hear of her till my return, three months hence."

I plucked my father by the coat, and whispered earnestly in his ear: "Oh! Papa, pray ask her to let her stay with us—it would be so delightful. Do, pray."

"If Madame will entrust her child to the care of my daughter, and of her good gouvernante, Madame Perrodon, and permit her to remain as our guest, under my charge, until her return, it will confer a distinction and an obligation upon us, and we shall treat her with all the care and devotion which so sacred a trust deserves."

"I cannot do that, sir, it would be to task your kindness and chivalry too cruelly," said the lady, distractedly.

"It would, on the contrary, be to confer on us a very great kindness at the moment when we most need it. My daughter has just been disappointed by a cruel misfortune, in a visit from which she had long anticipated a great deal of happiness. If you confide this young lady to our care it will be her best consolation. The nearest village on your route is distant, and affords no such inn as you could think of placing your daughter at; you cannot allow her to continue her journey for any considerable distance without danger. If, as you say, you cannot suspend your journey, you must part with her to-night, and nowhere could you do so with more honest assurances of care and tenderness than here."

There was something in this lady's air and appearance so distinguished, and even imposing, and in her manner so engaging, as to impress one, quite apart from the dignity of her equipage, with a conviction that she was a person of consequence.

By this time the carriage was replaced in its upright position, and the horses, quite tractable, in the traces again.

The lady threw on her daughter a glance which I fancied was not quite so affectionate as one might have anticipated from the beginning of the scene; then she beckoned slightly to my father, and withdrew two or three steps with him out of hearing; and talked to him with a fixed and stern countenance, not at all like that with which she had hitherto spoken.

I was filled with wonder that my father did not seem to perceive the change, and also unspeakably curious to learn what it could be that she was speaking, almost in his ear, with so much earnestness and rapidity.

Two or three minutes at most I think she remained thus employed, then she turned, and a few steps brought her to where her daughter lay, supported by Madame Perrodon. She kneeled beside her for a moment and whispered, as Madame supposed, a little benediction in her ear; then hastily kissing her she stepped into her carriage, the door was closed, the footmen in stately liveries jumped up behind, the outriders spurred on, the postillions cracked their whips, the horses plunged and broke suddenly into a furious canter that threatened soon again to become a gallop, and the carriage whirled away, followed at the same rapid pace by the two horsemen in the rear.

III

WE COMPARE NOTES

We followed the *cortège* with our eyes until it was swiftly lost to sight in the misty wood; and the very sound of the hoofs and the wheels died away in the silent night air.

Nothing remained to assure us that the adventure had not been an illusion of a moment but the young lady, who just at that moment opened her eyes. I could not see, for her face was turned from me, but she raised her head, evidently looking about her, and I heard a very sweet voice ask complainingly, "Where is mamma?"

Our good Madame Perrodon answered tenderly, and added some comfortable assurances.

I then heard her ask:

"Where am I? What is this place?" and after that she said, "I don't see the carriage; and Matska, where is she?"

Madame answered all her questions in so far as she understood them; and gradually the young lady remembered how the misadventure came about, and was glad to hear that no one in, or in attendance on, the carriage was hurt; and on learning that her mamma had left her here, till her return in about three months, she wept.

I was going to add my consolations to those of Madame Perrodon when Mademoiselle De Lafontaine placed her hand upon my arm, saying:

"Don't approach, one at a time is as much as she can at present converse with; a very little excitement would possibly overpower her now."

As soon as she is comfortably in bed, I thought, I will run up to her room and see her.

My father in the meantime had sent a servant on horseback for the physician, who lived about two leagues away; and a bedroom was being prepared for the young lady's reception.

The stranger now rose, and leaning on Madame's arm, walked slowly over the drawbridge and into the castle gate.

In the hall, servants waited to receive her, and she was conducted forthwith to her room.

The room we usually sat in as our drawing-room is long, having four windows, that looked over the moat and drawbridge, upon the forest scene I have just described.

It is furnished in old carved oak, with large carved cabinets, and the chairs are cushioned with crimson Utrecht velvet. The walls are covered with tapestry, and surrounded with great gold frames, the figures being as large as life, in ancient and very curious costume, and the subjects represented are hunting, hawking, and generally festive. It is not too stately to be extremely comfortable; and here we had our tea, for with his usual patriotic leanings Papa insisted that the national beverage should make its appearance regularly with our coffee and chocolate.

We sat here this night, and with candles lighted, were talking over the adventure of the evening.

Madame Perrodon and Mademoiselle De Lafontaine were both of our party. The young stranger had hardly lain down in her bed when she sank into a deep sleep; and those ladies had left her in the care of a servant.

"How do you like our guest?" I asked, as soon as Madame entered. "Tell me all about her?"

"I like her extremely," answered Madame, "she is, I almost think, the prettiest creature I ever saw; about your age, and so gentle and nice."

"She is absolutely beautiful," threw in Mademoiselle, who had peeped for a moment into the stranger's room.

"And such a sweet voice!" added Madame Perrodon.

"Did you remark a woman in the carriage, after it was set up again, who did not get out," inquired Mademoiselle, "but only looked from the window?"

"No, we had not seen her."

Then she described a hideous black woman, with a sort of coloured turban on her head, and who was gazing all the time from the carriage window, nodding and grinning derisively towards the ladies, with gleaming eyes and large white eye-balls, and her teeth set as if in fury.

"Did you remark what an ill-looking pack of men the servants were?" asked Madame.

"Yes," said my father, who had just come in, "ugly, hang-dog looking fellows, as ever I beheld in my life. I hope they mayn't rob the poor lady in the forest. They are clever rogues, however; they got everything to rights in a minute."

"I dare say they are worn out with too long travelling," said Madame. "Besides looking wicked, their faces were so strangely lean, and dark, and sullen. I am curious, I own; but I dare say the young lady will tell us all about it to-morrow, if she is sufficiently recovered."

"I don't think she will," said my father, with a mysterious smile, and a little nod of his head, as if he knew more about it than he cared to tell us.

This made us all the more inquisitive as to what had passed between him and the lady in the black velvet, in the brief but earnest interview that had immediately preceded her departure.

We were scarcely alone, when I entreated him to tell me. He did not need much pressing.

"There is no particular reason why I should not tell you. She expressed a reluctance to trouble us with the care of her daughter, saying she was in delicate health, and nervous, but not subject to any kind of seizure—she volunteered that—nor to any illusion; being, in fact, perfectly sane."

"How very odd to say all that!" I interpolated. "It was so unnecessary."

"At all events it *was* said," he laughed, "and as you wish to know all that passed, which was indeed very little, I tell you. She then said, 'I am making a long journey of *vital* importance—she emphasized the word—rapid and secret; I shall return for my child in three months; in the meantime, she will be silent as to who we are, whence we come, and whither we are travelling.' That is all she said. She spoke very pure French. When she said the word 'secret,' she paused for a few seconds, looking sternly, her eyes fixed on mine. I fancy she makes a great point of that. You saw how quickly she was gone. I hope I have not done a very foolish thing, in taking charge of the young lady."

For my part, I was delighted. I was longing to see and talk to her; and only waiting till the doctor should give me leave. You, who live in towns, can have no idea how great an event the introduction of a new friend is, in such a solitude as surrounded us.

The doctor did not arrive till nearly one o'clock; but I could no more have gone to my bed and slept, than I could have overtaken, on foot, the carriage in which the princess in black velvet had driven away.

When the physician came down to the drawing-room, it was to report very favourably upon his patient. She was now sitting up, her pulse quite regular, apparently perfectly well. She had sustained no injury, and the little shock to her nerves had passed away quite harmlessly. There could be no harm certainly in my seeing her, if we both wished it; and, with this permission, I sent, forthwith, to know whether she would allow me to visit her for a few minutes in her room.

The servant returned immediately to say that she desired nothing more.

You may be sure I was not long in availing myself of this permission.

Our visitor lay in one of the handsomest rooms in the schloss. It was, perhaps, a little stately. There was a sombre piece of tapestry opposite the foot of the bed, representing Cleopatra with the asps to her bosom; and other solemn classic scenes were displayed, a little faded, upon the other walls. But there was gold carving, and rich and varied colour enough in the other decorations of the room, to more than redeem the gloom of the old tapestry.

There were candles at the bed-side. She was sitting up; her slender pretty figure enveloped in the soft silk dressing-gown, embroidered with flowers, and lined with thick quilted silk, which her mother had thrown over her feet as she lay upon the ground.

What was it that, as I reached the bed-side and had just begun my little greeting, struck me dumb in a moment, and made me recoil a step or two from before her? I will tell you.

I saw the very face which had visited me in my childhood at night, which remained so fixed in my memory, and on which I had for so many years so often ruminated with horror, when no one suspected of what I was thinking.

It was pretty, even beautiful; and when I first beheld it, wore the same melancholy expression.

But this almost instantly lighted into a strange fixed smile of recognition.

There was a silence of fully a minute, and then at length *she* spoke; *I* could not.

"How wonderful!" she exclaimed. "Twelve years ago, I saw your face in a dream, and it has haunted me ever since."

"Wonderful indeed!" I repeated, overcoming with an effort the horror that had for a time suspended my utterances. "Twelve years ago, in vision or reality, *I* certainly saw you. I could not forget your face. It has remained before my eyes ever since."

Her smile had softened. Whatever I had fancied strange in it, was gone, and it and her dimpling cheeks were now delightfully pretty and intelligent.

I felt reassured, and continued more in the vein which hospitality indicated, to bid her welcome, and to tell her how much pleasure her accidental arrival had given us all, and especially what a happiness it was to me.

I took her hand as I spoke. I was a little shy, as lonely people are, but the situation made me eloquent, and even bold. She pressed my hand, she laid hers upon it, and her eyes glowed, as, looking hastily into mine, she smiled again, and blushed.

She answered my welcome very prettily. I sat down beside her, still wondering; and she said:

"I must tell you my vision about you; it is so very strange that you and I should have had, each of the other so vivid a dream, that each should have seen, I you and you me, looking as we do now, when of course we both were mere children. I was a child, about six years old, and I awoke from a confused and troubled dream, and found myself in a room, unlike my nursery, wainscoted clumsily in some dark wood, and with cupboards and bedsteads, and chairs, and benches placed about it. The beds were, I thought, all empty, and the room itself without anyone but myself in it; and I, after looking about me for some time, and admiring especially an iron candlestick with two branches, which I should certainly know again, crept under one of the beds to reach the window; but as I got from under the bed, I heard someone crying; and looking up, while I was still upon my knees, I saw *you*—most assuredly you—as I see you now; a beautiful young lady, with golden hair and large blue eyes, and lips—your lips—you, as you are here. Your looks won me; I climbed on the bed and put my arms about you, and I think we both fell asleep. I was aroused by a scream; you were sitting up screaming. I was frightened, and slipped down upon the ground, and, it seemed to me, lost consciousness for a moment; and when I came to myself, I was again in my nursery at home. Your face I have never forgotten since. I could not be misled by mere resemblance. You *are* the lady whom I saw then."

It was now my turn to relate my corresponding vision, which I did, to the undisguised wonder of my new acquaintance.

"I don't know which should be most afraid of the other," she said, again smiling—"If you were less pretty I think I should be very much afraid of you, but being as you are, and you and I both so young, I feel only that I have made your acquaintance twelve years ago, and have already a right to your intimacy; at all events it does seem as if we were destined, from our earliest childhood, to be friends. I wonder whether you feel as strangely drawn towards me as I do to you; I have never had a friend—shall I find one now?" She sighed, and her fine dark eyes gazed passionately on me.

Now the truth is, I felt rather unaccountably towards the beautiful stranger. I did feel, as she said, "drawn towards her," but there was also something of repulsion. In this ambiguous feeling, however, the sense of attraction immensely prevailed. She interested and won me; she was so beautiful and so indescribably engaging.

I perceived now something of languor and exhaustion stealing over her, and hastened to bid her good night.

"The doctor thinks," I added, "that you ought to have a maid to sit up with you to-night; one of ours is waiting, and you will find her a very useful and quiet creature."

"How kind of you, but I could not sleep, I never could with an attendant in my room. I shan't require any assistance—and, shall I confess my weakness, I am haunted with a terror of robbers. Our house was robbed once, and two servants murdered, so I always lock my door. It has become a habit—and you look so kind I know you will forgive me. I see there is a key in the lock."

She held me close in her pretty arms for a moment and whispered in my ear, "Good night, darling, it is very hard to part with you, but good night; to-morrow, but not early, I shall see you again."

She sank back on the pillow with a sigh, and her fine eyes followed me with a fond and melancholy gaze, and she murmured again "Good night, dear friend."

Young people like, and even love, on impulse. I was flattered by the evident, though as yet undeserved, fondness she showed me. I liked the confidence with which she at once received me. She was determined that we should be very near friends.

Next day came and we met again. I was delighted with my companion; that is to say, in many respects.

Her looks lost nothing in daylight—she was certainly the most beautiful creature I had ever seen, and the unpleasant remembrance of the face presented in my early dream, had lost the effect of the first unexpected recognition.

She confessed that she had experienced a similar shock on seeing me, and precisely the same faint antipathy that had mingled with my admiration of her. We now laughed together over our momentary horrors.

IV
HER HABITS—A SAUNTER

I told you that I was charmed with her in most particulars.

There were some that did not please me so well.

She was above the middle height of women. I shall begin by describing her. She was slender, and wonderfully graceful. Except that her movements were languid—*very* languid—indeed, there was nothing in her appearance to indicate an invalid. Her complexion was rich and brilliant; her features were small and beautifully formed; her eyes large, dark, and lustrous; her hair was quite wonderful, I never saw hair so magnificently thick and long when it was down about her shoulders; I have often placed my hands under it, and laughed with wonder at its weight. It was exquisitely fine and soft, and in colour a rich very dark brown, with something of gold. I loved to let it down, tumbling with its own weight, as, in her room, she lay back in her chair talking in her sweet low voice, I used to fold and braid it, and spread it out and play with it. Heavens! If I had but known all!

I said there were particulars which did not please me. I have told you that her confidence won me the first night I saw her; but I found that she exercised with respect to herself, her mother, her history, everything in fact connected with her life, plans, and people, an ever wakeful reserve. I dare say I was unreasonable, perhaps I was wrong; I dare say I ought to have respected the solemn injunction laid upon my father by the stately lady in black velvet. But curiosity is a restless and unscrupulous passion, and no one girl can endure, with patience, that hers should be baffled by another. What harm could it do anyone to tell me what I so ardently desired to know? Had she no trust in my good sense or honour? Why would she not believe me when I assured her, so solemnly, that I would not divulge one syllable of what she told me to any mortal breathing.

There was a coldness, it seemed to me, beyond her years, in her smiling melancholy persistent refusal to afford me the least ray of light.

I cannot say we quarrelled upon this point, for she would not quarrel upon any. It was, of course, very unfair of me to press her, very ill-bred, but I really could not help it; and I might just as well have let it alone.

What she did tell me amounted, in my unconscionable estimation—to nothing.

It was all summed up in three very vague disclosures:

First—Her name was Carmilla.

Second—Her family was very ancient and noble.

Third—Her home lay in the direction of the west.

She would not tell me the name of her family, nor their armorial bearings, nor the name of their estate, nor even that of the country they lived in.

You are not to suppose that I worried her incessantly on these subjects. I watched opportunity, and rather insinuated than urged my inquiries. Once or twice, indeed, I did attack her more directly. But no matter what my tactics, utter failure was invariably the result. Reproaches and caresses were all lost upon her. But I must add this, that her evasion was conducted with so pretty a melancholy and deprecation, with so many, and even passionate declarations of her liking for me, and trust in my honour, and with so many promises that I should at last know all, that I could not find it in my heart long to be offended with her.

She used to place her pretty arms about my neck, draw me to her, and laying her cheek to mine, murmur with her lips near my ear, "Dearest, your little heart is wounded; think me not cruel because I obey the irresistible law of my strength and weakness; if your dear heart is wounded, my wild heart bleeds with yours. In the rapture of my enormous humiliation I live in your warm life, and you shall die—die, sweetly die—into mine. I cannot help it; as I draw near to you, you, in your turn, will draw near to others, and learn the rapture of that cruelty, which yet is love; so, for a while, seek to know no more of me and mine, but trust me with all your loving spirit."

And when she had spoken such a rhapsody, she would press me more closely in her trembling embrace, and her lips in soft kisses gently glow upon my cheek.

Her agitations and her language were unintelligible to me.

From these foolish embraces, which were not of very frequent occurrence, I must allow, I used to wish to extricate myself; but my energies seemed to fail me. Her murmured words sounded like a lullaby in my ear, and soothed my resistance into a trance, from which I only seemed to recover myself when she withdrew her arms.

In these mysterious moods I did not like her. I experienced a strange tumultuous excitement that was pleasurable, ever and anon, mingled with a vague sense of fear and disgust. I had no distinct thoughts about her while such scenes lasted, but I was conscious of a love growing into adoration, and also of abhorrence. This I know is paradox, but I can make no other attempt to explain the feeling.

I now write, after an interval of more than ten years, with a trembling hand, with a confused and horrible recollection of certain occurrences and situations, in the ordeal through which I was unconsciously passing; though with a vivid and very sharp remembrance of the main current of my story. But, I suspect, in all lives there are certain emotional scenes, those in which our passions have been most wildly and terribly roused, that are of all others the most vaguely and dimly remembered.

Sometimes after an hour of apathy, my strange and beautiful companion would take my hand and hold it with a fond pressure, renewed again and again; blushing softly, gazing in my face with languid and burning eyes, and breathing so fast that her dress rose and fell with the tumultuous respiration. It was like the ardour of a lover; it embarrassed me; it was hateful and yet over-powering; and with gloating eyes she drew me to her, and her hot lips travelled along my cheek in kisses; and she would whisper, almost in sobs, "You are mine, you *shall* be mine, you and I are one for ever." Then she has thrown herself back in her chair, with her small hands over her eyes, leaving me trembling.

"Are we related," I used to ask, "what can you mean by all this? I remind you perhaps of some one whom you love; but you must not, I hate it; I don't know you—I don't know myself when you look so and talk so."

She used to sigh at my vehemence, then turn away and drop my hand.

Respecting these very extraordinary manifestations I strove in vain to form any satisfactory theory—I could not refer them to affectation or trick. It was unmistakably the momentary breaking out of suppressed instinct and emotion. Was she, notwithstanding her mother's volunteered denial, subject to brief visitations of insanity; or was there here a disguise and a romance? I had read in old story books of such things. What if a boyish lover had found his way into the house, and sought to prosecute his suit in masquerade, with the assistance of a clever old adventuress. But there were many things against this hypothesis, highly interesting as it was to my vanity.

I could boast of no little attentions such as masculine gallantry delights to offer. Between these passionate moments there were long intervals of common-place, of gaiety, of brooding melancholy, during which, except that I detected her eyes so full of melancholy fire, following me, at times I might have been as nothing to her. Except in these brief periods of mysterious excitement her ways were girlish; and there was always a languor about her, quite incompatible with a masculine system in a state of health.

In some respects her habits were odd. Perhaps not so singular in the opinion of a town lady like you, as they appeared to us rustic people. She used to come down very late, generally not till one o'clock, she would then take a cup of chocolate, but eat nothing; we then went out for a walk, which was a mere saunter, and she seemed, almost immediately, exhausted, and either returned to the schloss or sat on one of the benches that were placed, here and there, among the trees. This was a bodily languor in which her mind did not sympathise. She was always an animated talker, and very intelligent.

She sometimes alluded for a moment to her own home, or mentioned an adventure or situation, or an early recollection, which indicated a people of strange manners, and described customs of which we knew nothing. I gathered from these chance hints that her native country was much more remote than I had at first fancied.

As we sat thus one afternoon under the trees a funeral passed us by. It was that of a pretty young girl, whom I had often seen, the daughter of one of the rangers of the forest. The poor man was walking behind the coffin of his darling; she was his only child, and he looked quite heartbroken. Peasants walking two-and-two came behind, they were singing a funeral hymn.

I rose to mark my respect as they passed, and joined in the hymn they were very sweetly singing.

My companion shook me a little roughly, and I turned surprised.

She said brusquely, "Don't you perceive how discordant that is?"

"I think it is very sweet, on the contrary," I answered, vexed at the interruption, and very uncomfortable, lest the people who composed the little procession should observe and resent what was passing.

I resumed, therefore, instantly, and was again interrupted. "You pierce my ears," said Carmilla, almost angrily, and stopping her ears with her tiny fingers. "Besides, how can you tell that your religion and mine are the same; your forms wound me, and I hate funerals. What a fuss! Why *you* must die—*everyone* must die; and all are happier when they do. Come home."

"My father has gone on with the clergyman to the churchyard. I thought you knew she was to be buried to-day."

"*She?* I don't trouble my head about peasants. I don't know who she is," answered Carmilla, with a flash from her fine eyes.

"She is the poor girl who fancied she saw a ghost a fortnight ago, and has been dying ever since, till yesterday, when she expired."

"Tell me nothing about ghosts. I shan't sleep to-night if you do."

"I hope there is no plague or fever coming; all this looks very like it," I continued. "The swineherd's young wife died only a week ago, and she thought something seized her by the throat as she lay in her bed, and nearly strangled her. Papa says such horrible fancies do accompany some forms of fever. She was quite well the day before. She sank afterwards, and died before a week."

"Well, *her* funeral is over, I hope, and *her* hymn sung; and our ears shan't be tortured with that discord and jargon. It has made me nervous. Sit down here, beside me; sit close; hold my hand; press it hard—hard—harder."

We had moved a little back, and had come to another seat.

She sat down. Her face underwent a change that alarmed and even terrified me for a moment. It darkened, and became horribly livid; her teeth and hands were clenched, and she frowned and compressed her lips, while she stared down upon the ground at her feet, and trembled all over with a continued shudder as irrepressible as ague. All her energies seemed strained to suppress a fit, with which she was then breathlessly tugging; and at length a low convulsive cry of suffering broke from her, and gradually the hysteria subsided. "There! That comes of strangling people with hymns!" she said at last. "Hold me, hold me still. It is passing away."

And so gradually it did; and perhaps to dissipate the sombre impression which the spectacle had left upon me, she became unusually animated and chatty; and so we got home.

This was the first time I had seen her exhibit any definable symptoms of that delicacy of health which her mother had spoken of. It was the first time, also, I had seen her exhibit anything like temper.

Both passed away like a summer cloud; and never but once afterwards did I witness on her part a momentary sign of anger. I will tell you how it happened.

She and I were looking out of one of the long drawing-room windows, when there entered the courtyard, over the drawbridge, a figure of a wanderer whom I knew very well. He used to visit the schloss generally twice a year.

It was the figure of a hunchback, with the sharp lean features that generally accompany deformity. He wore a pointed black beard, and he was smiling from ear to ear, showing his white fangs. He was dressed in buff, black, and scarlet, and crossed with more straps and belts than I could count, from which hung all manner of things. Behind, he carried a magic-lantern, and two boxes, which I well knew, in one of which was a salamander, and in the other a mandrake. These monsters used to make my father laugh. They were compounded of parts of monkeys, parrots, squirrels, fish, and hedgehogs, dried and stitched together with great neatness and startling effect. He had a fiddle, a box of conjuring apparatus, a pair of foils and masks attached to his belt, several other mysterious cases dangling about him, and a black staff with copper ferrules in his hand. His companion was a rough spare dog, that followed at his heels, but stopped short, suspiciously at the drawbridge, and in a little while began to howl dismally.

In the meantime, the mountebank, standing in the midst of the courtyard, raised his grotesque hat, and made us a very ceremonious bow, paying his compliments very volubly in execrable French, and German not much better. Then, disengaging his fiddle, he began to scrape a lively air, to which he sang with a merry discord, dancing with ludicrous airs and activity, that made me laugh, in spite of the dog's howling.

Then he advanced to the window with many smiles and salutations, and his hat in his left hand, his fiddle under his arm, and with a fluency that never took breath, he gabbled a long advertisement of all his accomplishments, and the resources of the various arts which he placed at our service, and the curiosities and entertainments which it was in his power, at our bidding, to display.

"Will your ladyships be pleased to buy an amulet against the oupire, which is going like the wolf, I hear, through these woods," he said, dropping his hat on the pavement. "They are dying of it right and left, and here is a charm that never fails; only pinned to the pillow, and you may laugh in his face."

These charms consisted of oblong slips of vellum, with cabalistic ciphers and diagrams upon them.

Carmilla instantly purchased one, and so did I.

He was looking up, and we were smiling down upon him, amused; at least, I can answer for myself. His piercing black eye, as he looked up in our faces, seemed to detect something that fixed for a moment his curiosity.

In an instant he unrolled a leather case, full of all manner of odd little steel instruments.

"See here, my lady," he said, displaying it, and addressing me, "I profess, among other things less useful, the art of dentistry. Plague take the dog!" he interpolated. "Silence, beast! He howls so that your ladyships can scarcely hear a word. Your noble friend, the young lady at your right, has the sharpest tooth,—long, thin, pointed, like an awl, like a needle; ha, ha! With my sharp and long sight, as I look up, I have seen it distinctly; now if it happens to hurt the young lady, and I think it must, here am I, here are my file, my punch, my nippers; I will make it round and blunt, if her ladyship pleases; no longer the tooth of a fish, but of a beautiful young lady as she is. Hey? Is the young lady displeased? Have I been too bold? Have I offended her?"

The young lady, indeed, looked very angry as she drew back from the window.

"How dares that mountebank insult us so? Where is your father? I shall demand redress from him. My father would have had the wretch tied up to the pump, and flogged with a cart-whip, and burnt to the bones with the castle brand!"

She retired from the window a step or two, and sat down, and had hardly lost sight of the offender, when her wrath subsided as suddenly as it had risen, and she gradually recovered her usual tone, and seemed to forget the little hunchback and his follies.

My father was out of spirits that evening. On coming in he told us that there had been another case very similar to the two fatal ones which had lately occurred. The sister of a young peasant on his estate, only a mile away, was very ill, had been, as she described it, attacked very nearly in the same way, and was now slowly but steadily sinking.

"All this," said my father, "is strictly referable to natural causes. These poor people infect one another with their superstitions, and so repeat in imagination the images of terror that have infested their neighbours."

"But that very circumstance frightens one horribly," said Carmilla.

"How so?" inquired my father.

"I am so afraid of fancying I see such things; I think it would be as bad as reality."

"We are in God's hands; nothing can happen without his permission, and all will end well for those who love him. He is our faithful creator; He has made us all, and will take care of us."

"Creator! *Nature!*" said the young lady in answer to my gentle father. "And this disease that invades the country is natural. Nature. All things proceed from Nature—don't they? All things in the heaven, in the earth, and under the earth, act and live as Nature ordains? I think so."

"The doctor said he would come here to-day," said my father, after a silence. "I want to know what he thinks about it, and what he thinks we had better do."

"Doctors never did me any good," said Carmilla.

"Then you have been ill?" I asked.

"More ill than ever you were," she answered.

"Long ago?"

"Yes, a long time. I suffered from this very illness; but I forget all but my pain and weakness, and they were not so bad as are suffered in other diseases."

"You were very young then?"

"I dare say; let us talk no more of it. You would not wound a friend?" She looked languidly in my eyes, and passed her arm round my waist lovingly, and led me out of the room. My father was busy over some papers near the window.

"Why does your Papa like to frighten us?" said the pretty girl, with a sigh and a little shudder.

"He doesn't, dear Carmilla, it is the very furthest thing from his mind."

"Are you afraid, dearest?"

"I should be very much if I fancied there was any real danger of my being attacked as those poor people were."

"You are afraid to die?"

"Yes, every one is."

"But to die as lovers may—to die together, so that they may live together. Girls are caterpillars while they live in the world, to be finally butterflies when the summer comes; but in the meantime there are grubs and larvae, don't you see—each with their peculiar propensities, necessities and structure. So says Monsieur Buffon, in his big book, in the next room."

Later in the day the doctor came, and was closeted with Papa for some time. He was a skilful man, of sixty and upwards, he wore powder, and shaved his pale face as smooth as a pumpkin. He and Papa emerged from the room together, and I heard Papa laugh, and say as they came out:

"Well, I do wonder at a wise man like you. What do you say to hippogriffs and dragons?"

The doctor was smiling, and made answer, shaking his head—

"Nevertheless life and death are mysterious states, and we know little of the resources of either."

And so they walked on, and I heard no more. I did not then know what the doctor had been broaching, but I think I guess it now.

V

A WONDERFUL LIKENESS

This evening there arrived from Gratz the grave, dark-faced son of the picture cleaner, with a horse and cart laden with two large packing cases, having many pictures in each. It was a journey of ten leagues, and whenever a messenger arrived at the schloss from our little capital of Gratz, we used to crowd about him in the hall, to hear the news.

This arrival created in our secluded quarters quite a sensation. The cases remained in the hall, and the messenger was taken charge of by the servants till he had eaten his supper. Then with assistants, and armed with hammer, ripping-chisel, and turnscrew, he met us in the hall, where we had assembled to witness the unpacking of the cases.

Carmilla sat looking listlessly on, while one after the other the old pictures, nearly all portraits, which had undergone the process of renovation, were brought to light. My mother was of an old Hungarian family, and most of these pictures, which were about to be restored to their places, had come to us through her.

My father had a list in his hand, from which he read, as the artist rummaged out the corresponding numbers. I don't know that the pictures were very good, but they were, undoubtedly, very old, and some of them very curious also. They had, for the most part, the merit of being now seen by me, I may say, for the first time; for the smoke and dust of time had all but obliterated them.

"There is a picture that I have not seen yet," said my father. "In one corner, at the top of it, is the name, as well as I could read, 'Marcia Karnstein,' and the date '1698'; and I am curious to see how it has turned out."

I remembered it; it was a small picture, about a foot and a half high, and nearly square, without a frame; but it was so blackened by age that I could not make it out.

The artist now produced it, with evident pride. It was quite beautiful; it was startling; it seemed to live. It was the effigy of Carmilla!

"Carmilla, dear, here is an absolute miracle. Here you are, living, smiling, ready to speak, in this picture. Isn't it beautiful, Papa? And see, even the little mole on her throat."

My father laughed, and said "Certainly it is a wonderful likeness," but he looked away, and to my surprise seemed but little struck by it, and went on talking to the picture cleaner, who was also something of an artist, and discoursed with intelligence about the portraits or other works, which his art had just brought into light and colour, while I was more and more lost in wonder the more I looked at the picture.

"Will you let me hang this picture in my room, Papa?" I asked.

"Certainly, dear," said he, smiling, "I'm very glad you think it so like. It must be prettier even than I thought it, if it is."

The young lady did not acknowledge this pretty speech, did not seem to hear it. She was leaning back in her seat, her fine eyes under their long lashes gazing on me in contemplation, and she smiled in a kind of rapture.

"And now you can read quite plainly the name that is written in the corner. It is not Marcia; it looks as if it was done in gold. The name is Mircalla, Countess Karnstein, and this is a little coronet over it, and underneath A.D. 1698. I am descended from the Karnsteins; that is, mamma was."

"Ah!" said the lady languidly, "so am I, I think, a very long descent, very ancient. Are there any Karnsteins living now?"

"None who bear the name, I believe. The family were ruined, I believe, in some civil wars, long ago, but the ruins of the castle are only about three miles away."

"How interesting!" she said, languidly. "But see what beautiful moonlight!" She glanced through the hall-door, which stood a little open. "Suppose you take a little ramble round the court, and look down at the road and river."

"It is so like the night you came to us," I said.

She sighed, smiling.

She rose, and each with her arm about the other's waist, we walked out upon the pavement.

In silence, slowly we walked down to the drawbridge, where the beautiful landscape opened before us.

"And you asked for the picture you think like me, to hang in your room," she murmured with a sigh, as she drew her arm closer about my waist, and let her pretty head sink upon my shoulder.

"How romantic you are, Carmilla," I said. "Whenever you tell me your story, it will be made up chiefly of some one great romance."

She kissed me silently.

"I am sure, Carmilla, you have been in love; that there is, at this moment, an affair of the heart going on."

"I have been in love with no one, and never shall," she whispered, "unless it should be with you."

How beautiful she looked in the moonlight!

Shy and strange was the look with which she quickly hid her face in my neck and hair, with tumultuous sighs, that seemed almost to sob, and pressed in mine a hand that trembled.

Her soft cheek was glowing against mine. "Darling, darling," she murmured, "I live in you, and you would die for me, I love you so."

I started from her.

She was gazing on me with eyes from which all fire, all meaning had flown, and a face colourless and apathetic.

"Is there a chill in the air, dear?" she said drowsily. "I almost shiver; have I been dreaming? Let us come in. Come; come; come in."

"You look ill, Carmilla; a little faint. You certainly must take some wine," I said.

"Yes, I will. I'm better now. I shall be quite well in a few minutes. Yes, do give me a little wine," answered Carmilla, as we approached the door. "Let us look again for a moment; it is the last time, perhaps, I shall see the moonlight with you."

"How do you feel now, dear Carmilla? Are you really better?" I asked.

I was beginning to take alarm, lest she should have been stricken with the strange epidemic that they said had invaded the country about us.

"Papa would be grieved beyond measure," I added, "if he thought you were ever so little ill, without immediately letting us know. We have a very skilful doctor near this, the physician who was with Papa to-day."

"I'm sure he is. I know how kind you all are; but dear child, I am quite well again. There is nothing ever wrong with me, but a little weakness. People say I am languid; I am incapable of exertion; I can scarcely walk as far as a child of three years old; and every now and then the little strength I have falters, and I become as you have just seen me. But after all I am very easily set up again; in a moment I am perfectly myself. See how I have recovered."

So, indeed, she had; and she and I talked a great deal, and very animated she was; and the remainder of that evening passed without any recurrence of what I called her infatuations. I mean her crazy talk and looks, which embarrassed, and even frightened me.

But there occurred that night an event which gave my thoughts quite a new turn, and seemed to startle even Carmilla's languid nature into momentary energy.

VI

A VERY STRANGE AGONY

When we got into the drawing-room, and had sat down to our coffee and chocolate, although Carmilla did not take any, she seemed quite herself again, and Madame, and Mademoiselle De Lafontaine, joined us, and made a little card party, in the course of which Papa came in for what he called his "dish of tea."

When the game was over he sat down beside Carmilla on the sofa, and asked her, a little anxiously, whether she had heard from her mother since her arrival.

She answered "No."

He then asked whether she knew where a letter would reach her at present.

"I cannot tell," she answered ambiguously, "but I have been thinking of leaving you; you have been already too hospitable and too kind to me. I have given you an infinity of trouble, and I should wish to take a carriage to-morrow, and post in pursuit of her; I know where I shall ultimately find her, although I dare not tell you."

"But you must not dream of any such thing," exclaimed my father, to my great relief. "We can't afford to lose you so, and I won't consent to your leaving us, except under the care of your mother, who was so good as to consent to your remaining with us till she should herself return. I should be quite happy if I knew that you heard from her; but this evening the accounts of the progress of the mysterious disease that has invaded our neighbourhood, grow even more alarming; and my beautiful guest, I do feel the responsibility, unaided by advice from your mother, very much. But I shall do my best; and one thing is certain, that you must not think of leaving us without her distinct direction to that effect. We should suffer too much in parting from you to consent to it easily."

"Thank you, sir, a thousand times for your hospitality," she answered, smiling bashfully. "You have all been too kind to me; I have seldom been so happy in all my life before, as in your beautiful château, under your care, and in the society of your dear daughter."

So he gallantly, in his old-fashioned way, kissed her hand, smiling and pleased at her little speech.

I accompanied Carmilla as usual to her room, and sat and chatted with her while she was preparing for bed.

"Do you think," I said at length, "that you will ever confide fully in me?"

She turned round smiling, but made no answer, only continued to smile on me.

"You won't answer that?" I said. "You can't answer pleasantly; I ought not to have asked you."

"You were quite right to ask me that, or anything. You do not know how dear you are to me, or you could not think any confidence too great to look for. But I am under vows, no nun half so awfully, and I dare not tell my story yet, even to you. The time is very near when you shall know everything. You will think me cruel, very selfish, but love is always selfish; the more ardent the more selfish. How jealous I am you cannot know. You must come with me, loving me, to death; or else hate me and still come with me, and *hating* me through death and after. There is no such word as indifference in my apathetic nature."

"Now, Carmilla, you are going to talk your wild nonsense again," I said hastily.

"Not I, silly little fool as I am, and full of whims and fancies; for your sake I'll talk like a sage. Were you ever at a ball?"

"No; how you do run on. What is it like? How charming it must be."

"I almost forget, it is years ago."

I laughed.

"You are not so old. Your first ball can hardly be forgotten yet."

"I remember everything about it—with an effort. I see it all, as divers see what is going on above them, through a medium, dense, rippling, but transparent. There occurred that night what has confused the picture, and made its colours faint. I was all but assassinated in my bed, wounded *here*," she touched her breast, "and never was the same since."

"Were you near dying?"

"Yes, very—a cruel love—strange love, that would have taken my life. Love will have its sacrifices. No sacrifice without blood. Let us go to sleep now; I feel so lazy. How can I get up just now and lock my door?"

She was lying with her tiny hands buried in her rich wavy hair, under her cheek, her little head upon the pillow, and her glittering eyes followed me wherever I moved, with a kind of shy smile that I could not decipher.

I bid her good night, and crept from the room with an uncomfortable sensation.

I often wondered whether our pretty guest ever said her prayers. *I* certainly had never seen her upon her knees. In the morning she never came down until long after our family prayers were over, and at night she never left the drawing-room to attend our brief evening prayers in the hall.

If it had not been that it had casually come out in one of our careless talks that she had been baptised, I should have doubted her being a Christian. Religion was a subject on which I had never heard her speak a word. If I had known the world better, this particular neglect or antipathy would not have so much surprised me.

The precautions of nervous people are infectious, and persons of a like temperament are pretty sure, after a time, to imitate them. I had adopted Carmilla's habit of locking her bedroom door, having taken into my head all her whimsical alarms about midnight invaders and prowling assassins. I had also adopted her precaution of making a brief search through her room, to satisfy herself that no lurking assassin or robber was "ensconced."

These wise measures taken, I got into my bed and fell asleep. A light was burning in my room. This was an old habit, of very early date, and which nothing could have tempted me to dispense with.

Thus fortified I might take my rest in peace. But dreams come through stone walls, light up dark rooms, or darken light ones, and their persons make their exits and their entrances as they please, and laugh at locksmiths.

I had a dream that night that was the beginning of a very strange agony.

I cannot call it a nightmare, for I was quite conscious of being asleep. But I was equally conscious of being in my room, and lying in bed, precisely as I actually was. I saw, or fancied I saw, the room and its furniture just as I had seen it last, except that it was very dark, and I saw something moving round the foot of my bed, which at first I could not accurately distinguish. But I soon saw that it was a sooty-black animal that resembled a monstrous cat. It appeared to me about four or five feet long, for it measured fully the length of the hearth-rug as it passed over it; and it continued to-ing and fro-ing with the lithe, sinister restlessness of a beast in a cage. I could not cry out, although as you may suppose, I was terrified. Its pace was growing faster, and the room rapidly darker and darker, and at length so dark that I could no longer see anything of it but its eyes. I felt it spring lightly on the bed. The two broad eyes approached my face, and suddenly I felt a stinging pain as if two large needles darted, an inch or two apart, deep into my breast. I waked with a scream. The room was lighted by the candle that burnt there all through the night, and I saw a female figure standing at the foot of the bed, a little at the right side. It was in a dark loose dress, and its hair was down and covered its shoulders. A block of stone could not have been more still. There was not the slightest stir of respiration. As I stared at it, the figure appeared to have changed its place, and was now nearer the door; then close to it, the door opened, and it passed out.

I was now relieved, and able to breathe and move. My first thought was that Carmilla had been playing me a trick, and that I had forgotten to secure my door. I hastened to it, and found it locked as usual on the inside. I was afraid to open it—I was horrified. I sprang into my bed and covered my head up in the bed-clothes, and lay there more dead than alive till morning.

VII
DESCENDING

It would be vain my attempting to tell you the horror with which, even now, I recall the occurrence of that night. It was no such transitory terror as a dream leaves behind it. It seemed to deepen by time, and communicated itself to the room and the very furniture that had encompassed the apparition.

I could not bear next day to be alone for a moment. I should have told Papa, but for two opposite reasons. At one time I thought he would laugh at my story, and I could not bear its being treated as a jest; and at another, I thought he might fancy that I had been attacked by the mysterious complaint which had invaded our neighbourhood. I had myself no misgivings of the kind, and as he had been rather an invalid for some time, I was afraid of alarming him.

I was comfortable enough with my good-natured companions, Madame Perrodon and the vivacious Mademoiselle De Lafontaine. They both perceived that I was out of spirits and nervous, and at length I told them what lay so heavy at my heart.

Mademoiselle laughed, but I fancied that Madame Perrodon looked anxious.

"By-the-by," said Mademoiselle, laughing, "the long lime-tree walk, behind Carmilla's bedroom-window, is haunted!"

"Nonsense!" exclaimed Madame, who probably thought the theme rather inopportune, "and who tells that story, my dear?"

"Martin says that he came up twice, when the old yard-gate was being repaired, before sunrise, and twice saw the same female figure walking down the lime-tree avenue."

"So well he might, as long as there are cows to milk in the river fields," said Madame.

"I daresay; but Martin chooses to be frightened, and never did I see fool *more* frightened."

"You must not say a word about it to Carmilla, because she can see down that walk from her room window," I interposed, "and she is, if possible, a greater coward than I."

Carmilla came down rather later than usual that day.

"I was so frightened last night," she said, so soon as were together, "and I am sure I should have seen something dreadful if it had not been for that charm I bought from the poor little hunchback whom I called such hard names. I had a dream of something black coming round my bed, and I awoke in a perfect horror, and I really thought, for some seconds, I saw a dark figure near the chimney-piece, but I felt under my pillow for my charm, and the moment my fingers touched it, the figure disappeared, and I felt quite certain, only that I had it by me, that something frightful would have made its appearance, and, perhaps, throttled me, as it did those poor people we heard of."

"Well, listen to me," I began, and recounted my adventure, at the recital of which she appeared horrified.

"And you had the charm near you?" she asked, earnestly.

"No, I had dropped it into a china vase in the drawing-room, but I shall certainly take it with me to-night, as you have so much faith in it."

At this distance of time I cannot tell you, or even understand, how I overcame my horror so effectually as to lie alone in my room that night. I remember distinctly that I pinned the charm to my pillow. I fell asleep almost immediately, and slept even more soundly than usual all night.

Next night I passed as well. My sleep was delightfully deep and dreamless. But I wakened with a sense of lassitude and melancholy, which, however, did not exceed a degree that was almost luxurious.

"Well, I told you so," said Carmilla, when I described my quiet sleep, "I had such delightful sleep myself last night; I pinned the charm to the breast of my night-dress. It was too far away the night before. I am quite sure it was all fancy, except the dreams. I used to think that evil spirits made dreams, but our doctor told me it is no such thing. Only a fever passing by, or some other malady, as they often do, he said, knocks at the door, and not being able to get in, passes on, with that alarm."

"And what do you think the charm is?" said I.

"It has been fumigated or immersed in some drug, and is an antidote against the malaria," she answered.

"Then it acts only on the body?"

"Certainly; you don't suppose that evil spirits are frightened by bits of ribbon, or the perfumes of a druggist's shop? No, these complaints, wandering in the air, begin by trying the nerves, and so infect the brain, but before they can seize upon you, the antidote repels them. That I am sure is what the charm has done for us. It is nothing magical, it is simply natural."

I should have been happier if I could have quite agreed with Carmilla, but I did my best, and the impression was a little losing its force.

For some nights I slept profoundly; but still every morning I felt the same lassitude, and a languor weighed upon me all day. I felt myself a changed girl. A strange melancholy was stealing over me, a melancholy that I would not have interrupted. Dim thoughts of death began to open, and an idea that I was slowly sinking took gentle, and, somehow, not unwelcome, possession of me. If it was sad, the tone of mind which this induced was also sweet. Whatever it might be, my soul acquiesced in it.

I would not admit that I was ill, I would not consent to tell my Papa, or to have the doctor sent for.

Carmilla became more devoted to me than ever, and her strange paroxysms of languid adoration more frequent. She used to gloat on me with increasing ardour the more my strength and spirits waned. This always shocked me like a momentary glare of insanity.

Without knowing it, I was now in a pretty advanced stage of the strangest illness under which mortal ever suffered. There was an unaccountable fascination in its earlier symptoms that more than reconciled me to the incapacitating effect of that stage of the malady. This fascination increased for a time, until it reached a certain point, when gradually a sense of the horrible mingled itself with it, deepening, as you shall hear, until it discoloured and perverted the whole state of my life.

The first change I experienced was rather agreeable. It was very near the turning point from which began the descent of Avernus.

Certain vague and strange sensations visited me in my sleep. The prevailing one was of that pleasant, peculiar cold thrill which we feel in bathing, when we move against the current of a river. This was soon accompanied by dreams that seemed interminable, and were so vague that I could never recollect their scenery and persons, or any one connected portion of their action. But they left an awful impression, and a sense of exhaustion, as if I had passed through a long period of great mental exertion and danger. After all these dreams there remained on waking a remembrance of having been in a place very nearly dark, and of having spoken to people whom I could not see; and especially of one clear voice, of a female's, very deep, that spoke as if at a distance, slowly, and producing always the same sensation of indescribable solemnity and fear. Sometimes there came a sensation as if a hand was drawn softly along my cheek and neck. Sometimes it was as if warm lips kissed me, and longer and more lovingly as they reached my throat, but there the caress fixed itself. My heart beat faster, my breathing rose and fell rapidly and full drawn; a sobbing, that rose into a sense of strangulation, supervened, and turned into a dreadful convulsion, in which my senses left me and I became unconscious.

It was now three weeks since the commencement of this unaccountable state. My sufferings had, during the last week, told upon my appearance. I had grown pale, my eyes were dilated and darkened underneath, and the languor which I had long felt began to display itself in my countenance.

My father asked me often whether I was ill; but, with an obstinacy which now seems to me unaccountable, I persisted in assuring him that I was quite well.

In a sense this was true. I had no pain, I could complain of no bodily derangement. My complaint seemed to be one of the imagination, or the nerves, and, horrible as my sufferings were, I kept them, with a morbid reserve, very nearly to myself.

It could not be that terrible complaint which the peasants called the oupire, for I had now been suffering for three weeks, and they were seldom ill for much more than three days, when death put an end to their miseries.

Carmilla complained of dreams and feverish sensations, but by no means of so alarming a kind as mine. I say that mine were extremely alarming. Had I been capable of comprehending my condition, I would have invoked aid and advice on my knees. The narcotic of an unsuspected influence was acting upon me, and my perceptions were benumbed.

I am going to tell you now of a dream that led immediately to an odd discovery.

One night, instead of the voice I was accustomed to hear in the dark, I heard one, sweet and tender, and at the same time terrible, which said, "Your mother warns you to beware of the assassin." At the same time a light unexpectedly sprang up, and I saw Carmilla, standing near the foot of my bed, in her white nightdress, bathed, from her chin to her feet, in one great stain of blood.

I wakened with a shriek, possessed with the one idea that Carmilla was being murdered. I remember springing from my bed, and my next recollection is that of standing on the lobby, crying for help.

Madame and Mademoiselle came scurrying out of their rooms in alarm; a lamp burned always on the lobby, and seeing me, they soon learned the cause of my terror.

I insisted on our knocking on Carmilla's door. Our knocking was unanswered. It soon became a pounding and an uproar. We shrieked her name, but all was vain.

We all grew frightened, for the door was locked. We hurried back, in panic, to my room. There we rang the bell long and furiously. If my father's room had been at that side of the house, we would have called him up at once to our aid. But, alas! He was quite out of hearing, and to reach him involved an excursion for which we none of us had courage.

Servants, however, soon came running up the stairs; I had got on my dressing-gown and slippers meanwhile, and my companions were already similarly furnished. Recognising the voices of the servants on the lobby, we sallied out together; and having renewed, as fruitlessly, our summons at Carmilla's door, I ordered the men to force the lock. They did so, and we stood, holding our lights aloft, in the doorway, and so stared into the room.

We called her by name; but there was still no reply. We looked round the room. Everything was undisturbed. It was exactly in the state in which I had left it on bidding her good night. But Carmilla was gone.

VIII
SEARCH

At sight of the room, perfectly undisturbed except for our violent entrance, we began to cool a little, and soon recovered our senses sufficiently to dismiss the men. It had struck Mademoiselle that possibly Carmilla had been wakened by the uproar at her door, and in her first panic had jumped from her bed, and hid herself in a press, or behind a curtain, from which she could not, of course, emerge until the majordomo and myrmidons had withdrawn. We now recommenced our search, and began to call her by name again.

It was all to no purpose. Our perplexity and agitation increased. We examined the windows, but they were secured. I implored of Carmilla, if she had concealed herself, to play this cruel trick no longer—to come out, and to end our anxieties. It was all useless. I was by this time convinced that she was not in the room, nor in the dressing-room, the door of which was still locked on this side. She could not have passed it. I was utterly puzzled. Had Carmilla discovered one of those secret passages which the old housekeeper said were known to exist in the schloss, although the tradition of their exact situation had been lost? A little time would, no doubt, explain all—utterly perplexed as, for the present, we were.

It was past four o'clock, and I preferred passing the remaining hours of darkness in Madame's room. Daylight brought no solution of the difficulty.

The whole household, with my father at its head, was in a state of agitation next morning. Every part of the château was searched. The grounds were explored. Not a trace of the missing lady could be discovered. The stream was about to be dragged; my father was in distraction; what a tale to have to tell the poor girl's mother on her return. I, too, was almost beside myself, though my grief was quite of a different kind.

The morning was passed in alarm and excitement. It was now one o'clock, and still no tidings. I ran up to Carmilla's room, and found her standing at her dressing-table. I was astounded. I could not believe my eyes. She beckoned me to her with her pretty finger, in silence. Her face expressed extreme fear.

I ran to her in an ecstasy of joy; I kissed and embraced her again and again. I ran to the bell and rang it vehemently, to bring others to the spot, who might at once relieve my father's anxiety.

"Dear Carmilla, what has become of you all this time? We have been in agonies of anxiety about you," I exclaimed. "Where have you been? How did you come back?"

"Last night has been a night of wonders," she said.

"For mercy's sake, explain all you can."

"It was past two last night," she said, "when I went to sleep as usual in my bed, with my doors locked, that of the dressing-room, and that opening upon the gallery. My sleep was uninterrupted, and, so far as I know, dreamless; but I woke just now on the sofa in the dressing-room there, and I found the door between the rooms open, and the other door forced. How could all this have happened without my being wakened? It must have been accompanied with a great deal of noise, and I am particularly easily wakened; and how could I have been carried out of my bed without my sleep having been interrupted, I whom the slightest stir startles?"

By this time, Madame, Mademoiselle, my father, and a number of the servants were in the room. Carmilla was, of course, overwhelmed with inquiries, congratulations, and welcomes. She had but one story to tell, and seemed the least able of all the party to suggest any way of accounting for what had happened.

My father took a turn up and down the room, thinking. I saw Carmilla's eye follow him for a moment with a sly, dark glance.

When my father had sent the servants away, Mademoiselle having gone in search of a little bottle of valerian and salvolatile, and there being no one now in the room with Carmilla, except my father, Madame, and myself, he came to her thoughtfully, took her hand very kindly, led her to the sofa, and sat down beside her.

"Will you forgive me, my dear, if I risk a conjecture, and ask a question?"

"Who can have a better right?" she said. "Ask what you please, and I will tell you everything. But my story is simply one of bewilderment and darkness. I know absolutely nothing. Put any question you please. But you know, of course, the limitations mamma has placed me under."

"Perfectly, my dear child. I need not approach the topics on which she desires our silence. Now, the marvel of last night consists in your having been removed from your bed and your room, without being wakened, and this removal having occurred apparently while the windows were still secured, and the two doors locked upon the inside. I will tell you my theory, and first ask you a question."

Carmilla was leaning on her hand dejectedly; Madame and I were listening breathlessly.

"Now, my question is this. Have you ever been suspected of walking in your sleep?"

"Never, since I was very young indeed."

"But you did walk in your sleep when you were young?"

"Yes; I know I did. I have been told so often by my old nurse."

My father smiled and nodded.

"Well, what has happened is this. You got up in your sleep, unlocked the door, not leaving the key, as usual, in the lock, but taking it out and locking it on the outside; you again took the key out, and carried it away with you to some one of the five-and-twenty rooms on this floor, or perhaps upstairs or downstairs. There are so many rooms and closets, so much heavy furniture, and such accumulations of lumber, that it would require a week to search this old house thoroughly. Do you see, now, what I mean?"

"I do, but not all," she answered.

"And how, Papa, do you account for her finding herself on the sofa in the dressing-room, which we had searched so carefully?"

"She came there after you had searched it, still in her sleep, and at last awoke spontaneously, and was as much surprised to find herself where she was as any one else. I wish all mysteries were as easily and innocently explained as yours, Carmilla," he said, laughing. "And so we may congratulate ourselves on the certainty that the most natural explanation of the occurrence is one that involves no drugging, no tampering with locks, no burglars, or poisoners, or witches—nothing that need alarm Carmilla, or anyone else, for our safety."

Carmilla was looking charmingly. Nothing could be more beautiful than her tints. Her beauty was, I think, enhanced by that graceful languor that was peculiar to her. I think my father was silently contrasting her looks with mine, for he said:

"I wish my poor Laura was looking more like herself"; and he sighed.

So our alarms were happily ended, and Carmilla restored to her friends.

IX
THE DOCTOR

As Carmilla would not hear of an attendant sleeping in her room, my father arranged that a servant should sleep outside her door, so that she could not attempt to make another such excursion without being arrested at her own door.

That night passed quietly; and next morning early, the doctor, whom my father had sent for without telling me a word about it, arrived to see me.

Madame accompanied me to the library; and there the grave little doctor, with white hair and spectacles, whom I mentioned before, was waiting to receive me.

I told him my story, and as I proceeded he grew graver and graver.

We were standing, he and I, in the recess of one of the windows, facing one another. When my statement was over, he leaned with his shoulders against the wall, and with his eyes fixed on me earnestly, with an interest in which was a dash of horror.

After a minute's reflection, he asked Madame if he could see my father.

He was sent for accordingly, and as he entered, smiling, he said:

"I dare say, doctor, you are going to tell me that I am an old fool for having brought you here; I hope I am."

But his smile faded into shadow as the doctor, with a very grave face, beckoned him to him.

He and the doctor talked for some time in the same recess where I had just conferred with the physician. It seemed an earnest and argumentative conversation. The room is very large, and I and Madame stood together, burning with curiosity, at the farther end. Not a word could we hear, however, for they spoke in a very low tone, and the deep recess of the window quite concealed the doctor from view, and very nearly my father, whose foot, arm, and shoulder only could we see; and the voices were, I suppose, all the less audible for the sort of closet which the thick wall and window formed.

After a time my father's face looked into the room; it was pale, thoughtful, and, I fancied, agitated.

"Laura, dear, come here for a moment. Madame, we shan't trouble you, the doctor says, at present."

Accordingly I approached, for the first time a little alarmed; for, although I felt very weak, I did not feel ill; and strength, one always fancies, is a thing that may be picked up when we please.

My father held out his hand to me, as I drew near, but he was looking at the doctor, and he said:

"It certainly *is* very odd; I don't understand it quite. Laura, come here, dear; now attend to Doctor Spielsberg, and recollect yourself."

"You mentioned a sensation like that of two needles piercing the skin, somewhere about your neck, on the night when you experienced your first horrible dream. Is there still any soreness?"

"None at all," I answered.

"Can you indicate with your finger about the point at which you think this occurred?"

"Very little below my throat—*here*," I answered.

I wore a morning dress, which covered the place I pointed to.

"Now you can satisfy yourself," said the doctor. "You won't mind your Papa's lowering your dress a very little. It is necessary, to detect a symptom of the complaint under which you have been suffering."

I acquiesced. It was only an inch or two below the edge of my collar.

"God bless me!—so it is," exclaimed my father, growing pale.

"You see it now with your own eyes," said the doctor, with a gloomy triumph.

"What is it?" I exclaimed, beginning to be frightened.

"Nothing, my dear young lady, but a small blue spot, about the size of the tip of your little finger; and now," he continued, turning to Papa, "the question is what is best to be done?"

"Is there any danger?" I urged, in great trepidation.

"I trust not, my dear," answered the doctor. "I don't see why you should not recover. I don't see why you should not begin *immediately* to get better. That is the point at which the sense of strangulation begins?"

"Yes," I answered.

"And—recollect as well as you can—the same point was a kind of centre of that thrill which you described just now, like the current of a cold stream running against you?"

"It may have been; I think it was."

"Ay, you see?" he added, turning to my father. "Shall I say a word to Madame?"

"Certainly," said my father.

He called Madame to him, and said:

"I find my young friend here far from well. It won't be of any great consequence, I hope; but it will be necessary that some steps be taken, which I will explain by-and-by; but in the meantime, Madame, you will be so good as not to let Miss Laura be alone for one moment. That is the only direction I need give for the present. It is indispensable."

"We may rely upon your kindness, Madame, I know," added my father.

Madame satisfied him eagerly.

"And you, dear Laura, I know you will observe the doctor's direction."

"I shall have to ask your opinion upon another patient, whose symptoms slightly resemble those of my daughter, that have just been detailed to you—very much milder in degree, but I believe quite of the same sort. She is a young lady—

116

our guest; but as you say you will be passing this way again this evening, you can't do better than take your supper here, and you can then see her. She does not come down till the afternoon."

"I thank you," said the doctor. "I shall be with you, then, at about seven this evening."

And then they repeated their directions to me and to Madame, and with this parting charge my father left us, and walked out with the doctor; and I saw them pacing together up and down between the road and the moat, on the grassy platform in front of the castle, evidently absorbed in earnest conversation.

The doctor did not return. I saw him mount his horse there, take his leave, and ride away eastward through the forest.

Nearly at the same time I saw the man arrive from Dranfield with the letters, and dismount and hand the bag to my father.

In the meantime, Madame and I were both busy, lost in conjecture as to the reasons of the singular and earnest direction which the doctor and my father had concurred in imposing. Madame, as she afterwards told me, was afraid the doctor apprehended a sudden seizure, and that, without prompt assistance, I might either lose my life in a fit, or at least be seriously hurt.

The interpretation did not strike me; and I fancied, perhaps luckily for my nerves, that the arrangement was prescribed simply to secure a companion, who would prevent my taking too much exercise, or eating unripe fruit, or doing any of the fifty foolish things to which young people are supposed to be prone.

About half an hour after my father came in—he had a letter in his hand—and said:

"This letter has been delayed; it is from General Spielsdorf. He might have been here yesterday, he may not come till to-morrow or he may be here to-day."

He put the open letter into my hand; but he did not look pleased, as he used when a guest, especially one so much loved as the General, was coming. On the contrary, he looked as if he wished him at the bottom of the Red Sea. There was plainly something on his mind which he did not choose to divulge.

"Papa, darling, will you tell me this?" said I, suddenly laying my hand on his arm, and looking, I am sure, imploringly in his face.

"Perhaps," he answered, smoothing my hair caressingly over my eyes.

"Does the doctor think me very ill?"

"No, dear; he thinks, if right steps are taken, you will be quite well again, at least, on the high road to a complete recovery, in a day or two," he answered, a little dryly. "I wish our good friend, the General, had chosen any other time; that is, I wish you had been perfectly well to receive him."

"But do tell me, Papa," I insisted, "*what* does he think is the matter with me?"

"Nothing; you must not plague me with questions," he answered, with more irritation than I ever remember him to have displayed before; and seeing that I looked wounded, I suppose, he kissed me, and added, "You shall know all about it in a day or two; that is, all that *I* know. In the meantime you are not to trouble your head about it."

He turned and left the room, but came back before I had done wondering and puzzling over the oddity of all this; it was merely to say that he was going to Karnstein, and had ordered the carriage to be ready at twelve, and that I and Madame should accompany him; he was going to see the priest who lived near those picturesque grounds, upon business, and as Carmilla had never seen them, she could follow, when she came down, with Mademoiselle, who would bring materials for what you call a picnic, which might be laid for us in the ruined castle.

At twelve o'clock, accordingly, I was ready, and not long after, my father, Madame and I set out upon our projected drive.

Passing the drawbridge we turn to the right, and follow the road over the steep Gothic bridge, westward, to reach the deserted village and ruined castle of Karnstein.

No sylvan drive can be fancied prettier. The ground breaks into gentle hills and hollows, all clothed with beautiful wood, totally destitute of the comparative formality which artificial planting and early culture and pruning impart.

The irregularities of the ground often lead the road out of its course, and cause it to wind beautifully round the sides of broken hollows and the steeper sides of the hills, among varieties of ground almost inexhaustible.

Turning one of these points, we suddenly encountered our old friend, the General, riding towards us, attended by a mounted servant. His portmanteaus were following in a hired wagon, such as we term a cart.

The General dismounted as we pulled up, and, after the usual greetings, was easily persuaded to accept the vacant seat in the carriage and send his horse on with his servant to the schloss.

X

BEREAVED

It was about ten months since we had last seen him; but that time had sufficed to make an alteration of years in his appearance. He had grown thinner; something of gloom and anxiety had taken the place of that cordial serenity which used to characterise his features. His dark blue eyes, always penetrating, now gleamed with a sterner light from under his shaggy grey eyebrows. It was not such a change as grief alone usually induces, and angrier passions seemed to have had their share in bringing it about.

We had not long resumed our drive, when the General began to talk, with his usual soldierly directness, of the bereavement, as he termed it, which he had sustained in the death of his beloved niece and ward; and he then broke out in a tone of intense bitterness and fury, inveighing against the "hellish arts" to which she had fallen a victim, and expressing, with more exasperation than piety, his wonder that Heaven should tolerate so monstrous an indulgence of the lusts and malignity of hell.

My father, who saw at once that something very extraordinary had befallen, asked him, if not too painful to him, to detail the circumstances which he thought justified the strong terms in which he expressed himself.

"I should tell you all with pleasure," said the General, "but you would not believe me."

"Why should I not?" he asked.

"Because," he answered testily, "you believe in nothing but what consists with your own prejudices and illusions. I remember when I was like you, but I have learned better."

"Try me," said my father; "I am not such a dogmatist as you suppose. Besides which, I very well know that you generally require proof for what you believe, and am, therefore, very strongly predisposed to respect your conclusions."

"You are right in supposing that I have not been led lightly into a belief in the marvellous—for what I have experienced *is* marvellous—and I have been forced by extraordinary evidence to credit that which ran counter, diametrically, to all my theories. I have been made the dupe of a preternatural conspiracy."

Notwithstanding his professions of confidence in the General's penetration, I saw my father, at this point, glance at the General, with, as I thought, a marked suspicion of his sanity.

The General did not see it, luckily. He was looking gloomily and curiously into the glades and vistas of the woods that were opening before us.

"You are going to the Ruins of Karnstein?" he said. "Yes, it is a lucky coincidence; do you know I was going to ask you to bring me there to inspect them. I have a special object in exploring. There is a ruined chapel, ain't there, with a great many tombs of that extinct family?"

"So there are—highly interesting," said my father. "I hope you are thinking of claiming the title and estates?"

My father said this gaily, but the General did not recollect the laugh, or even the smile, which courtesy exacts for a friend's joke; on the contrary, he looked grave and even fierce, ruminating on a matter that stirred his anger and horror.

"Something very different," he said, gruffly. "I mean to unearth some of those fine people. I hope, by God's blessing, to accomplish a pious sacrilege here, which will relieve our earth of certain monsters, and enable honest people to sleep in their beds without being assailed by murderers. I have strange things to tell you, my dear friend, such as I myself would have scouted as incredible a few months since."

My father looked at him again, but this time not with a glance of suspicion—with an eye, rather, of keen intelligence and alarm.

"The house of Karnstein," he said, "has been long extinct: a hundred years at least. My dear wife was maternally descended from the Karnsteins. But the name and title have long ceased to exist. The castle is a ruin; the very village is deserted; it is fifty years since the smoke of a chimney was seen there; not a roof left."

"Quite true. I have heard a great deal about that since I last saw you; a great deal that will astonish you. But I had better relate everything in the order in which it occurred," said the General. "You saw my dear ward—my child, I may call her. No creature could have been more beautiful, and only three months ago none more blooming."

"Yes, poor thing! When I saw her last she certainly was quite lovely," said my father. "I was grieved and shocked more than I can tell you, my dear friend; I knew what a blow it was to you."

He took the General's hand, and they exchanged a kind pressure. Tears gathered in the old soldier's eyes. He did not seek to conceal them. He said:

"We have been very old friends; I knew you would feel for me, childless as I am. She had become an object of very near interest to me, and repaid my care by an affection that cheered my home and made my life happy. That is all gone. The years that remain to me on earth may not be very long; but by God's mercy I hope to accomplish a service to mankind before I die; and to subserve the vengeance of Heaven upon the fiends who have murdered my poor child in the spring of her hopes and beauty!"

"You said, just now, that you intended relating everything as it occurred," said my father. "Pray do; I assure you that it is not mere curiosity that prompts me."

By this time we had reached the point at which the Drunstall road, by which the General had come, diverges from the road which we were travelling to Karnstein.

"How far is it to the ruins?" inquired the General, looking anxiously forward.

"About half a league," answered my father. "Pray let us hear the story you were so good as to promise."

XI
THE STORY

"With all my heart," said the General, with an effort; and after a short pause in which to arrange his subject, he commenced one of the strangest narratives I ever heard.

"My dear child was looking forward with great pleasure to the visit you had been so good as to arrange for her to your charming daughter." Here he made me a gallant but melancholy bow. "In the meantime we had an invitation to my old friend the Count Carlsfeld, whose schloss is about six leagues to the other side of Karnstein. It was to attend the series of fêtes which, you remember, were given by him in honour of his illustrious visitor, the Grand Duke Charles."

"Yes; and very splendid, I believe, they were," said my father.

"Princely! But then his hospitalities are quite regal. He has Aladdin's lamp. The night from which my sorrow dates was devoted to a magnificent masquerade. The grounds were thrown open, the trees hung with coloured lamps. There was such a display of fireworks as Paris itself had never witnessed. And such music—music, you know is my weakness—such ravishing music! The finest instrumental band, perhaps, in the world, and the finest singers who could be collected from all the great operas in Europe. As you wandered through these fantastically illuminated grounds, the moon-lighted château throwing a rosy light from its long rows of windows, you would suddenly hear these ravishing voices stealing from the silence of some grove, or rising from boats upon the lake. I felt myself, as I looked and listened, carried back into the romance and poetry of my early youth.

"When the fireworks were ended, and the ball beginning, we returned to the noble suite of rooms that were thrown open to the dancers. A masked ball, you know, is a beautiful sight; but so brilliant a spectacle of the kind I never saw before.

"It was a very aristocratic assembly. I was myself almost the only 'nobody' present.

"My dear child was looking quite beautiful. She wore no mask. Her excitement and delight added an unspeakable charm to her features, always lovely. I remarked a young lady, dressed magnificently but wearing a mask, who appeared to me to be observing my ward with extraordinary interest. I had seen her, earlier in the evening, in the great hall, and again, for a few minutes, walking near us, on the terrace under the castle windows, similarly employed. A lady, also masked, richly and gravely dressed, and with a stately air, like a person of rank, accompanied her as a chaperon. Had the young lady not worn a mask, I could, of course, have been much more certain upon the question whether she was really watching my poor darling. I am now well assured that she was.

"We were now in one of the *salons*. My poor child had been dancing, and was resting a little in one of the chairs near the door; I was standing near. The two ladies I have mentioned had approached and the younger took the chair next my ward; while her companion stood beside me, and for a little time addressed herself, in a low tone, to her charge.

"Availing herself of the privilege of her mask, she turned to me, and in the tone of an old friend, and calling me by my name, opened a conversation with me, which piqued my curiosity a good deal. She referred to many scenes where she had met me—at Court, and at distinguished houses. She alluded to little incidents which I had long ceased to think of, but which, I found, had only lain in abeyance in my memory, for they instantly started into life at her touch.

"I became more and more curious to ascertain who she was, every moment. She parried my attempts to discover very adroitly and pleasantly. The knowledge she showed of many passages in my life seemed to me all but unaccountable; and she appeared to take a not unnatural pleasure in foiling my curiosity, and in seeing me flounder in my eager perplexity, from one conjecture to another.

"In the meantime the young lady, whom her mother called by the odd name of Millarca, when she once or twice addressed her, had, with the same ease and grace, got into conversation with my ward.

"She introduced herself by saying that her mother was a very old acquaintance of mine. She spoke of the agreeable audacity which a mask rendered practicable; she talked like a friend; she admired her dress, and insinuated very prettily her admiration of her beauty. She amused her with laughing criticisms upon the people who crowded the ballroom, and laughed at my poor child's fun. She was very witty and lively when she pleased, and after a time they had grown very good friends, and the young stranger lowered her mask, displaying a remarkably beautiful face. I had never seen it before, neither had my dear child. But though it was new to us, the features were so engaging, as well as lovely, that it was impossible not to feel the attraction powerfully. My poor girl did so. I never saw anyone more taken with another at first sight, unless, indeed, it was the stranger herself, who seemed quite to have lost her heart to her.

"In the meantime, availing myself of the licence of a masquerade, I put not a few questions to the elder lady.

"'You have puzzled me utterly,' I said, laughing. 'Is that not enough? Won't you, now, consent to stand on equal terms, and do me the kindness to remove your mask?'

"'Can any request be more unreasonable?' she replied. "Ask a lady to yield an advantage! Beside, how do you know you should recognise me? Years make changes.'

"'As you see,' I said, with a bow, and, I suppose, a rather melancholy little laugh.

"'As philosophers tell us,' she said; 'and how do you know that a sight of my face would help you?'

"'I should take chance for that,' I answered. 'It is vain trying to make yourself out an old woman; your figure betrays you.'

"'Years, nevertheless, have passed since I saw you, rather since you saw me, for that is what I am considering. Millarca, there, is my daughter; I cannot then be young, even in the opinion of people whom time has taught to be indulgent, and I may not like to be compared with what you remember me. You have no mask to remove. You can offer me nothing in exchange.'

"'My petition is to your pity, to remove it.'

"'And mine to yours, to let it stay where it is,' she replied.

"'Well, then, at least you will tell me whether you are French or German; you speak both languages so perfectly.'

"'I don't think I shall tell you that, General; you intend a surprise, and are meditating the particular point of attack.'

"'At all events, you won't deny this,' I said, 'that being honoured by your permission to converse, I ought to know how to address you. Shall I say Madame la Comtesse?'

"She laughed, and she would, no doubt, have met me with another evasion—if, indeed, I can treat any occurrence in an interview every circumstance of which was pre-arranged, as I now believe, with the profoundest cunning, as liable to be modified by accident.

"'As to that,' she began; but she was interrupted, almost as she opened her lips, by a gentleman, dressed in black, who looked particularly elegant and distinguished, with this drawback, that his face was the most deadly pale I ever saw, except in death. He was in no masquerade—in the plain evening dress of a gentleman; and he said, without a smile, but with a courtly and unusually low bow:—

"'Will Madame la Comtesse permit me to say a very few words which may interest her?'

"The lady turned quickly to him, and touched her lip in token of silence; she then said to me, 'Keep my place for me, General; I shall return when I have said a few words.'

"And with this injunction, playfully given, she walked a little aside with the gentleman in black, and talked for some minutes, apparently very earnestly. They then walked away slowly together in the crowd, and I lost them for some minutes.

"I spent the interval in cudgelling my brains for a conjecture as to the identity of the lady who seemed to remember me so kindly, and I was thinking of turning about and joining in the conversation between my pretty ward and the Countess's daughter, and trying whether, by the time she returned, I might not have a surprise in store for her, by having her name, title, château, and estates at my fingers' ends. But at this moment she returned, accompanied by the pale man in black, who said:

"'I shall return and inform Madame la Comtesse when her carriage is at the door.'

"He withdrew with a bow."

XII

A PETITION

"'Then we are to lose Madame la Comtesse, but I hope only for a few hours,' I said, with a low bow.

"'It may be that only, or it may be a few weeks. It was very unlucky his speaking to me just now as he did. Do you now know me?'

"I assured her I did not.

"'You shall know me,' she said, 'but not at present. We are older and better friends than, perhaps, you suspect. I cannot yet declare myself. I shall in three weeks pass your beautiful schloss, about which I have been making enquiries. I shall then look in upon you for an hour or two, and renew a friendship which I never think of without a thousand pleasant recollections. This moment a piece of news has reached me like a thunderbolt. I must set out now, and travel by a devious route, nearly a hundred miles, with all the dispatch I can possibly make. My perplexities multiply. I am only deterred by the compulsory reserve I practise as to my name from making a very singular request of you. My poor child has not quite recovered her strength. Her horse fell with her, at a hunt which she had ridden out to witness, her nerves have not yet recovered the shock, and our physician says that she must on no account exert herself for some time to come. We came here, in consequence, by very easy stages—hardly six leagues a day. I must now travel day and night, on a mission of life and death—a mission the critical and momentous nature of which I shall be able to explain to you when we meet, as I hope we shall, in a few weeks, without the necessity of any concealment.'

"She went on to make her petition, and it was in the tone of a person from whom such a request amounted to conferring, rather than seeking a favour. This was only in manner, and, as it seemed, quite unconsciously. Than the terms in which it was expressed, nothing could be more deprecatory. It was simply that I would consent to take charge of her daughter during her absence.

"This was, all things considered, a strange, not to say, an audacious request. She in some sort disarmed me, by stating and admitting everything that could be urged against it, and throwing herself entirely upon my chivalry. At the same moment, by a fatality that seems to have predetermined all that happened, my poor child came to my side, and, in an undertone, besought me to invite her new friend, Millarca, to pay us a visit. She had just been sounding her, and thought, if her mamma would allow her, she would like it extremely.

"At another time I should have told her to wait a little, until, at least, we knew who they were. But I had not a moment to think in. The two ladies assailed me together, and I must confess the refined and beautiful face of the young lady, about which there was something extremely engaging; as well as the elegance and fire of high birth, determined me; and, quite overpowered, I submitted, and undertook, too easily, the care of the young lady, whom her mother called Millarca.

"The Countess beckoned to her daughter, who listened with grave attention while she told her, in general terms, how suddenly and peremptorily she had been summoned, and also of the arrangement she had made for her under my care, adding that I was one of her earliest and most valued friends.

"I made, of course, such speeches as the case seemed to call for, and found myself, on reflection, in a position which I did not half like.

"The gentleman in black returned, and very ceremoniously conducted the lady from the room.

"The demeanour of this gentleman was such as to impress me with the conviction that the Countess was a lady of very much more importance that her modest title alone might have led me to assume.

"Her last charge to me was that no attempt was to be made to learn more about her than I might have already guessed, until her return. Our distinguished host, whose guest she was, knew her reasons.

"'But here,' she said, 'neither I nor my daughter could safely remain for more than a day. I removed my mask imprudently for a moment, about an hour ago, and, too late, I fancied you saw me. So I resolved to seek an opportunity of talking a little to you. Had I found that you *had* seen me, I should have thrown myself on your high sense of honour to keep my secret for some weeks. As it is, I am satisfied that you did not see me; but if you now *suspect*, or, on reflection, *should* suspect, who I am, I commit myself, in like manner, entirely to your honour. My daughter will observe the same secrecy, and I well know that you will, from time to time, remind her, lest she should thoughtlessly disclose it.'

"She whispered a few words to her daughter, kissed her hurriedly twice, and went away, accompanied by the pale gentleman in black, and disappeared in the crowd.

"'In the next room,' said Millarca, 'there is a window that looks upon the hall door. I should like to see the last of mamma, and to kiss my hand to her.'

"We assented, or course, and accompanied her to the window. We looked out, and saw a handsome old-fashioned carriage, with a troop of couriers and footmen. We saw the slim figure of the pale gentleman in black, as he held a thick velvet cloak, and placed it about her shoulders and threw the hood over her head. She nodded to him, and just touched his hand with hers. He bowed low repeatedly as the door closed, and the carriage began to move.

"'She is gone,' said Millarca, with a sigh.

"'She is gone,' I repeated to myself, for the first time—in the hurried moments that had elapsed since my consent—reflecting upon the folly of my act.

"'She did not look up,' said the young lady, plaintively.

"'The Countess had taken off her mask, perhaps, and did not care to show her face,' I said; 'and she could not know that you were in the window.'

"She sighed, and looked in my face. She was so beautiful that I relented. I was sorry I had for a moment repented of my hospitality, and I determined to make her amends for the unavowed churlishness of my reception.

"The young lady, replacing her mask, joined my ward in persuading me to return to the grounds, where the concert was soon to be renewed. We did so, and walked up and down the terrace that lies under the castle windows. Millarca became very intimate with us, and amused us with lively descriptions and stories of most of the great people whom we saw upon the terrace. I liked her more and more every minute. Her gossip, without being ill-natured, was extremely diverting to me, who had been so long out of the great world. I thought what life she would give to our sometimes lonely evenings at home.

"This ball was not over until the morning sun had almost reached the horizon. It pleased the Grand Duke to dance till then, so loyal people could not go away, or think of bed.

"We had just got through a crowded saloon, when my ward asked me what had become of Millarca. I thought she had been by her side, and she fancied she was by mine. The fact was, we had lost her.

"All my efforts to find her were vain. I feared that she had mistaken, in the confusion of a momentary separation from us, other people for her new friends, and had, possibly, pursued and lost them in the extensive grounds which were thrown open to us.

"Now, in its full force, I recognised a new folly in my having undertaken the charge of a young lady without so much as knowing her name; and fettered as I was by promises, of the reasons for imposing which I knew nothing, I could not even point my inquiries by saying that the missing young lady was the daughter of the Countess who had taken her departure a few hours before.

"Morning broke. It was clear daylight before I gave up my search. It was not till near two o'clock next day that we heard anything of my missing charge.

"At about that time a servant knocked at my niece's door, to say that he had been earnestly requested by a young lady, who appeared to be in great distress, to make out where she could find the General Baron Spielsdorf and the young lady his daughter, in whose charge she had been left by her mother.

"There could be no doubt, notwithstanding the slight inaccuracy, that our young friend had turned up; and so she had. Would to heaven we had lost her!

"She told my poor child a story to account for her having failed to recover us for so long. Very late, she said, she had got to the housekeeper's bedroom in despair of finding us, and had then fallen into a deep sleep which, long as it was, had hardly sufficed to recruit her strength after the fatigues of the ball.

"That day Millarca came home with us. I was only too happy, after all, to have secured so charming a companion for my dear girl."

XIII

THE WOODMAN

"There soon, however, appeared some drawbacks. In the first place, Millarca complained of extreme languor—the weakness that remained after her late illness—and she never emerged from her room till the afternoon was pretty far advanced. In the next place, it was accidentally discovered, although she always locked her door on the inside, and never disturbed the key from its place till she admitted the maid to assist her at her toilet, that she was undoubtedly sometimes absent from her room in the very early morning, and at various times later in the day, before she wished it to be understood that she was stirring. She was repeatedly seen from the windows of the schloss, in the first faint grey of the morning, walking through the trees, in an easterly direction, and looking like a person in a trance. This convinced me that she walked in her sleep. But this hypothesis did not solve the puzzle. How did she pass out from her room, leaving the door locked on the inside? How did she escape from the house without unbarring door or window?

"In the midst of my perplexities, an anxiety of a far more urgent kind presented itself.

"My dear child began to lose her looks and health, and that in a manner so mysterious, and even horrible, that I became thoroughly frightened.

"She was at first visited by appalling dreams; then, as she fancied, by a spectre, sometimes resembling Millarca, sometimes in the shape of a beast, indistinctly seen, walking round the foot of her bed, from side to side. Lastly came sensations. One, not unpleasant, but very peculiar, she said, resembled the flow of an icy stream against her breast. At a later time, she felt something like a pair of large needles pierce her, a little below the throat, with a very sharp pain. A few nights after, followed a gradual and convulsive sense of strangulation; then came unconsciousness."

I could hear distinctly every word the kind old General was saying, because by this time we were driving upon the short grass that spreads on either side of the road as you approach the roofless village which had not shown the smoke of a chimney for more than half a century.

You may guess how strangely I felt as I heard my own symptoms so exactly described in those which had been experienced by the poor girl who, but for the catastrophe which followed, would have been at that moment a visitor at my father's château. You may suppose, also, how I felt as I heard him detail habits and mysterious peculiarities which were, in fact, those of our beautiful guest, Carmilla!

A vista opened in the forest; we were on a sudden under the chimneys and gables of the ruined village, and the towers and battlements of the dismantled castle, round which gigantic trees are grouped, overhung us from a slight eminence.

In a frightened dream I got down from the carriage, and in silence, for we had each abundant matter for thinking; we soon mounted the ascent and were among the spacious chambers, winding stairs, and dark corridors of the castle.

"And this was once the palatial residence of the Karnsteins!" said the old General at length, as from a great window he looked out across the village, and saw the wide, undulating expanse of forest. "It was a bad family, and here its blood-stained annals were written," he continued. "It is hard that they should, after death, continue to plague the human race with their atrocious lusts. That is the chapel of the Karnsteins, down there."

He pointed down to the grey walls of the Gothic building, partly visible through the foliage, a little way down the steep. "And I hear the axe of a wood-man," he added, "busy among the trees that surround it; he possibly may give us the information of which I am in search, and point out the grave of Mircalla, Countess of Karnstein. These rustics preserve the local traditions of great families, whose stories die out among the rich and titled so soon as the families themselves become extinct."

"We have a portrait, at home, of Mircalla, the Countess Karnstein; should you like to see it?" asked my father.

"Time enough, dear friend," replied the General. "I believe that I have seen the original; and one motive which has led me to you earlier than I at first intended, was to explore the chapel which we are now approaching."

"What! See the Countess Mircalla," exclaimed my father; "why, she has been dead more than a century!"

"Not so dead as you fancy, I am told," answered the General.

"I confess, General, you puzzle me utterly," replied my father, looking at him, I fancied, for a moment with a return of the suspicion I detected before. But although there was anger and detestation, at times, in the old General's manner, there was nothing flighty.

"There remains to me," he said, as we passed under the heavy arch of the Gothic church—for its dimensions would have justified its being so styled—"but one object which can interest me during the few years that remain to me on earth, and that is to wreak on her the vengeance which, I thank God, may still be accomplished by a mortal arm."

"What vengeance can you mean?" asked my father, in increasing amazement.

"I mean, to decapitate the monster," he answered, with a fierce flush, and a stamp that echoed mournfully through the hollow ruin, and his clenched hand was at the same moment raised, as if it grasped the handle of an axe, while he shook it ferociously in the air.

"What?" exclaimed my father, more than ever bewildered.

"To strike her head off."

"Cut her head off!"

"Aye, with a hatchet, with a spade, or with anything that can cleave through her murderous throat. You shall hear," he answered, trembling with rage. And hurrying forward he said:

"That beam will answer for a seat; your dear child is fatigued; let her be seated, and I will, in a few sentences, close my dreadful story."

The squared block of wood, which lay on the grass-grown pavement of the chapel, formed a bench on which I was very glad to seat myself, and in the meantime the General called to the woodman, who had been removing some boughs which leaned upon the old walls; and, axe in hand, the hardy old fellow stood before us.

He could not tell us anything of these monuments; but there was an old man, he said, a ranger of this forest, at present sojourning in the house of a priest, about two miles away, who could point out every monument of the old Karnstein family; and, for a trifle, he undertook to bring him back with him, if we would lend him one of our horses, in little more than half an hour.

"Have you been long employed about this forest?" asked my father of the old man.

"I have been a woodman here," he answered in his *patois*, "under the forester, all my days; so has my father before me, and so on, as many generations as I can count up. I could show you the very house in the village here, in which my ancestors lived."

"How came the village to be deserted?" asked the General.

"It was troubled by *revenants*, sir; several were tracked to their graves, there detected by the usual tests, and extinguished in the usual way, by decapitation, by the stake, and by burning; but not until many of the villagers were killed.

"But after all these proceedings according to law," he continued—"so many graves opened, and so many vampires deprived of their horrible animation—the village was not relieved. But a Moravian nobleman, who happened to be travelling this way, heard how matters were, and being skilled—as many people are in his country—in such affairs, he offered to deliver the village from its tormentor. He did so thus: There being a bright moon that night, he ascended, shortly after sunset, the towers of the chapel here, from whence he could distinctly see the churchyard beneath him; you can see it from that window. From this point he watched until he saw the vampire come out of his grave, and place near it the linen clothes in which he had been folded, and then glide away towards the village to plague its inhabitants.

"The stranger, having seen all this, came down from the steeple, took the linen wrappings of the vampire, and carried them up to the top of the tower, which he again mounted. When the vampire returned from his prowlings and missed his clothes, he cried furiously to the Moravian, whom he saw at the summit of the tower, and who, in reply, beckoned him to ascend and take them. Whereupon the vampire, accepting his invitation, began to climb the steeple, and so soon as he had reached the battlements, the Moravian, with a stroke of his sword, clove his skull in twain, hurling him down to the churchyard, whither, descending by the winding stairs, the stranger followed and cut his head off, and next day delivered it and the body to the villagers, who duly impaled and burnt them.

"This Moravian nobleman had authority from the then head of the family to remove the tomb of Mircalla, Countess Karnstein, which he did effectually, so that in a little while its site was quite forgotten."

"Can you point out where it stood?" asked the General, eagerly.

The forester shook his head, and smiled.

"Not a soul living could tell you that now," he said; "besides, they say her body was removed; but no one is sure of that either."

Having thus spoken, as time pressed, he dropped his axe and departed, leaving us to hear the remainder of the General's strange story.

XIV
THE MEETING

"My beloved child," he resumed, "was now growing rapidly worse. The physician who attended her had failed to produce the slightest impression upon her disease, for such I then supposed it to be. He saw my alarm, and suggested a consultation. I called in an abler physician, from Gratz. Several days elapsed before he arrived. He was a good and pious, as well as a learned man. Having seen my poor ward together, they withdrew to my library to confer and discuss. I, from the adjoining room, where I awaited their summons, heard these two gentlemen's voices raised in something sharper than a strictly philosophical discussion. I knocked at the door and entered. I found the old physician from Gratz maintaining his theory. His rival was combating it with undisguised ridicule, accompanied with bursts of laughter. This unseemly manifestation subsided and the altercation ended on my entrance.

"'Sir,' said my first physician, 'my learned brother seems to think that you want a conjuror, and not a doctor.'

"'Pardon me,' said the old physician from Gratz, looking displeased, 'I shall state my own view of the case in my own way another time. I grieve, Monsieur le Général, that by my skill and science I can be of no use. Before I go I shall do myself the honour to suggest something to you.'

"He seemed thoughtful, and sat down at a table and began to write. Profoundly disappointed, I made my bow, and as I turned to go, the other doctor pointed over his shoulder to his companion who was writing, and then, with a shrug, significantly touched his forehead.

"This consultation, then, left me precisely where I was. I walked out into the grounds, all but distracted. The doctor from Gratz, in ten or fifteen minutes, overtook me. He apologised for having followed me, but said that he could not conscientiously take his leave without a few words more. He told me that he could not be mistaken; no natural disease exhibited the same symptoms; and that death was already very near. There remained, however, a day, or possibly two, of life. If the fatal seizure were at once arrested, with great care and skill her strength might possibly return. But all hung now upon the confines of the irrevocable. One more assault might extinguish the last spark of vitality which is, every moment, ready to die.

"'And what is the nature of the seizure you speak of?' I entreated.

"'I have stated all fully in this note, which I place in your hands upon the distinct condition that you send for the nearest clergyman, and open my letter in his presence, and on no account read it till he is with you; you would despise it else, and it is a matter of life and death. Should the priest fail you, then, indeed, you may read it.'

"He asked me, before taking his leave finally, whether I would wish to see a man curiously learned upon the very subject, which, after I had read his letter, would probably interest me above all others, and he urged me earnestly to invite him to visit him there; and so took his leave.

"The ecclesiastic was absent, and I read the letter by myself. At another time, or in another case, it might have excited my ridicule. But into what quackeries will not people rush for a last chance, where all accustomed means have failed, and the life of a beloved object is at stake?

"Nothing, you will say, could be more absurd than the learned man's letter. It was monstrous enough to have consigned him to a madhouse. He said that the patient was suffering from the visits of a vampire! The punctures which she described as having occurred near the throat, were, he insisted, the insertion of those two long, thin, and sharp teeth which, it is well known, are peculiar to vampires; and there could be no doubt, he added, as to the well-defined presence of the small livid mark which all concurred in describing as that induced by the demon's lips, and every symptom described by the sufferer was in exact conformity with those recorded in every case of a similar visitation.

"Being myself wholly sceptical as to the existence of any such portent as the vampire, the supernatural theory of the good doctor furnished, in my opinion, but another instance of learning and intelligence oddly associated with some one hallucination. I was so miserable, however, that, rather than try nothing, I acted upon the instructions of the letter.

"I concealed myself in the dark dressing-room, that opened upon the poor patient's room, in which a candle was burning, and watched there till she was fast asleep. I stood at the door, peeping through the small crevice, my sword laid on the table beside me, as my directions prescribed, until, a little after one, I saw a large black object, very ill-defined, crawl, as it seemed to me, over the foot of the bed, and swiftly spread itself up to the poor girl's throat, where it swelled, in a moment, into a great, palpitating mass.

"For a few moments I had stood petrified. I now sprang forward, with my sword in my hand. The black creature suddenly contracted towards the foot of the bed, glided over it, and, standing on the floor about a yard below the foot of the bed, with a glare of skulking ferocity and horror fixed on me, I saw Millarca. Speculating I know not what, I struck at her instantly with my sword; but I saw her standing near the door, unscathed. Horrified, I pursued, and struck again. She was gone; and my sword flew to shivers against the door.

"I can't describe to you all that passed on that horrible night. The whole house was up and stirring. The spectre Millarca was gone. But her victim was sinking fast, and before the morning dawned, she died."

The old General was agitated. We did not speak to him. My father walked to some little distance, and began reading the inscriptions on the tombstones; and thus occupied, he strolled into the door of a side-chapel to prosecute his researches. The General leaned against the wall, dried his eyes, and sighed heavily. I was relieved on hearing the voices of Carmilla and Madame, who were at that moment approaching. The voices died away.

In this solitude, having just listened to so strange a story, connected, as it was, with the great and titled dead, whose monuments were mouldering among the dust and ivy round us, and every incident of which bore so awfully upon my own mysterious case—in this haunted spot, darkened by the towering foliage that rose on every side, dense and high above its noiseless walls—a horror began to steal over me, and my heart sank as I thought that my friends were, after all, not about to enter and disturb this triste and ominous scene.

The old General's eyes were fixed on the ground, as he leaned with his hand upon the basement of a shattered monument.

Under a narrow, arched doorway, surmounted by one of those demoniacal grotesques in which the cynical and ghastly fancy of old Gothic carving delights, I saw very gladly the beautiful face and figure of Carmilla enter the shadowy chapel.

I was just about to rise and speak, and nodded smiling, in answer to her peculiarly engaging smile; when with a cry, the old man by my side caught up the woodman's hatchet, and started forward. On seeing him a brutalised change came over her features. It was an instantaneous and horrible transformation, as she made a crouching step backwards. Before I could utter a scream, he struck at her with all his force, but she dived under his blow, and unscathed, caught him in her tiny grasp by the wrist. He struggled for a moment to release his arm, but his hand opened, the axe fell to the ground, and the girl was gone.

He staggered against the wall. His grey hair stood upon his head, and a moisture shone over his face, as if he were at the point of death.

The frightful scene had passed in a moment. The first thing I recollect after, is Madame standing before me, and impatiently repeating again and again, the question, "Where is Mademoiselle Carmilla?"

I answered at length, "I don't know—I can't tell—she went there," and I pointed to the door through which Madame had just entered; "only a minute or two since."

"But I have been standing there, in the passage, ever since Mademoiselle Carmilla entered; and she did not return."

She then began to call "Carmilla," through every door and passage and from the windows, but no answer came.

"She called herself Carmilla?" asked the General, still agitated.

"Carmilla, yes," I answered.

"Aye," he said; "that is Millarca. That is the same person who long ago was called Mircalla, Countess Karnstein. Depart from this accursed ground, my poor child, as quickly as you can. Drive to the clergyman's house, and stay there till we come. Begone! May you never behold Carmilla more; you will not find her here."

XV
ORDEAL AND EXECUTION

As he spoke one of the strangest looking men I ever beheld entered the chapel at the door through which Carmilla had made her entrance and her exit. He was tall, narrow-chested, stooping, with high shoulders, and dressed in black. His face was brown and dried in with deep furrows; he wore an oddly-shaped hat with a broad leaf. His hair, long and grizzled, hung on his shoulders. He wore a pair of gold spectacles, and walked slowly, with an odd shambling gait, with his face sometimes turned up to the sky, and sometimes bowed down towards the ground, seemed to wear a perpetual smile; his long thin arms were swinging, and his lank hands, in old black gloves ever so much too wide for them, waving and gesticulating in utter abstraction.

"The very man!" exclaimed the General, advancing with manifest delight. "My dear Baron, how happy I am to see you, I had no hope of meeting you so soon." He signed to my father, who had by this time returned, and leading the fantastic old gentleman, whom he called the Baron to meet him. He introduced him formally, and they at once entered into earnest conversation. The stranger took a roll of paper from his pocket, and spread it on the worn surface of a tomb that stood by. He had a pencil case in his fingers, with which he traced imaginary lines from point to point on the paper, which from their often glancing from it, together, at certain points of the building, I concluded to be a plan of the chapel. He accompanied, what I may term, his lecture, with occasional readings from a dirty little book, whose yellow leaves were closely written over.

They sauntered together down the side aisle, opposite to the spot where I was standing, conversing as they went; then they began measuring distances by paces, and finally they all stood together, facing a piece of the side-wall, which they began to examine with great minuteness; pulling off the ivy that clung over it, and rapping the plaster with the ends of their sticks, scraping here, and knocking there. At length they ascertained the existence of a broad marble tablet, with letters carved in relief upon it.

With the assistance of the woodman, who soon returned, a monumental inscription, and carved escutcheon, were disclosed. They proved to be those of the long lost monument of Mircalla, Countess Karnstein.

The old General, though not I fear given to the praying mood, raised his hands and eyes to heaven, in mute thanksgiving for some moments.

"To-morrow," I heard him say; "the commissioner will be here, and the Inquisition will be held according to law."

Then turning to the old man with the gold spectacles, whom I have described, he shook him warmly by both hands and said:

"Baron, how can I thank you? How can we all thank you? You will have delivered this region from a plague that has scourged its inhabitants for more than a century. The horrible enemy, thank God, is at last tracked."

My father led the stranger aside, and the General followed. I knew that he had led them out of hearing, that he might relate my case, and I saw them glance often quickly at me, as the discussion proceeded.

My father came to me, kissed me again and again, and leading me from the chapel, said:

"It is time to return, but before we go home, we must add to our party the good priest, who lives but a little way from this; and persuade him to accompany us to the schloss."

In this quest we were successful: and I was glad, being unspeakably fatigued when we reached home. But my satisfaction was changed to dismay, on discovering that there were no tidings of Carmilla. Of the scene that had occurred in the ruined chapel, no explanation was offered to me, and it was clear that it was a secret which my father for the present determined to keep from me.

The sinister absence of Carmilla made the remembrance of the scene more horrible to me. The arrangements for that night were singular. Two servants, and Madame were to sit up in my room that night; and the ecclesiastic with my father kept watch in the adjoining dressing-room.

The priest had performed certain solemn rites that night, the purport of which I did not understand any more than I comprehended the reason of this extraordinary precaution taken for my safety during sleep.

I saw all clearly a few days later.

The disappearance of Carmilla was followed by the discontinuance of my nightly sufferings.

You have heard, no doubt, of the appalling superstition that prevails in Upper and Lower Styria, in Moravia, Silesia, in Turkish Servia, in Poland, even in Russia; the superstition, so we must call it, of the Vampire.

If human testimony, taken with every care and solemnity, judicially, before commissions innumerable, each consisting of many members, all chosen for integrity and intelligence, and constituting reports more voluminous perhaps than exist upon any one other class of cases, is worth anything, it is difficult to deny, or even to doubt the existence of such a phenomenon as the Vampire.

For my part I have heard no theory by which to explain what I myself witnessed and experienced, other than that supplied by the ancient and well-attested belief of the country.

The next day the formal proceedings took place in the Chapel of Karnstein. The grave of the Countess Mircalla was opened; and the General and my father recognised each his perfidious and beautiful guest, in the face now disclosed to view. The features, though a hundred and fifty years had passed since her funeral, were tinted with the warmth of life. Her eyes were open; no cadaverous smell exhaled from the coffin. The two medical men, one officially present, the other on the part of the promoter of the inquiry, attested the marvellous fact that there was a faint but appreciable respiration, and a corresponding action of the heart. The limbs were perfectly flexible, the flesh elastic; and the leaden coffin floated with blood, in which to a depth of seven inches, the body lay immersed. Here then, were all the admitted signs and proofs of vampirism. The body, therefore, in accordance with the ancient practice, was raised, and a sharp stake driven through the heart of the vampire, who uttered a piercing shriek at the moment, in all respects such as might escape from a living person in the last agony. Then the head was struck off, and a torrent of blood flowed from the severed neck. The body and head was next placed on a pile of wood, and reduced to ashes, which were thrown upon the river and borne away, and that territory has never since been plagued by the visits of a vampire.

My father has a copy of the report of the Imperial Commission, with the signatures of all who were present at these proceedings, attached in verification of the statement. It is from this official paper that I have summarized my account of this last shocking scene.

XVI
CONCLUSION

I write all this you suppose with composure. But far from it; I cannot think of it without agitation. Nothing but your earnest desire so repeatedly expressed, could have induced me to sit down to a task that has unstrung my nerves for months to come, and reinduced a shadow of the unspeakable horror which years after my deliverance continued to make my days and nights dreadful, and solitude insupportably terrific.

Let me add a word or two about that quaint Baron Vordenburg, to whose curious lore we were indebted for the discovery of the Countess Mircalla's grave.

He had taken up his abode in Gratz, where, living upon a mere pittance, which was all that remained to him of the once princely estates of his family, in Upper Styria, he devoted himself to the minute and laborious investigation of the marvellously authenticated tradition of Vampirism. He had at his fingers' ends all the great and little works upon the subject. "Magia Posthuma," "Phlegon de Mirabilibus," "Augustinus de curâ pro Mortuis," "Philosophicae et Christianae Cogitationes de Vampiris," by John Christofer Herenberg; and a thousand others, among which I remember only a few of those which he lent to my father. He had a voluminous digest of all the judicial cases, from which he had extracted a system of principles that appear to govern—some always, and others occasionally only—the condition of the vampire. I may mention, in passing, that the deadly pallor attributed to that sort of *revenants*, is a mere melodramatic fiction. They present, in the grave, and when they show themselves in human society, the appearance of healthy life. When disclosed to light in their coffins, they exhibit all the symptoms that are enumerated as those which proved the vampire-life of the long-dead Countess Karnstein.

How they escape from their graves and return to them for certain hours every day, without displacing the clay or leaving any trace of disturbance in the state of the coffin or the cerements, has always been admitted to be utterly inexplicable. The amphibious existence of the vampire is sustained by daily renewed slumber in the grave. Its horrible lust for living blood supplies the vigour of its waking existence. The vampire is prone to be fascinated with an engrossing vehemence, resembling the passion of love, by particular persons. In pursuit of these it will exercise inexhaustible patience and stratagem, for access to a particular object may be obstructed in a hundred ways. It will never desist until it has satiated its passion, and drained the very life of its coveted victim. But it will, in these cases, husband and protract its murderous enjoyment with the refinement of an epicure, and heighten it by the gradual approaches of an artful courtship. In these cases it seems to yearn for something like sympathy and consent. In ordinary ones it goes direct to its object, overpowers with violence, and strangles and exhausts often at a single feast.

The vampire is, apparently, subject, in certain situations, to special conditions. In the particular instance of which I have given you a relation, Mircalla seemed to be limited to a name which, if not her real one, should at least reproduce, without the omission or addition of a single letter, those, as we say, anagrammatically, which compose it. *Carmilla* did this; so did *Millarca*.

My father related to the Baron Vordenburg, who remained with us for two or three weeks after the expulsion of Carmilla, the story about the Moravian nobleman and the vampire at Karnstein churchyard, and then he asked the Baron how he had discovered the exact position of the long-concealed tomb of the Countess Millarca? The Baron's grotesque features puckered up into a mysterious smile; he looked down, still smiling on his worn spectacle-case and fumbled with it. Then looking up, he said:

"I have many journals, and other papers, written by that remarkable man; the most curious among them is one treating of the visit of which you speak, to Karnstein. The tradition, of course, discolours and distorts a little. He might have been termed a Moravian nobleman, for he had changed his abode to that territory, and was, beside, a noble. But he was, in truth, a native of Upper Styria. It is enough to say that in very early youth he had been a passionate and favoured lover of the beautiful Mircalla, Countess Karnstein. Her early death plunged him into inconsolable grief. It is the nature of vampires to increase and multiply, but according to an ascertained and ghostly law.

"Assume, at starting, a territory perfectly free from that pest. How does it begin, and how does it multiply itself? I will tell you. A person, more or less wicked, puts an end to himself. A suicide, under certain circumstances, becomes a vampire. That spectre visits living people in their slumbers; *they* die, and almost invariably, in the grave, develop into vampires. This happened in the case of the beautiful Mircalla, who was haunted by one of those demons. My ancestor, Vordenburg, whose title I still bear, soon discovered this, and in the course of the studies to which he devoted himself, learned a great deal more.

"Among other things, he concluded that suspicion of vampirism would probably fall, sooner or later, upon the dead Countess, who in life had been his idol. He conceived a horror, be she what she might, of her remains being profaned by the outrage of a posthumous execution. He has left a curious paper to prove that the vampire, on its expulsion from its amphibious existence, is projected into a far more horrible life; and he resolved to save his once beloved Mircalla from this.

"He adopted the stratagem of a journey here, a pretended removal of her remains, and a real obliteration of her monument. When age had stolen upon him, and from the vale of years, he looked back on the scenes he was leaving, he considered, in a different spirit, what he had done, and a horror took possession of him. He made the tracings and notes which have guided me to the very spot, and drew up a confession of the deception that he had practised. If he had intended any further action in this matter, death prevented him; and the hand of a remote descendant has, too late for many, directed the pursuit to the lair of the beast."

We talked a little more, and among other things he said was this:

"One sign of the vampire is the power of the hand. The slender hand of Mircalla closed like a vice of steel on the General's wrist when he raised the hatchet to strike. But its power is not confined to its grasp; it leaves a numbness in the limb it seizes, which is slowly, if ever, recovered from."

The following spring my father took me on a tour through Italy. We remained away for more than a year. It was long before the terror of recent events subsided; and to this hour the image of Carmilla returns to memory with ambiguous alternations—sometimes the playful, languid, beautiful girl; sometimes the writhing fiend I saw in the ruined church; and often from a reverie I have started, fancying I heard the light step of Carmilla at the drawing-room door.

MEMORIES
OF ULSTER

Lady Caroline Blackwood was a Sheridan on her father's side and a Guinness on her mother's. Although as an adult she lived in London, Paris, Los Angeles, and New York, she describes in this piece from 1972 how hailing from Ulster, "the world-famed trouble-spot," has been the defining influence on her and in her interactions with others.

And for all that I found there I might as well be
Where the Mountains of Mourne sweep down to the sea.

MANY PEOPLE FROM ULSTER have always felt that the man who wrote that song was a liar. "If the fellow once managed to get himself out of Northern Ireland," a woman from Belfast once said to me, "it's a bit hard to believe he's all that sincere when he pretends he was always fretting to get back. But the tune's all right, and the sentiment is all right. And in Ulster, of course," she added, "the tune and the sentiment have always been the thing."

That was long ago. But I still feel surprised whenever I hear Ulster mentioned in the news. It always used to seem like the archetypal place where nothing would, or could, ever happen. For as long as I can remember, boredom has seemed to be hanging over Northern Ireland like the grey mists that linger over her loughs. Boredom has seemed to be sweating out of the blackened Victorian buildings of Belfast, running down every tram-line of her dismal streets. Now, when Northern Ireland is mentioned, the word "internment" rattles through every sentence like the shots of a repeating rifle. And yet for years and years so many Ulster people, both Catholic and Protestant, have felt that they were "interned" in Ulster—interned by the gloom of her industrialised provinciality, by her backwaterishness, her bigotry and her tedium.

In 1940, war was seen as a solution. "All the American troops will liven things up a bit round here." But the last war never broke the back of Ulster's boredom. Everyone kept predicting—almost with pleasure—that the Belfast docks would be a prime German target, that Hitler would almost certainly launch his invasion via Northern Ireland. All the signposts were swivelled round in the Ulster lanes to trick his troops, and force tanks which had hoped to roll towards Ballynahinch into ending up in Ballygalley. However effective all these crafty precautions would have been in the event of a full-scale Axis landing, they turned out to be needless. There were very few raids, and one of these by error bombed what Protestant Northerners called "collaborationist" Dublin. This was said to be an act of God.

The American troops livened things up very little in Ulster. They hadn't much to do except hand out chewing-gum to the kids. They slouched miserably through their "duration"—and then they were gone. The few bonneted black faces which appeared in Ulster prams were the only memorable trace that they left of their unenjoyable stay.

And day after day—post-war, just as they had pre-war—in the grey squares of the Ulster villages groups of men in tweed caps, most of them toothless and out of work, went on standing around in huddles. They would rub their hands and mutter, and sometimes have a smoke, like people on a platform waiting endlessly for some cancelled train. And day after day—post-war, just as they had pre-war— in the wealthy suburbs of Belfast the wives of industrialists went on reading the Bible, drinking their sherry and eating scones. In those days all their houses were meant to contain that most curious of rooms known as "the parlour." The parlour was always musty and unused. There every stick of silver, every horse-show trophy and spoon, every candelabra and christening-cup, that the family had ever acquired was always laid out day and night, as though in defiant display of the rewards of Protestant virtue. Far too valuable to be used, and very heavily insured, there used to be a desolation to all this silver, which was polished daily by the maid and seemed to be perpetually waiting on its mahogany table as if in preparation for some longed-for, but never-arriving occasion. And very much the same effect used to be created, in the rooms which were in use for entertaining, by all the plaster Peter Scott geese, which were nailed so that they appeared to be flying past the photograph of the Royal Family in a freedom arc up the side of the wall. Sometimes one had the feeling that these status-symbol geese themselves secretly knew that their flight was an illusion: that they were just as static as their owners, that they would never fly out of these stifling, expensive interiors, where the light could hardly penetrate all the Gothic-cathedral stained-glass of the windows.

Then there were the Ulster Sundays. Post-war, there were still the Ulster Sundays: the war changed them not at all. On Sundays all the towns were still closed down, so that they seemed like the ghost towns of Colorado, and the Day of Rest went on being so well-observed that the serving of a cup of tea was still damned as a violation. When anyone died, people still went on saying that they feared it was a "judgment": that the dead one must have gone out driving, or drunk a Guinness, or read some novel on a Sunday.

And the war never changed the sermons which were preached on those Ulster Sundays, and the families still trailed off to listen to them. They would go all dressed up with hats and gloves and coins for the collection, taking their bored and dressed-up children. One particular sermon I heard in Ulster has always stayed with me. It was delivered on a Christmas Day, and the minister preached it from a pulpit decorated with holly. He said that on this special day he would like to start by quoting "the most beautiful words in the English language." His choice was curious: "The womb of a virgin hath he not abhorred." In his own terms, it was a daring choice. And some puritanical hesitation seemed to panic him, forcing him into a slip. He paused dramatically before delivering his words, and them boomed them out in ringing church-chant tones: "The worm of a virgin hath he not abhorred." I looked round his congregation. Surely they would have some reaction to this most unusual Christmas Day text. But all the scrubbed faces seemed to be in their usual trance. Glazed eyes just went on staring despondently at dusty hassocks, at the bleakness of the altar, stripped of all ornamentation to make a contrast with the idolatrous churches of the Papacy. Not one single person reacted to the minister's beautiful words—for not one person had heard them. His congregation had been interned by his sermons for far too long for his words to have any more power to penetrate the defensive depths of their devout deafness.

"Do you come from Northern Ireland?" I remember Foxy Falk barking the question at me years ago at an Oxford dinner. I was used to contemptuous responses from English people whenever I answered this question. "The South of Ireland is very nice," was all they would usually say. Or else, making one feel like some kind of mongrel imposter: "Oh, then you are not even proper Irish at all." But I felt that the question, when asked by Foxy Falk, was going to lead to something a little different. A collector of Ming vases, Cézannes and Persian carpets, he was a man who said that he believed in "the rule of the elite and the artist." He was tyrannical, reading Keats's letters aloud to people who had little desire to hear them, forbidding anyone in his household to use the telephone because he felt that it had ruined the art of conversation—and thereby creating daily difficulties as to grocery orders, etc. He would intimidate by his spluttering rages, which made one fear that the boil of his anger would crack his arteries. He was famous for the fact that he had once been Pavlova's lover.

"Do you come from Ulster?" I saw that the charge behind his question had already turned his whole face to a tomato-coloured balloon. Then his fist came smashing down on to the table so that the knives went shivering against the glasses. "All I can say is that the place where you come from ought to be blown up! It ought to be blown sky-high, and wiped from the face of this earth!" If he felt like that . . . I found myself staring blankly at his poor old turkey wattles, which were wobbling with agitation as they dripped down over his high Edwardian collar.

Then he calmed a little and explained that Pavlova at the height of her fame had danced in Belfast, and that the theatre had been totally empty except for two people. He claimed that she had never felt so insulted and distressed in her whole life—that Belfast was the only place in the world which had ever given her such a criminal reception.

Maybe because of the bombastic way the whole subject had been approached, and because I felt I was being personally blamed for the disastrous unsuccess of her visit, all I could feel was a sudden impatience with both Pavlova and her lover. Why were they so astounded by what to me seemed to be so very unastounding? What could have made them think that her dance could ever set the grimy dock-yards of Belfast dancing? When had that most austere of cities ever pretended for one moment that its prime interest was the dance?

I thought of the Ulster Protestants. Surely they had enough problems without having to be "wiped from the face of this earth" for being a poor audience. A fear of Catholics bred into them from childhood until it became instinctive like a ter-ror of spiders. Their lifelong drill of eccentric Ulster commandments. "Never drink from the same glass that a Catholic has drunk from. Any such glass should be broken immediately." And then their feeling of always being beleaguered, with the enemy pressing its full weight against the feeble ribbon of the border. Their suspicion that the enemy's prohibition on birth-control was a crafty long-term plan to out-breed them. Finally, their way of seeing the enemy—it's a very common way of seeing enemies—as dirty, lazy and cruel, plotting and promiscu-ous, and with one extra unforgivable vice—prone to dancing on a Sunday.

What happened? Everyone asks this as they look at the rubbled streets of Belfast and Londonderry on the television. The question never seems to be well answered, and only leads to more questions. If there had been no Catholics, would the Ulster Protestants have found it necessary to invent them? Certainly for years and years they provided the only spark of thrill and threat which could blast the monotony of the Ulster everyday. Month after month I remember lis-tening to the same repeating rumours that the Catholics were marching up from Dublin—"mustering" on the border—and infiltrating industry. Did all those interminable Ulster sermons seem less tedious when it was envisaged that iron-handed Papists might very soon try to put a stop to them? Did the polluted belch of Northern industry seem less hideous if it was felt that greedy Papal fingers were tentacling out to grasp the factories?

Can there be a boredom so powerful that it finally acts like an explosive? Marx said that the cottage must never be too near the castle. If England was the castle, was the provincial cottage of Ulster just a little bit too near?

"Wouldn't you think that people might be less bigoted in this day and age?" English people keep on asking me that. "You certainly would think so," I answer. And immediately I find myself doing a double-take. "Why would you think that they might be?" I wonder. "What reasons are there for thinking so?"

Every day the Ulster victims are flashed on the British television screens. They stutter out their tragedies in accents so unintelligible to the English that they might as well be speaking Swahili, and then they are cut off in mid-sentence for lack of television time.

When the Reverend Ian Paisley makes an occasional BBC appearance he seems awkward, oafish and provincial. He seems to lose all his rhetorical teeth when he is speaking to an English audience. He needs the roll and rattle of the Orange kettledrums to accompany his impassioned and oracular calls to duty. He needs to have his fanatical congregation, and King Billy of the Boyne, and The Lord, behind him. To see him on the BBC, who could believe that he could be idolised in Ulster? Who would ever think that he was an innovator—that back home in his Northern Irish church he has invented something quite as new as the "paper collection"? For Ian Paisley has said that the Lord wants no more coins . . . During his services, when the collection plate is passed round the congregation, the pounds pile up on it like great mounds of crumpled Kleenexes. But then when the plate is handed in to him, Dr. Paisley refuses to bless it. He just looks at it in sad silence and he shakes his enormous head. "The Lord," he says, "is not going to be very pleased with this." And the plate is sent back to the congregation for another round.

And while the Reverend's collection plate is circulating, the IRA seem less and less heroic as they blow the legs and arms off typists, and plant their gelignite wires across the routes of the school buses. And yet Ulster's rate of mental disease keeps on dropping as the troubles persist. Doctors claim they have never known it to be so low. All the while the Ulster Defence Association, dressed up like Ku Klux Klansmen, like Knights Templar from Outer Space, are drilling, and recruiting from the Orange Lodges of Scotland. They too set up their "no go" areas and their kangaroo courts. Last week I spoke to a Protestant who lives in County Down. "You don't like to go out at night," she said. "You feel that you might run into some roaming regiment of UDA with all their guns, and their goggles, and fish-net stockings over their mouths. And you feel that they might not like the look of you. They might set up a kangaroo court, and you'd be tried in their pouch." War games . . . And on both sides how many really want them to end one can sometimes despondently wonder. Has the whole province become intoxicated with its new-found power to seize the international headlines from its ancient overshadowing and world-important sister, England? Does it now feel some perverse and destructive terror of sinking back into a humdrum and peaceful obscurity in which the individual Ulsterman will no longer feel the superiority and glory of springing from a world-famed trouble-spot?

"Why not move all the Protestants out?" English liberals keep suggesting. "Why not move all the Catholics out?" Another common, and less liberal, suggestion. Both suggestions make it all sound so easy, like moving pinned flags on a staff map. Families, farms, occupations, the tie to the place of birth—all these things are made to seem like trifling, selfish quirks, which should be sacrificed for the greater good of the community. But who is going to decide which community most deserves this greater good? Then you are back again with an "Ulster problem."

"Why can't they all just get on with one another?" The English can seem very smug at the moment . . . If the IRA started hurling high explosives into the shopping-centres of Maidstone or Colchester, how long would it take before Catholic families living in the areas began to feel afraid of reprisals?

THOMAS MOORE

IRISH MELODIES

Between 1808 and 1834, Thomas Moore wrote 130 poems set to music, which are known collectively as Irish Melodies. *Two of the most enduring follow.*

BELIEVE ME, IF ALL THOSE ENDEARING YOUNG CHARMS

Believe me, if all those endearing young charms,
　　Which I gaze on so fondly to-day,
Were to change by to-morrow, and fleet in my arms,
　　Like fairy-gifts fading away,
Thou wouldst still be adored, as this moment thou art.
　　Let thy loveliness fade as it will.
And around the dear ruin each wish of my heart
　　Would entwine itself verdantly still.

It is not while beauty and youth are thine own,
　　And thy cheeks unprofaned by a tear,
That the fervor and faith of a soul can be known,
　　To which time will but make thee more dear;
No, the heart that has truly loved never forgets,
　　But as truly loves on to the close,
As the sun-flower turns on her god, when he sets,
　　The same look which she turned when he rose.

'T IS THE LAST ROSE OF SUMMER

'T is the last rose of summer
  Left blooming alone;
All her lovely companions
  Are faded and gone;
No flower of her kindred,
  No rose-bud is nigh,
To reflect back her blushes,
  Or give sigh for sigh.

I'll not leave thee, thou lone one!
  To pine on the stem;
Since the lovely are sleeping,
  Go, sleep thou with them.
Thus kindly I scatter
  Thy leaves o'er the bed,
Where thy mates of the garden
  Lie scentless and dead.

So soon may *I* follow,
  When friendships decay,
And from Love's shining circle
  The gems drop away.
When true hearts lie withered,
  And fond ones are flown,
Oh! who would inhabit
  This bleak world alone?

THOMAS MOORE

FROM
THE FUDGE FAMILY
IN PARIS

In The Fudge Family in Paris *(1818), Thomas Moore satirizes in epistolary verse the English tourists who began to infiltrate Paris after the Napoleonic era. The silly Fudges consist of father Phil, daughter Biddy, and son Bob, and these excerpts feature a letter each from Biddy and Bob to their friends back home; Biddy concerns herself with French fashion and men, while Bob likes to eat.*

LETTER I

FROM MISS BIDDY FUDGE TO MISS DOROTHY ———
OF CLONKILTY, IN IRELAND

Dear Doll, while the tails of our horses are plaiting,
    The trunks tying on, and Papa, at the door,
Into very bad French is as usual translating
    His English resolve not to give a *sou* more,
I sit down to write you a line—only think!—
A letter from France, with French pens and French ink,
How delightful! tho', would you believe it, my dear?
I have seen nothing yet *very* wonderful here;
No adventure, no sentiment, far as we've come,
But the corn-fields and trees quite as dull as at home;
And *but* for the post-boy, his boots and his queue,
I might *just* as well be at Clonkilty with you!
In vain, at Dessein's, did I take from my trunk
That divine fellow, Sterne, and fall reading "The Monk";

147

In vain did I think of his charming Dead Ass,
And remember the crust and the wallet—alas!
No monks can be had now for love or for money,
(All owing, Pa says, to that infidel Boney;)
And, tho' *one* little Neddy we saw in our drive
Out of classical Nampont, the beast was alive!

    By the by, tho' at Calais, Papa *had* a touch
Of romance on the pier, which affected me much,
At the sight of that spot, where our darling Dixhuit
Set the first of his own dear legitimate feet,
(Modelled out so exactly, and—God bless the mark!
'T is a foot, Dolly, worthy so *Grand a Monarque*),
He exclaimed, "*Oh, mon Roi!*" and, with tear-dropping eye,
Stood to gaze on the spot—while some Jacobin, nigh,
Muttered out with a shrug (what an insolent thing!)
"*Ma foi,* he be right—'t is de Englishman's King;
And dat *gros pied de cochon*—begar, me vil say
Dat de foot look mosh better, if turned toder way."
There's the pillar, too—Lord! I had nearly forgot—
What a charming idea!—raised close to the spot;
The mode being now, (as you've heard, I suppose,)
To build tombs over legs and raise pillars to toes.
    This is all that's occurred sentimental as yet;
Except indeed some little flower-nymphs we've met,
Who disturb one's romance with pecuniary views,
Flinging flowers in your path, and then—bawling for *sous!*
And some picturesque beggars, whose multitudes seem
To recall the good days of the *ancien régime,*
All as ragged and brisk, you'll be happy to learn,
And as thin as they were in the time of poor Sterne.

    Our party consists (in a neat Calais job)
Of Papa and myself, Mr. Connor and Bob.
You remember how sheepish Bob lookt at Kilrandy,
But, Lord! he's quite altered—they've made him a Dandy;
A thing, you know, whiskered, great-coated, and laced,
Like an hour-glass, exceedingly small in the waist:
Quite a new sort of creatures, unknown yet to scholars,
With heads so immovably stuck in shirt-collars,
That seats, like our music-stools, soon must be found them,

To twirl, when the creatures may wish to look round them,
In short, dear, "a Dandy" describes what I mean,
And Bob's far the best of the *genus* I've seen:
An improving young man, fond of learning, ambitious,
And goes now to Paris to study French dishes,
Whose names—think, how quick! he already knows pat,
A la braise, petits pâtés, and—what d'ye call that
They inflict on potatoes?—oh! *maitre d' hôtel*—
I assure you, dear Dolly, he knows them as well
As if nothing else all his life he had eat,
Tho' a bit of them Bobby has never touched yet;
But just knows the names of French dishes and cooks,
As dear Pa knows the titles of authors and books.

As to Pa, what d'ye think?—mind, it's all *entre nous*,
But you know, love, I never keep secrets from you—
Why, he's writing a book—what! a tale? a romance?
No, ye Gods, would it were!—but his travels in France;
At the special desire (he let out t' other day)
Of his great friend and patron, my Lord Castlereagh,
Who said, "My dear Fudge"—I forget the exact words,
And, it's strange, no one ever remembers my Lord's;
But 't was something to say that, as all must allow
A good orthodox work is much wanting just now,
To expound to the world the new—thingummie—science,
Found out by the—what's-its-name—Holy Alliance,
And prove to mankind that their rights are but folly,
Their freedom a joke (which it *is,* you know, Dolly),
"There's none," said his Lordship, "if *I* may be judge,
Half so fit for this great undertaking as Fudge!"

The matter's soon settled—Pa flies to *the Row*
(The *first* stage your tourists now usually go),
Settles all for his quarto—advertisements, praises—
Starts post from the door, with his tablets—French phrases—
"Scott's Visit," of course—in short, everything *he* has
An author can want, except words and ideas:—
And, lo! the first thing, in the spring of the year,
Is Phil Fudge at the front of a Quarto, my dear!
But, bless me, my paper's near out, so I'd better
Draw fast to a close:—this exceeding long letter

You owe to a *déjeûner à la fourchette,*
Which Bobby *would* have, and is hard at it yet.—
What's next? oh? the tutor, the last of the party,
Young Connor:—they say he's so like Bonaparte,
His nose and his chin—which Papa rather dreads,
As the Bourbons, you know, are suppressing all heads
That resemble old Nap's, and who knows but their honors
May think, in their fright, of suppressing poor Connor's?
Au reste (as we say), the young lad's well enough,
Only talks much of Athens, Rome, virtue and stuff;
A third cousin of ours, by the way—poor as Job
  (Tho' of royal descent by the side of Mamma),
And for charity made private tutor to Bob;
  Entre nous, too, a Papist—how liberal of Pa!

This is all, dear,—forgive me for breaking off thus,
But Bob's *déjeûner* 's done, and Papa's in a fuss.

B.F.

P.S.

How provoking of Pa! he will not let me stop
Just to run in and rummage some milliner's shop;
And my *début* in Paris, I blush to think on it,
Must now, Doll, be made in a hideous low bonnet.
But Paris, dear Paris!—oh, *there* will be joy,
And romance, and high bonnets, and Madame Le Roi!

⤋

LETTER III

FROM MR. BOB FUDGE TO RICHARD ———, ESQ.

Oh Dick! you may talk of your writing and reading,
Your Logic and Greek, but there's nothing like feeding;
And *this* is the place for it, Dicky, you dog,
Of all places on earth—the headquarters of Prog!
Talk of England—her famed *Magna Charta,* I swear, is
A humbug, a flam, to the Carte at old Véry's;
As as for your Juries—*who* would not set o'er 'em

A Jury of Tasters, with woodcocks before 'em?
Give Cartwright his Parliaments, fresh every year;
But those friends of *short Commons* would never do here;
And, let Romilly speak as he will on the question,
No Digest of Law 's like the laws of digestion!

By the by, Dick, *I* fatten—but *n'importe* for that,
'T is the mode—your Legitimates always get fat.
There's the Regent, there's Louis—and Boney tried too,
But, tho' somewhat imperial in paunch, 't would n't do:—
He improved indeed much in this point when he wed,
But he ne'er grew right royally fat *in the head.*

Dick, Dick, what a place is this Paris!—but stay—
As my raptures may bore you, I'll just sketch a Day,
As we pass it, myself and some comrades I've got,
All thorough-bred *Gnostics,* who know what is what.

After dreaming some hours of the land of Cocaigne,
    That Elysium of all that is *friand* and nice,
Where for hail they have *bon-bons,* and claret for rain,
    And the skaters in winter show off on *cream*-ice;
Where so ready all nature its cookery yields.
Macaroni au parmesan grows in the fields;
Little birds fly about with the true pheasant taint,
And the geese are all born with a liver complaint!
I rise—put on neck-cloth—stiff, tight, as can be—
For a lad who *goes into the world,* Dick, like me,
Should have his neck tied up, you know—there's no doubt of it—
Almost as tight as *some* lads who *go out of it.*
With whiskers well oiled, and with boots that "hold up
The mirror to nature"—so bright you could sup
Off the leather like china; with coat, too, that draws
On the tailor, who suffers, a martyr's applause!—
With head bridled up, like a four-in-hand leader,
And stays—devil's in them—too tight for a feeder,
I strut to the old Café Hardy, which yet
Beats the field at a *déjeûner a la fourchette.*
There, Dick, what a breakfast!—oh, not like your ghost
Of a breakfast in England, your curst tea and toast;
But a side-board, you dog, where one's eye roves about,

Like a turk's in the Haram, and thence singles out
One's *pâté* of larks, just to tune up the throat,
One's small limbs of chickens, done *en papillote.*
One's erudite cutlets, drest all ways but plain,
Or one's kidneys—imagine, Dick—done with champagne!
Then some glasses of *Beaune,* to dilute—or, mayhap,
Chambertin, which you know 's the pet tipple of Nap,
And which Dad, by the by, that legitimate stickler,
Much scruples to taste, but I'm not so partic'lar.—
Your coffee comes next, by prescription: and then Dick, 's
The coffee 's ne'er-failing and glorious appendix,
(If books had but such, my old Grecian, depend on 't,
I'd swallow e'en Watkins', for sake of the end on 't,)
A neat glass of *parfait-amour,* which one sips
Just as if bottled velvet tipt over one's lips.
This repast being ended, and *paid for*—how odd!
Till a man's used to paying, there 's something so queer in 't!)—
The sun now well out, and the girls all abroad,
    And the world enough aired for us Nobs to appear in 't,
We lounge up the boulevards, where—oh! Dick, the phizzes,
The turn-outs, we meet—what a nation of quizzes!
Here toddles along some old figure of fun,
With a coat you might date Anno Domini 1;
A laced hat, worsted stockings, and—noble old soul!
A fine ribbon and cross in his best button-hole;
Just such as our Prince, who nor reason nor fun dreads,
Inflicts, without even a court-martial, on hundreds.
Here trips a *grisette,* with a fond, roguish eye,
(Rather eatable things these *grisettes,* by the by);
And there an old *demoiselle,* almost as fond,
In a silk that has stood since the time of the Fronde.
There goes a French Dandy—ah, Dick! unlike some ones
We've seen about White's—the Mounseers are but rum ones;
Such hats!—fit for monkies—I'd back Mrs. Draper
To cut neater weather-boards out of brown paper:
And coats—how I wish, if it would n't distress 'em,
They 'd club for old Brummel, from Calais, to dress 'em!
The collar sticks out from the neck such a space,
    That you 'd swear 't was the plan of this head-lopping nation,
To leave there behind them a snug little place
    For the head to drop into, on decapitation.

In short, what with mountebanks, counts and friseurs,
Some mummers by trade and the rest amateurs—
What with captains in new jockey-boots and silk breeches,
    Old dustmen with swinging great opera-hats,
And shoeblacks, reclining by statues in niches,
    There never was seen such a race of Jack Sprats!

From the Boulevards—but hearken!
    —yes—as I'm a sinner.
The clock is just striking the half-hour to dinner:
So *no* more at present—short time for adorning—
My Day must be finisht some other fine morning.
Now, hey for old Beauvilliers's larder, my boy!
And, once *there,* if the Goddess of Beauty and Joy
Were to write "Come and kiss me, dear Bob!" I'd not budge—
Not a step, Dick, as sure as my name is

                    R. FUDGE

ON THOMAS
MOORE

In this essay celebrating Thomas Moore, "Ireland's national bard," acclaimed journalist Thomas D'Arcy McGee—who was only twenty years old in 1845 when it was published in his book Historical Sketches—*touches on the poet's friendship with Lord Byron and examines Moore's most important works, especially* Irish Melodies.

THOMAS MOORE, WHOSE biography, such as the public knows it, is as extensively read as the efforts of his genius are admired, contributed in a great degree, by his *Irish Melodies*, the epistles of the Fudge Family, and other political pieces, to establish the success of the Catholic cause. His life indeed, has been but one prolonged effort of patriotism—one endless succession of thoughts on Ireland. We find it under his theology in the *Travels of an Irish Gentleman*; we meet it in the groves of Persia, and on the Gheber's hill of refuge. In the melodies it melts us into tears, or rouses us to indignation; in the epistles it convulses us with laughter; in the memoirs of Captain Rock, it assumes as many colors as the chameleon—while it is the spirit and soul of all his thoughts throughout. Mr. Moore was born at No. 12 Angier Street, Dublin, on the 28th of May, 1780. His first teacher was Mr. Samuel Whyte of Grafton Street, who had likewise under his tuition Brinsley Sheridan. Under the teachings of this kind-hearted "Dominie," the tenacious memory of his pupil was stored with wonderful rapidity; in his twelfth year he meditated and actually commenced the translation of the odes of the Greek poet, Anacreon. His proficiency in the Latin and French languages was equally remarkable, and in the history of the middle ages, a study of which he was always fond. Amongst other peculiarities, Mr. Whyte had a rage for private theatricals; and so great was his experience in these matters, that he frequently managed the "getting up" of the amateur performances, in which the resident nobility of Dublin were anxious to excel. In these performances, his little pupil often figured, and occasionally wrote the prologues. Thus, at an age so tender, Moore by his own merit entered the high places of the aristocracy, and acquired an unhappy preference for their habits, which has remained with him through life. The relief bill of 1793 enabled Moore to enter Trinity College, where he resumed the translation of Anacreon, which he completed in 1799, and published, with a dedication—by permission—to George, Prince of Wales. The work is more admired as a beautiful version, than for the truthfulness of the translation.

In 1801, Moore, having gone to London, published a volume of original songs, odes and sonnets, under the title of *Poems, by Thomas Little the Younger,* which contains many splendid proofs of a fine imagination and sprightly wit, but greatly tarnished and obscured by a pervading spirit of lasciviousness. The result of this was, as may be expected, that the critics rose in arms *en masse*, and the only trouble amongst them seems to have been, who should devour the largest portion of the unfortunate Mr. Little. This point, however, was universally ceded to the celebrated Jeffrey, at that time editor of the *Edinburgh Review*, whose strictures, cutting with the easy voice of the south wind, were far less bearable than the stormy wrath of all the other defenders of morality and religion. The hot blood of the bard was stirred within him; he chose not to pay back scorn for ill usage, like Byron, but after his own Milesian method of revenge, he sent the critic a challenge, couched in words of fearful determination. They met at Chalk Farm, near London, a notorious duelling ground—but the authorities interfered, and on drawing the charges from the pistols of the hostile men of letters, discovered only *paper bullets!* This friendly invention of the seconds was seized upon by Byron, in 1809, in his masterly satire directed against "English Bards and Scotch Reviewers"; and he rallied both parties without mercy on the occasion. Once more the irritable Anacreon challenged; but this time there was no meeting, as Byron was on the shores of the Bosphorus before it reached him; on his return from the Childe Harold tour, matters were amicably arranged by the interference of Samuel Rogers, and the two bards became bosom friends. Moore's intimacy with the Prince of Wales is well known; the cause of its sudden irruption has been variously accounted for—but it appears that it was occasioned by the Regent's asking him if he was related to a certain peer whose family name is Moore; to which the poet promptly replied, "No, my liege! my father was a grocer of Dublin." A sneer of contempt rose on the noble faces at the board, and rested even on the lip of George; and from that night Moore was not seen again in royal company. The inheritors of the blood that triumphed at Hastings and Agincourt, whose bastard sires had enrolled their names on the roll of Battle Abbey, turned coldly from his conversation; and this was the true source of his falling into "contempt at court,"—disgrace, that, in the eyes of all upright men, will be a title to everlasting honor! In 1811 he was very busy at politics, and published two excellent pamphlets on the subject of the Catholic claims—one, "A Candid Appeal to the Public," and the other in the form of "A Letter to the Roman Catholics of Dublin"—both of which were of great usefulness at that time. In 1818 he produced *The Fudge Family in Paris,* a series of satiric letters on the then government, in which an agent of British diplomacy at Paris, Mr. Fudge, an expatriated Irishman, Phelim O'Connor, and one or two others, are the writers, and Lords Castlereagh, Liverpool and Eldon, Dr. Duigenan and others of that ilk, are the prominent butts. This work appeared with the anonymous signature of Thomas Brown. The "Two-Penny Post Bag," "The Skeptic," "Tom Crib's Memorial to Congress," and "Intolerance," are his other prominent satires, all written in a mingled vein of severity and humor, that teaches the reader to despise the objects of his spleen without sympathizing in the severity of their punishment. It was in 1808, we believe, that he commenced his *Irish Melodies,* the grandest combination of sweet sounds, historic truth, and the eloquent pleadings of suffering patriotism, ever produced by a single pen. These melodies are the proudest feature in his literary career; they are universally admired in Europe and America; they have been rendered into many languages, and furnished the gallant Poles with their last war songs. The Irish heart, barren after the sorrow of centuries, felt their reviving influence; and in some measure his own words of hope are verified:—

> The stranger shall hear thy lament on his plains;
>   The sound of thy harp shall be sent o'er the deep,
> Till thy tyrants themselves, as they rivet thy chains,
>   Shall pause at the song of the captive, and weep.

They have been so often judged and re-judged and so often eulogized, and by so many eminent critics, that it is needless to dwell on their claims to universal favor; for to those who are acquainted with them (and who is not?), all praise is needless. Moore's musical acumen has been matter of surprise to the most eminent composers; amongst others, Dr. Burney and Sir John Stevenson have borne evidence to its delicacy and ripeness. The airs he wrote to, although not originally known by very poetic names, are amongst the sweetest in the world. The great Gemanini declared he had heard nothing so original west of the Alps, and Handel has said he would rather have composed "Aileen Aroon," than his most prosperous operas. The historian of the Life of Godfrey of Boulogne, the leader of the second crusade, remarks that "but for the Irish harp, there would seem to be no music in these wars"; and an Italian professor of great skill exclaimed, on hearing for the first time the same instrument, "that must be the music of a people who have suffered slavery." To Moore, next to Bunting, is due the chief honor of reviving the fame, if not the use of his country's neglected melodies, and the resuscitation of her harp. For who but himself could have recognized the spirit of the "Red Fox," as chanted by some country crone, and infuse it into that glorious song, "Let Erin remember the days of old,"—or, that words divine might be wedded to the popular ballad air of "Thady ye gandher"?

As a prose writer, Mr. Moore's fame is not equal to his reputation as a poet. His *Memoirs of Captain Rock,* published in 1825, is, however, one of the very best books that was ever penned, on that prolific theme of many pens, the sufferings of Ireland. The knowledge, the philosophy, and the wit displayed in its composition, were never equalled, to our belief, in a similar work. The *Travels of an Irish Gentleman in Search of a Religion*, it has been bruited, was a penance imposed on Mr. Moore for the sins of Mr. Little—which, to judge from its pages, was performed with scrupulous diligence. The biographies of Byron, Sheridan, and Lord Edward Fitzgerald are all works of industry, and unblemished specimens of fine style. *The History of Ireland,* his most pretending prose work, is one of the best as yet written of that country, although very far removed from perfection. It is a singular truth that no Irish history now extant can be divested of some radical defect. Taafe is too declamatory, McDermott too metaphysical; Keating believes over much, and Tom Moore over little. But the latter has done more for Irish history than any other writer in our time who has made it his study or subject.

From this summary, and it may appear dogmatic, manner of speaking of the important productions of our national bard, we pass again to his poetry;—we pass with willingness from Ireland's sad realities to Persia's gay romance. Moore's *Lalla Rookh* needs no praise, can never feel censure, and stands impregnable to all the beleaguering hosts of criticism. Original in its conception as in its execution, it has appeared like one of those rare meteors, whose birth a seventh age is alone destined to witness. Our nature has no feeling that it does not reach; it puts in motion all the complex machinery of the heart. It is throughout "a string of gems"—a sheet of gold, scattered with every delicate and gorgeous flower that "the land of the sun" produces. With a little stretch of imagination, he has supposed that the pure-minded Emmet, or the great rebel chief (who seems fated to be the last of the Geraldines) stood before him for the portrait of his heroic Hafed. The betrayal is another trait of resemblance; and we would not desire a prettier epitaph for the late Mr. Reynolds of Kilkee Castle, or loyal Major Sirr, than that sublime malediction commencing with the line,—

"Oh! for a tongue to curse the slave."

It is only a little too good for either. *Lalla Rookh* has passed through the hands of millions; every dialect in Europe has its version, and of all the people who read it in the original, there is not one who does not ever after love the name of Moore. Shortly after its publication, it was dramatized and enacted at Berlin, the Queen of Prussia and the Emperor of Russia taking the characters of Feramoz and Lalla Rookh. In a letter written by Byron to Moore, he says, "I shall not suffer the

Misses Byron to read it lest they discover there is a greater poet than their father."

It is an honorable testimony to Moore's private character, that those who have written of his career or life, prefer dwelling on his social virtues and accomplishments, rather than the triumphs of his fancy or the splendor of his wit. His conversational powers are attractive and varied, while no man brings less of his literary pride into company than he does. With the ladies he is still successful, and, for a veteran adorer of the sex, he writes love songs with nearly as much spirit as he did forty years since. He sings, too, delightfully; for, like another Fitz Eustace, he

> Can frame love ditties, passing rare,
> And sing them to a lady fair.

After all the wear and tear affections suffer in passing through a life like his, his heart is still full of fresh feeling and vigorous attachment. When he visited Dublin in 1835, his stay was celebrated as a public event of great importance; the high hopes of his original designs for Ireland eked out, and discovered the same heart then, that once waked into life and gave a name to her national melodies. His public reception at Bannow, in the native county of his parents, was much after the manner of a Roman ovation. Nine peasant girls, bright as the beings of his own fancy, crowned him with a coronal of laurel and roses interwoven. The entire population sang his praises, in their own untutored style.

In his matrimonial affairs he has been happier than most men of letters. His cottage at Sloperton is as inviting a homestead as ever was the residence of a mind so active and an imagination so brilliant. His lady was chosen after his own mode of courtship. "You may go in for eighty years," was remarked by his friend Byron; he is now sixty-four, and the completion of the noble poet's prophecy, is, to human vision, nowise improbable.

A GLANCE AT THE
FUTURE DESTINY OF IRELAND

*In this hopeful essay from 1844 extolling what Thomas D'Arcy McGee
perhaps blindly foresees as a bright future for Ireland, the journalist
enumerates the virtues of the country: the improved educational system,
the mass adoption of a pledge against alcohol, the recent discovery of
Ireland's mineral wealth, and a gradual freedom from the tyranny of
England. Four years later he was forced to leave Ireland because of his
political activities; he eventually settled in Canada, where he stayed
active in that country's politics. After speaking out against the Fenian
movement, McGee was assassinated in 1868 in Ottawa, most likely by
Irish revolutionaries.*

THE DESTINY OF A PEOPLE IS in a great measure, indeed nearly altogether,
the work of their own creation. To penetrate the mysterious ways of
Providence, by unveiling the hidden face of futurity, has been given to
few even of the most favored of men, and for no trivial purposes. But hope and
observation are in some degree prophets; and it is because I have firm hope in
Ireland's ascension, and have observed for years past her growing mind, that I
have ventured to throw out the following reflections.

There is no enslaved people who within the present century have given such
cause for hope to their sympathizers, as the Irish. When we contemplate the self-
denial they have observed since arriving at a knowledge of their wrongs, we cannot but allow them the possession either of a more phlegmatic disposition than
they have hitherto been suspected of, or a deep and all-pervading religious sentiment. Within fifteen years the mental eye of Ireland has been opened; education
has been progressing; her history has been unsealed. The first lesson she learned
was indeed of surpassing bitterness. Her first triumph brought her to the knowledge of herself, of the high estate from which she had fallen, and of the almost

universally received calumnies on her character and name which England had propagated as wide as ships could sail, or travellers penetrate. There was no people in Europe less known, previous to the days of the Irish Volunteers. From 1782 to 1800, Ireland nobly vindicated her fame as a mother of genius and an ardent seeker after liberty. But the union demolished the fair rising structure, and again England ruled and libelled unopposed. In 1830, Ireland was again on her feet; looking around, she beheld all the horizon covered with the mists of prejudice and calumny. From one quarter alone, there came a ray of cheering light—from the land in whose service Sarsfield and Wolf Tone had died. Fourteen years are gone, and Ireland has learned something of her own history, and something also of the mournful truth that mankind are always more prone to give credit to the charge of the powerful, than the defence of the subjugated. A wise resolution was taken; the people resolved to undo practically before the eyes of the whole world, the filthy web of misrepresentation with which England had surrounded them. Every educational society and improvement was adopted, and a new one was formed which redounds to her great credit—I mean, "the Christian Brothers." Mr. Rice, a man of the most exalted purity of soul, the most generous enthusiasm, and the highest order of practical ability, was the founder of this admirable system. He realized in his own life many of those great qualities which distinguished Ignatius Loyola, with the shrinking modesty of a pure, devoted soul. His institution has conferred on Ireland innumerable advantages thus far, and many more and greater may fairly be anticipated from its rapid increase. Gerald Griffin, the inspired author of *Gysippius*—the poet, novelist and philosopher—the scholar of nature, and child of all the muses, was so deeply impressed with the utility of this excellent association, that, divesting himself of the world, he descended (or rather rose) from the instruction of kingdoms, to be a teacher of the poorest of the children of Ireland. The Ursuline community, devoted to the education of female children, are at present very numerous in Ireland, and the minds of the future mothers of the people are being expanded and improved to a degree which many generations before them have not been able to compass. The "national education" system, with all its faults, is also producing its effects; and, acting on the system of the ingenious Mr. Lancaster, is sowing the seeds of an abundant harvest. To these we cannot omit to add the lately-established method of "adult" self-culture, by the founding of reading-rooms and night-schools. The Dublin newspaper press deserve everlasting credit for their unceasing efforts to propagate this most useful and admirable system. Taking all things into consideration, we can very well agree with a late intelligent tourist, in the belief that the rising generation of the Irish men and women will be as well, or better educated, than any other portion of the European populace.[1]

There cannot be a truer maxim than Homer's:—

Jove makes it certain, that whatever day
Makes man a slave, takes half his worth away.

The Irish people, pressed down for so many ages—rendered reckless by an invariable infliction of want, incurred to a frightful extent, the odious habit of drunkenness. In this they are generally conceded the "bad eminence" of superiority; but there are unanswerable proofs that the Scottish people exceeded them in intemperance.[2] But of one fact there can be no question—that there are few among the population, on whom this terrible habit had not fastened. The Directory of the United Irishmen, in 1797, proposed to the people a pledge against all intoxicating liquors, which was not generally adopted. Mr. O'Connell, at Waterford, in 1826, and in the first Clare election, had pledged the peasantry to total abstinence until the contests should be decided; but the effects of these vows were limited by their duration. It is more than twenty years since the Rev. George Carr of New Ross introduced the system of Temperance Societies into Ireland, which languished through a fluctuating existence until the year 1838, when Theobald Mathew appeared as the moral regenerator of the people. Within five years, as many millions of the Irish people have taken a solemn vow, before God and their fellow-men, to abstain from all intoxicating drinks; this they have most rigidly adhered to, and faithfully endeavored to propagate. The contagion of their example has spread into Scotland and England, and accompanied the Irish emigrant to the Pacific, and America; and the world is now indebted for the brightest example of moral heroism which modern times produces, to the longest oppressed and worst ruled portion of its people. The career of Father Mathew is a miracle of success; quietly and humbly, without pomp, or bribe, or flattery, he has induced the people to cast off their prevalent and perilous habit. Sobriety has paved the way for study; the national love of music has been revived; the staple produce of the metropolis is poetry; the old airs are caught upon the mountains, as they were departing forever; and an emulative improvement actuates all the classes of society. Meanwhile, the good apostle, like another Patrick, traverses the island round and round, imitating that illustrious saint in the industry and self-sacrifice with which he pursues his mission, strengthening social bonds and virtuous societies, shedding peace and comfort into many a long-desolated home. His ways are not those of self-opinionated reformers, nor his wisdom as their wisdom. Yet in those distant ages when half a dozen names, at most, will be well remembered, out of the multitude of men dignified at this day by the cheap prefix of "great," that of Mathew will hold a first place. Political systems will perish; monuments of civilization will disappear; nations, leaving scarce a name, shall have expired—but his memory shall endure. The "abomination of desolation" shall fill cities and empires; false creeds shall have lived and died; false prophets and their rhapsodies will have vanished—but the name of this illustrious friar will not pass away. Their greatness is made with hands, or with the voice—while his is erected out of the inexhaustible energies of his own soul, and the edifice partakes of the immortality of the instrument of its erection. Their work is a work of pride, stimulated by passion—his, rising from humility, touches the heavens; and sustained by the most unbounded benevolence, makes all the earth its resting-place. In them we see the workings of man, the mere animal—but in him, the exhibition of one, all soul, and love, and disinterestedness.

There is no other phrase which so well expresses the character of Irish political history, as the single word, *extraordinary*. Singular, indeed, have been the fortunes of the Hibernian Celts, and their descendants. Ireland was old when Christianity exiled the Druids from their sacrificial forests; her commerce was known at Rome, but not her captives; Tyre and Sidon had bartered with her, before Romulus and his brother had forsaken Alba. Her military fame, at an early time, was equally celebrated; her soldiers trampled down the Roman fortifications, and were about to scale the Alps, when an arrow of lightning, launched from the thunder-cloud above, struck down Dathy, their daring general—yet a handful of needy Normans overran her sea-coast, and, profiting by the jealousies of rival chiefs, seized on the pleasant plains of Leinster. Seven hundred years of slavery have scarcely cured them of that besetting sin. Early in her Christian ages, when Europe was buried in barbarism, letters and science found a shelter amidst her glens, where like a conservatory, those precious plants were screened from the inclemency of that Gothic winter which had set in on all the cities and states of the continent. When literature "revived" abroad, in the latter part of the sixteenth century, penal laws and Protestantism had commenced the work of devastation in Ireland; then, what the Vandals had done for Rome, and the Saracens for Spain, Henry and Elizabeth performed for Ireland. With the accession of the Guelphs this was completed; and ignorance and the Reformation were established by law together. This eccentric destiny clung to the land even later; in the history of the Stuart war in Ireland, it is strangely exemplified. The revolution of 1688 gave new security to the liberties of the empire, but refastened the fetters of Ireland. Her soldiers went abroad to win glory in a foreign service; her scholars were proscribed and incarcerated; and while the reign of Anne is the brightest era in English literary history, it becomes the darkest in that of Ireland. In 1798, the Presbyterians and Catholics first combined to save the constitution, and enlarge its pale so as to take in all creeds; but again a blight came o'er their councils—and from willing comrades in danger, they were artfully turned into enemies, underrating and suspecting each other.

But, strange as it may appear, the singularity of this destiny has preserved through every change the great characteristics of the Milesian blood, which, although in some respects chilled or changed by slavery, is yet gushing from the heart. Their hatred of control has preserved the love of learning, because learning

164

was denied; and persecution has established Catholicism more firmly in the hearts of the people, than it would probably have been fixed, in an uninterrupted course of national prosperity. Every people west of the Alps have, at some time or other, yielded up their old faith and its imposing forms—but Ireland has only clung to them more fondly in the lapse of centuries. The sons of her rightful princes entered the sanctuary, and the expounders of Christian doctrine became also the hope of the bondsman. For nearly two centuries, the Catholic clergy were the only educated portion of the aboriginal population; and from this cause they were obliged to be the advocates and defenders of the people—the councillors and conveyancers, as well as the teachers, of the masses. The clergy became the conservers of antiquity, the narrators of history, and the preservers of a national spirit. In the gloomy glen, or in the cavern's darkness, haranguing their faithful flocks, it was impossible for them to avoid mentioning the laws which had driven them thither, and the transition thence was natural, to the men who made them. The upstart antiquity of the Saxon race—their treachery, injustice, and inferiority to those whom they oppressed, were kept constantly before the down-trodden masses; and thus was perpetuated that sturdy sense of ancestral dignity, which is always the companion of your true Irishman. Young patriots loved and cherished this useful vanity, feeding it with declamation, and celebrating it in fiery strains of never-dying song. At length, proscription wearied of its ineffectual labors, the penal laws were abolished, and the heart of Ireland swelled out to its original greatness. It has since voluntarily cast out much of the folly of a false pride, and in its place now wisely cultivates a knowledge of the defects of native character, with a view to their remedy.

It would be rash to assert, dogmatically, that the Irish of future times will be a great people; but we may say with certainty, that few countries ever had a fairer field, to win for themselves solid and legitimate greatness. In politics, they have produced the most remarkable statesman of the day; in morals, they possess the most wonderfully apostolic man; and in education, they are fast tracking up the steps of the best taught communities. It is true that in Austria and Prussia there are wider and deeper systems of study; but these are entirely governmental, and have not originated with the people. The peculiar genius of a nation ought to be represented in its system of culture; for if the system harmonizes not with that genius, it becomes a clog around its neck, rather than a beacon to light it onward. The Irish system, now rapidly tending to an established existence, will be of the people—all the better, insomuch that instead of being compulsory, it is formed by the same hands which are to use it. In this view its practicability is vastly superior to the schemes of the continental cabinets.

But there is a higher cause for hope, than all the workings of the national spirit convey, although these certainly are far from dubious or equivocal. It is the hope we all have (or should have) in the merciful guardianship of a just and retributive

Providence—Him, of whom it is written that a sparrow falls not to the earth, unknown to His all-pervading intelligence. To Him, on behalf of the oppressed, the freeman should always look—for the emancipation unsanctioned in heaven is valueless. We have many causes to look there on behalf of Ireland. The birth-land of five hundred canonized saints, and many thousands of beatified martyrs, cannot surely, in His justice, be left longer as the footstool of a hereditary despo-tism. The land from which the patrons of Scotland and Northumberland, of Germany and Gaul, swarmed forth, as St. Bernard says, "in an inundation" of pious zeal, is not to continue forever a nursery of paupers, partizans, and merce-nary soldiers. The vessel in which such goodly forms were moulded of old, has not been doomed—Oh! never can be doomed—to the shaping of hideous shapes, of slaves who go forth to make slaves, and maniacs who execute the laws of those who manacle them. Nations shall confess the justice of God, and kings tremble before his judgments. "Heaven and earth shall pass away," but his word never!

We see the evidences of this propitious Providence in the men now employed to raise up the people of Ireland, as well as in the improved temper of the people themselves. Their ancestors of old, revelling in plenty, and indulging in unat-tacked freedom, grafted on their hereditary Milesian impetuosity, a wilder and more hazardous daring. To this they joined an unsuspicious disposition, pam-pered by an overweening sense of their political security and military invincibility, which in reality "sold the pass" upon them, and gave their patrimony to the invad-er. But their sons, so long as they retained lands and gold, scorned to degenerate from the olden rule; it was only confiscation which could teach prudence, and beggary which introduced frugality. Two generations lay paralyzed in each of those extensive changes, which, under Elizabeth, James, Cromwell, and William, gave a new race of proprietors to the soil. Had the present and wisest attempt at national elevation been the work of impulse, or the promptings of a temporary resolution, we might well distrust it; for the swiftest steed is often the first to give out, and the wave which throws itself highest on the beach, returns most quickly to the bowels of the ocean. Such, however, is not the nature of the present Irish agitation, that, like a natural crop in a wholesome soil, has appeared faintly at first, but, overcoming the inclemency of many obstacles, flowers, and at last brings forth the long-expected fruit for general nourishment and preservation. The Providence which has given Ireland an O'Connell in political, and a Mathew in moral reformation, has also given her the heart to receive, and the understanding to follow the teachings of these great men. Without this innate virtue, and a strong native sense of duty, all preachings of peace and charity and forgiveness would be thrown away, and Father Mathew's reputation would still be limited to the congregation of Blackamoors Lane, and O'Connell would have been little more than " a stout special pleader." That consciousness of deserving better times, and hilarity of temper which distinguishes the people—their fervent Catholic enthusiasm, and lofty appreciation of the value of letters, are materials out of which sincere and industrious advocates can easily effect many salutary improvements. No country that endured slavery so long, has emerged from it less deteriorated by the contact. The sons of the Italian republics are wanderers on the earth, pedlars of bad music and retailers of comfits; the posterity of Greece lie most complacently beneath the heel of the Moslem, although their fathers were freemen before the Hegira, while yet Arabia slumbered in a state of tinselled barbarism.

The situation of Ireland, and her natural advantages, should long since have made her eminent amongst nations. An island compact and well watered, with as many harbors as there are leagues in her circumference; placed to the west of all Europe—the last Atlantic landmark of the old world, and the first European beacon for the new—she has been regarded by commerce as a mere Eddystone, useful when a wide berth is given her. Yet, what a mistake is here. Her northern coast—that wonderful museum of geology—instead of attracting attention only by its curiosities, should have invaded the ocean with moving monuments of art, more wonderful than the eternal pillars planted by giant hands, in defiance of the angry North Sea. Her southern shore tempts the approach of Mediterranean commerce, while her vast western havens ought to be covered with the fleets of the new world. Through the means of Ireland, a revolution will some day be effected in British commerce; and if the merchants of Liverpool and Bristol will not take time by the forelock, they may behold a time when the warehouses of Galway shall be large enough to oblige few ships to brave the dangers of Channel navigation.

Dr. Kane, in his recent admirable work, has demonstrated, with the most beautiful accuracy, the immense fund of mineral wealth which lies unemployed beneath the feet of the idle and half-starving peasantry. This laborious author has developed the extent of vast coal-fields, hitherto but little known, the wealth of which will be inexhaustible when Newcastle and Whitehaven are no longer productive. He has divided these fields into provincial classes, of which one is in Leinster, two in Munster, three in Ulster, and one in Connaught. The first occupies the greater portion of the county of Kilkenny, the Queen's county, and part of Carlow, and is bounded by the rivers Barrow and Nore. "This district," says the Doctor, "forms a great mineral basin; its strata consequently incline from the edge toward the centre—the undermost appear on the outer edge, and the uppermost in the interior of the district. Mr. Griffith estimates the area occupied by this coal at 5,000 acres, (Irish,) and its specific gravity is 1.591; the total quantity of pure solid coal may be calculated at rather more than sixty-three millions of tons." The Tipperary coal-field is about twenty miles in length by six in breadth; yet the quantity of coal at present raised from it does not exceed fifty thousand tons per annum. The great Munster "formation" is the most extensive coal-bed in the British islands. It occupies much of the counties of Clare, Kerry, Limerick, and Cork. Mr. Griffith has discovered in it six different layers; "three of the most valuable, locally known as the bulk-vein, the rack-vein, and the sweet-vein, have been recognized at the opposite sides of the undulations." Yet this vast source of wealth is almost untouched. The coal formations of Ulster, in Tyrone and Antrim, are not very extensive; in the former, however, there are between seven and eight thousand acres, comprising the Coal Island and Anahone districts. The hills around Lough Allen encompass the Connaught coal fields, which extend through Roscommon, Sligo, Leitrim, and a portion of Cavan, or about sixteen miles in each direction. This also has been to the present but little worked.

Such is the fuel power lying inactive in Ireland. Of her immense water power, it has been acknowledged that it could turn all the machinery of Britain and France. There is no other European country so well watered; an innumerable variety of streams dash down her declivities, and float onward to the ocean, like the unemployed hours of a sluggard, never to return. O, Nature! How thy boons are squandered upon slaves! What profits it to Irishmen that they live in a land flowing with milk and honey, when their hands are chained, and their limbs fettered? Of what avail are all the benefactions of a good Providence, when tyrant laws have reversed the order of nature, and reared up beggary in the very nursery of abundance? But the day of the destroyer is fading into twilight, and the sun of a new age is smiling serenely on "the plains and rivers of the land."

I have cast this hasty glance upon the moral, intellectual and physical capabilities of Ireland, for building up a name and nationality, because it is always an agreeable task to show that men are capable of better things than most philosophers suspect them of; but it is peculiarly so to believe that the slave is to have his turn of fortune, honor, enlightenment, and independence. It is delightful to contemplate the possibility of Ireland's ascension—to think that, when England's star shall pale, and her "felon flag" be furled forever, her long-oppressed sister-isle shall assume a glorious destiny, and practise toward her prostrate oppressor, "the noble vengeance of forgiveness."

Ireland has a deep, abiding faith; vast natural wealth; increasing intelligence; a firm sobriety, and a good share of political education. If she be but true to herself, no country ever shaped out a nobler futurity than she can. As the people are to themselves, so shall their posterity be to the world. The inheritance of liberty and eminence is before them, and over its portal, like the door of the enchanted chamber, it is written—"Be bold! be bold! but be not too bold!"

$$\downarrow$$

[1] Dr. James Johnson

[2] Among other documents tending to place the Irish people in their proper relation to other nations guilty of drunkenness, is the Parliamentary Report of the Excise Commissioners of 1835, in which their secondary proficiency is clearly established.

THE LEGEND OF KNOCKGRAFTON

This is a traditional tale retold by T. Crofton Croker, an early nineteenth-century antiquarian who was among the first to find literary merit in Irish folklore.

THERE WAS ONCE A POOR MAN who lived in the fertile glen of Aherlow, at the foot of the gloomy Galtee mountains, and he had a great hump on his back: he looked just as if his body had been rolled up and placed upon his shoulders; and his head was pressed down with the weight so much that his chin, when he was sitting, used to rest upon his knees for support. The country people were rather shy of meeting him in any lonesome place, for though, poor creature, he was as harmless and as inoffensive as a new-born infant, yet his deformity was so great that he scarcely appeared to be a human creature, and some ill-minded persons had set strange stories about him afloat. He was said to have a great knowledge of herbs and charms; but certain it was that he had a mighty skillful hand in plaiting straws and rushes into hats and baskets, which was the way he made his livelihood.

Lusmore, for that was the nickname put upon him by reason of his always wearing a sprig of the fairy cap, or lusmore (the foxglove), in his little straw hat, would ever get a higher penny for his plaited work than any one else and perhaps that was the reason why some one, out of envy, had circulated the strange stories about him. Be that as it may, it happened that he was returning one evening from the pretty town of Cahir towards Cappagh, and as little Lusmore walked very slowly, on account of the great hump upon his back, it was quite dark when he came to the old moat of Knockgrafton, which stood on the right-hand side of his road. Tired and weary was he, and noways comfortable in his own mind at thinking how much farther he had to travel, and that he should be walking all the night; so he sat down under the moat to rest himself, and began looking mournfully enough upon the moon, which

Rising in clouded majesty, at length
Apparent Queen, unveil'd her peerless light,
And o'er the dark her silver mantle threw.

Presently there rose a wild strain of unearthly melody upon the ear of little Lusmore; he listened, and he thought that he had never heard such ravishing music before. It was like the sound of many voices, each mingling and blending with the other so strangely that they seemed to be one, though all singing different strains, and the words of the song were these:

Da Luan, Da Mort, Da Luan, Da Mort, Da Luan, Da Mort

when there would be a moment's pause, and then the round of melody went on again.

Lusmore listened attentively, scarcely drawing his breath lest he might lose the slightest note. He now plainly perceived that the singing was within the moat; and though at first it had charmed him so much, he began to get tired of hearing the same round sung over and over so often without any change; so availing himself of the pause when *Da Luan, Da Mort,* had been sung three times, he took up the tune, and raised it with the words *augus Da Dardeen,* and then went on singing with the voices inside of the moat, *Da Luan, Da Mort,* finishing the melody, when the pause again came, with *augus Da Dardeen.*

The fairies within Knockgrafton, for the song was a fairy melody, when they heard this addition to the tune, were so much delighted that, with instant resolve, it was determined to bring the mortal among them, whose musical skill so far exceeded theirs, and little Lusmore was conveyed into their company with the eddying speed of a whirlwind.

Glorious to behold was the sight that burst upon him as he came down through the moat, twirling round and round, with the lightness of a straw, to the sweetest music that kept time to this motion. The greatest honour was then paid him, for he was put above all the musicians, and he had servants tending upon him, and everything to his heart's content, and a hearty welcome to all; and, in short, he was made as much of as if he had been the first man in the land.

Presently Lusmore saw a great consultation going forward among the fairies, and, notwithstanding all their civility, he felt very much frightened, until one stepping out from the rest came up to him and said:

Lusmore! Lusmore!
Doubt not, nor deplore,
For the hump which you bore
On your back is no more;
Look down on the floor,
And view it, Lusmore!

When these words were said, poor little Lusmore felt himself so light, and so happy, that he thought he could have bounded at one jump over the moon, like the cow in the history of the cat and the fiddle; and he saw, with inexpressible pleasure, his hump tumble down upon the ground from his shoulders. He then tried to lift up his head, and he did so with becoming caution, fearing that he might knock it against the ceiling of the grand hall, where he was; he looked round and round again with the greatest wonder and delight upon everything, which appeared more and more beautiful; and, overpowered at beholding such a resplendent scene, his head grew dizzy, and his eyesight became dim. At last he fell into a sound sleep, and when he awoke he found that it was broad daylight, the sun shining brightly, and the birds singing sweetly; and that he was lying just at the foot of the moat of Knockgrafton, with the cows and sheep grazing peaceably round about him. The first thing Lusmore did, after saying his prayers, was to put his hand behind to feel for his hump, but no sign of one was there on his back, and he looked at himself with great pride, for he had now become a well-shaped dapper little fellow, and more than that, found himself in a full suit of new clothes, which he concluded the fairies had made for him.

Towards Cappagh he went, stepping out as lightly, and springing up at every step as if he had been all his life a dancing-master. Not a creature who met Lusmore knew him without his hump, and he had a great work to persuade every one that he was the same man—in truth he was not, so far as the outward appearance went.

Of course it was not long before the story of Lusmore's hump got about, and a great wonder was made of it. Through the country, for miles round, it was the talk of every one, high and low.

One morning, as Lusmore was sitting contented enough at his cabin door, up came an old woman to him, and asked him if he could direct her to Cappagh.

"I need give you no directions, my good woman," said Lusmore, "for this is Cappagh; and whom may you want here?"

"I have come," said the woman, "out of Decie's country, in the county of Waterford, looking after one Lusmore, who, I have heard tell, had his hump taken off by the fairies; for there is a son of a gossip of mine who has got a hump on him that will be his death; and maybe, if he could use the same charm as Lusmore, the hump may be taken off him. And now I have told you the reason of my coming so far: 'tis to find out about this charm, if I can."

Lusmore, who was ever a good-natured little fellow, told the woman all the particulars, how he had raised the tune for the fairies at Knockgrafton, how his hump had been removed from his shoulders, and how he had got a new suit of clothes into the bargain.

The woman thanked him very much, and then went away quite happy and easy in her mind. When she came back to her gossip's house, in the county of Waterford, she told her everything that Lusmore had said, and they put the little hump-backed man, who was a peevish and cunning creature from his birth, upon a car, and took him all the way across the country. It was a long journey, but they did not care for that, so the hump was taken from off him; and they brought him, just at nightfall, and left him under the old moat of Knockgrafton.

Jack Madden, for that was the humpy man's name, had not been sitting there long when he heard the tune going on within the moat much sweeter than before; for the fairies were singing it the way Lusmore had settled their music for them, and the song was going on: *Da Luan, Da Mort, Da Luan, Da Mort, Da Luan, Da Mort, augus Da Dardeen,* without ever stopping. Jack Madden, who was in a great hurry to get quit of his hump, never thought of waiting until the fairies had done, or watching for a fit opportunity to raise the tune higher again than Lusmore had; so having heard them sing it over seven times without stopping, out he bawls, never minding the time or the humour of the tune, or how he could bring his words in properly, *augus Da Dardeen, augus Da Hena,* thinking that if one day was good, two were better; and that if Lusmore had one new suit of clothes given him, he should have two.

No sooner had the words passed his lips than he was taken up and whisked into the moat with prodigious force; and the fairies came crowding round about him with great anger, screeching and screaming, and roaring out:

"Who spoiled our tune? Who spoiled our tune?" and one stepped up to him above all the rest, and said:

> Jack Madden! Jack Madden!
> Your words came so bad in
> The tune we felt glad in;—
> This castle you're had in,
> That your life we may sadden;
> Here's two humps for Jack Madden!

And twenty of the strongest fairies brought Lusmore's hump, and put it down upon poor Jack's back, over his own, where it became fixed as firmly as if it was nailed on with twelve-penny nails, by the best carpenter that ever drove one. Out of their castle they then kicked him; and in the morning, when Jack Madden's mother and her gossip came to look after their little man, they found him half dead, lying at the foot of the moat, with the other hump upon his back. Well to be sure, how they did look at each other! but they were afraid to say anything, lest a hump might be put upon their own shoulders. Home they brought the unlucky Jack Madden with them, as downcast in their hearts and their looks as ever two gossips were; and what through the weight of his other hump, and the long journey, he died soon after, leaving, they say, his heavy curse to any one who would go to listen to fairy tunes again.

JOHN MITCHEL

THE FAMINE YEAR

When John Mitchel was asked to review a group of Irish travel guides for The Nation *in 1847, this poetic and frightening piece on the Great Famine resulted instead. The famine, which began in 1845 and was caused by the failure of three successive potato crops, brought on the death (through disease and starvation) of one million people before it ended in 1849. Politicized by this terrible chapter in Irish history, an event he called "deeper, darker than any bloody tragedy ever enacted under the sun," Mitchel went on to become an outspoken proponent of revolution in Ireland.*

AGAIN, THE GREAT SUN STANDS high at noon above the greenest island that lies within its ken on all the broad zodiac road he travels, and his glory, "like God's own head," will soon blaze forth from the solstitial tower. Once more, also—even in this June month of the rueful year—the trees have clothed themselves in their wonted pomp of leafy umbrage, and the warm air is trembling with the music of ten thousand singing-birds, and the great all-nourishing earth has arrayed herself in robes of glorious green—the greener for all the dead she has laid to rest within her bosom.

> What! alive and so bold, O Earth!
> Art thou not over bold?
> What! leapest thou forth as of old,
> In the light of thy morning mirth?

Why, we thought that the end of the world was at hand; we never looked to see a bright, genial summer, a bright rigorous winter again. To one who has been pent up for months, labouring with brain and heart in the panic-stricken city, haunted by the shadow of death, and has heard from afar the low, wailing moan of his patient, perishing brothers borne in upon every gale, black visions of the night might well come swarming; to his dulled eye a pall might visibly spread itself over the empyrean, to his weary ear the cope of heaven might ring from pole to pole with a muffled peal of Doom. Can such swinkt labourer believe that days will ever be wholesome any more, or nights ambrosial as they were wont to be? —for is not the sun in sick eclipse and like to die, and hangs there not upon the corner of the moon a vaporous drop profound, shedding plague and blight and the blackness of darkness over all the world?

Not so, heavy-laden labourer in the seed-field of time. Sow diligently what grain thou hast to sow, nothing doubting; for, indeed, there shall be hereafter, as of old, genial showers and ripening suns, and harvests shall whiten, and there shall verily be living men to reap them, be it with sword or sickle The sun is not yet turned into darkness, nor the moon into blood; neither is the abomination of desolation spoken of by Jeremy the Prophet yet altogether come to pass. Heaven and earth grow not old, as thou and thy plans and projects and speculations will all most assuredly do. Here have you been gnawing your heart all winter about the "state of the country," about a Railway Bill, about small rating districts, or about large; casting about for means to maintain your own paltry position; or else, perhaps, devising schemes, poor devil! for the regeneration of your country, and dreaming that in your own peculiar committee, clique, confederacy, caucus, council, conclave, or cabal, lay Ireland's last and only hope!—until you are nearly past hope yourself—until foul shadows are creeping over your light of life, and insanity is knocking at your parietal bone. Apparently you will be driven to this alternative—to commit suicide, or else, with a desperate rush, to fly into the country, leaving the spirits of evil and the whole rout of hell at the first running stream.

We advise the latter course; all the powers of nature enforce and conjure to it; every blushing evening woos thee westward; every blue morning sends its Favonian airs to search thee out in thy study and fan thy cheek, and tell thee over what soft, whispering woods; what bank of breathing field flowers; what heathery hills fragrant with bog myrtle and all the flora of the moors; what tracks of corn and waving meadows they have wandered before they came to mix with the foul city atmosphere, dim with coal smoke and the breath of multitudinous scoundreldom. On such blue morning, to us, lying wistfully dreaming with eyes wide open, rises many a vision of scenes that we know to be at this moment enacting themselves in far-off lonely glens we wot of. Ah! there is a green nook, high up amidst the foldings of certain granite mountains, forty leagues off and more, and there is gurgling through it, murmuring and flashing in the sun, a little stream clear as crystal—the mystic song of it, the gushing freshness of it, are seen now streaming cool through our adust and too cineritious brain; and, clearly as if present in the body, we seek the grey rock that hangs over one of its shallow pools, where the sun rays are broken by the dancing water into a network of tremulous golden light upon the pure sand that forms its basin; and close by, with quivering leaves and slender stem of silver, waves a solitary birch-tree; and the mountains stand solemn around, and by the heather-bells that are breaking from their sheaths everywhere under your steps, you know that soon a mantle of richest imperial purple will be spread over their mighty shoulders and envelop them to the very feet. Lie down upon the emerald sward that banks this little pool, and gaze and listen. Through one gorge that breaks the mountain pass to the right hand, you see a vast cultivated plain, with trees and fields and whitened houses, stretching away into the purple distance, studded here and there with lakes that gleam like mirrors of polished silver. Look to the left, through another deep valley, and lo—! the blue Western Sea! And aloft over all, over land and sea, over plain and mountain, rock and river, go slowly floating the broad shadows of clouds, rising slowly from the south, borne in the lap of the soft, south wind, slowly climbing the blue dome by the meridian line, crossing the path of the sun, nimbus after nimbus, cirrus and cumulus, and every other cloud after his cloud, each flinging his mighty shadow on the passes, and then majestically melting off northward. What battalions and broad-winged hosts of clouds are these? Here have we lain but two hours, and there have been continually looming upward from behind the wind, continually sailing downward beyond the northern horizon, such wondrous drifts and piled up mountain of vapour as would shed another Noachian deluge and quench the stars if the floodgates were once let loose and the windows of heaven opened, yet this fragrant, soft-blowing southern gale bears them up bravely on its invisible pinions and softly winnows them on their destined way. They have a mission; they are going to build themselves up, somewhere over the Hebrides, into a huge, many-towered Cumulostratus; and to-morrow or the day after will come down in thunder and storm and hissing sheets of grey rain, sweeping the Sound of Mull with their trailing skirt, and making the billows of Corrievrechan seethe and roar around his cliffs and caves. Ben Cruachan, with his head wrapped in thick night, will send down Awe River in raging spate, in a tumult of tawny foam, and Morven shall echo through all his groaning woods.

But one cannot be everywhere at once. We are not now among the Western Isles, buffeting a summer storm in the Sound of Mull; but here in this green nook, among our own Irish granite mountains, at our feet the clear, poppling water, over our head the birch leaves quivering in the warm June air; and the far-off sea smooth and blue as a burnished sapphire. Let the cloud-hosts go and fulfil their destiny; and let us, with open eye and ear and soul, gaze and listen. Not only are mysterious splendours around us, but mysterious song gushes forth above us and beneath us. In this little brook alone what a scale of notes! from where the first faint tinkle of it is heard far up as it gushes from the heart of the mountain, down through countless cascades and pools and gurgling rapids, swelling and growing till it passes our grassy couch and goes on its murmuring way singing to the sea;

but it is only one of the instruments. Hark! the eloquent wind that comes sighing up the valley and whispering with the wavering fern! And at intervals comes from above or beneath, you know not which, the sullen croak of a solitary raven, without whose hoarse bass you never find nature's mountain symphony complete; and we defy you to say why the obscene fowl sits there and croaks upon his grey stone for half a day, unless it is that nature puts him in requisition to make up her orchestra, as the evil beast ought to be proud to do. And hark again! the loud hum of innumerable insects, first begotten of the Sun, that flit among the green heather stalks and sing all their summer life through—and then, if you listen beyond all that, you hear, faintly at first as the weird murmur in a wreathed shell, but swelling till it almost overwhelms all the other sounds, the mighty voice of the distant sea. For it is a peculiarity ever of this earth-music that you can separate every tone of it, untwist every strand of its linked sweetness, and listen to that and dwell upon it by itself. You may shut your senses to all save that far-off ocean murmur until it fills your ear as with the roar and rush of ten thousand tempests, and you can hear the strong billows charging against every beaked promontory from pole to pole; or you may listen to the multitudinous insect hum till it booms painfully upon your ear-drum, and you know that here is the mighty hymn or spiritual song of life, as it surges ever upward from the abyss; louder, louder, it booms into your brain—oh, heaven! it is the ground-tone of that thunder-song wherein the earth goes singing in her orbit among the stars. Yes, such and so grand are the separate parts of this harmony; but blend them all and consider what a diapason! Cathedral organs of all stops, and instruments of thousand strings, and add extra additional keys to your pianofortes, and sweetest silver flutes, and the voices of men and of angels; all these, look you, all these, and the prima donnas of all sublunary operas, and the thrills of a hundred Swedish Nightingales, have not the compass nor the flexibility, nor the pathos, nor the loudness, nor the sweetness required for the execution of this wondrous symphony among the hills.

> Loud as from numbers without number, sweet,
> As of blest voices uttering joy.

Loud and high as the hallelujahs of choiring angels—yet, withal, what a trance of *Silence?* Here in this mountain dell, all the while we lie, breathes around such a solemn overpowering stillness, that the rustle of an unfolding heath-bell, too near breaks it offensively; and if you linger *near* enough—by heaven! you can hear the throb of your own pulse. For, indeed, the divine silence is also a potent instrument of that eternal harmony, and bears melodious part.

"Such concord is in heaven!" Yea, and on the earth, too, if only *we*—we who call ourselves the beauty of the world and paragon of animals—did not mar it. Out of a man's heart proceedeth evil thoughts; out of his mouth revilings and bitterness and evil-speaking. In us, and not elsewhere, lies the fatal note that jars all the harmonies of the universe, and makes them like sweet bells jangled out of tune. Who will show us a way to escape from ourselves and from one another? Even, you, reader, whom we have invited up into this mountain, we begin to abhor you in our soul; you are transfigured before us; your eyes are become as the eyes of an evil demon, and now we know that this gushing stream of living water could not in a life-time wash away the iniquity from the chambers of thine heart; the arch-chemist sun could not burn it out of thee. For know, reader, thou hast a devil: it were better thy mother had not borne thee; and almost we are impelled to murder thee where thou liest.

"Poor human nature! Poor human nature!" So men are accustomed to cry out when there is talk of any meanness or weakness committed, especially by themselves; and they seem to make no doubt that if we could only get rid of our poor human nature we should get on much more happily. Yet human nature is not the worst element that enters into our composition—there is also a large diabolical ingredient—also, if we would admit it, a vast mixture of the brute, especially the donkey nature—and then, also, on the other hand, some irradiation of the god-like, and by that only is mankind *redeemed*.

For the sake whereof we forgive thee, comrade, and will forbear to do thee a mischief upon the present occasion. But note well how the very thought of all these discords has silenced, or made inaudible to us, all these choral songs of earth and sky. We listen, but there is silence—mere common silence; it is no use crying *Encore!* either the performers are dumb or we are stone deaf. Moreover, as evening comes on, the grass and heath grow somewhat damp, and one may get cold in his human nature. Rise, then, and we shall show you the way through the mountain to seaward, where we shall come down upon a little cluster of seven or eight cabins, in one of which cabins, two summers ago, we supped sumptuously on potatoes and salt with the decent man who lives there, and the black-eyed woman of the house and five small children. We had a hearty welcome though the fare was poor; and as we toasted our potatoes in the *greeshaugh*, our ears drank in the honey-sweet tones of the well-beloved Gaelic. If it were only to hear, though you did not understand, mothers and children talking together in their own blessed Irish, you ought to betake you to the mountains every summer. The sound of it is venerable, majestic, almost sacred. You hear in it the tramp of the clans, the judgment of the Brehons, the song of bards. There is no name for "modern enlightenment" in Irish, no word corresponding with the "masses," or with "reproductive labour"; in short, the "nineteenth century" would not know itself, could not express itself in Irish. For the which, let all men bless the brave old tongue, and pray that it may never fall silent by the hills and streams of holy Ireland—never until long after the great nineteenth century of centuries, with its "enlightenment" and its "paupers," shall be classed in its true category the darkest of all the Dark Ages.

THE FAMINE YEAR

As we come down towards the roots of the mountains, you may feel, loading the evening air, the heavy balm of hawthorn blossoms; here are whole thickets of white-mantled hawthorn, every mystic tree (save us all from fairy thrall!) smothered with snow-white and showing like branching coral in the South Pacific. And be it remembered that never in Ireland, since the last of her chiefs sailed away from her, did that fairy tree burst into such luxuriant beauty and fragrance as this very year. The evening, too, is delicious; the golden sun has deepened into crimson, over the sleeping sea, as we draw near the hospitable cottages; almost you might dream that you beheld a vision of the Connacht of the thirteenth century; for that—

> The clime, indeed, is a clime to praise,
>   The clime is Erin's, the green and bland;
> And this is the time—these be the days—
>   Of Cathal Mor of the Wine-Red Hand—

Cathal Mor, in whose days both land and sea were fruitful, and the yeanlings of the flocks were doubled, and the horses champed yellow wheat in the mangers.

But why do we not see the smoke curling from those lowly chimneys? And surely we ought by this time to scent the well-known aroma of the turf-fires. But what (may Heaven be about us this night)—what reeking breath of hell is this oppressing the air, heavier and more loathsome than the smell of death rising from the fresh carnage of a battlefield. Oh, misery! had we forgotten that this was the *Famine Year*? And we are here in the midst of those thousand Golgothas that border our island with a ring of death from Cork Harbour all round to Lough Foyle. There is no need of inquiries here—no need of words; the history of this little society is plain before us. Yet we go forward, though with sick hearts and swimming eyes, to examine the Place of Skulls nearer. There is a horrible silence; grass grows before the doors; we fear to look into any door, though they are all open or off the hinges; for we fear to see yellow skeletons grinning there; but our footfalls rouse two lean dogs, that run from us with doleful howling, and we know by the felon-gleam in the wolfish eyes how *they* have lived after their masters died. We walk amidst the houses of the dead, and out at the other side of the cluster, and there is not one where we dare to enter. We stop before the threshold of our host of two years ago, put our head, with eyes shut, inside the door-jamb, and say, with shaking voice, "God save all here!"—No answer—ghastly silence, and a mouldy stench, as from the mouth of burial-vaults. Ah! they are dead! they are dead! the strong man and the fair, dark-eyed woman and the little ones, with their liquid Gaelic accents that melted into music for us two years ago; they shrunk and withered together until their voices dwindled to a rueful gibbering, and they hardly knew one another's faces; but their horrid eyes scowled on each other with a cannibal glare. We know the whole story—the father was on a "public work," and earned the sixth part of what would have maintained his family, which was not always paid him, but still it kept them half alive for three months, and so instead of dying in December they died in March. And the agonies of those three months who can tell?—the poor wife wasting and weeping over her stricken children; the heavy-laden weary man, with black night thickening around him— thickening within him—feeling his own arm shrink and his step totter with the cruel hunger that gnaws away his life, and knowing too surely that all this will soon be over. And he has grown a rogue, too, on those public works; with roguery and lying about him, he has begun to say in his heart that there is no God; from a poor but honest farmer he has sunk down into a swindling, sturdy beggar; for him there is nothing firm or stable; the pillars of the world are rocking around him; "the sun to him is dark and silent, as the moon when she deserts the night." Even ferocity or thirst for vengeance he can never feel again; for the very blood of him is starved into a thin, chill *serum*, and if you prick him he will not bleed. Now he can totter forth no longer, and he stays at home to die. But his darling wife is dear to him no longer; alas! and alas! there is a dull, stupid malice in their looks: they forget that they had five children, all dead weeks ago, and flung coffinless into shallow graves—nay, in the frenzy of their despair they would rend one another for the last morsel in that house of doom; and at last, in misty dreams of drivelling idiocy, they die utter strangers.

Oh! Pity and Terror! what a tragedy is here—deeper, darker than any *bloody* tragedy ever enacted under the sun, with all its dripping daggers and sceptred palls. Who will compare the fate of men burned at the stake, or cut down in bat-tle—men with high hearts and the pride of life in their veins, and an eye to look up to heaven, or to defy the slayer to his face—who will compare it with *this*?

↓

No shelter here to-night, then; and here we are far on in the night, still gazing on the hideous ruin. *O Bœtho!* a man might gaze and think on such a scene, till curs-es breed about his heart of hearts, and the *hysterica passio* swells in his throat.

But we have twelve miles to walk along the coast before we reach our inn; so come along with us and we will tell you as we walk together in the shadows of the night——

JOHN MITCHEL

FROM
JAIL JOURNAL

This is the first chapter of Irish patriot John Mitchel's Jail Journal, *which he began on May 27, 1848, the day he was sentenced to fourteen years' transportation for what the Irish government defined as treason. Mitchel alternates his outrage at being deemed a felon with an entertaining measure of sarcasm aimed at the policies of the unstable government, which wants to keep him confined but not to treat him too severely since it fears upsetting the public to whom Mitchel is a hero. He was transported finally to Tasmania, then called Van Diemen's Land, and escaped to the United States in 1853, enabling this book to be published the following year.*

MAY 27, 1848—ON THIS DAY, about four o'clock in the afternoon, I, John Mitchel, was kidnapped, and carried off from Dublin, in chains, as a convicted "Felon."

I had been in Newgate prison for a fortnight. An apparent *trial* had been enacted before twelve of the castle jurors in ordinary—much legal palaver, and a "conviction" (as if there were *law*, *order*, *government*, or *justice* in Ireland). Sentence had been pronounced, with much gravity, by that ancient Purple Brunswicker, Baron Lefroy—*fourteen years' transportation*; and I had returned to my cell and taken leave of my wife and two poor boys. A few minutes after they had left me a gaoler came in with a suit of coarse grey clothes in his hand. "You are to put on these," said he, "directly." I put them on directly. A voice then shouted from the foot of the stairs, "Let him be removed in his own clothes"; so I was ordered to change again, which I did. I asked to what place I was to be removed. "Can't tell," said the man. "Make haste." There was a travelling bag of mine in the cell, containing a change of clothes; and I asked whether I might take it with me. "No; make haste." "I am ready, then"; and I followed him down the stairs.

When we came into the small paved court, some constables and gaolers were standing there. One of them had in his hand a pair of iron fetters; and they all appeared in a hurry, as if they had some very critical neck-or-nothing business in hand; but they might as well have taken their time and done the business with their usual unconcerned and sullen dignity of demeanour.

I was ordered to put my foot upon a stone seat that was by the wall; and a constable fastened one of the bolts upon my ankle. But the other peopled hurried him so much that he said quickly, "Here, take the other in your hand, and come along." I took it, and held up the chain which connected the two, to keep it from dragging along the pavement, as I followed through the hall of the prison (where a good many persons had gathered to see the vindication of the "law") and so on to the outer door. I stood on the steps for one moment, and gazed round: the black police-omnibus—a strong force of the city constabulary occupying the street on either side; outside of them dark crowds of people, standing in perfect silence; parties of cavalry drawn up at the openings of the streets hard by. I walked down the steps; and amidst all that multitude the clanking of my chain was the loudest sound. The moment I stepped into the carriage the door was dashed to with a bang. Someone shouted, "To the North Wall!" and instantly the horses set forward at a gallop. The dragoons, with drawn sabres, closed both in front and rear and on both sides; and in this style we dashed along, but not by the shortest, or the usual way to the North Wall, as I could see through a slit in the panel. The carriage was full of police-constables. Two of them, in plain clothes, seemed to have special charge of me, as they sat close by me, on right and left, one of them holding a pistol with a cap on the nipple. After a long and furious drive along the North Circular road, I could perceive that we were coming near the river. The machine suddenly stopped, and I was ushered to the quay-wall between two ranks of carbineers, with naked swords. A Government steamer, the *Shearwater*, lay in the river, with steam up, and a large man-of-war's boat, filled with men armed to the teeth, was alongside the wall. I descended the ladder with some difficulty, owing to the chain, took my seat beside a naval officer, who sat in the stern, and a dozen pulls brought us to the steamer's side. A good many people who stood on the quay and in two or three vessels close by, looked on in silence. One man bade God bless me; a police-inspector roared out to him that he had better make no disturbance.

As soon as we came on board, the naval officer who had brought me off, a short, dark man of five-and-forty or thereabouts, conducted me to the cabin, ordered my fetters to be removed, called for sherry and water to be placed before us, and began to talk. He told me I was to be brought to Spike Island, a convict prison in Cork Harbour, in the first place; that he himself, however, was only going as far as Kingstown, where his own ship lay; that he was Captain Hall, of the *Dragon* steam-frigate; and that he dared to say I had heard of the unfortunate *Nemesis*. "Then," quoth I, "you are the Captain Hall who was in China lately, and wrote a book." He said he was, and seemed quite pleased. If he had a copy of his work there, he said he should be most happy to present it to me. Then he appeared apprehensive that I might confound him with Captain Basil Hall. So he told me that he was not Basil Hall, who in fact was dead; but that though not actually Basil Hall, he had sailed with Basil Hall, as a youngster, on board the *Lyra*. "I presume," he said, "you have read his voyage to the Loo Choo Islands." I said I had, and also another book of his which I liked far better: his "Account of the Chilian and Peruvian Revolutions," and of that splendid fellow, San Martin. Captain Hall laughed. "Your mind," said he, "has been running upon revolutions." "Yes, very much—almost exclusively." "Ah, sir!" quoth he, "dangerous things, these revolutions." Whereto I replied, "You may say that." We were now near Kingstown Pier, and my friend, looking at his watch, said he should still be in time for dinner; that he was to dine with the Lord Lieutenant; that he had been at a review in the Park this morning, and was suddenly ordered off to escort me with a boat's crew from the *Dragon*; further, that he was sorry to have to perform such a service; and that he had been credibly informed my father was a very good man. I answered I know not what. He invited me to go with him upon deck, where his crew were preparing to man the boat; they were all dressed like seamen, but well armed. I pointed to them, and asked, "Are those fellows marines?" He looked at me with a peculiar smile—"Well, come now, they *are* marines." He was evidently amazed at my penetration in detecting marines without their uniform (I asked the question in mere ignorance and absence of mind); "but," he quickly added, "our marines are all seamen." "I suppose so," quoth I.

Captain Hall, of the *Dragon,* now bade me good evening, saying he should just have time to dress for dinner. I wished him a good appetite, and he went off to his ship. No doubt he thought me an amazingly cool character; but God knoweth the heart. There was a huge lump in my throat all the time of this bald chat, and my thoughts were far enough away from both Peru and Loo Choo. At Charlemont Bridge, in Dublin, this evening, there is a desolate house—my mother and sisters, who came up to town to see me (for the last time in case of the worst)—five little children, very dear to me; none of them old enough to understand the cruel blow that has fallen on them this day, and above all—above all—my wife.[1]

What will they do? What is to become of them? By this time, undoubtedly, my office, my newspaper, types, books, all that I had, are seized on by the Government burglar. And then they will have to accept that public "tribute"—the thought of which I abhor. And did I not know this? And, knowing it, did I not run the risk? Yes; and I did well. The possible sacrifice indeed was terrible; but the enterprise was great, and was needful. And, moreover, that sacrifice shall not have been made in vain. And I know that my wife and little ones shall not want. He that feedeth the young ravens—but then, indeed, as I remember, young ravens and other carrion-birds have been better fed in Ireland than the Christians, these latter years.

After all, for what has this sacrifice been made? *Why* was it needful? What did I hope to gain by this struggle with the enemy's "Government," if successful? What, if unsuccessful? What *have* I gained? Questions truly which it behoves me to ask and answer on this evening of my last day (it may be) of civil existence. Dublin City, with its bay and pleasant villas—city of bellowing slaves—villas of genteel dastards—lies now behind us, and the sun has set behind the blue peaks of Wicklow, as we steam past Bray Head, where the Vale of Shanganagh, sloping softly from the Golden Spears, sends its bright river murmuring to the sea. And I am on the first stage of my way, faring to what regions of unknown horror? And may never, never—never more, O, Ireland!—my mother and queen!—see vale, or hill, or murmuring stream of thine. And *why?* What is gained?

Let me set it down:—

First, then, I have compelled the enlightened "Government"—the Whig Government—after repeated warnings, challenges, taunts (so that everybody should know what I was about), compelled them publicly and notoriously to pack a jury, most strictly, in order to crush one man ; and thus compelled them to prove that there is no "constitution" in Ireland at all; that the "Government" is not under, but above the Law; that trial by jury is a fraud; that all Whig professions about conciliatory and impartial government in Ireland, were as false as the Father of Whiggery himself.

☞ They *dared* not have given me a fair trial before my countrymen. If I had beaten them on that trial, it would have been a victory which I could have followed up to their utter smash. I would soon have shown all Ireland the way—not to drive a coach-and-six through, but to ride roughshod over their laws and them.

Second,—By demonstrating that there is no law or Constitution for us, I have put an end, one may hope, to "constitutional agitation," and shamed the country out of "moral force" (in the O'Connellite sense). So, that delusion being put out of the way, there is a chance of my countrymen seeing, what is a solemn truth, that, for Ireland's "grievances," her famines, her party spirit, her packed juries, her exterminations, there is but one and all-sufficient remedy, *the edge of the sword*.

☞ As God is above me, this is *true*. On the truth of it I have staked body and soul, and will abide the issue. Those who consider that all through O'Connell's forty years of "agitation," the people had been industriously taught by him and the priests to keep the peace, and abhor bloodshed, and also to "keep within the law" (thus falsely and fatally acknowledging the existence of government, and the validity of London law) will understand the difficulty of making any way in respect of this matter, and also the need there was to enforce the true doctrine openly, and so to break the canting spell.

Third.—I have shown the Catholics of Ireland that they are not yet emancipated, for all their Clare-elections; that they are deliberately, ostentatiously debarred from executing the common civic office of jurors in any case of public concernment—that is to say, that they are not citizens in their own land—that is to say, that they are *slaves*—for there is no middle term. They are ruled now, as ever, by the sword; if they go on quietly obeying this kind of rule, let them obey, and be hanged!

☞I do not know what they will *do* upon being made to learn this lesson. I only know what they ought to do. All Catholic judges, assistant-barristers, magistrates, and other functionaries, ought to resign their employments; all Catholic policemen ought to strip off their ignominious livery; all Catholic officers ought to desert—in one word, what the Catholics ought to do is tear up society from its roots, but they will be citizens in their own land. What they *will* do, for the present, is the reverse of all this. Some of the respectable Castle-Catholics will thank me little for bringing their degradation so prominently into public view; *they* think they are emancipated enough, and will curse me by their gods, if they have any. Heaven! where is the great heart of chief and tanist? How has the rich blood of O'Conor and O'Donnell Roe grown pale! Is this, the stateliest family of the Caucasian race, indeed, starved and kicked into incurable Helotism?

But *young* Catholics are growing up—even, I trust, in the Castle-going rank of life—who will shame their fathers, and do honour to their ancestors.

Fourth.—I have made sure—for the thing is not going to stop here—that the breach between the Irish people and the Carthaginian government will be made henceforth wider and deeper than ever—that disaffection will grow and thrive—that Nice, Queen of Carthage, will not steer her yacht to Ireland this summer of 1848, as she graciously intended[2]—that Ireland will become *ungovernable* to all Carthaginian governments; and, finally, that the struggle will become a republican one in the long run.[3]

Now, if I have indeed done, or helped to do, or materially furthered and provided for the doing of these things—and if my zeal in this matter has not been born of greediness, or ambition, or vain-glory, shall I not say that I have done well? Shall I not go on my dark voyage with a stout heart—aye, and wear my fetters lightly, as garlands of flowers? I may not know, indeed, how the great game goes; newspapers will probably be wholly out of my reach. The cause may prosper soon and suddenly beyond all my hope—or may be shipwrecked by fools, or sold by traitors, for a time. I, myself (but that is no great matter), may be named patriot and martyr—Heaven help me!—or, contrariwise, may be "sung and proverbed for a *fool* in every street"; or, indeed, clean lost sight of within a month. And I, in some far latitude, perhaps under the Southern Constellations, will be unconsciously doing my daily convict-work. What would I not give, six months hence, for a bulletin from Reilly or Martin, to tell me how it goes!

I am not afraid of either cowardice or treachery on the part of our chiefest men. [Thomas Francis] Meagher is eloquent and ardent—brave to act; brave, if need be, to suffer. I would that he took the trouble to think for himself. [William

Smith] O'Brien is bold and high-minded, but capricious, unaccountable, intractable; also, he is an aristocrat born and bred, and, being a genuine Irishman himself, he cannot be brought to see that his fellow-aristocrats are not Irish, but the irreconcilable enemies of Ireland. Then who will dare to write or publish one word of bold truth? *The Freeman* will be tame and legal till the evil days are over-past. *The Nation* will be so busy giving "the party" a properly Girondesque character, and discriminating carefully between the wild Montagnards—to wit, me and the like of me—on the one hand, and the truly respectable Lafayette-Lamartinists, on the other, that he will be of little use in dealing with the substantial Irish affair that lies before him. [John Blake] Dillon—O'Gorman—good and brave men, but not sufficiently desperate. My chief trust is in Martin and Reilly; but then they will probably be the very first devoured by the Carthaginian sea-monster. God be with them all and direct them; and, above all, put some heart into the poor people!

It darkened over the sea, and the stars came out; and the dark hills of Wicklow had shrouded themselves in the night-fog before I moved from the shoreward gunwale of the quarter-deck. My two guardians, the police-constables in plain clothes, who had never left my side, now told me it was growing late, and that tea was ready below. Went down, accordingly, and had an "aesthetic tea" with two detectives. Asked my two friends if they knew my destination. They knew nothing, they said; but thought it probable I would not be removed from Spike Island; supposed that Government would just keep me there "till matters were a little quieted down," and then let me go. Well, I think differently, my plain-coated, plain-witted friends. On Ireland, or anywhere near it, assuredly I will not be allowed to live. But where then? The Carthaginians have convict colonies everywhere: at Gibraltar, at Bermuda, in the Atlantic; at Norfolk Island, in the Pacific; besides Van Diemen's Land, and the various settlements in New South Wales; for on British felony the sun never sets. To any one of these I may find myself steering within the twenty-four hours. But be my prison where it will, I suppose there is a heaven above that place.

There is a good berth provided for me here, and I am as sleepy as a tired ploughman. Good night, then, Ireland, and Irish tumults, strugglings and vociferations, quackery, puffery, and endless talk! Good night, friends and enemies. And good night, my sweet wife and widow!—yet shall we meet again.

28th.—Sunday morning. A bright morning, but no land in sight. Found the *United Irishman* of yesterday in my cabin. The sixteenth and *last* number. Read all the articles. Good Martin! Brave Reilly! but you will be swallowed, my fine fellows. "Government" has adopted the vigorous policy.

Was invited to breakfast with the lieutenants and surgeon. All very polite to me. One of them, whom I take to be the second lieutenant, is a fine young fellow, who has lately returned from the Pacific, after cruising there seven years, and is as brown as Queen Pomare. He is an Irishman, but far more familiar with the politics of Taïti and Hawaii, than with Irish affairs. About ten o'clock the land-fog rose, and far to the northward I could recognise the coast about Youghal, the opening of the Blackwater, and beyond these, faint and blue, the summits of Knockmeldown. We had kept a wide berth from the land all night, but were now making straight for Cork Harbour. Soon it opened; within half-an-hour more we came to anchor opposite Cove, and within five hundred yards of Spike Island—a rueful looking place, where I could discern, crowning the hill, the long walls of the prison, and a battery commanding the harbour. A boat was instantly lowered and manned. My friends in plain clothes told me they would "take it on their own responsibility" (policemen have high responsibilities in Ireland) *not* to put me in irons as I went ashore. The Commander and first lieutenant buckled on their swords, and took their seats in the stern of the boat beside me. We were rowed rapidly to the island, and as we walked up the approach we met an elderly, grave-looking gentleman, who said, "Mr. Mitchel, I presume!" How on earth, thought I, did you know already that I was coming to you?—forgetting that Lord Clarendon, before I was "tried," made sure of my conviction. However, I bowed, and then he turned and escorted us to his den, over a drawbridge, past several sen-tries, through several gratings, and at last into a small square court. At one side of this court a door opened into a large vaulted room, furnished with a bed, table, chair, and basin-stand, and I was told that I was in my cell. The two naval offi-cers took their leave politely, saying they hoped to meet me under happier cir-cumstances; and they seemed really sorry. I bowed and thanked them; and I was left alone. I found I had the range of the cell and the court before it, no prisoner being there but myself. Mr. Grace, the Governor, came in to tell me I might write home if I chose, submitting the letter to him. I did write, telling where I was, and desiring a trunk to be sent to me with some clothes and a few books. Mr. Grace also offered to lend me books while I should stay. A turnkey, or guard in blue uni-form, kept sauntering up and down the court, and sometimes lounged into the room. Asked him what he wanted. He told me he was not to leave me until lock-up hour—thought this a great grievance, and wished for lock-up hour. It came at last: my door was shut, and for the first time I was quite alone.

And now—as this is to be a faithful record of whatsoever befalls me—I do confess, and will write down the confession, that I flung myself on the bed, and broke into a raging passion of tears—tears bitter and salt—tears of wrath, pity, regret, remorse—but not of base lamentation for my own fate. The thoughts and feelings that have so shaken me for this once, language was never made to describe; but if any austere censor could find it in his heart to vilipend my man-hood therefor, I would advise him to wait until he finds himself in a somewhat similar position. Believe me, O Stoic! if your soul were in my soul's stead, I also could heap up words against you, and shake mine head at you.

It is over, and finally over. In half-an-hour I rose, bathed my head in water, and walked a while up and down my room. I know that all weakness is past, and that I am ready for my fourteen years' ordeal, and for whatsoever the same may bring me—toil, sickness, ignominy, death. Fate, thou are defied.

29th.—In this court nothing is to be seen but the high walls and the blue sky. And beyond these walls I know is the beautiful bay lying in the bosom of its soft green hills. If they keep me here for many years I will forget what the fair, outer world is like. Gazing on grey stones, my eyes will grow stony.

After breakfast to-day Mr. Grace came into my cell with a turnkey. He had a suit of brown convict-clothes in his hand, and said it was an unpleasant duty he had to perform, but that I must put on those clothes. I obeyed without remark, and in a few minutes after this a fat, red man came in to look at me. This was the governor of Smithfield Prison in Dublin, who is about to return home, and who desires to be enabled to attest at headquarters that he had seen me in convict costume. To me the whole affair is totally indifferent.

Drew my chair to the door, sat down in the sun, and spent an hour or two in reading the "Merry Wives of Windsor." Thank God for Shakespeare at any rate. Baron Lefroy cannot sentence Shakespeare to death, nor so much as mulct him for damages, though I am told he deserves it for defamation of character, in the case of Sir John Falstaff. The real Falstaff, or Fastolf, I am assured, was a very grave and valiant knight, and built himself the great castle of Caistor to dwell in; never drank sack in Eastcheap, nor made love in Windsor; was neither poor, fat, nor witty, like our Sir John, but was, in fact, as like to other good knights of the period as one shotten herring is like another shotten herring. Well; suppose all this to be what you call "true," which, then, is the more real and substantial man? I hold that our Sir John is the authentic Sir John, and that your Fastolf was an impostor. Why, I have seen the man, and laughed with him a hundred times: for though he is fat and groweth old, and his hair is grey, yet the fine old fellow will never die—in truth, he was born with a grey head and something of a round belly. And so he can take his sack still, witty himself, and the cause of wit in others even to this day. Oh! I have much to say in the behalf of that Falstaff.

While I sat in the sun, a large and important-looking gentleman came into the yard, who is, I understand, "Inspector": four or five well-dressed young gentlemen were with him. They passed into my room, made a few muttered remarks to one another, and went out again, looking very sharply at me as they passed. I gazed at them abstractedly, as if I were looking through them, and thinking of something else. They came, I believe, only to see me. Very well: I wish them much comfort.

30th.—My turnkey, who is desired never to leave me, I find to be a good, quiet sort of creature. He is some kind of Dissenter, hums psalm-tunes almost under his breath, and usually stays as far away from me as our bonds will allow him. There is a door in the high wall leading into another inclosure, and as I was taking a turn through my territory to-day, the turnkey was near that door, and he said to me in a low voice—"This way, sir, if you please"; he held the door open, I passed through, and immediately a tall, gentleman-like person, in black but rather over-worn clothes, came up to me and grasped both my hands with every demonstration of reverence. I knew his face, but could not at first remember who he was; he was Edward Walsh, author of "Mo Chraoibhin Chno," and other sweet songs, and of some very musical translations from old Irish ballads. Tears stood in his eyes as he told me he had contrived to get an opportunity of seeing and shaking hands with me before I should leave Ireland. I asked him what he was doing at Spike Island, and he told me he had accepted the office of teacher to a school they keep here for small convicts—a very wretched office, indeed, and to a shy, sensitive creature, like Walsh, it must be daily torture. He stooped down and kissed my hands "Ah!" he said, "you are now the man in all Ireland most *to be envied.*" I answered that I thought there might be room for difference of opinion about that; and then, after another kind word or two, being warned by my turnkey, I bade him farewell, and retreated into my own den. Poor Walsh! He has a family of young children; he seems broken in health and spirits. Ruin has been on his traces for years, and I think has him in the wind at last. There are more contented galley-slaves moiling at Spike than the schoolmaster. Perhaps this man does really envy me; and most assuredly I do not envy him.

31st.—The important Inspector came to me to-day, accompanied by Mr. Grace. He asked me if I had any complaint to make to him? "None whatever," I answered. He hesitated a moment, and then said, "It has become my duty to inform you that Government have determined on sending you out of the country." "Indeed! How soon?" "To-morrow morning." "May I ask to what part of the world?" "Bermuda." "And by what conveyance?" "A man-of-war, which has arrived to-day in the harbour." "Very good," quoth I, and they left me. Presently Mr. Grace returned, said he was glad to tell me matters did not promise to go so hard with me as he had expected—that he had a letter from the castle, directing him to treat me quite differently from "a common convict," to let me wear my own clothes, not to put me in irons, etc. Further, that he had been already on board the ship which was to carry me to Bermuda—the *Scourge*, a large war steamer; that he had seen the instructions which had been delivered to the commander before he left Portsmouth, and which bore that I was to be treated on the passage "as a person of education and a gentleman"—so it ran; and to have accommodations thereunto correspondent.

A person of education and a gentleman! And if such a person has indeed committed a felony, is he not just all the more felonious? If a person of education commit the real crime of endeavouring to subvert social order, to break down the sanction of law, and to destroy the Government under which he lives (supposing order, law, and government to exist), how does his education entitle him to indulgence above other felons? But possibly you begin to see, Gaffer John Bull, that I am no felon at all, and have committed no crime at all, notwithstanding your new "Act of Parliament," in that case made and provided; and you think it impolitic, or else you are ashamed, to proceed to the uttermost rigour with me. Cowardly John! You ought either not to take up the vigorous policy at all, or else to carry it through with a high hand. This is child's play. Positively I am either a felon or no felon; that is to say, either I am a felon, or you, John, are a felon.

Mr. Grace excuses himself for putting me into convict dress—says he had no instructions to the contrary at first, and did not know *how they might feel towards me* at the castle; and so he was afraid to refuse when the Smithfield gaoler required to see me in felon array, that he might report it in Dublin. Curious that this should have happened twice. In Dublin also I had to put on the convict dress and strip it off again instantly. Come, my Lord Clarendon, either I am a felon or not a felon.

But perhaps they do this to vex and hurt me, not knowing how callous I am.

Wrote this evening to my wife, a cheerful letter, telling her everything that is pleasant in my situation, and how I am to be a gentleman, at least while on board the *Scourge*. But I fear now that her expected letter will not arrive before I sail, and then I may not hear for months anything that has befallen since I took leave of her in Newgate: what seizures have been made by the police; what she is going to do with the house in Dublin; where she means to live; how my children are. My wardrobe, too, is somewhat scanty, for a "gentleman," seeing that they brought me away from Newgate in an old brown summer coat, old shoes, and a glazed cap; and the trunk I wrote for cannot come in time. Mr. Grace, however, has kindly taken the trouble of procuring for me at Cove a few changes of linen and other small indispensables. The surgeon of the establishment, a young man from the county Monaghan, came to request some *autographs* from me. It seems the women in Cove importuned him; so I indulged him with half-a-dozen, and wish the sweet girls much joy with them.

Speaking of this surgeon, I must not forget to record that the first time he saw me he made most minute inquires about my health; and when I told him I was in perfect health, and never had been better in my life, he remarked that I looked rather delicate—perhaps I had been subject occasionally to some complaint? Told him I had—to asthma, now and then; but was at present quite free from it. He said that would *do*. "Do what?" I asked. Whereupon he told me that it might be necessary, in order to justify Mr. Grace in *not setting me to work*, to have a certificate from him that my health was rather delicate. All this passed on Monday last, and before Mr. Grace had received orders from the castle not to use me as a convict.

I set down all these trifling particulars relating to my usage here because I foresee the worthy "Government" will have occasion to tell official falsehoods on the subject before all is over; otherwise, they are of no importance to me at all.

At five o'clock to-morrow morning a boat is to come ashore for me.

June 1st.—It was a raw, damp morning that I took my last look of Irish land. The first lieutenant of the *Scourge*, in full costume, with cocked hat and sword, came for me with a boat full of marines. The *Scourge* lay about a mile distant—a long, low rakish-looking steamer, with black hull and two funnels. In a few minutes I stepped on deck, and was presented to the captain, who was walking on the quarter deck. He lifted his cap, and asked me to go below, and he would show me my quarter. The principal cabin is very handsome, divided into two rooms, of which the one farthest aft is to be occupied by me as a sleeping-cabin. It has couches, chairs, and a table, and is lighted by all the stern windows. During the day both rooms are to be open to me: and the captain said, that as he is obliged to consider me as a prisoner, there will be a marine always stationed on sentry at the foot of the companion-ladder; and that whenever I desire to go upon deck, which I may do when I please, I am to inform the sentry, who will summon a sergeant—that for the rest, he hoped his hours would suit me, when breakfast, dinner, and so forth, will be served in the chief cabin. He is a quiet, saturnine, bilious, thin man of about fifty, with a very low voice—not at all a bluff seaman, or a jolly tar, or the like; yet I dare say he is an excellent officer, and will execute his orders.

Mr. Grace had promised to go to Cove and inquire for my letter; and the vessel lay for an hour, waiting his return. He came and brought a letter. I snatched it eagerly, and found in it *a small religious tract*, which an unknown lady had sent me. No letter from home. Ten minutes after this we were steaming southward, at ten knots an hour. So my moorings are cut.

It rained dismally. The wind sung ruefully in shrouds and rigging; and huge grey rain-clouds darkened over shore and sea. We were out of sight of land almost as soon as the ship had cleared the headlands of the bay. I waved my hand north-east-by-north, then went below, and ate a tremendous breakfast.

So my moorings are cut. I am a banished man. And this is no mere *relegatio*, like Ovid's, at Tomi; it is utter *exsilium*—interdiction of fire and water; the loss of citizenship, if citizenship I had; the brand of whatsoever ignominy law can inflict, if law there be. Be it so; I am content. There are no citizens in Ireland; there is no citizenship—no law. I cannot lose what I never had; for no Irishman has any rights at present. As for the disgrace of "felony," that sits very easy upon me. To make me a felon needs an *act* of my own. No "Act of Parliament" can do it! and what ignominy London "law" can stain an Irishman withal, I am content to underlie till my dying hour. Be that disgrace on my head and on the heads of my children.

But for the thought of those children and their mother, and what temporary inconveniences they may suffer before arrangements can be made for their leaving Ireland—but for that I should absolutely feel jolly to-day. There is something independent in setting forth on a voyage of three thousand miles, with an old brown coat on my back, and a few shillings in my *tricolor* purse. The onus is not upon me. You Sovereign Lady, Queen Nice, have charge of me now; look you take good care of me. I am in your majesty's hands at last; but you may find, O Queen! that I am too dear at the price you have paid, and are like to pay. I will cost you, most dread sovereign, rather more than my rations.

It has come on to blow hard this evening. Dined on four teaspoonfuls of arrowroot.

2nd.—Blowing still worse. Hoped fervently for a thorough-going storm. When one is at sea, one may as well have trial of all the sea can do. Steward came into my cabin; asked him if it was a storm. "No, sir; only half a gale of wind." I cursed its halfness, and tried to sleep.

3rd.—Ship still pitching and rolling heavily; part of the bulwark, the steward told us, is stove in—still no storm. Went on deck. Storm or no storm, this Atlantic rears grand, mountainous waves. Porpoises tumbling—Storm-Petrel skimming. *This bird is the Mother Carey's Chicken or procellaria*—but I scorn it. All these things, are they not written in the journal of any young lady sailing to India for a husband—or missionary, or "literary" (that is, book-spinning) naval officer, spinning as he goes, for a manufacturer in Paternoster Row?

Went over the *Scourge*, and surveyed her fore and aft. She is a fine ship. A long unbroken flush deck; one huge mortar, containing five tons of metal, close behind the mainmast—one "long gun" pointed over the bow—one brass field-piece mounted on a carriage in the stern—and four carronades. She is manned by 180 men and boys. The long gun is a tremendous instrument. The sergeant of marines who has charge of me, a very fat and good-humoured fellow who rolls in his waddle, as only a fat Englishman can roll, seems greatly attached to this gun. He saw me looking at it, and he came over to show me all the conditions of it—how it traverses—how it is raised and lowered by a graduated scale for taking aim, and so forth. "Ah! Sir," said he, "she's a clever piece—she's just a *clever* piece," he repeated, slapping her affectionately on the breech as he said it. The men were called to drill by beat of drum, and here was a new thing to me; for it seems all the sailors, as well as marines on board a man-of-war are regularly drilled as soldiers. They were armed with musket and bayonet, cutlasses, boarding-pikes, and hatchets—altogether most formidable looking pirates. They were drilled by the principal gunner, and certainly know how to handle their arms; but the ship rolled so much that, as they were ranged along the deck, they had to balance themselves very cunningly, on toes and heels alternately; and sometimes seemed on the point of making an involuntary charge across the deck with fixed bayonets, pinning the gunner and half-a-dozen officers to the opposite bulwark.

The organiser and chief mover on board the *Scourge* is the first lieutenant. By the first word he addressed to me, I perceived he was a Derry or Tyrone Irishman—told him so, and found that I was right. He is a native of Tyrone; and he and I went to school in the same city, Derry, at the same time, more than twenty years ago, but not at the same school. For twenty-four years he has been in the navy, and is (the captain tells me), a most admirable officer; but seems to think he will never be anything but a lieutenant. He has not parliamentary connections, and is an Irishman.

Dined with the captain, whose name is Wingrove. After dinner, the saturnine man relaxed a little, and even grew cheerful. He thought I ought to be deeply impressed by my survey of his ship, and duly awed by a contemplation of the power and majesty of "England." Yes, it is all very terrible and very grand, Captain, but if Irishmen had only the sense and spirit to take the management of their own concerns, you would want carriages for some of your guns: some of the gilding would be rubbed off your epaulettes, I apprehend. The herds and harvests that we send every year to England (getting neither money nor value for them) would build and man dozens of your spitfire *Scourges*, besides frigates, and line of battle ships, what may suffice. Wood, iron, hemp, gunpowder, would obey Irish hands as well as Carthaginian.

Captain Wingrove has good wine. He had just come from Madeira and Portugal, when he was ordered off to Bermuda, so that he has had opportunities. He is evidently curious about late events in Ireland, but does not like to ask me much about them. Said he understood there was a practice in Ireland, in the law courts there, called *packing juries*, and asked what it meant. I explained it to him; but it is clear that he hardly believes me: indeed, he listens to everything I say with a kind of quiet smile—and sometimes looks doubtfully at me, as if he thought me slightly insane, and expected me to break out in some strange manner.

7th.—The weather has been very beautiful and warm, for some days; but today it is rather foggy, to my sorrow, for we are passing through the Azores between Terceira and St. Michael's, and cannot see them. They are most lovely islands, with fine mountains and rivers, rich in grain and fruit. Portugal has these and Madeira yet; but perhaps the next war will give an excuse to the bullying pirates of Carthage to take the Azores for coal depots, or convict depots, and so create some situations to relieve the pressure of younger sons.

The officers of the ship seem desirous to make my voyage as little irksome to me as possible. Several of them have offered to lend me books—and though I had vowed to look on no book save sea and sky during the passage, I find I must have recourse to them. A sea voyage is a very tedious affair: the weather indeed is warm and serene, but I 'gin to be aweary of the sun: he is advancing fast to his summer solstice, and we are rushing to meet him at the rate of 180 miles per day. The pure profound blue of the ocean is most glorious to see. One whose navigation has been confined to crossing St. George's Channel, with its short chopping waves and dull leaden colour, has never seen the sea.

[1] Mitchel's Dublin residence in 1848 was No. 8 Ontario Terrace, Charlemont Bridge, Rathmines.

[2] But the *next* year Her Gracious Majesty did carry her beneficent intention into effect, and the debased nation set its neck under her feet in a paroxysm of fictitious "loyalty." It is painful to relate, but it is the disgraceful fact.—J.M.

[3] All these reflections, inferences, and predictions, I give exactly as I wrote them down at the time. I stand to them all; though I know that many will say subsequent events have belied them. We shall yet see whether those subsequent events will not have events subsequent to them also, and belying them; the remotion of the negative is the position of the affirmative.—J.M.

THE
DIAMOND LENS

After squandering a large inheritance in 1851, native Irishman Fitz-James O'Brien relocated to New York, where he wrote for magazines and newspapers. "The Diamond Lens," one of the most famous stories of the nineteenth century, appeared in The Atlantic Monthly *in 1858. Featuring a most unusual love object, the story is also celebrated for being one of the earliest works of science fiction. O'Brien died in 1862 of wounds received while fighting in the American Civil War.*

I
THE BENDING OF THE TWIG

FROM A VERY EARLY PERIOD of my life the entire bent of my inclinations had been towards microscopic investigations. When I was not more than ten years old, a distant relative of our family, hoping to astonish my inexperience, constructed a simple microscope for me, by drilling in a disk of copper a small hole, in which a drop of pure water was sustained by capillary attraction. This very primitive apparatus, magnifying some fifty diameters, presented, it is true, only indistinct and imperfect forms, but still sufficiently wonderful to work up my imagination to a preternatural state of excitement.

Seeing me so interested in this rude instrument, my cousin explained to me all that he knew about the principles of the microscope, related to me a few of the wonders which had been accomplished through its agency, and ended by promising to send me one regularly constructed, immediately on his return to the city. I counted the days, the hours, the minutes, that intervened between that promise and his departure.

Meantime I was not idle. Every transparent substance that bore the remotest resemblance to a lens I eagerly seized upon, and employed in vain attempts to realise that instrument, the theory of whose construction I as yet only vaguely comprehended. All panes of glass containing those oblate spheroidal knots familiarly known as "bull's-eyes" were ruthlessly destroyed, in the hope of obtaining lenses of marvellous power. I even went so far as to extract the crystalline humour from the eyes of fishes and animals, and endeavoured to press it into the microscopic service. I plead guilty to having stolen the glasses from my Aunt Agatha's spectacles, with a dim idea of grinding them into lenses of wondrous magnifying properties,—in which attempt it is scarcely necessary to say that I totally failed.

At last the promised instrument came. It was of that order known as Field's simple microscope, and had cost perhaps about fifteen dollars. As far as educational purposes went, a better apparatus could not have been selected. Accompanying it was a small treatise on the microscope,—its history, uses, and discoveries. I comprehended then for the first time the "Arabian Nights' Entertainments." The dull veil of ordinary existence that hung across the world seemed suddenly to roll away, and to lay bare a land of enchantments. I felt towards my companions as the seer might feel towards the ordinary masses of men. I held conversations with nature in a tongue which they could not understand. I was in daily communication with living wonders, such as they never imagined in their wildest visions. I penetrated beyond the external portal of things, and roamed through the sanctuaries. Where they beheld only a drop of rain slowly rolling down the window-glass, I saw a universe of beings animated with all the passions common to physical life, and convulsing their minute sphere with struggles as fierce and protracted as those of men. In the common spots of mould, which my mother, good housekeeper that she was, fiercely scooped away from her jam pots, there abode for me, under the name of mildew, enchanted gardens, filled with dells and avenues of the densest foliage and most astonishing verdure, while from the fantastic boughs of these microscopic forests hung strange fruits glittering with green, and silver, and gold.

It was no scientific thirst that at this time filled my mind. It was the pure enjoyment of a poet to whom a world of wonders has been disclosed. I talked of my solitary pleasures to none. Alone with my microscope, I dimmed my sight, day after day and night after night, poring over the marvels which it unfolded to me. I was like one who, having discovered the ancient Eden still existing in all its primitive glory, should resolve to enjoy it in solitude, and never betray to mortal the secret of its locality. The rod of my life was bent at this moment. I destined myself to be a microscopist.

Of course, like every novice, I fancied myself a discoverer. I was ignorant at the time of the thousands of acute intellects engaged in the same pursuit as myself, and with the advantage of instruments a thousand times more powerful than mine. The names of Leeuwenhoek, Williamson, Spencer, Ehrenberg, Schultz, Dujardin, Schact, and Schleiden were then entirely unknown to me, or if known, I was ignorant of their patient and wonderful researches. In every fresh specimen of cryptogamia which I placed beneath my instrument I believed that I discovered wonders of which the world was as yet ignorant. I remember well the thrill of delight and admiration that shot through me the first time that I discovered the common wheel animacule (*Rotifera vulgaris*) expanding and contracting its flexible spokes, and seemingly rotating through the water. Alas! as I grew older, and obtained some works treating of my favourite study, I found that I was only on the threshold of a science to the investigation of which some of the greatest men of the age were devoting their lives and intellects.

As I grew up, my parents, who saw but little likelihood of anything practical resulting from the examination of bits of moss and drops of water through a brass tube and a piece of glass, were anxious that I should choose a profession. It was their desire that I should enter the counting-house of my uncle, Ethan Blake, a prosperous merchant, who carried on business in New York. This suggestion I decisively combated. I had no taste for trade; I should only make a failure; in short, I refused to become a merchant.

But it was necessary for me to select some pursuit. My parents were staid New England people, who insisted on the necessity of labour; and therefore, although, thanks to the bequest of my poor aunt Agatha, I should, on coming of age, inherit a small fortune sufficient to place me above want, it was decided that, instead of waiting for this, I should act the nobler part, and employ the intervening years in rendering myself independent.

After much cogitation I complied with the wishes of my family, and selected a profession. I determined to study medicine at the New York Academy. This disposition of my future suited me. A removal from my relatives would enable me to dispose of my time as I pleased without fear of detection. As long as I paid my Academy fees, I might shirk attending the lectures if I chose; and, as I never had the remotest intention of standing an examination, there was no danger of my being "plucked." Besides, a metropolis was the place for me. There I could obtain excellent instruments, the newest publications, intimacy with men of pursuits kindred with my own,—in short, all things necessary to insure a profitable devotion of my life to my beloved science. I had an abundance of money, few desires that were not bounded by my illuminating mirror on one side and my object-glass on the other; what, therefore, was to prevent my becoming an illustrious investigator of the veiled worlds? It was with the most buoyant hope that I left my New England home and established myself in New York.

II

THE LONGING OF A MAN OF SCIENCE

My first step, of course, was to find suitable apartments. These I obtained, after a couple of days' search, in Fourth Avenue; a very pretty second-floor unfurnished, containing sitting-room, bedroom, and a smaller apartment which I intended to fit up as a laboratory. I furnished my lodgings simply, but rather elegantly, and then devoted all my energies to the adornment of the temple of my worship. I visited Pike, the celebrated optician, and passed in review his splendid collection of microscopes,—Field's Compound, Hinghams's, Spencer's, Nachet's Binocular, (that founded on the principles of the stereoscope,) and at length fixed upon that form known as Spencer's Trunnion Microscope, as combining the greatest number of improvements with an almost perfect freedom from tremor. Along with this I purchased every possible accessory,—draw-tubes, micrometers, a *camera-lucida*, lever-stage, achromatic condensers, white cloud illuminators, prisms, parabolic condensers, polarising apparatus, forceps, aquatic boxes, fishing-tubes, with a host of other articles, all of which would have been useful in the hands of an experienced microscopist, but, as I afterwards discovered, were not of the slightest present value to me. It takes years of practice to know how to use a complicated microscope. The optician looked suspiciously at me as I made these wholesale purchases. He evidently was uncertain whether to set me down as some scientific celebrity or a madman. I think he inclined to the latter belief. I suppose I was mad. Every great genius is mad upon the subject in which he is greatest. The unsuccessful madman is disgraced and called a lunatic.

Mad or not, I set myself to work with a zeal which few scientific students have ever equalled. I had everything to learn relative to the delicate study upon which I had embarked,—a study involving the most earnest patience, the most rigid analytic powers, the steadiest hand, the most untiring eye, the most refined and subtle manipulation.

For a long time half my apparatus lay inactively on the shelves of my laboratory, which was now most amply furnished with every possible contrivance for facilitating my investigations. The fact was that I did not know how to use some of my scientific implements,—never having been taught microscopics,—and those whose use I understood theoretically were of little avail, until by practice I could attain the necessary delicacy of handling. Still, such was the fury of my ambition, such the untiring perseverance of my experiments, that, difficult of credit as it may be, in the course of one year I became theoretically and practically an accomplished microscopist.

During this period of my labours, in which I submitted specimens of every substance that came under my observation to the action of my lenses, I became a discoverer,—in a small way, it is true, for I was very young, but still a discoverer. It was I who destroyed Ehrenberg's theory that the *Volvox globator* was an animal, and proved that his "monads" with stomachs and eyes were merely phases of the formation of a vegetable cell, and were, when they reached their mature state, incapable of the act of conjugation, or any true generative act, without which no organism rising to any stage of life higher than vegetable can be said to be complete. It was I who resolved the singular problem of rotation in the cells and hairs of plants into ciliary attraction, in spite of the assertions of Mr. Wenham and others, that my explanation was the result of an optical illusion.

But notwithstanding these discoveries, laboriously and painfully made as they were, I felt horribly dissatisfied. At every step I found myself stopped by the imperfections of my instruments. Like all active microscopists, I gave my imagination full play. Indeed, it is a common complaint against many such, that they supply the defects of their instruments with the creations of their brains. I imagined depths beyond depths in nature which the limited power of my lenses prohibited me from exploring. I lay awake at night constructing imaginary microscopes of immeasurable power, with which I seemed to pierce through all the envelopes of matter down to its original atom. How I cursed those imperfect mediums which necessity through ignorance compelled me to use! How I longed to discover the secret of some perfect lens, whose magnifying power should be limited only by the resolvability of the object, and which at the same time should be free from spherical and chromatic aberrations, in short from all the obstacles over which the poor microscopist finds himself continually stumbling! I felt convinced that the simple microscope, composed of a single lens of such vast yet perfect power was possible of construction. To attempt to bring the compound microscope up to such a pitch would have been commencing at the wrong end; this latter being simply a partially successful endeavour to remedy those very defects of the simple instrument, which, if conquered, would leave nothing to be desired.

It was in this mood of mind that I became a constructive microscopist. After another year passed in this new pursuit, experimenting on every imaginable substance,—glass, gems, flints, crystals, artificial crystals formed of the alloy of various vitreous materials,—in short, having constructed as many varieties of lenses as Argus had eyes, I found myself precisely where I had started, with nothing gained save an extensive knowledge of glass-making. I was almost dead with despair. My parents were surprised at my apparent want of progress in my medical studies, (I had not attended one lecture since my arrival in the city,) and the expenses of my mad pursuit had been so great as to embarrass me very seriously.

I was in this frame of mind one day, experimenting in my laboratory on a small diamond,—that stone, from its great refracting power, having always occupied my attention more than any other,—when a young Frenchman, who lived on the second floor above me, and who was in the habit of occasionally visiting me, entered the room.

I think that Jules Simon was a Jew. He had many traits of the Hebrew character: a love of jewelry, of dress, and of good living. There was something mysterious about him. He always had something to sell, and yet went into excellent society. When I say sell, I should perhaps have said peddle; for his operations were generally confined to the disposal of single articles,—a picture, for instance, or a rare carving in ivory, or a pair of duelling-pistols, or the dress of a Mexican *caballero*. When I was first furnishing my rooms, he paid me a visit, which ended in my purchasing an antique silver lamp, which he assured me was a Cellini, —it was handsome enough even for that,— and some other knickknacks for my sitting-room. Why Simon should pursue this petty trade I never could imagine. He apparently had plenty of money, and had the *entrée* of the best houses in the city, —taking care, however, I suppose, to drive no bargains within the enchanted circle of the Upper Ten. I came at length to the conclusion that this peddling was but a mask to cover some greater object, and even went so far as to believe my young acquaintance to be implicated in the slave-trade. That, however, was none of my affair.

On the present occasion, Simon entered my room in a state of considerable excitement.

"*Ah! mon ami!*" he cried, before I could even offer him the ordinary salutation, "it has occurred to me to be the witness of the most astonishing things in the world. I promenade myself to the house of Madame ———. How does the little animal—*le renard*—name himself in the Latin?"

"Vulpes," I answered.

"Ah! yes,—Vulpes. I promenade myself to the house of Madame Vulpes."

"The spirit medium?"

"Yes, the great medium. Great heavens! what a woman! I write on a slip of paper many of questions concerning affairs the most secret,—affairs that conceal themselves in the abysses of my heart the most profound; and behold! by example! what occurs?—This devil of a woman makes me replies the most truthful to all of them. She talks to me of things that I do not love to talk of to myself. What am I to think? I am fixed to the earth!"

"Am I to understand you, M. Simon, that this Mrs. Vulpes replied to questions secretly written by you, which questions related to events known only to yourself?"

"Ah! more than that, more than that," he answered with an air of some alarm. "She related to me things—But," he added, after a pause, and suddenly changing his manner, "why occupy ourselves with these follies? It was all the biology, without doubt. It goes without saying that it has not my credence.—But why are we here, *mon ami*? It has occurred to me to discover the most beautiful thing as you can imagine,—a vase with green lizards on it, composed by the great Bernard Palissy. It is in my apartment; let us mount. I go to show it to you."

I followed Simon mechanically; but my thoughts were far from Palissy and his enamelled ware, although I, like him, was seeking in the dark a great discovery. This casual mention of the spiritualist, Madame Vulpes, set me on a new track. What if this spiritualism should be really a great fact? What if, through communication with more subtle organisms than my own, I could reach at a single bound the goal, which perhaps a life of agonising mental toil would never enable me to attain?

While purchasing the Palissy vase from my friend Simon, I was mentally arranging a visit to Madame Vulpes.

III

THE SPIRIT OF LEEUWENHOEK

Two evenings after this, thanks to an arrangement by letter and the promise of an ample fee, I found Madame Vulpes awaiting me at her residence alone. She was a coarse-featured woman, with keen and rather cruel dark eyes, and an exceedingly sensual expression about her mouth and under jaw. She received me in perfect silence, in an apartment on the ground floor, very sparely furnished. In the centre of the room, close to where Mrs. Vulpes sat, there was a common round mahogany table. If I had come for the purpose of sweeping her chimney, the woman could not have looked more indifferent to my appearance. There was no attempt to inspire the visitor with awe. Everything bore a simple and practical aspect. This intercourse with the spiritual world was evidently as familiar an occupation with Mrs. Vulpes as eating her dinner or riding in an omnibus.

"You come for a communication, Mr. Linley?" said the medium, in a dry business-like tone of voice.

"By appointment,—yes."

"What sort of communication do you want?—a written one?"

"Yes,—I wish for a written one."

"From any particular spirit?"

"Yes."

"Have you ever known this spirit on this earth?"

"Never. He died long before I was born. I wish merely to obtain from him some information which he ought to be able to give better than any other."

"Will you seat yourself at the table, Mr. Linley," said the medium, "and place your hands upon it?"

I obeyed,—Mrs. Vulpes being seated opposite to me, with her hands also on the table. We remained thus for about a minute and a half, when a violent succession of raps came on the table, on the back of my chair, on the floor immediately under my feet, and even on the windowpanes. Mrs. Vulpes smiled composedly.

"They are very strong tonight," she remarked. "You are fortunate." She then continued, "Will the spirits communicate with this gentleman?"

Vigorous affirmative.

"Will the particular spirit he desires to speak with communicate?"

A very confused rapping followed this question.

"I know what they mean," said Mrs. Vulpes, addressing herself to me; "they wish you to write down the name of the particular spirit that you desire to converse with. Is that so?" she added, speaking to her invisible guests.

That it was so was evident from the numerous affirmatory responses. While this was going on, I tore a slip from my pocket-book, and scribbled a name, under the table.

"Will this spirit communicate in writing with this gentleman?" asked the medium once more.

After a moment's pause, her hand seemed to be seized with a violent tremor, shaking so forcibly that the table vibrated. She said that a spirit had seized her hand and would write. I handed her some sheets of paper that were on the table and a pencil. The latter she held loosely in her hand, which presently began to move over the paper with a singular and seemingly involuntary motion. After a few moments had elapsed, she handed me the paper, on which I found written, in a large uncultivated hand, the words, "He is not here, but has been sent for." A pause of a minute or so now ensued, during which Mrs. Vulpes remained perfectly silent, but the raps continued at regular intervals. When the short period I mentioned had elapsed, the hand of the medium was again seized with its convulsive tremor, and she wrote, under this trance influence, a few words on the paper, which she handed to me. They were as follows:—

"I am here. Question me.
Leeuwenhoek."

I was astounded. The name was identical with that I had written beneath the table, and carefully kept concealed. Neither was it at all probable that an uncultivated woman like Mrs. Vulpes should know even the name of the great father of microscopics. It may have been biology; but this theory was soon doomed to be destroyed. I wrote on my slip—still concealing it from Mrs. Vulpes—a series of questions, which, to avoid tediousness, I shall place with the responses in the order in which they occurred:—

I.—Can the microscope be brought to perfection?
Spirit.—Yes.
I.—Am I destined to accomplish this great task?
Spirit.—You are.
I.—I wish to know how to proceed to attain this end. For the love which you bear to science, help me!
Spirit.—A diamond of one hundred and forty carats, submitted to electro-magnetic currents for a long period, will experience a rearrangement of its atoms *inter se*, and from that stone you will form the universal lens.
I.—Will great discoveries result from the use of such a lens?
Spirit.—So great that all that has gone before is as nothing.
I.—But the refractive power of the diamond is so immense, that the image will be formed within the lens. How is that difficulty to be surmounted?
Spirit. —Pierce the lens through its axis, and the difficulty is obviated.

The image will be formed in the pierced space, which will itself serve as a tube to look through. Now I am called. Good night.

I cannot at all describe the effect that these extraordinary communications had upon me. I felt completely bewildered. No biological theory could account for the *discovery* of the lens. The medium might, by means of biological *rapport* with my mind, have gone so far as to read my questions, and reply to them coherently. But biology could not enable her to discover that magnetic currents would so alter the crystals of the diamond as to remedy its previous defects, and admit of its being polished into a perfect lens. Some such theory may have passed through my head, it is true; but if so, I had forgotten it. In my excited condition of mind there was no course left but to become a convert, and it was in a state of the most painful nervous exaltation that I left the medium's house that evening. She accompanied me to the door, hoping that I was satisfied. The raps followed us as we went through the hall, sounding on the balusters, the flooring, and even the lintels of the door. I hastily expressed my satisfaction, and escaped hurriedly into the cool night air. I walked home with but one thought possessing me,—how to obtain a diamond of the immense size required. My entire means multiplied a hundred times over would have been inadequate to its purchase. Besides, such stones are rare, and become historical. I could find such only in the regalia of Eastern or European monarchs.

IV
THE EYE OF MORNING

There was a light in Simon's room as I entered my house. A vague impulse urged me to visit him. As I opened the door of his sitting-room unannounced, he was bending, with his back toward me, over a carcel lamp, apparently engaged in minutely examining some object which he held in his hands. As I entered, he started suddenly, thrust his hand into his breast pocket and turned to me with a face crimson with confusion.

"What!" I cried, "poring over the miniature of some fair lady? Well, don't blush so much; I won't ask to see it."

Simon laughed awkwardly enough, but made none of the negative protestations usual on such occasions. He asked me to take a seat.

"Simon," I said, "I have just come from Madame Vulpes."

This time Simon turned as white as a sheet, and seemed stupefied, as if a sudden electric shock had smitten him. He babbled some incoherent words, and went hastily to a small closet where he usually kept his liquors. Although astonished at his emotions, I was too preoccupied with my own idea to pay much attention to anything else.

"You say truly when you call Madame Vulpes a devil of a woman," I continued. "Simon, she told me wonderful things tonight, or rather was the means of telling me wonderful things. Ah! if I could only get a diamond that weighed one hundred and forty carats!"

Scarcely had the sigh with which I uttered this desire died upon my lips, when Simon, with the aspect of a wild beast, glared at me savagely, and, rushing to the mantelpiece, where some foreign weapons hung on the wall, caught up a Malay creese, and brandished it furiously before him.

"No!" he cried in French, into which he always broke when he was excited. "No! you shall not have it! You are perfidious! You have consulted with that demon, and desire my treasure! But I will die first! Me! I am brave! You cannot make me fear!"

All this, uttered in a loud voice trembling with excitement, astounded me. I saw at a glance that I had accidentally trodden upon the edges of Simon's secret, whatever it was. It was necessary to reassure him.

"My dear Simon," I said, "I am entirely at a loss to know what you mean. I went to Madame Vulpes to consult with her on a scientific problem, to the solution of which I discovered that a diamond of the size I just mentioned was necessary. You were never alluded to during the evening, nor, so far as I was concerned, even thought of. What can be the meaning of this outburst? If you happen to have a set of valuable diamonds in your possession, you need fear nothing from me. The diamond which I require you could not possess; or, if you did possess it, you would not be living here."

Something in my tone must have completely reassured him; for his expression immediately changed to a sort of constrained merriment, combined, however, with a certain suspicious attention to my movements. He laughed, and said that I must bear with him; that he was at certain moments subject to a species of vertigo, which betrayed itself in incoherent speeches, and that the attacks passed off as rapidly as they came. He put his weapon aside while making this explanation, and endeavoured, with some success, to assume a more cheerful air.

All this did not impose on me in the least. I was too much accustomed to analytical labours to be baffled by so flimsy a veil. I was determined to probe the mystery to the bottom.

"Simon," I said, gayly, "let us forget all this over a bottle of burgundy. I have a case of Lausseure's *Clos Vougeot* downstairs, fragrant with the odours and ruddy with the sunlight of the Côte d'Or. Let us have up a couple of bottles. What say you?"

"With all my heart," answered Simon, smilingly.

I produced the wine and we seated ourselves to drink. It was a famous vintage, that of 1848, a year when war and wine throve together,—and its pure but powerful juice seemed to impart renewed vitality to the system. By the time we had half finished the second bottle, Simon's head, which I knew was a weak one, had begun to yield, while I remained calm as ever, only that every draught seemed to send a flush of vigour through my limbs. Simon's utterance became more and more indistinct. He took to singing French *chansons* of a not very moral tendency. I rose suddenly from the table just at the conclusion of one of those incoherent verses, and, fixing my eyes on him with a quiet smile, said: "Simon, I have deceived you. I learned your secret this evening. You may as well be frank with me. Mrs. Vulpes, or rather one of her spirits, told me all."

He started with horror. His intoxication seemed for the moment to fade away, and he made a movement towards the weapon that he had a short time before laid down. I stopped him with my hand.

"Monster!" he cried passionately, "I am ruined! What shall I do? You shall never have it! I swear by my mother!"

"I don't want it," I said; "rest secure, but be frank with me. Tell me all about it."

The drunkenness began to return. He protested with maudlin earnestness that I was entirely mistaken,—that I was intoxicated; then asked me to swear eternal secrecy, and promised to disclose the mystery to me. I pledged myself, of course, to all. With an uneasy look in his eyes, and hands unsteady with drink and nervousness, he drew a small case from his breast and opened it. Heavens! How the mild lamp-light was shivered into a thousand prismatic arrows, as it fell upon a vast rose-diamond that glittered in the case! I was no judge of diamonds, but I saw at a glance that this was a gem of rare size and purity. I looked at Simon with wonder, and—must I confess it?—with envy. How could he have obtained this treasure? In reply to my question, I could just gather from his drunken state-ments (of which, I fancy, half the incoherence was affected) that he had been superintending a gang of slaves engaged in diamond washing in Brazil; that he had seen one of them secret a diamond, but, instead of informing his employers, had quietly watched the negro until he saw him bury his treasure; that he had dug it up and fled with it, but that as yet he was afraid to attempt to dispose of it pub-licly,—so valuable a gem being almost certain to attract too much attention to its owner's antecedents,—and he had not been able to discover any of those obscure channels by which such matters are conveyed away safely. He added, that, in accordance with oriental practice, he had named his diamond with the fanciful title of "The Eye of Morning."

While Simon was relating this to me, I regarded the great diamond attentively. Never had I beheld anything so beautiful. All the glories of light, ever imagined or described, seemed to pulsate in its crystalline chambers. Its weight, as I learned from Simon, was exactly one hundred and forty carats. Here was an amazing coin-cidence. The hand of destiny seemed in it. On the very evening when the spirit of Leeuwenhoek communicates to me the great secret of the microscope, the priceless means which he directs me to employ start up within my easy reach! I deter-mined, with the most perfect deliberation, to possess myself of Simon's diamond.

I sat opposite to him while he nodded over his glass, and calmly revolved the whole affair. I did not for an instant contemplate so foolish an act as a common theft, which would of course be discovered, or at least necessitate flight and concealment, all of which must interfere with my scientific plans. There was but one step to be taken,—to kill Simon. After all, what was the life of a little peddling Jew, in comparison with the interests of science? Human beings are taken every day from the condemned prisons to be experimented on by surgeons. This man, Simon, was by his own confession a criminal, a robber, and I believed on my soul a murderer. He deserved death quite as much as any felon condemned by the laws: why should I not, like government, contrive that his punishment should contribute to the progress of human knowledge?

The means for accomplishing everything I desired lay within my reach. There stood upon the mantelpiece a bottle half full of French laudanum. Simon was so occupied with his diamond, which I had just restored to him, that it was an affair of no difficulty to drug his glass. In a quarter of an hour he was in a profound sleep.

I now opened his waistcoat, took the diamond from the inner pocket in which he had placed it, and removed him to the bed, on which I laid him so that his feet hung down over the edge; I had possessed myself of the Malay creese, which I held in my right hand, while with the other I discovered as accurately as I could by pulsation the exact location of the heart. It was essential that all the aspects of his death should lead to the surmise of self-murder. I calculated the exact angle at which it was probable that the weapon, if levelled by Simon's own hand, would enter his breast; then with one powerful blow I thrust it up to the hilt in the very spot which I desired to penetrate. A convulsive thrill ran through Simon's limbs. I heard a smothered sound issue from his throat, precisely like the bursting of a large air-bubble, sent up by a diver, when it reaches the surface of the water; he turned half round on his side, and, as if to assist my plans more effectually, his right hand, moved by some mere spasmodic impulse, clasped the handle of the creese, which it remained holding with extraordinary muscular tenacity. Beyond this there was no apparent struggle. The laudanum, I presume, paralysed the usual nervous action. He must have died instantly.

There was yet something to be done. To make it certain that all suspicion of the act should be diverted from any inhabitant of the house to Simon himself, it was necessary that the door should be found in the morning *locked on the inside*. How to do this, and afterwards escape myself? Not by the window; that was a physical impossibility. Besides, I was determined that the windows *also* should be found bolted. The solution was simple enough. I descended softly to my own room for a peculiar instrument which I had used for holding small slippery substances, such as minute spheres of glass, etc. This instrument was nothing more than a long slender hand-vice, with a very powerful grip, and a considerable leverage, which last was accidentally owing to the shape of the handle. Nothing was simpler than, when the key was in the lock, to seize the end of its stem in this vice, through the keyhole, from the outside, and so lock the door. Previously, however, to doing this, I burned a numbers of papers on Simon's hearth. Suicides almost always burn papers before they destroy themselves. I also emptied some more laudanum into Simon's glass,—having first removed from it all traces of wine,—cleaned the other wine glass, and brought the bottles away with me. If traces of two persons drinking had been found in the room, the question naturally would have arisen, Who was the second? Besides, the wine bottles might have been identified as belonging to me. The laudanum I poured out to account for its presence in his stomach, in case of a *post-mortem* examination. The theory naturally would be, that he first intended to poison himself, but after swallowing a little of the drug, was either disgusted with its taste, or changed his mind from other motives, and chose the dagger. These arrangements made, I walked out, leaving the gas burning, locked the door with my vice, and went to bed.

Simon's death was not discovered until nearly three in the afternoon. The servant, astonished at seeing the gas burning,—the light streaming on the dark landing from under the door,—peeped through the keyhole and saw Simon on the bed. She gave the alarm. The door was burst open and the neighbourhood was in a fever of excitement.

Every one in the house was arrested, myself included. There was an inquest; but no clue to his death beyond that of suicide could be obtained. Curiously enough, he had made several speeches to his friends the preceding week, that seemed to point to self-destruction. One gentleman swore that Simon had said in his presence that "he was tired of life." His landlord affirmed that Simon, when paying him his last month's rent, remarked that "he should not pay him rent much longer." All the other evidence corresponded,—the door locked inside, the position of the corpse, the burnt papers. As I anticipated, no one knew of the possession of the diamond by Simon, so that no motive was suggested for his murder. The jury, after a prolonged examination, brought in the usual verdict, and the neighbourhood once more settled down into its accustomed quiet.

V

ANIMULA

The three months succeeding Simon's catastrophe I devoted night and day to my diamond lens. I had constructed a vast galvanic battery, composed of nearly two thousand pairs of plates,—a higher power I dared not use, lest the diamond should be calcined. By means of this enormous engine I was enabled to send a power current of electricity continually through my great diamond, which it seemed to me gained in lustre every day. At the expiration of a month I commenced the grinding and polishing of the lens, a work of intense toil and exquisite delicacy. The great density of the stone, and the care required to be taken with the curvatures of the surfaces of the lens, rendered the labour the severest and most harassing that I had yet undergone.

At last the eventful moment came; the lens was completed. I stood trembling on the threshold of new worlds. I had the realisation of Alexander's famous wish before me. The lens lay on the table, ready to be placed upon its platform. My hand fairly shook as I enveloped a drop of water with a thin coating of oil of turpentine, preparatory to its examination,—a process necessary in order to prevent the rapid evaporation of the water. I now placed the drop on a thin slip of glass under the lens, and throwing upon it, by the combined aid of a prism and a mirror, a powerful stream of light, I approached my eye to the minute hole drilled through the axis of the lens. For an instant I saw nothing save what seemed to be an illuminated chaos, a vast luminous abyss. A pure white light, cloudless and serene, and seemingly limitless as space itself, was my first impression. Gently, and with the greatest care, I depressed the lens a few hair's-breadths. The wondrous illumination still continued, but as the lens approached the object a scene of indescribable beauty was unfolded to my view.

I seemed to gaze upon a vast space, the limits of which extended far beyond my vision. An atmosphere of magical luminousness permeated the entire field of view. I was amazed to see no trace of animalculous life. Not a living thing, apparently, inhabited that dazzling expanse. I comprehended instantly that, by the wondrous power of my lens, I had penetrated beyond the grosser particles of aqueous matter, beyond the realms of infusoria and protozoa, down to the original gaseous globule, into whose luminous interior I was gazing, as into an almost boundless dome filled with a supernatural radiance.

It was, however, no brilliant void into which I looked. On every side I beheld beautiful inorganic forms, of unknown texture, and coloured with the most enchanting hues. These forms presented the appearance of what might be called, for want of a more specific definition, foliated clouds of the highest rarity; that is, they undulated and broke into vegetable formations, and were tinged with splendours compared with which the gilding of our autumn woodlands is as dross compared with gold. Far away into the illimitable distance stretched long avenues of these gaseous forests, dimly transparent, and painted with prismatic hues of unimaginable brilliancy. The pendent branches waved along the fluid glades until every vista seemed to break through half-lucent ranks of many coloured drooping silken pennons. What seemed to be either fruits or flowers, pied with a thousand hues, lustrous and ever varying, bubbled from the crowns of this fairy foliage. No hills, no lakes, no rivers, no forms animate or inanimate, were to be seen, save those vast auroral copses that floated serenely in the luminous stillness, with leaves and fruits and flowers gleaming with unknown fires, unrealisable by mere imagination.

How strange, I thought, that this sphere should be thus condemned to solitude! I had hoped, at least, to discover some new form of animal life,—perhaps of a lower class than any with which we are at present acquainted, but still, some living organism. I found my newly discovered world, if I may so speak, a beautiful chromatic desert.

While I was speculating on the singular arrangements of the internal economy of Nature, with which she so frequently splinters into atoms our most compact theories, I thought I beheld a form moving slowly through the glades of one of the prismatic forests. I looked more attentively, and found that I was not mistaken. Words cannot depict the anxiety with which I awaited the nearer approach of this mysterious object. Was it merely some inanimate substance, held in suspense in the attenuated atmosphere of the globule? or was it an animal endowed with vitality and motion? It approached, flitting behind the gauzy, coloured veils of cloud-foliage, for seconds dimly revealed, then vanishing. At last the violet pennons that trailed nearest to me vibrated; they were gently pushed aside, and the form floated out into the broad light.

It was a female human shape. When I say human, I mean it possessed the outline of humanity,—but there the analogy ends. Its adorable beauty lifted it illimitable heights beyond the loveliest daughter of Adam.

I cannot, I dare not, attempt to inventory the charms of this divine revelation of perfect beauty. Those eyes of mystic violet, dewy and serene, evade my words. Her long, lustrous hair following her glorious head in a golden wake, like the track sown in heaven by a falling star, seems to quench my most burning phrases with its splendours. If all the bees of Hybla nestled upon my lips, they would still sing but hoarsely the wondrous harmonies of outline that enclosed her form.

She swept out from between the rainbow-curtains of the cloud-trees into the broad sea of light that lay beyond. Her motions were those of some graceful naiad, cleaving, by a mere effort of her will, the clear, unruffled waters that fill the chambers of the sea. She floated forth with the serene grace of a frail bubble ascending through the still atmosphere of a June day. The perfect roundness of her limbs formed suave and enchanting curves. It was like listening to the most spiritual symphony of Beethoven the divine, to watch the harmonious flow of lines. This, indeed, was a pleasure cheaply purchased at any price. What cared I, if I had waded to the portal of this wonder through another's blood? I would have given my own to enjoy one such moment of intoxication and delight.

Breathless with gazing on this lovely wonder, and forgetful for an instant of everything save her presence, I withdrew my eye from the microscope eagerly,—alas! As my gaze fell on the thin slide that lay beneath my instrument, the bright light from mirror and from prism sparkled on a colourless drop of water! There, in that tiny bead of dew, this beautiful being was forever imprisoned. The planet Neptune was not more distant from me than she. I hastened once more to apply my eye to the microscope.

Animula (let me now call her by that dear name which I subsequently bestowed on her) had changed her position. She had again approached the wondrous forest, and was gazing earnestly upwards. Presently one of the trees—as I must call them—unfolded a long ciliary process, with which it seized one of the gleaming fruits that glittered on its summit, and, sweeping slowly down, held it within reach of Animula. The sylph took it in her delicate hand and began to eat. My attention was so entirely absorbed by her, that I could not apply myself to the task of determining whether this singular plant was or was not instinct with volition.

I watched her, as she made her repast, with the most profound attention. The suppleness of her motions sent a thrill of delight through my frame; my heart beat madly as she turned her beautiful eyes in the direction of the spot in which I stood. What would I have not given to have had the power to precipitate myself into that luminous ocean, and float with her through those groves of purple and gold! While I was thus breathlessly following her every movement, she suddenly started, seemed to listen for a moment, and then cleaving the brilliant ether in which she was floating, like a flash of light, pierced through the opaline forest, and disappeared.

Instantly a series of the most singular sensations attacked me. It seemed as if I had suddenly gone blind. The luminous sphere was still before me, but my daylight had vanished. What caused this sudden disappearance? Had she a lover or a husband? Yes, that was the solution! Some signal from a happy fellow-being had vibrated through the avenues of the forest, and she had obeyed the summons.

The agony of my sensations, as I arrived at this conclusion, startled me. I tried to reject the conviction that my reason forced upon me. I battled against the fatal conclusion,—but in vain. It was so. I had no escape from it. I loved an animalcule!

It is true that thanks to the marvellous power of my microscope, she appeared of human proportions. Instead of presenting the revolting aspect of the coarser creatures, that live and struggle and die, in the more easily resolvable portions of the water-drop, she was fair and delicate and of surpassing beauty. But of what account was all that? Every time that my eye was withdrawn from the instrument, it fell on a miserable drop of water, within which, I must be content to know, dwelt all that could make my life lovely.

Could she but see me once! Could I for one moment pierce the mystical walls that so inexorably rose to separate us, and whisper all that filled my soul, I might consent to be satisfied for the rest of my life with the knowledge of her remote sympathy. It would be something to have established even the faintest personal link to bind us together,—to know that at times, when roaming through those enchanted glades, she might think of the wonderful stranger, who had broken the monotony of her life with his presence, and left a gentle memory in her heart!

But it could not be. No invention of which human intellect was capable could break down the barriers that nature had erected. I might feast my soul upon her wondrous beauty, yet she must always remain ignorant of the adoring eyes that day and night gazed down upon her, and, even when closed, beheld her in dreams. With a bitter cry of anguish I fled from the room, and, flinging myself on my bed, sobbed myself to sleep like a child.

VI
THE SPILLING OF THE CUP

I arose the next morning almost at daybreak, and rushed to my microscope. I trembled as I sought the luminous world in miniature that contained my all. Animula was there. I had left the gas-lamp, surrounded by its moderators, burning, when I went to bed the night before. I found the sylph bathing, as it were, with an expression of pleasure animating her features, in the brilliant light which surrounded her. She tossed her lustrous golden hair over her shoulders with innocent coquetry. She lay at full length in the transparent medium, in which she supported herself with ease, and gambolled with the enchanting grace that the nymph Salmacis might have exhibited when she sought to conquer the modest Hermaphroditus. I tried an experiment to satisfy myself if her powers of reflection were developed. I lessened the lamp-light considerably. By the dim light that remained, I could see an expression of pain flit across her face. She looked upward suddenly, and her brows contracted. I flooded the stage of the microscope again with a full stream of light, and her whole expression changed. She sprang forward like some substance deprived of all weight. Her eyes sparkled and her lips moved. Ah! if science had only the means of conducting and reduplicating sounds, as it does the rays of light, what carols of happiness would then have entranced my ears! what jubilant hymns to Adonais would have thrilled the illumined air!

I now comprehended how it was that the Count de Gabalis peopled his mystic world with sylphs,—beautiful beings whose breath of life was lambent fire, and who sported forever in regions of purest ether and purest light. The Rosicrucian had anticipated the wonder that I had practically realised.

How long this worship of my divinity went on thus I scarcely know. I lost all note of time. All day from early dawn, and far into the night, I was to be found peering through that wonderful lens. I saw no one, went nowhere, and scarce allowed myself sufficient time for my meals. My whole life was absorbed in contemplation as rapt as that of any of the Romish saints. Every hour that I gazed upon the divine form strengthened my passion,—a passion that was always overshadowed by the maddening conviction, that, although I could gaze on her at will, she never, never could behold me!

At length, I grew so pale and emaciated, from want of rest, and continual brooding over my insane love and its cruel conditions, that I determined to make some effort to wean myself from it. "Come," I said, "this is at best but a fantasy. Your imagination has bestowed on Animula charms which in reality she does not possess. Seclusion from female society has produced this morbid condition of mind. Compare her with the beautiful women of your own world, and this false enchantment will vanish."

I looked over the newspapers by chance. There I beheld the advertisement of a celebrated *danseuse* who appeared nightly at Niblo's. The Signorina Caradolce had the reputation of being the most beautiful as well as the most graceful woman in the world. I instantly dressed and went to the theatre.

The curtain drew up. The usual semicircle of fairies in white muslin were standing on the right toe around the enamelled flower-bank, of green canvas, on which the belated prince was sleeping. Suddenly a flute is heard. The fairies start. The trees open, the fairies all stand on the left toe, and the queen enters. It was the Signorina. She bounded forward amid thunders of applause, and, lighting on one foot, remained poised in the air. Heavens! was this the great enchantress that had drawn monarchs at her chariot-wheels? Those heavy muscular limbs, those thick ankles, those cavernous eyes, that stereotyped smile, those crudely painted cheeks! Where were the vermeil blooms, the liquid expressive eyes, the harmonious limbs of Animula?

The Signorina danced. What gross, discordant movements! The play of her limbs was all false and artificial. Her bounds were painful athletic efforts; her poses were angular and distressed the eye. I could bear it no longer; with an exclamation of disgust that drew every eye upon me, I rose from my seat in the very middle of the Signorina's *pas-de-fascination*, and abruptly quitted the house.

I hastened home to feast my eyes once more on the lovely form of my sylph. I felt that henceforth to combat this passion would be impossible. I applied my eye to the lens. Animula was there,—but what could have happened? Some terrible change seemed to have taken place during my absence. Some secret grief seemed to cloud the lovely features of her I gazed upon. Her face had grown thin and haggard; her limbs trailed heavily; the wondrous lustre of her golden hair had faded. She was ill!—ill, and I could not assist her! I believe at that moment I would have gladly forfeited all claims to my human birthright, if I could only have been dwarfed to the size of an animalcule, and permitted to console her from whom fate had forever divided me.

I racked my brain for the solution of this mystery. What was it that afflicted the sylph? She seemed to suffer intense pain. Her features contracted, and she even writhed, as if with some internal agony. The wondrous forests appeared also to have lost half their beauty. Their hues were dim and in some places faded away altogether. I watched Animula for hours with a breaking heart, and she seemed absolutely to wither away under my very eye. Suddenly I remembered that I had not looked at the water-drop for several days. In fact I hated to see it; for it reminded me of the natural barrier between Animula and myself. I hurriedly looked down on the stage of the microscope. The slide was still there,—but, great heavens! the water-drop had vanished! The awful truth burst upon me; it had evaporated, until it had become so minute as to be invisible to the naked eye; I had been gazing on its last atom, the one that contained Animula, and she was dying!

I rushed again to the front of the lens, and looked through. Alas! the last agony had seized her. The rainbow-hued forests had all melted away, and Animula lay struggling feebly in what seemed to be a spot of dim light. Ah! the sight was horrible: the limbs once so round and lovely shrivelling up into nothings; the eyes—those eyes that shone like heaven—being quenched into black dust; the lustrous golden hair now lank and discoloured. The last throe came. I beheld that final struggle of the blackening form—and I fainted.

When I awoke out of a trance of many hours, I found myself lying amid the wreck of my instrument, myself as shattered in mind and body as it. I crawled feebly to my bed, from which I did not rise for months.

They say now that I am mad; but they are mistaken. I am poor, for I have neither the heart nor the will to work; all my money is spent, and I live on charity. Young men's associations that love a joke invite me to lecture on Optics before them, for which they pay me, and laugh at me while I lecture. "Linley, the mad microscopist," is the name I go by. I suppose that I talk incoherently while I lecture. Who could talk sense when his brain is haunted by such ghastly memories, while ever and anon among the shapes of death I behold the radiant form of my lost Animula!

DOUGLAS HYDE

THE STUDENT
WHO LEFT COLLEGE

*Douglas Hyde, the scholar who became the first president of the Irish
Republic in 1938, was instrumental in the revival of Gaelic in Ireland
earlier this century. His translations of traditional Irish folktales, such as
"The Student Who Left College," which dates from somewhere around
1888, are considered the finest.*

HERE CAME A NUMBER OF YOUNG people from the County of Galway to
a great college, to learn and gain instruction, so as to become priests. I
often heard the name of this college from my mother, but I do not
remember it. It was not Maynooth. There was a man of these of the name of
Patrick O'Flynn. He was the son of a rich farmer. His father and his mother
desired to make a priest of him. He was a nice, gentle lad. He used not to go dancing with the other boys in the evening, but it was his habit to go out with the grey-
light of day, and he used to be walking by himself up and down under the shadow
of the great trees that were round about the college, and he used to remain there
thinking and meditating by himself, until some person would come and bring
him into his room.

One evening, in the month of May, he went out, as was his custom, and he was
taking his walk under the trees when he heard a melodious music. There came a
darkness or a sort of blindness over his eyes, and when he found his sight again
he beheld a great high wall on every side of him, and out in front of him a shining road. The musicians were on the road, and playing melodiously, and he heard
a voice saying, "Come with us to the land of delight and rest." He looked back
and beheld a great high wall behind him and on each side of him, and he was not
able to return back again across the wall, although he desired to return. He went
forward then after the music. He did not know how long he walked, but the great
high wall kept ever on each side of him and behind him.

He was going, and ever-going, until they came to a great river, and water in it as red as blood. Wonder came upon him then, and great fear. But the musicians walked across the river without wetting their feet, and Patrick O'Flynn followed them without wetting his own. He thought at first that the musicians belonged to the Fairy-Host, and next he thought that he had died and that it was a group of angels that were in it, taking him to heaven.

The walls fell away from them then, on each side, and they came to a great wide plain. They were going then, and ever-going, until they came to a fine castle that was in the midst of the plain. The musicians went in, but Patrick O'Flynn remained outside. It was not long until the chief of the musicians came out to him and brought him into a handsome chamber. He spoke not a word, and Patrick O'Flynn never heard one word spoken so long as he remained there.

There was no night in that place, but the light of day throughout. He never ate and he never drank a single thing there, and he never saw anyone eating or drinking, and the music never ceased. Every half-hour, as he thought, he used to hear a bell, as it were a church-bell being rung, but he never beheld the bell, and he was unable to see it in any place.

When the musicians used to go out upon the plain before the castle, there used to come a tribe of every sort of bird in the heavens, playing the most melodious music that ear ever heard. It was often Patrick O'Flynn said to himself, "It is certain that I am in heaven, but is it not curious that I have no remembrance of sickness, nor of death, nor of judgment, and that I have not seen God nor his Blessed Mother, as is promised to us?"

Patrick O'Flynn did not know how long he was in that delightful place. He thought that he had been in it only for a short little time, but he was in it for a hundred years and one.

One day the musicians were out in the field and he was listening to them, when the chief came to him. He brought him out and put him behind the musicians. They departed on their way, and they made neither stop nor stay until they came to the river that was as red as blood. They went across that, without wetting their foot-soles, and went forward until they came to the field near the college where they found him at the first. Then they departed out of his sight like a mist.

He looked round him, and recognized the college, but he thought that the trees were higher and that there was some change in the college itself. He went in, then, but he did not recognise a single person whom he met, and not a person recognised him.

The principal of the college came to him, and said to him, "Where are you from, son, or what is your name?"

"I am Patrick O'Flynn from the County of Galway," said he.

"How long are you here?" said the principal.

"I am here since the first day of March," said he.

216

"I think that you are out of your senses," said the principal. "There is no person of your name in the college, and there has not been for twenty years, for I am more than twenty years here."

"Though you were in it since you were born, yet I am here since last March, and I can show you my room and my books."

With that he went up the stairs, and the principal after him. He went into his room and looked round him, and said, "This is my room, but that is not my furniture, and those are not my books that are in it." He saw an old Bible upon the table and he opened it, and said: "This is my Bible—my mother gave it to me when I was coming here; and, see, my name is written in it."

The principal looked at the Bible, and there, as sure as God is in heaven, was the name of Patrick O'Flynn written in it, and the day of the month that he left home.

Now there was great trouble of mind on the principal, and he did not know what he should do. He sent for the masters and the professors and he told them the story.

"By my word," said an old priest that was in it, "I heard talk when I was young, of a student who went away out of this college, and there was no account of him since, whether living or dead. The people searched the river and the bog holes, but there was no account to be had of him, and they never got the body."

The principal called to them then and bade them bring him a great book in which the name of every person was written who had come to that college since it was founded. He looked through the book, and see! Patrick O'Flynn's name was in it, and the day of the month that he came, and this was written opposite to his name, that the same Patrick O'Flynn had departed on such a day, and that nobody knew what had become of him. Now it was exactly one hundred and one years from the day he went until the day he came back in that fashion.

"This is a wonderful, and a very wonderful story," said the principal. "But, do you wait here quietly, my son," said he, "and I shall write to the bishop." He did that, and he got an account from the bishop to keep the man until he should come himself.

At the end of a week after that the bishop came and sent for Patrick O'Flynn. There was nobody present except the two. "Now, son," said the bishop, "go on your knees and make a confession." Then he made an act of contrition, and the bishop gave him absolution.

Immediately there came a fainting and a heavy sleep over him, and he was, as it were, for three days and three nights a dead person. When he came to himself the bishop and priests were round about him. He rose up, shook himself, and told them his story, as I have told it, and he put excessive wonder upon every man of them. "Now," said he, "here I am alive and safe, and do as ye please."

The bishop and the priests took counsel together. "It is a saintly man you are," said the bishop then, "and we shall give you holy orders on the spot."

They made a priest of him then, and no sooner were holy orders given him than he fell dead upon the altar, and they all heard at the same time the most melodious music that ear ever listened to, above them in the sky, and they all said that it was the angels who were in it, carrying the soul of Father O'Flynn up to heaven with them.

THE
WILDES

✣

O SCAR WILDE CUT SUCH a distinctive—if not unique—figure in world literature, it is not completely surprising that each of his parents also lived a somewhat eccentric life in letters. His father, Sir William Wilde, was an eminent Dublin physician (specializing in eye and ear surgery) who also built a reputation as an amateur archaeologist and writer. One of his books advanced some theories on the nature of the diseases that plagued Jonathan Swift (*The Closing Years of Dean Swift's Life*), but his best known work was *Irish Popular Superstitions.* In addition to his career as a writer, it may not be irrelevant that Dr. Wilde led a somewhat scandalous life for the times (he sired and acknowledged a number of illegitimate offspring, or, as he called them, his "breed," and was the central figure in a libel trial related to a sexual assault he was alleged to have committed). Dr. Wilde's wife, Lady Jane Francesca Elgee Wilde (Oscar's mother) was a redoubtable figure in her own right. Using the pen name Speranza she became notorious for writing nationalistic polemics that appeared in such radical journals as *The Nation*, as well as works on Irish folklore. The Wilde home at Merrion Square in Dublin became an active social center in the middle of the nineteenth century, and Lady Wilde continued to hold a fashionable salon in London when she relocated there after the death of her husband in 1876. By that time Oscar was twenty-two years old and was already beginning to make his presence known at Oxford and elsewhere. After embodying the Aesthetic Movement in his life and art, and writing some of the most memorable plays and stories of his time, he became mired in a sexual scandal that ruined his career and his life, sending him first to jail and then to exile in France. Lying on her deathbed in 1896, his mother asked that Oscar might be temporarily released from prison to visit her. On being told that this was not possible, she is said to have responded, "I hope prison will do him good" and turned her face to the wall.

FAIRY INTERFERENCE

This is taken from William Wilde's Irish Popular Superstitions *(1852),
a collection of tales that Wilde remembered from his childhood. One of
Wilde's children was Oscar Wilde, and it is said that if it were not for
the looming shadow of the son, the father would be more remembered
today for his many works of folklore and travel writing. There are
more than a few clues in "Fairy Interference" that its author was also a
doctor who specialized in surgery of the eye and ear.*

THE FOLLOWING INSTANCE OF popular superstitious prejudice has been
afforded the writer by a person who was present at the transaction; and,
as it is best expressed in the words of the narrator, it is here inserted as a
quotation: "I well remember in the year 1818, that Mary, the wife of Daniel Kelly,
a bouncing, full, auburn-haired, snow-white-skinned woman, about twenty-
eight years of age, died suddenly on a summer's day, while in the act of cutting
cabbages in her garden. Great was the consternation throughout the entire parish
of Moyarta, in the southwest of Clare, at this sad event, the more particularly as
several persons who were in a westerly direction from her at the time, declared
that they had *seen* and felt a violent gust of wind pass by and *through* them in the
exact direction of Kelly's house, carrying with it all the dust and straws, etc.,
which came in its way. This confirmed the husband and friends of the deceased
in their impression that she had been carried off to nurse for the fairies.
Immediately Mary Quin, alias the Pet (*Maire an Pheata*), and Margaret
MacInerheny, alias Black Peg, two famous fairy-women in the neighbourhood,
were called in, who, for three days and three nights, kept up a constant but
unavailing assault on a neighbouring fort or rath for the recovery of the abducted
woman. But at the end of that time it was found that the body, or what in their
belief appeared to be the body, of Mary Kelly, could not be kept over ground,

wherefore it was placed in the grave, but still with a total unbelief of its identity. Her bereaved husband and her brothers watched her grave day and night for three weeks after, and then they opened it, in the full conviction of finding only a birch broom, a log of wood, or the skeleton of some deformed monster in it. In this, however, they were mistaken, for they found in it what they had put into it, but in a much more advanced state of decomposition."

Whenever the good people venture abroad, or suddenly change their residence in the open day, their transit is marked by a whirlwind, in the eddies of which dust, straws, and other light substances, are taken up and carried along. When such occur, the Irish peasant, if conversing, ceases to speak, crosses himself, holds his breath, looks down, and mentally repeats a short prayer; and no irreverent expression with regard to the supernatural movement ever drops from him. Many persons have told us that they have often heard and FELT the fairies pass by them with a sound like that of a swarm of bees, or a flock of sparrows on the wing. An instance of this occurred lately during the hurricane at Limerick.

There is no prejudice more firmly rooted than the belief in the abduction of recently-confined females, for the purpose of acting as nurses either to the children of the fairy queen, or to some of those carried away from earth. In certain cases of mental aberration which sometimes occur at this period, the unhappy state of the patient is always attributed to fairy interference. It is believed that the real person is not physically present, but that the patient is one of the fairies who has assumed the features and general appearance of the abducted individual, while the actual person is "giving the breast" to one of Fin Varra's children in the fairy halls of the hill of Knockmaah, in the county Galway. In such cases, if there has been any delay in recovery, the medical attendant is at once discarded, and if a friar had been called in to read prayers over her, and that this did not prove immediately effectual, all legalised practitioners, medical or ecclesiastical, are dismissed, and the fairy doctor is applied to. His mode of proceeding is usually as follows: he fills a cup, or wine-glass with oaten meal, and mutters over it an Irish prayer. He then covers it with a cloth, and applies it to the heart, back, and sides, repeating the incantation on each application. If it is a fairy that is present, one-half of the meal disappears at one side of the vessel, as if it were cut down from above. That which remains is made into three small cakes and baked upon the hearth. The sick person is to eat one of these every morning, "fasting"; when the spell is broken, the fairy departs, and is once more replaced by the real mortal, sound and whole.

The "meal-cure" is likewise employed, with some modification, for the heartache, and in that case, the expression, "*Foir an Cridhe*—ease the heart, ease the heart," is made use of by the charmer on each application. The patient generally visits the doctor on a Monday, Thursday, and Monday, and the meal in the cup is lessened each time in proportion to the amount of disease removed, until at last the vessel is completely emptied. The remnant is brought home each day by the patient, who must not lose any of it, nor speak to any person by the way. The invalid then makes it into a cake, and sits by the fire until it is baked, taking care that neither cat, dog, nor any other living thing passes between him and his cake until it is baked and eaten with three sprigs of watercress, in the name of the Trinity. The meal cure is a very good specimen of fairy sleight of hand, and worthy the attention of modern wizards.

As the person is not always conscious of her state while labouring under what is termed by physicians, "puerpural mania," it is rather difficult to get any very accurate or collected account of the fairy nursery in which they pass their time; and when the cures and charms prove ineffectual, and they "die all out," the truth becomes more difficult to attain; nevertheless it is not quite impossible. In proof of this, we would refer our readers to a very poetic and well-told legend in the Rev. Mr. Neilson's "Introduction to the Irish Language" (1808), where we have an account of one Mary Rourke, who, having died in childbirth, in the county of Galway, was washed, laid out, waked, keened, and buried with all due form and ceremonial. Mary, however, "was in Knockmagha, three quarters of a year, nursing a child, entertained with mirth and sweet songs; but notwithstanding, she was certainly in affliction. At length the host of the castle told her that her husband was now married to another woman, and that she should indulge no longer in sorrow and melancholy; that Fin Varra and all his family were about to pay a visit to the province of Ulster. They set out at cock-crowing, from smooth Knockmaah forth, both Fin Varra and his valiant host. And many a fairy castle, rath and mount they shortly visited from dawn of day till fall of night, on beautiful winged coursers:

> Around Knock Greine and Knock-na-Rae,
> Ben Bulbin and Keis-Corainn,
> To Ben Echlann and Loch Da éan
> From thence northeast to Slieve Guilin,
> They traveled the lofty hills of Mourne,
> Round high Slieve Donard and Ballachanèry,
> Down to Dundrim, Dundrum and Dunardalay,
> Right forward to Knock-na-Feadala."

These are all the celebrated haunts of the fairy people in the west and north. Now at the foot of Knock-na-Feadala there lived with his mother, who was a widow woman, a boy named Thady Hughes, an honest, pious, hard-working bachelor. Well, Thady went out on Hallow Eve night, about the very time that the court of Fin Varra were passing through the air, and as he stood in the gap of an old fort looking up at the stars that were shining bright through the clear frosty air, he observed a dark cloud moving towards him from the southwest, with a great whirlwind; and he heard the sound of horses upon the wind, as a mighty troop of cavalry came over the ford, and straight along the valley, to the very rath on which he stood. Thady was in a mighty flustrification, and trembled all over; but he remembered that he had often heard it said by knowledgable people, that if you cast the dust that is under your foot against the whirlwind at the instant that it passes you, "them that's in it" (that is, if they have any human being along with them) are obliged to be released. So, being of a humane disposition, he lifted a handful of the gravel that was under his foot, and threw it lustily, in the name of the Trinity, against the blast, when, lo and behold! down falls a young woman, neither more nor less than Mary Rourke from Galway, all the way; but mighty wake entirely. Thady took courage, having heard her groan like a Christian, so he spoke softly to her, and lifted her up, and brought her home to his mother, who took care of her till she recovered. In process of time the heart of Thady was soft-ened, and he took Mary to wife, and they lived mighty happy and contented for a year and a day, the lovingest couple in the whole county Down, till a stocking merchant from Connemara, passing that way, recognized her as the wife of Michael Joyce, of Gort, who shortly after came all the ways from Connaught to claim her: and it took six clergy and a bishop to say whose wife she was.

A few, however, of those who have been carried away have returned, and have left us faithful records of all they saw, and what was said and done in the court of his elfin majesty.

There lived a woman in Innis Shark—one of the group of islands on the east-ern coast—named Biddy Mannion, as handsome and likely a fisherman's wife as you would meet in a day's walk. She was tall, and fair in the face, with skin like an egg, and hair that might vie with the gloss of the raven's wing. She was mar-ried about a twelvemonth, when the midwife presented her husband, Patsy-Andrew M'Intire, with as fine a man-child as could be found between Shark and America, and sure they are the next parishes, with only the Atlantic for a mear-ing between them. The young one throve apace, and all the women and gossips said that Biddy Mannion was the lucky woman, and the finest nurse seen in the island for many a day. Now the king of the fairies had a child about the same age, or a little older; but the queen was not able to nurse it, for she was mighty weakly after her lying-in, as her husband had a falling-out with another fairy potentate that lives down one side of the Giant's Causeway, who, by the force of magic and *pishrogues,* banished the suck from the Connaught princess for spite. The gentry had their eye upon Biddy Mannion for a long time, but as she always wore a *gospel* round her neck, and kept an *errub* and a bit of a burnt sod from St. John's Night sewed up in her clothes, she was proof against all their machinations and seduc-tions. At long run, however, she lost this herb, and one fine summer's night the young *gaurlough* [a very young infant], being mighty cross with the teeth, wouldn't sleep in the cradle at all, but was evermore starting and crying, as if the life was leaving him, so she got up at last, determined to take him to bed to herself, and she went down to the kitchen to light a candle. Well, just as she was blowing a coal, three men caught a hold of her, before she could bless herself, and she was unable to shout or say a word, so they brought her out of the house quite easy, and put her upon a pillion, behind one of themselves, on a fine black horse that was ready waiting outside the door. She was no sooner seated behind one of the men than away they all galloped, without saying a word. It was as calm and beautiful a night as ever came out of the sky, just before the moon rose "between day and dark," with the gloom of parting twilight softening every break upon the surrounding landscape, and not a breath of air was to be felt. They rode on a long time, and she didn't know where they were going to; but she thought to herself they must be on the mainland, for she heard the frogs croaking in the ditches, the *bunnaun lena* [heron] was sounding away in the bogs, and the *minnaun airigh* [snipe] was wheeling over their heads. At last the horse stopped of itself all of a sudden before the gate of a "big house," at the butt of a great hill, with trees growing all round it, where she had never been before in her life. There was much light in the house, and presently a grand looking gentleman dressed all in scarlet, with a cocked hat on his head and a sword by his side, and his fingers so covered with rings that they shone "like *lassar lena* [a brilliant-yellow plant] in a bog-hole," lifted her off the pillion as polite as possible, handed her into the house, and bid her a *cead mile failte,* just the same as if he had known her all his lifetime.

The gentleman left her sitting in one of the rooms, and when he was gone she saw a young woman standing at the *thrashal* of the door, and looking very earnestly at her, as if she wanted to speak to her. "Troth I'll speak, anyway" says Biddy Mannion, "for if I didn't, I'm sure I'd burst." And with that she bid her the time of day, and asked her why she was looking at her so continuously. The woman then gave a great sigh, and whispered to her, "If you take my advice, Biddy Mannion, you'll not taste bit, bite, or sup, while you are in this house, for if you do you'll be sorry for it, and maybe never get home again to your child or husband. I ate and drank my fill, *forrior geraugh* [great grief], the first night I came, and that's the reason that I am left here now in this enchanted place, where everything you meet is bewitched, even to the mate itself. But when you go home send word to them that's after me, Tim Conneely, that lives on side of the Killaries, that I am here, and maybe he'd try what Father Pat Prendergast, the blessed abbot of Cong, could do to get me out of it."

Biddy was just going to make further inquiries, when in the clapping of your hand the woman was gone, and the man with the scarlet coat came back, and the same strange woman, bringing a young child in her arms. The man took the child from the woman, and gave it to Biddy to put it to the breast, and when it had drank its *fill* he took it away, and invited her into another room, where the queen—a darling, fine-looking lady, as you'd meet in a day's walk—was seated

225

in an arm-chair, surrounded by a power of quality, dressed up for all the world like judges with big wigs, and red gowns upon them. There was a table laid out with all sorts of eating, which the man in the cocked hat pressed her to take. She made answer that she was no ways hungry, but that if they could give her a cure for a little girl belonging to one of her neighbours, who was mighty *dauny,* and never well in herself since she had a fit of the *feur-gurtagh* [a weakness from hunger], while crossing the Minaune Pass in Achill, and to send herself home to Shark, she would be for ever obliged to them. The king, for that was the gentleman with cocked hat, said he had ne'er a cure.

"Indeed, then," said the mother of the child, "as I was the cause of your coming here, honest woman, you must get the cure; go home," says she, speaking for all the world like an Englishwoman, "and get ten green rishes from the side of the well of Aughavalla [a holy well near Murrisk], throw the tenth away, and squeeze the juice of the rest of them into the bottom of a taycup, and give it to the colleen to drink, and she will get well in no time."

The king then put a ring on her finger and told her not to lose it by any manner of means, and that as long as she wore this ring no person could hurt or harm her. He then rubbed a sort of an ointment on her eyes, and no sooner had he done so than she found herself in a frightful cave where she couldn't see her hand before her. "Don't be any ways afeard," says he; "this is to let you know what kind of a people we are that took you away. We are the fallen angels that the people up above upon the earth call the fairies"; and then after a while she began to see about her, and the place was full of dead men's bones, and had a terrible musty smell; and after a while he took her into another room where there was more light, and here she found a wonderful sight of young children, and them all blindfolded, and doing nothing but sitting upon *pookauns* [mushroom fairy-stools]. These were the souls of infants that were never baptised, and are believed "to go into naught." After that he showed her a beautiful garden, and at the end of it there was a large gate, which he opened with a key that was hung to his watch-chain. "Now," says he, "you are not far from your own house"; so he let her out, and then says he, "who is that that is coming down the boreen"; and when she turned her back to look who it was, behold the man with the red coat and the cocked hat had disappeared.

Biddy Mannion could not see anybody, but she knew full well the place where she was in a minute, and that it was the little road that led down to the bog just beside her own house, and when she went up to the door she met another woman the very *moral* of herself, just as fair as if she saw her in the looking-glass, who said to her as she passed, "What a *gomal* your husband is that didn't know the difference between you and me." She said no more, but Biddy went in and found her child in a beautiful sleep, with his face smiling, like the buttercups in May.

THE PRIEST'S SOUL

The rather harrowing tale that appears here is a version written by Lady Wilde, Oscar Wilde's mother, in the late nineteenth century. Some readers may feel that the eerie dialogue between the fallen priest and the angel of death is worthy of her son.

IN FORMER DAYS THERE WERE great schools in Ireland where every sort of learning was taught to the people, and even the poorest had more knowledge at that time than many a gentleman has now. But as to the priests, their learning was above all, so that the fame of Ireland went over the whole world, and many kings from foreign lands used to send their sons all the way to Ireland to be brought up in the Irish schools.

Now, at this time there was a little boy learning at one of them who was a wonder to everyone for his cleverness. His parents were only labouring people, and of course poor; but young as he was, and poor as he was, no king's or lord's son could come up to him in learning. Even the masters were put to shame; for when they were trying to teach him he would tell them something they never heard of before, and show them their ignorance. One of his great triumphs was in argument; and he would go on till he proved to you that black was white, and then when you gave in, for no one could beat him in talk, he would turn round and show you that white was black, or maybe that there was no colour at all in the world. When he grew up his poor father and mother were so proud of him that they resolved to make him a priest, which they did at last, though they nearly starved themselves to get the money. Well, such another learned man was not in Ireland, and he was as great in argument as ever, so that no one could stand before him. Even the bishops tried to talk to him, but he showed them at once they knew nothing at all.

Now, there were no schoolmasters in those times, but it was the priests taught the people; and as this man was the cleverest in Ireland, all the foreign kings sent their sons to him, as long as he had house room to give them. So he grew very proud, and began to forget how low he had been, and worst of all, even to forget God, who had made him what he was. And the pride of arguing got hold of him, so that from one thing to another he went on to prove that there was no Purgatory, and then no Hell, and then no Heaven, and then no God; and at last that men had no souls, but were no more than a dog or a cow, and when they died there was an end of them. "Whoever saw a soul?" he would say. "If you can show me one, I will believe." No one could make any answer to this; and at last they all came to believe that as there was no other world, everyone might do what they liked in this; the priest setting the example, for he took a beautiful young girl to wife. But as no priest or bishop in the whole land could be got to marry them, he was obliged to read the service over for himself. It was a great scandal, yet no one dared to say a word, for all the king's sons were on his side, and would have slaughtered anyone who tried to prevent his wicked goings-on. Poor boys; they all believed in him, and thought every word he said was the truth. In this way his notions began to spread about, and the whole world was going to the bad, when one night an angel came down from Heaven, and told the priest he had but twenty-four hours to live. He began to tremble, and asked for a little more time.

But the angel was stiff, and told him that could not be.

"What do you want time for, you sinner?" he asked.

"Oh, sir, have pity on my poor soul!" urged the priest.

"Oh, no! You have a soul then," said the angel. "Pray, how did you find that out?"

"It has been fluttering in me ever since you appeared," answered the priest. "What a fool I was not to think of it before."

"A fool, indeed," said the angel. "What good was all your learning, when it could not tell you that you had a soul?"

"Ah, my lord," said the priest, "if I am to die, tell me how soon I may be in Heaven?"

"Never," replied the angel. "You denied there was a Heaven."

"Then, my lord, may I go to Purgatory?"

"You denied Purgatory also; you must go straight to Hell," said the angel.

"But, my lord, I denied Hell also," answered the priest, "so you can't send me there either."

The angel was a little puzzled.

"Well," said he, "I'll tell you what I can do for you. You may either live now on earth for a hundred years, enjoying every pleasure, and then be cast into Hell for ever; or you may die in twenty-four hours in the most horrible torments, and pass through Purgatory, there to remain till the Day of Judgment, if only you can find some one person that believes, and through his belief mercy will be vouchsafed to you, and your soul will be saved."

The priest did not take five minutes to make up his mind.

"I will have death in the twenty-four hours," he said, "so that my soul may be saved at last."

On this the angel gave him directions as to what he was to do, and left him.

Then immediately the priest entered the large room where all the scholars and the kings' sons were seated, and called out to them:

"Now tell me the truth, and let none fear to contradict me; tell me what is your belief—have men souls?"

"Master," they answered, "once we believed that men had souls; but thanks to your teaching, we believe so no longer. There is no Hell, and no Heaven, and no God. This is our belief, for it is thus you taught us."

Then the priest grew pale with fear and cried out: "Listen! I taught you a lie. There is a God, and man has an immortal soul. I believe now all I denied before."

But the shouts of laughter that rose up drowned the priest's voice, for they thought he was only trying them for argument.

"Prove it, master," they cried. "Prove it. Who has ever seen God? Who has ever seen the soul?"

And the room was stirred with their laughter.

The priest stood up to answer them, but no word could he utter. All his eloquence, all his powers of argument had gone from him; and he could do nothing but wring his hands and cry out, "There is a God! there is a God! Lord have mercy on my soul!"

And they all began to mock him and repeat his own words that he had taught them:

"Show him to us; show us your God." And he fled from them groaning with agony, for he saw that none believed; and how, then, could his soul be saved?

But he thought next of his wife. "She will believe," he said to himself; "women never give up God."

And he went to her; but she told him that she believed only what he had taught her, and that a good wife should believe in her husband first and before and above all things in Heaven or earth.

Then despair came on him, and he rushed from the house, and began to ask every one he met if they believed. But the same answer came from one and all: "We believe only what you have taught us," for his doctrine had spread far and wide through the country.

Then he grew half mad with fear, for the hours were passing. And he flung himself down on the ground in a lonesome spot, and wept and groaned in terror, for the time was coming fast when he must die.

Just then a little child came by. "God save you kindly," said the child to him.

The priest started up.

"Do you believe in God?" he asked.

"I have come from a far country to learn about Him," said the child. "Will your honour direct me to the best school that they have in these parts?"

"The best school and the best teacher is close by," said the priest, and he named himself.

"Oh, not to that man," answered the child, "for I am told he denies God, and Heaven, and Hell, and even that man has a soul, because he cannot see it; but I would soon put him down."

The priest looked at him earnestly. "How?" he inquired.

"Why," said the child, "I would ask him if he believed he had life to show me his life."

"But he could not do that, my child," said the priest. "Life cannot be seen; we have it, but it is invisible."

"Then if we have life, though we cannot see it, we may also have a soul, though it is invisible," answered the child.

When the priest heard him speak these words he fell down on his knees before him, weeping for joy, for now he knew his soul was safe; he had met one at last that believed. And he told the child his whole story—all his wickedness, and pride, and blasphemy against the great God; and how the angel had come to him, and told him of the only way in which he could be saved, through the faith and prayers of someone that believed.

"Now, then," he said to the child, "take this penknife and strike it into my breast, and go on stabbing the flesh until you see the paleness of death on my face. Then watch—for a living thing will soar up from my body as I die, and you will then know that my soul has ascended to the presence of God. And when you see this thing, make haste and run to my school, and call on all my scholars to come and see that the soul of their master has left the body, and that all he taught them was a lie, for that there is a God who punishes sin, and a Heaven and a Hell, and that man has an immortal soul destined for eternal happiness or misery."

"I will pray," said the child, "to have courage to do this work." And he kneeled down and prayed. Then he rose up and took the penknife and struck it into the priest's heart, and struck and struck again till all the flesh was lacerated; but still the priest lived, though the agony was horrible, for he could not die until the twenty-four hours had expired.

At last the agony seemed to cease, and the stillness of death settled on his face. Then the child, who was watching, saw a beautiful living creature, with four snow-white wings, mount from the dead man's body into the air and go fluttering round his head.

So he ran to bring the scholars; and when they saw it, they all knew it was the soul of their master; and they watched with wonder and awe until it passed from sight into the clouds.

And this was the first butterfly that was ever seen in Ireland; and now all men know that the butterflies are the souls of the dead waiting for the moment when they may enter Purgatory, and so pass through torture to purification and peace.

But the schools of Ireland were quite deserted after that time, for people said, What is the use of going so far to learn, when the wisest man in all Ireland did not know if he had a soul till he was near losing it, and was only saved at last through the simple belief of a little child?

FROM
THE PICTURE OF
DORIAN GRAY

*The Picture of Dorian Gray (1891), Oscar Wilde's only novel, is the
story of a startlingly handsome young man, Dorian Gray, who is so
delighted by the image of himself in a portrait painted by a friend that
he unwisely wishes that he could forever remain exactly as depicted. In
this excerpt he attempts to make sense of the events of the previous night,
when he heartlessly broke his engagement to a young actress, Sybil Vane,
and upon returning home was horrified at a change in the cherished
portrait: new lines of cruelty had somehow formed around the mouth.*

IT WAS LONG PAST NOON WHEN he awoke. His valet had crept several times
on tiptoe into the room to see if he was stirring, and had wondered what
made his young master sleep so late. Finally his bell sounded, and Victor came
softly in with a cup of tea, and a pile of letters, on a small tray of old Sèvres china,
and drew back the olive-satin curtains, with their shimmering blue lining, that
hung in front of the three tall windows.

"Monsieur has slept well this morning," he said, smiling.

"What o'clock is it, Victor?" asked Dorian Gray, drowsily.

"One hour and a quarter, Monsieur."

How late it was! He sat up, and, having sipped some tea, turned over his letters. One of them was from Lord Henry, and had been brought by hand that
morning. He hesitated for a moment, and then put it aside. The others he opened
listlessly. They contained the usual collection of cards, invitations to dinner, tickets
for private views, programmes of charity concerts, and the like, that are showered
on fashionable young men every morning during the season. There was a rather
heavy bill, for a chased silver Louis-Quinze toilet-set, that he had not yet had the
courage to send on to his guardians, who were extremely old-fashioned people
and did not realise that we live in an age when unnecessary things are our only

necessities; and there were several very courteously worded communications from Jermyn Street money-lenders offering to advance any sum of money at a moment's notice and at the most reasonable rates of interest.

After about ten minutes he got up, and, throwing on an elaborate dressing-gown of silk-embroidered cashmere wool, passed into the onyx-paved bathroom. The cool water refreshed him after his long sleep. He seemed to have forgotten all that he had gone through. A dim sense of having taken part in some strange tragedy came to him once or twice, but there was the unreality of a dream about it.

As soon as he was dressed, he went into the library and sat down to a light French breakfast, that had been laid out for him on a small round table close to the open window. It was an exquisite day. The warm air seemed laden with spices. A bee flew in, and buzzed round the blue-dragon bowl that, filled with sulphur-yellow roses, stood before him. He felt perfectly happy.

Suddenly his eye fell on the screen that he had placed in front of the portrait, and he started.

"Too cold for Monsieur?" asked his valet, putting an omelette on the table. "I shut the window?"

Dorian shook his head. "I am not cold," he murmured.

Was it all true? Had the portrait really changed? Or had it been simply his own imagination that had made him see a look of evil where there had been a look of joy? Surely a painted canvas could not alter? The thing was absurd. It would serve as a tale to tell Basil some day. It would make him smile.

And, yet, how vivid was his recollection of the whole thing! First in the dim twilight, and then in the bright dawn, he had seen the touch of cruelty round the warped lips. He almost dreaded his valet leaving the room. He knew that when he was alone he would have to examine the portrait. He was afraid of certainty. When the coffee and cigarettes had been brought and the man turned to go, he felt a wild desire to tell him to remain. As the door was closing behind him he called him back. The man stood waiting for his orders. Dorian looked at him for a moment. "I am not at home to any one, Victor," he said, with a sigh. The man bowed and retired.

Then he rose from the table, lit a cigarette, and flung himself down on a lux-uriously-cushioned couch that stood facing the screen. The screen was an old one, of gilt Spanish leather, stamped and wrought with a rather florid Louis-Quatorze pattern. He scanned it curiously, wondering if ever before it had concealed the secret of a man's life.

Should he move it aside, after all? Why not let it stay there? What was the use of knowing? If the thing was true, it was terrible. If it was not true, why trouble about it? But what if, by some fate or deadlier chance, eyes other than his spied behind, and saw the horrible change? What should he do if Basil Hallward came and asked to look at his own picture? Basil would be sure to do that. No; the thing had to be examined, and at once. Anything would be better than this dreadful state of doubt.

He got up, and locked both doors. At least he would be alone when he looked upon the mask of his shame. Then he drew the screen aside, and saw himself face to face. It was perfectly true. The portrait had altered.

As he often remembered afterwards, and always with no small wonder, he found himself at first gazing at the portrait with a feeling of almost scientific interest. That such a change should have taken place was incredible to him. And yet it was a fact. Was there some subtle affinity between the chemical atoms, that shaped themselves into form and colour on the canvas, and the soul that was within him? Could it be that what that soul thought, they realised?—that what it dreamed, they made true? Or was there some other, more terrible reason? He shuddered, and felt afraid, and, going back to the couch, lay there, gazing at the picture in sickened horror.

One thing, however, he felt that it had done for him. It had made him conscious how unjust, how cruel, he had been to Sibyl Vane. It was not too late to make reparation for that. She could still be his wife. His unreal and selfish love would yield to some higher influence, would be transformed into some nobler passion, and the portrait that Basil Hallward had painted of him would be a guide to him through life, would be to him what holiness is to some, and conscience to others, and the fear of God to us all. There were opiates for remorse, drugs that could lull the moral sense to sleep. But here was a visible symbol of the degradation of sin. Here was an ever-present sign of the ruin men brought upon their souls.

Three o'clock struck, and four, and the half-hour rang its double chime, but Dorian Gray did not stir. He was trying to gather up the scarlet threads of life, and to weave them into a pattern; to find his way through the sanguine labyrinth of passion through which he was wandering. He did not know what to do, or what to think. Finally, he went over to the table, and wrote a passionate letter to the girl he had loved, imploring her forgiveness, and accusing himself of madness. He covered page after page with wild words of sorrow, and wilder words of pain. There is a luxury in self-reproach. When we blame ourselves we feel that no one else has a right to blame us. It is the confession, not the priest, that gives us absolution. When Dorian had finished the letter, he felt that he had been forgiven.

Suddenly there came a knock to the door, and he heard Lord Henry's voice outside. "My dear boy, I must see you. Let me in at once. I can't bear your shutting yourself up like this."

He made no answer at first, but remained quite still. The knocking still continued, and grew louder. Yes, it was better to let Lord Henry in, and to explain to him the new life he was going to lead, to quarrel with him if it became necessary to quarrel, to part if parting was inevitable. He jumped up, drew the screen hastily across the picture, and unlocked the door.

"I am so sorry for it all, Dorian," said Lord Henry, as he entered. "But you must not think too much about it."

"Do you mean about Sibyl Vane?" asked the lad.

"Yes, of course," answered Lord Henry, sinking into a chair, and slowly pulling off his yellow gloves. "It is dreadful, from one point of view, but it was not your fault. Tell me, did you go behind and see her, after the play was over?"

"Yes."

"I felt sure you had. Did you make a scene with her?"

"I was brutal, Harry—perfectly brutal. But it is all right now. I am not sorry for anything that has happened. It has taught me to know myself better."

"Ah, Dorian, I am so glad you take it in that way! I was afraid I would find you plunged in remorse, and tearing that nice curly hair of yours."

"I have got through all that," said Dorian, shaking his head, and smiling. "I am perfectly happy now. I know what conscience is, to begin with. It is not what you told me it was. It is the divinest thing in us. Don't sneer at it, Harry, any more—at least not before me. I want to be good. I can't bear the idea of my soul being hideous."

"A very charming artistic basis for ethics, Dorian! I congratulate you on it. But how are you going to begin?"

"By marrying Sibyl Vane."

"Marrying Sibyl Vane!" cried Lord Henry, standing up, and looking at him in perplexed amazement. "But, my dear Dorian——"

"Yes, Harry, I know what you are going to say. Something dreadful about marriage. Don't say it. Don't ever say things of that kind to me again. Two days ago I asked Sibyl to marry me. I am not going to break my word to her. She is to be my wife!"

"Your wife! Dorian! . . . Didn't you get my letter? I wrote to you this morning, and sent the note down, by my own man."

"Your letter? Oh, yes, I remember. I have not read it yet, Harry. I was afraid there might be something in it that I wouldn't like. You cut life to pieces with your epigrams."

"You know nothing then?"

"What do you mean?"

Lord Henry walked across the room and, sitting down by Dorian Gray, took both his hands in his own, and held them tightly. "Dorian," he said, "my letter—don't be frightened—was to tell you that Sibyl Vane is dead."

A cry of pain broke from the lad's lips, and he leaped to his feet, tearing his hands away from Lord Henry's grasp. "Dead! Sibyl dead! It is not true! It is a horrible lie! How dare you say it?"

"It is quite true, Dorian," said Lord Henry, gravely. "It is in all the morning papers. I wrote down to you to ask you not to see any one till I came. There will have to be an inquest, of course, and you must not be mixed up in it. Things like that make a man fashionable in Paris. But in London people are so prejudiced. Here, one should never make one's *début* with a scandal. One should reserve that to give an interest to one's old age. I suppose they don't know your name at the theatre? If they don't, it is all right. Did any one see you going round to her room? That is an important point."

Dorian did not answer for a few moments. He was dazed with horror. Finally he stammered in a stifled voice, "Harry, did you say an inquest? What did you mean by that? Did Sibyl——? Oh, Harry, I can't bear it! But be quick. Tell me everything at once."

"I have no doubt it was not an accident, Dorian, though it must be put in that way to the public. It seems that as she was leaving the theatre with her mother, about half-past twelve or so, she said she had forgotten something upstairs. They waited some time for her, but she did not come down again. They ultimately found her lying dead on the floor of her dressing-room. She had swallowed something by mistake, some dreadful thing they use at theatres. I don't know what it was, but it had either prussic acid or white lead in it. I should fancy it was prussic acid, as she seems to have died instantaneously."

"Harry, Harry, it is terrible!" cried the lad.

"Yes; it is very tragic, of course, but you must not get yourself mixed up in it. I see by *The Standard* that she was seventeen. I should have thought she was almost younger than that. She looked such a child, and seemed to know so little about acting. Dorian, you mustn't let this thing get on your nerves. You must come and dine with me, and afterwards we will look in at the Opera. It is a Patti night, and everybody will be there. You can come to my sister's box. She has got some smart women with her."

"So I have murdered Sibyl Vane," said Dorian Gray, half to himself—"murdered her as surely as if I had cut her little throat with a knife. Yet the roses are not less lovely for all that. The birds sing just as happily in my garden. And to-night I am to dine with you, and then go on to the Opera, and sup somewhere, I suppose, afterwards. How extraordinary dramatic life is! If I had read all this in a book, Harry, I think I would have wept over it. Somehow, now that it has happened actually, and to me, it seems far too wonderful for tears. Here is the first passionate love-letter I have ever written in my life. Strange, that my first passionate love-letter should have been addressed to a dead girl. Can they feel, I wonder, those white silent people we call the dead? Sibyl! Can she feel, or know, or listen? Oh, Harry, how I loved her once! It seems years ago to me now. She was everything to me. Then came that dreadful night—was it really only last night?—when she played so badly, and my heart almost broke. She explained it all to me. It was terribly pathetic. But I was not moved a bit. I thought her shallow. Suddenly something happened that made me afraid. I can't tell you what it was, but it was terrible. I said I would go back to her. I felt I had done wrong. And now she is dead. My God! My God! Harry, what shall I do? You don't know the danger I am in, and there is nothing to keep me straight. She would have done that for me. She had no right to kill herself. It was selfish of her."

"My dear Dorian," answered Lord Henry, taking a cigarette from his case, and producing a gold-latten match-box, "the only way a woman can ever reform a man is by boring him so completely that he loses all possible interest in life. If you had married this girl you would have been wretched. Of course, you would have treated her kindly. One can always be kind to people about whom one cares nothing. But she would have soon found out that you were absolutely indifferent to her. And when a woman finds that out about her husband, she either becomes dreadfully dowdy, or wears very smart bonnets that some other woman's husband has to pay for. I say nothing about the social mistake, which would have been abject, which, of course, I would not have allowed, but I assure you that in any case the whole thing would have been an absolute failure."

"I suppose it would," muttered the lad, walking up and down the room and looking horribly pale. "But I thought it was my duty. It is not my fault that this terrible tragedy has prevented my doing what was right. I remember your saying once that there is a fatality about good resolutions—that they are always made too late. Mine certainly were."

"Good resolutions are useless attempts to interfere with scientific laws. Their origin is pure vanity. Their result is absolutely *nil*. They give us, now and then, some of those luxurious sterile emotions that have a certain charm for the weak. That is all that can be said for them. They are simply cheques that men draw on a bank where they have no account."

"Harry," cried Dorian Gray, coming over and sitting down beside him, "why is it that I cannot feel this tragedy as much as I want to? I don't think I am heartless. Do you?"

"You have done too many foolish things during the last fortnight to be entitled to give yourself that name, Dorian," answered Lord Henry, with his sweet, melancholy smile.

The lad frowned. "I don't like that explanation, Harry," he rejoined, "but I am glad you don't think I am heartless. I am nothing of the kind. I know I am not. And yet I must admit that this thing that has happened does not affect me as it should. It seems to me to be simply like a wonderful ending to a wonderful play. It has all the terrible beauty of a Greek tragedy, a tragedy in which I took a great part, but by which I have not been wounded."

"It is an interesting question," said Lord Henry, who found an exquisite pleasure in playing on the lad's unconscious egotism—"an extremely interesting question. I fancy that the true explanation is this. It often happens that the real tragedies of life occur in such an inartistic manner that they hurt us by their crude violence, their absolute incoherence, their absurd want of meaning, their entire lack of style. They affect us just as vulgarity affects us. They give us an impression of sheer brute force, and we revolt against that. Sometimes, however, a tragedy that possesses artistic elements of beauty crosses our lives. If these elements of beauty are real, the whole thing simply appeals to our sense of dramatic effect. Suddenly we find that we are no longer the actors, but the spectators of the play. Or rather we are both. We watch ourselves, and the mere wonder of the spectacle enthralls us. In the present case, what is it that has really happened? Some one has killed herself for love of you. I wish that I had ever had such an experience. It would have made me in love with love for the rest of my life. The people who have adored me— there have not been very many, but there have been some—have always insisted on living on, long after I had ceased to care for them, or they to care for me. They have become stout and tedious, and when I meet them they go in at once for reminiscences. That awful memory of woman! What a fearful thing it is. And what an utter intellectual stagnation it reveals! One should absorb the colour of life, but one should never remember its details. Details are always vulgar."

"I must sow poppies in my garden," sighed Dorian.

"There is no necessity," rejoined his companion. "Life has always poppies in her hands. Of course, now and then things linger. I once wore nothing but violets all through one season, as a form of artistic mourning for a romance that would not die. Ultimately, however, it did die. I forget what killed it. I think it was her proposing to sacrifice the whole world for me. That is always a dreadful moment. It fills one with the terror of eternity. Well—would you believe it?—a week ago, at Lady Hampshire's, I found myself seated at dinner next to the lady in question, and she insisted on going over the whole thing again, and digging up the past, and raking up the future. I had buried my romance in a bed of asphodel. She dragged it out again, and assured me that I had spoiled her life. I am bound to state that she ate an enormous dinner, so I did not feel any anxiety. But what a lack of taste she showed! The one charm of the past is that it is the past. But women never know when the curtain has fallen. They always want a sixth act, and as soon as the interest of the play is entirely over they propose to continue it. If they were allowed their own way, every comedy would have a tragic ending, and every tragedy would culminate in a farce. They are charmingly artificial, but they have no sense of art. You are more fortunate than I am. I assure you, Dorian, that not one of the women I have known would have done for me what Sibyl Vane did for you. Ordinary women always console themselves. Some of them do it by going in for sentimental colours. Never trust a woman who wears mauve, whatever her age may be, or a woman over thirty-five who is fond of pink ribbons. It always means that they have a history. Others find a great consolation in suddenly discovering the good qualities of their husbands. They flaunt their conjugal felicity in one's face, as if it were the most fascinating of sins. Religion consoles some. Its mysteries have all the charm of a flirtation, a woman once told me; and I can quite understand it. Besides, nothing makes one so vain as being told that one is a sinner. Conscience makes egotists of us all. Yes; there is really no end to the consolations that women find in modern life. Indeed, I have not mentioned the most important one."

"What is that, Harry?" said the lad listlessly.

"Oh, the obvious consolation. Taking some one else's admirer when one loses one's own. In good society that always whitewashes a woman. But really, Dorian, how different Sibyl Vane must have been from all the women one meets! There is something to me quite beautiful about her death. I am glad I am living in a century when such wonders happen. They make one believe in the reality of the things we all play with, such as romance, passion, and love."

"I was terribly cruel to her. You forget that."

"I am afraid that women appreciate cruelty, downright cruelty, more than anything else. They have wonderfully primitive instincts. We have emancipated them, but they remain slaves looking for their masters, all the same. They love being dominated. I am sure you were splendid. I have never seen you really and absolutely angry, but I can fancy how delightful you looked. And, after all, you said something to me the day before yesterday that seemed to me at the time to be merely fanciful, but that I see now was absolutely true, and it holds the key to everything."

"What was that, Harry?"

"You said to me that Sibyl Vane represented to you all the heroines of romance—that she was Desdemona one night, and Ophelia the other; that she died as Juliet, she came to life as Imogen."

"She will never come to life again now," muttered the lad, burying his face in his hands.

"No, she will never come to life. She has played her last part. But you must think of that lonely death in the tawdry dressing-room simply as a strange lurid fragment from some Jacobean tragedy, as a wonderful scene from Webster, or Ford, or Cyril Tourneur. The girl never really lived, and so she has never really died. To you at least, she was always a dream, a phantom that flitted through Shakespeare's plays and left them lovelier for its presence, a reed through which Shakespeare's music sounded richer and more full of joy. The moment she touched actual life, she marred it, and it marred her, and so she passed away. Mourn for Ophelia, if you like. Put ashes on your head because Cordelia was strangled. Cry out against Heaven because the daughter of Brabantio died. But don't waste your tears over Sibyl Vane. She was less real than they are."

There was a silence. The evening darkened in the room. Noiselessly, and with silver feet, the shadows crept in from the garden. The colours faded wearily out of things.

After some time, Dorian Gray looked up. "You have explained me to myself, Harry," he murmured, with something of a sigh of relief. "I felt all that you have said, but somehow I was afraid of it, and I could not express it to myself. How well you know me! But we will not talk again of what has happened. It has been a marvellous experience. That is all. I wonder if life has still in store for me anything as marvellous."

"Life has everything in store for you, Dorian. There is nothing that you, with your extraordinary good looks, will not be able to do."

"But suppose, Harry, I became haggard, and old, and wrinkled? What then?"

"Ah, then," said Lord Henry, rising to go—"then, my dear Dorian, you would have to fight for your victories. As it is, they are brought to you. No, you must keep your good looks. We live in an age that reads too much to be wise, and that thinks too much to be beautiful. We cannot spare you. And now you had better dress, and drive down to the club. We are rather late, as it is."

"I think I shall join you at the Opera, Harry. I feel too tired to eat anything. What is the number of your sister's box?"

"Twenty-seven, I believe. It is on the grand tier. You will see her name on the door. But I am sorry you won't come and dine."

"I don't feel up to it," said Dorian, listlessly. "But I am awfully obliged to you for all that you have said to me. You are certainly my best friend. No one has ever understood me as you have."

"We are only at the beginning of our friendship, Dorian," answered Lord Henry, shaking him by the hand. "Good-bye. I shall see you before nine-thirty, I hope. Remember, Patti is singing."

As he closed the door behind him, Dorian Gray touched the bell, and in a few minutes Victor appeared with the lamps and drew the blinds down.

He waited impatiently for him to go. The man seemed to take an interminable time over everything.

As soon as he had left, he rushed to the screen, and drew it back. No; there was no further change in the picture. It had received the news of Sibyl Vane's death before he had known of it himself. It was conscious of the events of life as they occurred. The vicious cruelty that marred the fine lines of the mouth had, no doubt, appeared at the very moment that the girl had drunk the poison, whatever it was. Or was it indifferent to results? Did it merely take cognizance of what passed within the soul? He wondered, and hoped that some day he would see the change taking place before his very eyes, shuddering as he hoped it.

Poor Sibyl! What a romance it had all been! She had often mimicked death on the stage. Then Death himself had touched her, and taken her with him. How had she played that dreadful last scene? Had she cursed him, as she died? No; she had died for love of him, and love would always be a sacrament to him now. She had atoned for everything, by the sacrifice she had made of her life. He would not think any more of what she had made him go through, on that horrible night at the theatre. When he thought of her, it would be as a wonderful tragic figure sent on to the world's stage to show the supreme reality of Love. A wonderful tragic figure? Tears came to his eyes as he remembered her child-like look, and winsome fanciful ways, and shy tremulous grace. He brushed them away hastily, and looked again at the picture.

He felt that the time had really come for making his choice. Or had his choice already been made? Yes, life had decided that for him—life, and his own infinite curiosity about life. Eternal youth, infinite passion, pleasures subtle and secret, wild joys and wilder sins—he was to have all these things. The portrait was to bear the burden of his shame: that was all.

A feeling of pain crept over him, as he thought of the desecration that was in store for the fair face on the canvas. Once, in boyish mockery of Narcissus, he had kissed, or feigned to kiss, those painted lips that now smiled so cruelly at him. Morning after morning he had sat before the portrait, wondering at its beauty, almost enamoured of it, as it seemed to him at times. Was it to alter now with every mood to which he yielded? Was it to become a monstrous and loathsome thing, to be hidden away in a locked room, to be shut out from the sunlight that had so often touched to brighter gold the waving wonder of its hair? The pity of it! The pity of it!

For a moment he thought of praying that the horrible sympathy that existed between him and the picture might cease. It had changed in answer to a prayer; perhaps in answer to a prayer it might remain unchanged. And yet, who, that knew anything about Life, would surrender the chance of remaining always young, however fantastic that chance might be, or with what fateful consequences it might be fraught? Besides, was it really under his control? Had it indeed been prayer that had produced the substitution? Might there not be some curious scientific reason for it all? If thought could exercise its influence upon a living organism, might not thought exercise an influence upon dead and inorganic things? Nay, without thought or conscious desire, might not things external to ourselves vibrate in unison with our moods and passions, atom calling to atom in secret love of strange affinity? But the reason was of no importance. He would never again tempt by a prayer any terrible power. If the picture was to alter, it was to alter. That was all. Why inquire too closely into it?

For there would be a real pleasure in watching it. He would be able to follow his mind into its secret places. This portrait would be to him the most magical of mirrors. As it had revealed to him his own body, so it would reveal to him his own soul. And when winter came upon it, he would still be standing where spring trembles on the verge of summer. When the blood crept from its face, and left behind a pallid mask of chalk with leaden eyes, he would keep the glamour of boyhood. Not one blossom of his loveliness would ever fade. Not one pulse of his life would ever weaken. Like the gods of the Greeks, he would be strong, and fleet, and joyous. What did it matter what happened to the coloured image on the canvas? He would be safe. That was everything.

He drew the screen back into its former place in front of the picture, smiling as he did so, and passed into his bedroom, where his valet was already waiting for him. An hour later he was at the Opera, and Lord Henry was leaning over his chair.

PHRASES AND PHILOSOPHIES FOR THE USE OF THE YOUNG

A lighthearted Oscar Wilde published this group of aphorisms in the December 1894 issue of Chameleon, *a few months before the start of the legal troubles that would eventually ruin his life.*

THE FIRST DUTY IN LIFE IS to be as artificial as possible. What the second duty is no one has as yet discovered.

Wickedness is a myth invented by good people to account for the curious attractiveness of others.

If the poor only had profiles there would be no difficulty in solving the problem of poverty.

Those who see any difference between soul and body have neither.

A really well-made buttonhole is the only link between Art and Nature.

Religions die when they are proved to be true. Science is the record of dead religions.

The well-bred contradict other people. The wise contradict themselves.

Nothing that actually occurs is of the smallest importance.

Dullness is the coming of age of seriousness.

In all unimportant matters, style, not sincerity, is the essential. In all important matters, style, not sincerity, is the essential.

If one tells the truth, one is sure, sooner or later, to be found out.

Pleasure is the only thing one should live for. Nothing ages like happiness.

It is only by not paying one's bills that one can hope to live in the memory of the commercial classes.

No crime is vulgar, but all vulgarity is crime. Vulgarity is the conduct of others.

Only the shallow know themselves.

Time is waste of money.

One should always be a little improbable.

PHRASES AND PHILOSOPHIES FOR THE USE OF THE YOUNG

There is a fatality about all good resolutions. They are invariably made too soon.

The only way to atone for being occasionally a little over-dressed is by being always absolutely over-educated.

To be premature is to be perfect.

Any preoccupation with ideas of what is right or wrong in conduct shows an arrested intellectual development.

Ambition is the last refuge of the failure.

A truth ceases to be true when more than one person believes in it.

In examinations the foolish ask questions that the wise cannot answer.

Greek dress was in its essence inartistic. Nothing should reveal the body but the body.

One should either be a work of art, or wear a work of art.

It is only the superficial qualities that last. Man's deeper nature is soon found out.

Industry is the root of all ugliness.

The ages live in history through their anachronisms.

It is only the gods who taste of death. Apollo has passed away, but Hyacinth, whom men say he slew, lives on. Nero and Narcissus are always with us.

The old believe everything: the middle-aged suspect everything: the young know everything.

The condition of perfection is idleness: the aim of perfection is youth.

Only the great masters of style ever succeed in being obscure.

There is something tragic about the enormous number of young men there are in England at the present moment who start life with perfect profiles, and end by adopting some useful profession.

To love oneself is the beginning of a life-long romance.

OSCAR WILDE

THE BALLAD OF READING GAOL

After his release from prison in 1897, Oscar Wilde resisted requests to write about the experience but he did compose this very long poem, The Ballad of Reading Gaol. *Here he expresses the outrage he felt at the hanging of a prison mate, Charles Thomas Wooldridge, who had murdered his wife. (The poem's overlength was a conscious choice and symbolically important, Wilde said, to stress the problems of the English penal system.)* The Ballad of Reading Gaol *sold phenomenally well (for poetry) when published in book form in 1898; four of its lines appear on Wilde's monument at the Père Lachaise cemetery in Paris: "And alien tears will fill for him / Pity's long-broken urn, / For his mourners will be outcast men, / And outcasts always mourn."*

1.

He did not wear his scarlet coat,
　　For blood and wine are red,
And blood and wine were on his hands,
　　When they found him with the dead,
The poor dead woman whom he loved,
　　And murdered in her bed.

He walked amongst the Trial Men
　　In a suit of shabby grey;
A cricket cap was on his head,
　　And his step seemed light and gay;
But I never saw a man who looked
　　So wistfully at the day.

I never saw a man who looked
　　With such a wistful eye

Upon that little tent of blue
    Which prisoners call the sky,
And at every drifting cloud that went
    With sails of silver by.

I walked, with other souls in pain,
    Within another ring,
And was wondering if the man had done
    A great or little thing,
When a voice behind me whispered low,
    "That fellow's got to swing."

Dear Christ! the very prison walls
    Suddenly seemed to reel,
And the sky above my head became
    Like a casque of scorching steel;
And, though I was a soul in pain,
    My pain I could not feel.

I only knew what hunted thought
    Quickened his step, and why
He looked upon the garish day
    With such a wistful eye;
The man who killed the thing he loved,
    And so he had to die.

↓

Yet each man kills the thing he loves,
    By each let this be heard,
Some do it with a bitter look,
    Some with a flattering word.
The coward does it with a kiss,
    The brave man with a sword!

Some kill their love when they are young,
    And some when they are old;
Some strangle with the hands of Lust,
    Some with the hands of Gold:
The kindest use a knife, because
    The dead so soon grow cold.

Some love too little, some too long,
    Some sell, and others buy;
Some do the deed with many tears,
    And some without a sigh:

For each man kills the thing he loves,
   Yet each man does not die.

He does not die a death of shame
   On a day of dark disgrace,
Nor have a noose about his neck,
   Nor a cloth upon his face,
Nor drop feet foremost through the floor
   Into an empty space.

He does not sit with silent men
   Who watch him night and day;
Who watch him when he tries to weep,
   And when he tries to pray;
Who watch him lest himself should rob
   The prison of its prey.

He does not wake at dawn to see
   Dread figures throng his room,
The shivering Chaplain robed in white,
   The Sheriff stern with gloom,
And the Governor all in shiny black,
   With the yellow face of Doom.

He does not rise in piteous haste
   To put on convict-clothes,
While some coarse-mouthed Doctor gloats, and notes
   Each new and nerve-twitched pose,
Fingering a watch whose little ticks
   Are like horrible hammer-blows.

He does not feel that sickening thirst
   That sands one's throat, before
The hangman with his gardener's gloves
   Comes through the padded door,
And binds one with three leathern thongs,
   That the throat may thirst no more.

He does not bend his head to hear
   The Burial Office read,
Nor, while the anguish of his soul
   Tells him he is not dead,
Cross his own coffin, as he moves
   Into the hideous shed.

He does not stare upon the air
    Through a little roof of glass:
He does not pray with lips of clay
    For his agony to pass;
Nor feel upon his shuddering cheek
    The kiss of Caiaphas.

2.

Six weeks the guardsman walked the yard,
    In the suit of shabby grey:
His cricket cap was on his head,
    And his step seemed light and gay,
But I never saw a man who looked
    So wistfully at the day.

I never saw a man who looked
    With such a wistful eye
Upon that little tent of blue
    Which prisoners call the sky,
And at every wandering cloud that trailed
    Its ravelled fleeces by.

He did not wring his hands, as do
    Those witless men who dare
To try to rear the changeling Hope
    In the cave of black Despair:
He only looked upon the sun,
    And drank the morning air.

He did not wring his hands nor weep,
    Nor did he peek or pine,
But he drank the air as though it held
    Some healthful anodyne;
With open mouth he drank the sun
    As though it had been wine!

And I and all the souls in pain,
    Who tramped the other ring,
Forgot if we ourselves had done
    A great or little thing,
And watched with gaze of dull amaze
    The man who had to swing.

For strange it was to see him pass
    With a step so light and gay,

And strange it was to see him look
　　So wistfully at the day,
And strange it was to think that he
　　Had such a debt to pay.

✢

For oak and elm have pleasant leaves
　　That in the spring-time shoot;
But grim to see is the gallows-tree
　　With its adder-bitten root,
And, green or dry, a man must die
　　Before it bears its fruit!

The loftiest place is that seat of grace
　　For which all worldlings try:
But who would stand in hempen band
　　Upon a scaffold high,
And through a murderer's collar take
　　His last look at the sky?

It is sweet to dance to violins
　　When Love and Life are fair:
To dance to flutes, to dance to lutes
　　Is delicate and rare:
But it is not sweet with nimble feet
　　To dance upon the air!

So with curious eyes and sick surmise
　　We watched him day by day,
And wondered if each one of us
　　Would end the self-same way,
For none can tell to what red Hell
　　His sightless soul may stray.

At last the dead man walked no more
　　Amongst the Trial Men,
And I knew that he was standing up
　　In the black dock's dreadful pen,
And that never would I see his face
　　For weal or woe again.

Like two doomed ships that pass in storm
　　We had crossed each other's way:
But we made no sign, we said no word,
　　We had no word to say;

For we did not meet in the holy night,
    But in the shameful day.

A prison wall was round us both,
    Two outcast men we were:
The world had thrust us from its heart,
    And God from out His care:
And the iron gin that waits for Sin
    Had caught us in its snare.

3.

In Debtor's Yard the stones are hard,
    And the dripping wall is high,
So it was there he took the air
    Beneath the leaden sky,
And by each side a Warder walked,
    For fear the man might die.

Or else he sat with those who watched
    His anguish night and day;
Who watched him when he rose to weep,
    And when he crouched to pray;
Who watched him lest himself should rob
    Their scaffold of its prey.

The Governor was strong upon
    The Regulations Act:
The Doctor said that Death was but
    A scientific fact:
And twice a day the Chaplain called,
    And left a little tract.

And twice a day he smoked his pipe,
    And drank his quart of beer:
His soul was resolute, and held
    No hiding-place for fear;
He often said that he was glad
    The hangman's day was near.

But why he said so strange a thing
    No warder dared to ask:
For he to whom a watcher's doom
    Is given as his task,
Must set a lock upon his lips
    And make his face a mask.

Or else he might be moved, and try
    To comfort or console:
And what should Human Pity do
    Pent up in Murderer's Hole?
What word of grace in such a place
    Could help a brother's soul?

With slouch and swing around the ring
    We trod the Fools' Parade!
We did not care: we knew we were
    The Devil's Own Brigade:
And shaven head and feet of lead
    Make a merry masquerade.

We tore the tarry rope to shreds
    With blunt and bleeding nails,
We rubbed the doors, and scrubbed the floors,
    And cleaned the shining rails:
And, rank by rank, we soaped the plank,
    And clattered with the pails.

We sewed the sacks, we broke the stones,
    We turned the dusty drill:
We banged the tins, and bawled the hymns,
    And sweated on the mill:
But in the heart of every man
    Terror was lying still.

So still it lay that every day
    Crawled like a weed-clogged wave:
And we forgot the bitter lot
    That waits for fool and knave,
Till once, as we tramped in from work,
    We passed an open grave.

With yawning mouth the yellow hole
    Gaped for a living thing;
The very mud cried out for blood
    To the thirsty asphalte ring:
And we knew that ere one dawn grew fair
    Some prisoner had to swing.

Right in we went, with soul intent
    On Death and Dread and Doom:
The hangman, with his little bag,
    Went shuffling through the gloom:

And I trembled as I groped my way
    Into my numbered tomb.

↓

That night the empty corridors
    Were full of forms of Fear,
And up and down the iron town
    Stole feet we could not hear,
And through the bars that hide the stars
    White faces seemed to peer.

He lay as one who lies and dreams
    In a pleasant meadow-land,
The watchers watched him as he slept,
    And could not understand
How one could sleep so sweet a sleep
    With a hangman close at hand.

But there is no sleep when men must weep
    Who never yet have wept:
So we—the fool, the fraud, the knave—
    That endless vigil kept,
And through each brain on hands of pain
    Another's terror crept.

Alas! it is a fearful thing
    To feel another's guilt!
For, right, within, the Sword of Sin
    Pierced to its poisoned hilt,
And as molten lead were the tears we shed
    For the blood we had not spilt.

The warders with their shoes of felt
    Crept by each padlocked door,
And peeped and saw, with eyes of awe,
    Grey figures on the floor,
And wondered why men knelt to pray
    Who never prayed before.

All through the night we knelt and prayed,
    Mad mourners of a corse!
The troubled plumes of midnight shook
    The plumes upon a hearse:
And bitter wine upon a sponge
    Was the savour of Remorse.

✧

The grey cock crew, the red cock crew,
 But never came the day:
And crooked shapes of Terror crouched,
 In the corners where we lay:
And each evil sprite that walks by night
 Before us seemed to play.

They glided past, they glided fast,
 Like travellers through a mist:
They mocked the moon in a rigadoon
 Of delicate turn and twist,
And with formal pace and loathsome grace
 The phantoms kept their tryst.

With mop and mow, we saw them go,
 Slim shadows hand in hand:
About, about, in ghostly rout
 They trod a saraband:
And the damned grotesques made arabesques,
 Like the wind upon the sand!

With the pirouettes of marionettes,
 They tripped on pointed tread:
But with flutes of Fear they filled the ear,
 As their grisly masque they led,
And loud they sang, and long they sang,
 For they sang to wake the dead.

"Oho!" they cried, "The world is wide,
 But fettered limbs go lame!
And once, or twice, to throw the dice
 Is a gentlemanly game,
But he does not win who plays with Sin
 In the secret House of Shame."

No things of air these antics were,
 That frolicked with such glee:
To men whose lives were held in gyves,
 And whose feet might not go free,
Ah! wounds of Christ! they were living things
 Most terrible to see.

Around, around, they waltzed and wound;
    Some wheeled in smirking pairs;
With the mincing step of a demirep
    Some sidled up the stairs:
And with subtle sneer, and fawning leer,
    Each helped us at our prayers.

The morning wind began to moan,
    But still the night went on:
Through its giant loom the web of gloom
    Crept till each thread was spun:
And, as we prayed, we grew afraid
    Of the Justice of the Sun.

The moaning wind went wandering round
    The weeping prison-wall:
Till like a wheel of turning steel
    We felt the minutes crawl:
O moaning wind! what had we done
    To have such a seneschal?

At last I saw the shadowed bars,
    Like a lattice wrought in lead,
Move right across the whitewashed wall
    That faced my three-plank bed,
And I knew that somewhere in the world
    God's dreadful dawn was red.

At six o'clock we cleaned our cells,
    At seven all was still,
But the sough and swing of a mighty wing
    The prison seemed to fill,
For the Lord of Death with icy breath
    Had entered in to kill.

He did not pass in purple pomp,
    Nor ride a moon-white steed.
Three yards of cord and a sliding board
    Are all the gallows' need:
So with rope of shame the Herald came
    To do the secret deed.

We were as men who through a fen
    Of filthy darkness grope:
We did not dare to breathe a prayer,
    Or to give our anguish scope:

Something was dead in each of us,
　　And what was dead was Hope.

For Man's grim Justice goes its way,
　　And will not swerve aside:
It slays the weak, it slays the strong,
　　It has a deadly stride:
With iron heel it slays the strong,
　　The monstrous parricide!

We waited for the stroke of eight:
　　Each tongue was thick with thirst:
For the stroke of eight is the stroke of Fate
　　That makes a man accursed,
And Fate will use a running noose
　　For the best man and the worst.

We had no other thing to do,
　　Save to wait for the sign to come:
So, like things of stone in a valley lone,
　　Quiet we sat and dumb:
But each man's heart beat thick and quick,
　　Like a madman on a drum!

With sudden shock the prison-clock
　　Smote on the shivering air,
And from all the gaol rose up a wail
　　Of impotent despair,
Like the sound that frightened marches hear
　　From some leper in his lair.

And as one sees most fearful things
　　In the crystal of a dream,
We saw the greasy hempen rope
　　Hooked to the blackened beam,
And heard the prayer the hangman's snare
　　Strangled into a scream.

And all the woe that moved him so
　　That he gave that bitter cry,
And the wild regrets, and the bloody sweats,
　　None knew so well as I:
For he who lives more lives than one
　　More deaths than one must die.

4.

There is no chapel on the day
    On which they hang a man:
The Chaplain's heart is far too sick,
    Or his face is far too wan,
Or there is that written in his eyes
    Which none should look upon.

So they kept us close till nigh on noon,
    And then they rang the bell,
And the warders with their jingling keys
    Opened each listening cell,
And down the iron stair we tramped,
    Each from his separate Hell.

Out into God's sweet air we went,
    But not in wonted way,
For this man's face was white with fear,
    And that man's face was grey,
And I never saw sad men who looked
    So wistfully at the day.

I never saw sad men who looked
    With such a wistful eye
Upon that little tent of blue
    We prisoners called the sky,
And at every happy cloud that passed
    In such strange freedom by.

But there were those amongst us all
    Who walked with downcast head,
And knew that, had each got his due,
    They should have died instead:
He had but killed a thing that lived,
    Whilst they had killed the dead.

For he who sins a second time
    Wakes a dead soul to pain,
And draws it from its spotted shroud,
    And makes it bleed again,
And makes it bleed great gouts of blood,
    And makes it bleed in vain!

↓

Like ape or clown, in monstrous garb
    With crooked arrows starred,
Silently we went round and round
    The slippery asphalte yard;
Silently we went round and round,
    And no man spoke a word.

Silently we went round and round,
    And through each hollow mind
The Memory of dreadful things
    Rushed like a dreadful wind,
And Horror stalked before each man,
    And Terror crept behind.

✤

The warders strutted up and down,
    And watched their herd of brutes,
Their uniforms were spick and span,
    And they wore their Sunday suits,
But we knew the work they had been at,
    By the quicklime on their boots.

For where a grave had opened wide,
    There was no grave at all:
Only a stretch of mud and sand
    By the hideous prison-wall,
And a little heap of burning lime,
    That the man should have his pall.

For he has a pall, this wretched man,
    Such as few men can claim:
Deep down below a prison-yard,
    Naked for greater shame,
He lies, with fetters on each foot,
    Wrapt in a sheet of flame!

And all the while the burning lime
    Eats flesh and bone away,
It eats the brittle bone by night,
    And the soft flesh by day,
It eats the flesh and bone by turns,
    But it eats the heart alway.

✤

For three long years they will not sow
    Or root or seedling there:
For three long years the unblessed spot
    Will sterile be and bare,
And look upon the wondering sky
    With unreproachful stare.

They think a murderer's heart would taint
    Each simple seed they sow.
It is not true! God's kindly earth
    Is kindlier than men know,
And the red rose would but blow more red,
    The white rose whiter blow.

Out of his mouth a red, red rose!
    Out of his heart a white!
For who can say by what strange way,
    Christ brings His will to light,
Since the barren staff the pilgrim bore
    Bloomed in the great Pope's sight?

But neither milk-white rose nor red
    May bloom in prison-air;
The shard, the pebble, and the flint,
    Are what they give us there:
For flowers have been known to heal
    A common man's despair.

So never will wine-red rose or white,
    Petal by petal, fall
On that stretch of mud and sand that lies
    By the hideous prison-wall,
To tell the men who tramp the yard
    That God's Son died for all.

Yet though the hideous prison-wall
    Still hems him round and round,
And a spirit may not walk by night
    That is with fetters bound,
And a spirit may but weep that lies
    In such unholy ground,

He is at peace—this wretched man—
    At peace, or will be soon:
There is no thing to make him mad,
    Nor does Terror walk at noon,

For the lampless Earth in which he lies
    Has neither Sun nor Moon.

They hanged him as a beast is hanged!
    They did not even toll
A requiem that might have brought
    Rest to his startled soul,
But hurriedly they took him out,
    And hid him in a hole.

The warders stripped him of his clothes,
    And gave him to the flies:
They mocked the swollen purple throat,
    And the stark and staring eyes:
And with laughter loud they heaped the shroud
    In which the convict lies.

The Chaplain would not kneel to pray
    By his dishonoured grave:
Nor mark it with that blessed Cross
    That Christ for sinners gave,
Because the man was one of those
    Whom Christ came down to save.

Yet all is well; he has but passed
    To Life's appointed bourne:
And alien tears will fill for him
    Pity's long-broken urn
For his mourners will be outcast men,
    And outcasts always mourn

5.

I know not whether Laws be right,
    Or whether Laws be wrong;
All that we know who lie in gaol
    Is that the wall is strong;
And that each day is like a year,
    A year whose days are long.

But this I know, that every Law
    That men hath made for Man,
Since first Man took his brother's life,
    And the sad world began,
But straws the wheat and saves the chaff
    With a most evil fan.

This too I know—and wise it were
    If each could know the same—
That every prison that men build
    Is built with bricks of shame,
And bound with bars lest Christ should see
    How men their brothers maim.

With bars they blur the gracious moon,
    And blind the goodly sun;
And they do well to hide their Hell,
    For in it things are done
That Son of God nor son of Man
    Ever should look upon!

↓

The vilest deeds like poison weeds,
    Bloom well in prison-air;
It is only what is good in Man
    That wastes and withers there:
Pale Anguish keeps the heavy gate,
    And the Warder is Despair.

For they starve the little frightened child
    Till it weeps both night and day:
And they scourge the weak, and flog the fool,
    And gibe the old and grey,
And some grow mad, and all grow bad,
    And none a word may say.

Each narrow cell in which we dwell
    Is a foul and dark latrine,
And the fetid breath of living Death
    Chokes up each grated screen,
And all, but Lust, is turned to dust
    In Humanity's machine.

The brackish water that we drink
    Creeps with a loathsome slime,
And the bitter bread they weigh in scales
    Is full of chalk and lime,
And Sleep will not lie down, but walks
    Wild-eyed, and cries to Time.

↓

But though lean Hunger and green Thirst
   Like asp with adder fight,
We have little care of prison fare,
   For what chills and kills outright
Is that every stone one lifts by day
   Becomes one's heart by night.

With midnight always in one's heart,
   And twilight in one's cell,
We turn the crank, or tear the rope,
   Each in his separate Hell,
And the silence is more awful far
   Than the sound of a brazen bell.

And never a human voice comes near
   To speak a gentle word:
And the eye that watches through the door
   Is pitiless and hard:
And by all forgot, we rot and rot,
   With soul and body marred.

And thus we rust Life's iron chain
   Degraded and alone:
And some men curse, and some men weep,
   And some men make no moan:
But God's eternal Laws are kind
   And break the heart of stone.

And every human heart that breaks,
   In prison-cell or yard,
Is as that broken box that gave
   Its treasure to the Lord,
And filled the unclean leper's house
   With the scent of costliest nard.

Ah! happy they whose hearts can break
   And peace of pardon win!
How else may man make straight his plan
   And cleanse his soul from Sin?
How else but through a broken heart
   May Lord Christ enter in?

↓

And he of the swollen purple throat,
    And the stark and staring eyes,
Waits for the holy hands that took
    The Thief to Paradise;
And a broken and a contrite heart
    The Lord will not despise.

The man in red who reads the Law
    Gave him three weeks of life,
Three little weeks in which to heal
    His soul of his soul's strife,
And cleanse from every blot of blood
    The hand that held the knife.

And with tears of blood he cleansed the hand,
    The hand that held the steel:
For only blood can wipe out blood,
    And only tears can heal:
And the crimson stain that was of Cain
    Became Christ's snow-white seal.

6.

In Reading gaol by Reading town
    There is a pit of shame,
And in it lies a wretched man
    Eaten by teeth of flame,
In a burning winding-sheet he lies,
    And his grave has got no name.

And there, till Christ call forth the dead,
    In silence let him lie:
No need to waste the foolish tear,
    Or heave the windy sigh:
The man had killed the thing he loved,
    And so he had to die.

And all men kill the thing they love,
    By all let this be heard,
Some do it with a bitter look,
    Some with a flattering word,
The coward does it with a kiss,
    The brave man with a sword!

SOME EXPERIENCES OF AN IRISH R.M.

OH LOVE! OH FIRE!

Some Experiences of an Irish R.M. *(1899) features the adventures of a fish out of water, Major Sinclair Yeates, sent from England to act as resident magistrate in a small Irish country town called Skebawn, filled with eccentricities of every sort. In this chapter Yeates attends a tenants' dance at Aussolas, a large estate owned by the grandmother of his land-lord and friend, Flurry Knox. The momentous party ends in flames, as the puzzled Yeates watches the unfolding of a forbidden romantic rela-tionship between Flurry and his cousin Sally.*

IT WAS ON ONE OF THE HOTTEST days of a hot August that I walked over to Tory Lodge to inform Mr. Flurry Knox, M.F.H., that the limits of human endurance had been reached, and that either Venus and her family, or I and mine, must quit Shreelane. In a moment of impulse I had accepted her and her numerous progeny as guests in my stable-yard, since when Mrs. Cadogan had given warning once or twice a week, and Maria, lawful autocrat of the ashpit, had had—I quote the kitchen-maid—"tin battles for every male she'd ate."

The walk over the hills was not of a nature to lower the temperature, moral or otherwise. The grassy path was as slippery as glass, the rocks radiated heat, the bracken radiated horseflies. There was no need to nurse my wrath to keep it warm.

I found Flurry seated in the kennel-yard in a long and unclean white linen coat, engaged in clipping hieroglyphics on the ears of a young outgoing draft, an occupation in itself unfavourable to argument. The young draft had already monopolised all possible forms of remonstrance, from snarling in the obscurity behind the meal sack in the boiler-house, to hysterical yelling as they were dragged forth by the tail; but through these alarms and excursions I denounced Venus and all her works, from slaughtered Wyandottes to broken dishes. Even as I did so I was conscious of something chastened in Mr. Knox's demeanour, some touch of remoteness and melancholy with which I was quite unfamiliar; my indictment weakened and my grievances became trivial when laid before this grave and almost religiously gentle young man.

"I'm sorry you and Mrs. Yeates should be vexed by her. Send her back when you like. I'll keep her. Maybe it'll not be for so long after all."

When pressed to expound this dark saying, Flurry smiled wanly and snipped a second line in the hair of the puppy that was pinned between his legs. I was almost relieved when a hard try to bite on the part of the puppy imparted to Flurry's language a transient warmth; but the reaction was only temporary.

"It'd be as good for me to make a present of this lot to old Welby as to take the price he's offering me," he went on, as he got up and took off his highly scented kennel-coat; "but I couldn't be bothered fighting him. Come on in and have something. I drink tea myself at this hour."

If he had said toast-and-water it would have seemed no more than was suitable to such a frame of mind. As I followed him to the house I thought that when the day came that Flurry Knox could not be bothered with fighting old Welby things were becoming serious, but I kept this opinion to myself and merely offered an admiring comment on the roses that were blooming in the front of the house.

"I put up every stick of that trellis myself with my own hands," said Flurry, still gloomily; "the roses were trailing all over the place for the want of it. Would you like to have a look at the garden while they're getting tea? I settled it up a bit since you saw it last."

I acceded to this almost alarmingly ladylike suggestion, marvelling greatly.

Flurry certainly was a changed man, and his garden was a changed garden. It was a very old garden, with unexpected arbours madly overgrown with flowering climbers, and a flight of grey steps leading to a terrace, where a moss-grown sundial and ancient herbaceous plants strove with nettles and briars; but I chiefly remembered it as a place where washing was wont to hang on black-currant bushes, and the kennel terrier matured his bones and hunted chickens. There was now rabbit-wire on the gate, the walks were cleaned, the beds weeded. There was even a bed of mignonette, a row of sweet-pea, and a blazing party of sunflowers, and Michael, once second in command in many a filibustering expedition, was now on his knees, ingloriously tying carnations to little pieces of cane.

We walked up the steps to the terrace. Down below us the rich and southern blue of the sea filled the gaps between scattered fir-trees; the hillside above was purple with heather; a bay mare and her foal were moving lazily through the bracken, with the sun glistening on it and them. I looked back at the house, nestling in the hollow of the hill, I smelled the smell of the mignonette in the air, I regarded Michael's labouring back among the carnations, and without any connection of ideas I seemed to see Miss Sally Knox, with her golden-red hair and slight figure, standing on the terrace beside her kinsman.

"Michael! Do ye know where's Misther Flurry?" squalled a voice from the garden gate, the untrammelled voice of the female domestic at large among her fellows. "The tay's wet, and there's a man over with a message from Aussolas. He was tellin' me the owld hairo beyant is givin' out invitations——"

A stricken silence fell, induced, no doubt, by hasty danger signals from Michael.

"Who's 'the old hero beyant'?" I asked, as we turned towards the house.

"My grandmother," said Flurry, permitting himself a smile that had about as much sociability in it as skim milk; "she's giving a tenants' dance at Aussolas. She gave one about five years ago, and I declare you might as well get the influenza into the country, or a mission at the chapel. There won't be a servant in the place will be able to answer their name for a week after it, what with toothache and headache, and blathering in the kitchen!"

We had tea in the drawing-room, a solemnity which I could not but be aware was due to the presence of a new carpet, a new wall-paper, and a new piano. Flurry made no comment on these things, but something told me that I was expected to do so, and I did.

"I'd sell you the lot to-morrow for half what I gave for them," said my host, eyeing them with morose respect as he poured out this third cup of tea.

I have all my life been handicapped by not having the courage of my curiosity. Those who have the nerve to ask direct questions on matters that do not concern them seldom fail to extract direct answers, but in my lack of this enviable gift I went home in the dark as to what had befallen my landlord, and fully aware of how my wife would despise me for my shortcomings. Philippa always says that she never asks questions, but she seems none the less to get a lot of answers.

On my own avenue I met Miss Sally Knox riding away from the house on her white cob; she had found no one at home, and she would not turn back with me, but she did not seem to be in any hurry to ride away. I told her that I had just been over to see her relative, Mr. Knox, who had informed me that he meant to give up the hounds, a fact in which she seemed only conventionally interested. She looked pale, and her eyelids were slightly pink; I checked myself on the verge of asking her if she had hay-fever, and inquired instead if she had heard of the tenants' dance at Aussolas. She did not answer at first, but rubbed her cane up and down the cob's clipped toothbrush of a mane. Then she said:

"Major Yeates—look here—there's a most awful row at home!"

I expressed incoherent regret, and wished to my heart that Philippa had been there to cope with the situation.

"It began when Mamma found out about Flurry's racing Sultan, and then came our dance——"

Miss Sally stopped; I nodded, remembering certain episodes of Lady Knox's dance.

"And—Mamma says—she says——"

I waited respectfully to hear what Mamma had said; the cob fidgeted under the attention of the horseflies, and nearly trod on my toe.

"Well, the end of it is," she said with a gulp, "she said such things to Flurry that he can't come near the house again, and I'm to go over to England to Aunt Dora next week. Will you tell Philippa I came to say good-bye to her? I don't think I can get over here again."

Miss Sally was a sufficiently old friend of mine for me to take her hand and press it in a fatherly manner, but for the life of me I could not think of anything to say, unless I expressed my sympathy with her mother's point of view about detrimentals, which was obviously not the thing to do.

Philippa accorded to my news the rare tribute of speechless attention, and then was despicable enough to say that she had foreseen the whole affair from the beginning.

"From the day that she refused him in the ice-house, I suppose," said I sarcastically.

"That *was* the beginning," replied Philippa.

"Well," I went on judicially, "whenever it began, it was high time for it to end. She can do a good deal better than Flurry."

Philippa became rather red in the face.

"I call that a thoroughly commonplace thing to say," she said. "I daresay he has not many ideas beyond horses, but no more has she, and he really does come and borrow books from me——"

"*Whitaker's Almanack,*" I murmured.

"Well, I don't care, I like him very much, and I know what you're going to say, and you're wrong, and I'll tell you why——"

Here Mrs. Cadogan came into the room, her cap at rather more than its usual warlike angle over her scarlet forehead, and in her hand a kitchen plate, on which a note was ceremoniously laid forth.

"But this is for you, Mrs. Cadogan," said Philippa, as she looked at it.

"Ma'am," returned Mrs. Cadogan with immense dignity, "I have no learning, and from what the young man's afther telling me that brought it from Aussolas, I'd sooner yerself read it for me than thim gerrls."

My wife opened the envelope, and drew forth a gilt-edged sheet of pink paper.

"Miss Margaret Nolan presents her compliments to Mrs. Cadogan," she read, "and I have the pleasure of telling you that the servants of Aussolas is inviting you and Mr. Peter Cadogan, Miss Mulrooney, and Miss Gallagher"—Philippa's voice quavered perilously—"to a dance on next Wednesday. Dancing to begin at seven o'clock, and to go on till five.—Yours affectionately, Maggie Nolan."

"How affectionate she is!" snorted Mrs. Cadogan; "them's Dublin manners, I daresay!"

"P.S.," continued Philippa; "steward, Mr. Denis O'Loughlin; stewardess, Mrs. Mahony."

"Thoughtful provision," I remarked; "I suppose Mrs. Mahony's duties will begin after supper."

"Well, Mrs. Cadogan," said Philippa, quelling me with a glance, "I suppose you'd all like to go?"

"As for dancin'," said Mrs. Cadogan, with her eyes fixed on a level with the curtain-pole, "I thank God I'm a widow, and the only dancin' I'll do is to dance to my grave."

"Well, perhaps Julia, and Annie, and Peter——" suggested Philippa, considerably overawed.

"I'm not one of them that holds with loud mockery and harangues," continued Mrs. Cadogan, "but if I had any wish for dhrawing down talk I could tell you, ma'am, that the like o' them has their share of dances without going to Aussolas! Wasn't it only last Sunday week I wint follyin' the turkey that's layin' out in the plantation, and the whole o' thim hysted their sails and back with them to their lovers at the gatehouse, and the kitchen-maid having a Jew-harp to be playing for them!"

"That was very wrong," said the truckling Philippa. "I hope you spoke to the kitchen-maid about it."

"Is it spake to thim?" rejoined Mrs. Cadogan. "No, but what I done was to dhrag the kitchen-maid round the passages by the hair o' the head!"

"Well, after that, I think you might let her go to Aussolas," said I venturously.

The end of it was that every one in and about the house went to Aussolas on the following Wednesday, including Mrs. Cadogan. Philippa had gone over to stay at the Shutes', ostensibly to arrange about a jumble sale, the real object being (as a matter of history) to inspect the Scotch young lady before whom Bernard Shute had dumped his affections in his customary manner. Being alone, with every prospect of a bad dinner, I accepted with gratitude an invitation to dine and sleep at Aussolas and see the dance; it is only on very special occasions that I have the heart to remind Philippa that she had neither part nor lot in what occurred— it is too serious a matter for trivial gloryings.

Mrs. Knox had asked me to dine at six o'clock, which meant that I arrived, in blazing sunlight and evening clothes, punctually at that hour, and that at seven o'clock I was still sitting in the library, reading heavily bound classics, while my hostess held loud conversations down staircases with Denis O'Loughlin, the red-bearded Robinson Crusoe who combined in himself the offices of coachman, butler, and, to the best of my belief, valet to the lady of the house. The door opened at last, and Denis, looking as furtive as his prototype after he had sighted the footprint, put in his head and beckoned to me.

"The misthress says will ye go to dinner without her," he said very confidentially; "sure she's greatly vexed ye should be waitin' on her. 'Twas the kitchin chimney cot fire, and faith she's afther giving Biddy Mahony the sack, on the head of it! Though, indeed, 'tis little we'd regard a chimney on fire here any other day."

Mrs. Knox's woolly dog was the sole occupant of the dining-room when I entered it; he was sitting on his mistress's chair, with all the air of outrage peculiar to a small and self-important dog when routine has been interfered with. It was difficult to discover what had caused the delay, the meal, not excepting the soup, being a cold collation; it was heavily flavoured with soot, and was hurled on to the table by Crusoe in spasmodic bursts, contemporaneous, no doubt, with Biddy Mahony's fits of hysterics in the kitchen. Its most memorable feature was a noble lake trout, which appeared in two jagged pieces, a matter lightly alluded to by Denis as the result of "a little argument" between himself and Biddy as to the dish on which it was to be served. Further conversation elicited the interesting fact that the combatants had pulled the trout in two before the matter was settled. A brief glance at my attendant's hands decided me to let the woolly dog justify his existence by consuming my portion for me, when Crusoe left the room.

Old Mrs. Knox remained invisible till the end of dinner, when she appeared in the purple velvet bonnet that she was reputed to have worn since the famine, and a dun-coloured woollen shawl fastened by a splendid diamond brooch, that flashed rainbow fire against the last shafts of sunset. There was a fire in the old lady's eye, too, the light that I had sometimes seen in Flurry's in moments of crisis.

"I have no apologies to offer that are worth hearing," she said, "but I have come to drink a glass of port wine with you, if you will so far honour me, and then we must go out and see the ball. My grandson is late, as usual."

She crumbled a biscuit with a brown and preoccupied hand; her claw-like fingers carried a crowded sparkle of diamonds upwards as she raised her glass to her lips.

The twilight was falling when we left the room and made our way downstairs. I followed the little figure in the purple bonnet through dark regions of passages and doorways, where strange lumber lay about; there was a rusty suit of armour, an upturned punt, mouldering pictures, and finally, by a door that opened into the yard, a lady's bicycle, white with the dust of travel. I suppose this latter to have been imported from Dublin by the fashionable Miss Maggie Nolan, but on the other hand it was well within the bounds of possibility that it belonged to old Mrs. Knox. The coach-house at Aussolas was on a par with the rest of the establishment, being vast, dilapidated, and of unknown age. Its three double doors were wide open, and the guests overflowed through them into the cobble-stoned yard; above their heads the tin reflectors of paraffin lamps glared at us from among the Christmas decorations of holly and ivy that festooned the walls. The voices of a fiddle and a concertina, combined, were uttering a polka with shrill and hideous fluency, to which the scraping and stamping of hobnailed boots made a ponderous bass accompaniment.

Mrs. Knox's donkey-chair had been placed in a commanding position at the top of the room, and she made her way slowly to it, shaking hands with all varieties of tenants and saying right things without showing any symptom of that flustered boredom that I have myself exhibited when I went round the men's messes on Christmas Day. She took her seat in the donkey-chair, with the white dog in her lap, and looked with her hawk's eyes round the array of faces that hemmed in the space where the dancers were solemnly bobbing and hopping.

"Will you tell me who that tomfool is, Denis?" she said, pointing to a young lady in a ball dress who was circling in conscious magnificence and somewhat painful incongruity in the arms of Mr. Peter Cadogan.

"That's the lady's-maid from Castle Knox, yer honour, ma'am," replied Denis, with something remarkably like a wink at Mrs. Knox.

"When did the Castle Knox servants come?" asked the old lady, very sharply.

"The same time yer honour left the table, and—— Pillilew! What's this?"

There was a clatter of galloping hoofs in the courtyard, as of a troop of cavalry, and out of the heart of it Flurry's voice shouting to Denis to drive out the colts and shut the gates before they had the people killed. I noticed that the colour had risen to Mrs. Knox's face, and I put it down to anxiety about her young horses. I may admit that when I heard Flurry's voice, and saw him collaring his grandmother's guests and pushing them out of the way as he came into the coach-house, I rather feared that he was in the condition so often defined to me at Petty Sessions as "not dhrunk, but having dhrink taken." His face was white, his eyes glittered, there was a general air of exaltation about him that suggested the solace of the pangs of love according to the most ancient convention.

"Hullo!" he said, swaggering up to the orchestra, "what's this humbugging thing they're playing? A polka, is it? Drop that, John Casey, and play a jig."

John Casey ceased abjectly.

"What'll I play, Masther Flurry?"

"What the devil do I care? Here, Yeates, put a name on it! You're a sort of musicianer yourself!"

I know the names of three or four Irish jigs; but on this occasion my memory clung exclusively to one, I suppose because it was the one I felt to be peculiarly inappropriate.

"Oh, well, *Haste to the Wedding*," I said, looking away.

Flurry gave a shout of laughter.

"That's it!" he exclaimed. "Play it up, John! Give us *Haste to the Wedding*. That's Major Yeates's fancy!"

Decidedly Flurry was drunk.

"What's wrong with you all that you aren't dancing?" he continued, striding up the middle of the room. "Maybe you don't know how. Here, I'll soon get one that'll show you!"

He advanced upon his grandmother, snatched her out of the donkey-chair, and, amid roars of applause, led her out, while the fiddle squealed its way through the inimitable twists of the tune, and the concertina surged and panted after it. Whatever Mrs. Knox may have thought of her grandson's behaviour, she was evidently going to make the best of it. She took her station opposite to him, in the purple bonnet, the dun-coloured shawl, and the diamonds; she picked up her skirt at each side, affording a view of narrow feet in elastic-sided cloth boots, and for three repeats of the tune she stood up to her grandson, and footed it on the coach-house floor. What the cloth boots did I could not exactly follow; they were, as well as I could see, extremely scientific, while there was hardly so much as a nod from the plumes of the bonnet. Flurry was also scientific, but his dancing did not alter my opinion that he was drunk; in fact, I thought he was making rather an exhibition of himself. They say that that jig was twenty pounds in Mrs. Knox's pocket at the next rent day; but though this statement is open to doubt, I believe that if she and Flurry had taken the hat round there and then she would have got in the best part of her arrears.

After this the company settled down to business. The dances lasted a sweltering half-hour, old women and young dancing with equal and tireless zest. At the end of each the gentlemen abandoned their partners without ceremony or comment, and went out to smoke, while the ladies retired to the laundry, where families of teapots stewed on the long bars of the fire, and Mrs. Mahony cut up mighty "barm-bracks," and the tea-drinking was illimitable.

At ten o'clock Mrs. Knox withdrew from the revel; she said that she was tired, but I have seldom seen any one look more wide awake. I thought that I might unobtrusively follow her example, but I was intercepted by Flurry.

"Yeates," he said seriously, "I'll take it as a kindness if you'll see this thing out with me. We must keep them pretty sober, and get them out of this by daylight. I—I have to get home early."

I at once took back my opinion that Flurry was drunk; I almost wished he had been, as I could then have deserted him without a pang. As it was, I addressed myself heavily to the night's enjoyment. Wan with heat, but conscientiously cheerful, I danced with Miss Maggie Nolan, with the Castle Knox lady's-maid, with my own kitchen-maid, who fell into wild giggles of terror whenever I spoke to her, with Mrs. Cadogan, who had apparently postponed the interesting feat of dancing to her grave, and did what she could to dance me into mine. I am bound to admit that though an ex-soldier and a major, and, therefore, equipped with a ready-made character for gallantry, Mrs. Cadogan was the only one of my partners with whom I conversed with any comfort.

At intervals I smoked cigarettes in the yard, seated on the old mounting-block by the gate, and overheard such conversation about the price of pigs in Skebawn; at intervals I plunged again into the coach-house, and led forth a perspiring wallflower into the scrimmage of a polka, or shuffled meaninglessly opposite to her in the long double line of dancers who were engaged with serious faces in executing a jig or a reel, I neither knew nor cared which. Flurry remained as undefeated as ever; I could only suppose it was his method of showing that his broken heart had mended.

"It's time to be making the punch, Masther Flurry," said Denis, as the harness-room clock struck twelve; "sure the night's warm, and the men's all gaping for it, the craytures!"

"What'll we make it in?" said Flurry, as we followed him into the laundry.

"The boiler, to be sure," said Crusoe, taking up a stone of sugar, and preparing to shoot it into the laundry copper.

"Stop, you fool, it's full of cockroaches!" shouted Flurry, amid sympathetic squalls from the throng of countrywomen. "Go get a bath!"

"Sure yerself knows there's but one bath in it," retorted Denis, "and that's within in the Major's room. Faith, the tinker got his own share yesterday with the same bath, sthriving to quinch the holes, and they as thick in it as the stars in the sky, and 'tis weeping still, afther all he done!"

"Well, then, here goes for the cockroaches!" said Flurry. "What doesn't sicken will fatten? Give me the kettle, and come on, you Kitty Collins, and be skimming them off!"

There were no complaints of the punch when the brew was completed, and the dance thundered on with a heavier stamping and a louder hilarity than before. The night wore on; I squeezed through the unyielding pack of frieze coats and shawls in the doorway, and with feet that momently swelled in my pumps I limped over the cobblestones to smoke my eighth cigarette on the mounting-block. It was a dark, hot night. The old castle loomed above me in piled-up roofs and gables, and high up in it somewhere a window sent a shaft of light into the sleeping leaves of a walnut-tree that overhung the gateway. At the bars of the gate two young horses peered in at the medley of noise and people; away in an outhouse a cock crew hoarsely. The gaiety in the coach-house increased momently, till, amid shrieks and bursts of laughter, Miss Maggie Nolan fled coquettishly from it with a long yell, like a train coming out of a tunnel, pursued by the fascinating Peter Cadogan brandishing a twig of mountain ash, in imitation of mistletoe. The young horses stampeded in horror, and immediately a voice proceeded from the lighted window above, Mrs. Knox's voice, demanding what the noise was, and announcing that if she heard any more of it she would have the place cleared.

An awful silence fell, to which the young horses' fleeing hoofs lent the final touch of consternation. Then I heard the irrespressible Maggie Nolan say: "Oh God! Merry-come-sad!" which I take to be a reflection on the mutability of all earthly happiness.

Mrs. Knox remained for a moment at the window, and it struck me as remarkable that at 2:30 A.M. she should still have on her bonnet. I thought I heard her speak to some one in the room, and there followed a laugh, a laugh that was not a servant's, and was puzzlingly familiar. I gave it up, and presently dropped into a cheerless doze.

With the dawn there came a period when even Flurry showed signs of failing. He came and sat down beside me with a yawn; it struck me that there was more impatience and nervousness than fatigue in the yawn.

"I think I'll turn them all out of this after the next dance is over," he said; "I've a lot to do, and I can't stay here."

I grunted in drowsy approval. It must have been a few minutes later that I felt Flurry grip my shoulder.

"Yeates!" he said, "look up at the roof. Do you see anything up there by the kitchen chimney?"

He was pointing at a heavy stack of chimneys in a tower that stood up against the grey and pink of the morning sky. At the angle where one of them joined the roof smoke was oozing busily out, and, as I stared, a little wisp of flame stole through.

The next thing that I distinctly remember is being in the van of a rush through the kitchen passages, every one shouting "Water! Water!" and not knowing where to find it, then up several flights of the narrowest and darkest stairs it has ever been my fate to ascend, with a bucket of water that I snatched from a woman, spilling as I ran. At the top of the stairs came a ladder leading to a trap-door, and up in the dark loft above was the roar and the wavering glare of flames.

"My God! That's sthrong fire!" shouted Denis, tumbling down the ladder with a brace of empty buckets; "we'll never save it! The lake won't quinch it!"

The flames were squirting out through the bricks of the chimney, through the timbers, through the slates; it was barely possible to get through the trap-door, and the booming and crackling strengthened every instant.

"A chain to the lake!" gasped Flurry, coughing in the stifling heat as he slashed the water at the blazing rafters; "the well's no good! Go on, Yeates!"

The organising of a double chain out of the mob that thronged and shouted and jammed in the passages and yard was no mean feat of generalship; but it got done somehow. Mrs. Cadogan and Biddy Mahony rose magnificently to the occasion, cursing, thumping, shoving; and stable buckets, coal buckets, milk pails, and kettles were unearthed and sent swinging down the grass slope to the lake that lay in glittering unconcern in the morning sunshine. Men, women, and children worked in a way that only Irish people can work on an emergency. All their cleverness, and their good-heartedness, and all their love of a ruction came to the front; the screaming and the exhortations were incessant, but so were also the buckets that flew from hand to hand up to the loft. I hardly know how long we were at it, but there came a time when I looked up from the yard and saw that the billows of reddened smoke from the top of the tower were dying down, and

I bethought me of old Mrs. Knox.

I found her at the door of her room, engaged in tying up a bundle of old clothes in a sheet; she looked as white as a corpse, but she was not in any way quelled by the situation.

"I'd be obliged to you all the same, Major Yeates, to throw this over the balusters," she said, as I advanced with the news that the fire had been got under. "'Pon my honour, I don't know when I've been as vexed as I've been this night, what with one thing and another! 'Tis a monstrous thing to use a guest as we've used you, but what could we do? I threw all the silver out of the dining-room window myself, and the poor peahen that had her nest there was hurt by an *entrée*-dish, and half her eggs were——"

There was a curious sound not unlike a titter in Mrs. Knox's room.

"However, we can't make omelettes without breaking eggs—as they say—" she went on rather hurriedly; "I declare I don't know what I'm saying! My old head is confused——"

Here Mrs. Knox went abruptly into her room and shut the door. Obviously there was nothing further to do for my hostess, and I fought my way up the dripping back staircase to the loft. The flames had ceased, the supply of buckets had been stopped, and Flurry, standing on a ponderous crossbeam, was poking his head and shoulders out into the sunlight through the hole that had been burned in the roof. Denis and others were pouring water over charred beams, the atmosphere was still stifling, everything was black, everything dripped with inky water. Flurry descended from his beam and stretched himself, looking like a drowned chimney-sweep.

"We've made a night of it, Yeates, haven't we?" he said, "but we've bested it anyhow. We were done for only for you!" There was more emotion about him than the occasion seemed to warrant, and his eyes had a Christy Minstrel brightness, not wholly to be attributed to the dirt on his face. "What's the time?—I must get home."

The time, incredible as it seemed, was half-past six. I could almost have sworn that Flurry changed colour when I said so.

"I must be off," he said; "I had no idea it was so late."

"Why, what's the hurry?" I asked.

He stared at me, laughed foolishly, and fell to giving directions to Denis. Five minutes afterwards he drove out of the yard and away at a canter down the long stretch of avenue that skirted the lake, with a troop of young horses flying on either hand. He whirled his whip round his head and shouted at them, and was lost to sight in a clump of trees. It is a vision of him that remains with me, and it always carried with it the bitter smell of wet charred wood.

Reaction had begun to set in among the volunteers. The chain took to sitting in the kitchen, cups of tea began mysteriously to circulate, and personal narratives of the fire were already foreshadowing the amazing legends that have since gathered round the night's adventure. I left to Denis the task of clearing the house, and went up to change my wet clothes, with a feeling that I had not been to bed for a year. The ghost of a waiter who had drowned himself in a bog-hole would have presented a cheerier aspect than I, as I surveyed myself in the prehistoric mirror in my room, with the sunshine falling on my unshorn face and begrimed shirt-front.

I made my toilet at considerate length, and, it being now nearly eight o'clock, went downstairs to look for something to eat. I had left the house humming with people; I found it silent as Pompeii. The sheeted bundles containing Mrs. Knox's wardrobe were lying about the hall; a couple of ancestors who in the first alarm had been dragged from the walls were leaning drunkenly against the bundles; last night's dessert was still on the dining-room table. I went out on to the hall-door steps, and saw the *entrée*-dishes in a glittering heap in a nasturtium bed, and realised that there was no breakfast for me this side of lunch at Shreelane.

There was a sound of wheels on the avenue, and a brougham came into view, driving fast up the long open stretch by the lake. It was the Castle Knox brougham, driven by Norris, whom I had last seen drunk at the athletic sports, and as it drew up at the door I saw Lady Knox inside.

"It's all right, the fire's out," I said, advancing genially and full of reassurance.

"What fire?" said Lady Knox, regarding me with an iron countenance.

I explained.

"Well, as the house isn't burned down," said Lady Knox, cutting short my details, "perhaps you would kindly find out if I could see Mrs. Knox."

Lady Knox's face was many shades redder than usual. I began to understand that something awful had happened, or would happen, and I wished myself safe at Shreelane, with the bedclothes over my head.

"If 'tis for the misthress you're looking, me lady," said Denis's voice behind me, in tones of the utmost respect, "she went out to the kitchen garden a while ago to get a blasht o' the fresh air afther the night. Maybe your ladyship would sit inside in the library till I call her?"

Lady Knox eyed Crusoe suspiciously.

"Thank you, I'll fetch her myself," she said.

"Oh, sure, that's too throuble——" began Denis.

"Stay where you are!" said Lady Knox, in a voice like the slam of a door.

"Bedad, I'm best plased she went," whispered Denis, as Lady Knox set forth alone down the shrubbery walk.

"But *is* Mrs. Knox in the garden?" said I.

"The Lord preserve your innocence, sir!" replied Denis, with seeming irrelevance.

At this moment I became aware of the incredible fact that Sally Knox was silently descending the stairs; she stopped short as she got into the hall, and looked almost wildly at me and Denis. Was I looking at her wraith? There was again a sound of wheels on the gravel; she went to the hall door, outside which was now drawn up Mrs. Knox's donkey-carriage, as well as Lady Knox's brougham, and, as if overcome by this imposing spectacle, she turned back and put her hands over her face.

"She's gone round to the garden, asthore," said Denis in a hoarse whisper; "go in the donkey-carriage. 'Twill be all right!" He seized her by the arm, pushed her down the steps and into the little carriage, pulled up the hood over her to its furthest stretch, snatched the whip out of the hand of the broadly grinning Norris, and with terrific objurgations lashed the donkey into a gallop. The donkey-boy grasped the position, whatever it might be; he took up the running on the other side, and the donkey-carriage swung away down the avenue, with all its incongruous air of hooded and rowdy invalidism.

I have never disguised that fact that I am a coward, and, therefore, when, at this dynamitical moment, I caught a glimpse of Lady Knox's hat over a laurustinus, as she returned at high speed from the garden, I slunk into the house and faded away round the dining-room door.

"This minute I seen the misthress going down through the plantation beyond," said the voice of Crusoe outside the window, "and I'm after sending Johnny Regan to her with the little carriage, not to put any more delay on yer ladyship. Sure you can see him making all the haste he can. Maybe you'd sit inside in the library till she comes."

Silence followed. I peered cautiously round the window curtain. Lady Knox was looking defiantly at the donkey-carriage as it reeled at top speed into the shades of the plantation, strenuously pursued by the woolly dog. Norris was regarding his horses' ears in expressionless respectability. Denis was picking up the *entrée*-dishes with decorous solicitude. Lady Knox turned and came into the house; she passed the dining-room door with an ominous step, and went on into the library.

It seemed to me that now or never was the moment to retire quietly to my room, put my things into my portmanteau, and——

Denis rushed into the room with the *entrée*-dishes piled up to his chin.

"She's diddled!" he whispered, crashing them down on the table. He came at me with his hand out. "Three cheers for Masther Flurry and Miss Sally," he hissed, wringing my hand up and down, "and 'twas yerself called for *Haste to the Weddin'* last night, long life to ye! The Lord save us! There's the misthress going into the library!"

Through the half-open door I saw old Mrs. Knox approach the library from the staircase with a dignified slowness; she had on a wedding garment, a long white burnous, in which she might easily have been mistaken for a small, stout clergyman. She waved back Crusoe, the door closed upon her, and the battle of giants was entered upon. I sat down—it was all I was able for—and remained for a full minute in stupefied contemplation of the *entrée*-dishes.

Perhaps of all conclusions to a situation so portentous, that which occurred was the least possible. Twenty minutes after Mrs. Knox met her antagonist I was summoned from strapping my portmanteau to face the appalling duty of escorting the combatants, in Lady Knox's brougham, to the church outside the back gate, to which Miss Sally had preceded them in the donkey-carriage. I pulled myself together, went downstairs, and found that the millennium had suddenly set in. It had apparently dawned with the news that Aussolas and all things therein were bequeathed to Flurry by his grandmother, and had established itself finally upon the considerations that the marriage was past praying for, and that the diamonds were intended for Miss Sally.

We fetched the bride and bridegroom from the church; we fetched old Eustace Hamilton, who married them; we dug out the champagne from the cellar; we even found rice and threw it.

The hired carriage that had been ordered to take the runaways across country to a distant station was driven by Slipper. He was shaved; he wore an old livery coat and a new pot-hat; he was wondrous sober. On the following morning he was found asleep on a heap of stones ten miles away; somewhere in the neighbourhood one of the horses was grazing in a field with a certain amount of harness hanging about it. The carriage and the remaining horse were discovered in a roadside ditch, two miles farther on; one of the carriage doors had been torn off, and in the interior the hens of the vicinity were conducting an exhaustive search after the rice that lurked in the cushions.

CLONMACNOISE

This lovely elegy takes its name from a monastic ruin—an ancient seat of Celtic learning—on the east bank of the Shannon, from which the poet contemplates the fallen glory of the Irish past.

In a quiet water'd land, a land of roses,
    Stands Saint Kieran's city fair;
And the warriors of Erin in their famous generations
    Slumber there.

There beneath the dewy hillside sleep the noblest
    Of the clan of Conn,
Each below his stone with name in branching Ogham
    And the sacred knot thereon.

There they laid to rest the seven Kings of Tara,
    There the sons of Cairbrè sleep—
Battle-banners of the Gael that in Kieran's plain of crosses
    Now their final hosting keep.

And in Clonmacnoise they laid the men of Teffia,
    And right many a lord of Breagh;
Deep the sod above Clan Creidè and Clan Conaill,
    Kind in hall and fierce in fray

Many and many a son of Conn the Hundred-fighter
    In the red earth lies at rest;
Many a blue eye of Clan Colman the turf covers,
    Many a swan-white breast.

THE ONLY SON OF AOIFE

The legend of a father and son unknowingly facing each other in battle is found in many cultures. This version, featuring the mythical warrior Cuchulain, was adapted from Old Irish heroic literature in 1902 by Lady Gregory, a major figure of the Irish Literary Renaissance.

THE TIME CUCHULAIN CAME back from Alban, after he had learned the use of arms under Scathach, he left Aoife, the queen he had overcome in battle, with child.

And when he was leaving her, he told her what name to give the child, and he gave her a gold ring, and bade her keep it safe till the child grew to be a lad, and till his thumb would fill it; and he bade her to give it to him then, and to send him to Ireland, and he would know he was his son by that token. She promised to do so, and with that Cuchulain went back to Ireland.

It was not long after the child was born, word came to Aoife that Cuchulain had taken Emer to be his wife in Ireland. When she heard that, great jealousy came on her, and great anger, and her love for Cuchulain was turned to hatred; and she remembered her three champions that he had killed, and how he had overcome herself, and she determined in her mind that when her son would come to have the strength of a man, she would get her revenge through him. She told Conlaoch her son nothing of this, but brought him up like any king's son; and when he was come to sensible years, she put him under the teaching of Scathach, to be taught the use of arms and the art of war. He turned out as apt a scholar as his father, and it was not long before he had learnt all Scathach had to teach.

Then Aoife gave him the arms of a champion, and bade him go to Ireland, but first she laid three commands on him: the first, never to give way to any living person, but to die sooner than be made to turn back; the second, not to refuse a challenge from the greatest champion alive, but to fight him at all risks, even if he

279

was sure to lose his life; the third, not to tell his name on any account, though he might be threatened with death for hiding it. She put him under *geasa*, that is, under bonds, not to do these things.

Then the young man, Conlaoch, set out, and it was not long before his ship brought him to Ireland, and the place he landed at was Baile's Strand, near Dundealgan.

It chanced that at that time Conchubar, the High King, was holding court there, for it was a convenient gathering-place for his chief men, and they were settling some business that belonged to the government of that district.

When word was brought to Conchubar that there was a ship come to the strand, and a young lad in it armed as if for fighting, and armed men with him, he sent one of the chief men of his household to ask his name, and on what business he was come.

The messenger's name was Cuinaire, and he went down to the strand, and when he saw the young man he said: "A welcome to you, young hero from the east, with the merry face. It is likely, seeing you come armed as if for fighting, you are gone astray on your journey; but as you are come to Ireland, tell me your name and what your deeds have been, and your victories in the eastern bounds of the world."

"As to my name," said Conlaoch, "it is of no great account; but whatever it is, I am under bonds not to tell it to the stoutest man living."

"It is best for you to tell it at the king's desire," said Cuinaire, "before you get your death through refusing it, as many a champion from Alban and from Britain has done before now." "If that is the order you put on us when we land here, it is I will break it," said Conlaoch, "and no one will obey it any longer from this out."

So Cuinaire went back and told the king what the young lad had said. Then Conchubar said to his people: "Who will go out into the field, and drag the name and the story out of this young man?" "I will go," said Conall, for his hand was never slow in fighting. And he went out, and found the lad angry and destroying, handling his arms, and they attacked one another with a great noise of swords and shouts, and they were gripped together, and fought for a while, and then Conall was overcome, and the great name and the praise that was on Conall, it was on the head of Conlaoch it was now.

Word was sent then to where Cuchulain was, in pleasant, bright-faced Dundealgan. And the messenger told him the whole story, and he said: "Conall is lying humbled, and it is slow the help is in coming; it is a welcome there would be before the Hound."

Cuchulain rose up then and went to where Conlaoch was, and he still handling his arms. And Cuchulain asked him his name and said: "It would be well for you, young hero of unknown name, to loosen yourself from this knot, and not to bring down my hand upon you, for it will be hard for you to escape death." But

Conlaoch said: "If I put you down in the fight, the way I put down your comrade, there will be a great name on me; but if I draw back now, there will be mockery on me, and it will be said I was afraid of the fight. I will never give in to any man to tell the name, or to give an account of myself. But if I was not held with a command," he said, "there is no man in the world I would sooner give it to than to yourself, since I saw your face. But do not think, brave champion of Ireland, that I will let you take away the fame I have won, for nothing."

With that they fought together, and it is seldom such a battle was seen, and all wondered that the young lad could stand so well against Cuchulain.

So they fought a long while, neither getting the better of the other, but at last Cuchulain was charged so hotly by the lad that he was forced to give way, and although he had fought so many good fights, and killed so many great champions, and understood the use of arms better than any man living, he was pressed very hard.

And he called for the Gae Bulg, and his anger came on him, and the flames of the hero-light began to shine about his head, and by that sign Conlaoch knew him to be Cuchulain, his father. And just at that time he was aiming his spear at him, and when he knew it was Cuchulain, he threw his spear crooked that it might pass beside him. But Cuchulain threw his spear, the Gae Bulg, at him with all his might, and it struck the lad in the side and went into his body, so that he fell to the ground.

And Cuchulain said: "Now, boy, tell your name and what you are, for it is short your life will be, for you will not live after that wound."

And Conlaoch showed the ring that was on his hand, and he said: "Come here where I am lying on the field, let my men from the east come round me. I am suffering for revenge. I am Conlaoch, son of the Hound, heir of dear Dundealgan; I was bound to this secret in Dun Scathach, the secret in which I have found my grief."

And Cuchulain said: "It is a pity your mother not to be here to see you brought down. She might have stretched out her hand to stop the spear that wounded you." And Conlaoch said: "My curse be on my mother, for it was she put me under bonds; it was she sent me here to try my strength against yours." And Cuchulain said: "My curse be on your mother, the woman that is full of treachery; it is through her harmful thoughts these tears have been brought on us." And Conlaoch said: "My name was never forced from my mouth till now; I never gave an account of myself to any man under the sun. But, O Cuchulain of the sharp sword, it was a pity you not to know me the time I threw the slanting spear behind you in the fight."

And then the sorrow of death came upon Conlaoch, and Cuchulain took his sword and put it through him, sooner than leave him in the pain and the punishment he was in.

And then great trouble and anguish came on Cuchulain, and he made this complaint:

"It is a pity it is, O son of Aoife, that ever you came into the province of Ulster, that you ever met with the Hound of Cuailgne.

"If I and my fair Conlaoch were doing feats of war on the one side, the men of Ireland from sea to sea would not be equal to us together. It is no wonder I to be under grief when I see the shield and the arms of Conlaoch. A pity it is there is no one at all, a pity there are not hundreds of men on whom I could get satisfaction for his death.

"If it was the king himself had hurt your fair body, it is I would have shortened his days.

"It is well for the House of the Red Branch, and for the heads of its fair army of heroes, it was not they that killed my only son.

"It is well for Laegaire of Victories it is not from him you got your heavy pain.

"It is well for the heroes of Conall they did not join in the killing of you; it is well that travelling across the plain of Macha they did not fall in with me after such a fight.

"It is well for the tall, well-shaped Forbuide; well for Dubthach, your Black Beetle of Ulster.

"It is well for you, Cormac Conloingeas, your share of arms gave no help, that it is not from your weapons he got his wound, the hard-skinned shield or the blade.

"It is a pity it was not one on the plains of Munster, or in Leinster of the sharp blades, or at Cruachan of the rough fighters, that struck down my comely Conlaoch.

"It is a pity it was not in the country of the Cruithne, of the fierce Fians, you fell in a heavy quarrel, or in the country of the Greeks, or in some other place of the world, you died, and I could avenge you.

"Or in Spain, or in Sorcha, or in the country of the Saxons of the free armies; there would not then be this death in my heart.

"It is very well for the men of Alban it was not they that destroyed your fame; and it is well for the men of the Gall.

"Och! It is bad that it happened; my grief! it is on me is the misfortune, O Conlaoch of the Red Spear, I myself to have spilled your blood.

"I to be under defeat, without strength. It is a pity Aoife never taught you to know the power of my strength in the fight.

"It is no wonder I to be blinded after such a fight and such a defeat.

"It is no wonder I to be tired out, and without the sons of Usnach beside me.

"Without a son, without a brother, with none to come after me; without Conlaoch, without a name to keep my strength.

"To be without Naoise, without Ainnle, without Ardan; is it not with me is my fill of trouble?

"I am the father that killed his son, the fine green branch; there is no hand or shelter to help me.

"I am a raven that has no home; I am a boat going from wave to wave; I am a ship that has lost its rudder; I am the apple left on the tree; it is little I thought of falling from it; grief and sorrow will be with me from this time."

Then Cuchulain stood up and faced all the men of Ulster. "There is trouble on Cuchulain," said Conchubar; "he is after killing his own son, and if I and all my men were to go against him, by the end of the day he would destroy every man of us. Go now," he said to Cathbad, the Druid, "and bind him to go down to Baile's Strand, and to give three days fighting against the waves of the sea, rather than to kill us all."

So Cathbad put an enchantment on him, and bound him to go down. And when he came to the strand, there was a great white stone before him, and he took his sword in his right hand, and he said: "If I had the head of the woman that sent her son to his death, I would split it as I split this stone." And he made four quarters of the stone.

Then he fought with the waves three days and three nights, till he fell from hunger and weakness, so that some men said he got his death there. But it was not there he got his death, but on the plain of Muirthemne.

FROM
MRS. WARREN'S
PROFESSION

George Bernard Shaw wrote Mrs. Warren's Profession *in 1898, but, because it involved prostitution, it wasn't performed in public until more than a quarter of a century later. In Act I of the play, Mrs. Warren and two friends pay a surprise visit to her twenty-two-year-old daughter, whom she hardly knows.*

ACT I

Summer afternoon in a cottage garden on the eastern slope of a hill a little south of Haslemere in Surrey. Looking up the hill, the cottage is seen in the left hand corner of the garden, with its thatched roof and porch, and a large latticed window to the left of the porch. Farther back a little wing is built out, making an angle with the right side wall. From the end of this wing a paling curves across and forward, completely shutting in the garden, except for a gate on the right. The common rises uphill beyond the paling to the sky line. Some folded canvas garden chairs are leaning against the side bench in the porch. A lady's bicycle is propped against the wall, under the window. A little to the right of the porch a hammock is slung from two posts. A big canvas umbrella, stuck in the ground, keeps the sun off the hammock, in which a young lady lies reading and making notes, her head towards the cottage and her feet towards the gate. In front of the hammock, and within reach of her hand, is a common kitchen chair, with a pile of serious-looking books and a supply of writing paper upon it.

A gentleman walking on the common comes into sight from behind the cottage. He is hardly past middle age, with something of the artist about him, unconventionally but carefully dressed, and clean-shaven except for a moustache, with an eager susceptible face and very amiable and considerate manners. He has silky black hair, with waves of grey and white in it. His eyebrows are white, his moustache black. He seems not certain of his way. He looks over the paling; takes stock of the place; and sees the young lady.

THE GENTLEMAN [*taking off his hat*]. I beg your pardon. Can you direct me to Hindhead View—Mrs. Alison's?

THE YOUNG LADY [*glancing up from her book*]. This is Mrs. Alison's [*She resumes her work*].

THE GENTLEMAN. Indeed! Perhaps—may I ask are you Miss Vivie Warren?

THE YOUNG LADY [*sharply, as she turns on her elbow to get a good look at him*]. Yes.

THE GENTLEMAN [*daunted and conciliatory*]. I'm afraid I appear intrusive. My name is Praed. [*Vivie at once throws her books upon the chair, and gets out of the hammock.*] Oh, pray don't let me disturb you.

VIVIE [*striding to the gate and opening it for him*]. Come in, Mr. Praed. [*He comes in.*] Glad to see you. [*She proffers her hand and takes his with a resolute and hearty grip. She is an attractive specimen of the sensible, able, highly-educated middle-class Englishwoman. Age 22. Prompt, strong, confident, self-possessed. Plain, business-like dress, but not dowdy. She wears a chatelaine at her belt, with a fountain pen and a paper knife among its pendants*].

PRAED. Very kind of you indeed, Miss Warren. [*She shuts the gate with a vigorous slam: he passes in to the middle of the garden, exercising his fingers, which are slightly numbed by her greetings.*] Has your mother arrived?

VIVIE [*quickly, evidently scenting aggression*]. Is she coming?

PRAED [*surprised*]. Didn't you expect us?

VIVIE. No.

PRAED. Now, goodness me, I hope I've not mistaken the day. That would be just like me, you know. Your mother arranged that she was to come down from London and that I was to come over from Horsham to be introduced to you.

VIVIE [*not at all pleased*]. Did she? H'm! My mother has rather a trick of taking me by surprise—to see how I behave myself when she's away, I suppose. I fancy I shall take my mother very much by surprise one of these days, if she makes arrangements that concern me without consulting me beforehand. She hasn't come.

PRAED [*embarrassed*]. I'm really very sorry.

VIVIE [*throwing off her displeasure*]. It's not your fault, Mr. Praed, is it? And I'm very glad you've come, believe me. You are the only one of my mother's friends I have asked her to bring to see me.

PRAED [*relieved and delighted*]. Oh, now this is really very good of you, Miss Warren!

VIVIE. Will you come indoors; or would you rather sit out here whilst we talk?

PRAED. It will be nicer out here, don't you think?

VIVIE. Then I'll go and get you a chair. [*She goes to the porch for a garden chair.*]

PRAED [*following her*]. Oh, pray, pray! Allow me. [*He lays hands on the chair.*]

VIVIE [*letting him take it*]. Take care of your fingers: they're rather dodgy things, those chairs. [*She goes across to the chair with the books on it; pitches them into the hammock; and brings the chair forward with one swing.*]

PRAED [*who has just unfolded his chair*]. Oh, now do let me take that hard chair! I like hard chairs.

VIVIE. So do I. [*She sits down.*] Sit down, Mr. Praed. [*This invitation is given with genial peremptoriness, his anxiety to please her clearly striking her as a sign of weakness of character on his part.*]

PRAED. By the way, though, hadn't we better go to the station to meet your mother?

VIVIE [*coolly*]. Why? She knows the way. [*Praed hesitates, and then sits down in the garden chair, rather disconcerted*]. Do you know, you are just like what I expected. I hope you are disposed to be friends with me?

PRAED [*again beaming*]. Thank you, my dear Miss Warren; thank you. Dear me! I'm so glad your mother hasn't spoilt you!

VIVIE How?

PRAED. Well, in making you too conventional. You know, my dear Miss Warren, I am a born anarchist. I hate authority. It spoils the relations between parent and child—even between mother and daughter. Now I was always afraid that your mother would strain her authority to make you very conventional. It's such a relief to find that she hasn't.

VIVIE. Oh! have I been behaving unconventionally?

PRAED. Oh, no: oh, dear no. At least not conventionally unconventionally, you understand. [*She nods. He goes on, with a cordial outburst.*] But it was so charming of you to say that you were disposed to be friends with me! You modern ladies are splendid—perfectly splendid!

VIVIE [*dubiously*]. Eh? [*watching him with dawning disappointment as to the quality of his brains and character.*]

PRAED. When I was your age, young men and women were afraid of each other: there was no good fellowship—nothing real—only gallantry copied out of novels, and as vulgar and affected as it could be. Maidenly reserve!—gentlemanly chivalry!—always saying no when you meant yes!—simple purgatory for shy and sincere souls!

VIVIE. Yes, I imagine there must have been a frightful waste of time—especially women's time.

PRAED. Oh, waste of life, waste of everything. But things are improving. Do you know, I have been in a positive state of excitement about meeting you ever since your magnificent achievements at Cambridge—a thing unheard of in my day. It was perfectly splendid, your tieing with the third wrangler. Just the right place, you know. The first wrangler is always a dreamy, morbid fellow, in whom the thing is pushed to the length of a disease.

VIVIE. It doesn't pay. I wouldn't do it again for the same money.

PRAED [aghast]. The same money!

VIVIE. I did it for £50. Perhaps you don't know how it was. Mrs. Latham, my tutor at Newnham, told my mother that I could distinguish myself in the mathematical tripos if I went for it in earnest. The papers were full just then of Phillipa Summers beating the senior wrangler—you remember about it; and nothing would please my mother but that I should do the same thing. I said flatly that it was not worth my while to face the grind since I was not going in for teaching; but I offered to try for fourth wrangler or thereabouts for £50. She closed with me at that, after a little grumbling; and I was better than my bargain. But I wouldn't do it again for that. £200 would have been nearer the mark.

PRAED [much damped]. Lord bless me! That's a very practical way of looking at it.

VIVIE. Did you expect to find me an unpractical person?

PRAED. No, no. But surely it's practical to consider not only the work these honors cost, but also the culture they bring.

VIVIE. Culture! My dear Mr. Praed: do you know what the mathematical tripos means? It means grind, grind, grind, for six to eight hours a day at mathematics, and nothing but mathematics. I'm supposed to know something about science; but I know nothing except the mathematics it involves. I can make calculations for engineers, electricians, insurance companies, and so on; but I know next to nothing about engineering or electricity or insurance. I don't even know arithmetic well. Outside mathematics, lawn-tennis, eating, sleeping, cycling, and walking, I'm a more ignorant barbarian than any woman could possibly be who hadn't gone in for the tripos.

PRAED [revolted]. What a monstrous, wicked, rascally system! I knew it! I felt at once that it meant destroying all that makes womanhood beautiful.

VIVIE. I don't object to it on that score in the least. I shall turn it to very good account, I assure you.

PRAED. Pooh! In what way?

VIVIE. I shall set up in chambers in the city and work at actuarial calculations and conveyancing. Under cover of that I shall do some law, with one eye on the Stock Exchange all the time. I've come down here by myself to read law —not for a holiday, as my mother imagines. I hate holidays.

PRAED. You make my blood turn cold. Are you to have no romance, no beauty in your life?

VIVIE. I don't care for either, I assure you.

PRAED. You can't mean that.

VIVIE. Oh yes I do. I like working and getting paid for it. When I'm tired of working, I like a comfortable chair, a cigar, a little whisky, and a novel with a good detective story in it.

PRAED [*in a frenzy of repudiation*]. I don't believe it. I am an artist; and I can't believe it: I refuse to believe it. [*Enthusiastically.*] Ah, my dear Miss Warren, you haven't discovered yet, I see, what a wonderful world art can open up to you.

VIVIE. Yes, I have. Last May I spent six weeks in London with Honoria Fraser. Mamma thought we were doing a round of sight-seeing together; but I was really at Honoria's chambers in Chancery Lane every day, working away at actuarial calculations for her, and helping her as well as a greenhorn could. In the evenings we smoked and talked, and never dreamt of going out except for exercise. And I never enjoyed myself more in my life. I cleared all my expenses and got initiated into the business without a fee into the bargain.

PRAED. But bless my heart and soul, Miss Warren, do you call that trying art?

VIVIE. Wait a bit. That wasn't the beginning. I went up to town on an invitation from some artistic people in Fitzjohn's Avenue: one of the girls was a Newnham chum. They took me to the National Gallery, to the Opera, and to a concert where the band played all the evening—Beethoven and Wagner and so on. I wouldn't go through that experience again for anything you could offer me. I held out for civility's sake until the third day; and then I said, plump out, that I couldn't stand any more of it, and went off to Chancery Lane. Now you know the sort of perfectly splendid modern young lady I am. How do you think I shall get on with my mother?

PRAED [*startled*]. Well, I hope—er—

VIVIE. It's not so much what you hope as what you believe, that I want to know.

PRAED. Well, frankly, I am afraid your mother will be a little disappointed. Not from any shortcoming on your part—I don't mean that. But you are so different from her ideal.

VIVIE. What is her ideal like?

PRAED. Well, you must have observed, Miss Warren, that people who are dissatisfied with their own bringing up generally think that the world would be all right if everybody were to be brought up quite differently. Now your mother's life has been—er—I suppose you know—

VIVIE. I know nothing. [*Praed is appalled. His consternation grows as she continues.*] That's exactly my difficulty. You forget, Mr. Praed, that I hardly know my mother. Since I was a child I have lived in England, at school or college, or with people paid to take charge of me. I have been boarded out all my life; and my mother has lived in Brussels or Vienna and never let me go to her. I only see her when she visits England for a few days. I don't complain; it's been very pleasant; for people have been very good to me; and there has always been plenty of money to make things smooth. But don't imagine I know anything about my mother. I know far less than you do.

PRAED [*very ill at ease*]. In that case— [*He stops, quite at a loss. Then, with a forced attempt at gaiety.*] But what nonsense we are talking! Of course you and your mother will get on capitally. [*He rises, and looks abroad at the view.*] What a charming little place you have here!

VIVIE [*unmoved*]. If you think you are doing anything but confirming my worst suspicions by changing the subject like that, you must take me for a much greater fool than I hope I am.

PRAED. Your worst suspicions! Oh, pray don't say that. Now don't.

VIVIE. Why won't my mother's life bear being talked about?

PRAED. Pray think, Miss Vivie. It is natural that I should have a certain delicacy in talking to my old friend's daughter about her behind her back. You will have plenty of opportunity of talking to her about it when she comes. [*Anxiously.*] I wonder what is keeping her.

VIVIE. No: She won't talk about it either. [*Rising.*] However, I won't press you. Only mind this, Mr. Praed. I strongly suspect there will be a battle royal when my mother hears of my Chancery Lane project.

PRAED [*ruefully*]. I'm afraid there will.

VIVIE. I shall win the battle, because I want nothing but my fare to London to start there to-morrow earning my own living by devilling for Honoria. Besides, I have no mysteries to keep up; and it seems she has. I shall use that advantage over her if necessary.

PRAED [*greatly shocked*]. Oh, no. No, pray. You'd not do such a thing.

VIVIE. Then tell me why not.

PRAED. I really cannot. I appeal to your good feeling. [*She smiles at his sentimentality.*] Besides, you may be too bold. Your mother is not to be trifled with when she's angry.

VIVIE. You can't frighten me, Mr. Praed. In that month at Chancery Lane I had opportunities of taking the measure of one or two women very like my mother who came to consult Honoria. You may back me to win. But if I hit harder in my ignorance than I need, remember that it is you who refuse to enlighten me. Now let us drop the subject. [*She takes her chair and replaces it near the hammock with the same vigorous swing as before.*]

PRAED [*taking a desperate resolution*]. One word, Miss Warren. I had better tell you. It's very difficult; but—

[*Mrs. Warren and Sir George Crofts arrive at the gate. Mrs. Warren is a woman between 40 and 50, good-looking, showily dressed in a brilliant hat and a gay blouse fitting tightly over her bust and flanked by fashionable sleeves. Rather spoiled and domineering, but, on the whole, a genial and fairly presentable old blackguard of a woman.*

Crofts is a tall, powerfully-built man of about 50, fashionably dressed in the style of a young man. Nasal voice, reedier than might be expected from his strong frame. Clean-shaven, bull-dog jaws, large flat ears, and thick neck, gentlemanly combination of the most brutal types of city man, sporting man, and man about town.]

VIVIE. Here they are. [*Coming to them as they enter the garden.*] How do, mater. Mr. Praed's been here this half hour, waiting for you.

MRS. WARREN. Well, if you've been waiting, Praddy, it's your own fault: I thought you'd have had the gumption to know I was coming by the 3:10 train. Vivie, put your hat on, dear; you'll get sunburnt. Oh, forgot to introduce you. Sir George Crofts, my little Vivie.

[*Crofts advances to Vivie with his most courtly manner. She nods, but makes no motion to shake hands.*]

CROFTS. May I shake hands with a young lady whom I have known by reputation very long as the daughter of one of my oldest friends?

VIVIE [*who has been looking him up and down sharply*]. If you like. [*She takes his tenderly proffered hand and gives it a squeeze that makes him open his eyes; then turns away and says to her mother*] Will you come in, or shall I get a couple more chairs? [*She goes into the porch for the chairs.*]

MRS. WARREN. Well, George, what do you think of her?

CROFTS [*ruefully*]. She has a powerful fist. Did you shake hands with her, Praed?

PRAED. Yes: it will pass off presently.

CROFTS. I hope so. [*Vivie reappears with two more chairs. He hurries to her assistance.*] Allow me.

MRS. WARREN [*patronizingly*]. Let Sir George help you with the chairs, dear.

VIVIE [*almost pitching two into his arms*]. Here you are. [*She dusts her hands and turns to Mrs. Warren*]. You'd like some tea, wouldn't you?

MRS. WARREN [*sitting in Praed's chair and fanning herself*]. I'm dying for a drop to drink.

VIVIE. I'll see about it. [*She goes into the cottage. Sir George has by this time managed to unfold a chair and plant it beside Mrs. Warren, on her left. He throws the other on the grass and sits down, looking dejected and rather foolish, with the handle of his stick in his mouth. Praed, still very uneasy, fidgets about the garden on their right.*]

MRS. WARREN [*to Praed, looking at Crofts*]. Just look at him, Praddy; he looks cheerful, don't he? He's been worrying my life out these three years to have that little girl of mine shewn to him; and now that I've done it, he's quite out of countenance. [*Briskly.*] Come! sit up, George; and take your stick out of your mouth. [*Crofts sulkily obeys.*]

PRAED. I think, you know—if you don't mind my saying so—that we had better get out of the habit of thinking of her as a little girl. You see she has really distinguished herself; and I'm not sure, from what I have seen of her, that she is not older than any of us.

MRS. WARREN [*greatly amused*]. Only listen to him, George! Older than any of us! Well, she has been stuffing you nicely with her importance.

PRAED. But young people are particularly sensitive about being treated in that way.

MRS. WARREN. Yes; and young people have to get all that nonsense taken out of them, and a good deal more besides. Don't you interfere, Praddy. I know how to treat my own child as well as you do. [*Praed, with a grave shake of his head, walks up the garden with his hands behind his back. Mrs. Warren pretends to laugh, but looks after him with perceptible concern. Then she whispers to Crofts.*] What's the matter with him? What does he take it like that for?

CROFTS [*morosely*]. You're afraid of Praed.

MRS. WARREN. What! Me! Afraid of dear old Praddy! Why, a fly wouldn't be afraid of him.

CROFTS. You're afraid of him.

MRS. WARREN [*angry*]. I'll trouble you to mind your own business, and not try any of your sulks on me. I'm not afraid of you, anyhow. If you can't make yourself agreeable, you'd better go home. [*She gets up, and, turning her back on him, finds herself face to face with Praed.*] Come, Praddy, I know it was only your tender-heartedness. You're afraid I'll bully her.

PRAED. My dear Kitty: you think I'm offended. Don't imagine that: pray don't. But you know I often notice things that escape you; and though you never take my advice, you sometimes admit afterwards that you ought to have taken it.

MRS. WARREN. Well, what do you notice now?

PRAED. Only that Vivie is a grown woman. Pray, Kitty, treat her with every respect.

MRS. WARREN [*with genuine amazement*]. Respect! Treat my own daughter with respect! What next, pray!

VIVIE [*appearing at the cottage door and calling to Mrs. Warren*]. Mother: will you come up to my room and take your bonnet off before tea?

MRS. WARREN. Yes, dearie. [*She laughs indulgently at Praed and pats him on the cheek as she passes him on her way to the porch. She follows Vivie into the cottage.*]

CROFTS [*furtively*]. I say, Praed.

PRAED. Yes.

CROFTS. I want to ask you a rather particular question.

PRAED. Certainly. [*He takes Mrs. Warren's chair and sits close to Crofts.*]

CROFTS. That's right: they might hear us from the window. Look here: did Kitty ever tell you who that girl's father is?

PRAED. Never.

CROFTS. Have you any suspicion of who it might be?

PRAED. None.

CROFTS [*not believing him*]. I know, of course, that you perhaps might feel bound not to tell if she had said anything to you. But it's very awkward to be uncertain about it now that we shall be meeting the girl every day. We don't exactly know how we ought to feel towards her.

PRAED. What difference can that make? We take her on her own merits. What does it matter who her father was?

CROFTS [*suspiciously*]. Then you know who he was?

PRAED [*with a touch of temper*]. I said no just now. Did you not hear me?

CROFTS. Look here, Praed. I ask you as a particular favor. If you do know [*movement of protest from Praed*]—I only say, if you know, you might at least set my mind at rest about her. The fact is I feel attracted towards her. Oh, don't be alarmed: it's quite an innocent feeling. That's what puzzles me about it. Why, for all I know, *I* might be her father.

PRAED. You! Impossible! Oh, no, nonsense!

CROFTS [*catching him up cunningly*]. You know for certain that I'm not?

PRAED. I know nothing about it, I tell you, any more than you. But really, Crofts—oh, no, it's out of the question. There's not the least resemblance.

CROFTS. As to that, there's no resemblance between her and her mother that I can see. I suppose she's not your daughter, is she?

PRAED [*He meets the question with an indignant stare; then recovers himself with an effort and answers gently and gravely*]. Now listen to me, my dear Crofts. I have nothing to do with that side of Mrs. Warren's life, and never had. She has never spoken to me about it; and of course I have never spoken to her about it. Your delicacy will tell you that a handsome woman needs some friends who are not—well, not on that footing with her. The effect of her own beauty would become a torment to her if she could not escape from it occasionally. You are probably on much more confidential terms with Kitty than I am. Surely you can ask her the question yourself.

CROFTS [*rising impatiently*]. I have asked her often enough. But she's so determined to keep the child all to herself that she would deny that it ever had a father if she could. No: there's nothing to be got out of her—nothing that one can believe, anyhow. I'm thoroughly uncomfortable about it, Praed.

PRAED [*rising also*]. Well, as you are, at all events, old enough to be her father, I don't mind agreeing that we both regard Miss Vivie in a parental way, as a young girl whom we are bound to protect and help. All the more, as the real father, whoever he was, was probably a blackguard. What do you say?

CROFTS [*aggressively*]. I'm no older than you, if you come to that.

PRAED. Yes, you are, my dear fellow: you were born old. I was born a boy: I've never been able to feel the assurance of a grown-up man in my life.

MRS. WARREN [*calling from within the cottage*]. Prad-dee! George! Tea-ea-ea-ea!

CROFTS [*hastily*]. She's calling us. [*He hurries in. Praed shakes his head bodingly, and is following slowly when he is hailed by a young gentleman who has just appeared on the common, and is making for the gate. He is a pleasant, pretty, smartly dressed, and entirely good-for-nothing young fellow, not long turned 20, with a charming voice and agreeably disrespectful manner. He carries a very light sporting magazine rifle.*]

THE YOUNG GENTLEMAN. Hallo! Praed!

PRAED. Why, Frank Gardner! [*Frank comes in and shakes hands cordially.*] What on earth are you doing here?

FRANK. Staying with my father.

PRAED. The Roman father?

FRANK. He's rector here. I'm living with my people this autumn for the sake of economy. Things came to a crisis in July: the Roman father had to pay my debts. He's stony broke in consequence; and so am I. What are you up to in these parts? Do you know the people here?

PRAED. Yes: I'm spending the day with a Miss Warren.

FRANK [*enthusiastically*]. What! Do you know Vivie? Isn't she a jolly girl! I'm teaching her to shoot—you see [*shewing the rifle.*]! I'm so glad she knows you: you're just the sort of fellow she ought to know. [*He smiles, and raises the charming voice almost to a singing tone as he exclaims*] It's ever so jolly to find you here, Praed. Ain't it, now?

PRAED. I'm an old friend of her mother's. Mrs. Warren brought me over to make her daughter's acquaintance.

FRANK. The mother! Is she here?

PRAED. Yes—inside at tea.

MRS. WARREN [*calling from within*]. Prad-dee-ee-ee-eee! The tea-cake'll be cold.

PRAED [*calling*]. Yes, Mrs. Warren. In a moment. I've just met a friend here.

MRS. WARREN. A what?

PRAED [*louder*]. A friend.

MRS. WARREN. Bring him up.

PRAED. All right. [*To Frank.*] Will you accept the invitation?

FRANK [*incredulous, but immensely amused*]. Is that Vivie's mother?

PRAED. Yes.

FRANK. By Jove! What a lark! Do you think she'll like me?

PRAED. I've no doubt you'll make yourself popular, as usual. Come in and try [*moving towards the house*].

FRANK. Stop a bit. [*Seriously.*] I want to take you into my confidence.

PRAED. Pray don't. It's only some fresh folly, like the barmaid at Redhill.

FRANK. It's ever so much more serious than that. You say you've only just met Vivie for the first time?

PRAED. Yes.

FRANK [*rhapsodically*]. Then you can have no idea what a girl she is. Such character! Such sense! And her cleverness! Oh, my eye, Praed, but I can tell you she is clever! And the most loving little heart that—

CROFTS [*putting his head out of the window*]. I say, Praed: what are you about? Do come along. [*He disappears.*]

FRANK. Hallo! Sort of chap that would take a prize at a dog show, ain't he? Who's he?

PRAED. Sir George Crofts, an old friend of Mrs. Warren's. I think we had better come in.

[*On their way to the porch they are interrupted by a call from the gate. Turning, they see an elderly clergyman looking over it.*]

THE CLERGYMAN [*calling*]. Frank!

FRANK. Hallo! [*To Praed.*] The Roman father. [*To the clergyman.*] Yes, gov'nor: all right: presently. [*To Praed.*] Look here, Praed: you'd better go in to tea. I'll join you directly.

PRAED. Very good. [*He raises his hat to the clergyman, who acknowledges the salute distantly. Praed goes into the cottage. The clergyman remains stiffly outside the gate, with his hands on the top of it. The Rev. Samuel Gardner, a beneficed clergyman of the Established Church, is over 50. He is a pretentious, booming, noisy person, hopelessly asserting himself as a father and a clergyman without being able to command respect in either capacity.*]

REV. S. Well, sir. Who are your friends here, if I may ask?

FRANK. Oh, it's all right, gov'nor! Come in.

REV. S. No, sir; not until I know whose garden I am entering.

FRANK. It's all right. It's Miss Warren's.

REV. S. I have not seen her at church since she came.

FRANK. Of course not: she's a third wrangler—ever so intellectual!—took a higher degree than you did; so why should she go to hear you preach?

REV. S. Don't be disrespectful, sir.

FRANK. Oh, it don't matter: nobody hears us. Come in. [*He opens the gate, unceremoniously pulling his father with it into the garden.*] I want to introduce you to her. She and I get on rattling well: she's charming. Do you remember the advice you gave me last July, gov'nor?

REV. S. [*severely*]. Yes. I advised you to conquer your idleness and flippancy, and to work your way into an honorable profession and live on it and not upon me.

FRANK. No: that's what you thought of afterwards. What you actually said was that since I had neither brains nor money, I'd better turn my good looks to account by marrying somebody with both. Well, look here. Miss Warren has brains: you can't deny that.

REV. S. Brains are not everything.

FRANK. No, of course not: there's the money—

REV. S. [*interrupting him austerely*]. I was not thinking of money, sir. I was speaking of higher things—social position, for instance.

FRANK. I don't care a rap about that.

REV. S. But I do, sir.

FRANK. Well, nobody wants you to marry her. Anyhow, she has what amounts to a high Cambridge degree; and she seems to have as much money as she wants.

REV. S. [sinking into a feeble vein of humor]. I greatly doubt whether she has as much money as you will want.

FRANK. Oh, come: I haven't been so very extravagant. I live ever so quietly; I don't drink; I don't bet much; and I never go regularly on the razzle-dazzle as you did when you were my age.

REV. S. [booming hollowly]. Silence, sir.

FRANK. Well, you told me yourself, when I was making ever such an ass of myself about the barmaid at Redhill, that you once offered a woman £50 for the letters you wrote to her when—

REV. S. [terrified]. Sh-sh-sh, Frank, for Heaven's sake! [He looks round apprehensively. Seeing no one within earshot he plucks up courage to boom again, but more subduedly.] You are taking an ungentlemanly advantage of what I confided to you for your own good, to save you from an error you would have repented all your life long. Take warning by your father's follies, sir; and don't make them an excuse for your own.

FRANK. Did you ever hear the story of the Duke of Wellington and his letters?

REV. S. No, sir; and I don't want to hear it.

FRANK. The old Iron Duke didn't throw away £50—not he. He just wrote: "My dear Jenny: Publish and be damned! Yours affectionately, Wellington." That's what you should have done.

REV. S. [piteously]. Frank, my boy; when I wrote those letters I put myself into that woman's power. When I told you about her I put myself, to some extent, I am sorry to say, in your power. She refused my money with these words, which I shall never forget: "Knowledge is power," she said; "and I never sell power." That's more than twenty years ago; and she has never made use of her power or caused me a moment's uneasiness. You are behaving worse to me than she did, Frank.

FRANK. Oh, yes, I dare say! Did you ever preach at her the way you preach at me every day?

REV. S. [wounded almost to tears]. I leave you, sir. You are incorrigible. [He turns towards the gate.]

FRANK [utterly unmoved]. Tell them I shan't be home to tea, will you, gov'nor, like a good fellow? [He goes towards the cottage door and is met by Vivie coming out, followed by Praed, Crofts, and Mrs. Warren.]

VIVIE [to Frank]. Is that your father, Frank? I do so want to meet him.

FRANK. Certainly. [Calling after his father.] Gov'nor! [The Rev. S. turns at the *gate, fumbling nervously at his hat. Praed comes down the garden on the opposite side, beaming in anticipation of civilities. Crofts prowls about near the hammock, poking it with his stick to make it swing. Mrs. Warren halts on the threshold, staring hard at the clergyman.*] Let me introduce—my father: Miss Warren.

VIVIE [*going to the clergyman and shaking his hand*]. Very glad to see you here, Mr. Gardner. Let me introduce everybody. Mr. Gardner—Mr. Frank Gardner— Mr. Praed—Sir George Crofts, and—[*As the men are raising their hats to one another, Vivie is interrupted by an exclamation from her mother, who swoops down on the Reverend Samuel*].

MRS. WARREN. Why, it's Sam Gardner, gone into the church! Don't you know us, Sam? This is George Crofts, as large as life and twice as natural. Don't you remember me?

REV. S. [*very red*]. I really—er—

MRS. WARREN. Of course you do. Why, I have a whole album of your letters still: I came across them only the other day.

REV. S. [*miserably confused*]. Miss Vavasour, I believe.

MRS. WARREN [*correcting him quickly in a loud whisper*]. Tch! Nonsense— Mrs. Warren: don't you see my daughter there?

OSCAR WILDE

*In this letter to his friend Frank Harris, which was used as an intro-
duction to a revised edition of Harris's* Life of Wilde *(1918), George
Bernard Shaw writes his own impressions of his "fellow-townsman"
Oscar Wilde. It's not exactly clear whether Shaw considers himself
friend or foe, but most of his criticism focuses on Wilde's purported snobbery; what Shaw saw as a complete lack of knowledge of music and art;
and the fact that Wilde was a huge man, "a giant in the pathological
sense." Wilde, though, believed Shaw had his own issues: Richard
Ellmann describes an encounter in his biography,* Oscar Wilde, *in
which Shaw informs Wilde that he plans a new publication, telling him
"I'd call it* Shaw's Magazine: Shaw—Shaw—Shaw!" *Wilde retorts,
"Yes, and how would you spell it?" (Frank Harris, who was also Irish,
published a biography of Shaw in 1931.)*

MY DEAR HARRIS:—
Why was Wilde so good a subject for a biography that none of the
previous attempts which you have just wiped out are bad? Just because
his stupendous laziness simplified his life almost as if he knew instinctively that
there must be no episodes to spoil the great situation at the end of the last act but
one. It was a well-made life in the Scribe sense. It was as simple as the life of Des
Grieux, Manon Lescaut's lover; and it beat that by omitting Manon and making
Des Grieux his own lover and his own hero.

Des Grieux was a worthless rascal by all conventional standards; and we forgive him everything. We think we forgive him because he was unselfish and
loved greatly. Oscar seems to have said: "I will love nobody: I will be utterly selfish; and I will be not merely a rascal but a monster; and you shall forgive me
everything. In other words, I will reduce your standards to absurdity, not by writ-

ing them down, though I could do that so well—in fact, *have* done it—but by actually living them down and dying them down."

However, I mustn't start writing a book to you about Wilde: I must just tumble a few things together and tell you them. To take things in the order of your book, I can remember only one occasion on which I saw Sir William Wilde [Oscar's father], who, by the way, operated on my father to correct a squint, and overdid the correction so much that my father squinted the other way all the rest of his life. To this day I never notice a squint: it is as normal to me as a nose or a tall hat.

I was a boy at a concert in the Antient Concert Rooms in Brunswick Street in Dublin. Everybody was in evening dress; and—unless I am mixing up this concert with another (in which case I doubt if the Wildes would have been present)—the Lord-Lieutenant was there with his courtiers in blue facings. Wilde was dressed in snuffy brown; and as he had the sort of skin that never looks clean, he produced a dramatic effect beside Lady Wilde (in full fig) of being, like Frederick the Great, Beyond Soap and Water, as his Nietzschean son was beyond Good and Evil. He was currently reported to have a family in every farmhouse; and the wonder was that Lady Wilde didn't mind—evidently a tradition from the Travers case, which I did not know about until I read your account, as I was only eight in 1864.

Lady Wilde was nice to me in London during the desperate days between my arrival in 1876 and my first earning of an income by my pen in 1885, or rather until, a few years earlier, I threw myself into Socialism and cut myself contemptuously loose from everything of which her at-homes—themselves desperate affairs enough, as you saw for yourself—were part. I was at two or three of them; and I once dined with her in company with an ex-tragedy queen named Miss Glynn, who, having no visible external ears, reared a head like a turnip. Lady Wilde talked about Schopenhauer; and Miss Glynn told me that Gladstone formed his oratorical style on Charles Kean.

I ask myself where and how I came across Lady Wilde; for we had no social relations in the Dublin days. The explanation must be that my sister, then a very attractive girl who sang beautifully, had met and made some sort of innocent conquest of both Oscar and Willie [Oscar's older brother]. I met Oscar once at one of the at-homes; and he came and spoke to me with an evident intention of being specially kind to me. We put each other out frightfully; and this odd difficulty persisted between us to the very last, even when we were no longer mere boyish novices and had become men of the world with plenty of skill in social intercourse. I saw him very seldom, as I avoided literary and artistic coteries like the plague, and refused the few invitations I received to go into society with burlesque ferocity, so as to keep out of it without offending people past their willingness to indulge me as a privileged lunatic.

The last time I saw him was at that tragic luncheon of yours at the Café Royal; and I am quite sure our total of meetings from first to last did not exceed twelve, and may not have exceeded six.

I definitely recollect six: (1) At the at-home aforesaid. (2) At Macmurdo's house in Fitzroy Street in the days of the Century Guild and its paper *The Hobby Horse*. (3) At a meeting somewhere in Westminster at which I delivered an address on Socialism, and at which Oscar turned up and spoke. Robert Ross surprised me greatly by telling me, long after Oscar's death, that it was this address of mine that moved Oscar to try his hand at a similar feat by writing "The Soul of Man Under Socialism." (4) A chance meeting near the stage door of the Haymarket Theatre, at which our queer shyness of one another made our resolutely cordial and appreciative conversation so difficult that our final laugh and shakehands was almost a reciprocal confession. (5) A really pleasant afternoon we spent together on catching one another in a place where our presence was an absurdity. It was some exhibition in Chelsea: a naval commemoration, where there was a replica of Nelson's Victory and a set of P.&O. cabins which made one seasick by mere association of ideas. I don't know why I went or why Wilde went; but we did; and the question what the devil we were doing in that galley tickled us both. It was my sole experience of Oscar's wonderful gift as a raconteur. I remember particularly an amazingly elaborate story which you have no doubt heard from him: an example of the cumulation of a single effect, as in Mark Twain's story of the man who was persuaded to put lightning conductor after lightning conductor at every possible point on his roof until a thunderstorm came and all the lightning in the heavens went for his house and wiped it out.

Oscar's much more carefully and elegantly worked out story was of a young man who invented a theatre stall which economized space by ingenious contrivances which were all described. A friend of his invited twenty millionaires to meet him at dinner so that he might interest them in the invention. The young man convinced them completely by his demonstration of the saving in a theatre holding, in ordinary seats, six hundred people, leaving them eager and ready to make his fortune. Unfortunately he went on to calculate the annual saving in all the theatres of the world; then in all the churches of the world; then in all the legislatures; estimating finally the incidental and moral and religious effects of the invention until at the end of an hour he had estimated a profit of several thousand millions: the climax of course being that the millionaires folded their tents and silently stole away, leaving the ruined inventor a marked man for life.

Wilde and I got on extraordinarily well on this occasion. I had not to talk myself, but to listen to a man telling me stories better than I could have told them. We did not refer to Art, about which, excluding literature from the definition, he knew only what could be picked up by reading about it. He was in a tweed suit and low hat like myself, and had been detected and had detected me in the act of

clandestinely spending a happy day at Rosherville Gardens instead of pontificat-
ing in his frock-coat and so forth. And he had an audience on whom not one of
his subtlest effects was lost. And so for once our meeting was a success; and I
understood why Morris, when he was dying slowly, enjoyed a visit from Wilde
more than from anybody else, as I understand why you say in your book that you
would rather have Wilde back than any friend you have ever talked to, even
though he was incapable of friendship, though not of the most touching kindness
on occasion.

Our sixth meeting, the only other one I can remember, was the one at the Café
Royal. On that occasion he was not too preoccupied with his danger to be disgusted with me because I, who had praised his first plays handsomely, had turned
traitor over *The Importance of Being Earnest.* Clever as it was, it was his first really
heartless play. In the others the chivalry of the eighteenth-century Irishman and
the romance of the disciple of Théophile Gautier (Oscar was old-fashioned in the
Irish way, except as a critic of morals) not only gave a certain kindness and gallantry to the serious passages and to the handling of the women, but provided that
proximity of emotion without which laughter, however irresistible, is destructive
and sinister. In *The Importance of Being Earnest* this had vanished; and the play,
though extremely funny, was essentially hateful. I had no idea that Oscar was
going to the dogs, and that this represented a real degeneracy produced by his
debaucheries. I thought he was still developing; and I hazarded the unhappy
guess that *The Importance of Being Earnest* was in idea a young work written or
projected long before under the influence of Gilbert and furbished up for
Alexander as a potboiler. At the Café Royal that day I calmly asked him whether
I was not right. He indignantly repudiated my guess, and said loftily (the only
time he ever tried on me the attitude he took to John Gray and his more abject
disciples) that he was disappointed in me. I suppose I said, "Then what on earth
has happened to you?" but I recollect nothing more on that subject except that we
did not quarrel over it.

When he was sentenced I spent a railway journey on a Socialist lecturing
excursion to the North drafting a petition for his release. After that I met Willie
Wilde at a theatre which I think must have been the Duke of York's, because I
connect it vaguely with St. Martin's Lane. I spoke to him about the petition, asking him whether anything of the sort was being done, and warning him that
though I and Stewart Headlam would sign it, that would be no use, as we were
two notorious cranks, and our names would by themselves reduce the petition to
absurdity and do Oscar more harm than good. Willie cordially agreed, and
added, with maudlin pathos and an inconceivable want of tact: "Oscar was NOT
a man of bad character: you could have trusted him with a woman anywhere."
He convinced me, as you discovered later, that signatures would not be obtain-
able; so the petition project dropped; and I don't know what became of my draft.

When Wilde was in Paris during his last phase I made a point of sending him inscribed copies of all my books as they came out; and he did the same to me.

In writing about Wilde and Whistler, in the days when they were treated as witty triflers, and called Oscar and Jimmy in print, I always made a point of taking them seriously and with scrupulous good manners. Wilde on his part also made a point of recognizing me as a man of distinction by his manner, and repudiating the current estimate of me as a mere jester. This was not the usual reciprocal-admiration trick: I believe he was sincere, and felt indignant at what he thought was a vulgar underestimate of me; and I had the same feeling about him. My impulse to rally to him in his misfortune, and my disgust at "the man Wilde" scurrilities of the newspapers, was irresistible: I don't quite know why; for my charity to his perversion, and my recognition of the fact that it does not imply any general depravity or coarseness of character, came to me through reading and observation, not through sympathy. I have all the normal violent repugnance to homosexuality—if it be really normal, which nowadays one is sometimes provoked to doubt.

Also, I was in no way predisposed to like him: he was my fellow-townsman, and a very prime specimen of the sort of fellow-townsman I most loathed: to wit, the Dublin snob. His Irish charm, potent with Englishmen, did not exist for me; and on the whole it may be claimed for him that he got no regard from me that he did not earn.

What first established a friendly feeling in me was, unexpectedly enough, the affair of the Chicago anarchists, whose Homer you constituted yourself by your story called *The Bomb*. I tried to get some literary men in London, all heroic rebels and sceptics on paper, to sign a memorial asking for the reprieve of these unfortunate men. The only signature I got was Oscar's. It was a completely disinterested act on his part; and it secured my distinguished consideration for him for the rest of his life.

To return for a moment to Lady Wilde. You know that there is a disease called giantism, caused by "a certain morbid process in the sphenoid bone of the skull—viz., an excessive development of the anterior lobe of the pituitary body" (this is from the nearest encyclopedia). "When this condition does not become active until after the age of twenty-five, by which time the long bones are consolidated, the result is acromegaly, which chiefly manifests itself in an enlargement of the hands and feet." I never saw Lady Wilde's feet; but her hands were enormous, and never went straight to their aim when they grasped anything, but minced about, feeling for it. And the gigantic splaying of her palm was reproduced in her lumbar region.

Now Oscar was an overgrown man, with something not quite normal about his bigness: something that made Lady Colin Campbell, who hated him, describe him as "that great white caterpillar." You yourself describe the disagreeable impression he made on you physically, in spite of his fine eyes and style. Well, I have always maintained that Oscar was a giant in the pathological sense, and that this explains a good deal of his weakness.

I think you have affectionately underrated his snobbery, mentioning only the pardonable and indeed justifiable side of it; the love of fine names and distinguished associations and luxury and good manners. You say repeatedly, and *on certain planes*, truly, that he was not bitter and did not use his tongue to wound people. But this is not true on the snobbish plane. On one occasion he wrote about T. P. O'Connor with deliberate, studied, wounding insolence, with his Merrion Square Protestant pretentiousness in full cry against the Catholic. He repeatedly declaimed against the vulgarity of the British journalist, not as you or I might, but as an expression of the odious class feeling that is itself the vilest vulgarity. He made the mistake of not knowing his place. He objected to be addressed as Wilde, declaring that he was Oscar to his intimates and Mr. Wilde to others, quite unconscious of the fact that he was imposing on the men with whom, as a critic and journalist, he had to live and work, the alternative of granting him an intimacy he had no right to ask or a deference to which he had no claim. The vulgar hated him for snubbing them; and the valiant men damned his impudence and cut him. Thus he was left with a band of devoted satellites on the one hand, and a dining-out connection on the other, with here and there a man of talent and personality enough to command his respect, but utterly without that fortifying body of acquaintance among plain men in which a man must move as himself a plain man, and be Smith and Jones and Wilde and Shaw and Harris instead of Bosie and Robbie and Oscar and Mister. This is the sort of folly that does not last forever in a man of Wilde's ability; but it lasted long enough to prevent Oscar laying any solid social foundations.

Another difficulty I have already hinted at. Wilde started as an apostle of Art; and in that capacity he was a humbug. The notion that a Portora [Ireland's version of Eton] boy, passed on to T.C.D. [Trinity College, Dublin] and thence to Oxford and spending his vacations in Dublin, could without special circumstances have any genuine intimacy with music and painting, is to me ridiculous. When Wilde was at Portora, I was at home in a house where important musical works, including several typical masterpieces, were being rehearsed from the point of blank amateur ignorance up to fitness for public performance. I could whistle them from the first bar to the last as a butcher's boy whistles music-hall songs, before I was twelve. The toleration of popular music—Strauss's waltzes, for instance—was to me positively a painful acquirement, a sort of republican duty.

I was so fascinated by painting that I haunted the National Gallery, which Doyle had made perhaps the finest collection of its size in the world; and I longed for money to buy painting materials with. This afterwards saved me from starving: it was as a critic of music and painting in *The World* that I won through my ten years of journalism before I finished up with you on *The Saturday Review*. I could make deaf stockbrokers read my two pages on music, the alleged joke being that I knew nothing about it. The real joke was that I knew all about it.

Now it was quite evident to me, as it was to Whistler and Beardsley, that Oscar knew no more about pictures than anyone of his general culture and with his opportunities can pick up as he goes along. He could be witty about Art, as I could be witty about engineering; but that is no use when you have to seize and hold the attention and interest of people who really love music and painting. Therefore, Oscar was handicapped by a false start, and got a reputation for shallowness and insincerity which he never retrieved until too late.

Comedy: the criticism of morals and manners *viva voce,* was his real forte. When he settled down to that he was great. But, as you found when you approached Meredith about him, his initial mistake had produced that "rather low opinion of Wilde's capacities," that "deep-rooted contempt for the showman in him," which persisted as a first impression and will persist until the last man who remembers his aesthetic period has perished. The world has been in some ways so unjust to him that one must be careful not to be unjust to the world.

In the preface on education, called "Parents and Children," to my volume of plays beginning with *Misalliance*, there is a section headed "Artist Idolatry," which is really about Wilde. Dealing with "the powers enjoyed by brilliant persons who are also connoisseurs in art," I say, "the influence they can exercise on young people who have been brought up in the darkness and wretchedness of a home without art, and in whom a natural bent towards art has always been baffled and snubbed, is incredible to those who have not witnessed and understood it. He (or she) who reveals the world of art to them opens heaven to them. They become satellites, disciples, worshippers of the apostle. Now the apostle may be a voluptuary without much conscience. Nature may have given him enough virtue to suffice in a reasonable environment. But this allowance may not be enough to defend him against the temptation and demoralization of finding himself a little god on the strength of what ought to be a quite ordinary culture. He may find adorers in all directions in our uncultivated society among people of stronger character than himself, not one of whom, if they had been artistically educated, would have had anything to learn from him, or regarded him as in any way extraordinary apart from his actual achievements as an artist. Tartufe is not always a priest. Indeed, he is not always a rascal: he is often a weak man absurdly credited with omniscience and perfection, and taking unfair advantages only because they are offered to him and he is too weak to refuse. Give everyone his culture, and no one will offer him more than his due."

That paragraph was the outcome of a walk and talk I had one afternoon at Chartres with Robert Ross.

You reveal Wilde as a weaker man than I thought him: I still believe that his fierce Irish pride had something to do with his refusal to run away from the trial. But in the main your evidence is conclusive. It was part of his tragedy that people asked more moral strength from him than he could bear the burden of, because they made the very common mistake—of which actors get the benefit—of regarding style as evidence of strength, just as in the case of women they are apt to regard paint as evidence of beauty. Now Wilde was so in love with style that he never realized the danger of biting off more than he could chew: in other words, of putting up more style than his matter would carry. Wise kings wear shabby clothes, and leave the gold lace to the drum major.

I was at your *Saturday Review* lunch at the Café Royal when Wilde came in just before the trial. He said he had come to ask you to go into the witness box next day and testify that *Dorian Gray* was a highly moral work. Your answer was something like this: "For God's sake, man, put everything on that plane out of your head. You don't realize what is going to happen to you. It is not going to be a matter of clever talk about your books. They are going to bring up a string of witnesses that will put art and literature out of the question. Clarke will throw up his brief. He will carry the case to a certain point; and then, when he sees the avalanche coming, he will back out and leave you in the dock. What you have to do is to cross to France tonight. Leave a letter saying that you cannot face the squalor and horror of a law case; that you are an artist and unfitted for such things. Don't stay here clutching at straws like testimonials to *Dorian Gray*. *I tell you I know.* I know what is going to happen. I know Clarke's sort. I know what evidence they have got. You must go."

It was no use. Wilde was in a curious double temper. He made no pretence either of innocence or of questioning the folly of his proceedings against Queensberry. But he had an infatuate haughtiness as to the impossibility of his retreating, and as to his right to dictate your course. Oscar finally rose with a mixture of impatience and his grand air, and walked out with the remark that he had now found out who were his real friends.

What your book needs to complete it is a portrait of yourself as good as your portrait of Wilde. Oscar was not combative, though he was supercilious in his early pose. When his snobbery was not in action, he liked to make people devoted to him and to flatter them exquisitely with that end. Mrs. Calvert, whose great final period as a stage old woman began with her appearance in my *Arms and the Man*, told me one day, when apologizing for being, as she thought, a bad rehearser, that no author had ever been so nice to her except Mr. Wilde.

Pugnacious people, if they did not actually terrify Oscar, were at least the sort of people he could not control, and whom he feared as possibly able to coerce him. You suggest that the Queensberry pugnacity was something that Oscar could not deal with successfully. But how in that case could Oscar have felt quite safe with you? You were more pugnacious than six Queensberrys rolled into one. When people asked, "What has Frank Harris been?" the usual reply was, "Obviously a pirate from the Spanish Main."

Oscar, from the moment he gained your attachment, could never have been afraid of what you might do to him, as he was sufficient of a connoisseur in Blut Bruderschaft to appreciate yours; but he must always have been mortally afraid of what you might do or say to his friends.

You had quite an infernal scorn for nineteen out of twenty of the men and women you met in the circles he most wished to propitiate; and nothing could induce you to keep your knife in its sheath when they jarred on you. The Spanish Main itself would have blushed rosy red at your language when classical invective did not suffice to express your feelings.

It may be that if, say, Edmund Gosse had come to Oscar when he was out on bail, with a couple of first-class tickets in his pocket, and gently suggested a mild trip to Folkestone, or the Channel Islands, Oscar might have let himself be coaxed away. But to be called on to gallop *ventre à terre* to Erith—it might have been Deal—and hoist the Jolly Roger on board your lugger, was like casting a light comedian and first lover for Richard III. Oscar could not see himself in the part.

I must not press the point too far; but it illustrates, I think, what does not come out at all in your book: that you were a very different person from the submissive and sympathetic disciples to whom he was accustomed. There are things more terrifying to a soul like Oscar's than an as yet unrealized possibility of a sentence of hard labor. A voyage with Captain Kidd may have been one of them. Wilde was a conventional man: his unconventionality was the very pedantry of convention: never was there a man less an outlaw than he. You were a born outlaw, and will never be anything else.

That is why, in his relations with you, he appears as a man always shirking action—more of a coward (all men are cowards more or less) than so proud a man can have been. Still this does not affect the truth and power of your portrait. Wilde's memory will have to stand or fall by it.

You will be blamed, I imagine, because you have not written a lying epitaph instead of a faithful chronicle and study of him; but you will not lose your sleep over that. As a matter of fact, you could not have carried kindness further without sentimental folly. I should have made a far sterner summing up. I am sure Oscar has not found the gates of heaven shut against him: he is too good company to be excluded; but he can hardly have been greeted as "Thou good and faithful servant." The first thing we ask a servant for is a testimonial to honesty, sobriety, and industry; for we soon find out that these are the scarce things, and that geniuses and clever people are as common as rats. Well, Oscar was not sober, not honest, not industrious. Society praised him for being idle, and persecuted him savagely for an aberration which it had better have left unadvertized, thereby making a hero of him; for it is in the nature of people to worship those who have been made to suffer horribly: indeed I have often said that if the Crucifixion could be proved a myth, and Jesus convicted of dying of old age in comfortable circumstances, Christianity would lose ninety-nine percent of its devotees.

We must try to imagine what judgment we should have passed on Oscar if he had been a normal man, and had dug his grave with his teeth in the ordinary respectable fashion, as his brother Willie did. This brother, by the way, gives us some cue; for Willie, who had exactly the same education and the same chances, must be ruthlessly set aside by literary history as a vulgar journalist of no account. Well, suppose Oscar and Willie had both died the day before Queensberry left that card at the Club! Oscar would still have been remembered as a wit and a dandy, and would have had a niche beside Congreve in the drama. A volume of his aphorisms would have stood creditably on the library shelf with La Rochefoucauld's Maxims. We should have missed the *Ballad of Reading Gaol* and *De Profundis*; but he would still have cut a considerable figure in the *Dictionary of National Biography*, and been read and quoted outside the British Museum reading room.

As to the *Ballad* and *De Profundis*, I think it is greatly to Oscar's credit that, whilst he was sincere and deeply moved when he was protesting against the cruelty of our present system to children and to prisoners generally, he could not write about his own individual share in that suffering with any conviction or sympathy. Except for the passage where he describes his exposure at Clapham Junction, there is hardly a line in *De Profundis* that he might not have written as a literary feat five years earlier. But in the *Ballad*, even in borrowing form and melody from Coleridge, he shews that he could pity others when he could not seriously pity himself. And this, I think, may be pleaded against the reproach that he was selfish. Externally, in the ordinary action of life as distinguished from the literary action proper to his genius, he was no doubt sluggish and weak because of his giantism. He ended as an unproductive drunkard and swindler; for his repeated sales of the Daventry plot, in so far as they imposed on the buyers and were not transparent excuses for begging, were undeniably swindles. For all that, he does not appear in his writings a selfish or base-minded man. He is at his worst and weakest in the suppressed part of *De Profundis*; but in my opinion it had better be published, for several reasons. It explains some of his personal weakness by the stifling narrowness of his daily round, ruinous to a man whose proper place was in a large public life. And its concealment is mischievous because, first, it leads people to imagine all sorts of horrors in a document which contains nothing worse than any record of the squabbles of two touchy men on a holiday; and, second, it is clearly a monstrous thing that one of them should have a torpedo launched at him and timed to explode after his death.

Now that you have written the best life of Oscar Wilde, let us have the best life of Frank Harris. Otherwise the man behind your works will go down to posterity as the hero of my very inadequate preface to *The Dark Lady of the Sonnets*.

W. B. YEATS

POEMS

Nobel laureate William Butler Yeats's poems range from the lyrical to the narrative, from passionate songs of love to somber visions of life in a nation torn by uprising and war. All follow in the great Irish bardic storytelling tradition; all are infused with a quintessentially Irish lushness of language. In Yeats's poems we discover exquisitely crafted surfaces and deft musical phrasing perhaps unrivaled in the whole of literature.

Yeats's recastings of Irish myths and Celtic lore are made richer under his artful touch, wherein potent symbols, sound, and sense fuse. Throughout, we follow his amassing philosophical system, his mystical conceptions of the turns of history, and his fervent linking of the personal with the universal, the mundane with the spiritual, the psychological with the vast eternal.

The poems selected here showcase these qualities and provide a vivid snapshot of Yeats's poetic genius. "The Lake Isle of Innisfree" borrows from the tradition of Celtic song. Yeats evokes the magical lure of nature, the very heartbeat of a charmed landscape—buzzing, glimmering, singing. It is here, in the bosom of nature, in a cabin at the shore (one thinks of links with Wordsworth, Whitman, Walden), we will find the cradle of peace.

"No Second Troy" is one of the most famous odes to unrequited love ever penned. Much has been written of Yeats's tortured infatuation with the beautiful Maud Gonne. Here he likens her to Helen of Troy, and depicts her dangerous power as an archer's bow about to spring.

In "The Wild Swans at Coole," Yeats crafts a sublimely graceful scene (what could be more timeless and tranquil than to watch lovely swans adrift on a mirror of water?). But this Keatsean eternal moment proves ephemeral, and the poem reveals the sweet melancholy that underlies contentment, love, and peace.

Another sort of resignedness permeates Yeats's poem "The Second Coming"; specifically an attitude of acceptance and an air of gloomy expectedness toward the 2,000-year cycles of history that are central to Yeats's mystical philosophy. A decidedly ominous portend of apocalypse, of the unknown which follows an epoch when "the centre cannot hold."

Myth made startlingly personal, urgent, and inevitable makes for violent drama in "Leda and the Swan." The rape is experienced in sensual terms to an almost uncomfortable degree of clarity; what Leda feels and suffers and knows will not only alter her own world but will change the course of history as well.

"Sailing to Byzantium" also concerns the cycles of time, the "gyres" of ages. Yet here the poet crafts an eerie ars poetica, and links his own personal search for something permanent to the universal cycles of decay, violence, and rebirth. He relinquishes the natural world for artifice, "Of hammered gold and gold enamelling," choosing aesthetic mastery as his own consolation for immortality.

The human and the sublime merge to more extended effect in "Lapis Lazuli," Yeats's dizzying depiction of ever-crumbling civilizations, where every measure of aesthetic richness becomes overwrought, even physically disfigured. But the vital power of transcendent imagination is affirmed, and the all-knowing Chinamen's ancient eyes remain "glittering," and "are gay."

The fate of civilization rests on the measured grace of a leader lost in thought, of the movements of a single mind, in "Long-Legged Fly." The precision of language in this poem plays fit counterpoint to the exactingly beautiful recurrent image: a fly walking on water. Silent thought—well-turned, agile, seemingly miraculous—has its own sort of sensuality, erotic allure, maybe even spiritual significance.

These brilliant pairings of the ineffable and the tangible, apocalypse and permanence, physical and spiritual, artifice and reality—all rendered in language that sounds only as it should, inevitable—make for the most satisfying of reading experiences. This, then, is the singular and innovative yet tradition-hewn voice that could emanate only from an Irish bard named W. B. Yeats.

THE LAKE ISLE OF INNISFREE

I will arise and go now, and go to Innisfree,
And a small cabin build there, of clay and wattles made:
Nine bean-rows will I have there, a hive for the honey-bee,
And live alone in the bee-loud glade.

And I shall have some peace there, for peace comes dropping slow,
Dropping from the veils of the morning to where the cricket sings;
There midnight's all a glimmer, and noon a purple glow,
And evening full of the linnet's wings.

I will arise and go now, for always night and day
I hear lake water lapping with low sounds by the shore;
While I stand on the roadway, or on the pavements grey,
I hear it in the deep heart's core.

[1893]

NO SECOND TROY

Why should I blame her that she filled my days
With misery, or that she would of late
Have taught to ignorant men most violent ways,
Or hurled the little streets upon the great,
Had they but courage equal to desire?
What could have made her peaceful with a mind
That nobleness made simple as a fire,
With beauty like a tightened bow, a kind
That is not natural in an age like this,
Being high and solitary and most stern?
Why, what could she have done, being what she is?
Was there another Troy for her to burn?

[1910]

THE WILD SWANS AT COOLE

The trees are in their autumn beauty,
The woodland paths are dry,
Under the October twilight the water
Mirrors a still sky;
Upon the brimming water among the stones
Are nine-and-fifty swans.

The nineteenth autumn has come upon me
Since I first made my count;
I saw, before I had well finished,
All suddenly mount
And scatter wheeling in great broken rings
Upon their clamorous wings.

I have looked upon those brilliant creatures,
And now my heart is sore.
All's changed since I, hearing at twilight,
The first time on this shore,
The bell-beat of their wings above my head,
Trod with a lighter tread.

Unwearied still, lover by lover,
They paddle in the cold
Companionable streams or climb the air;
Their hearts have not grown old;
Passion or conquest, wander where they will,
Attend upon them still.

But now they drift on the still water,
Mysterious, beautiful;
Among what rushes will they build,
By what lake's edge or pool
Delight men's eyes when I awake some day
To find they have flown away?

[1919]

THE SECOND COMING

Turning and turning in the widening gyre
The falcon cannot hear the falconer;
Things fall apart; the centre cannot hold;
Mere anarchy is loosed upon the world,
The blood-dimmed tide is loosed, and everywhere
The ceremony of innocence is drowned;
The best lack all conviction, while the worst
Are full of passionate intensity.

Surely some revelation is at hand;
Surely the Second Coming is at hand.
The Second Coming! Hardly are those words out
When a vast image out of *Spiritus Mundi*
Troubles my sight: somewhere in sands of the desert
A shape with lion body and the head of a man,
A gaze blank and pitiless as the sun,
Is moving its slow thighs, while all about it
Reel shadows of the indignant desert birds.
The darkness drops again; but now I know
That twenty centuries of stony sleep
Were vexed to nightmare by a rocking cradle,
And what rough beast, its hour come round at last,
Slouches towards Bethlehem to be born?

[1921]

LEDA AND THE SWAN

A sudden blow: the great wings beating still
Above the staggering girl, her thighs caressed
By the dark webs, her nape caught in his bill,
He holds her helpless breast upon his breast.

How can those terrified vague fingers push
The feathered glory from her loosening thighs?
And how can body, laid in that white rush,
But feel the strange heart beating where it lies?

A shudder in the loins engenders there
The broken wall, the burning roof and tower
And Agamemnon dead.
                              Being so caught up,
So mastered by the brute blood of the air,
Did she put on his knowledge with his power
Before the indifferent beak could let her drop?

[1923]

SAILING TO BYZANTIUM

I

That is no country for old men. The young
In one another's arms, birds in the trees,
—Those dying generations—at their song,
The salmon-falls, the mackerel-crowded seas,
Fish, flesh, or fowl, commend all summer long
Whatever is begotten, born, and dies.
Caught in that sensual music all neglect
Monuments of unageing intellect.

II

An aged man is but a paltry thing,
A tattered coat upon a stick, unless
Soul clap its hands and sing, and louder sing
For every tatter in its mortal dress,
Nor is there singing school but studying
Monuments of its own magnificence;
And therefore I have sailed the seas and come
To the holy city of Byzantium.

III

O sages standing in God's holy fire
As in the gold mosaic of a wall,
Come from the holy fire, perne in a gyre,
And be the singing-masters of my soul.
Consume my heart away; sick with desire
And fastened to a dying animal
It knows not what it is; and gather me
Into the artifice of eternity.

IV

Once out of nature I shall never take
My bodily form from any natural thing,
But such a form as Grecian goldsmiths make
Of hammered gold and gold enamelling
To keep a drowsy Emperor awake;
Or set upon a golden bough to sing
To lords and ladies of Byzantium
Of what is past, or passing, or to come.

[1927]

LAPIS LAZULI
(For Harry Clifton)

I have heard that hysterical women say
They are sick of the palette and fiddle-bow,
Of poets that are always gay,
For everybody knows or else should know
That if nothing drastic is done
Aeroplane and Zeppelin will come out,
Pitch like King Billy bomb-balls in
Until the town lie beaten flat.

All perform their tragic play,
There struts Hamlet, there is Lear,
That's Ophelia, that Cordelia;
Yet they, should the last scene be there,
The great stage curtain about to drop,
If worthy their prominent part in the play,
Do not break up their lines to weep.
They know that Hamlet and Lear are gay;
Gaiety transfiguring all that dread.
All men have aimed at, found and lost;
Black out; Heaven blazing into the head:
Tragedy wrought to its uttermost.
Though Hamlet rambles and Lear rages,
And all the drop scenes drop at once
Upon a hundred thousand stages,
It cannot grow by an inch or an ounce.

On their own feet they came, or on shipboard,
Camel-back, horse-back, ass-back, mule-back,
Old civilisations put to the sword.
Then they and their wisdom went to rack:
No handiwork of Callimachus
Who handled marble as if it were bronze,
Made draperies that seemed to rise
When sea-wind swept the corner, stands;
His long lamp chimney shaped like the stem
Of a slender palm, stood but a day;
All things fall and are built again
And those that build them again are gay.

Two Chinamen, behind them a third,
Are carved in Lapis Lazuli,
Over them flies a long-legged bird
A symbol of longevity;
The third, doubtless a serving-man,
Carries a musical instrument.

Every discolouration of the stone,
Every accidental crack or dent
Seems a water-course or an avalanche,
Or lofty slope where it still snows
Though doubtless plum or cherry-branch
Sweetens the little half-way house
Those Chinamen climb towards, and I
Delight to imagine them seated there;
There, on the mountain and the sky,
On all the tragic scene they stare.
One asks for mournful melodies;
Accomplished fingers begin to play.
Their eyes mid many wrinkles, their eyes,
Their ancient, glittering eyes, are gay.

[1938]

LONG-LEGGED FLY

That civilisation may not sink
Its great battle lost,
Quiet the dog, tether the pony
To a distant post.
Our master Caesar is in the tent
Where the maps are spread,
His eyes fixed upon nothing,
A hand under his head.

Like a long-legged fly upon the stream
His mind moves upon silence.

That the topless towers be burnt
And men recall that face,
Move most gently if move you must
In this lonely place.
She thinks, part woman, three parts a child,
That nobody looks; her feet
Practise a tinker shuffle
Picked up on the street.

Like a long-legged fly upon the stream
Her mind moves upon silence.

That girls at puberty may find
The first Adam in their thought,
Shut the door of the Pope's chapel,
Keep those children out.
There on the scaffolding reclines
Michael Angelo.
With no more sound than the mice make
His hand moves to and fro.

Like a long-legged fly upon the stream
His mind moves upon silence.

[1938-39]

W. B. YEATS

FROM
MEMOIRS

These excerpts come from W. B. Yeats's Memoirs, *which first appeared in 1972, and consists of material that Yeats left out of his many published works of autobiography. In these excerpts, which span a period of about ten years, Yeats describes how "the troubling of my life began" in 1889, when he met the beautiful Irish nationalist Maud Gonne, who would be the great (though unrequited) love of his life. The footnotes placed at the end are by Denis Donoghue, who edited* Memoirs, *and they point out when manuscript readings may be doubtful, indicate when words have been crossed out by Yeats on the original, and offer brief biographical notations on individuals mentioned within the text.*

I WAS TWENTY-THREE YEARS OLD when the troubling of my life began. I had heard from time to time in letters from Miss O'Leary,[1] John O'Leary's old sister, of a beautiful girl who had left the society of the Viceregal Court for Dublin nationalism. In after years I persuaded myself that I felt premonitory excitement at the first reading of her name.[2] Presently she drove up to our house in Bedford Park with an introduction from John O'Leary to my father.[3] I had never thought to see in a living woman so great beauty. It belonged to famous pictures, to poetry, to some legendary past. A complexion like the blossom of apples, and yet face and body had the beauty of lineaments which Blake calls the highest beauty because it changes least from youth to age, and a stature so great that she seemed of a divine race. Her movements were worthy of her form, and I understood at last why the poet of antiquity, where we would but speak of face and form, sings, loving some lady, that she paces like a goddess. I remember nothing of her speech that day except that she vexed my father by praise of war, for she too was of the Romantic movement and found those uncontrovertible Victorian reasons, that seemed to announce so prosperous a future, a little grey. As I look back-

319

ward, it seems to me that she brought into my life in those days—for as yet I saw only what lay upon the surface—the middle of the tint, a sound as of a Burmese gong, an overpowering tumult that had yet many pleasant secondary notes.

She asked [me] to dine with her that evening in her rooms in Ebury Street, and I think that I dined with her all but every day during her stay in London of perhaps nine days, and there was something so exuberant in her ways that it seemed natural she should give her hours in overflowing abundance. She had heard of me from O'Leary; he had praised me, and it was natural that she should give and take without stint. She lived surrounded by cages of innumerable singing birds and with these she always travelled, it seemed, taking them even upon short journeys, and they and she were now returning to Paris where their home was.

She spoke to me of her wish for a play that she could act in Dublin. Somebody had suggested Todhunter's[4] *Helena in Troas*, but he had refused. I told her of a story I had found when compiling my *Fairy and Folk Tales of the Irish Peasantry*, and offered to write for her the play I have called *The Countess Cathleen*. When I told her I wished to become an Irish Victor Hugo, was I wholly sincere?—for though a volume of bad verse translations from Hugo had been my companion at school, I had begun to simplify myself with great toil. I had seen upon her table *Tristram of Lyonesse*[5] and *Les Contemplations*, and besides it was natural to commend myself by claiming a very public talent, for her beauty as I saw it in those days seemed incompatible with private, intimate life.

She, like myself, had received the political tradition of Davis[6] with an added touch of hardness and heroism from the hand of O'Leary, and when she spoke of William O'Brien,[7] [who] was in jail making a prolonged struggle against putting on the prison clothes, she said, "There was a time when men sacrificed their lives for their country, but now they sacrifice their dignity." But mixed with this feeling for what is permanent in human life there was something declamatory, Latin in a bad sense, and perhaps even unscrupulous. She spoke of her desire for power, apparently for its own sake, and when we talked of politics spoke much of mere effectiveness, or the mere winning of this or that election. Her two and twenty years had taken some colour, I thought, from French Boulangist adventurers and journalist *arrivistes* of whom she had seen too much, and [she] already had made some political journey into Russia in their interest. I was full of that thought of the "Animula Vagula" chapter, I had heard it at the feet of a young Brahmin[8] in Dublin, "Only the means can justify the end." She meant her ends to be unselfish, but she thought almost any means justified in their success. We were seeking different things: she, some memorable action for final consecration of her youth, and I, after all, but to discover and communicate a state of being. Perhaps even in politics it would in the end be enough to have lived and thought passionately and have, like O'Leary, a head worthy of a Roman coin.

I spoke much of my spiritual philosophy. How important it all seemed to me;

what would I not have given that she might think exactly right on all those great questions of the day? All is but faint to me beside a moment when she passed before a window, dressed in white, and rearranged a spray of flowers in a vase. Twelve years afterwards I put that impression into verse: ("she pulled down the pale blossom." Quote):

> [Blossom pale, she pulled down the pale blossom
> At the moth hour and hid it in her bosom.] [9]

I felt in the presence of a great generosity and courage, and of a mind without peace, and when she and all her singing birds had gone my melancholy was not the mere melancholy of love. I had what I thought was a "clairvoyant" perception but was, I can see now, but an obvious deduction of an awaiting immediate disaster. I was compiling for an American publisher a selection from the Irish novelists, [10] and I can remember that all the tribulations of their heroes but reminded me of that dread. They too, according to a fashion of the writers of early Victoria, had been so often thrown without father or mother or guardian amid a world of deception, and they too, in their different way, were incurably romantic. I was in love but had not spoken of love and never meant to speak, and as the months passed I grew master of myself again. "What wife could she make," I thought, "what share could she have in the life of a student?"

↓

One evening we [Gonne and Yeats] were joined by a friend I had made at the art school in Kildare Street.[11] This was George Russell.[12] He had given up art and was now an accountant in a draper's shop, for his will was weak and an emotional occupation would have weakened it still further. He had seen many visions, and some of them had contained information about matters of fact that were afterwards verified; but, though his own personal revelation was often original and very remarkable, he accepted in the main the conclusions of Theosophy. He spoke of reincarnation, and Maud Gonne asked him, "How soon a child was reborn, and if [reborn], where?" He said, "It may be reborn in the same family." I could see that Maud Gonne was deeply impressed, and I quieted my more sceptical intelligence, as I have so often done in her presence. I remember a pang of conscience. Ought I not to say, "The whole doctrine of the reincarnation of the soul is hypothetical. It is the most plausible of the explanations of the world, but can we say more than that?" or some like sentence?

I had already taken a decision that will not suggest scepticism. She now told me of an apparition of a woman dressed in grey and with a grey veil covering the lower part of her face, which had appeared to her [in] childhood. Perhaps when one loves one is not quite sane, or perhaps one can pierce—in sudden intuition—

behind the veil.[13] I decided to make this woman visible at will. I had come to believe that she was an evil spirit troubling Maud Gonne's life unseen, weakening affections and above all creating a desire for power and excitement. But, if it were visible, it would speak, it would put its temptation into words and she would face it with her intellect, and at last banish it. I made a symbol according to the rules of my Order, considering it as an inhabitant of the fifth element with another element subordinate, and almost at once it became visible. I of course saw nothing beyond an uncertain impression on the mind, but Maud Gonne saw it almost as if palpably present. It told its story, taking up what was perhaps a later event of her dream of the desert. It was a past personality of hers, now seeking to be reunited with her. She had been priestess in a temple somewhere in Egypt and under the influence of a certain priest who was her lover gave false oracles for money, and because of this the personality of that life had split off from the soul and remained a half-living shadow. I would have taken all this for but a symbolic event, expressing a psychological state or spirit (is not Rahab "an Eternal State" in William Blake?),[14] but for a coincidence. When I had been in the Esoteric Section of the Theosophical Society, I had been taught as one of the secrets of that initiation that a just such separated, half-living personality might haunt the soul in its new life and seek a reunion that must be always refused. I had not then the evidence that I have now of the most profound knowledge of all that passes in our minds and in the minds of those with whom we are even in remote contact, upon the part of beings of whom I know nothing except that they are invisible, subtle, and perhaps full of a secret laughter.

She had come [to] have need of me, as it seemed, and I had no doubt that need would become love, that it was already coming so. I had even as I watched her a sense of cruelty, as though I were a hunter taking captive some beautiful wild creature.[15] We went to London and were initiated in the Hermetic Students, and I began to form plans of our lives devoted to mystic truth, and spoke to her of Nicholas Flamel and his wife, Pernella.[16] In a propaganda, secret and seeking out only the most profound and subtle minds, that great beauty would be to others, as it was always to me, symbolic and mysterious. She stayed with her sister in London. I noticed that one evening when I paid her some compliment her face was deeply tinted. She returned to Paris, and her cousin, a young girl of like age, meeting me in the street, asked me "why I was not in Paris." I had no money. I had spent in Ireland all my earnings, and now instead of earning more as quickly as possible I spent more than half my time writing to her. Surely if I told her all my thoughts, all my hopes and ambitions, she would never leave me.

↓

I came to hate her politics, my one visible rival. One day when [she] spent all day playing with a hawk somebody had sent her from Donegal I was delighted, because she gave up for that play a political caucus. The candidate she was interested in was defeated by half-a-dozen votes. "But for you," she said, "he would have been returned," and I was scornful at the idea that an Irish member the more would have been worth spoiling our day for, when we had so few days. I thought that the forces I had myself begun to organize, and like forces, would settle all such things, give them but time. We had a quarrel, and even after she had gone to France and returned again there was a slight estrangement. I was on my side deeply moved because she seemed to take my own work, especially a quarrel that had arisen, too lightly. To her it was only, it often seemed, a troublesome dispute among her friends that she kept herself apart from out of decent tact. I believed that the intellectual future of Ireland was at stake.

$$\downarrow$$

On a visit to Dr. Hyde I had seen the Castle Rock, as it was called, in Lough Key.[17] There is this small island entirely covered by what was a still habitable but empty castle. The last man who had lived there had been Dr. Hyde's father who, when a young man, lived there for a few weeks. All round were the wooded and hilly shores, a place of great beauty. I believed that the castle could be hired for little money, and had long been dreaming of making it an Irish Eleusis or Samothrace. An obsession more constant than anything but my love itself was the need of mystical rites—a ritual system of evocation and meditation—to reunite the perception of the spirit, of the divine, with natural beauty. I believed that instead of thinking of Judea as holy we should [think] our own land holy, and most holy where most beautiful. Commerce and manufacture had made the world ugly; the death of pagan nature-worship had robbed visible beauty of its inviolable sanctity. I was convinced that all lonely and lovely places were crowded with invisible beings and that it would be possible to communicate with them. I meant to initiate young men and women in this worship, which would unite the radical truths of Christianity to those of a more ancient world, and to use the Castle Rock for their occasional retirement from the world.

For years to come it was in my thought, as in much of my writing, to seek also to bring again in[to] imaginative life the old sacred places—Slievenamon, Knocknarea—all that old reverence that hung—above all—about conspicuous hills. But I wished by my writings and those of the school I hoped to found to have a secret symbolical relation to these mysteries, for in that way, I thought, there will be a greater richness, a greater claim upon the love of the soul, doctrine without exhortation and rhetoric. Should not religion hide within the work of art as God is within His world, and how can the interpreter do more than whisper? I did not wish to compose rites as if for the theatre. They must in their main outline be the work of invisible hands.

My own seership was, I thought, inadequate; it was to be Maud Gonne's work and mine. Perhaps that was why we had been thrown together. Were there not strange harmonies amid discord? My outer nature was passive—but for her I should never perhaps have left my desk—but I knew my spiritual nature was passionate, even violent. In her all this was reversed, for it was her spirit only that was gentle and passive and full of charming fantasy, as though it touched the world only with the point of its finger. When I had first met her I had used as a test the death symbol, imagining it in my own mind, but not wishing to alarm her had asked that it should take the form not of a human but of a dog's skull. She said, "I see a figure holding out its hand with a skull on it. No, there is a bruise[18] on the hand, but I was compelled to say it was a skull." I, who could not influence her actions, could dominate her inner being. I could therefore use her clairvoyance to produce forms that would arise from both minds, though mainly seen by one, and escape therefore from what is mere[ly] personal. There would be, as it were, a spiritual birth from the soul of a man and a woman. I knew that the incomprehensible life could select from our memories and, I believed, from the memory of the race itself; could realize of ourselves, beyond personal predilection, all it required, of symbol and of myth. I believed we were about to attain a revelation.

Maud Gonne entirely shared these ideas, and I did not doubt that in carrying them out I should win her for myself. Politics were merely a means of meeting, but this was a link so perfect that [it] would restore at once, even [after] a quarrel, the sense of intimacy. At every moment of leisure we obtained in vision long lists of symbols. Various trees corresponded to cardinal points, and the old gods and heroes took their places gradually in a symbolic fabric that had for its centre the four talismans of the Tuatha de Danaan, the sword, the stone, the spear and the cauldron, which related themselves in my mind with the suits of the Tarot. George Pollexfen, though already an old man, shared my plans, and his slow and difficult clairvoyance added certain symbols. He and Maud Gonne only met once—in politics he was an extreme Unionist—but he and she worked with each other's symbols and I did much of the work in his house. The forms became very continuous in my thoughts, and when AE came to stay at Coole he asked who was the white jester he had seen about the corridors. It was a form I associated with the god Aengus.

It was a time of great personal strain and sorrow. Since my mistress had left me, no other woman had come into my life, and for nearly seven years none did. I was tortured by sexual desire and disappointed love. Often as I walked in the woods at Coole it would have been a relief to have screamed aloud.[19] When desire became an unendurable torture, I would masturbate, and that, no matter how moderate I was, would make me ill. It never occurred to me to seek another love.

I would repeat to myself again and again the last confession of Lancelot, and indeed it was my greatest pride, "I have loved a queen beyond measure and exceeding long." I was never before or since so miserable as in those years that followed my first visit to Coole. In the second as during the first visit my nervous system was worn out. The toil of dressing in the morning exhausted me, and Lady Gregory began to send me cups of soup when I was called.

✥

I joined Maud Gonne from time to time, once at Belfast, where she [had] gone on some political mission, sometimes at Paris, often in Dublin. In Dublin I never went to the same hotel, fearing to compromise her, though she often laughed at my scruple. Once she complained that she saw too much of me. "I do not say," she said, "that the crowds are in love with me, but they would hate anybody who was." But I never failed to get my letter saying when we could meet. One morning I woke in my hotel somewhere near Rutland Square with the fading vision of her face bending over mine and the knowledge that she had just kissed me. I joined her after breakfast in the Nassau Hotel. We were to spend the day together and visit in the afternoon the old Fenian leader, James Stephens. She said, "Had you a strange dream last night?" I said, "I dreamed this morning for the first time in my life that you kissed me." She made no answer, but late that night when dinner was over and I was about to return home she said, "I will tell you now what happened. When I fell asleep last night I saw standing at my bedside a great spirit. He took me to a great throng of spirits, and you were among them. My hand was put into yours and I was told that we were married. After that, I remember nothing." Then and there for the first time with the bodily mouth, she kissed me.

The next day I found her sitting very gloomily over the fire. "I should not have spoken to you in that way," she said, "for I can never be your wife in reality." I said, "Do you love anybody else?" and she said "No" but added that there was somebody else, and that she had to be a moral nature for two. Then bit by bit came out the story of her life, things I had heard all twisted awry by scandal, and disbelieved.

She had met in the South of France the French Boulangist deputy, Millevoye,[20] while staying with a relative in her nineteenth year, and had at once and without any urging on his part fallen in love with him. She then returned to Dublin where her father[21] had a military command.[22] She had sat one night over the fire thinking over her future life. She longed to have control over her own life, and chance discovery of some book on magic among her father's books had made her believe that the Devil, if she prayed to him, might help her. He was rather a real personage to her, for in her earlier girlhood she had wanted to join a convent. She asked the Devil to give her control of her own life and offered in return her soul. At that moment the clock struck twelve, and she felt of a sudden that the prayer had been heard and answered. Within a fortnight her father died suddenly, and she was stricken with remorse.

She had control of her life now, and when she was of age settled in Paris, and after some months became Millevoye's mistress. She was often away from him, for sexual love soon began to repel her, but was for all that very much in love. Then he failed her in various ways. But [she] gave me no coherent account and when I asked some questions clenched her hands together and said it was not well to speak of such things. He had, I discovered, at one time urged her to become the mistress of one man to help his political projects, and that she had refused. Then a little boy was born, the adopted child I had been told of—she thought that sexual love was only justified by children. If the boy had not died, she would have broken with Millevoye altogether and lived in Ireland. As it was, after its death she had thought of breaking with him, and had engaged herself for a week to someone else—I thought, I may have had that poor betrothal for my reward— but had broken it off. The idea came to her that the lost child might be reborn, and she had gone back to Millevoye, in the vault under the memorial chapel. A girl child was born, now two years old.[23] Since the child's birth, I understood her to say amid so much broken speech, she and Millevoye had lived apart.

But she was necessary to him, "She did not know what would happen to him if her influence was not there." I wonder as I write these words if I rightly understood, if she had not [in] mind some service he might fall from, to a political idea. I thought at the time that [she] was appeasing a troubled conscience by performing to the last tittle every duty, and Lady Gregory confirmed me later in this thought. And in all that followed I was careful to touch [her] as one might a sister. If she was to come to me, it must be from no temporary passionate impulse, but with the approval of her conscience. Many a time since then, as I lay awake at night, have I accused myself of acting, not as I thought from a high scruple, but from a dread of moral responsibility, and my thoughts have gone round and round, as do miserable thoughts, coming to no solution.

A little later, how many days I do not remember, we were sitting together when she said, "I hear a voice saying, 'You are about to receive the initiation of the spear.'" We became silent; a double vision unfolded itself, neither speaking till all was finished. She thought herself a great stone statue through which passed flame, and I felt myself becoming flame and mounting up through and looking out of the eyes of a great stone Minerva. Were the beings which stand behind human life trying to unite us, or had we brought it by our own dreams? She was now always very emotional, and would kiss me very tenderly, but when I spoke of marriage on the eve of her leaving said, "No, it seems to me impossible." And then, with clenched hands, "I have a horror and terror of physical love." Lady Gregory was in Venice, but had come home at once on receiving from me an incoherent letter. She offered me money to travel, and told me not to leave Maud Gonne till I had her promise of marriage, but I said, "No, I am too exhausted; I can do no more."

✟

[1] Ellen O'Leary (1831-89). Yeats wrote a brief Introduction to a selection of her poems in 1892.

[2] Maud Gonne (December 20, 1865-April 27, 1953).

[3] January 30, 1889. O'Leary (1830-1907), the Fenian leader, had returned to Ireland in 1885 after five years' imprisonment and fifteen years' exile.

[4] John Todhunter (1839-1916), poet, dramatist, man of letters, author of *A Study of Shelley* (1880) and *Life of Patrick Sarsfield* (1895).

[5] Swinburne's *Tristram of Lyonesse, and Other Poems* (1882) included the poem "The Statue of Victor Hugo," one of Swinburne's many tributes to Hugo.

[6] Thomas Davis (1814-45), leader of the Young Ireland movement, and one of the founders of *The Nation* in 1842.

[7] William O'Brien (1852-1928), journalist, Nationalist member of Parliament, founder of the agrarian and Nationalist paper, *United Ireland*, in 1881.

[8] Mohini Chatterji, the Indian sage, arrived in London in 1884 and visited Dublin, where Yeats met him, in late 1885 or early 1886. See *Collected Poems*, pp. 279-80.

[9] From "The Arrow," in the version which appeared in *In the Seven Woods* (1903).

[10] *Representative Irish Tales,* compiled by W. B. Yeats (New York, Putnam's Sons, 1891).

[11] Metropolitan School of Art, Leinster House, Kildare Street, Dublin, where Yeats studied, 1884-6.

[12] George W. Russell (AE) (1867-1935), poet and mystic. At this time he was working in Pim's, South Great George's Street, Dublin.

[13] "I have often wondered if I did great evil." deleted.

[14] "Rahab is an Eternal State," "Jerusalem," plate 52, *Complete Writings,* p. 681.

[15] "I began to talk to her of my plan, which I thought she felt only less emphatically. I wished now to make her my lover." deleted.

[16] In the Cuala Press edition of *The Green Helmet, and Other Poems* (1910) the first eight poems are linked under the title, "Raymond Lully and his wife Pernella." An erratum note reads, in part: "By a slip of the pen when I was writing out the heading for the first group of poems, I put Raymond Lully's name in the room of the later Alchemist, Nicholas Flamel."

[17] Yeats stayed at Frenchpark from April 13 to May 1, 1895.

[18] Doubtful reading.

[19] "It was the most miserable time of my life." deleted.

[20] Lucien Millevoye, French political journalist, editor of *La Patrie.*

[21] The words from the beginning of the present paragraph up to this point are deleted, but they are required by the narrative.

[22] Colonel Thomas Gonne was Assistant Adjutant-General in Dublin. Sean O'Casey has the following passage in *Inishfallen, Fare Thee Well:* "There she sits stonily silent, once a sibyl of patriotism from whom no oracle ever came; now silent and aged; her deep-set eyes now sad, agleam with disappointment; never quite at ease with the crowd, whose cheers she loved; the colonel's daughter still." O'Casey, *Autobiographies II* (London, Macmillan, 1963 edition), pp. 152-3.

[23] Iseult Gonne (1895-1954)

J. M. SYNGE

THE PLAYBOY OF
THE WESTERN WORLD

John Millington Synge's 1907 play caused a disturbance upon its first performance at Dublin's Abbey Theatre because of one mention of a woman's slip. Synge sets the play in a small county Mayo village and uses the poetic yet simple language of the ordinary people who live there to explore hypocrisy and identity. Christy Mahon, a colorless young man and the playboy of the title, arrives in the village claiming to have murdered his father. He is lionized by all, but especially by the young women who vie for his attention. By the way, the "Western World" of the title refers only to the west of Ireland.

PREFACE

IN WRITING *The Playboy of the Western World*, as in my other plays, I have used one or two words only that I have not heard among the country people of Ireland, or spoken in my own nursery before I could read the newspapers. A certain number of the phrases I employ I have heard also from herds and fishermen along the coast from Kerry to Mayo or from beggar-women and ballad-singers nearer Dublin; and I am glad to acknowledge how much I owe to the folk-imagination of these fine people. Anyone who has lived in real intimacy with the Irish peasantry will know that the wildest sayings and ideas in this play are tame indeed, compared with the fancies one may hear in any little hillside cabin in Geesala, or Carraroe, or Dingle Bay. All art is a collaboration; and there is little doubt that in the happy ages of literature, striking and beautiful phrases were as ready to the story-teller's or the playwright's hand, as the rich cloaks and dresses of his time. It is probable that when the Elizabethan dramatist took his ink-horn and sat down to his work he used many phrases that he had just heard, as he sat at dinner, from his mother or his children. In Ireland, those of us who know the

329

people have the same privilege. When I was writing *The Shadow of the Glen*, some years ago, I got more aid than any learning could have given me from a chink in the floor of the old Wicklow house where I was staying, that let me hear what was being said by the servant girls in the kitchen. This matter, I think, is of importance, for in countries where the imagination of the people, and the language they use, is rich and living, it is possible for a writer to be rich and copious in his words, and at the same time to give the reality, which is the root of all poetry, in a comprehensive and natural form. In the modern literature of towns, however, richness is found only in sonnets, or prose poems, or in one or two elaborate books that are far away from the profound and common interests of life. One has, on one side, Mallarmé and Huysmans producing this literature; and on the other, Ibsen and Zola dealing with the reality of life in joyless and pallid words. On the stage one must have reality, and one must have joy; and that is why the intellectual modern drama has failed, and people have grown sick of the false joy of the musical comedy, that has been given them in place of the rich joy found only in what is superb and wild in reality. In a good play every speech should be as fully flavoured as a nut or apple, and such speeches cannot be written by anyone who works among people who have shut their lips on poetry. In Ireland, for a few years more, we have a popular imagination that is fiery, and magnificent, and tender; so that those of us who wish to write start with a chance that is not given to writers in places where the springtime of the local life has been forgotten, and the harvest is a memory only, and the straw has been turned into bricks.

J. M. S.
January 21, 1907

PERSONS IN THE PLAY

CHRISTOPHER MAHON
OLD MAHON, *his father, a squatter*
MICHAEL JAMES FLAHERTY (called MICHAEL JAMES), *a publican*
MARGARET FLAHERTY (called PEGEEN MIKE), *his daughter*
WIDOW QUIN, *a woman of about thirty*
SHAWN KEOGH, *her cousin, a young farmer*
PHILLY CULLEN and JIMMY FARRELL, *small farmers*
SARA TANSEY, SUSAN BRADY and HONOR BLAKE, *village girls*
A BELLMAN
SOME PEASANTS

The action takes place near a village, on a wild coast of Mayo. The first Act passes on an evening of autumn, the other two Acts on the following day.

ACT I

Country public-house or shebeen, very rough and untidy. There is a sort of counter on the right with shelves, holding many bottles and jugs, just seen above it. Empty barrels stand near the counter. At back, a little to left of counter, there is a door into the open air, then, more to the left, there is a settle with shelves above it, with more jugs, and a table beneath a window. At the left there is a large open fireplace, with turf fire, and a small door into inner room. PEGEEN, a wild-looking but fine girl, of about twenty, is writing at table. She is dressed in the usual peasant dress.

PEGEEN [*slowly as she writes*]. Six yards of stuff for to make a yellow gown. A pair of lace boots with lengthy heels on them and brassy eyes. A hat is suited for a wedding-day. A fine-tooth comb. To be sent with three barrels of porter in Jimmy Farrell's creel cart on the evening of the coming fair to Mister Michael James Flaherty. With the best compliments of the season. Margaret Flaherty.

SHAWN KEOGH [*a fat and fair young man comes in as she signs, looks round awkwardly, when he sees she is alone*]. Where's himself?

PEGEEN [*without looking at him*]. He's coming. [*She directs letter.*] To Mister Sheamus Mulroy, Wine and Spirit Dealer, Castlebar.

SHAWN [*uneasily*]. I didn't see him on the road.

PEGEEN. How would you see him [*licks stamp and puts it on letter*] and it dark night this half-hour gone by?

SHAWN [*turning towards door again*]. I stood a while outside wondering would I have a right to pass on or to walk in and see you, Pegeen Mike [*comes to fire*], and I could hear the cows breathing and sighing in the stillness of the air, and not a step moving any place from this gate to the bridge.

PEGEEN [*putting letter in envelope*]. It's above at the crossroads he is, meeting Philly Cullen and a couple more are going along with him to Kate Cassidy's wake.

SHAWN [*looking at her blankly*]. And he's going that length in the dark night.

PEGEEN [*impatiently*]. He is surely, and leaving me lonesome on the scruff of the hill. [*She gets up and puts envelope on dresser, then winds clock.*] Isn't it long the nights are now, Shawn Keogh, to be leaving a poor girl with her own self counting the hours to the dawn of day?

SHAWN [*with awkward humour*]. If it is, when we're wedded in a short while you'll have no call to complain, for I've little will to be walking off to wakes or weddings in the darkness of the night.

PEGEEN [*with rather scornful good-humour*]. You're making mighty certain Shaneen, that I'll wed you now.

SHAWN. Aren't we after making a good bargain, the way we're only waiting these days on Father Reilly's dispensation from the bishops, or the Court of Rome.

PEGEEN [*looking at him teasingly, washing up at dresser*]. It's a wonder, Shaneen, the Holy Father'd be taking notice of the likes of you; for if I was him I wouldn't bother with this place where you'll meet none but Red Linahan, has a squint in his eye, and Patcheen is lame in his heel, or the mad Mulrannies were driven from California and they lost in their wits. We're a queer lot these times to go troubling the Holy Father on his sacred seat.

SHAWN [*scandalized*]. If we are, we're as good this place as another, maybe, and as good these times as we were for ever.

PEGEEN [*with scorn*]. As good, is it? Where now will you meet the like of Daneen Sullivan knocked the eye from a peeler; or Marcus Quin, God rest him, got six months for maiming ewes, and he a great warrant to tell stories of holy Ireland till he'd have the old women shedding down tears about their feet. Where will you find the like of them, I'm saying?

SHAWN [*timidly*]. If you don't, it's a good job, maybe; for [*with peculiar emphasis on the words*] Father Reilly has small conceit to have that kind walking around and talking to the girls.

PEGEEN [*impatiently throwing water from basin out of the door*]. Stop tormenting me with Father Reilly [*imitating his voice*] when I'm asking only what way I'll pass these twelve hours of dark, and not take my death with the fear. [*Looking out of door.*]

SHAWN [*timidly*]. Would I fetch you the Widow Quin, maybe?

PEGEEN. Is it the like of that murderer? You'll not, surely.

SHAWN [*going to her, soothingly*]. Then I'm thinking himself will stop along with you when he sees you taking on; for it'll be a long night-time with great darkness, and I'm after feeling a kind of fellow above in the furzy ditch, groaning wicked like a maddening dog, the way it's good cause you have, maybe, to be fearing now.

PEGEEN [*turning on him sharply*]. What's that? Is it a man you seen?

SHAWN [*retreating*]. I couldn't see him at all; but I heard him groaning out, and breaking his heart. It should have been a young man from his words speaking

PEGEEN [*going after him*]. And you never went near to see was he hurted or what ailed him at all?

SHAWN. I did not, Pegeen Mike. It was a dark, lonesome place to be hearing the like of him.

PEGEEN. Well, you're a daring fellow, and if they find his corpse stretched above in the dews of dawn, what'll you say then to the peelers, or the Justice of the Peace?

SHAWN [*thunderstruck*]. I wasn't thinking of that. For the love of God, Pegeen Mike, don't let on I was speaking of him. Don't tell your father and the men is coming above; for if they heard that story they'd have great blabbing this night at the wake.

PEGEEN. I'll maybe tell them, and I'll maybe not.

SHAWN. They are coming at the door. Will you whisht, I'm saying?

PEGEEN. Whisht yourself.

> *She goes behind counter. MICHAEL JAMES, fat jovial publican, comes in followed by PHILLY CULLEN, who is thin and mistrusting, and JIMMY FARRELL, who is fat and amorous, about forty-five.*

MEN [*together*]. God bless you! The blessing of God on this place!

PEGEEN. God bless you kindly.

MICHAEL [*to men, who go to the counter*]. Sit down now, and take your rest. [*Crosses to SHAWN at the fire.*] And how is it you are, Shawn Keogh? Are you coming over the sands to Kate Cassidy's wake?

SHAWN. I am not, Michael James. I'm going home the short cut to my bed.

PEGEEN [*speaking across the counter*]. He's right, too, and have you no shame, Michael James, to be quitting off for the whole night, and leaving myself lonesome in the shop?

MICHAEL [*good-humouredly*]. Isn't it the same whether I go for the whole night or a part only? and I'm thinking it's a queer daughter you are if you'd have me crossing backward through the Stooks of the Dead Women, with a drop taken.

PEGEEN. If I am a queer daughter, it's a queer father'd be leaving me lonesome these twelve hours of dark, and I piling the turf with the dogs barking, and the calves mooing, and my own teeth rattling with the fear.

JIMMY [*flatteringly*]. What is there to hurt you, and you a fine, hardy girl would knock the head of any two men in the place?

PEGEEN [*working herself up*]. Isn't there the harvest boys with their tongues red for drink, and the ten tinkers is camped in the east glen, and the thousand militia—bad cess to them!—walking idle through the land. There's lots surely to hurt me, and I won't stop alone in it, let himself do what he will.

MICHAEL. If you're that afeard, let Shawn Keogh stop along with you. It's the will of God, I'm thinking, himself should be seeing to you now.

> *They all turn on SHAWN.*

SHAWN [*in horrified confusion*]. I would and welcome, Michael James, but I'm afeard of Father Reilly; and what at all would the Holy Father and the Cardinals of Rome be saying if they heard I did the like of that?

MICHAEL [*with contempt*]. God help you! Can't you sit in by the hearth with the light lit and herself beyond in the room? You'll do that surely, for I've heard tell there's a queer fellow above, going mad or getting his death, maybe, in the gripe of the ditch, so she'd be safer this night with a person here.

SHAWN [*with plaintive despair*]. I'm afeard of Father Reilly, I'm saying. Let you not be tempting me, and we near married itself.

PHILLY [*with cold contempt*]. Lock him in the west room. He'll stay then and have no sin to be telling to the priest.

MICHAEL [*to SHAWN, getting between him and the door*]. Go up now.

SHAWN [*at the top of his voice*]. Don't stop me, Michael James. Let me out of the door, I'm saying, for the love of the Almighty God. Let me out [*trying to dodge past him*]. Let me out of it, and may God grant you His indulgence in the hour of need.

MICHAEL [*loudly*]. Stop your noising, and sit down by the hearth.

Gives him a push and goes to counter laughing.

SHAWN [*turning back, wringing his hands*]. Oh, Father Reilly, and the saints of God, where will I hide myself today? Oh, St. Joseph and St. Patrick and St. Brigid and St. James, have mercy on me now!

SHAWN turns round, sees door clear, and makes a rush for it.

MICHAEL [*catching him by the coat-tail*]. You'd be going, is it?

SHAWN [*screaming*]. Leave me go, Michael James, leave me go, you old Pagan, leave me go, or I'll get the curse of the priests on you, and of the scarlet-coated bishops of the Courts of Rome.

With a sudden movement he pulls himself out of his coat, and disappears out of the door, leaving his coat in MICHAEL'S hands.

MICHAEL [*turning round, and holding up coat*]. Well, there's the coat of a Christian man. Oh, there's sainted glory this day in the lonesome west; and by the will of God I've got you a decent man, Pegeen, you'll have no call to be spying after if you've a score of young girls, maybe, weeding in your fields.

PEGEEN [*taking up the defence of her property*]. What right have you to be making game of a poor fellow for minding the priest, when it's your own the fault is, not paying a penny pot-boy to stand along with me and give me courage in the doing of my work?

She snaps the coat away from him, and goes behind counter with it.

MICHAEL [*taken aback*]. Where would I get a pot-boy? Would you have me send the bellman screaming in the streets of Castlebar?

SHAWN [*opening the door a chink and putting in his head, in a small voice*]. Michael James!

MICHAEL [*imitating him*]. What ails you?

SHAWN. The queer dying fellow's beyond looking over the ditch. He's come up, I'm thinking, stealing your hens. [*Looks over his shoulder.*] God help me, he's following me now [*he runs into room*], and if he's heard what I said, he'll be having my life, and I going home lonesome in the darkness of the night.

For a perceptible moment they watch the door with curiosity. Someone coughs outside. Then CHRISTY MAHON, a slight young man, comes in very tired and frightened and dirty.

CHRISTY [*in a small voice*]. God save all here!

MEN. God save you kindly!

CHRISTY [*going to the counter*]. I'd trouble you for a glass of porter, woman of the house.

> *He puts down coin.*

PEGEEN [*serving him*]. You're one of the tinkers, young fellow, is beyond camped in the glen?

CHRISTY. I am not; but I'm destroyed walking.

MICHAEL [*patronizingly*]. Let you come up then to the fire. You're looking famished with the cold.

CHRISTY. God reward you. [*He takes up his glass and goes a little way across to the left, then stops and looks about him.*] Is it often the polis do be coming into this place, master of the house?

MICHAEL. If you'd come in better hours, you'd have seen "Licensed for the Sale of Beer and Spirits, to be Consumed on the Premises," written in white letters above the door, and what would the polis want spying on me, and not a decent house within four miles, the way every living Christian is a bona fide, saving one widow alone?

CHRISTY [*with relief*]. It's a safe house, so.

> *He goes over to the fire, sighing and moaning. Then he sits down, putting his glass beside him, and begins gnawing a turnip, too miserable to feel the others staring at him with curiosity.*

MICHAEL [*going after him*]. Is it yourself is fearing the polis? You're wanting, maybe?

CHRISTY. There's many wanting.

MICHAEL. Many, surely, with the broken harvest and the ended wars. [*He picks up some stockings, etc., that are near the fire, and carries them away furtively.*] It should be larceny, I'm thinking?

CHRISTY [*dolefully*]. I had it in my mind it was a different word and a bigger.

PEGEEN. There's a queer lad. Were you never slapped in school, young fellow, that you don't know the name of your deed?

CHRISTY [*bashfully*]. I'm slow at learning, a middling scholar only.

MICHAEL. If you're a dunce itself, you'd have a right to know that larceny's robbing and stealing. Is it for the like of that you're wanting?

CHRISTY [*with a flash of family pride*]. And I the son of a strong farmer [*with a sudden qualm*], God rest his soul, could have bought up the whole of your old house a while since, from the butt of his tail-pocket, and not have missed the weight of it gone.

MICHAEL [*impressed*]. If it's not stealing, it's maybe something big.

CHRISTY [*flattered*]. Aye; it's maybe something big.

JIMMY. He's a wicked-looking young fellow. Maybe he followed after a young woman on a lonesome night.

CHRISTY [*shocked*]. Oh, the saints forbid, mister; I was all times a decent lad.

PHILLY [*turning on JIMMY*]. You're a silly man, Jimmy Farrell. He said his father was a farmer a while since, and there's himself now in a poor state. Maybe the land was grabbed from him, and he did what any decent man would do.

MICHAEL [*to CHRISTY, mysteriously*]. Was it bailiffs?

CHRISTY. The divil a one.

MICHAEL. Agents?

CHRISTY. The divil a one.

MICHAEL. Landlords?

CHRISTY [*peevishly*]. Ah, not at all, I'm saying. You'd see the like of them stories on any little paper of a Munster town. But I'm not calling to mind any person, gentle, simple, judge or jury, did the like of me.

> *They all draw nearer with delighted curiosity.*

PHILLY. Well, that lad's a puzzle-the-world.

JIMMY. He'd beat Dan Davies' circus, or the holy missioners making sermons on the villainy of man. Try him again, Philly.

PHILLY. Did you strike golden guineas out of solder, young fellow, or shilling coins itself?

CHRISTY. I did not, mister, not sixpence nor a farthing coin.

JIMMY. Did you marry three wives maybe? I'm told there's a sprinkling have done that among the holy Luthers of the preaching north.

CHRISTY [*shyly*]. I never married with one, let alone with a couple or three.

PHILLY. Maybe he went fighting for the Boers, the like of the man beyond, was judged to be hanged, quartered, and drawn. Were you off east, young fellow, fighting bloody wars for Kruger and the freedom of the Boers?

CHRISTY. I never left my own parish till Tuesday was a week.

PEGEEN [*coming from counter*]. He's done nothing, so. [*To CHRISTY.*] If you didn't commit murder or a bad, nasty thing; or false coining, or robbery, or butchery, or the like of them, there isn't anything that would be worth your troubling for to run from now. You did nothing at all.

CHRISTY [*his feelings hurt*]. That's an unkindly thing to be saying to a poor orphaned traveller, has a prison behind him, and hanging before, and hell's gap gaping below.

PEGEEN [*with a sign to the men to be quiet*]. You're only saying it. You did nothing at all. A soft lad the like of you wouldn't slit the windpipe of a screeching sow..

CHRISTY [*offended*]. You're not speaking the truth.

PEGEEN [*in mock rage*]. Not speaking the truth, is it? Would you have me knock the head of you with the butt of the broom?

CHRISTY [*twisting round on her with a sharp cry of horror*]. Don't strike me. I killed my poor father, Tuesday was a week, for doing the like of that.

PEGEEN [*with blank amazement*]. Is it killed your father?

CHRISTY [*subsiding*]. With the help of God I did, surely, and that the Holy Immaculate Mother may intercede for his soul.

PHILLY [*retreating with JIMMY*]. There's a daring fellow.

JIMMY. Oh, glory be to God!

MICHAEL [*with great respect*]. That was a hanging crime, mister honey. You should have had good reason for doing the like of that.

CHRISTY [*in a very reasonable tone*]. He was a dirty man, God forgive him, and he getting old and crusty, the way I couldn't put up with him at all.

PEGEEN. And you shot him dead?

CHRISTY [*shaking his head*]. I never used weapons. I've no licence, and I'm a law-fearing man.

MICHAEL. It was with a hilted knife maybe? I'm told, in the big world, it's bloody knives they use.

CHRISTY [*loudly, scandalized*]. Do you take me for a slaughter-boy?

PEGEEN. You never hanged him, the way Jimmy Farrell hanged his dog from the licence, and had it screeching and wriggling three hours at the butt of a string, and himself swearing it was a dead dog, and the peelers swearing it had life?

CHRISTY. I did not, then. I just riz the loy and let fall the edge of it on the ridge of his skull, and he went down at my feet like an empty sack, and never let a grunt or groan from him at all.

MICHAEL [*making a sign to PEGEEN to fill CHRISTY'S glass*]. And what way weren't you hanged, mister? Did you bury him then?

CHRISTY [*considering*]. Aye. I buried him then. Wasn't I digging spuds in the field?

MICHAEL. And the peelers never followed after you the eleven days that you're out?

CHRISTY [*shaking his head*]. Never a one of them, and I walking forward facing hog, dog, or divil on the highway of the road.

PHILLY [*nodding wisely*]. It's only with a common weekday kind of a murderer them lads would be trusting their carcase, and that man should be a great terror when his temper's roused.

MICHAEL. He should then. [*To CHRISTY.*] And where was it, mister honey, that you did the deed?

CHRISTY [*looking at him with suspicion*]. Oh, a distant place, master of the house, a windy corner of high, distant hills.

PHILLY [*nodding with approval*]. He's a close man, and he's right, surely.

PEGEEN. That'd be a lad with the sense of Solomon to have for a pot-boy, Michael James, if it's the truth you're seeking one at all.

PHILLY. The peelers is fearing him, and if you'd that lad in the house there isn't one of them would come smelling around if the dogs itself were lapping poteen from the dung-pit of the yard.

JIMMY. Bravery's a treasure in a lonesome place, and a lad would kill his father, I'm thinking, would face a foxy divil with a pitchpike on the flags of hell.

PEGEEN. It's the truth they're saying, and if I'd that lad in the house, I wouldn't be fearing the looséd kharki cut-throats, or the walking dead.

CHRISTY [*swelling with surprise and triumph*]. Well, glory be to God!

MICHAEL [*with deference*]. Would you think well to stop here and be pot-boy, mister honey, if we gave you good wages, and didn't destroy you with the weight of work.

SHAWN [*coming forward uneasily*]. That'd be a queer kind to bring into a decent, quiet household with the like of Pegeen Mike.

PEGEEN [*very sharply*]. Will you whisht? Who's speaking to you?

SHAWN [*retreating*]. A bloody-handed murderer the like of . . .

PEGEEN [*snapping at him*]. Whisht, I am saying; we'll take no fooling from your like at all. [*To CHRISTY with a honeyed voice.*] And you, young fellow, you'd have a right to stop, I'm thinking, for we'd do our all and utmost to content your needs.

CHRISTY [*overcome with wonder*]. And I'd be safe this place from the searching law?

MICHAEL. You would, surely. If they're not fearing you, itself, the peelers in this place is decent, drouthy poor fellows, wouldn't touch a cur dog and not give warning in the dead of night.

PEGEEN [*very kindly and persuasively*]. Let you stop a short while anyhow. Aren't you destroyed walking with your feet in bleeding blisters, and your whole skin needing washing like a Wicklow sheep.

CHRISTY [*looking round with satisfaction*]. It's a nice room, and if it's not humbugging me you are, I'm thinking that I'll surely stay.

JIMMY [*jumps up*]. Now, by the grace of God, herself will be safe this night, with a man killed his father holding danger from the door, and let you come on, Michael James, or they'll have the best stuff drunk at the wake.

MICHAEL [*going to the door with men*]. And begging your pardon, mister, what name will we call you, for we'd like to know?

CHRISTY. Christopher Mahon.

MICHAEL. Well, God bless you, Christy, and a good rest till we meet again when the sun'll be rising to the noon of day.

CHRISTY. God bless you all.

MEN. God bless you.

> They go out, except SHAWN, who lingers at the door.

SHAWN [*to PEGEEN*]. Are you wanting me to stop along with you and keep you from harm?

PEGEEN [*gruffly*]. Didn't you say you were fearing Father Reilly?

SHAWN. There'd be no harm staying now, I'm thinking, and himself in it too.

PEGEEN. You wouldn't stay when there was need for you, and let you step off nimble this time when there's none.

SHAWN. Didn't I say it was Father Reilly . . .

PEGEEN. Go on, then, to Father Reilly [*in a jeering tone*], and let him put you in the holy brotherhoods, and leave that lad to me.

SHAWN. If I meet the Widow Quin . . .

PEGEEN. Go on, I'm saying, and don't be waking this place with your noise. [*She hustles him out and bolts door.*] That lad would wear the spirits from the saints of peace. [*Bustles about, then takes off her apron and pins it up in the window as a blind, CHRISTY watching her timidly. Then she comes to him and speaks with bland good-humour.*] Let you stretch out now by the fire, young fellow. You should be destroyed travelling.

CHRISTY [*shyly again, drawing off his boots*]. I'm tired surely, walking wild eleven days, and waking fearful in the night.

> *He holds up one of his feet, feeling his blisters, and looking at them with compassion.*

PEGEEN [*standing beside him, watching him with delight*]. You should have had great people in your family, I'm thinking, with the little, small feet you have, and you with a kind of a quality name, the like of what you'd find on the great powers and potentates of France and Spain.

CHRISTY [*with pride*]. We were great, surely, with wide and windy acres of rich Munster land.

PEGEEN. Wasn't I telling you, and you a fine, handsome young fellow with a noble brow?

CHRISTY [*with a flash of delighted surprise*]. Is it me?

PEGEEN. Aye. Did you never hear that from the young girls where you come from in the west or south?

CHRISTY [*with venom*]. I did not, then. Oh, they're bloody liars in the naked parish where I grew a man.

PEGEEN. If they are itself, you've heard it these days, I'm thinking, and you walking the world telling out your story to young girls or old.

CHRISTY. I've told my story no place till this night, Pegeen Mike, and it's foolish I was here, maybe, to be talking free; but you're decent people, I'm thinking, and yourself a kindly woman, the way I wasn't fearing you at all.

PEGEEN [*filling a sack with straw*]. You've said the like of that, maybe, in every cot and cabin where you've met a young girl on your way.

CHRISTY [*going over to her, gradually raising his voice*]. I've said it nowhere till this night, I'm telling you; for I've seen none the like of you the eleven long days I am walking the world, looking over a low ditch or a high ditch on my north or south, into stony, scattered fields, or scribes of bog, where you'd see young, limber girls, and fine, prancing women making laughter with the men.

PEGEEN. If you weren't destroyed travelling, you'd have as much talk and streeleen, I'm thinking, as Owen Roe O'Sullivan or the poets of the Dingle Bay; and I've heard all times it's the poets are your like—fine, fiery fellows with great rages when their temper's roused.

CHRISTY [*drawing a little nearer to her*]. You've a power of rings, God bless you, and would there be any offence if I was asking are you single now?

PEGEEN. What would I want wedding so young?

CHRISTY [*with relief*]. We're alike, so.

PEGEEN [*she puts sack on settle and beats it up*]. I never killed my father. I'd be afeard to do that, except I was the like of yourself with blind rages tearing me within, for I'm thinking you should have had great tussling when the end was come.

CHRISTY [*expanding with delight at the first confidential talk he has ever had with a woman*]. We had not then. It was a hard woman was come over the hill; and if he was always a crusty kind when he'd a hard woman setting him on, not the divil himself or his four fathers could put up with him at all.

PEGEEN [*with curiosity*]. And isn't it a great wonder that one wasn't fearing you?

CHRISTY [*very confidentially*]. Up to the day I killed my father, there wasn't a person in Ireland knew the kind I was, and I there drinking, waking, eating, sleeping, a quiet, simple poor fellow with no man giving me heed.

PEGEEN [*getting a quilt out of cupboard and putting it on the sack*]. It was the girls were giving you heed, maybe, and I'm thinking it's most conceit you'd have to be gaming with their like.

CHRISTY [*shaking his head, with simplicity*]. Not the girls itself, and I won't tell you a lie. There wasn't anyone heeding me in that place saving only the dumb beasts of the field. [*He sits down at fire.*]

PEGEEN [*with disappointment*]. And I thinking you should have been living the like of a king of Norway or the eastern world.

She comes and sits beside him after placing bread and mug of milk on the table.

CHRISTY [*laughing piteously*]. The like of a king, is it? And I after toiling, moiling, digging, dodging from the dawn till dusk; with never a sight of joy or sport saving only when I'd be abroad in the dark night poaching rabbits on hills, for I was a divil to poach, God forgive me, [*very naïvely*] and I near got six months for going with a dung fork and stabbing a fish.

PEGEEN. And it's that you'd call sport, is it, to be abroad in the darkness with yourself alone?

CHRISTY. I did, God help me, and there I'd be as happy as the sunshine of St. Martin's Day, watching the light passing the north or the patches of fog, till I'd hear a rabbit starting to screech and I'd go running in the furze. Then, when I'd my full share, I'd come walking down where you'd see the ducks and geese stretched sleeping on the highway of the road, and before I'd pass the dunghill, I'd hear himself snoring out—a loud, lonesome snore he'd be making all times, the while he was sleeping; and he a man'd be raging all times, the while he was waking, like a gaudy officer you'd hear cursing and damning and swearing oaths.

PEGEEN. Providence and Mercy, spare us all!

CHRISTY. It's that you'd say surely if you seen him and he after drinking for weeks, rising up in the red dawn, or before it maybe, and going out into the yard as naked as an ash-tree in the moon of May, and shying clods against the visage of the stars he'd till put the fear of death into the banbhs and the screeching sows.

PEGEEN. I'd be well-nigh afeard of that lad myself, I'm thinking. And there was no one in it but the two of you alone?

CHRISTY. The divil a one, though he'd sons and daughters walking all great states and territories of the world, and not a one of them, to this day, but would say their seven curses on him, and they rousing up to let a cough or sneeze, maybe, in the deadness of the night.

PEGEEN [*nodding her head*]. Well, you should have been a queer lot. I never cursed my father the like of that, though I'm twenty and more years of age.

CHRISTY. Then you'd have cursed mine, I'm telling you, and he a man never gave peace to any, saving when he'd get two months or three, or be locked in the asylums for battering peelers or assaulting men [*with depression*], the way it was a bitter life he led me till I did up a Tuesday and halve his skull.

PEGEEN [*putting her hand on his shoulder*]. Well, you'll have peace in this place, Christy Mahon, and none to trouble you, and it's near time a fine lad like you should have your good share of the earth.

CHRISTY. It's time surely, and I a seemly fellow with great strength in me and bravery of . . . [*Someone knocks.*]

CHRISTY [*clinging to PEGEEN*]. Oh, glory! it's late for knocking, and this last while I'm in terror of the peelers, and the walking dead. [*Knocking again.*]

PEGEEN. Who's there?

VOICE [*outside*]. Me.

PEGEEN. Who's me?

VOICE. The Widow Quin.

PEGEEN [*jumping up and giving him the bread and milk*]. Go on now with your supper, and let on to be sleepy, for if she found you were such a warrant to talk, she'd be stringing gabble till the dawn of day.

    He takes bread and sits shyly with his back to the door.

PEGEEN [*opening the door, with temper*]. What ails you, or what is it you're wanting at this hour of the night?

WIDOW QUIN [*coming in a step and peering at CHRISTY*]. I'm after meeting

Shawn Keogh and Father Reilly below, who told me of your curiosity man, and they fearing by this time he was maybe roaring, romping on your hands with drink.

PEGEEN [*pointing to CHRISTY*]. Look now is he roaring, and he stretched out drowsy with his supper and his mug of milk. Walk down and tell that to Father Reilly and to Shaneen Keogh.

WIDOW QUIN [*coming forward*]. I'll not see them again, for I've their word to lead that lad forward for to lodge with me.

PEGEEN [*in blank amazement*]. This night is it?

WIDOW QUIN [*going over*]. This night. "It isn't fitting," says the priesteen, "to have his likeness lodging with an orphaned girl." [*To CHRISTY.*] God save you, mister!

CHRISTY [*shyly*]. God save you kindly!

WIDOW QUIN [*looking at him with half-amused curiosity*]. Well, aren't you a little smiling fellow? It should have been great and bitter torments did rouse your spirits to a deed of blood.

CHRISTY [*doubtfully*]. It should, maybe.

WIDOW QUIN. It's more than "maybe" I'm saying, and it'd soften my heart to see you sitting so simple with your cup and cake, and you fitter to be saying your catechism than slaying your da.

PEGEEN [*at counter, washing glasses*]. There's talking when any'd see he's fit to be holding his head high with the wonders of the world. Walk on from this, for I'll not have him tormented, and he destroyed travelling since Tuesday was a week.

WIDOW QUIN [*peaceably*]. We'll be walking surely when his supper's done, and you'll find we're great company, young fellow, when it's of the like of you and me you'd hear the penny poets singing in an August Fair.

CHRISTY [*innocently*]. Did you kill your father?

PEGEEN [*contemptuously*]. She did not. She hit himself with a worn pick, and the rusted poison did corrode his blood the way he never overed it, and died after. That was a sneaky kind of murder did win small glory with the boys itself.
She crosses to CHRISTY'S left.

WIDOW QUIN [*with good humour*]. If it didn't, maybe all knows a widow woman has buried her children and destroyed her man is a wiser comrade for a young lad than a girl, the like of you, who'd go helter-skeltering after any man would let you a wink upon the road.

PEGEEN [*breaking out into wild rage*]. And you'll say that, Widow Quin, and you gasping with the rage you had racing the hill beyond to look on his face.

WIDOW QUIN [*laughing derisively*]. Me, is it? Well, Father Reilly has cuteness to divide you now. [*She pulls CHRISTY up.*] There's great temptation in a man did slay his da, and we'd best be going, young fellow; so rise up and come with me.

PEGEEN [*seizing his arm*]. He'll not stir. He's pot-boy in this place, and I'll not have him stolen off and kidnapped while himself's abroad.

WIDOW QUIN. It'd be a crazy pot-boy'd lodge him in the shebeen where he works by day, so you'd have a right to come on, young fellow, till you see my little houseen, a perch off on the rising hill.

PEGEEN. Wait till morning, Christy Mahon. Wait till you lay eyes on her leaky thatch is growing more pasture for her buck goat than her square of fields, and she without a tramp itself to keep in order her place at all.

WIDOW QUIN. When you see me contriving in my little gardens, Christy Mahon, you'll swear the Lord God formed me to be living lone, and that there isn't my match in Mayo for thatching, or mowing, or shearing a sheep.

PEGEEN [*with noisy scorn*]. It's true the Lord God formed you to contrive indeed. Doesn't the world know you reared a black ram at your own breast, so that the Lord Bishop of Connaught felt the elements of a Christian, and he eating it after in a kidney stew? Doesn't the world know you've been seen shaving the foxy skipper from France for a threepenny-bit and a sop of grass tobacco would wring the liver from a mountain goat you'd meet leaping the hills?

WIDOW QUIN [*with amusement*]. Do you hear her now, young fellow? Do you hear the way she'll be rating at your own self when a week is by?

PEGEEN [*to CHRISTY*]. Don't heed her. Tell her to go on into her pigsty and not plague us here.

WIDOW QUIN. I'm going; but he'll come with me.

PEGEEN [*shaking him*]. Are you dumb, young fellow?

CHRISTY [*timidly to WIDOW QUIN*]. God increase you; but I'm pot-boy in this place, and it's here I liefer stay.

PEGEEN [*triumphantly*]. Now you have heard him, and go on from this.

WIDOW QUIN [*looking round the room*]. It's lonesome this hour crossing the hill, and if he won't come along with me, I'd have a right maybe to stop this night with yourselves. Let me stretch out on the settle, Pegeen Mike; and himself can lie by the hearth.

PEGEEN [*short and fiercely*]. Faith, I won't. Quit off or I will send you now.

WIDOW QUIN [*gathering her shawl up*]. Well, it's a terror to be aged a score. [*To CHRISTY.*] God bless you now, young fellow, and let you be wary, or there's right torment will await you here if you go romancing with her like, and she waiting only, as they bade me say, on a sheepskin parchment to be wed with Shawn Keogh of Killakeen.

CHRISTY [*going to PEGEEN as she bolts door*]. What's that she's after saying?

PEGEEN. Lies and blather, you've no call to mind. Well, isn't Shawn Keogh an impudent fellow to send up spying on me? Wait till I lay hands on him. Let him wait, I'm saying.

CHRISTY. And you're not wedding him at all?

PEGEEN. I wouldn't wed him if a bishop came walking for to join us here.

CHRISTY. That God in glory may be thanked for that.

PEGEEN. There's your bed now. I've put a quilt upon you. I'm after quilting a while since with my own two hands, and you'd best stretch out now for your sleep, and may God give you a good rest till I call you in the morning when the cocks will crow.

CHRISTY [*as she goes to inner room*]. May God and Mary and St. Patrick bless you and reward you for your kindly talk. [*She shuts the door behind her. He settles his bed slowly, feeling the quilt with immense satisfaction.*] Well, it's a clean bed and soft with it, and it's great luck and company I've won me in the end of time—two fine women fighting for the likes of me—till I'm thinking this night wasn't I a foolish fellow not to kill my father in the years gone by.

CURTAIN

ACT II

Scene as before. Brilliant morning light. CHRISTY, looking bright and cheerful, is cleaning a girl's boots.

CHRISTY [*to himself, counting jugs on dresser*]. Half a hundred beyond. Ten there. A score that's above. Eighty jugs. Six cups and a broken one. Two plates. A power of glasses. Bottles, a schoolmaster'd be hard set to count, and enough in them, I'm thinking, to drunken all the wealth and wisdom of the county Clare. [*He puts down the boot carefully.*] There's her boots now, nice and decent for her evening use, and isn't it grand brushes she has? [*He puts them down and goes by degrees to the looking-glass.*] Well, this'd be a fine place to be my whole life talking out with swearing Christians, in place of my old dogs and cat; and I stalking around, smoking my pipe and drinking my fill, and never a day's work but drawing a cork an odd time, or wiping a glass, or rinsing out a shiny tumbler for a decent man. [*He takes the looking-glass from the wall and puts it on the back of a chair; then sits down in front of it and begins washing his face.*] Didn't I know rightly, I was handsome, though it was the divil's own mirror we had beyond, would twist a squint across an angel's brow; and I'll be growing fine from this day, the way I'll have a soft lovely skin on me and won't be the like of the clumsy young fellows do be ploughing all times in the earth and dung. [*He starts.*] Is she coming again? [*He looks out.*] Stranger girls. God help me, where'll I hide myself away and my long neck naked to the world? [*He looks out.*] I'd best go to the room maybe till I'm dressed again.

He gathers up his coat and the looking-glass, and runs into the inner room. *The door is pushed open, and* SUSAN BRADY *looks in, and knocks on door.*

SUSAN. There's nobody in it. [*Knocks again.*]

NELLY [*Pushing her in and following her, with* HONOR BLAKE *and* SARA TANSEY]. It'd be early for them both to be out walking the hill.

SUSAN. I'm thinking Shawn Keogh was making game of us, and there's no such man in it at all.

HONOR [*pointing to straw and quilt*]. Look at that. He's been sleeping there in the night. Well, it'll be a hard case if he's gone off now, the way we'll never set our eyes on a man killed his father, and we after rising early and destroying ourselves running fast on the hill.

NELLY. Are you thinking them's his boots?

SARA [*taking them up*]. If they are, there should be his father's track on them. Did you never read in the papers the way murdered men do bleed and drip?

SUSAN. Is that blood there, Sara Tansey?

SARA [*smelling it*]. That's bog water, I'm thinking; but it's his own they are, surely, for I never seen the like of them for whitey mud, and red mud, and turf on them, and the fine sands of the sea. That man's been walking, I'm telling you.
She goes down right, putting on one of his boots.

SUSAN [*going to window*]. Maybe he's stolen off to Belmullet with the boots of Michael James, and you'd have a right so to follow after him, Sara Tansey, and you the one yoked the ass cart and drove ten miles to set your eyes on the man bit the yellow lady's nostril on the northern shore. [*She looks out.*]

SARA [*running to window, with one boot on*]. Don't be talking, and we fooled today. [*Putting on the other boot.*] There's a pair do fit me well and I'll be keeping them for walking to the priest, when you'd be ashamed this place, going up winter and summer with nothing worth while to confess at all.

HONOR [*who has been listening at door*]. Whisht! there's someone inside the room. [*She pushes door a chink open.*] It's a man.
SARA kicks off boots and puts them where they were. They all stand in a line looking through chink.

SARA. I'll call him. Mister! Mister! [*He puts in his head.*] Is Pegeen within?

CHRISTY [*coming in as meek as a mouse, with the looking-glass held behind his back*]. She's above on the cnuceen, seeking the nanny goats, the way she'd have a sup of goats' milk for to colour my tea.

SARA. And asking your pardon, is it you's the man killed his father?

CHRISTY [*sidling toward the nail where the glass was hanging*]. I am, God help me!

SARA [*taking eggs she has brought*]. Then my thousand welcomes to you, and I've run up with a brace of duck's eggs for your food to-day. Pegeen's ducks is no use, but these are the real rich sort. Hold out your hand and you'll see it's no lie I'm telling you.

CHRISTY [*coming forward shyly, and holding out his left hand*]. They're a great and weighty size.

SUSAN. And I run up with a pat of butter, for it'd be a poor thing to have you eating your spuds dry, and you after running a great way since you did destroy your da.

CHRISTY. Thank you kindly.

HONOR. And I brought you a little cut of a cake, for you should have a thin stomach on you, and you that length walking the world.

NELLY. And I brought you a little laying pullet—boiled and all she is—was crushed at the fall of night by the curate's car. Feel the fat of that breast, mister.

CHRISTY. It's bursting, surely.

He feels it with the back of his hand, in which he holds the presents.

SARA. Will you pinch it? Is your right hand too sacred for to use at all? [*She slips round behind him.*] It's a glass he has. Well, I never seen to this day a man with a looking-glass held to his back. Them that kills their fathers is a vain lot surely.

GIRLS giggle.

CHRISTY [*smiling innocently and piling presents on glass*]. I'm very thankful to you all to-day. . . .

WIDOW QUIN [*coming in quickly, at door*]. Sara Tansey, Susan Brady, Honor Blake! What in glory has you here at this hour of day?

GIRLS [*giggling*]. That's the man killed his father.

WIDOW QUIN [*coming to them*]. I know well it's the man; and I'm after putting him down in the sports below for racing, leaping, pitching, and the Lord knows what.

SARA [*exuberantly*]. That's right, Widow Quin. I'll bet my dowry that he'll lick the world.

WIDOW QUIN. If you will, you'd have a right to have him fresh and nourished in place of nursing a feast. [*Taking presents.*] Are you fasting or fed, young fellow?

CHRISTY. Fasting, if you please.

WIDOW QUIN [*loudly*]. Well, you're the lot. Stir up now and give him his breakfast. [*To CHRISTY.*] Come here to me [*she puts him on bench beside her while the GIRLS make tea and get his breakfast*], and let you tell us your story before Pegeen will come, in place of grinning your ears off like the moon of May.

CHRISTY [*beginning to be pleased*]. It's a long story; you'd be destroyed listening.

WIDOW QUIN. Don't be letting on to be shy, a fine, gamey, treacherous lad the like of you. Was it in your house beyond you cracked his skull?

CHRISTY [*shy but flattered*]. It was not. We were digging spuds in his cold, sloping, stony, divil's patch of a field.

WIDOW QUIN. And you went asking money of him, or making talk of getting a wife would drive him from his farm?

CHRISTY. I did not, then; but there I was digging and digging, and "You squint-

346

ing idiot," says he, "let you walk down now and tell the priest you'll wed the
Widow Casey in a score of days."

WIDOW QUIN. And what kind was she?

CHRISTY [*with horror*]. A walking terror from beyond the hills, and she two
score and five years, and two hundred-weights and five pounds in the weigh-
ing scales, with a limping leg on her, and a blinded eye, and she a woman of
noted misbehaviour with the old and young.

GIRLS [*clustering round him, serving him*]. Glory be.

WIDOW QUIN. And what did he want driving you to wed with her?

She takes a bit of the chicken.

CHRISTY [*eating with growing satisfaction*]. He was letting on I was wanting a
protector from the harshness of the world, and he without a thought the whole
while but how he'd have her hut to live in and her gold to drink.

WIDOW QUIN. There's maybe worse than a dry hearth and a widow woman
and your glass at night. So you hit him then?

CHRISTY [*getting almost excited*]. I did not. "I won't wed her," says I, "when all
know she did suckle me for six weeks when I came into the world, and she a
hag this day with a tongue on her has the crows and seabirds scattered, the way
they wouldn't cast a shadow on her garden with the dread of her curse."

WIDOW QUIN [*teasingly*]. That one should be right company.

SARA [*eagerly*]. Don't mind her. Did you kill him then?

CHRISTY. "She's too good for the like of you," says he, "and go on now or I'll
flatten you out like a crawling beast has passed under a dray." "You will not if
I can help it," says I. "Go on," says he, "or I'll have the divil making garters of
your limbs tonight!" "You will not if I can help it," says I.

He sits up brandishing his mug.

SARA. You were right surely.

CHRISTY [*impressively*]. With that the sun came out between the cloud and the
hill, and it shining green in my face. "God have mercy on your soul," says he,
lifting a scythe. "Or on your own," said I, raising the loy.

SUSAN. That's a grand story.

HONOR. He tells it lovely.

CHRISTY [*flattered and confident, waving bone*]. He gave a drive with the scythe,
and I gave a lep to the east. Then I turned around with my back to the north,
and I hit a blow on the ridge of his skull, laid him stretched out, and he split
to the knob of his gullet.

He raises the chicken bone to his Adam's apple.

GIRLS [*together*]. Well, you're a marvel! Oh, God bless you! You're the lad, surely!

SUSAN. I'm thinking the Lord God sent him this road to make a second husband to the Widow Quin, and she with a great yearning to be wedded, though
all dread her here. Lift him on her knee, Sara Tansey.

WIDOW QUIN. Don't tease him.

SARA [*going over to dresser and counter very quickly, and getting two glasses and porter*]. You're heroes, surely, and let you drink a supeen with your arms linked like the outlandish lovers in the sailor's song. [*She links their arms and gives them the glasses.*] There now. Drink a health to the wonders of the western world, the pirates, preachers, poteen-makers, with the jobbing jockies; parching peelers, and the juries fill their stomachs selling judgments of the English law.

> *Brandishing the bottle.*

WIDOW QUIN. That's a right toast, Sara Tansey. Now, Christy.

> *They drink with their arms linked, he drinking with his left hand, she with her right. As they are drinking, PEGEEN MIKE comes in with a milk-can and stands aghast. They all spring away from CHRISTY. He goes down left. WIDOW QUIN remains seated.*

PEGEEN [*angrily to SARA*]. What is it you're wanting?

SARA [*twisting her apron*]. An ounce of tobacco.

PEGEEN. Have you tuppence?

SARA. I've forgotten my purse.

PEGEEN. Then you'd best be getting it and not be fooling us here. [*To the WIDOW QUIN, with more elaborate scorn.*] And what is it you're wanting, Widow Quin?

WIDOW QUIN [*insolently*]. A penn'orth of starch.

PEGEEN [*breaking out*]. And you without a white shift or a shirt in your whole family since the drying of the flood. I've no starch for the like of you, and let you walk on now to Killamuck.

WIDOW QUIN [*turning to CHRISTY, as she goes out with the GIRLS*]. Well, you're mighty huffy this day, Pegeen Mike, and you, young fellow, let you not forget the sports and racing when the noon is by. [*They go out.*]

PEGEEN [*imperiously*]. Fling out that rubbish and put them cups away. [*CHRISTY tidies away in great haste.*] Shove in the bench by the wall. [*He does so.*] And hang that glass on the nail. What disturbed it at all?

CHRISTY [*very meekly*]. I was making myself decent only, and this a fine country for young lovely girls.

PEGEEN [*sharply*]. Whisht your talking of girls. [*Goes to counter on right.*]

CHRISTY. Wouldn't any wish to be decent in a place . . .

PEGEEN. Whisht, I'm saying.

CHRISTY [*looks at her face for a moment with great misgivings, then as a last effort takes up a loy, and goes towards her, with feigned assurance*]. It was with a loy the like of that I killed my father.

PEGEEN [*still sharply*]. You've told me that story six times since the dawn of day.

CHRISTY [*reproachfully*]. It's a queer thing you wouldn't care to be hearing it and them girls after walking four miles to be listening to me now.

PEGEEN [*turning round astonished*]. Four miles?

CHRISTY [*apologetically*]. Didn't himself say there were only bona fides living in the place?

PEGEEN. It's bona fides by the road they are, but that lot came over the river lepping the stones. It's not three perches when you go like that, and I was down this morning looking on the papers the post-boy does have in his bag. [*With meaning and emphasis.*] For there was great news this day, Christopher Mahon.

    She goes into room on left.

CHRISTY [*suspiciously*]. Is it news of my murder?

PEGEEN [*inside*]. Murder, indeed.

CHRISTY [*loudly*]. A murdered da?

PEGEEN [*coming in again and crossing right*]. There was not, but a story filled half a page of the hanging of a man. Ah, that should be a fearful end, young fellow, and it worst of all for a man destroyed his da; for the like of him would get small mercies, and when it's dead he is they'd put him in a narrow grave, with cheap sacking wrapping him round, and pour down quicklime on his head, the way you'd see a woman pouring any frish-frash from a cup.

CHRISTY [*very miserably*]. Oh, God help me. Are you thinking I'm safe? You were saying at the fall of night I was shut of jeopardy and I here with yourselves.

PEGEEN [*severely*]. You'll be shut of jeopardy no place if you go talking with a pack of wild girls the like of them do be walking abroad with the peelers, talking whispers at the fall of night.

CHRISTY [*with terror*]. And you're thinking they'd tell?

PEGEEN [*with mock sympathy*]. Who knows, God help you?

CHRISTY [*loudly*]. What joy would they have to bring hanging to the likes of me?

PEGEEN. It's queer joys they have, and who knows the thing they'd do, if it'd make the green stones cry itself to think of you swaying and swiggling at the butt of a rope, and you with a fine, stout neck, God bless you! the way you'd be a half an hour, in great anguish, getting your death.

CHRISTY [*getting his boots and putting them on*]. If there's that terror of them, it'd be best, maybe, I went on wandering like Esau or Cain and Abel on the sides of Neifin or the Erris plain.

PEGEEN [*beginning to play with him*]. It would, maybe, for I've heard the Circuit Judges this place is a heartless crew.

CHRISTY [*bitterly*]. It's more than Judges this place is a heartless crew. [*Looking up at her.*] And isn't it a poor thing to be starting again, and I a lonesome fellow will be looking out on women and girls the way the needy fallen spirits do be looking on the Lord?

PEGEEN. What call have you to be that lonesome when there's poor girls walking Mayo in their thousands now?

CHRISTY [*grimly*]. It's well you know what call I have. It's well you know it's a lonesome thing to be passing small towns with the lights shining sideways when the night is down, or going in strange places with a dog noising before you and a dog noising behind, or drawn to the cities where you'd hear a voice kissing and talking deep love in every shadow of the ditch, and you passing on with an empty, hungry stomach failing from your heart.

PEGEEN. I'm thinking you're an odd man, Christy Mahon. The oddest walking fellow I ever set my eyes on to this hour today.

CHRISTY. What would any be but odd men and they living lonesome in the world?

PEGEEN. I'm not odd, and I'm my whole life with my father only.

CHRISTY [*with infinite admiration*]. How would a lovely, handsome woman the like of you be lonesome when all men should be thronging around to hear the sweetness of your voice, and the little infant children should be pestering your steps, I'm thinking, and you walking the roads.

PEGEEN. I'm hard set to know what way a coaxing fellow the like of yourself should be lonesome either.

CHRISTY. Coaxing.

PEGEEN. Would you have me think a man never talked with the girls would have the words you've spoken today? It's only letting on you are to be lonesome, the way you'd get around me now.

CHRISTY. I wish to God I was letting on; but I was lonesome all times, and born lonesome, I'm thinking, as the moon of dawn.

> *Going to door.*

PEGEEN [*puzzled by his talk*]. Well, it's a story I'm not understanding at all why you'd be worse than another, Christy Mahon, and you a fine lad with the great savagery to destroy your da.

CHRISTY. It's little I'm understanding myself, saving only that my heart's scalded this day, and I going off stretching out the earth between us, the way I'll not be waking near you another dawn of the year till the two of us do arise to hope or judgment with the saints of God, and now I'd best be going with my wattle in my hand, for hanging is a poor thing [*turning to go*], and it's little welcome only is left me in this house today.

PEGEEN [*sharply*]. Christy. [*He turns round.*] Come here to me. [*He goes towards her.*] Lay down that switch and throw some sods on the fire. You're pot-boy in this place, and I'll not have you mitch off from us now.

CHRISTY. You were saying I'd be hanged if I stay.

PEGEEN [*quite kindly at last*]. I'm after going down and reading the fearful crimes of Ireland for two weeks or three, and there wasn't a word of your murder. [*Getting up and going over to the counter.*] They've likely not found the body. You're safe so with ourselves.

CHRISTY [*astonished, slowly*]. It's making game of me you were [*following her with fearful joy*], and I can stay so, working at your side, and I not lonesome from this mortal day.

PEGEEN. What's to hinder you staying, except the widow woman or the young girls would inveigle you off?

CHRISTY [*with rapture*]. And I'll have your words from this day filling my ears, and that look is come upon you meeting my two eyes, and I watching you loafing around in the warm sun, or rinsing your ankles when the night is come.

PEGEEN [*kindly, but a little embarrassed*]. I'm thinking you'll be a loyal young lad to have working around, and if you vexed me a while since with your leaguing with the girls, I wouldn't give a thraneen for a lad hadn't a mighty spirit in him and a gamey heart.

SHAWN KEOGH runs in carrying a cleeve on his back, followed by the WIDOW QUIN.

SHAWN [*to PEGEEN*]. I was passing below, and I seen your mountainy sheep eating cabbages in Jimmy's field. Run up or they'll be bursting, surely.

PEGEEN. Oh, God mend them!

She puts a shawl over her head and runs out.

CHRISTY [*looking from one to the other. Still in high spirits*]. I'd best go to her aid maybe. I'm handy with ewes.

WIDOW QUIN [*closing the door*]. She can do that much, and there is Shaneen has long speeches for to tell you now.

She sits down with an amused smile.

SHAWN [*taking something from his pocket and offering it to CHRISTY*]. Do you see that, mister?

CHRISTY [*looking at it*]. The half of a ticket to the Western States!

SHAWN [*trembling with anxiety*]. I'll give it to you and my new hat [*pulling it out of hamper*]; and my breeches with the double seat [*pulling it out*]; and my new coat is woven from the blackest shearings for three miles around [*giving him the coat*]; I'll give you the whole of them, and my blessing, and the blessing of Father Reilly itself, maybe, if you'll quit from this and leave us in the peace we had till last night at the fall of dark.

CHRISTY [*with a new arrogance*]. And for what is it you're wanting to get shut of me?

SHAWN [*looking to the WIDOW for help*]. I'm a poor scholar with middling faculties to coin a lie, so I'll tell you the truth, Christy Mahon. I'm wedding with Pegeen beyond, and I don't think well of having a clever, fearless man the like of you dwelling in her house.

CHRISTY [*almost pugnaciously*]. And you'd be using bribery for to banish me?

SHAWN [*in an imploring voice*]. Let you not take it badly, mister honey; isn't beyond the best place for you, where you'll have golden chains and shiny coats and you riding upon hunters with the ladies of the land.

He makes an eager sign to the WIDOW QUIN to come to help him.

WIDOW QUIN [*coming over*]. It's true for him, and you'd best quit off and not have that poor girl setting her mind on you, for there's Shaneen thinks she wouldn't suit you, though all is saying that she'll wed you now.

CHRISTY beams with delight.

SHAWN [*in terrified earnest*]. She wouldn't suit you, and she with the divil's own temper the way you'd be strangling one another in a score of days. [*He makes the movement of strangling with his hands.*] It's the like of me only that she's fit for; a quiet simple fellow wouldn't raise a hand upon her if she scratched itself.

WIDOW QUIN [*putting SHAWN's hat on CHRISTY*]. Fit them clothes on you anyhow, young fellow, and he'd maybe loan them to you for the sports. [*Pushing him towards inner door.*] Fit them on and you can give your answer when you have them tried.

CHRISTY [*beaming, delighted with the clothes*]. I will then. I'd like herself to see me in them tweeds and hat.

He goes into room and shuts the door.

SHAWN [*in great anxiety*]. He'd like herself to see them. He'll not leave us, Widow Quin. He's a score of divils in him the way it's well-nigh certain he will wed Pegeen.

WIDOW QUIN [*jeeringly*]. It's true all girls are fond of courage and do hate the like of you.

SHAWN [*walking about in desperation*]. Oh, Widow Quin, what'll I be doing now? I'd inform again him, but he'd burst from Kilmainham and he'd be sure and certain to destroy me. If I wasn't so God-fearing, I'd near have courage to come behind him and run a pike into his side. Oh, it's a hard case to be an orphan and not to have your father that you're used to, and you'd easy kill and make yourself a hero in the sight of all. [*Coming up to her.*] Oh, Widow Quin, will you find me some contrivance when I've promised you a ewe?

WIDOW QUIN. A ewe's a small thing, but what would you give me if I did wed him and did save you so?

SHAWN [*with astonishment*]. You?

WIDOW QUIN. Aye. Would you give me the red cow you have and the mountainy ram, and the right of way across your rye path, and a load of dung at Michaelmas, and turbary upon the western hill?

SHAWN [*radiant with hope*]. I would, surely, and I'd give you the wedding-ring I have, and the loan of a new suit, the way you'd have him decent on the wedding-day. I'd give you two kids for your dinner, and a gallon of poteen, and I'd call the piper on the long car to your wedding from Crossmolina or from Ballina. I'd give you . . .

WIDOW QUIN. That'll do, so, and let you whisht, for he's coming now again.

*CHRISTY comes in very natty in the new clothes. WIDOW QUIN
goes to him admiringly.*

WIDOW QUIN. If you seen yourself now, I'm thinking you'd be too proud to
speak to at all, and it'd be a pity surely to have your like sailing from Mayo to
the western world.

CHRISTY [*as proud as a peacock*]. I'm not going. If this is a poor place itself, I'll
make myself contented to be lodging here.

WIDOW QUIN makes a sign to SHAWN to leave them.

SHAWN. Well, I'm going measuring the racecourse while the tide is low, so I'll
leave you the garments and my blessing for the sports today. God bless you!

He wriggles out.

WIDOW QUIN [*admiring CHRISTY*]. Well, you're mighty spruce, young fellow. Sit down now while you're quiet till you talk with me.

CHRISTY [*swaggering*]. I'm going abroad on the hillside for to seek Pegeen.

WIDOW QUIN. You'll have time and plenty for to seek Pegeen, and you heard
me saying at the fall of night the two of us should be great company.

CHRISTY. From this out I'll have no want of company when all sorts is bringing me their food and clothing [*he swaggers to the door, tightening his belt*], the
way they'd set their eyes upon a gallant orphan cleft his father with one blow
to the breeches belt. [*He opens door, then staggers back.*] Saints of glory! Holy
angels from the throne of light!

WIDOW QUIN [*going over*]. What ails you?

CHRISTY. It's the walking spirit of my murdered da!

WIDOW QUIN [*looking out*]. Is it that tramper?

CHRISTY [*wildly*]. Where'll I hide my poor body from that ghost of hell?

*The door is pushed open, and OLD MAHON appears on threshold.
CHRISTY darts in behind door.*

WIDOW QUIN [*in great amusement*]. God save you, my poor man.

MAHON [*gruffly*]. Did you see a young lad passing this way in the early morning or the fall of night?

WIDOW QUIN. You're a queer kind to walk in not saluting at all.

MAHON. Did you see the young lad?

WIDOW QUIN [*stiffly*]. What kind was he?

MAHON. An ugly young streeler with a murderous gob on him, and a little
switch in his hand. I met a tramper seen him coming this way at the fall of
night.

WIDOW QUIN. There's harvest hundreds do be passing these days for the Sligo
boat. For what is it you're wanting him, my poor man?

MAHON. I want to destroy him for breaking the head on me with the clout of a
loy. [*He takes off a big hat, and shows his head in a mass of bandages and plaster,
with some pride.*] It was he did that, and amn't I a great wonder to think I've

353

traced him ten days with that rent in my crown?

WIDOW QUIN [*taking his head in both hands and examining it with extreme delight*]. That was a great blow. And who hit you? A robber maybe?

MAHON. It was my own son hit me, and he the divil a robber, or anything else, but a dirty, stuttering lout.

WIDOW QUIN [*letting go his skull and wiping her hands in her apron*]. You'd best be wary of a mortified scalp, I think they call it, lepping around with that wound in the splendour of the sun. It was a bad blow, surely, and you should have vexed him fearful to make him strike that gash in his da.

MAHON. Is it me?

WIDOW QUIN [*amusing herself*]. Aye. And isn't it a great shame when the old and hardened do torment the young?

MAHON [*raging*]. Torment him is it? And I after holding out with the patience of a martyred saint till there's nothing but destruction on, and I'm driven out in my old age with none to aid me.

WIDOW QUIN [*greatly amused*]. It's a sacred wonder the way that wickedness will spoil a man.

MAHON. My wickedness, is it? Amn't I after saying it is himself has me destroyed, and he a lier on walls, a talker of folly, a man you'd see stretched the half of the day in the brown ferns, with his belly to the sun.

WIDOW QUIN. Not working at all?

MAHON. The divil a work, or if he did itself, you'd see him raising up a haystack like the stalk of a rush, or driving our last cow till he broke her leg at the hip, and when he wasn't at that he'd be fooling over little birds he had— finches and felts—or making mugs at his own self in the bit of a glass we had hung on the wall.

WIDOW QUIN [*looking at CHRISTY*]. What way was he so foolish? It was running wild after the girls maybe?

MAHON [*with a shout of derision*]. Running wild, is it? If he seen a red petticoat coming swinging over the hill, he'd be off to hide in the sticks, and you'd see him shooting out his sheep's eyes between the little twigs and the leaves, and his two ears rising like a hare looking out through a gap. Girls, indeed!

WIDOW QUIN. It was drink maybe?

MAHON. And he a poor fellow would get drunk on the smell of a pint. He'd a queer rotten stomach, I'm telling you, and when I gave him three pulls from my pipe a while since, he was taken with contortions till I had to send him in the ass-cart to the females' nurse.

WIDOW QUIN [*clasping her hands*]. Well, I never, till this day, heard tell of a man the like of that!

MAHON. I'd take a mighty oath you didn't, surely, and wasn't he the laughing joke of every female woman where four baronies meet, the way the girls would stop their weeding if they seen him coming the road to let a roar at him, and call him the looney of Mahon's.

WIDOW QUIN. I'd give the world and all to see the like of him. What kind was he?

MAHON. A small, low fellow.

WIDOW QUIN. And dark?

MAHON. Dark and dirty.

WIDOW QUIN [*considering*]. I'm thinking I seen him.

MAHON [*eagerly*]. An ugly young blackguard.

WIDOW QUIN. A hideous, fearful villain, and the spit of you.

MAHON. What way is he fled?

WIDOW QUIN. Gone over the hills to catch a coasting steamer to the north or south.

MAHON. Could I pull up on him now?

WIDOW QUIN. If you'll cross the sands below where the tide is out, you'll be in it as soon as himself, for he had to go round ten miles by the top of the bay. [*She points to the door.*] Strike down by the head beyond and then follow on the roadway to the north and east.

MAHON goes abruptly.

WIDOW QUIN [*shouting after him*]. Let you give him a good vengeance when you come up with him, but don't put yourself in the power of the law, for it'd be a poor thing to see a judge in his black cap reading out his sentence on a civil warrior the like of you. [*She swings the door to and looks at CHRISTY, who is cowering in terror, for a moment, then she bursts into a laugh.*] Well, you're the walking Playboy of the Western World, and that's the poor man you had divided to his breeches belt.

CHRISTY [*looking out; then, to her*]. What'll Pegeen say when she hears that story? What'll she be saying to me now?

WIDOW QUIN. She'll knock the head of you, I'm thinking, and drive you from the door. God help her to be taking you for a wonder, and you a little schemer making up a story you destroyed your da.

CHRISTY [*turning to the door, nearly speechless with rage, half to himself*]. To be letting on he was dead, and coming back to his life, and following after me like an old weasel tracing a rat, and coming in here laying desolation between my own self and the fine women of Ireland, and he a kind of carcase that you'd fling upon the sea. . . .

WIDOW QUIN [*more soberly*]. There's talking for a man's one only son.

CHRISTY [*breaking out*]. His one son, is it? May I meet him with one tooth and it aching, and one eye to be seeing seven and seventy divils in the twists of the road, and one old timber leg on him to limp into the scalding grave. [*Looking out.*] There he is now crossing the strands, and that the Lord God would send a high wave to wash him from the world.

WIDOW QUIN [*scandalized*]. Have you no shame? [*putting her hand on his shoulder and turning him round*]. What ails you? Near crying, is it?

CHRISTY [*in despair and grief*]. Amn't I after seeing the love-light of the star of knowledge shining from her brow, and hearing words would put you thinking on the holy Brigid speaking to the infant saints, and now she'll be turning again, and speaking hard words to me, like an old woman with a spavindy ass she'd have, urging on a hill.

WIDOW QUIN. There's poetry talk for a girl you'd see itching and scratching, and she with a stale stink of poteen on her from selling in the shop.

CHRISTY [*impatiently*]. It's her like is fitted to be handling merchandise in the heavens above, and what'll I be doing now, I ask you, and I a kind of wonder was jilted by the heavens when a day was by.

There is a distant noise of GIRLS' voices. WIDOW QUIN looks from window and comes to him, hurriedly.

WIDOW QUIN. You'll be doing like myself, I'm thinking, when I did destroy my man, for I'm above many's the day, odd times in great spirits, abroad in the sunshine, darning a stocking or stitching a shift; and odd times again looking out on the schooners, hookers, trawlers is sailing the sea, and I thinking on the gallant hairy fellows are drifting beyond, and myself long years living alone.

CHRISTY [*interested*]. You're like me, so.

WIDOW QUIN. I am your like, and it's for that I'm taking a fancy to you, and I with my little houseen above where there'd be myself to tend you, and none to ask were you a murderer or what at all.

CHRISTY. And what would I be doing if I left Pegeen?

WIDOW QUIN. I've nice jobs you could be doing—gathering shells to make a white-wash for our hut within, building up a little goosehouse, or stretching a new skin on an old curagh I have, and if my hut is far from all sides, it's there you'll meet the wisest old men, I tell you, at the corner of my wheel, and it's there yourself and me will have great times whispering and hugging. . . .

VOICES [*outside, calling far away*]. Christy! Christy Mahon! Christy!

CHRISTY. Is it Pegeen Mike?

WIDOW QUIN. It's the young girls, I'm thinking, coming to bring you to the sports below, and what is it you'll have me to tell them now?

CHRISTY. Aid me for to win Pegeen. It's herself only that I'm seeking now. [*WIDOW QUIN gets up and goes to window.*] Aid me for to win her, and I'll be asking God to stretch a hand to you in the hour of death, and lead you short cuts through the Meadows of Ease, and up the floor of Heaven to the Footstool of the Virgin's Son.

WIDOW QUIN. There's praying!

VOICES [*nearer*]. Christy! Christy Mahon!

CHRISTY [*with agitation*]. They're coming. Will you swear to aid and save me, for the love of Christ?

WIDOW QUIN [*looks at him for a moment*]. If I aid you, will you swear to give me a right of way I want, and a mountainy ram, and a load of dung at Michaelmas, the time that you'll be master here?

CHRISTY. I will, by the elements and stars of night.

WIDOW QUIN. Then we'll not say a word of the old fellow, the way Pegeen won't know your story till the end of time.

CHRISTY. And if he chances to return again?

WIDOW QUIN. We'll swear he's a maniac and not your da. I could take an oath I seen him raving on the sands today.

GIRLS run in.

SUSAN. Come on to the sports below. Pegeen says you're to come.

SARA TANSEY. The lepping's beginning, and we've a jockey's suit to fit upon you for the mule race on the sands below.

HONOR. Come on, will you?

CHRISTY. I will then if Pegeen's beyond.

SARA. She's in the boreen making game of Shaneen Keogh.

CHRISTY. Then I'll be going to her now.

He runs out, followed by the GIRLS.

WIDOW QUIN. Well, if the worst comes in the end of all, it'll be great game to see there's none to pity him but a widow woman, the like of me, has buried her children and destroyed her man.

She goes out.

CURTAIN.

ACT III

Scene as before. Later in the day. JIMMY comes in, slightly drunk.

JIMMY [*calls*]. Pegeen! [*Crosses to inner door.*] Pegeen Mike! [*Comes back again into the room.*] Pegeen! [*PHILLY comes in in the same state. To PHILLY.*] Did you see herself?

PHILLY. I did not; but I sent Shawn Keogh with the ass-cart for to bear him home. [*Trying cupboards, which are locked.*] Well, isn't he a nasty man to get into such staggers at a morning wake; and isn't herself the divil's daughter for locking, and she so fussy after that young gaffer, you might take your death with drouth and none to heed you?

JIMMY. It's little wonder she'd be fussy, and he after bringing bankrupt ruin on the roulette man, and the trick-o'-the-loop man, and breaking the nose of the cockshot-man, and winning all in the sports below, racing, lepping, dancing, and the Lord knows what! He's right luck, I'm telling you.

PHILLY. If he has, he'll be rightly hobbled yet, and he not able to say ten words without making a brag of the way he killed his father, and the great blow he hit with the loy.

JIMMY. A man can't hang by his own informing, and his father should be rotten by now.

    OLD MAHON passes window slowly.

PHILLY. Supposing a man's digging spuds in that field with a long spade, and supposing he flings up the two halves of that skull, what'll be said then in the papers and the courts of law?

JIMMY. They'd say it was an old Dane, maybe, was drowned in the flood. [*OLD MAHON comes in and sits down near door listening.*] Did you never hear tell of the skulls they have in the city of Dublin, ranged out like blue jugs in a cabin of Connaught?

PHILLY. And you believe that?

JIMMY [*pugnaciously*]. Didn't a lad see them and he after coming from harvesting in the Liverpool boat? "They have them there," says he, "making a show of the great people there was one time walking the world. White skulls and black skulls and yellow skulls, and some with full teeth, and some haven't only but one."

PHILLY. It was no lie, maybe, for when I was a young lad there was a graveyard beyond the house with the remnants of a man who had thighs as long as your arm. He was a horrid man, I'm telling you, and there was many a fine Sunday I'd put him together for fun, and he with shiny bones, you wouldn't meet the like of these days in the cities of the world.

MAHON [*getting up*]. You wouldn't, is it? Lay your eyes on that skull, and tell me where and when there was another the like of it, is splintered only from the blow of a loy.

PHILLY. Glory be to God! And who hit you at all?

MAHON [*triumphantly*]. It was my own son hit me. Would you believe that?

JIMMY. Well, there's wonders hidden in the heart of man!

PHILLY [*suspiciously*]. And what way was it done?

MAHON [*wandering about the room*]. I'm after walking hundreds and long scores of miles, winning clean beds and the fill of my belly four times in the day, and I doing nothing but telling stories of that naked truth. [*He comes to them a little aggressively.*] Give me a supeen and I'll tell you now.

    WIDOW QUIN comes in and stands aghast behind him. He is facing
    JIMMY and PHILLY, who are on the left.

JIMMY. Ask herself beyond. She's the stuff hidden in her shawl.

WIDOW QUIN [*coming to MAHON quickly*]. You here, is it? You didn't go far at all?

MAHON. I seen the coasting steamer passing, and I got a drouth upon me and a cramping leg, so I said, 'The divil go along with him,' and turned again. [*Looking under her shawl.*] And let you give me a supeen, for I'm destroyed travelling since Tuesday was a week.

WIDOW QUIN [*getting a glass, in a cajoling tone*]. Sit down then by the fire and take your ease for a space. You've a right to be destroyed indeed, with your walking, and fighting, and facing the sun [*giving him poteen from a stone jar she has brought in*]. There now is a drink for you, and may it be to your happiness and length of life.

MAHON [*taking glass greedily, and sitting down by fire*]. God increase you!

WIDOW QUIN [*taking men to the right stealthily*]. Do you know what? That man's raving from his wound today, for I met him a while since telling a rambling tale of a tinker had him destroyed. Then he heard of Christy's deed, and he up and says it was his son had cracked his skull. Oh, isn't madness a fright, for he'll go killing someone yet, and he thinking it's the man has struck him so?

JIMMY [*entirely convinced*]. It's a fright surely. I knew a party was kicked in the head by a red mare, and he went killing horses a great while, till he eat the insides of a clock and died after.

PHILLY [*with suspicion*]. Did he see Christy?

WIDOW QUIN. He didn't. [*With a warning gesture.*] Let you not be putting him in mind of him, or you'll be likely summoned if there's murder done. [*Looking round at MAHON.*] Whisht! He's listening. Wait now till you hear me taking him easy and unravelling all. [*She goes to MAHON.*] And what way are you feeling, mister? Are you in contentment now?

MAHON [*slightly emotional from his drink*]. I'm poorly only, for it's a hard story the way I'm left today, when it was I did tend him from his hour of birth, and he a dunce never reached his second book, the way he'd come from school, many's the day, with his legs lamed under him, and he blackened with his beatings like a tinker's ass. It's a hard story, I'm saying, the way some do have their next and nighest raising up a hand of murder on them, and some is lonesome getting their death with lamentation in the dead of night.

WIDOW QUIN [*not knowing what to say*]. To hear you talking so quiet, who'd know you were the same fellow we seen pass today?

MAHON. I'm the same surely. The wrack and ruin of threescore years; and it's a terror to live that length, I tell you, and to have your sons going to the dogs against you, and you wore out scolding them, and skelping them, and God knows what.

PHILLY [*to JIMMY*]. He's not raving. [*To WIDOW QUIN.*] Will you ask him what kind was his son?

WIDOW QUIN [*to MAHON, with a peculiar look*]. Was your son that hit you a lad of one year and a score maybe, a great hand at racing and lepping and licking the world?

MAHON [*turning on her with a roar of rage*]. Didn't you hear me say he was the fool of men, the way from this out he'll know the orphan's lot, with old and young making game of him, and they swearing, raging, kicking at him like a mangy cur.

> *A great burst of cheering outside, some way off.*

MAHON [*putting his hands to his ears*]. What in the name of God do they want roaring below?

WIDOW QUIN [*with the shade of a smile*]. They're cheering a young lad, the champion Playboy of the Western World.

> *More cheering.*

MAHON [*going to window*]. It'd split my heart to hear them, and I with pulses in my brain-pan for a week gone by. Is it racing they are?

JIMMY [*looking from door*]. It is, then. They are mounting him for the mule race will be run upon the sands. That's the playboy on the winkered mule.

MAHON [*puzzled*]. That lad, is it? If you said it was a fool he was, I'd have laid a mighty oath he was the likeness of my wandering son. [*Uneasily, putting his hand to his head.*] Faith, I'm thinking I'll go walking for to view the race.

WIDOW QUIN [*stopping him, sharply*]. You will not. You'd best take the road to Belmullet, and not be dilly-dallying in this place where there isn't a spot you could sleep.

PHILLY [*coming forward*]. Don't mind her. Mount there on the bench and you'll have a view of the whole. They're hurrying before the tide will rise, and it'd be near over if you went down the pathway through the crags below.

MAHON [*mounts on bench, WIDOW QUIN beside him*]. That's a right view again the edge of the sea. They're coming now from the point. He's leading. Who is he at all?

WIDOW QUIN. He's the champion of the world, I tell you, and there isn't a hap'orth isn't falling lucky to his hands today.

PHILLY [*looking out, interested in the race*]. Look at that. They're pressing him now.

JIMMY. He'll win it yet.

PHILLY. Take your time, Jimmy Farrell. It's too soon to say.

WIDOW QUIN [*shouting*]. Watch him taking the gate. There's riding.

JIMMY [*cheering*]. More power to the young lad!

MAHON. He's passing the third.

JIMMY. He'll lick them yet.

WIDOW QUIN. He'd lick them if he was running races with a score itself.

MAHON. Look at the mule he has, kicking the stars.

WIDOW QUIN. There was a lep! [*Catching hold of MAHON in her excitement.*] He's fallen? He's mounted again! Faith, he's passing them all!

JIMMY. Look at him skelping her!

PHILLY. And the mountain girls hooshing him on!

JIMMY. It's the last turn! The post's cleared for them now!

MAHON. Look at the narrow place. He'll be into the bogs! [*With a yell.*] Good rider! He's through it again!

JIMMY. He neck and neck!

PHILLY. Good boy to him! Flames, but he's in! [*Great cheering, in which all join.*]

MAHON [*with hesitation*]. What's that? They're raising him up. They're coming this way. [*With a roar of rage and astonishment.*] It's Christy, by the stars of God! I'd know his way of spitting and he astride the moon.

> *He jumps down and makes a run for the door, but WIDOW QUIN*
> *catches him and pulls him back.*

WIDOW QUIN. Stay quiet, will you? That's not your son. [*To JIMMY.*] Stop him, or you'll get a month for the abetting of manslaughter and be fined as well.

JIMMY. I'll hold him.

MAHON [*struggling*]. Let me out! Let me out, the lot of you, till I have my vengeance on his head today.

WIDOW QUIN [*shaking him, vehemently*]. That's not your son. That's a man is going to make a marriage with the daughter of this house, a place with fine trade, with a licence, and with poteen too.

MAHON [*amazed*]. That man marrying a decent and a moneyed girl! Is it mad yous are? Is it in a crazy-house for females that I'm landed now?

WIDOW QUIN. It's mad yourself is with the blow upon your head. That lad is the wonder of the western world.

MAHON. I seen it's my son.

WIDOW QUIN. You seen that you're mad. [*Cheering outside.*] Do you hear them cheering him in the zig-zags of the road? Aren't you after saying that your son's a fool, and how would they be cheering a true idiot born?

MAHON [*getting distressed*]. It's maybe out of reason that that man's himself. [*Cheering again.*] There's none surely will go cheering him. Oh, I'm raving with a madness that would fright the world! [*He sits down with his hand to his head.*] There was one time I seen ten scarlet divils letting on they'd cork my spirit in a gallon can; and one time I seen rats as big as badgers sucking the lifeblood from the butt of my lug; but I never till this day confused that dribbling idiot with a likely man. I'm destroyed surely.

WIDOW QUIN. And who'd wonder when it's your brain-pan that is gaping now?

MAHON. Then the blight of the sacred drouth upon myself and him, for I never went mad to this day, and I not three weeks with the Limerick girls drinking myself silly and parlatic from the dusk to dawn. [*To WIDOW QUIN, suddenly.*] Is my visage astray?

WIDOW QUIN. It is, then. You're a sniggering maniac, a child could see.

MAHON [*getting up more cheerfully*]. Then I'd best be going to the union

361

beyond, and there'll be a welcome before me, I tell you [*with great pride*], and I a terrible and fearful case, the way that there I was one time, screeching in a straightened waistcoat, with seven doctors writing out my sayings in a printed book. Would you believe that?

WIDOW QUIN. If you're a wonder itself, you'd best be hasty, for them lads caught a maniac one time and pelted the poor creature till he ran out, raving and foaming, and was drowned in the sea.

MAHON [*with philosophy*]. It's true mankind is the divil when your head's astray. Let me out now and I'll slip down the boreen, and not see them so.

WIDOW QUIN [*showing him out*]. That's it. Run to the right, and not a one will see.

> *He runs off.*

PHILLY [*wisely*]. You're at some gaming, Widow Quin; but I'll walk after him and give him his dinner and a time to rest, and I'll see then if he's raving or as sane as you.

WIDOW QUIN [*annoyèd*]. If you go near that lad, let you be wary of your head, I'm saying. Didn't you hear him telling he was crazed at times?

PHILLY. I heard him telling a power; and I'm thinking we'll have right sport before night will fall. [*He goes out.*]

JIMMY. Well, Philly's a conceited and foolish man. How could that madman have his senses and his brain-pan slit? I'll go after them and see him turn on Philly now.

> *He goes; WIDOW QUIN hides poteen behind counter. Then hubbub outside.*

VOICES. There you are! Good jumper! Grand lepper! Darlint boy! He's the racer! Bear him on, will you!

> *CHRISTY Comes in, in jockey's dress, with PEGEEN MIKE, SARA, and other GIRLS and MEN.*

PEGEEN [*to crowd*]. Go on now and don't destroy him and he drenching with sweat. Go along, I'm saying, and have your tug-of-warring till he's dried his skin.

CROWD. Here's his prizes! A bagpipes! A fiddle was played by a poet in the years gone by! A flat and three-thorned blackthorn would lick the scholars out of Dublin town!

CHRISTY [*taking prizes from the MEN*]. Thank you kindly, the lot of you. But you'd say it was little only I did this day if you'd seen me a while since striking my one single blow.

TOWN CRIER [*outside ringing a bell*]. Take notice, last event of this day! Tug-of-warring on the green below! Come on, the lot of you! Great achievements for all Mayo men!

PEGEEN. Go on and leave him for to rest and dry. Go on, I tell you, for he'll do no more.

She hustles crowd out; WIDOW QUIN following them.

MEN [*going*]. Come on, then. Good luck for the while!

PEGEEN [*radiantly, wiping his face with her shawl*]. Well, you're the lad, and you'll have great times from this out when you could win that wealth of prizes, and you sweating in the heat of noon!

CHRISTY [*looking at her with delight*]. I'll have great times if I win the crowning prize I'm seeking now, and that's your promise that you'll wed me in a fortnight, when our banns is called.

PEGEEN [*backing away from him*]. You've right daring to go ask me that, when all knows you'll be starting to some girl in your own townland, when your father's rotten in four months, or five.

CHRISTY [*indignantly*]. Starting from you, is it? [*He follows her.*] I will not, then, and when the airs is warming, in four months or five, it's then yourself and me should be pacing Neifin in the dews of night, the times sweet smells do be rising, and you'd see a little, shiny new moon, maybe, sinking on the hills.

PEGEEN [*looking at him playfully*]. And it's that kind of a poacher's love you'd make, Christy Mahon, on the sides of Neifin, when the night is down?

CHRISTY. It's little you'll think if my love's a poacher's, or an earl's itself, when you'll feel my two hands stretched around you, and I squeezing kisses on your puckered lips, till I'd feel a kind of pity for the Lord God is all ages sitting lonesome in His golden chair.

PEGEEN. That'll be right fun, Christy Mahon, and any girl would walk her heart out before she'd meet a young man was your like for eloquence, or talk at all.

CHRISTY [*encouraged*]. Let you wait, to hear me talking, till we're astray in Erris, when Good Friday's by, drinking a sup from a well, and making mighty kisses with our wetted mouths, or gaming in a gap of sunshine, with yourself stretched back unto your necklace, in the flowers of the earth.

PEGEEN [*in a low voice, moved by his tone*]. I'd be nice so, is it?

CHRISTY [*with rapture*]. If the mitred bishops seen you that time, they'd be the like of the holy prophets, I'm thinking, do be straining the bars of Paradise to lay eyes on the Lady Helen of Troy, and she abroad, pacing back and forward, with a nosegay in her golden shawl.

PEGEEN [*with real tenderness*]. And what is it I have, Christy Mahon, to make me fitting entertainment for the like of you, that has such poet's talking, and such bravery of heart.

CHRISTY [*in a low voice*]. Isn't there the light of seven heavens in your heart alone, the way you'll be an angel's lamp to me from this out, and I abroad in the darkness, spearing salmons in the Owen or the Carrowmore?

PEGEEN. If I was your wife I'd be along with you those nights, Christy Mahon, the way you'd see I was a great hand at coaxing bailiffs, or coining funny nicknames for the stars of night.

CHRISTY. You, is it? Taking your death in the hailstones, or in the fogs of dawn.

PEGEEN. Yourself and me would shelter easy in a narrow bush [*with a qualm of dread*]; but we're only talking, maybe, for this would be a poor, thatched place to hold a fine lad is the like of you.

CHRISTY [*putting his arm round her*]. If I wasn't a good Christian, it's on my naked knees I'd be saying my prayers and paters to every jackstraw you have roofing your head, and every stony pebble is paving the laneway to your door.

PEGEEN [*radiantly*]. If that's the truth I'll be burning candles from this out to the miracles of God that have brought you from the south today, and I with my gowns bought ready, the way that I can wed you, and not wait at all.

CHRISTY. It's miracles, and that's the truth. Me there toiling a long while, and walking a long while, not knowing at all I was drawing all times nearer to this holy day.

PEGEEN. And myself, a girl, was tempted often to go sailing the seas till I'd marry a Jew-man, with ten kegs of gold, and I not knowing at all there was the like of you drawing nearer, like the stars of God.

CHRISTY. And to think I'm long years hearing women talking that talk, to all bloody fools, and this the first time I've heard the like of your voice talking sweetly for my own delight.

PEGEEN. And to think it's me is talking sweetly, Christy Mahon, and I the fright of seven townlands for my biting tongue. Well, the heart's a wonder; and, I'm thinking, there won't be our like in Mayo, for gallant lovers, from this hour today. [*Drunken singing is heard outside.*] There's my father coming from the wake, and when he's had his sleep we'll tell him, for he's peaceful then.

   They separate.

MICHAEL [*singing outside*].

> The jailer and the turnkey.
> They quickly ran us down,
> And brought us back as prisoners.
> Once more to Cavan town.

He comes in supported by SHAWN.

> There we lay bewailing.
> All in a prison bound. . . .

He sees CHRISTY. Goes and shakes him drunkenly by the hand, while PEGEEN and SHAWN talk on the left.

MICHAEL [*to CHRISTY*]. The blessing of God and the holy angels on your head, young fellow. I hear tell you're after winning all in the sports below; and wasn't it a shame I didn't bear you along with me to Kate Cassidy's wake, a fine,

364

stout lad, the like of you, for you'd never see the match of it for flows of drink, the way when we sunk her bones at noonday in her narrow grave, there were five men, aye, and six men, stretched out retching speechless on the holy stones.

CHRISTY [*uneasily, watching PEGEEN*]. Is that the truth?

MICHAEL. It is, then; and aren't you a louty schemer to go burying your poor father unbeknownst when you'd a right to throw him on the crupper of a Kerry mule and drive him westwards, like holy Joseph in the days gone by, the way we could have given him a decent burial, and not have him rotting beyond, and not a Christian drinking a smart drop to the glory of his soul?

CHRISTY [*gruffly*]. It's well enough he's lying, for the likes of him.

MICHAEL [*slapping him on the back*]. Well, aren't you a hardened slayer? It'll be a poor thing for the household man where you go sniffing for a female wife; and [*pointing to SHAWN*] look beyond at that shy and decent Christian I have chosen for my daughter's hand, and I after getting the gilded dispensation this day for to wed them now.

CHRISTY. And you'll be wedding them this day, is it?

MICHAEL [*drawing himself up*]. Aye. Are you thinking, if I'm drunk itself, I'd leave my daughter living single with a little frisky rascal is the like of you?

PEGEEN [*breaking away from SHAWN*]. Is it the truth the dispensation's come?

MICHAEL [*triumphantly*]. Father Reilly's after reading it in gallous Latin, and "It's come in the nick of time," says he; "so I'll wed them in a hurry, dreading that young gaffer who'd capsize the stars."

PEGEEN [*fiercely*]. He's missed his nick of time, for it's that lad, Christy Mahon, that I'm wedding now.

MICHAEL [*loudly, with horror*]. You'd be making him a son to me, and he wet and crusted with his father's blood?

PEGEEN. Aye. Wouldn't it be a bitter thing for a girl to go marrying the like of Shaneen, and he a middling kind of a scarecrow, with no savagery or fine words in him at all?

MICHAEL [*gasping and sinking on a chair*]. Oh, aren't you a heathen daughter to go shaking the fat of my heart, and I swamped and drownded with the weight of drink? Would you have them turning on me the way that I'd be roaring to the dawn of day with the wind upon my heart? Have you not a word to aid me, Shaneen? Are you not jealous at all?

SHAWN [*in great misery*]. I'd be afeard to be jealous of a man did slay his da?

PEGEEN. Well, it'd be a poor thing to go marrying your like. I'm seeing there's a world of peril for an orphan girl, and, isn't it a great blessing I didn't wed you before himself came walking from the west or south?

SHAWN. It's a queer story you'd go picking a dirty tramp up from the highways of the world.

PEGEEN [*playfully*]. And you think you're a likely beau to go straying along with the shiny Sundays of the opening year, when it's sooner on a bullock's liver you'd put a poor girl thinking than on the lily or the rose?

SHAWN. And have you no mind of my weight of passion, and the holy dispensation, and the drift of heifers I'm giving, and the golden ring?

PEGEEN. I'm thinking you're too fine for the like of me, Shawn Keogh of Killakeen, and let you go off till you'd find a radiant lady with droves of bullocks on the plains of Meath, and herself bedizened in the diamond jewelleries of Pharaoh's ma. That'd be your match, Shaneen. So God save you now!

She retreats behind CHRISTY.

SHAWN. Won't you hear me telling you . . . ?

CHRISTY [*with ferocity*]. Take yourself from this, young fellow, or I'll maybe add a murder to my deeds today.

MICHAEL [*springing up with a shriek*]. Murder is it? Is it mad yous are? Would you go making murder in this place, and it piled with poteen for our drink tonight? Go on to the foreshore if it's fighting you want, where the rising tide will wash all traces from the memory of man.

Pushing SHAWN towards CHRISTY.

SHAWN [*shaking himself free, and getting behind MICHAEL*]. I'll not fight him, Michael James. I'd liefer live a bachelor, simmering in passions to the end of time, than face a lepping savage the like of him has descended from the Lord knows where. Strike him yourself, Michael James, or you'll lose my drift of heifers and my blue bull from Sneem.

MICHAEL. Is it me fight him, when it's father-slaying he's bred to now? [*Pushing SHAWN.*] Go on, you fool, and fight him now.

SHAWN [*coming forward a little*]. Will I strike him with my hand?

MICHAEL. Take the loy is on your western side.

SHAWN. I'd be afeard of the gallows if I struck with that.

CHRISTY [*taking up the loy*]. Then I'll make you face the gallows or quit off from this. [*SHAWN flies out of the door.*]

CHRISTY. Well, fine weather be after him [*going to MICHAEL, coaxingly*], and I'm thinking you wouldn't wish to have that quaking blackguard in your house at all. Let you give us your blessing and hear her swear her faith to me, for I'm mounted on the spring-tide of the stars of luck, the way it'll be good for any to have me in the house.

PEGEEN [*at the other side of MICHAEL*]. Bless us now, for I swear to God I'll wed him, and I'll not renege.

MICHAEL [*standing up in the centre, holding on to both of them*]. It's the will of God, I'm thinking, that all should win an easy or a cruel end, and it's the will of God that all should rear up lengthy families for the nurture of the earth. What's a single man, I ask you, eating a bit in one house and drinking a sup in another, and he with no place of his own, like an old braying jackass strayed upon the rocks? [*To CHRISTY.*] It's many would be in dread to bring your like into their house for to end them, maybe, with a sudden end; but I'm a decent man of Ireland, and I liefer face the grave untimely and I seeing a score of grandsons growing up little gallant swearers by the name of God, than go peopling my bedside with puny weeds the like of what you'd breed, I'm think-ing, out of Shaneen Keogh. [*He joins their hands.*] A daring fellow is the jewel of the world, and a man did split his father's middle with a single clout should have the bravery of ten, so may God and Mary and St. Patrick bless you, and increase you from this mortal day.

CHRISTY and PEGEEN. Amen, O Lord!

> *Hubbub outside. OLD MAHON rushes in, followed by all the crowd, and WIDOW QUIN. He makes a rush at CHRISTY, knocks him down, and begins to beat him.*

PEGEEN [*digging back his arm*]. Stop that, will you? Who are you at all?

MAHON. His father, God forgive me!

PEGEEN [*drawing back*]. Is it rose from the dead?

MAHON. Do you think I look so easy quenched with the tap of a loy?

> *Beats CHRISTY again.*

PEGEEN [*glaring at CHRISTY*]. And it's lies you told, letting on you had him slitted, and you nothing at all.

CHRISTY [*catching MAHON's stick*]. He's not my father. He's a raving maniac would scare the world. [*Pointing to WIDOW QUIN.*] Herself knows it is true.

CROWD. You're fooling Pegeen! The Widow Quin seen him this day, and you likely knew! You're a liar!

CHRISTY [*dumbfounded*]. It's himself was a liar, lying stretched out with an open head on him, letting on he was dead.

MAHON. Weren't you off racing the hills before I got my breath with the start I had seeing you turn on me at all?

PEGEEN. And to think of the coaxing glory we had given him, and he after doing nothing but hitting a soft blow and chasing northward in a sweat of fear. Quit off from this.

CHRISTY [*piteously*]. You've seen my doings this day, and let you save me from the old man; for why would you be in such a scorch of haste to spur me to destruction now?

PEGEEN. It's there your treachery is spurring me, till I'm hard set to think you're the one I'm after lacing in my heartstrings half an hour gone by. [*To MAHON.*] Take him on from this, for I think bad the world should see me raging for a Munster liar, and the fool of men.

MAHON. Rise up now to retribution, and come on with me.

CROWD [*jeeringly*]. There's the playboy! There's the lad thought he'd rule the roost in Mayo! Slate him now, mister.

CHRISTY [*getting up in shy terror*]. What is it drives you to torment me here, when I'd asked the thunders of the might of God to blast me if I ever did hurt to any saving only that one single blow.

MAHON [*loudly*]. If you didn't, you're a poor good-for-nothing, and isn't it by the like of you the sins of the whole world are committed?

CHRISTY [*raising his hands*]. In the name of the Almighty God . . .

MAHON. Leave troubling the Lord God. Would you have Him sending down droughts, and fevers, and the old hen and the cholera morbus?

CHRISTY [*to WIDOW QUIN*]. Will you come between us and protect me now?

WIDOW QUIN. I've tried a lot, God help me, and my share is done.

CHRISTY [*looking round in desperation*]. And I must go back into my torment is it, or run off like a vagabond straying through the unions with the dust of August making mudstains in the gullet of my throat; or the winds of March blowing on me till I'd take an oath I felt them making whistles of my ribs within?

SARA. Ask Pegeen to aid you. Her like does often change.

CHRISTY. I will not, then, for there's torment in the splendour of her like, and she a girl any moon of midnight would take pride to meet, facing southwards on the heaths of Keel. But what did I want crawling forward to scorch my understanding at her flaming brow?

PEGEEN [*to MAHON, vehemently, fearing she will break into tears*]. Take him on from this or I'll set the young lads to destroy him here.

MAHON [*going to him, shaking his stick*]. Come on now if you wouldn't have the company to see you skelped.

PEGEEN [*half-laughing, through her tears*]. That's it, now the world will see him pandied, and he an ugly liar was playing off the hero, and the fright of men.

CHRISTY [*to MAHON, very sharply*]. Leave me go!

CROWD. That's it. Now, Christy. If them two set fighting, it will lick the world.

MAHON [*making a grab at CHRISTY*]. Come here to me.

CHRISTY [*more threateningly*]. Leave me go, I'm saying.

MAHON. I will, maybe, when your legs is limping, and your back is blue.

CROWD. Keep it up, the two of you. I'll back the old one. Now the playboy.

CHRISTY [*in low and intense voice*]. Shut your yelling, for if you're after making a mighty man of me this day by the power of a lie, you're setting me now to think if it's a poor thing to be lonesome it's worse, maybe, go mixing with the fools of earth.

    MAHON makes a movement towards him.

CHRISTY [*almost shouting*]. Keep off . . . lest I do show a blow unto the lot of you would set the guardian angels winking in the clouds above.

    He swings round with a sudden rapid movement and picks up a loy.

CROWD [*half-frightened, half-amused*]. He's going mad! Mind yourselves! Run from the idiot!

CHRISTY. If I am an idiot, I'm after hearing my voice this day saying words would raise the top-knot on a poet in a merchant's town. I've won your racing, and your lepping, and . . .

MAHON. Shut your gullet and come on with me.

CHRISTY. I'm going, but I'll stretch you first.

He runs at OLD MAHON with the loy, chases him out of the door, followed by crowd and WIDOW QUIN. There is a great noise outside, then a yell, and dead silence for a moment. CHRISTY comes in, half-dazed, and goes to fire.

WIDOW QUIN [*coming in hurriedly, and going to him*]. They're turning again you. Come on, or you'll be hanged, indeed.

CHRISTY. I'm thinking, from this out, Pegeen'll be giving me praises, the same as in the hours gone by.

WIDOW QUIN [*impatiently*]. Come by the back door. I'd think bad to have you stifled on the gallows tree.

CHRISTY [*indignantly*]. I will not, then. What good'd be my lifetime if I left Pegeen?

WIDOW QUIN. Come on, and you'll be no worse than you were last night; and you with a double murder this time to be telling to the girls.

CHRISTY. I'll not leave Pegeen Mike.

WIDOW QUIN [*impatiently*]. Isn't there the match of her in every parish public, from Binghamstown unto the plain of Meath? Come on, I tell you, and I'll find you finer sweethearts at each waning moon.

CHRISTY. It's Pegeen I'm seeking only, and what'd I care if you brought me a drift of chosen females, standing in their shifts itself, maybe, from this place to the eastern world?

SARA [*runs in, pulling off one of her petticoats*]. They're going to hang him. [*Holding out petticoat and shawl.*] Fit these upon him, and let him run off to the east.

WIDOW QUIN. He's raving now; but we'll fit them on him, and I'll take him to the ferry to the Achill boat.

CHRISTY [*struggling feebly*]. Leave me go, will you? when I'm thinking of my luck today, for she will wed me surely, and I a proven hero in the end of all.

They try to fasten petticoat round him.

WIDOW QUIN. Take his left hand, and we'll pull him now. Come on, young fellow.

CHRISTY [*suddenly starting up*]. You'll be taking me from her? You're jealous, is it, of her wedding me? Go on from this.

He snatches up a stool, and threatens them with it.

WIDOW QUIN [*going*]. It's in the madhouse they should put him, not in jail, at all. We'll go by the back door to call the doctor, and we'll save him so.

She goes out, with SARA, through inner room. MEN crowd in the doorway. CHRISTY sits down again by the fire.

MICHAEL [*in a terrified whisper*]. Is the old lad killed surely?

PHILLY. I'm after feeling the last gasps quitting his heart. [*They peer in at CHRISTY.*]

MICHAEL [*with a rope*]. Look at the way he is. Twist a hangman's knot on it, and slip it over his head, while he's not minding at all.

PHILLY. Let you take it, Shaneen. You're the soberest of all that's here.

SHAWN. Is it me to go near him, and he the wickedest and the worst with me? Let you take it, Pegeen Mike.

PEGEEN. Come on, so.

She goes forward with the others, and they drop the double hitch over his head.

CHRISTY. What ails you?

SHAWN [*triumphantly, as they pull the rope tight on his arms*]. Come on to the peelers, till they stretch you now.

CHRISTY. Me!

MICHAEL. If we took pity on you the Lord God would, maybe, bring us ruin from the law today, so you'd best come easy, for hanging is an easy and a speedy end.

CHRISTY. I'll not stir. [*To PEGEEN.*] And what is it you'll say to me, and I after doing it this time in the face of all?

PEGEEN. I'll say, a strange man is a marvel, with his mighty talk; but what's a squabble in your backyard, and the blow of a loy, have taught me that there's a great gap between a gallous story and a dirty deed. [*To MEN.*] Take him on from this, or the lot of us will be likely put on trial for his deed today.

CHRISTY [*with horror in his voice*]. And it's yourself will send me off, to have a horny-fingered hangman hitching his bloody slipknots at the butt of my ear.

MEN [*pulling rope*]. Come on, will you?

He is pulled down on the floor.

CHRISTY [*twisting his legs round the table*]. Cut the rope, Pegeen, and I'll quit the lot of you, and live from this out, like the madmen of Keel, eating muck and green weeds on the faces of the cliffs.

PEGEEN. And leave us to hang, is it, for a saucy liar, the like of you? [*To MEN.*] Take him on, out from this.

SHAWN. Pull a twist on his neck, and squeeze him so.

PHILLY. Twist yourself. Sure he cannot hurt you, if you keep your distance from his teeth alone.

SHAWN. I'm afeard of him. [*To PEGEEN.*] Lift a lighted sod, will you, and scorch his leg.

PEGEEN [*blowing the fire with a bellows*]. Leave go now, young fellow, or I'll scorch your shins.

CHRISTY. You're blowing for to torture me. [*His voice rising and growing stronger.*] That's your kind, is it? Then let the lot of you be wary, for, if I've to face the gallows, I'll have a gay march down, I tell you, and shed the blood of some of you before I die.

SHAWN [*in terror*]. Keep a good hold, Philly. Be wary, for the love of God. For I'm thinking he would liefest wreak his pains on me.

CHRISTY [*almost gaily*]. If I do lay my hands on you, it's the way you'll be at the fall of night, hanging as a scarecrow for the fowls of hell. Ah, you'll have a gallous jaunt, I'm saying, coaching out through Limbo with my father's ghost.

SHAWN [*to PEGEEN*]. Make haste, will you? Oh, isn't he a holy terror, and isn't it true for Father Reilly, that all drink's a curse that has the lot of you so shaky and uncertain now?

CHRISTY. If I can wring a neck among you, I'll have a royal judgment looking on the trembling jury in the courts of law. And won't there be crying out in Mayo the day I'm stretched upon the rope, with ladies in their silks and satins snivelling in their lacy kerchiefs, and they rhyming songs and ballads on the terror of my fate?

He squirms round on the floor and bites SHAWN's leg.

SHAWN [*shrieking*]. My leg's bit on me. He's the like of a mad dog, I'm thinking, the way that I will surely die.

CHRISTY [*delighted with himself*]. You will, then, the way you can shake out hell's flags of welcome for my coming in two weeks or three, for I'm thinking Satan hasn't many have killed their da in Kerry, and in Mayo too.

OLD MAHON comes in behind on all fours and looks on unnoticed.

MEN [*to PEGEEN*]. Bring the sod, will you?

PEGEEN [*coming over*]. God help him so. [*Burns his leg.*]

CHRISTY [*kicking and screaming*]. Oh, glory be to God!

He kicks loose from the table, and they all drag him towards the door.

JIMMY [*seeing OLD MAHON*]. Will you look what's come in?

They all drop CHRISTY and run left.

CHRISTY [*scrambling on his knees face to face with OLD MAHON*]. Are you coming to be killed a third time, or what ails you now?

MAHON. For what is it they have you tied?

CHRISTY. They're taking me to the peelers to have me hanged for slaying you.

MICHAEL [*apologetically*]. It is the will of God that all should guard their little cabins from the treachery of law, and what would my daughter be doing if I was ruined or was hanged itself?

MAHON [*grimly, loosening CHRISTY*]. It's little I care if you put a bag on her back, and went picking cockles till the hour of death; but my son and myself will be going our own way, and we'll have great times from this out telling stories of the villainy of Mayo, and the fools is here. [*To CHRISTY, who is freed.*] Come on now.

CHRISTY. Go with you, is it? I will then, like a gallant captain with his heathen slave. Go on now and I'll see you from this day stewing my oatmeal and washing my spuds, for I'm master of all fights from now. [*Pushing MAHON.*] Go on, I'm saying.

MAHON. Is it me?

CHRISTY. Not a word out of you. Go on from this.

MAHON [*walking out and looking back at CHRISTY over his shoulder*]. Glory be to God! [*With a broad smile.*] I am crazy again. [*Goes.*]

CHRISTY. Ten thousand blessings upon all that's here, for you've turned me a likely gaffer in the end of all, the way I'll go romancing through a romping lifetime from this hour to the dawning of the judgment day. [*He goes out.*]

MICHAEL. By the will of God, we'll have peace now for our drinks. Will you draw the porter, Pegeen?

SHAWN [*going up to her*]. It's a miracle Father Reilly can wed us in the end of all, and we'll have none to trouble us when his vicious bite is healed.

PEGEEN [*hitting him a box on the ear*]. Quit my sight. [*Putting her shawl over her head and breaking out into wild lamentations.*] Oh, my grief, I've lost him surely. I've lost the only Playboy of the Western World.

CURTAIN

LORD DUNSANY

THE HASHISH MAN

This imaginative little drug story comes from Lord Dunsany's collection
Dreamers Tales, *which was published in 1910.*

I WAS AT DINNER IN LONDON the other day. The ladies had gone upstairs, and
no one sat on my right; on my left there was a man I did not know, but he
knew my name somehow, apparently, for he turned to me after a while, and
said, "I read a story of yours about Bethmoora in a review."

Of course I remembered the tale. It was about a beautiful Oriental city that
was suddenly deserted in a day—nobody quite knew why. I said, "Oh, yes," and
slowly searched in my mind for some more fitting acknowledgment of the compliment that his memory had paid me.

I was greatly astonished when he said, "You were wrong about the gnousar
sickness; it was not that at all."

I said, "Why! Have you been there?"

And he said, "Yes; but I do it with hashish. I know Bethmoora well." And he
took out of his pocket a small box full of some black stuff that looked like tar, but
had a stranger smell. He warned me not to touch it with my finger, as the stain
remained for days. "I got it from a gipsy," he said. "He had a lot of it, as it had
killed his father." But I interrupted him, for I wanted to know for certain what it
was that had made desolate that beautiful city, Bethmoora, and why they fled from
it swiftly in a day. "Was it because of the Desert's curse?" I asked. And he said,
"Partly it was the fury of the Desert and partly the advice of the Emperor Thuba
Mleen, for that fearful beast is in some way connected with the Desert on his mother's side." And he told me this strange story: "You remember the sailor with the
black scar, who was there on the day that you described when the messengers came
on mules to the gate of Bethmoora, and all the people fled. I met this man in a tavern, drinking rum, and he told me all about the flight from Bethmoora, but knew

373

no more than you did what the message was, or who had sent it. However, he said he would see Bethmoora once more whenever he touched again at an eastern port, even if he had to face the Devil. He often said that he would face the Devil to find out the mystery of that message that emptied Bethmoora in a day. And in the end he had to face Thuba Mleen, whose weak ferocity he had not imagined. For one day the sailor told me he had found a ship, and I met him no more after that in the tavern drinking rum. It was about that time that I got the hashish from the gipsy, who had a quantity that he did not want. It takes one literally out of oneself. It is like wings. You swoop over distant countries and into other worlds. Once I found out the secret of the universe. I have forgotten what it was, but I know that the Creator does not take Creation seriously, for I remember that He sat in Space with all His work in front of Him and laughed. I have seen incredible things in fearful worlds. As it is your imagination that takes you there, so it is only by your imagination that you can get back. Once out in æther I met a battered, prowling spirit, that had belonged to a man whom drugs had killed a hundred years ago; and he led me to regions that I had never imagined; and we parted in anger beyond the Pleiades, and I could not imagine my way back. And I met a huge grey shape that was the Spirit of some great people, perhaps of a whole star, and I besought It to show me my way home, and It halted beside me like sudden wind and pointed, and, speaking quite softly, asked me if I discerned a certain tiny light, and I saw a far star faintly, and then It said to me, 'That is the Solar System,' and strode tremendously on. And somehow I imagined my way back, and only just in time, for my body was already stiffening in a chair in my room; and the fire had gone out and everything was cold, and I had to move each finger one by one, and there were pins and needles in them, and dreadful pains in the nails, which began to thaw; and at last I could move one arm, and reached a bell, and for a long time no one came, because every one was in bed. But at last a man appeared, and they got a doctor; and *he* said that it was hashish poisoning, but it would have been all right if I hadn't met that battered, prowling spirit.

"I could tell you astounding things that I have seen, but you want to know who sent that message to Bethmoora. Well, it was Thuba Mleen. And this is how I know. I often went to the city after that day that you wrote of (I used to take hashish of an evening in my flat), and I always found it uninhabited. Sand had poured into it from the desert, and the streets were yellow and smooth, and through open, swinging doors the sand had drifted.

"One evening I had put the guard in front of the fire, and settled into a chair and eaten my hashish, and the first thing that I saw when I came to Bethmoora was the sailor with the black scar, strolling down the street, and making footprints in the yellow sand. And now I knew that I should see what secret power it was that kept Bethmoora uninhabited.

"I saw that there was anger in the Desert, for there were storm clouds heaving along the skyline, and I heard a muttering amongst the sand.

"The sailor strolled on down the street, looking into the empty house as he went; sometimes he shouted and sometimes he sang, and sometimes he wrote his name on a marble wall. Then he sat down on a step and ate his dinner. After a while he grew tired of the city, and came back up the street. As he reached the gate of green copper three men on camels appeared.

"I could do nothing. I was only a consciousness, invisible, wandering: my body was in Europe. The sailor fought well with his fists, but he was over-powered and bound with ropes, and led away through the Desert.

"I followed for as long as I could stay, and found that they were going by the way of the Desert round the Hills of Hap towards Utnar Véhi, and then I knew that the camel men belonged to Thuba Mleen.

"I work in an insurance office all day, and I hope you won't forget me if ever you want to insure—life, fire, or motor—but that's no part of my story. I was desperately anxious to get back to my flat, though it is not good to take hashish two days running; but I wanted to see what they would do to the poor fellow, for I had heard bad rumours about Thuba Mleen. When at last I got away I had a letter to write; then I rang for my servant, and told him that I must not be disturbed, though I left my door unlocked in case of accidents. After that I made up a good fire, and sat down and partook of the pot of dreams. I was going to the palace of Thuba Mleen.

"I was kept back longer than usual by noises in the street, but suddenly I was up above the town; the European countries rushed by beneath me, and there appeared the thin white palace spires of horrible Thuba Mleen. I found him presently at the end of a little narrow room. A curtain of red leather hung behind him, on which all the names of God, written in Yannish, were worked with a golden thread. Three windows were small and high. The Emperor seemed no more than about twenty, and looked small and weak. No smiles came on his nasty yellow face, though he tittered continually. As I looked from his low forehead to his quivering under lip, I became aware that there was some horror about him, though I was not able to perceive what it was. And then I saw it—the man never blinked; and though later on I watched those eyes for a blink, it never happened once.

"And then I followed the Emperor's rapt glance, and I saw the sailor lying on the floor, alive but hideously rent, and the royal torturers were at work all round him. They had torn long strips from him, but had not detached them, and they were torturing the ends of them far away from the sailor." The man that I met at dinner told me many things which I must omit. "The sailor was groaning softly, and every time he groaned Thuba Mleen tittered. I had no sense of smell, but I could hear and see, and I do not know which was the most revolting—the terrible condition of the sailor or the happy unblinking face of horrible Thuba Mleen.

"I wanted to go away, but the time had not yet come, and I had to stay where I was.

"Suddenly the Emperor's face began to twitch violently and his under lip quivered faster, and he whimpered with anger, and cried with a shrill voice, in Yannish, to the captain of his torturers that there was a spirit in the room. I feared not, for living men cannot lay hands on a spirit, but all the torturers were appalled at his anger, and stopped their work, for their hands trembled with fear. Then two men of the spear-guard slipped from the room, and each of them brought back presently a golden bowl, with knobs on it, full of hashish; and the bowls were large enough for heads to have floated in had they been filled with blood. And the two men fell to rapidly, each eating with two great spoons—there was enough in each spoonful to have given dreams to a hundred men. And there came upon them soon the hashish state, and their spirits hovered, preparing to go free, while I feared horribly, but ever and anon they fell back again to the bodies, recalled by some noise in the room. Still the men ate, but lazily now, and without ferocity. At last the great spoons dropped out of their hands, and their spirits rose and left them. I could not flee. And the spirits were more horrible than the men, because they were young men, and not yet wholly moulded to fit their fearful souls. Still the sailor groaned softly, evoking little titters from the Emperor Thuba Mleen. Then the two spirits rushed at me, and swept me thence as gusts of wind sweep butterflies, and away we went from that small, pale, heinous man. There was no escaping from these spirits' fierce insistence. The energy in my minute lump of the drug was overwhelmed by the huge spoonsful that these men had eaten with both hands. I was whirled over Arvle Woondery, and brought to the lands of Snith, and swept on still until I came to Kragua, and beyond this to those bleak lands that are nearly unknown to fancy. And we came at last to those ivory hills that are named the Mountains of Madness, and I tried to struggle against the spirits of that frightful Emperor's men, for I heard on the other side of the ivory hills the pittering of those beasts that prey on the mad, as they prowled up and down. It was no fault of mine that my little lump of hashish could not fight with their horrible spoonsful. . . ."

Some one was tugging at the hall-door bell. Presently a servant came and told our host that a policeman in the hall wished to speak to him at once. He apologised to us, and went outside, and we heard a man in heavy boots, who spoke in a low voice to him. My friend got up and walked over to the window, and opened it, and looked outside. "I should think it will be a fine night," he said. Then he jumped out. When we put our astonished heads out of the window to look for him, he was already out of sight.

JAMES JOYCE

FROM
CHAMBER
MUSIC

One of Irish literature's most curious—and most seldom-read—gems,
culled from James Joyce's earliest poetical output, is Chamber Music
(1907), a symphony of thirty-six poems about the bittersweet pleasures of
youth and the exquisite pain of a failed love affair. It reads like a fairy tale
gone sour. Critics have commented on how the elements of the story told
here parallel the concerns of A Portrait of the Artist as a Young Man:
a sensitive and smitten youth chases after love, attains near-happiness,
only to lose his lover to a rival. Could this also be a metaphor for a writer's
frustrated attempt to court his muse?

Another intriguing aspect of Chamber Music is its title. There are
several versions of the real-life events that are said to have fueled Joyce's
imagination. The details are by turns comic and tawdry, including an
afternoon visit with a woman in her private quarters, the gift of ladies
underwear, and something musical that transpired due to the traditional
or invented use of a chamberpot.

A selection of eleven of the thirty-six poems appears below.

I

Strings in the earth and air
Make music sweet;
Strings by the river where
The willows meet.

There's music along the river
For Love wanders there,
Pale flowers on his mantle,
Dark leaves on his hair.

All softly playing,
    With head to the music bent,
And fingers straying
    Upon an instrument.

III

At that hour when all things have repose,
    O lonely watcher of the skies,
    Do you hear the night wind and the sighs
Of harps playing unto Love to unclose
    The pale gates of sunrise?

When all things repose do you alone
    Awake to hear the sweet harps play
    To Love before him on his way,
And the night wind answering in antiphon
    Till night is overgone?

Play on, invisible harps, unto Love
    Whose way in heaven is aglow
    At that hour when soft lights come and go,
Soft sweet music in the air above
    And in the earth below.

V

Lean out of the window,
    Goldenhair,
I heard you singing
    A merry air.

My book was closed;
    I read no more,
Watching the fire dance
    On the floor.

I have left my book,
    I have left my room,
For I heard you singing
    Through the gloom.

Singing and singing
    A merry air,
Lean out of the window,
    Goldenhair.

VI

I would in that sweet bosom be
    (O sweet it is and fair it is!)
Where no rude wind might visit me.
    Because of sad austerities
I would in that sweet bosom be.

I would be ever in that heart
    (O soft I knock and soft entreat her!)
Where only peace might be my part.
    Austerities were all the sweeter
So I were ever in that heart.

XI

Bid adieu, adieu, adieu,
    Bid adieu to girlish days,
Happy Love is come to woo
    Thee and woo thy girlish ways—
The zone that doth become thee fair,
The snood upon thy yellow hair.

When thou hast heard his name upon
    The bugles of the cherubim
Begin thou softly to unzone
    Thy girlish bosom unto him
And softly to undo the snood
That is the sign of maidenhood.

XVII

Because your voice was at my side
    I gave him pain,
Because within my hand I held
    Your hand again.

There is no word nor any sign
    Can make amend—
He is a stranger to me now
    Who was my friend.

XVIII

O Sweetheart, hear you
    Your lover's tale;
A man shall have sorrow
    When friends him fail.

For he shall know then
    Friends be untrue
And a little ashes
    Their words come to.

But one unto him
    Will softly move
And softly woo him
    In ways of love.

His hand is under
    Her smooth round breast;
So he who has sorrow
    Shall have rest.

XXVIII

Gentle lady, do not sing
    Sad songs about the end of love;
Lay aside sadness and sing
    How love that passes is enough.

Sing about the long deep sleep
    Of lovers that are dead, and how
In the grave all love shall sleep:
    Love is aweary now.

XXX

Love came to us in time gone by
    When one at twilight shyly played
And one in fear was standing nigh—
    For Love at first is all afraid.

We were grave lovers. Love is past
    That had his sweet hours many a one;
Welcome to us now at the last
    The ways that we shall go upon.

XXXIII

Now, O now, in this brown land
    Where Love did so sweet music make
We two shall wonder, hand in hand,
    Forbearing for old friendship sake,
Nor grieve because our love was gay
Which now is ended in this way.

A rogue in red and yellow dress
    Is knocking, knocking at the tree;
And all around our loneliness
    The wind is whistling merrily.
The leaves—they do not sigh at all
When the year takes them in the fall.

Now, O now, we hear no more
    The vilanelle and roundelay!
Yet will we kiss, sweetheart, before
    We take sad leave at close of day.
Grieve not, sweetheart, for anything—
The year, the year is gathering.

XXXV

All day I hear the noise of waters
    Making moan,
Sad as the sea-bird is, when going
    Forth alone,
He hears the winds cry to the waters'
    Monotone.

The grey winds, the cold winds are blowing
    Where I go.
I hear the noise of many waters
    Far below.
All day, all night, I hear them flowing
    To and fro.

A PORTRAIT OF THE ARTIST AS A YOUNG MAN

James Joyce's autobiographical first novel, A Portrait of the Artist as a Young Man, *first appeared as twenty-five installments in the literary magazine* The Egoist *during 1914 and 1915, and was brought out the following year in book form.*

"Et ignotas animum dimittit in artes."
OVID, *Metamorphoses*, VIII., 18.

I

ONCE UPON A TIME AND A very good time it was there was a moocow coming down along the road and this moocow that was down along the road met a nicens little boy named baby tuckoo. . . .

His father told him that story: his father looked at him through a glass: he had a hairy face.

He was baby tuckoo. The moocow came down the road where Betty Byrne lived: she sold lemon platt.

> *O, the wild rose blossoms*
> *On the little green place.*

He sang that song. That was his song.

> *O, the green wothe botheth.*

When you wet the bed, first it is warm then it gets cold. His mother put on the oilsheet. That had the queer smell.

His mother had a nicer smell than his father. She played on the piano the sailor's hornpipe for him to dance. He danced:

> *Tralala lala,*
> *Tralala tralaladdy,*
> *Tralala lala,*
> *Tralala lala.*

Uncle Charles and Dante clapped. They were older than his father and mother but uncle Charles was older than Dante.

Dante had two brushes in her press. The brush with the maroon velvet back was for Michael Davitt and the brush with the green velvet back was for Parnell. Dante gave him a cachou every time he brought her a piece of tissue paper.

The Vances lived in number seven. They had a different father and mother. They were Eileen's father and mother. When they were grown up he was going to marry Eileen. He hid under the table. His mother said:

—O, Stephen will apologise.

Dante said:

—O, if not, the eagles will come and pull out his eyes.—

> Pull out his eyes,
> Apologise,
> Apologise,
> Pull out his eyes.

> Apologise,
> Pull out his eyes,
> Pull out his eyes,
> Apologise.

☙

The wide playgrounds were swarming with boys. All were shouting and the prefects urged them on with strong cries. The evening air was pale and chilly and after every charge and thud of the foot-ballers the greasy leather orb flew like a heavy bird through the grey light. He kept on the fringe of his line, out of sight of his prefect, out of the reach of the rude feet, feigning to run now and then. He felt his body small and weak amid the throng of players and his eyes were weak and watery. Rody Kickham was not like that: he would be captain of the third line all the fellows said.

Rody Kickham was a decent fellow but Nasty Roche was a stink. Rody Kickham had greaves in his number and a hamper in the refectory. Nasty Roche had big hands. He called the Friday pudding dog-in-the-blanket. And one day he had asked:

—What is your name?

Stephen had answered: Stephen Dedalus.

Then Nasty Roche had said:

—What kind of a name is that?

And when Stephen had not been able to answer Nasty Roche had asked:

—What is your father?

Stephen had answered:

—A gentleman.

Then Nasty Roche had asked:

—Is he a magistrate?

He crept about from point to point on the fringe of his line, making little runs now and then. But his hands were bluish with cold. He kept his hands in the side pockets of his belted grey suit. That was a belt round his pocket. And belt was also to give a fellow a belt. One day a fellow had said to Cantwell:

—I'd give you such a belt in a second.

Cantwell had answered:

—Go and fight your match. Give Cecil Thunder a belt. I'd like to see you. He'd give you a toe in the rump for yourself.

That was not a nice expression. His mother had told him not to speak with the rough boys in the college. Nice mother! The first day in the hall of the castle when she had said goodbye she had put up her veil double to her nose to kiss him: and her nose and eyes were red. But he had pretended not to see that she was going to cry. She was a nice mother but she was not so nice when she cried. And his father had given him two five-shilling pieces for pocket money. And his father had told him if he wanted anything to write home to him and, whatever he did, never to peach on a fellow. Then at the door of the castle the rector had shaken hands with his father and mother, his soutane fluttering in the breeze, and the car had driven off with his father and mother on it. They had cried to him from the car, waving their hands:

—Good-bye, Stephen, goodbye!

—Good-bye, Stephen, goodbye!

He was caught in the whirl of a scrimmage and, fearful of the flashing eyes and muddy boots, bent down to look through the legs. The fellows were struggling and groaning and their legs were rubbing and kicking and stamping. Then Jack Lawton's yellow boots dodged out the ball and all the other boots and legs ran after. He ran after them a little way and then stopped. It was useless to run on. Soon they would be going home for the holidays. After supper in the study hall he would change the number pasted up inside his desk from seventyseven to seventysix.

It would be better to be in the study hall than out there in the cold. The sky was pale and cold but there were lights in the castle. He wondered from which window Hamilton Rowan had thrown his hat on the haha and had there been flowerbeds at that time under the windows. One day when he had been called to the castle the butler had shown him the marks of the soldiers' slugs in the wood of the door and had given him a piece of shortbread that the community ate. It was nice and warm to see the lights in the castle. It was like something in a book. Perhaps Leicester Abbey was like that. And there were nice sentences in Doctor Cornwell's Spelling Book. They were like poetry but they were only sentences to learn the spelling from.

> *Wolsey died in Leicester Abbey*
> *Where the abbots buried him.*
> *Canker is a disease of plants,*
> *Cancer one of animals.*

It would be nice to lie on the hearthrug before the fire, leaning his head upon his hands, and think on those sentences. He shivered as if he had cold slimy water next his skin. That was mean of Wells to shoulder him into the square ditch because he would not swop his little snuffbox for Wells's seasoned hacking chestnut, the conqueror of forty. How cold and slimy the water had been! A fellow had once seen a big rat jump into the scum. Mother was sitting at the fire with Dante waiting for Brigid to bring in the tea. She had her feet on the fender and her jewelly slippers were so hot and they had such a lovely warm smell! Dante knew a lot of things. She had taught him where the Mozambique Channel was and what was the longest river in America and what was the name of the highest mountain in the moon. Father Arnall knew more than Dante because he was a priest but both his father and uncle Charles said that Dante was a clever woman and a well-read woman. And when Dante made that noise after dinner and then put up her hand to her mouth: that was heartburn.

A voice cried far out on the playground:

—All in!

Then other voices cried from the lower and third lines:

—All in! All in!

The players closed around, flushed and muddy, and he went among them, glad to go in. Rody Kickham held the ball by its greasy lace. A fellow asked him to give it one last: but he walked on without even answering the fellow. Simon Moonan told him not to because the prefect was looking. The fellow turned to Simon Moonan and said:

—We all know why you speak. You are McGlade's suck.

Suck was a queer word. The fellow called Simon Moonan that name because Simon Moonan used to tie the prefect's false sleeves behind his back and the prefect used to let on to be angry. But the sound was ugly. Once he had washed his hands in the lavatory of the Wicklow Hotel and his father pulled the stopper up by the chain after and the dirty water went down through the hole in the basin.

And when it had all gone down slowly the hole in the basin had made a sound like that: suck. Only louder.

To remember that and the white look of the lavatory made him feel cold and then hot. There were two cocks that you turned and water came out: cold and hot. He felt cold and then a little hot: and he could see the names printed on the cocks. That was a very queer thing.

And the air in the corridor chilled him too. It was queer and wettish. But soon the gas would be lit and in burning it made light noise like a little song. Always the same: and when the fellows stopped talking in the playroom you could hear it.

It was the hour for sums. Father Arnall wrote a hard sum on the board and then said:

—Now then, who will win? Go ahead, York! Go ahead, Lancaster!

Stephen tried his best but the sum was too hard and he felt confused. The little silk badge with the white rose on it that was pinned on the breast of his jacket began to flutter. He was no good at sums but he tried his best so that York might not lose. Father Arnall's face looked very black but he was not in a wax: he was laughing. Then Jack Lawton cracked his fingers and Father Arnall looked at his copybook and said:

—Right. Bravo Lancaster! The red rose wins. Come on now, York! Forge ahead!

Jack Lawton looked over from his side. The little silk badge with the red rose on it looked very rich because he had a blue sailor top on. Stephen felt his own face red too, thinking of all the bets about who would get first place in Elements, Jack Lawton or he. Some weeks Jack Lawton got the card for first and some weeks he got the card for first. His white silk badge fluttered and fluttered as he worked at the next sum and heard Father Arnall's voice. Then all his eagerness passed away and he felt his face quite cool. He thought his face must be white because it felt so cool. He could not get out the answer for the sum but it did not matter. White roses and red roses: those were beautiful colours to think of. And the cards for first place and third place were beautiful colours too: pink and cream and lavender. Lavender and cream and pink roses were beautiful to think of. Perhaps a wild rose might be like those colours and he remembered the song about the wild rose blossoms on the little green place. But you could not have a green rose. But perhaps somewhere in the world you could.

The bell rang and then the classes began to file out of the rooms and along the corridors towards the refectory. He sat looking at the two prints of butter on his plate but could not eat the damp bread. The tablecloth was damp and limp. But he drank off the hot weak tea which the clumsy scullion, girt with a white apron, poured into his cup. He wondered whether the scullion's apron was damp too or whether all white things were cold and damp. Nasty Roche and Saurin drank cocoa that their people sent them in tins. They said they could not drink the tea;

that it was hogwash. Their fathers were magistrates, the fellows said.

All the boys seemed to him very strange. They had all fathers and mothers and different clothes and voices. He longed to be at home and lay his head on his mother's lap. But he could not: and so he longed for the play and study and prayers to be over and to be in bed.

He drank another cup of hot tea and Fleming said:

—What's up? Have you a pain or what's up with you?

—I don't know, Stephen said.

—Sick in your bread basket—Fleming said—because your face looks white. It will go away.

—O yes, Stephen said.

But he was not sick there. He thought that he was sick in his heart if you could be sick in that place. Fleming was very decent to ask him. He wanted to cry. He leaned his elbows on the table and shut and opened the flaps of his ears. Then he heard the noise of the refectory every time he opened the flaps of his ears. It made a roar like a train at night. And when he closed the flaps the roar was shut off like a train going into a tunnel. That night at Dalkey the train had roared like that and then, when it went into the tunnel, the roar stopped. He closed his eyes and the train went on, roaring and then stopping; roaring again, stopping. It was nice to hear it roar and stop and then roar out of the tunnel again and then stop.

Then the higher line fellows began to come down along the matting in the middle of the refectory, Paddy Rath and Jimmy Magee and the Spaniard who was allowed to smoke cigars and the little Portuguese who wore the woolly cap. And then the lower line tables and the tables of the third line. And every single fellow had a different way of walking.

He sat in a corner of the playroom pretending to watch a game of dominos and once or twice he was able to hear for an instant the little song of the gas. The prefect was at the door with some boys and Simon Moonan was knotting his false sleeves. He was telling them something about Tullabeg.

Then he went away from the door and Wells came over to Stephen and said:

—Tell us, Dedalus, do you kiss your mother before you go to bed?

Stephen answered:

—I do.

Wells turned to the other fellows and said:

—O, I say, here's a fellow says he kisses his mother every night before he goes to bed.

The other fellows stopped their game and turned round, laughing. Stephen blushed under their eyes and said:

—I do not.

Wells said:

—O, I say, here's a fellow says he doesn't kiss his mother before he goes to bed.

They all laughed again. Stephen tried to laugh with them. He felt his whole body hot and confused in a moment. What was the right answer to the question? He had given two and still Wells laughed. But Wells must know the right answer for he was in third of grammar. He tried to think of Wells's mother but he did not dare to raise his eyes to Wells's face. He did not like Wells's face. It was Wells who had shouldered him into the square ditch the day before because he would not swop his little snuffbox for Wells's seasoned hacking chestnut, the conqueror of forty. It was a mean thing to do; all the fellows said it was. And how cold and slimy the water had been! And a fellow had once seen a big rat jump plop into the scum.

The cold slime of the ditch covered his whole body; and, when the bell rang for study and the lines filed out of the playrooms, he felt the cold air of the corridor and staircase inside his clothes. He still tried to think what was the right answer. Was it right to kiss his mother or wrong to kiss his mother? What did that mean, to kiss? You put your face up like that to say goodnight and then his mother put her face down. That was to kiss. His mother put her lips on his cheek; her lips were soft and they wetted his cheek; and they made a tiny little noise: kiss. Why did people do that with their two faces?

Sitting in the study hall he opened the lid of his desk and changed the number pasted up inside from seventyseven to seventysix. But the Christmas vacation was very far away: but one time it would come because the earth moved round always.

There was a picture of the earth on the first page of his geography: a big ball in the middle of clouds. Fleming had a box of crayons and one night during free study he had coloured the earth green and the clouds maroon. That was like the two brushes in Dante's press, the brush with the green velvet back for Parnell and the brush with the maroon velvet back for Michael Davitt. But he had not told Fleming to colour them those colours. Fleming had done it himself.

He opened the geography to study the lesson; but he could not learn the names of places in America. Still they were all different places that had different names. They were all in different countries and the countries were in continents and the continents were in the world and the world was in the universe.

He turned to the flyleaf of the geography and read what he had written there: himself, his name and where he was.

> *Stephen Dedalus*
> *Class of Elements*
> *Clongowes Wood College*
> *Sallins*
> *County Kildare*
> *Ireland*
> *Europe*
> *The World*
> *The Universe*

That was in his writing: and Fleming one night for a cod had written on the opposite page:

Stephen Dedalus is my name,
Ireland is my nation.
Clongowes is my dwellingplace
And heaven my expectation.

He read the verses backwards but then they were not poetry. Then he read the flyleaf from the bottom to the top till he came to his own name. That was he: and he read down the page again. What was after the universe? Nothing. But was there anything round the universe to show where it stopped before the nothing place began? It could not be a wall but there could be a thin thin line there all round everything. It was very big to think about everything and everywhere. Only God could do that. He tried to think what a big thought that must be but he could think only of God. God was God's name just as his name was Stephen. *Dieu* was the French for God and that was God's name too; and when anyone prayed to God and said Dieu then God knew at once that it was a French person that was praying. But though there were different names for God in all the different languages in the world and God understood what all the people who prayed said in their different languages still God remained always the same God and God's real name was God.

It made him very tired to think that way. It made him feel his head very big. He turned over the flyleaf and looked wearily at the green round earth in the middle of the maroon clouds. He wondered which was right, to be for the green or for the maroon, because Dante had ripped the green velvet back off the brush that was for Parnell one day with her scissors and had told him that Parnell was a bad man. He wondered if they were arguing at home about that. That was called politics. There were two sides in it: Dante was on one side and his father and Mr. Casey were on the other side but his mother and uncle Charles were on no side. Every day there was something in the paper about it.

It pained him that he did not know well what politics meant and that he did not know where the universe ended. He felt small and weak. When would he be like the fellows in Poetry and Rhetoric? They had big voices and big boots and they studied trigonometry. That was very far away. First came the vacation and then the next term and then vacation again and then again another term and then again the vacation. It was like a train going in and out of tunnels and that was like the noise of the boys eating in the refectory when you opened and closed the flaps of the ears. Term, vacation; tunnel, out; noise, stop. How far away it was! It was better to go to bed to sleep. Only prayers in the chapel and then bed. He shivered and yawned. It would be lovely in bed after the sheets got a bit hot. First they were so cold to get into. He shivered to think how cold they were first. But then they got hot and then he could sleep. It was lovely to be tired. He yawned again. Night prayers and then bed: he shivered and wanted to yawn. It would be lovely in a few minutes. He felt a warm glow creeping up from the cold shivering sheets, warmer and warmer till he felt warm all over, ever so warm and yet he shivered a little and still wanted to yawn.

The bell rang for night prayers and he filed out of the study hall after the others and down the staircase and along the corridors to the chapel. The corridors were darkly lit and the chapel was darkly lit. Soon all would be dark and sleeping. There was cold night air in the chapel and the marbles were the colour the sea was at night. The sea was cold day and night: but it was colder at night. It was cold and dark under the seawall beside his father's house. But the kettle would be on the hob to make punch.

The prefect of the chapel prayed above his head and his memory knew the responses:

> *O Lord, open our lips*
> *And our mouths shall announce Thy praise.*
> *Incline unto our aid, O God!*
> *O Lord, make haste to help us!*

There was a cold night smell in the chapel. But it was a holy smell. It was not like the smell of the old peasants who knelt at the back of the chapel at Sunday mass. That was a smell of air and rain and turf and corduroy. But they were very holy peasants. They breathed behind him on his neck and sighed as they prayed. They lived in Clane, a fellow said: there were little cottages there and he had seen a woman standing at the halfdoor of a cottage with a child in her arms, as the cars had come past from Sallins. It would be lovely to sleep for one night in that cottage before the fire of smoking turf, in the dark lit by the fire, in the warm dark, breathing the smell of the peasants, air and rain and turf and corduroy. But, O, the road there between the trees was dark! You would be lost in the dark. It made him afraid to think of how it was.

He heard the voice of the prefect of the chapel saying the last prayer. He prayed it too against the dark outside under the trees.

> *Visit, we beseech Thee, O Lord, this habitation and*
> *drive away from it all the snares of the enemy. May*
> *Thy holy angels dwell herein to preserve us in peace*
> *and may Thy blessing be always upon us through*
> *Christ our Lord. Amen.*

His fingers trembled as he undressed himself in the dormitory. He told his fingers to hurry up. He had to undress and then kneel and say his own prayers and be in bed before the gas was lowered so that he might not go to hell when he died. He rolled his stockings off and put on his nightshirt quickly and knelt trembling at his bedside and repeated his prayers quickly, fearing that the gas would go down. He felt his shoulders shaking as he murmured:

God bless my father and my mother and spare them to me!
God bless my little brothers and sisters and spare them to me!
God bless Dante and uncle Charles and spare them to me!

He blessed himself and climbed quickly into bed and, tucking the end of the nightshirt under his feet, curled himself together under the cold white sheets, shaking and trembling. But he would not go to hell when he died; and the shaking would stop. A voice bade the boys in the dormitory goodnight. He peered out for an instant over the coverlet and saw the yellow curtains round and before his bed that shut him off on all sides. The light was lowered quietly.

The prefect's shoes went away. Where? Down the staircase and along the corridors or to his room at the end? He saw the dark. Was it true about the black dog that walked there at night with eyes as big as carriagelamps? They said it was the ghost of a murderer. A long shiver of fear flowed over his body. He saw the dark entrance hall of the castle. Old servants in old dress were in the ironingroom above the staircase. It was long ago. The old servants were quiet. There was a fire there but the hall was still dark. A figure came up the staircase from the hall. He wore the white cloak of a marshal; his face was pale and strange; he held his hand pressed to his side. He looked out of strange eyes at the old servants. They looked at him and saw their master's face and cloak and knew that he had received his death wound. But only the dark was where they looked: only dark silent air. Their master had received his death wound on the battlefield of Prague far away over the sea. He was standing on the field; his hand was pressed to his side; his face was pale and strange and he wore the white cloak of a marshal.

O how cold and strange it was to think of that! All the dark was cold and strange. There were pale strange faces there, great eyes like carriagelamps. They were the ghosts of murderers, the figures of marshals who had received their death wound on battlefields far away over the sea. What did they wish to say that their faces were so strange?

Visit, we beseech Thee, O Lord, this habitation
and drive away from it all . . .

Going home for the holidays! That would be lovely: the fellows had told him. Getting up on the cars in the early wintry morning outside the door of the castle. The cars were rolling on the gravel. Cheers for the rector!

Hurray! Hurray! Hurray!

The cars drove past the chapel and all caps were raised. They drove merrily along the country roads. The drivers pointed with their whips to Bodenstown. The fellows cheered. They passed the farmhouse of the Jolly Farmer. Cheer after cheer after cheer. Through Clane they drove, cheering and cheered. The peasant women stood at the halfdoors, the men stood here and there. The lovely smell there was in the wintry air: the smell of Clane: rain and wintry air and turf smouldering and corduroy.

The train was full of fellows: a long long chocolate train with cream facings. The guards went to and fro opening, closing, locking, unlocking the doors. They were men in dark blue and silver; they had silvery whistles and their keys made a quick music: click, click: click, click.

And the train raced on over the flat lands and past the Hill of Allen. The telegraph poles were passing, passing. The train went on and on. It knew. There were lanterns in the hall of his father's house and ropes of green branches. There were holly and ivy round the pierglass and holly and ivy, green and red, twined round the chandeliers. There were red holly and green ivy round the old portraits on the walls. Holly and ivy for him and for Christmas.

Lovely . . .

All the people. Welcome home, Stephen! Noises of welcome. His mother kissed him. Was that right? His father was a marshal now: higher than a magistrate. Welcome home, Stephen!

Noises . . .

There was a noise of curtainrings running back along the rods, of water being splashed in the basins. There was a noise of rising and dressing and washing in the dormitory: a noise of clapping of hands as the prefect went up and down telling the fellows to look sharp. A pale sunlight showed the yellow curtains drawn back, the tossed beds. His bed was very hot and his face and body were very hot.

He got up and sat on the side of his bed. He was weak. He tried to pull on his stocking. It had a horrid rough feel. The sunlight was queer and cold.

Fleming said:

—Are you not well?

He did not know; and Fleming said:

—Get back into bed. I'll tell McGlade you're not well.

—He's sick.

—Who is?

—Tell McGlade.

—Get back into bed.

—Is he sick?

A fellow held his arms while he loosened the stocking clinging to his foot and climbed back into the hot bed.

He crouched down between the sheets, glad of their tepid glow.

He heard the fellows talk among themselves about him as they dressed for mass. It was a mean thing to do, to shoulder him into the square ditch, they were saying.

Then their voices ceased; they had gone. A voice at his bed said:

—Dedalus, don't spy on us, sure you won't?

Wells's face was there. He looked at it and saw that Wells was afraid.

—I didn't mean to. Sure you won't?

His father had told him, whatever he did, never to peach on a fellow. He shook his head and answered no and felt glad.

Wells said:

—I didn't mean to, honour bright. It was only for cod. I'm sorry.

The face and the voice went away. Sorry because he was afraid. Afraid that it was some disease. Canker was a disease of plants and cancer one of animals: or another different. That was a long time ago then out on the playgrounds in the evening light, creeping from point to point on the fringe of his line, a heavy bird flying low through the grey light. Leicester Abbey lit up. Wolsey died there. The abbots buried him themselves.

It was not Wells's face, it was the prefect's. He was not foxing. No, no: he was sick really. He was not foxing. And he felt the prefect's hand on his forehead; and he felt his forehead warm and damp against the prefect's cold damp hand. That was the way a rat felt, slimy and damp and cold. Every rat had two eyes to look out of. Sleek slimy coats, little little feet tucked up to jump, black slimy eyes to look out of. They could understand how to jump. But the minds of rats could not understand trigonometry. When they were dead they lay on their sides. Their coats dried then. They were only dead things.

The prefect was there again and it was his voice that was saying that he was to get up, that Father Minister had said he was to get up and dress and go to the infirmary. And while he was dressing himself as quickly as he could the prefect said:

—We must pack off to Brother Michael because we have the collywobbles!

He was very decent to say that. That was all to make him laugh. But he could not laugh because his cheeks and lips were all shivery: and then the prefect had to laugh by himself.

The prefect cried:

—Quick march! Hayfoot! Strawfoot!

They went together down the staircase and along the corridor and past the bath. As he passed the door he remembered with a vague fear the warm turf-coloured bogwater, the warm moist air, the noise of plunges, the smell of the towels, like medicine.

Brother Michael was standing at the door of the infirmary and from the door of the dark cabinet on his right came a smell like medicine. That came from the bottles on the shelves. The prefect spoke to Brother Michael and Brother Michael answered and called the prefect sir. He had reddish hair mixed with grey and a queer look. It was queer that he would always be a brother. It was queer too that you could not call him sir because he was a brother and had a different kind of look. Was he not holy enough or why could he not catch up on the others?

There were two beds in the room and in one bed there was a fellow: and when they went in he called out:

—Hello! It's young Dedalus! What's up?

—The sky is up, Brother Michael said.

He was a fellow out of the third of grammar and, while Stephen was undressing, he asked Brother Michael to bring him a round of buttered toast.

—Ah, do! he said.

—Butter you up! said Brother Michael. You'll get your walking papers in the morning when the doctor comes.

—Will I? the fellow said. I'm not well yet.

Brother Michael repeated:

—You'll get your walking papers. I tell you.

He bent down to rake the fire. He had a long back like the long back of a tramhorse. He shook the poker gravely and nodded his head at the fellow out of third of grammar.

Then Brother Michael went away and after a while the fellow out of third of grammar turned in towards the wall and fell asleep.

That was the infirmary. He was sick then. Had they written home to tell his mother and father? But it would be quicker for one of the priests to go himself to tell them. Or he would write a letter for the priest to bring.

> Dear Mother,
>   I am sick. I want to go home. Please come and take
> me home. I am in the infirmary.
> Your fond son,
Stephen.

How far away they were! There was cold sunlight outside the window. He wondered if he would die. You could die just the same on a sunny day. He might die before his mother came. Then he would have a deadmass in the chapel like the way the fellows had told him it was when Little had died. All the fellows would be at the mass, dressed in black, all with sad faces. Wells too would be there but no fellow would look at him. The rector would be there in a cope of black and gold and there would be tall yellow candles on the altar and round the catafalque. And they would carry the coffin out of the chapel slowly and he would be buried in the little graveyard of the community off the main avenue of limes. And Wells would be sorry then for what he had done. And the bell would toll slowly.

He could hear the tolling. He said over to himself the song that Brigid had taught him.

Dingdong! The castle bell!
Farewell, my mother!
Bury me in the old churchyard
Beside my eldest brother.
My coffin shall be black,
Six angels at my back,
Two to sing and two to pray
And two to carry my soul away.

How beautiful and sad that was! How beautiful the words were where they said *Bury me in the old churchyard!* A tremor passed over his body. How sad and how beautiful! He wanted to cry quietly but not for himself: for the words, so beautiful and sad, like music. The bell! The bell! Farewell! O farewell!

The cold sunlight was weaker and Brother Michael was standing at his beside with a bowl of beeftea. He was glad for his mouth was hot and dry. He could hear them playing in the playgrounds. And the day was going on in the college just as if he were there.

Then Brother Michael was going away and the fellow out of third of grammar told him to be sure and come back and tell him all the news in the paper. He told Stephen that his name was Athy and that his father kept a lot of racehorses that were spiffing jumpers and that his father would give a good tip to Brother Michael any time he wanted it because Brother Michael was very decent and always told him the news out of the paper they got every day up in the castle. There was every kind of news in the paper: accidents, shipwrecks, sports and politics.

—Now it is all about politics in the papers, he said. Do your people talk about that too?

—Yes, Stephen said.

—Mine too, he said.

Then he thought for a moment and said:

—You have a queer name, Dedalus, and I have a queer name too, Athy. My name is the name of a town. Your name is like Latin.

Then he asked:

—Are you good at riddles?

Stephen answered:

—Not very good.

Then he said:

—Can you answer me this one? Why is the county of Kildare like the leg of a fellow's breeches?

Stephen thought what could be the answer and then said:

—I give it up.

—Because there is a thigh in it, he said. Do you see the joke? Athy is the town in the county Kildare, and a thigh is the other thigh.

—O, I see, Stephen said.

—That's an old riddle, he said.

After a moment he said:

—I say!

—What? asked Stephen.

—You know, he said, you can ask that riddle another way.

—Can you? said Stephen

—The same riddle, he said. Do you know the other way to ask it?

—No, said Stephen.

—Can you not think of the other way? he said.

He looked at Stephen over the bedclothes as he spoke. Then he lay back on the pillow and said:

—There is another way but I won't tell you what it is.

Why did he not tell it? His father, who kept the racehorses, must be a magistrate too like Saurin's father and Nasty Roche's father. He thought of his own father, of how he sang songs while his mother played and of how he always gave him a shilling when he asked for sixpence and he felt sorry for him that he was not a magistrate like the other boys' fathers. Then why was he sent to that place with them? But his father had told him that he would be no stranger there because his granduncle had presented an address to the Liberator there fifty years before. You could know the people of that time by their old dress. It seemed to him a solemn time: and he wondered if that was the time when the fellows in Clongowes wore blue coats with brass buttons and yellow waistcoats and caps of rabbit-skin and drank beer like grownup people and kept greyhounds of their own to course the hares with.

He looked at the window and saw that the daylight had grown weaker. There would be cloudy grey light over the playgrounds. There was no noise on the playgrounds. The class must be doing the themes or perhaps Father Arnall was reading out of the book.

It was queer that they had not given him any medicine. Perhaps Brother Michael would bring it back when he came. They said you got stinking stuff to drink when you were in the infirmary. But he felt better now than before. It would be nice getting better slowly. You could get a book then. There was a book in the library about Holland. There was lovely foreign names in it and pictures of strange-looking cities and ships. It made you feel so happy.

How pale the light was at the window! But that was nice. The fire rose and fell on the wall. It was like waves. Someone had put coal on and he heard voices. They were talking. It was the noise of the waves. Or the waves were talking among themselves as they rose and fell.

He saw the sea of waves, long dark waves rising and falling, dark under the

moonless night. A tiny light twinkled at the pierhead where the ship was entering: and he saw a multitude of people gathered by the waters' edge to see the ship
that was entering their harbour. A tall man stood on the deck, looking out
towards the flat dark land: and by the light at the pierhead he saw his face, the
sorrowful face of Brother Michael.

He saw him lift his hand towards the people and heard him say in a loud voice
of sorrow over the waters:

—He is dead. We saw him lying upon the catafalque. A wail of sorrow went
up from the people.

—Parnell! Parnell! He is dead!

They fell upon their knees, moaning in sorrow.

And he saw Dante in a maroon velvet dress and with a green velvet mantle
hanging from her shoulders walking proudly and silently past the people who
knelt by the waters' edge.

A great fire, banked high and red, flamed in the grate and under the ivy
twined branches of the chandelier the Christmas table was spread. They had
come home a little late and still dinner was not ready: but it would be ready in a
jiffy, his mother had said. They were waiting for the door to open and for the servants to come in, holding the big dishes covered with their heavy metal covers.

All were waiting: uncle Charles, who sat far away in the shadow of the window, Dante and Mr. Casey, who sat in the easy chairs at either side of the hearth,
Stephen, seated on a chair between them, his feet resting on the toasted boss. Mr.
Dedalus looked at himself in the pierglass above the mantelpiece, waxed out his
moustache ends and then, parting his coat tails, stood with his back to the glowing fire: and still from time to time he withdrew a hand from his coat tail to wax
out one of his moustache ends. Mr. Casey leaned his head to one side and, smiling, tapped the gland of his neck with his fingers. And Stephen smiled too for he
knew now that it was not true that Mr. Casey had a purse of silver in his throat.
He smiled to think how the silvery noise which Mr. Casey used to make had
deceived him. And when he had tried to open Mr. Casey's hand to see if the purse
of silver was hidden there he had seen that the fingers could not be straightened
out: and Mr. Casey had told him that he had got those three cramped fingers
making a birthday present for Queen Victoria.

Mr. Casey tapped the gland of his neck and smiled at Stephen with sleepy eyes:
and Mr. Dedalus said to him:

—Yes. Well now, that's all right. O, we had a good walk, hadn't we, John?
Yes . . . I wonder if there's any likelihood of dinner this evening. Yes. . . . O, well
now, we got a good breath of ozone round the Head today. Ay, bedad.

He turned to Dante and said:

—You didn't stir out at all, Mrs. Riordan?

Dante frowned and said shortly:

—No.

Mr. Dedalus dropped his coat tails and went over to the sideboard. He brought forth a great stone jar of whisky from the locker and filled the decanter slowly, bending now and then to see how much he had poured in. Then replacing the jar in the locker he poured a little of the whisky into two glasses, added a little water and came back with them to the fireplace.

—A thimbleful, John, he said, just to whet your appetite.

Mr. Casey took the glass, drank, and placed it near him on the mantelpiece. Then he said:

—Well, I can't help thinking of our friend Christopher manufacturing . . .

He broke into a fit of laughter and coughing and added:

—. . . manufacturing that champagne for those fellows.

Mr. Dedalus laughed loudly.

—Is it Christy? he said. There's more cunning in one of those warts on his bald head than in a pack of jack foxes.

He inclined his head, closed his eyes, and, licking his lips profusely, began to speak with the voice of the hotel keeper.

—And he has such a soft mouth when he's speaking to you, don't you know. He's very moist and watery about the dewlaps, God bless him.

Mr. Casey was still struggling through his fit of coughing and laughter. Stephen, seeing and hearing the hotel keeper through his father's face and voice, laughed.

Mr. Dedalus put up his eyeglass and, staring down at him, said quietly and kindly:

—What are you laughing at, you little puppy, you?

The servants entered and placed the dishes on the table. Mrs. Dedalus followed and the places were arranged.

—Sit over, she said.

Mr. Dedalus went to the end of the table and said:

—Now, Mrs. Riordan, sit over. John, sit you down, my hearty.

He looked round to where uncle Charles sat and said:

—Now then, sir there's a bird here waiting for you.

When all had taken their seats he laid his hand on the cover and then said quickly, withdrawing it:

—Now, Stephen.

Stephen stood up in his place to say the grace before meals:

> *Bless us, O Lord, and these Thy gifts which through Thy bounty*
> *we are about to receive through Christ our Lord. Amen.*

All blessed themselves and Mr. Dedalus with a sigh of pleasure lifted from the dish the heavy cover pearled around the edge with glistening drops.

Stephen looked at the plump turkey which had lain, trussed and skewered, on the kitchen table. He knew that his father had paid a guinea for it in Dunn's of D'Olier Street and that the man had prodded it often at the breastbone to show how good it was: and he remembered the man's voice when he had said:

—Take that one, sir. That's the real Ally Daly.

Why did Mr. Barrett in Clongowes call his pandybat a turkey? But Clongowes was far away: and the warm heavy smell of turkey and ham and celery rose from the plates and dishes and the great fire was banked high and red in the grate and the green ivy and red holly made you feel so happy and when dinner was ended the big plum pudding would be carried in, studded with peeled almonds and sprigs of holly, with bluish fire running around it and a little green flag flying from the top.

It was his first Christmas dinner and he thought of his little brothers and sisters who were waiting in the nursery, as he had often waited, till the pudding came. The deep low collar and the Eton jacket made him feel queer and oldish: and that morning when his mother had brought him down to the parlour, dressed for mass, his father cried. That was because he was thinking of his own father. And uncle Charles had said so too.

Mr. Dedalus covered the dish and began to eat hungrily. Then he said:

—Poor old Christy, he's nearly lopsided now with roguery.

—Simon, said Mrs. Dedalus, you haven't given Mrs. Riordan any sauce.

Mr. Dedalus seized the sauceboat.

—Haven't I? he cried. Mrs. Riordan, pity the poor blind.

Dante covered her plate with her hands and said:

—No, thanks.

Mr. Dedalus turned to uncle Charles.

—How are you off, sir?

—Right as the mail, Simon.

—You, John?

—I'm all right. Go on yourself.

—Mary? Here, Stephen, here's something to make your hair curl.

He poured sauce freely over Stephen's plate and set the boat again on the table. Then he asked uncle Charles was it tender. Uncle Charles could not speak because his mouth was full but he nodded that it was.

—That was a good answer our friend made to the canon. What? said Mr. Dedalus.

—I didn't think he had that much in him, said Mr. Casey.

—*I'll pay your dues, father, when you cease turning the house of God into a polling-booth.*

—A nice answer, said Dante, for any man calling himself a catholic to give to his priest.

·—They have only themselves to blame, said Mr. Dedalus suavely. If they took

400

a fool's advice they would confine their attention to religion.

—It is religion, Dante said. They are doing their duty in warning the people.

—We go to the house of God, Mr. Casey said, in all humility to pray to our Maker and not to hear election addresses.

—It is religion, Dante said again. They are right. They must direct their flocks.

—And preach politics from the altar, is it? asked Mr. Dedalus.

—Certainly, said Dante. It is a question of public morality. A priest would not be a priest if he did not tell his flock what is right and what is wrong.

Mrs. Dedalus laid down her knife and fork, saying:

—For pity sake and for pity sake let us have no political discussion on this day of all days in the year.

—Quite right, ma'am, said uncle Charles. Now Simon, that's quite enough now. Not another word now.

—Yes, yes, said Mr. Dedalus quickly.

He uncovered the dish boldly and said:

—Now then, who's for more turkey?

Nobody answered. Dante said:

—Nice language for any catholic to use!

—Mrs. Riordan, I appeal to you, said Mrs. Dedalus, to let the matter drop now.

Dante turned on her and said:

—And am I to sit here and listen to the pastors of my church being flouted?

—Nobody is saying a word against them, said Mr. Dedalus, so long as they don't meddle in politics.

—The bishops and priests of Ireland have spoken, said Dante, and they must be obeyed.

—Let them leave politics alone, said Mr. Casey; or the people may leave their church alone.

—You hear? said Dante turning to Mrs. Dedalus.

—Mr. Casey! Simon! said Mrs. Dedalus, let it end now.

—Too bad! Too bad! said uncle Charles.

—What? cried Mr. Dedalus. Were we to desert him at the bidding of the English people?

—He was no longer worthy to lead, said Dante. He was a public sinner.

—We are all sinners and black sinners, said Mr. Casey coldly.

—Woe be to the man by whom the scandal cometh! said Mrs. Riordan. *It would be better for him that a millstone were tied about his neck and that he were cast into the depths of the sea rather than that he should scandalise one of these, my least little ones.* That is the language of the Holy Ghost.

—And very bad language if you ask me, said Mr. Dedalus coolly.

—Simon! Simon! said uncle Charles. The boy.

—Yes, yes, said Mr. Dedalus. I meant about the . . . I was thinking about the bad language of that railway porter. Well now, that's all right. Here, Stephen, show me your plate, old chap. Eat away now. Here.

He heaped up the food on Stephen's plate and served uncle Charles and Mr. Casey to large pieces of turkey and splashes of sauce. Mrs. Dedalus was eating little and Dante sat with her hands in her lap. She was red in the face. Mr. Dedalus rooted with the carvers at the end of the dish and said:

—There's a tasty bit here we call the pope's nose. If any lady or gentleman . . .

He held a piece of fowl up on the prong of the carvingfork. Nobody spoke. He put it on his own plate, saying:

—Well, you can't say but you were asked. I think I had better eat it myself because I'm not well in my health lately.

He winked at Stephen and, replacing the dish-cover, began to eat again.

There was a silence while he ate. Then he said:

—Well now, the day kept up fine after all. There were plenty of strangers down too.

Nobody spoke. He said again:

—I think there were more strangers down than last Christmas.

He looked round at the others whose faces were bent towards their plates and, receiving no reply, waited for a moment and said bitterly:

—Well, my Christmas dinner has been spoiled anyhow.

—There could be neither luck nor grace, Dante said, in a house where there is no respect for the pastors of the church.

Mr. Dedalus threw his knife and fork noisily on his plate.

—Respect! he said. Is it for Billy with the lip or for the tub of guts up in Armagh? Respect!

—Princes of the church, said Mr. Casey with slow scorn.

—Lord Leitrim's coachman, yes, said Mr. Dedalus.

—They are the Lord's anointed, Dante said. They are an honour to their country.

—Tub of guts, said Mr. Dedalus coarsely. He has a handsome face, mind you, in repose. You should see that fellow lapping up his bacon and cabbage of a cold winter's day. O Johnny!

He twisted his features into a grimace of heavy bestiality and made a lapping noise with his lips.

—Really, Simon, you should not speak that way before Stephen. It's not right.

—O, he'll remember all this when he grows up, said Dante hotly—the language he heard against God and religion and priests in his own home.

—Let him remember too, cried Mr. Casey to her from across the table, the language with which the priests and the priests' pawn broke Parnell's heart and hounded him into his grave. Let him remember that too when he grows up.

—Sons of bitches! cried Mr. Dedalus. When he was down they turned on him to betray him and rend him like rats in a sewer. Lowlived dogs! And they look it! By Christ, they look it!

—They behaved rightly, cried Dante. They obeyed their bishops and their priests. Honour to them!

—Well, it is perfectly dreadful to say that not even for one day in the year, said Mrs. Dedalus, can we be free from these dreadful disputes!

—Come now, come now, come now! Can we not have our opinions whatever they are without this bad temper and this bad language? It is too bad surely.

Mrs. Dedalus spoke to Dante in a low voice but Dante said loudly:

—I will not say nothing. I will defend my church and my religion when it is insulted and spit on by renegade catholics.

Mr. Casey pushed his plate rudely into the middle of the table and, resting his elbows before him, said in a hoarse voice to his host:

—Tell me, did I tell you that story about a very famous split?

—You did not, John, said Mr. Dedalus.

—Why then, said Mr. Casey, it is a most instructive story. It happened not long ago in the county Wicklow where we are now.

He broke off and, turning towards Dante, said with quiet indignation:

—And I may tell you, ma'am, that I, if you mean me, am no renegade catholic. I am a catholic as my father was and his father before him and his father before him again when we gave up our lives rather than sell our faith.

—The more shame to you now, Dante said, to speak as you do.

—The story, John, said Mr. Dedalus smiling. Let us have the story anyhow.

—Catholic indeed! repeated Dante ironically. The blackest protestant in the land would not speak the language I have heard this evening.

Mr. Dedalus began to sway his head to and fro, crooning like a country singer.

—I am no protestant, I tell you again, said Mr. Casey flushing.

Mr. Dedalus, still crooning and swaying his head, began to sing in a grunting nasal tone:

O, come all you Roman catholics
That never went to mass.

He took up his knife and fork again in good humour and set to eating, saying to Mr. Casey:

—Let us have the story, John. It will help us to digest.

Stephen looked with affection at Mr. Casey's face which stared across the table over his joined hands. He like to sit near him at the fire, looking up at his dark fierce face. But his dark eyes were never fierce and his slow voice was good to listen to. But why was he then against the priests? Because Dante must be right then. But he had heard his father say that she was a spoiled nun and that she had come out of the convent in the Alleghanies when her brother had got the money from the savages for the trinkets and the chainies. Perhaps that made her severe against Parnell. And she did not like him to play with Eileen because Eileen was a protestant and when she was young she knew children that used to play with protestants and the protestants used to make fun of the litany of the Blessed Virgin. *Tower of Ivory,* they used to say, *House of Gold!* How could a woman be a tower of ivory or a house of gold! Who was right then? And he remembered the evening in the infirmary in Clongowes, the dark waters, the light at the pierhead and the moan of sorrow from the people when they had heard.

Eileen had long white hands. One evening when playing tig she had put her hands over his eyes: long and white and thin and cold and soft. That was ivory: a cold white thing. That was the meaning of *Tower of Ivory.*

—The story is very short and sweet, Mr. Casey said. It was one day down in Arklow, a cold bitter day, not long before the chief died. May God have mercy on him!

He closed his eyes wearily and paused. Mr. Dedalus took a bone from his plate and tore some meat from it with his teeth, saying:

—Before he was killed, you mean.

Mr. Casey opened his eyes, sighed and went on:

—He was down in Arklow one day. We were down there at a meeting and after the meeting was over we had to make our way to the railway station through the crowd. Such booing and baaing, man, you never heard. They called us all the names in the world. Well there was one old lady, and a drunken old harridan she was surely, that paid all her attention to me. She kept dancing along beside me in the mud bawling and screaming into my face: *Priest hunter! The Paris Funds! Mr. Fox! Kitty O'Shea!*

—And what did you do, John? asked Mr. Dedalus.

—I let her bawl away, said Mr. Casey. It was a cold day and to keep up my heart I had (saving your presence, ma'am) a quid of Tullamore in my mouth and sure I couldn't say a word in any case because my mouth was full of tobacco juice.

—Well, John?

—Well. I let her bawl away, to her heart's content, *Kitty O'Shea* and the rest of it till at last she called that lady a name that I won't sully this Christmas board nor your ears, ma'am, nor my own lips by repeating.

He paused. Mr. Dedalus, lifting his head from the bone, asked:

—And what did you do, John?

—Do! said Mr. Casey. She stuck her ugly old face up at me when she said it and I had my mouth full of tobacco juice. I bent down to her and *Phth!* says I to her like that.

He turned aside and made the act of spitting.

—Phth! says I to her like that, right into her eye. He clapped a hand to his eye and gave a hoarse scream of pain.

—*O Jesus, Mary and Joseph!* says she. *I'm blinded! I'm blinded and drownded!*

He stopped in a fit of coughing and laughter, repeating:

—*I'm blinded entirely.*

Mr. Dedalus laughed loudly and lay back in his chair while uncle Charles swayed his head to and fro.

Dante looked terribly angry and repeated while they laughed:

—Very nice! Ha! Very nice!

It was not nice about the spit in the woman's eye.

But what was the name the woman had called Kitty O'Shea that Mr. Casey would not repeat? He thought of Mr. Casey walking through the crowds of people and making speeches from a wagonette. That was what he had been in prison for and he remembered that one night Sergeant O'Neill had come to the house and had stood in the hall, talking in a low voice with his father and chewing nervously at the chinstrap of his cap. And that night Mr. Casey had not gone to Dublin by train but a car had come to the door and he had heard his father say something about the Cabinteely road.

He was for Ireland and Parnell and so was his father: and so was Dante too for one night at the band on the esplanade she had hit a gentleman on the head with her umbrella because he had taken off his hat when the band played *God save the Queen* at the end.

Mr. Dedalus gave a snort of contempt.

—Ah, John, he said. It is true for them. We are an unfortunate priestridden race and always were and always will be till the end of the chapter.

Uncle Charles shook his head, saying:

—A bad business! A bad business!

Mr. Dedalus repeated:

—A priestridden Godforsaken race!

He pointed to the portrait of his grandfather on the wall to his right.

—Do you see that old chap up there, John? he said. He was a good Irishman when there was no money in the job. He was condemned to death as a whiteboy. But he had a saying about our clerical friends, that he would never let one of them put his two feet under his mahogany.

Dante broke in angrily:

—If we are a priestridden race we ought to be proud of it! They are the apple of God's eye. *Touch them not,* says Christ, *for they are the apple of My eye.*

—And can we not love our country then? asked Mr. Casey. Are we not to follow the man that was born to lead us?

—A traitor to his country! replied Dante. A traitor, an adulterer! The priests were right to abandon him. The priests were always the true friends of Ireland.

—Were they, faith? said Mr. Casey.

He threw his fist on the table and, frowning angrily, protruded one finger after another.

—Didn't the bishops of Ireland betray us in the time of the union when Bishop Lanigan presented an address of loyalty to the Marquess Cornwallis? Didn't the bishops and priests sell the aspirations of their country in 1829 in return for catholic emancipation? Didn't they denounce the fenian movement from the pulpit and in the confession box? And didn't they dishonour the ashes of Terence Bellew MacManus?

His face was glowing with anger and Stephen felt the glow rise to his own cheek as the spoken words thrilled him. Mr. Dedalus uttered a guffaw of coarse scorn.

—O, by God—he cried—I forgot little old Paul Cullen! Another apple of God's eye!

Dante bent across the table and cried to Mr. Casey:

—Right! Right! They were always right! God and morality and religion come first.

Mrs. Dedalus, seeing her excitement, said to her:

—Mrs. Riordan, don't excite yourself answering them.

—God and religion before everything! Dante cried. God and religion before the world!

Mr. Casey raised his clenched fist and brought it down on the table with a crash.

—Very well, then, he shouted hoarsely, if it comes to that, no God for Ireland!

—John! John! cried Mr. Dedalus, seizing his guest by the coat sleeve.

Dante stared across the table, her cheeks shaking. Mr. Casey struggled up from his chair and bent across the table towards her, scraping the air from before his eyes with one hand as though he were tearing aside a cobweb.

—No God for Ireland! he cried. We have had too much God in Ireland. Away with God!

—Blasphemer! Devil! screamed Dante, starting to her feet and almost spitting in his face.

Uncle Charles and Mr. Dedalus pulled Mr. Casey back into his chair again, talking to him from both sides reasonably. He stared before him out of his dark flaming eyes, repeating:

—Away with God, I say!

Dante shoved her chair violently aside and left the table, upsetting her napkinring which rolled slowly along the carpet and came to rest against the foot of an easychair. Mrs. Dedalus rose quickly and followed her towards the door. At the door Dante turned round violently and shouted down the room, her cheeks flushed and quivering with rage:

—Devil out of hell! We won! We crushed him to death! Fiend!

The door slammed behind her.

Mr. Casey, freeing his arms from his holders, suddenly bowed his head on his hands with a sob of pain.

—Poor Parnell! he cried loudly. My dead king!

He sobbed loudly and bitterly.

Stephen, raising his terrorstricken face, saw that his father's eyes were full of tears.

⇓

The fellows talked together in little groups.

One fellow said:

—They were caught near the Hill of Lyons.

—Who caught them?

—Mr. Gleeson and the minister. They were on a car.

The same fellow added:

—A fellow in the higher line told me.

Fleming asked:

—But why did they run away, tell us?

—I know why, Cecil Thunder said. Because they had fecked cash out of the rector's room.

—Who fecked it?

—Kickham's brother. And they all went shares in it.

But that was stealing. How could they have done that?

—A fat lot you know about it, Thunder! Wells said. I know why they scut.

—Tell us why.

—I was told not to, Wells said.

—O, go on, Wells, all said. You might tell us. We won't let it out.

Stephen bent forward his head to hear. Wells looked round to see if anyone was coming. Then he said secretly:

—You know the altar wine they keep in the press in the sacristy?

—Yes.

—Well, they drank that and it was found out who did it by the smell. And that's why they ran away, if you want to know.

And the fellow who had spoken first said:

—Yes, that's what I heard too from the fellow in the higher line.

The fellows were all silent. Stephen stood among them, afraid to speak, listening. A faint sickness of awe made him feel weak. How could they have done that? He thought of the dark silent sacristy. There were dark wooden presses there where the crimped surplices lay quietly folded. It was not the chapel but still you had to speak under your breath. It was a holy place. He remembered the summer evening he had been there to be dressed as boat-bearer, the evening of the procession to the little altar in the wood. A strange and holy place. The boy that held the censer had swung it gently to and fro near the door with the silvery cap lifted by the middle chain to keep the coals lighting. That was called charcoal: and it had burned quietly as the fellow had swung it gently and had given off a weak sour smell. And then when all were vested he had stood holding out the boat to the rector and the rector had put a spoonful of incense in and it had hissed on the red coals.

The fellows were talking together in little groups here and there on the playground. The fellows seemed to him to have grown smaller: that was because a sprinter had knocked him down the day before, a fellow out of second of grammar. He had been thrown by the fellow's machine lightly on the cinderpath and his spectacles had been broken in three pieces and some of the grit of the cinders had gone into his mouth.

That was why the fellows seemed to him smaller and farther away and the goalposts so thin and far and the soft grey sky so high up. But there was no play on the football grounds for cricket was coming: and some said that Barnes would be the prof and some said it would be Flowers. And all over the playgrounds they were playing rounders and bowling twisters and lobs. And from here and from there came the sounds of the cricket bats through the soft grey air. They said: pick, pack, pock, puck: little drops of water in a fountain slowly falling in the brimming bowl.

Athy, who had been silent, said quietly:

—You are all wrong.

All turned towards him eagerly.

—Why?

—Do you know?

—Who told you?

—Tell us, Athy.

Athy pointed across the playground to where Simon Moonan was walking by himself kicking a stone before him.

—Ask him, he said.

The fellows looked there and then said:

—Why him?

—Is he in it?

Athy lowered his voice and said:

—Do you know why those fellows scut? I will tell you but you must not let on you know.

—Tell us, Athy. Go on. You might if you know.

He paused for a moment and then said mysteriously:

—They were caught with Simon Moonan and Tusker Boyle in the square one night.

The fellows looked at him and asked:

—Caught?

—What doing?

Athy said:

—Smugging.

All the fellows were silent: and Athy said:

—And that's why?

Stephen looked at the faces of the fellows but they were all looking across the playground. He wanted to ask somebody about it. What did that mean about the smugging in the square? Why did the five fellows out of the higher line run away for that? It was a joke, he thought. Simon Moonan had nice clothes and one night he had shown him a ball of creamy sweets that the fellows of the football fifteen had rolled down to him along the carpet in the middle of the refectory when he was at the door. It was the night of the match against the Bective Rangers and the ball was made just like a red and green apple only it opened and it was full of the creamy sweets. And one day Boyle had said that an elephant had two tuskers instead of two tusks and that was why he was called Tusker Boyle but some fellows called him Lady Boyle because he was always at his nails, paring them.

Eileen had long thin cool white hands too because she was a girl. They were like ivory; only soft. That was the meaning of *Tower of Ivory* but protestants could not understand it and made fun of it. One day he had stood beside her looking into the hotel grounds. A waiter was running up a trail of bunting on the flagstaff and a fox terrier was scampering to and fro on the sunny lawn. She had put her hand into his pocket where his hand was and he had felt how cool and thin and soft her hand was. She had said that pockets were funny things to have: and then all of a sudden she had broken away and had run laughing down the sloping curve of the path. Her fair hair had streamed out behind her like gold in the sun. *Tower of Ivory. House of Gold.* By thinking of things you could understand them.

But why in the square? You went there when you wanted to do something. It was all thick slabs of slate and water trickled all day out of tiny pinholes and there was a queer smell of stale water there. And behind the door of one of the closets there was a drawing in red pencil of a bearded man in a Roman dress with a brick in each hand and underneath was the name of the drawing:

Balbus was building a wall.

Some fellows had drawn it there for a cod. It had a funny face but it was very like a man with a beard. And on the wall of another closet there was written in backhand in beautiful writing:

Julius Caesar wrote The Calico Belly.

Perhaps that was why they were there because it was a place where some fellows wrote things for cod. But all the same it was queer what Athy said and the way he said it. It was not a cod because they had run away. He looked with the others across the playground and began to feel afraid.

At last Fleming said:

—And we are all to be punished for what other fellows did?

—I won't come back, see if I do, Cecil Thunder said. Three days' silence in the refectory and sending us up for six and eight every minute.

—Yes, said Wells. And old Barrett has a new way of twisting the note so that you can't open it and fold it again to see how many ferulæ you are to get. I won't come back too.

—Yes, said Cecil Thunder, and the prefect of studies was in second of grammar this morning.

—Let us get up a rebellion, Fleming said. Will we?

All the fellows were silent. The air was very silent and you could hear the cricket bats but more slowly than before: pick, pock.

Wells asked:

—What is going to be done to them?

—Simon Moonan and Tusker are going to be flogged, Athy said, and the fellows in the higher line got their choice of flogging or being expelled.

—And which are they taking? asked the fellow who had spoken first.

—All are taking expulsion except Corrigan, Athy answered. He's going to be flogged by Mr. Gleeson.

—I know why, Cecil Thunder said. He is right and the other fellows are wrong because a flogging wears off after a bit but a fellow that has been expelled from college is known all his life on account of it. Besides Gleeson won't flog him hard.

—It's best of his play not to, Fleming said.

—I wouldn't like to be Simon Moonan and Tusker, Cecil Thunder said. But I don't believe they will be flogged. Perhaps they will be sent up for twice nine.

—No, no, said Athy. They'll both get it on the vital spot.

Wells rubbed himself and said in a crying voice:

—Please, sir, let me off!

Athy grinned and turned up the sleeves of his jacket, saying:

> *It can't be helped;*
> *It must be done.*
> *So down with your breeches*
> *And out with your bum.*

The fellows laughed; but he felt that they were a little afraid. In the silence of the soft grey air he heard the cricket bats from here and from there: pock. That was a sound to hear but if you were hit then you would feel a pain. The pandybat made a sound too but not like that. The fellows said it was made of whalebone and leather with lead inside: and he wondered what was the pain like. There were different kinds of sounds. A long thin cane would have a high whistling sound and he wondered what was that pain like. It made him shivery to think of it and cold: and what Athy said too. But what was there to laugh at in it? It made him shivery: but that was because you always felt like a shiver when you let down your trousers. It was the same in the bath when you undressed yourself. He wondered who had to let them down, the master or the boy himself. O how could they laugh about it that way?

He looked at Athy's rolled-up sleeves and knuckly inky hands. He had rolled up his sleeves to show how Mr. Gleeson would roll up his sleeves. But Mr. Gleeson had round shiny cuffs and clean white wrists and fattish white hands and the nails of them were long and pointed. Perhaps he pared them too like Lady Boyle. But they were terribly long and pointed nails. So long and cruel they were though the white fattish hands were not cruel but gentle. And though he trembled with cold and fright to think of the cruel long nails and of the high whistling sound of the cane and of the chill you felt at the end of your shirt when you undressed yourself yet he felt a feeling of queer quiet pleasure inside him to think of the white fattish hands, clean and strong and gentle. And he thought of what Cecil Thunder had said; that Mr. Gleeson would not flog Corrigan hard. And Fleming had said he would not because it was best of his play not to. But that was not why.

A voice from far out on the playground cried:

—All in!

And other voices cried:

—All in! All in!

During the writing lesson he sat with his arms folded, listening to the slow scraping of the pens. Mr. Harford went to and fro making little signs in red pencil and sometimes sitting beside the boy to show him how to hold his pen. He had tried to spell out the headline for himself though he knew already what it was for it was the last of the book. *Zeal without prudence is like a ship adrift.* But the lines of the letters were like fine invisible threads and it was only by closing his right eye tight tight and staring out of the left eye that he could make out the full curves of the capital.

But Mr. Harford was very decent and never got into a wax. All the other masters got into dreadful waxes. But why were they to suffer for what fellows in the higher line did? Wells had said that they had drunk some of the altar wine out of the press in the sacristy and that it had been found out who had done it by the smell. Perhaps they had stolen a monstrance to run away with it and sell it somewhere. That must have been a terrible sin, to go in there quietly at night, to open the dark press and steal the flashing gold thing into which God was put on the altar in the middle of flowers and candles at benediction while the incense went up in clouds at both sides as the fellow swung the censer and Dominic Kelly sang the first part by himself in the choir. But God was not in it of course when they stole it. But still it was a strange and a great sin even to touch it. He thought of it with deep awe; a terrible and strange sin: it thrilled him to think of it in the silence when the pens scraped lightly. But to drink the altar wine out of the press and be found out by the smell was a sin too: but it was not terrible and strange. It only made you feel a little sickish on account of the smell of the wine. Because on the day when he had made his first holy communion in the chapel he had shut his eyes and opened his mouth and put out his tongue a little: and when the rector had stooped down to give him the holy communion he had smelt a faint winy smell off the rector's breath after the wine of the mass. The word was beautiful: wine. It made you think of dark purple because the grapes were dark purple that grew in Greece outside houses like white temples. But the faint smell off the rector's breath had made him feel a sick feeling on the morning of his first communion. The day of your first communion was the happiest day of your life. And once a lot of generals had asked Napoleon what was the happiest day of his life. They thought he would say the day he won some great battle or the day he was made an emperor. But he said:

—Gentlemen, the happiest day of my life was the day on which I made my first holy communion.

Father Arnall came in and the Latin lesson began and he remained still leaning on the desk with his arms folded. Father Arnall gave out the theme-books and he said that they were scandalous and that they were all to be written out again with the corrections at once. But the worst of all was Fleming's theme because the pages were stuck together by a blot: and Father Arnall held it up by a corner and said it was an insult to any master to send him up such a theme. Then he asked Jack Lawton to decline the noun *mare* and Jack Lawton stopped at the ablative singular and could not go on with the plural.

—You should be ashamed of yourself, said Father Arnall sternly. You, the leader of the class!

Then he asked the next boy and the next and the next. Nobody knew. Father Arnall became very quiet, more and more quiet as each boy tried to answer it and could not. But his face was black looking and his eyes were staring though his voice was so quiet. Then he asked Fleming and Fleming said that that word had no plural. Father Arnall suddenly shut the book and shouted at him:

—Kneel out there in the middle of the class. You are one of the idlest boys I ever met. Copy out your themes again the rest of you.

Fleming moved heavily out of his place and knelt between the two last benches. The other boys bent over their theme-books and began to write. A silence filled the classroom and Stephen, glancing timidly at Father Arnall's dark face, saw that it was a little red from the wax he was in.

Was that a sin for Father Arnall to be in a wax or was he allowed to get into a wax when the boys were idle because that made them study better or was he only letting on to be in a wax? It was because he was allowed because a priest would know what a sin was and would not do it. But if he did it one time by mistake what would he do to go to confession? Perhaps he would go to confession to the minister. And if the minister did it he would go to the rector: and the rector to the provincial: and the provincial to the general of the jesuits. That was called the order: and he had heard his father say that they were all clever men. They could all have become high-up people in the world if they had not become jesuits. And he wondered what Father Arnall and Paddy Barrett would have become and what Mr. McGlade and Mr. Gleeson would have become if they had not become jesuits. It was hard to think what because you would have to think of them in a different way with different coloured coats and trousers and with beards and moustaches and different kinds of hats.

The door opened quietly and closed. A quick whisper ran through the class: the prefect of studies. There was an instant of dead silence and then the loud crack of a pandybat on the last desk. Stephen's heart leapt up in fear.

—Any boys want flogging here, Father Arnall? cried the prefect of studies. Any lazy idle loafers that want flogging in this class?

He came to the middle of the class and saw Fleming on his knees.

—Hoho! he cried. Who is this boy? Why is he on his knees? What is your name, boy?

—Fleming, sir.

—Hoho, Fleming! An idler of course. I can see it in your eye. Why is he on his knees, Father Arnall?

—He wrote a bad Latin theme, Father Arnall said, and he missed all the questions in grammar.

—Of course he did! cried the prefect of studies, of course he did! A born idler! I can see it in the corner of his eye.

He banged his pandybat down on the desk and cried:

—Up, Fleming! Up, my boy!

Fleming stood up slowly.

—Hold out! cried the prefect of studies.

Fleming held out his hand. The pandybat came down on it with a loud smacking sound: one, two, three, four, five, six.

—Other hand!

The pandybat came down again in six loud quick smacks.

—Kneel down! cried the prefect of studies.

Fleming knelt down squeezing his hands under his armpits, his face contorted with pain, but Stephen knew how hard his hands were because Fleming was always rubbing rosin into them. But perhaps he was in great pain for the noise of the pandybat was terrible. Stephen's heart was beating and fluttering.

—At your work, all of you! shouted the prefect of studies. We want no lazy idle loafers here, lazy idle little schemers. At your work, I tell you. Father Dolan will be in to see you every day. Father Dolan will be in tomorrow.

He poked one of the boys in the side with the pandybat, saying:

—You, boy! When will Father Dolan be in again?

—Tomorrow, sir, said Tom Furlong's voice.

—Tomorrow and tomorrow and tomorrow, said the prefect of studies. Make up your minds for that. Every day Father Dolan. Write away. You, boy, who are you?

Stephen's heart jumped suddenly.

—Dedalus, sir.

—Why are you not writing like the others?

—I . . . my . . .

He could not speak with fright.

—Why is he not writing, Father Arnall?

—He broke his glasses, said Father Arnall, and I exempted him from work.

—Broke? What is this I hear? What is this? Your name is? said the prefect of studies.

—Dedalus, sir.

—Out here, Dedalus. Lazy little schemer. I see schemer in your face. Where did you break your glasses?

Stephen stumbled into the middle of the class, blinded by fear and haste.

—Where did you break your glasses? repeated the prefect of studies.

—The cinderpath, sir.

—Hoho! The cinderpath! cried the prefect of studies. I know that trick.

Stephen lifted his eyes in wonder and saw for a moment Father Dolan's white-grey not young face, his baldy whitegrey head with fluff at the sides of it, the steel rims of his spectacles and his no-coloured eyes looking through the glasses. Why did he say he knew that trick?

—Lazy idle little loafer! cried the prefect of studies. Broke my glasses! An old schoolboy trick! Out with your hand this moment!

Stephen closed his eyes and held out in the air his trembling hand with the palm upwards. He felt the prefect of studies touch it for a moment at the fingers to straighten it and then the swish of the sleeve of the soutane as the pandybat was lifted to strike. A hot burning stinging tingling blow like the loud crack of a broken stick made his trembling hand crumple together like a leaf in the fire: and at the sound and the pain scalding tears were driven into his eyes. His whole body was shaking with fright, his arm was shaking and his crumpled burning livid hand shook like a loose leaf in the air. A cry sprang to his lips, a prayer to be let off. But though the tears scalded his eyes and his limbs quivered with pain and fright he held back the hot tears and the cry that scalded his throat.

—Other hand! shouted the prefect of studies.

Stephen drew back his maimed and quivering right arm and held out his left hand. The soutane sleeve swished again as the pandybat was lifted and a loud crashing sound and a fierce maddening tingling burning pain made his hand shrink together with the palms and fingers in a livid quivering mass. The scalding water burst forth from his eyes and, burning with shame and agony and fear, he drew back his shaking arm in terror and burst out into a whine of pain. His body shook with a palsy of fright and in shame and rage he felt the scalding cry come from his throat and the scalding tears falling out of his eyes and down his flaming cheeks.

—Kneel down! cried the prefect of studies.

Stephen knelt down quickly pressing his beaten hands to his sides. To think of them beaten and swollen with pain all in a moment made him feel so sorry for them as if they were not his own but someone else's that he felt sorry for. And as he knelt, calming the last sobs in his throat and feeling the burning tingling pain pressed in to his sides, he thought of the hands which he had held out in the air with the palms up and of the firm touch of the prefect of studies when he had steadied the shaking fingers and of the beaten swollen reddened mass of palm and fingers that shook helplessly in the air.

—Get at your work, all of you, cried the prefect of studies from the door. Father Dolan will be in every day to see if any boy, any lazy idle little loafer wants flogging. Every day. Every day.

The door closed behind him.

The hushed class continued to copy out the themes. Father Arnall rose from his seat and went among them, helping the boys with gentle words and telling them the mistakes they had made. His voice was very gentle and soft. Then he returned to his seat and said to Fleming and Stephen:

—You may return to your places, you two.

Fleming and Stephen rose and, walking to their seats, sat down. Stephen, scarlet with shame, opened a book quickly with one weak hand and bent down upon it, his face close to the page.

It was unfair and cruel because the doctor had told him not to read without glasses and he had written home to his father that morning to send him a new pair. And Father Arnall had said that he need not study till the new glasses came. Then to be called a schemer before the class and to be pandied when he always got the card for first or second and was the leader of the Yorkists! How could the prefect of studies know that it was a trick? He felt the touch of the prefect's fingers as they had steadied his hand and at first he had thought he was going to shake hands with him because the fingers were soft and firm: but then in an instant he had heard the swish of the soutane sleeve and the crash. It was cruel and unfair to make him kneel in the middle of the class then: and Father Arnall had told them both that they might return to their places without making any difference between them. He listened to Father Arnell's low and gentle voice as he corrected the themes. Perhaps he was sorry now and wanted to be decent. But it was unfair and cruel. The prefect of studies was a priest but that was cruel and unfair. And his whitegrey face and the no-coloured eyes behind the steel rimmed spectacles were cruel looking because he had steadied the hand first with his firm soft fingers and that was to hit it better and louder.

—It's a stinking mean thing, that's what it is, said Fleming in the corridor as the classes were passing out in file to the refectory, to pandy a fellow for what is not his fault.

—You really broke your glasses by accident, didn't you? Nasty Roche asked.

Stephen felt his heart filled by Fleming's words and did not answer.

—Of course he did! said Fleming. I wouldn't stand it. I'd go up and tell the rector on him.

—Yes, said Cecil Thunder eagerly, and I saw him lift the pandybat over his shoulder and he's not allowed to do that.

—Did they hurt much? Nasty Roche asked.

—Very much, Stephen said.

—I wouldn't stand it, Fleming repeated, from Baldyhead or any other Baldyhead. It's a stinking mean low trick, that's what it is. I'd go straight up to the rector and tell him about it after dinner.

—Yes, do. Yes, do, said Cecil Thunder.

—Yes, do. Yes, go up and tell the rector on him, Dedalus, said Nasty Roche, because he said that he'd come in tomorrow again and pandy you.

—Yes, yes. Tell the rector, all said.

And there were some fellows out of second of grammar listening and one of them said:

—The senate and the Roman people declared that Dedalus had been wrongly punished.

It was wrong; it was unfair and cruel: and, as he sat in the refectory, he suffered time after time in memory the same humiliation until he began to wonder whether it might not really be that there was something in his face which made him look like a schemer and he wished he had a little mirror to see. But there could not be; and it was unjust and cruel and unfair.

He could not eat the blackish fish fritters they got on Wednesdays in Lent and one of his potatoes had the mark of the spade in it. Yes, he would do what the fellows had told him. He would go up and tell the rector that he had been wrongly punished. A thing like that had been done before by somebody in history, by some great person whose head was in the books of history. And the rector would declare that he had been wrongly punished because the senate and the Roman people always declared that the men who did that had been wrongly punished. Those were the great men whose names were in Richmal Magnall's Questions. History was all about those men and what they did and that was what Peter Parley's Tales about Greece and Rome were all about. Peter Parley himself was on the first page in a picture. There was a road over a heath with grass at the side and little bushes: and Peter Parley had a broad hat like a protestant minister and a big stick and he was walking fast along the road to Greece and Rome.

It was easy what he had to do. All he had to do was when the dinner was over and he came out in his turn to go on walking but not out to the corridor but up the staircase on the right that led to the castle. He had nothing to do but that; to turn to the right and walk fast up the staircase and in half a minute he would be in the low dark narrow corridor that led through the castle to the rector's room. And every fellow had said that it was unfair, even the fellow out of second of grammar who had said that about the senate and the Roman people.

What would happen? He heard the fellows of the higher line stand up at the top of the refectory and heard their steps as they came down the matting: Paddy Rath and Jimmy Magee and the Spaniard and the Portuguese and the fifth was big Corrigan who was going to be flogged by Mr. Gleeson. That was why the prefect of studies had called him a schemer and pandied him for nothing: and, straining his weak eyes, tired with the tears, he watched big Corrigan's broad shoulders and big hanging black head passing in the file. But he had done something and besides Mr. Gleeson would not flog him hard: and he remembered how big Corrigan looked in the bath. He had skin the same colour as the turf-coloured bogwater in the shallow end of the bath and when he walked along the side his feet slapped loudly on the wet tiles and at every step his thighs shook a little because he was fat.

The refectory was half empty and the fellows were still passing out in file. He could go up the staircase because there was never a priest or a prefect outside the refectory door. But he could not go. The rector would side with the prefect of studies and think it was a schoolboy trick and then the prefect of studies would come in every day the same, only it would be worse because he would be dreadfully waxy at any fellow going up to the rector about him. The fellows had told him to go but they would not go themselves. They had forgotten all about it. No, it was best to forget all about it and perhaps the prefect of studies had only said he would come in. No, it was best to hide out of the way because when you were small and young you could often escape that way.

The fellows at his table stood up. He stood up and passed out among them in the file. He had to decide. He was coming near the door. If he went on with the fellows he could never go up to the rector because he could not leave the playground for that. And if he went and was pandied all the same all the fellows would make fun and talk about young Dedalus going up to the rector to tell on the prefect of studies.

He was walking down along the matting and he saw the door before him. It was impossible: he could not. He thought of the baldy head of the prefect of studies with the cruel no-coloured eyes looking at him and he heard the voice of the prefect of studies asking him twice what his name was. Why could he not remember the name when he was told the first time? Was he not listening the first time or was it to make fun out of the name? The great men in the history had names like that and nobody made fun of them. It was his own name that he should have made fun of if he wanted to make fun. Dolan: it was like the name of a woman who washed clothes.

He had reached the door and, turning quickly up to the right, walked up the stairs; and, before he could make up his mind to come back, he had entered the low dark narrow corridor that led to the castle. And as he crossed the threshold of the door of the corridor he saw, without turning his head to look, that all the fellows were looking after him as they went filing by.

He passed along the narrow dark corridor, passing little doors that were the doors of the rooms of the community. He peered in front of him and right and left through the gloom and thought that those must be portraits. It was dark and silent and his eyes were weak and tired with tears so that he could not see. But he thought they were the portraits of the saints and great men of the order who were looking down on him silently as he passed: Saint Ignatius Loyola holding an open book and pointing to the words *Ad Majorem Dei Gloriam* in it, saint Francis Xavier pointing to his chest, Lorenzo Ricci with his berretta on his head like one of the prefects of the lines, the three patrons of holy youth, saint Stanislaus Kostka, saint Aloysius Gonzaga and Blessed John Berchmans, all with young faces because they died when they were young, and Father Peter Kenny sitting in a chair wrapped in a big cloak.

He came out on the landing above the entrance hall and looked about him. That was where Hamilton Rowan had passed and the marks of the soldiers' slugs were there. And it was there that the old servants had seen the ghost in the white cloak of a marshal.

An old servant was sweeping at the end of the landing. He asked him where was the rector's room and the old servant pointed to the door at the far end and looked after him as he went on to it and knocked.

There was no answer. He knocked again more loudly and his heart jumped when he heard a muffled voice say:

—Come in!

He turned the handle and opened the door and fumbled for the handle of the green baize door inside. He found it and pushed it open and went in.

He saw the rector sitting at a desk writing. There was a skull on the desk and a strange solemn smell in the room like the old leather of chairs.

His heart was beating fast on account of the solemn place he was in and the silence of the room: and he looked at the skull and at the rector's kind-looking face.

—Well, my little man, said the rector, what is it?

Stephen swallowed down the thing in his throat and said:

—I broke my glasses, sir.

The rector opened his mouth and said:

—O!

Then he smiled and said:

—Well, if we broke our glasses we must write home for a new pair.

—I wrote home, sir, said Stephen, and Father Arnall said I am not to study till they come.

—Quite right! said the rector.

Stephen swallowed down the thing again and tried to keep his legs and his voice from shaking.

—But, sir . . .

—Yes?

—Father Dolan came in today and pandied me because I was not writing my theme.

The rector looked at him in silence and he could feel the blood rising to his face and the tears about to rise to his eyes.

The rector said:

—Your name is Dedalus, isn't it?

—Yes, sir.

—And where did you break your glasses?

—On the cinderpath, sir. A fellow was coming out of the bicycle house and I fell and they got broken. I don't know the fellow's name.

The rector looked at him again in silence. Then he smiled and said:

—O, well, it was a mistake, I am sure Father Dolan did not know.

—But I told him I broke them, sir, and he pandied me.

—Did you tell him that you had written home for a new pair? the rector asked.

—No, sir.

—O well then, said the rector, Father Dolan did not understand. You can say that I excuse you from your lessons for a few days.

Stephen said quickly for fear his trembling would prevent him:

—Yes, sir, but Father Dolan said he will come in tomorrow to pandy me again for it.

—Very well, the rector said, it is a mistake and I shall speak to Father Dolan myself. Will that do now?

Stephen felt the tears wetting his eyes and murmured:

—O yes sir, thanks.

The rector held his hand across the side of the desk where the skull was and Stephen, placing his hand in it for a moment, felt a cool moist palm.

—Good day now, said the rector, withdrawing his hand and bowing.

—Good day, sir, said Stephen.

He bowed and walked quietly out of the room, closing the doors carefully and slowly.

But when he had passed the old servant on the landing and was again in the low narrow dark corridor he began to walk faster and faster. Faster and faster he hurried on through the gloom excitedly. He bumped his elbow against the door at the end and, hurrying down the staircase, walked quickly through the two corridors and out into the air.

He could hear the cries of the fellows on the playgrounds. He broke into a run and, running quicker and quicker, ran across the cinderpath and reached the third line playground, panting.

The fellows had seen him running. They closed round him in a ring, pushing one against another to hear.

—Tell us! Tell us!

—What did he say?

—Did you go in?

—What did he say?

—Tell us! Tell us!

He told them what he had said and what the rector had said and, when he had told them, all the fellows flung their caps spinning up into the air and cried:

—Hurroo!

They caught their caps and sent them up again spinning skyhigh and cried again:

—Hurroo! Hurroo!

They made a cradle of their locked hands and hoisted him up among them and carried him along till he struggled to get free. And when he had escaped from them they broke away in all directions, flinging their caps again into the air and whistling as they went spinning up and crying:

—Hurroo!

And they gave three groans for Baldyhead Dolan and three cheers for Conmee and they said he was the decentest rector that was ever in Clongowes.

The cheers died away in the soft grey air. He was alone. He was happy and free: but he would not be anyway proud with Father Dolan. He would be very quiet and obedient: and he wished that he could do something kind for him to show him that he was not proud.

The air was soft and grey and mild and evening was coming. There was the smell of evening in the air, the smell of the fields in the country where they digged up turnips to peel them and eat them when they went out for a walk to Major Barton's, the smell there was in the little wood beyond the pavilion where the gallnuts were.

The fellows were practising long shies and bowling lobs and slow twisters. In the soft grey silence he could hear the bump of the balls: and from here and from there through the quiet air the sound of the cricket bats: pick, pack, pock, puck: like drops of water in a fountain falling softly in the brimming bowl.

II

Uncle Charles smoked such black twist that at last his nephew suggested to him to enjoy his morning smoke in a little outhouse at the end of the garden.

—Very good, Simon. All serene, Simon, said the old man tranquilly. Anywhere you like. The outhouse will do me nicely: it will be more salubrious.

—Damn me, said Mr. Dedalus frankly, if I know how you can smoke such villainous awful tobacco. It's like gunpowder, by God.

—It's very nice, Simon, replied the old man. Very cool and mollifying.

Every morning, therefore, uncle Charles repaired to his outhouse but not before he had creased and brushed scrupulously his back hair and brushed and put on his tall hat. While he smoked the brim of his tall hat and the bowl of his pipe were just visible beyond the jambs of the outhouse door. His arbour, as he called the reeking outhouse which he shared with the cat and the garden tools, served him also as a soundingbox: and every morning he hummed contentedly one of his favourite songs: *O, twine me a bower* or *Blue eyes and golden hair* or *The Groves of Blarney* while the grey and blue coils of smoke rose slowly from his pipe and vanished in the pure air.

During the first part of the summer in Blackrock uncle Charles was Stephen's constant companion. Uncle Charles was a hale old man with a well tanned skin, rugged features and white side whiskers. On week days he did messages between the house in Carysfort Avenue and those shops in the main street of the town with which the family dealt. Stephen was glad to go with him on these errands for uncle Charles helped him very liberally to handfuls of whatever was exposed in open boxes and barrels outside the counter. He would seize a handful of grapes and sawdust or three or four American apples and thrust them generously into his grandnephew's hand while the shopman smiled uneasily; and, on Stephen's feigning reluctance to take them, he would frown and say:

—Take them, sir. Do you hear me, sir? They're good for your bowels.

When the order list had been booked the two would go on to the park where an old friend of Stephen's father, Mike Flynn, would be found seated on a bench, waiting for them. Then would begin Stephen's run round the park. Mike Flynn would stand at the gate near the railway station, watch in hand, while Stephen ran round the track in the style Mike Flynn favoured, his head high lifted, his knees well lifted and his hands held straight down by his sides. When the morning practice was over the trainer would make his comments and sometimes illustrate them by shuffling along for a yard or so comically in an old pair of blue canvas shoes. A small ring of wonderstruck children and nursemaids would gather to watch him and linger even when he and uncle Charles had sat down again and were talking athletics and politics. Though he had heard his father say that Mike

Flynn had put some of the best runners of modern times through his hands Stephen often glanced at his trainer's flabby stubble-covered face, as it bent over the long stained fingers through which he rolled his cigarette, and with pity at the mild lustreless blue eyes which would look up suddenly from the task and gaze vaguely into the blue distance while the long swollen fingers ceased their rolling and grains and fibres of tobacco fell back into the pouch.

On the way home uncle Charles would often pay a visit to the chapel and, as the font was above Stephen's reach, the old man would dip his hand and then sprinkle the water briskly about Stephen's clothes and on the floor of the porch. While he prayed he knelt on his red handkerchief and read above his breath from a thumb blackened prayer-book wherein catchwords were printed at the foot of every page. Stephen knelt at his side respecting, though he did not share, his piety. He often wondered what his granduncle prayed for so seriously. Perhaps he prayed for the souls in purgatory or for the grace of a happy death or perhaps he prayed that God might send him back a part of the big fortune he had squandered in Cork.

On Sundays Stephen with his father and his granduncle took their constitutional. The old man was a nimble walker in spite of his corns and often ten or twelve miles of the road were covered. The little village of Stillorgan was the parting of the ways. Either they went to the left towards the Dublin mountains or along the Goatstown road and thence into Dundrum, coming home by Sandyford. Trudging along the road or standing in some grimy wayside public house his elders spoke constantly of the subjects nearer their hearts, of Irish politics, of Munster and of the legends of their own family, to all of which Stephen lent an avid ear. Words which he did not understand he said over and over to himself till he had learnt them by heart: and through them he had glimpses of the real world about him. The hour when he too would take part in the life of that world seemed drawing near and in secret he began to make ready for the great part which he felt awaited him the nature of which he only dimly apprehended.

His evenings were his own; and he pored over a ragged translation of *The Count of Monte Cristo.* The figure of that dark avenger stood forth in his mind for whatever he had heard or divined in childhood of the strange and terrible. At night he built up on the parlour table an image of the wonderful island cave out of transfers and paper flowers and coloured tissue paper and strips of the silver and golden paper in which chocolate is wrapped. When he had broken up this scenery, weary of its tinsel, there would come to his mind the bright picture of Marseilles, of sunny trellises and of Mercedes.

Outside Blackrock, on the road that led to the mountains, stood a small whitewashed house in the garden of which grew many rosebushes: and in this house, he told himself, another Mercedes lived. Both on the outward and on the homeward journey he measured distance by this landmark: and in his imagination he lived through a long train of adventures, marvellous as those in the book itself, towards the close of which there appeared an image of himself, grown older and sadder, standing in a moonlit garden with Mercedes who had so many years before slighted his love, and with a sadly proud gesture of refusal, saying:

—Madam, I never eat muscatel grapes.

He became the ally of a boy named Aubrey Mills and founded with him a gang of adventurers in the avenue. Aubrey carried a whistle dangling from his buttonhole and a bicycle lamp attached to his belt while the others had short sticks thrust daggerwise through theirs. Stephen, who had read of Napoleon's plain style of dress, chose to remain unadorned and thereby heightened for himself the pleasure of taking counsel with his lieutenant before giving orders. The gang made forays into the gardens of old maids or went down to the castle and fought a battle on the shaggy weedgrown rocks, coming home after it weary stragglers with the stale odours of the foreshore in their nostrils and the rank oils of the sea-wrack upon their hands and in their hair.

Aubrey and Stephen had a common milkman and often they drove out in the milkcar to Carrickmines where the cows were at grass. While the men were milking the boys would take turns in riding the tractable mare round the field. But when autumn came the cows were driven home from the grass: and the first sight of the filthy cowyard at Stradbrook with its foul green puddles and clots of liquid dung and steaming bran troughs sickened Stephen's heart. The cattle which had seemed so beautiful in the country on sunny days revolted him and he could not even look at the milk they yielded.

The coming of September did not trouble him this year for he was not to be sent back to Clongowes. The practice in the park came to an end when Mike Flynn went into hospital. Aubrey was at school and had only an hour or two free in the evening. The gang fell asunder and there were no more nightly forays or battles on the rocks. Stephen sometimes went round with the car which delivered the evening milk: and these chilly drives blew away his memory of the filth of the yard and he felt no repugnance at seeing the cow hairs and hayseeds on the milkman's coat. Whenever the car drew up before a house he waited to catch a glimpse of a well scrubbed kitchen or of a softly lighted hall and to see how the servant would hold the jug and how she would close the door. He thought it should be a pleasant life enough, driving along the roads every evening to deliver milk, if he had warm gloves and a fat bag of gingernuts in his pocket to eat from. But the same foreknowledge which had sickened his heart and made his legs sag suddenly as he raced round the park, the same intuition which had made him glance with mistrust at his trainer's flabby stubblecovered face as it bent heavily over his long stained fingers, dissipated any vision of the future. In a vague way he understood that his father was in trouble and that this was the reason why he himself had not been sent back to Clongowes. For some time he had felt the slight change in his house; and those changes in what he had deemed unchangeable were so many slight shocks to his boyish conception of the world. The ambition which he felt astir at times in the darkness of his soul sought no outlet. A dusk like that of the outer world obscured his mind as he heard the mare's hoofs clattering along the tramtrack on the Rock Road and the great can swaying and rattling behind him.

He returned to Mercedes and, as he brooded upon her image, a strange unrest crept into his blood. Sometimes a fever gathered within him and led him to rove alone in the evening along the quiet avenue. The peace of the gardens and the kindly lights in the windows poured a tender influence into his restless heart. The noise of children at play annoyed him and their silly voices made him feel, even more keenly than he had felt at Clongowes, that he was different from others. He did not want to play. He wanted to meet in the real world the unsubstantial image which his soul so constantly beheld. He did not know where to seek it or how but a premonition which led him on told him that this image would, without any overt act of his, encounter him. They would meet quietly as if they had known each other and had made their tryst, perhaps at one of the gates or in some more secret place. They would be along, surrounded by darkness and silence: and in that moment of supreme tenderness he would be transfigured. He would fade into something impalpable under her eyes and then in a moment, he would be transfigured. Weakness and timidity and inexperience would fall from him in that magic moment.

↓

Two great yellow caravans had halted one morning before the door and men had come tramping into the house to dismantle it. The furniture had been hustled out through the front garden which was strewn with wisps of straw and rope ends and into the huge vans at the gate. When all had been safely stowed the vans had set off noisily down the avenue: and from the window of the railway carriage, in which he had sat with his red eyed mother, Stephen had seen them lumbering along the Merrion Road.

The parlour fire would not draw that evening and Mr. Dedalus rested the poker against the bars of the grate to attract the flame. Uncle Charles dozed in a corner of the half furnished uncarpeted room and near him the family portraits leaned against the wall. The lamp on the table shed a weak light over the boarded floor, muddied by the feet of the vanmen. Stephen sat on a footstool beside his father listening to a long and incoherent monologue. He understood little or nothing of it at first but he became slowly aware that his father had enemies and that some flight was going to take place. He felt, too, that he was being enlisted for the fight, that some duty was being laid upon his shoulders. The sudden flight from the comfort and revery of Blackrock, the passage through the gloomy foggy city, the thought of the bare cheerless house in which they were now to live made his heart heavy: and again an intuition, a foreknowledge of the future came to him. He understood also why the servants had often whispered together in the hall and why his father had often stood on the hearthrug, with his back to the fire, talking loudly to uncle Charles who urged him to sit down and eat his dinner.

—There's a crack of the whip left in me yet, Stephen, old chap, said Mr. Dedalus, poking at the dull fire with fierce energy. We're not dead yet, sonny. No, by the Lord Jesus (God forgive me) nor half dead.

Dublin was a new and complex sensation. Uncle Charles had grown so witless that he could no longer be sent out on errands and the disorder in settling in the new house left Stephen freer than he had been in Blackrock. In the beginning he contented himself with circling timidly round the neighbouring square or, at most, going half way down one of the side streets: but when he had made a skeleton map of the city in his mind he followed boldly one of its central lines until he reached the Custom House. He passed unchallenged among the docks and along the quays wondering at the multitude of corks that lay bobbing on the surface of the water in a thick yellow scum, at the crowds of quay porters and the rumbling carts and the ill dressed bearded policeman. The vastness and strangeness of the life suggested to him by the bales of merchandise stocked along the walls or swung aloft out of the holds of steamers wakened again in him the unrest which had sent him wandering in the evening from garden to garden in search of Mercedes. And amid this new bustling life he might have fancied himself in another Marseilles but that he missed the bright sky and the sun-warmed trellisses of the wineshops. A vague dissatisfaction grew up within him as he looked on the quays and on the river and on the lowering skies and yet he continued to wander up and down day after day as if he really sought someone that eluded him.

He went once or twice with his mother to visit their relatives: and though they passed a jovial array of shops lit up and adorned for Christmas his mood of embittered silence did not leave him. The causes of his embitterment were many, remote and near. He was angry with himself for being young and the prey of restless foolish impulses, angry also with the change of fortune which was reshaping the world about him into a vision of squalor and insincerity. Yet his anger lent nothing to the vision. He chronicled with patience what he saw, detaching himself from it and testing its mortifying flavour in secret.

He was sitting on the backless chair in his aunt's kitchen. A lamp with a reflector hung on the japanned wall of the fireplace and by its light his aunt was reading the evening paper that lay on her knees. She looked a long time at a smiling picture that was set in it and said musingly:

—The beautiful Mabel Hunter!

A ringletted girl stood on tiptoe to peer at the picture and said softly:

—What is she in, mud?

—In a pantomime, love.

The child leaned her ringletted head against her mother's sleeve, gazing on the picture and murmured as if fascinated:

—The beautiful Mabel Hunter!

As if fascinated, her eyes rested long upon those demurely taunting eyes and she murmured devotedly:

—Isn't she an exquisite creature?

And the boy who came in from the street, stamping crookedly under his stone of coal, heard her words. He dropped his load promptly on the floor and hurried to her side to see. He mauled the edges of the paper with his reddened and blackened hands, shouldering her aside and complaining that he could not see.

He was sitting in the narrow breakfast room high up in the old dark windowed house. The firelight flickered on the wall and beyond the window a spectral dusk was gathering upon the river. Before the fire an old woman was busy making tea and, as she bustled at the task, she told in a low voice of what the priest and the doctor had said. She told too of certain changes they had seen in her of late and of her odd ways and sayings. He sat listening to the words and following the ways of adventure that lay open in the coals, arches and vaults and winding galleries and jagged caverns.

Suddenly he became aware of something in the doorway. A skull appeared suspended in the gloom of the doorway. A feeble creature like a monkey was there, drawn there by the sound of voices at the fire. A whining voice came from the door asking:

—Is that Josephine?

The old bustling woman answered cheerily from the fireplace:

—No, Ellen, it's Stephen.

—O . . . O, good evening, Stephen.

He answered the greeting and saw a silly smile break over the face in the doorway.

—Do you want anything, Ellen? asked the old woman at the fire.

But she did not answer the question and said,

—I thought it was Josephine. I thought you were Josephine, Stephen.

And, repeating this several times, she fell to laughing feebly.

He was sitting in the midst of a children's party at Harold's Cross. His silent watchful manner had grown upon him and he took little part in the games. The children, wearing the spoils of their crackers, danced and romped noisily and, though he tried to share their merriment, he felt himself a gloomy figure amid the gay cocked hats and sunbonnets.

But when he had sung his song and withdrawn into a snug corner of the room he began to taste the joy of his loneliness. The mirth, which in the beginning of the evening had seemed to him false and trivial, was like a soothing air to him, passing gaily by his senses, hiding from other eyes the feverish agitation of his blood while through the circling of the dancers and amid the music and laughter her glance travelled to his corner, flattering, taunting, searching, exciting his heart.

In the hall the children who had stayed latest were putting on their things: the party was over. She had thrown a shawl about her and, as they went together towards the tram, sprays of her fresh warm breath flew gaily above her cowled head and her shoes tapped blithely on the glassy road.

It was the last tram. The lank brown horses knew it and shook their bells to the clear night in admonition. The conductor talked with the driver, both nodding often in the green light of the lamp. On the empty seats of the tram were scattered a few coloured tickets. No sound of footsteps came up or down the road. No sound broke the peace of the night save when the lank brown horses rubbed their noses together and shook their bells.

They seemed to listen, he on the upper step and she on the lower. She came up to his step many times and went down to hers again between their phrases and once or twice stood close beside him for some moments on the upper step, forgetting to go down, and then went down. His heart danced upon her movements like a cork upon a tide. He heard what her eyes said to him from beneath their cowl and knew that in some dim past, whether in life or revery, he had heard their tale before. He saw her urge her vanities, her fine dress and sash and long black stockings, and knew that he had yielded to them a thousand times. Yet a voice within him spoke above the noise of his dancing heart, asking him would he take her gift to which he had only to stretch out his hand. And he remembered the day when he and Eileen had stood looking into the Hotel Grounds, watching the waiters running up a trail of bunting on the flagstaff and the fox terrier scampering to and fro on the sunny lawn, and how, all of a sudden, she had broken out into a peal of laughter and had run down the sloping curve of the path. Now, as then, he stood listlessly in his place, seemingly a tranquil watcher of the scene before him.

—She too wants me to catch hold of her, he thought. That's why she came with me to the tram. I could easily catch hold of her when she comes up to my step: nobody is looking. I could hold her and kiss her.

But he did neither: and, when he was sitting alone in the deserted tram he tore his ticket into shreds and stared gloomily at the corrugated footboard.

The next day he sat at his table in the bare upper room for many hours. Before him lay a new pen, a new bottle of ink and a new emerald exercise. From force of habit he had written at the top of the first page the initial letters of the jesuit motto: A.M.D.G. On the first line of the page appeared the title of the verses he was trying to write: To E____C___. He knew it was right to begin so for he had seen similar titles in the collected poems of Lord Byron. When he had written this title and drawn an ornamental line underneath he fell into a day dream and began to draw diagrams on the cover of the book. He saw himself sitting at his table in Bray the morning after the discussion at the Christmas dinner table, trying to write a poem about Parnell on the back of one of his father's second moiety notices. But his brain had then refused to grapple with the theme and, desisting, he had covered the page with the names and addresses of certain of his classmates:

Roderick Kickham
John Lawton
Anthony MacSwiney
Simon Moonan

Now it seemed as if he would fail again but, by dint of brooding on the incident, he thought himself into confidence. During this process all those elements which he deemed common and insignificant fell out of the scene. There remained no trace of the tram itself nor of the trammen nor of the horses: nor did he and she appear vividly. The verses told only of the night and the balmy breeze and the maiden lustre of the moon. Some undefined sorrow was hidden in the hearts of the protagonists as they stood in silence beneath the leafless trees and when the moment of farewell had come the kiss, which had been withheld by one, was given by both. After this the letters L. D. S. were written at the foot of the page and, having hidden the book, he went into his mother's bedroom and gazed at his face for a long time in the mirror of her dressing table.

But his long spell of leisure and liberty was drawing to its end. One evening his father came home full of news which kept his tongue busy all through dinner. Stephen had been awaiting his father's return for there had been mutton hash that day and he knew that his father would make him dip his bread in the gravy. But he did not relish the hash for the mention of Clongowes had coated his palate with a scum of disgust.

—I walked bang into him, said Mr. Dedalus for the fourth time, just at the corner of the square.

—Then I suppose, said Mrs. Dedalus, he will be able to arrange it. I mean about Belvedere.

—Of course, he will, said Mr. Dedalus. Don't I tell you he's provincial of the order now?

—I never liked the idea of sending him to the christian brothers myself, said Mrs. Dedalus.

—Christian brothers be damned! said Mr. Dedalus. Is it with Paddy Stink and Mickey Mud? No, let him stick to the jesuits in God's name since he began with them. They'll be of service to him in after years. Those are the fellows that can get you a position.

—And they're a very rich order, aren't they, Simon?

—Rather. They live well, I tell you. You saw their table at Clongowes. Fed up, by God, like gamecocks.

Mr. Dedalus pushed his plate over to Stephen and bade him finish what was on it.

—Now then, Stephen, he said, you must put your shoulder to the wheel, old chap. You've had a fine long holiday.

—O, I'm sure he'll work very hard now, said Mrs. Dedalus, especially when he has Maurice with him.

—O, Holy Paul, I forgot about Maurice, said Mr. Dedalus. Here, Maurice! Come here, you thick-headed ruffian! Do you know I'm going to send you to a college where they'll teach you to spell c.a.t. cat. And I'll buy you a nice little penny handkerchief to keep your nose dry. Won't that be grand fun?

Maurice grinned at his father and then at his brother. Mr. Dedalus screwed his glass into his eye and stared hard at both of his sons. Stephen mumbled his bread without answering his father's gaze.

—By the bye, said Mr. Dedalus at length, the rector or provincial rather, was telling me that story about you and Father Dolan. You're an impudent thief, he said.

—O, he didn't, Simon!

—Not he! said Mr. Dedalus. But he gave me a great account of the whole affair. We were chatting, you know, and one word borrowed another. And, by the way, who do you think he told me will get that job in the corporation? But I'll tell you that after. Well, as I was saying, we were chatting away quite friendly and he asked me did our friend here wear glasses still and then he told me the whole story.

—And was he annoyed, Simon?

—Annoyed! Not he! *Manly little chap!* he said.

Mr. Dedalus imitated the mincing nasal tone of the provincial.

—Father Dolan and I, when I told them all at dinner about it, Father Dolan and I had a great laugh over it. *You better mind yourself, Father Dolan,* said I, *or young Dedalus will send you up for twice nine.* We had a famous laugh together over it. Ha! Ha! Ha!

Mr. Dedalus turned to his wife and interjected in his natural voice:

—Shows you the spirit in which they take the boys there. O, a jesuit for your life, for diplomacy!

He reassumed the provincial's voice and repeated:

—I told them all at dinner about it and Father Dolan and I and all of us we all had a hearty laugh together over it. Ha! Ha! Ha!

The night of the Whitsuntide play had come and Stephen from the window of the dressing room looked out on the small grassplot across which lines of Chinese lanterns were stretched. He watched the visitors come down the steps from the house and pass into the theatre. Stewards in evening dress, old

Belvestoreans, loitered in groups about the entrance to the theatre and ushered in
the visitors with ceremony. Under the sudden glow of a lantern he could recognise the smiling face of a priest.

The Blessed Sacrament had been removed from the tabernacle and the first
benches had been driven back so as to leave the daïs of the altar and the space
before it free. Against the walls stood companies of barbells and Indian clubs; the
dumb bells were piled in one corner: and in the midst of countless hillocks of
gymnasium shoes and sweaters and singlets in untidy brown parcels there stood
the stout leatherjacketed vaulting horse waiting its turn to be carried up on the
stage and set in the middle of the winning team at the end of the gymnastic display.

Stephen, though in deference to his reputation for essay writing he had been
elected secretary to the gymnasium, had had no part in the first section of the programme, but in the play which formed the second section he had the chief part,
that of a farcical pedagogue. He had been cast for it on account of his stature and
grave manners for he was now at the end of his second year at Belvedere and in
number two.

A score of the younger boys in white knickers and singlets came pattering
down from the stage, through the vestry and into the chapel. The vestry and
chapel were peopled with eager masters and boys. The plump bald sergeant
major was testing with his foot the springboard of the vaulting horse. The lean
young man in a long overcoat, who was to give a special display of intricate club
swinging, stood near watching with interest, his silver coated clubs peeping out of
his deep sidepockets. The hollow rattle of the wooden dumb bells was heard as
another team made ready to go up on the stage: and in another moment the excited
prefect was hustling the boys through the vestry like a flock of geese, flapping the
wings of his soutane nervously and crying to the laggards to make haste. A little
troop of Neapolitan peasants were practising their steps at the end of the chapel,
some circling their arms above their heads, some swaying their baskets of paper
violets and curtseying. In a dark corner of the chapel at the gospel side of the altar
a stout old lady knelt amid her copious black skirts. When she stood up a pink
dressed figure, wearing a curly golden wig and an old fashioned straw sunbonnet, with black pencilled eyebrows and cheeks delicately rouged and powdered,
was discovered. A low murmur of curiosity ran round the chapel at the discovery
of this girlish figure. One of the prefects, smiling and nodding his head, approached
the dark corner and, having bowed to the stout old lady, said pleasantly:

—Is this a beautiful young lady or a doll that you have here, Mrs. Tallon?

Then, bending down to peer at the smiling painted face under the leaf of the
bonnet, he exclaimed:

—No! Upon my word I believe it's little Bertie Tallon after all!

Stephen at his post by the window heard the old lady and the priest laugh
together and heard the boys' murmurs of admiration behind him as they passed

430

forward to see the little boy who had to dance the sunbonnet dance by himself. A movement of impatience escaped him. He let the edge of the blind fall and, stepping down from the bench on which he had been standing, walked out of the chapel.

He passed out of the schoolhouse and halted under the shed that flanked the garden. From the theatre opposite came the muffled noise of the audience and sudden brazen clashes of the soldiers' band. The light spread upwards from the glass roof making the theatre seem a festive ark, anchored among the hulks of houses, her frail cables of lanterns looping her to her moorings. A side door of the theatre opened suddenly and a shaft of light flew across the grassplots. A sudden burst of music issued from the ark, the prelude of a waltz: and when the side door closed again the listener could hear the faint rhythm of the music. The sentiment of the opening bars, their languor and supple movement, evoked the incommunicable emotion which had been the cause of all his day's unrest and of his impatient movement of a moment before. His unrest issued from him like a wave of sound: and on the tide of flowing music the ark was journeying, trailing her cables of lanterns in her wake. Then a noise like dwarf artillery broke the movement. It was the clapping that greeted the entry of the dumb bell team on the stage.

At the far end of the shed near the street a speck of pink light showed in the darkness and as he walked towards it he became aware of a faint aromatic odour. Two boys were standing in the shelter of a doorway, smoking, and before he reached them he had recognised Heron by his voice.

—Here comes the noble Dedalus! cried a high throaty voice. Welcome to our trusty friend!

This welcome ended in a soft peal of mirthless laughter as Heron salaamed and then began to poke the ground with his cane.

—Here I am, said Stephen, halting and glancing from Heron to his friend.

The latter was a stranger to him but in the darkness, by the aid of the glowing cigarette tips, he could make out a pale dandyish face, over which a smile was travelling slowly, a tall overcoated figure and a hard hat. Heron did not trouble himself about an introduction but said instead:

—I was just telling my friend Wallis what a lark it would be tonight if you took off the rector in the part of the schoolmaster. It would be a ripping good joke.

Heron made a poor attempt to imitate for his friend Wallis the rector's pedantic bass and then, laughing at his failure, asked Stephen to do it.

—Go on, Dedalus, he urged, you can take him off rippingly. *He that will not hear the churcha let him be to theea as the heathena and the publicana.*

The imitation was prevented by a mild expression of anger from Wallis in whose mouthpiece the cigarette had become too tightly wedged.

—Damn this blankety blank holder, he said, taking it from his mouth and smiling and frowning upon it tolerantly. It's always getting stuck like that. Do you use a holder?

—I don't smoke, answered Stephen.

—No, said Heron, Dedalus is a model youth. He doesn't smoke and he doesn't go to bazaars and he doesn't flirt and he doesn't damn anything or damn all.

Stephen shook his head and smiled in his rival's flushed and mobile face, beaked like a bird's. He had often thought it strange that Vincent Heron had a bird's face as well as a bird's name. A shock of pale hair lay on the forehead like a ruffled crest: the forehead was narrow and bony and a thin hooked nose stood out between the closeset prominent eyes which were light and inexpressive. The rivals were school friends. They sat together in class, knelt together in the chapel, talked together after beads over their lunches. As the fellows in number one were undistinguished dullards Stephen and Heron had been during the year the virtual heads of the school. It was they who went up to the rector together to ask for a free day or to get a fellow off.

—O by the way, said Heron suddenly, I saw your governor going in.

The smile waned on Stephen's face. Any allusion made to his father by a fellow or by a master put his calm to rout in a moment. He waited in timorous silence to hear what Heron might say next. Heron, however, nudged him expressively with his elbow and said:

—You're a sly dog.

—Why so? said Stephen.

—You'd think butter wouldn't melt in your mouth, said Heron. But I'm afraid you're a sly dog.

—Might I ask you what you are talking about? said Stephen urbanely.

—Indeed you might, answered Heron. We saw her, Wallis, didn't we? And deucedly pretty she is too. And inquisitive! *And what part does Stephen take, Mr. Dedalus? And will Stephen not sing, Mr. Dedalus?* Your governor was staring at her through that eyeglass of his for all he was worth so that I think the old man has found you out too. I wouldn't care a bit, by Jove. She's ripping, isn't she. Wallis?

—Not half bad, answered Wallis quietly as he placed his holder once more in a corner of his mouth.

A shaft of momentary anger flew through Stephen's mind at these indelicate allusions in the hearing of a stranger. For him there was nothing amusing in a girl's interest and regard. All day he had thought of nothing but their leavetaking on the steps of the tram at Harold's Cross, the stream of moody emotions it had made to course through him, and the poem he had written about it. All day he had imagined a new meeting with her for he knew that she was to come to the play. The old restless moodiness had again filled his breast as it had done on the night of the party but had not found an outlet in verse. The growth and knowledge of two years of boyhood stood between them and now, forbidding such an outlet: and all day the stream of gloomy tenderness within him had started forth and returned upon itself in dark courses and eddies, wearying him in the end until the pleasantry of the prefect and the painted little boy had drawn from him a movement of impatience.

—So you may as well admit, Heron went on, that we've fairly found you out this time. You can't play the saint on me any more, that's one sure five.

A soft peal of mirthless laughter escaped from his lips and, bending down as before, he struck Stephen lightly across the calf of the leg with his cane, as if in jesting reproof.

Stephen's movement of anger had already passed. He was neither flattered nor confused but simply wished the banter to end. He scarcely resented what had seemed to him a silly indelicateness for he knew that the adventure in his mind stood in no danger from these words: and his face mirrored his rival's false smile.

—Admit! repeated Heron, striking him again with his cane across the calf of the leg.

The stroke was playful but not so lightly given as the first one had been. Stephen felt the skin tingle and glow slightly and almost painlessly; and, bowing submissively, as if to meet his companion's jesting mood, began to recite the *Confiteor*. The episode ended well for both Heron and Wallis laughed indulgently at the irreverence.

The confession came only from Stephen's lips and, while they spoke the words, a sudden memory had carried him to another scene called up, as if by magic, at the moment when he had noted the faint cruel dimples at the corners of Heron's smiling lips and had felt the familiar stroke of the cane against his calf and had heard the familiar word of admonition:

—Admit.

It was towards the close of his first term in the college when he was in number six. His sensitive nature was still smarting under the lashes of an undivined and squalid way of life. His soul was still disquieted and cast down by the dull phenomenon of Dublin. He had emerged from a two years' spell of reverie to find himself in the midst of a new scene, every event and figure of which affected him intimately, disheartened him or allured and, whether alluring or disheartening, filled him always with unrest and bitter thoughts. All the leisure which his school life left him was passed in the company of subversive writers whose gibes and violence of speech set up a ferment in his brain before they passed out of it into his crude writings.

The essay was for him the chief labour of his week and every Tuesday, as he marched from home to the school, he read his fate in the incidents of the way, pitting himself against some figure ahead of him and quickening his pace to outstrip it before a certain goal was reached or planting his steps scrupulously in the spaces of the patchwork of the pathway and telling himself that he would be first and not first in the weekly essay.

On a certain Tuesday the course of his triumphs was rudely broken. Mr. Tate, the English master, pointed his finger at him and said bluntly:

—This fellow has heresy in his essay.

A hush fell on the class. Mr. Tate did not break it but dug with his hand between his thighs while his heavily starched linen creaked about his neck and wrists. Stephen did not look up. It was a raw spring morning and his eyes were still smarting and weak. He was conscious of failure and of detection, of the squalor of his own mind and home, and felt against his neck the raw edge of his turned and jagged collar.

A short loud laugh from Mr. Tate set the class more at ease.

—Perhaps you didn't know that, he said.

—Where? asked Stephen.

Mr. Tate withdrew his delving hand and spread out the essay.

—Here. It's about the Creator and the soul. Rrm . . . rrm . . . rrm. . . . Ah! *without a possibility of ever approaching nearer*. That's heresy.

Stephen murmured:

—I meant *without a possibility of ever reaching*.

It was a submission and Mr. Tate, appeased, folded up the essay and passed it across to him, saying:

—O . . . Ah! *ever reaching*. That's another story.

But the class was not so soon appeased. Though nobody spoke to him of the affair after class he could feel about him a vague general malignant joy.

A few nights after this public chiding he was walking with a letter along the Drumcondra Road when he heard a voice cry:

—Halt!

He turned and saw three boys of his own class coming towards him in the dusk. It was Heron who had called out and, as he marched forward between his two attendants, he cleft the air before him with a thin cane, in time to their steps. Boland, his friend, marched beside him, a large grin on his face, while Nash came on a few steps behind, blowing from the pace and wagging his great red head.

As soon as the boys had turned into Clonliffe Road together they began to speak about books and writers, saying what books they were reading and how many books there were in their fathers' bookcases at home. Stephen listened to them in some wonderment for Boland was the dunce and Nash the idler of the class. In fact after some talk about their favourite writers Nash declared for Captain Marryat who, he said, was the greatest writer.

—Fudge! said Heron. Ask Dedalus. Who is the greatest writer, Dedalus?

Stephen noted the mockery in the question and said:

—Of prose do you mean?

—Yes.

—Newman, I think.

—Is it Cardinal Newman? asked Boland.

—Yes, answered Stephen.

The grin broadened on Nash's freckled face as he turned to Stephen and said:

—And do you like Cardinal Newman, Dedalus?

—O, many say that Newman has the best prose style, Heron said to the other two in explanation; of course he's not a poet.

—And who is the best poet, Heron? asked Boland.

—Lord Tennyson, of course, answered Heron.

—O, yes, Lord Tennyson, said Nash. We have all his poetry at home in a book.

At this Stephen forgot the silent vows he had been making and burst out:

—Tennyson a poet! Why, he's only a rhymester!

—O, get out! said Heron. Everyone knows that Tennyson is the greatest poet.

—And who do you think is the greatest poet? asked Boland, nudging his neighbour.

—Byron, of course, answered Stephen.

Heron gave the lead and all three joined in a scornful laugh.

—What are you laughing at? asked Stephen.

—You, said Heron. Byron the greatest poet! He's only a poet for uneducated people.

—He must be a fine poet! said Boland.

—You may keep your mouth shut, said Stephen, turning on him boldly. All you know about poetry is what you wrote up on the slates in the yard and were going to be sent to the loft for.

Boland, in fact, was said to have written on the slates in the yard a couplet about a classmate of his who often rode home from the college on a pony:

> *As Tyson was riding into Jerusalem*
> *He fell and hurt his Alec Kafoozelum.*

This thrust put the two lieutenants to silence but Heron went on:

—In any case Byron was a heretic and immoral too.

—I don't care what he was, cried Stephen hotly.

—You don't care whether he was a heretic or not? said Nash.

—What do you know about it? shouted Stephen. You never read a line of anything in your life except a trans or Boland either.

—I know that Byron was a bad man, said Boland.

—Here, catch hold of this heretic, Heron called out.

In a moment Stephen was a prisoner.

—Tate made you buck up the other day, Heron went on, about the heresy in your essay.

—I'll tell him tomorrow, said Boland.

—Will you? said Stephen. You'd be afraid to open your lips.

—Afraid?

—Ay. Afraid of your life.

—Behave yourself! cried Heron, cutting at Stephen's legs with his cane.

It was the signal for their onset. Nash pinioned his arms behind while Boland seized a long cabbage stump which was lying in the gutter. Struggling and kicking under the cuts of the cane and the blows of the knotty stump Stephen was borne back against a barbed wire fence.

—Admit that Byron was no good.

—No.

—Admit.

—No.

—Admit.

—No. No.

At last after a fury of plunges he wrenched himself free. His tormentors set off towards Jones's Road, laughing and jeering at him, while he, half blinded with tears, stumbled on, clenching his fists madly and sobbing.

While he was still repeating the *Confiteor* amid the indulgent laughter of his hearers and while the scenes of that malignant episode were still passing sharply and swiftly before his mind he wondered why he bore no malice now to those who had tormented him. He had not forgotten a whit of their cowardice and cruelty but the memory of it called forth no anger from him. All the description of fierce love and hatred which he had met in books had seemed to him therefore unreal. Even that night as he stumbled homewards along Jones's Road he had felt that some power was divesting him of that sudden woven anger as easily as a fruit is divested of its soft ripe peel.

He remained standing with his two companions at the end of the shed listening idly to their talk or to the bursts of applause in the theatre. She was sitting there among the others perhaps waiting for him to appear. He tried to recall her appearance but could not. He could remember only that she had worn a shawl about her head like a cowl and that her dark eyes had invited and unnerved him. He wondered had he been in her thoughts as she had been in his. Then in the dark and unseen by the other two he rested the tips of the fingers of one hand upon the palm of the other hand, scarcely touching it lightly. But the pressure of her fingers had been lighter and steadier: and suddenly the memory of their touch traversed his brain and body like an invisible wave.

A boy came towards them, running along under the shed. He was excited and breathless.

—O, Dedalus, he cried, Doyle is in a great bake about you. You're to go in at once and get dressed for the play. Hurry up, you better.

—He's coming now, said Heron to the messenger with a haughty drawl, when he wants to.

The boy turned to Heron and repeated:

—But Doyle is in an awful bake.

—Will you tell Doyle with my best compliments that I damned his eyes? answered Heron.

—Well, I must go now, said Stephen, who cared little for such points of honour.

—I wouldn't, said Heron, damn me if I would. That's no way to send for one of the senior boys. In a bake, indeed! I think it's quite enough that you're taking a part in his bally old play.

This spirit of quarrelsome comradeship which he had observed lately in his rival had not seduced Stephen from his habits of quiet obedience. He mistrusted the turbulence and doubted the sincerity of such comradeship which seemed to him a sorry anticipation of manhood. The question of honour here raised was, like all such questions, trivial to him. While his mind had been pursuing its intangible phantoms and turning in irresolution from such pursuit he had heard about him the constant voices of his father and of his masters, urging him to be a gentleman above all things and urging him to be a good catholic above all things. These voices had now come to be hollow sounding in his ears. When the gymnasium had been opened he had heard another voice urging him to be strong and manly and healthy and when the movement towards national revival had begun to be felt in the college yet another voice had bidden him be true to his country and help to raise up her language and tradition. In the profane world, as he foresaw, a worldly voice would bid him raise up his father's fallen state by his labours and, meanwhile, the voice of his school-comrades urged him to be a decent fellow, to shield others from blame or to beg them off and to do his best to get free days for the school. And it was the din of all these hollowsounding voices that made him halt irresolutely in the pursuit of phantoms. He gave them ear only for a time but he was happy only when he was far from them, beyond their call, alone or in the company of phantasmal comrades.

In the vestry a plump freshfaced jesuit and an elderly man, in shabby blue clothes, were dabbling in a case of paints and chalks. The boys who had been painted walked about or stood still awkwardly, touching their faces in a gingerly fashion with their furtive fingertips. In the middle of the vestry a young jesuit, who was then on a visit to the college, stood rocking himself rhythmically from the tips of his toes to his heels and back again, his hands thrust well forward into his side pockets. His small head set off with glossy red curls and his newly shaven face agreed well with the spotless decency of his soutane and with his spotless shoes.

As he watched this swaying form and tried to read for himself the legend of the priest's mocking smile there came into Stephen's memory a saying which he had heard from his father before he had been sent to Clongowes, that you could always tell a jesuit by the style of his clothes. At the same moment he thought he saw a likeness between his father's mind and that of this smiling welldressed priest: and he was aware of some desecration of the priest's office or of the vestry itself whose silence was now routed by loud talk and joking and its air pungent with the smells of the gasjets and the grease.

While his forehead was being wrinkled and his jaws painted black and blue by the elderly man he listened distractedly to the voice of the plump young jesuit which bade him speak up and make his points clearly. He could hear the band playing *The Lily of Killarney* and knew that in a few moments the curtain would go up. He felt no stage fright but the thought of the part he had to play humiliated him. A remembrance of some of his lines made a sudden flush rise to his painted cheeks. He saw her serious alluring eyes watching him from among the audience and their image at once swept away his scruples, leaving his will compact. Another nature seemed to have been lent him: the infection of the excitement and youth about him entered into and transformed his moody mistrustfulness. For one rare moment he seemed to be clothed in the real apparel of boyhood: and, as he stood in the wings among the other players, he shared the common mirth amid which the drop scene was hauled upwards by two ablebodied priests with violent jerks and all awry.

A few moments after he found himself on the stage amid the garish gas and the dim scenery, acting before the innumerable faces of the void. It surprised him to see that the play which he had known at rehearsals for a disjointed lifeless thing had suddenly assumed a life of its own. It seemed now to play itself, he and his fellow actors aiding it with their parts. When the curtain fell on the last scene he heard the void filled with applause and, through a rift in a side scene, saw the simple body before which he had acted magically deformed, the void of faces breaking at all points and falling asunder into busy groups.

He left the stage quickly and rid himself of his mummery and passed out through the chapel into the college garden. Now that the play was over his nerves cried for some further adventure. He hurried onwards as if to overtake it. The doors of the theatre were all open and the audience had emptied out. On the lines which he had fancied the moorings of an ark a few lanterns swung in the night breeze, flickering cheerlessly. He mounted the steps from the garden in haste, eager that some prey should not elude him, and forced his way through the crowd in the hall and past the two jesuits who stood watching the exodus and bowing and shaking hands with the visitors. He pushed onward nervously, feigning a still greater haste and faintly conscious of the smiles and stares and nudges which his powdered head left in its wake.

When he came out on the steps he saw his family waiting for him at the first lamp. In a glance he noted that every figure of the group was familiar and ran down the steps angrily.

—I have to leave a message down in George's Street, he said to his father quickly. I'll be home after you.

Without waiting for his father's questions he ran across the road and began to walk at breakneck speed down the hill. He hardly knew where he was walking. Pride and hope and desire like crushed herbs in his heart sent up vapours of maddening incense before the eyes of his mind. He strode down the hill amid the tumult of suddenrisen vapours of wounded pride and fallen hope and baffled desire. They streamed upwards before his anguished eyes in dense and maddening fumes and passed away above him till at last the air was clear and cold again.

A film still veiled his eyes but they burned no longer. A power, akin to that which had often made anger or resentment fall from him, brought his steps to rest. He stood still and gazed up at the sombre porch of the morgue and from that to the dark cobbled laneway at its side. He saw the word *Lotts* on the wall of the lane and breathed slowly the rank heavy air.

—That is horse piss and rotted straw, he thought. It is a good odour to breathe. It will calm my heart. My heart is quite calm now. I will go back.

Stephen was once again seated beside his father in the corner of a railway carriage at Kingsbridge. He was travelling with his father by the night mail to Cork. As the train steamed out of the station he recalled his childish wonder of years before and every event of his first day at Clongowes. But he felt no wonder now. He saw the darkening lands slipping away past him, the silent telegraphpoles passing his window swiftly every four seconds, the little glimmering stations, manned by a few silent sentries, flung by the mail behind her and twinkling for a moment in the darkness like fiery grains flung backwards by a runner.

He listened without sympathy to his father's evocation of Cork and of scenes of his youth—a tale broken by sighs or draughts from his pocket flask whenever the image of some dead friend appeared in it, or whenever the evoker remembered suddenly the purpose of his actual visit. Stephen heard, but could feel no pity. The images of the dead were all strangers to him save that of uncle Charles, an image which had lately been fading out of memory. He knew, however, that his father's property was going to be sold by auction and in the manner of his own dispossession he felt the world give the lie rudely to his phantasy.

At Maryborough he fell asleep. When he awoke the train had passed out of Mallow and his father was stretched asleep on the other seat. The cold light of the dawn lay over the country, over the unpeopled fields and the closed cottages. The terror of sleep fascinated his mind as he watched the silent country or heard from time to time his father's deep breath or sudden sleepy movement. The neighbourhood of unseen sleepers filled him with strange dread, as though they could harm him, and he prayed that the day might come quickly. His prayer, addressed neither to God nor saint, began with a shiver, as the chilly morning breeze crept through the chink of the carriage door to his feet, and ended in a trail of foolish words which he made to fit the insistent rhythm of the train; and silently, at intervals of four seconds, the telegraphpoles held the galloping notes of the music between punctual bars. This furious music allayed his dread and, leaning against the window ledge, he let his eyelids close again.

They drove in a jingle across Cork while it was still early morning and Stephen finished his sleep in a bedroom of the Victoria Hotel. The bright warm sunlight was streaming through the window and he could hear the din of traffic. His father was standing before the dressingtable, examining his hair and face and moustache with great care, craning his neck across the water jug and drawing it back sideways to see the better. While he did so he sang softly to himself with quaint accent and phrasing:

"'Tis youth and folly
  Makes young men marry,
  So here, my love, I'll
    No longer stay.
  What can't be cured, sure,
  Must be injured, sure,
    So I'll go to Amerikay.

"My love she's handsome,
  My love she's bony:
  She's like good whisky
    When it is new;
  But when 'tis old
  And growing cold
  It fades and dies like
    The mountain dew."

The consciousness of the warm sunny city outside his window and the tender tremors with which his father's voice festooned the strange sad happy air, drove off all the mists of the night's ill humour from Stephen's brain. He got up quickly to dress and, when the song had ended, said:

—That's much prettier than any of your other *come-all-yous*.

—I like it, said Stephen.

—It's a pretty old air, said Mr. Dedalus, twirling the points of his moustache. Ah, but you should have heard Mick Lacy sing it! Poor Mick Lacy! He had little turns for it, grace notes he used to put in that I haven't got. That was the boy who could sing a *come-all-you,* if you like.

Mr. Dedalus had ordered drisheens for breakfast and during the meal he cross-examined the waiter for local news. For the most part they spoke at cross purposes when a name was mentioned, the waiter having in mind the present holder and Mr. Dedalus his father or perhaps his grandfather.

Well, I hope they haven't moved the Queen's College anyhow, said Mr. Dedalus, for I want to show it to this youngster of mine.

Along the Mardyke the trees were in bloom. They entered the grounds of the college and were led by the garrulous porter across the quadrangle. But their progress across the gravel was brought to a halt after every dozen or so paces by some reply of the porter's—

—Ah, do you tell me so? And is poor Pottlebelly dead?

—Yes, sir. Dead, sir.

During these halts Stephen stood awkwardly behind the two men, weary of the subject and waiting restlessly for the slow march to begin again. By the time they had crossed the quadrangle his restlessness had risen to fever. He wondered how his father, whom he knew for a shrewd suspicious man, could be duped by the servile manners of the porter; and the lively southern speech which had entertained him all the morning now irritated his ears.

They passed into the anatomy theatre where Mr. Dedalus, the porter aiding him, searched the desks for his initials. Stephen remained in the background, depressed more than ever by the darkness and silence of the theatre and by the air it wore of jaded and formal study. On the desk he read the word Fœtus cut several times in the dark stained wood. The sudden legend startled his blood: he seemed to feel the absent students of the college about him and to shrink from their company. A vision of their life, which his father's words had been powerless to evoke, sprang up before him out of the word cut in the desk. A broad shouldered student with a moustache was cutting in the letters with a jack knife, seriously. Other students stood or sat near him laughing at his handiwork. One jogged his elbow. The big student turned on him, frowning. He was dressed in loose grey clothes and had tan boots.

Stephen's name was called. He hurried down the steps of the theatre so as to be as far away from the vision as he could be and, peering closely at his father's initials, hid his flushed face.

But the word and the vision capered before his eyes as he walked back across the quadrangle and towards the college gate. It shocked him to find in the outer world a trace of what he had deemed till then a brutish and individual malady of his own mind. His monstrous reveries came thronging into his memory. They too had sprung up before him, suddenly and furiously, out of mere words. He had soon given in to them, and allowed them to sweep across and abase his intellect, wondering always where they came from, from what den of monstrous images, and always weak and humble towards others, restless and sickened of himself when they had swept over him.

—Ay, bedad! And there's the Groceries sure enough! cried Mr. Dedalus. You often heard me speak of the Groceries, didn't you, Stephen. Many's the time we went down there when our names had been marked, a crowd of us, Harry Peard and little Jack Mountain and Bob Dyas and Maurice Moriarty, the Frenchman, and Tom O'Grady and Mick Lacy that I told you of this morning and Joey Corbet and poor little good hearted Johnny Keevers of the Tantiles.

The leaves of the trees along the Mardyke were astir and whispering in the sunlight. A team of cricketers passed, agile young men in flannels and blazers, one of them carrying the long green wicket bag. In a quiet by street a German band of five players in faded uniforms and with battered brass instruments was playing to an audience of street arabs and leisurely messenger boys. A maid in a white cap and apron was watering a box of plants on a sill which shone like a slab of limestone in the warm glare. From another window open to the air came the sound of a piano, scale after scale rising into the treble.

Stephen walked on at his father's side, listening to stories he had heard before, hearing again the names of the scattered and dead revellers who had been the companions of his father's youth. And a faint sickness sighed in his heart. He recalled his own equivocal position in Belvedere, a free boy, a leader afraid of his own authority, proud and sensitive and suspicious, battling against the squalor of his life and against the riot of his mind. The letters cut in the stained wood of the desk stared upon him, mocking his bodily weakness and futile enthusiasms and making him loathe himself for his own mad and filthy orgies. The spittle in his throat grew bitter and foul to swallow and the faint sickness climbed to his brain so that for a moment he closed his eyes and walked on in darkness.

He could still hear his father's voice—

—When you kick out for yourself, Stephen—as I daresay you will one of those days—remember, whatever you do, to mix with gentlemen. When I was a young fellow I tell you I enjoyed myself. I mixed with fine decent fellows. Everyone of us could do something. One fellow had a good voice, another fellow was a good actor, another could sing a good comic song, another was a good oarsman or a good racket player, another could tell a good story and so on. We kept the ball rolling anyhow and enjoyed ourselves and saw a bit of life and we were none the worse of it either. But we were all gentlemen, Stephen—at least I hope we were—and bloody good honest Irishmen too. That's the kind of fellows I want you to associate with, fellows of the right kidney. I'm talking to you as a friend, Stephen. I don't believe a son should be afraid of his father. No, I treat you as your grandfather treated me when I was a young chap. We were more like brothers than father and son. I'll never forget the first day he caught me smoking. I was standing at the end of the South Terrace one day with some maneens like myself and sure we thought we were grand fellows because we had pipes stuck in the corners of our mouths. Suddenly the governor passed. He didn't say a word, or stop even. But the next day, Sunday, we were out for a walk together and when we were coming home he took out his cigar case and said:—By the by, Simon, I didn't know you smoked, or something like that. Of course I tried to carry it off as best I could. —If you want a good smoke, he said, try one of these cigars. An American captain made me a present of them last night in Queenstown.

Stephen heard his father's voice break into a laugh which was almost a sob.

—He was the handsomest man in Cork at that time, by God he was! The women used to stand to look after him in the street.

He heard the sob passing loudly down his father's throat and opened his eyes with a nervous impulse. The sunlight breaking suddenly on his sight turned the sky and clouds into a fantastic world of sombre masses with lakelike spaces of dark rosy light. His very brain was sick and powerless. He could scarcely interpret the letters of the signboards of the shops. By his monstrous way of life he seemed to have put himself beyond the limits of reality. Nothing moved him or spoke to him from the real world unless he heard in it an echo of the infuriated cries within him. He could respond to no earthly or human appeal, dumb and insensible to the call of summer and gladness and companionship, wearied and dejected by his father's voice. He could scarcely recognise as his his own thoughts, and repeated slowly to himself:

—I am Stephen Dedalus. I am walking beside my father whose name is Simon Dedalus. We are in Cork, in Ireland. Cork is a city. Our room is in the Victoria Hotel. Victoria and Stephen and Simon. Simon and Stephen and Victoria. Names.

The memory of his childhood suddenly grew dim. He tried to call forth some of its vivid moments but could not. He recalled only names. Dante, Parnell, Clane, Clongowes. A little boy had been taught geography by an old woman who kept two brushes in her wardrobe. Then he had been sent away from home to a college, he had made his first communion and eaten slim jim out of his cricket cap and watched the firelight leaping and dancing on the wall of a little bedroom in the infirmary and dreamed of being dead, of mass being said for him by the rector in a black and gold cope, of being buried then in the little graveyard of the community off the main avenue of lines. But he had not died then. Parnell had died. There had been no mass for the dead in the chapel, and no procession. He had not died but he had faded out like a film in the sun. He had been lost or had wandered out of existence for he no longer existed. How strange to think of him passing out of existence in such a way, not by death, but by fading out in the sun or by being lost and forgotten somewhere in the universe! It was strange to see his small body appear again for a moment: a little boy in a grey belted suit. His hands were in his side pockets and his trousers were tucked in at the knees by elastic bands.

On the evening of the day on which the property was sold Stephen followed his father meekly about the city from bar to bar. To the sellers in the market, to the barmen and barmaids, to the beggars who importuned him for a lob Mr. Dedalus told the same tale, that he was an old Corkonian, that he had been trying for thirty years to get rid of his Cork accent up in Dublin and that Peter Pickackafax beside him was his eldest son but that he was only a Dublin jackeen.

They had set out early in the morning from Newcombe's coffeehouse, where Mr. Dedalus' cup had rattled noisily against its saucer, and Stephen had tried to cover that shameful sign of his father's drinking-bout of the night before by moving his chair and coughing. One humiliation had succeeded another—the false smiles of the market sellers, the curvetings and oglings of the barmaids with whom his father flirted, the compliments and encouraging words of his father's friends. They had told him that he had a great look of his grandfather and Mr. Dedalus had agreed that he was an ugly likeness. They had unearthed traces of a Cork accent in his speech and made him admit that the Lee was a much finer river than the Liffey. One of them, in order to put his Latin to the proof, had made him translate short passages from Dilectus, and asked him whether it was correct to say: *Tempora mutantur nos et mutamur in illis,* or *Tempora mutantur et nos mutamur in illis.* Another, a brisk old man, whom Mr. Dedalus called Johnny Cashman, had covered him with confusion by asking him to say which were prettier, the Dublin girls or the Cork girls.

—He's not that way built, said Mr. Dedalus. Leave him alone. He's a level-headed thinking boy who doesn't bother his head about that kind of nonsense.

—Then he's not his father's son, said the little old man.

—I don't know, I'm sure, said Mr. Dedalus, smiling complacently.

—Your father, said the little old man to Stephen, was the boldest flirt in the city of Cork in his day. Do you know that?

Stephen looked down and studied the tiled floor of the bar into which they had drifted.

—Now don't be putting ideas into his head, said Mr. Dedalus. Leave him to his Maker.

—Yerra, sure I wouldn't put any ideas into his head. I'm old enough to be his grandfather. And I am a grandfather, said the little old man to Stephen. Do you know that?

—Are you? asked Stephen.

—Bedad I am, said the little old man. I have two bouncing grandchildren out at Sunday's Well. Now, then! What age do you think I am! And I remember seeing your grandfather in his red coat riding out to hounds. That was before you were born.

—Ay, or thought of, said Mr. Dedalus.

—Bedad I did, repeated the little old man. And, more than that, I can remember even your great grandfather, old John Stephen Dedalus, and a fierce old fire-eater he was. Now, then! There's a memory for you!

—That's three generations—four generations, said another of the company. Why, Johnny Cashman, you must be nearing the century.

—Well, I'll tell you the truth, said the little old man. I'm just twentyseven years of age.

—We're as old as we feel, Johnny, said Mr. Dedalus.

—And just finish what you have there, and we'll have another. Here, Tim or Tom or whatever your name is, give us the same again here. By God, I don't feel more than eighteen myself. There's that son of mine there not half my age and I'm a better man than he is any day of the week.

—Draw it mild now, Dedalus. I think it's time for you to take a back seat, said the gentleman who had spoken before.

—No, by God! asserted Mr. Dedalus. I'll sing a tenor song against him or I'll vault a fire-barred gate against him or I'll run with him after the hounds across the country as I did thirty years ago along with the Kerry Boy and the best man for it.

—But he'll beat you here, said the little old man, tapping his forehead and raising his glass to drain it.

—Well, I hope he'll be as good a man as his father. That's all I can say, said Mr. Dedalus.

—If he is, he'll do, said the little old man.

—And thanks be to God, Johnny, said Mr. Dedalus, that we lived so long and did so little harm.

—But did so much good, Simon, said the little old man gravely. Thanks be to God we lived so long and did so much good.

Stephen watched the three glasses being raised from the counter as his father and his two cronies drank to the memory of their past. An abyss of fortune or of temperament sundered him from them. His mind seemed older than theirs: it shone coldly on their strifes and happiness and regrets like a moon upon a younger earth. No life or youth stirred in him as it had stirred in them. He had known neither the pleasure of companionship with others nor the vigour of rude male health nor filial piety. Nothing stirred within his soul but a cold and cruel and loveless lust. His childhood was dead or lost and with it his soul capable of simple joys and he was drifting amid life like the barren shell of the moon.

> "Art thou pale for weariness
> Of climbing heaven and gazing on the earth,
> Wandering companionless?..."

He repeated to himself the lines of Shelley's fragment. Its alternation of sad human ineffectualness with vast inhuman cycles of activity chilled him, and he forgot his own human and ineffectual grieving.

✧

Stephen's mother and his brother and one of his cousins waited at the corner of quiet Foster Place while he and his father went up the steps and along the colonnade where the Highland sentry was parading. When they had passed into the great hall and stood at the counter Stephen drew forth his orders on the governor of the bank of Ireland for thirty and three pounds; and these sums, the moneys of his exhibition and essay prize, were paid over to him rapidly by the teller in notes and in coin respectively. He bestowed them in his pockets with feigned composure and suffered the friendly teller, to whom his father chatted, to take his hand across the broad counter and wish him a brilliant career in after life. He was impatient of their voices and could not keep his feet at rest. But the teller still deferred the serving of others to say he was living in changed times and that there was nothing like giving a boy the best education that money could buy. Mr. Dedalus lingered in the hall gazing about him and up at the roof and telling Stephen, who urged him to come out, that they were standing in the house of commons of the old Irish parliament.

—God help us! he said piously, to think of the men of those times, Stephen, Hely Hutchinson and Flood and Henry Grattan and Charles Kendal Bushe, and the noblemen we have now, leaders of the Irish people at home and abroad. Why, by God, they wouldn't be seen dead in a ten acre field with them. No, Stephen, old chap, I'm sorry to say that they are only as I roved out one fine May morning in the merry month of sweet July.

A keen October wind was blowing round the bank. The three figures standing at the edge of the muddy path had pinched cheeks and watery eyes. Stephen looked at his thinly clad mother and remembered that a few days before he had seen a mantle priced at twenty guineas in the windows of Barnardo's.

—Well that's done, said Mr. Dedalus.

—We had better go to dinner, said Stephen. Where?

—Dinner? said Mr. Dedalus. Well, I suppose we had better, what?

—Some place that's not too dear, said Mrs. Dedalus.

—Underdone's?

—Yes. Some quiet place.

—Come along, said Stephen quickly. It doesn't matter about the dearness.

He walked on before them with short nervous steps, smiling. They tried to keep up with him, smiling also at his eagerness.

—Take it easy like a good young fellow, said his father. We're not out for the half mile, are we?

For a swift season of merrymaking the money of his prizes ran through Stephen's fingers. Great parcels of groceries and delicacies and dried fruits arrived from the city. Every day he drew up a bill of fare for the family and every night led a party of three or four to the theatre to see *Ingomar* or *The Lady of Lyons.* In his coat pockets he carried squares of Vienna chocolate for his guests while his trousers' pockets bulged with masses of silver and copper coins. He bought presents for everyone, overhauled his room, wrote out resolutions, marshalled his books up and down their shelves, pored upon all kinds of price lists, drew up a form of commonwealth for the household by which every member of it held some office, opened a loan bank for his family and pressed loans on willing borrowers so that he might have the pleasure of making out receipts and reckoning the interests on the sums lent. When he could do no more he drove up and down the city in trams. Then the season of pleasure came to an end. The pot of pink enamel paint gave out and the wainscot of his bedroom remained with its unfinished and ill plastered coat.

His household returned to its usual way of life. His mother had no further occasion to upbraid him for squandering his money. He, too, returned to his old life at school and all his novel enterprises fell to pieces. The commonwealth fell, the loan bank closed its coffers and its books on a sensible loss, the rules of life which he had drawn about himself fell into desuetude.

How foolish his aim had been! He had tried to build a breakwater of order and elegance against the sordid tide of life without him and to dam up, by rules of conduct and active interests and new filial relations, the powerful recurrence of the tide within him. Useless. From without as from within the water had flowed over his barriers: their tides began once more to jostle fiercely above the crumbled mole.

He saw clearly, too, his own futile isolation. He had not gone one step nearer the lives he had sought to approach nor bridged the restless shame and rancour that had divided him from mother and brother and sister. He felt that he was hardly of the one blood with them but stood to them rather in the mystical kinship of fosterage, foster child and foster brother.

He turned to appease the fierce longings of his heart before which everything else was idle and alien. He cared little that he was in mortal sin, that his life had grown to be a tissue of subterfuge and falsehood. Beside the savage desire within him to realise the enormities which he brooded on nothing was sacred. He bore cynically with the shameful details of his secret riots in which he exulted to defile with patience whatever image had attracted his eyes. By day and by night he moved among distorted images of the outer world. A figure that had seemed to him by day demure and innocent came towards him by night through the winding darkness of sleep, her face transfigured by a lecherous cunning, her eyes bright with brutish joy. Only the morning pained him with its dim memory of dark orgiastic riot, its keen and humiliating sense of transgression.

He returned to his wanderings. The veiled autumnal evenings led him from street to street as they had led him years before along the quiet avenues of Blackrock. But no vision of trim front gardens or of kindly lights in the windows poured a tender influence upon him now. Only at times, in the pauses of his desire, when the luxury that was wasting him gave room to a softer languor, the image of Mercedes traversed the background of his memory. He saw again the small white house and the garden of rosebushes on the road that led to the mountains and he remembered the sadly proud gesture of refusal which he was to make there, standing with her in the moonlit garden after years of estrangement and adventure. At those moments the soft speeches of Claude Melnotte rose to his lips and eased his unrest. A tender premonition touched him of the tryst he had then looked forward to and, in spite of the horrible reality which lay between his hope of then and now, of the holy encounter he had then imagined at which weakness and timidity and inexperience were to fall from him.

Such moments passed and the wasting fires of lust sprang up again. The verses passed from his lips and the inarticulate cries and the unspoken brutal words rushed forth from his brain to force a passage. His blood was in revolt. He wandered up and down the dark slimy streets peering into the gloom of lanes and doorways, listening eagerly for any sound. He moaned to himself like some baffled prowling beast. He wanted to sin with another of his kind, to force another being to sin with him and to exult with her in sin. He felt some dark presence moving irresistibly upon him from the darkness, a presence subtle and murmurous as a flood filling him wholly with itself. Its murmur besieged his ears like the murmur of some multitude in sleep; its subtle streams penetrated his being. His hands clenched convulsively and his teeth set together as he suffered the agony of its penetration. He stretched out his arms in the street to hold fast the frail swooning form that eluded him and incited him: and the cry that he had strangled for so long in his throat issued from his lips. It broke from him like a wail of despair from a hell of sufferers and died in a wail of furious entreaty, a cry for an iniquitous abandonment, a cry which was but the echo of an obscene scrawl which he had read on the oozing wall of a urinal.

He had wandered into a maze of narrow and dirty streets. From the foul laneways he heard bursts of hoarse riot and wrangling and the drawling of drunken singers. He walked onward, undismayed, wondering whether he had strayed into the quarter of the Jews. Women and girls dressed in long vivid gowns traversed the street from house to house. They were leisurely and perfumed. A trembling seized him and his eyes grew dim. The yellow gasflames arose before his troubled vision against the vapoury sky, burning as if before an altar. Before the doors and in the lighted halls groups were gathered arrayed as for some rite. He was in another world: he had awakened from a slumber of centuries.

He stood still in the middle of the roadway, his heart clamouring against his bosom in a tumult. A young woman dressed in a long pink gown laid her hand on his arm to detain him and gazed into his face. She said gaily:

—Good night, Willie dear!

Her room was warm and lightsome. A huge doll sat with her legs apart in the copious easychair beside the bed. He tried to bid his tongue speak that he might seem at ease, watching her as she undid her gown, noting the proud conscious movements of her perfumed head.

As he stood silent in the middle of the room she came over to him and embraced him gaily and gravely. Her round arms held him firmly to her and he, seeing her face lifted to him in serious calm and feeling the warm calm rise and fall of her breast, all but burst into hysterical weeping. Tears of joy and relief shone in his delighted eyes and his lips parted though they would not speak.

She passed her tinkling hand through his hair, calling him a little rascal.

—Give me a kiss, she said.

His lips would not bend to kiss her. He wanted to be held firmly in her arms, to be caressed slowly, slowly, slowly. In her arms he felt that he had suddenly become strong and fearless and sure of himself. But his lips would not bend to kiss her.

With a sudden movement she bowed his head and joined her lips to his and he read the meaning of her movements in her frank uplifted eyes. It was too much for him. He closed his eyes, surrendering himself to her, body and mind, conscious of nothing in the world but the dark pressure of her softly parting lips. They pressed upon his brain as upon his lips as though they were the vehicle of a vague speech; and between them he felt an unknown and timid pressure, darker than the swoon of sin, softer than sound or odour.

III

The swift December dusk had come tumbling clownishly after its dull day and as he stared through the dull square of the window of the schoolroom he felt his belly crave for its food. He hoped there would be stew for dinner, turnips and carrots and bruised potatoes and fat mutton pieces to be ladled out in thick peppered flour-fattened sauce. Stuff it into you, his belly counselled him.

It would be a gloomy secret night. After early nightfall the yellow lamps would light up, here and there, the squalid quarter of the brothels. He would follow a devious course up and down the streets, circling always nearer and nearer in a tremor of fear and joy, until his feet led him suddenly round a dark corner. The whores would be just coming out of their houses making ready for the night, yawning lazily after their sleep and settling the hairpins in their clusters of hair. He would pass by them calmly waiting for a sudden movement of his own will or a sudden call to his sin-loving soul from their soft perfumed flesh. Yet as he prowled in quest of that call, his senses, stultified only by his desire, would note keenly all that wounded or shamed them; his eyes, a ring of porter froth on a clothless table or a photograph of two soldiers standing to attention on a gaudy playbill; his ears, the drawling jargon of greeting:

—Hello, Bertie, any good in your mind?

—Is that you, pigeon?

—Number ten. Fresh Nelly is waiting on you.

—Good night, husband! Coming in to have a short time?

The equation on the page of his scribbler began to spread out a widening tail, eyed and starred like a peacock's; and, when the eyes and stars of its indices had been eliminated, began slowly to fold itself together again. The indices appearing and disappearing were eyes opening and closing; the eyes opening and closing were stars being born and being quenched. The vast cycle of starry life bore his weary mind outward to its verge and inward to its centre, a distant music accompanying him outward and inward. What music? The music came nearer and he recalled the words, the words of Shelley's fragment upon the moon wandering companionless, pale for weariness. The stars began to crumble and a cloud of fine stardust fell through space.

The dull light fell more faintly upon the page whereon another equation began to unfold itself slowly and to spread abroad its widening tail. It was his own soul going forth to experience, unfolding itself sin by sin, spreading abroad the balefire of its burning stars and folding back upon itself, fading slowly, quenching its own lights and fires. They were quenched: and the cold darkness filled chaos.

A cold lucid indifference reigned in his soul. At his first violent sin he had felt a wave of vitality pass out of him and had feared to find his body or his soul maimed by the excess. Instead the vital wave had carried him on its bosom out of himself and back again when it receded: and no part of body or soul had been maimed, but a dark peace had been established between them. The chaos in which his ardour extinguished itself was a cold indifferent knowledge of himself. He had sinned mortally not once by many times and he knew that, while he stood in danger of eternal damnation for the first sin alone, by every succeeding sin he multiplied his guilt and his punishment. His days and works and thoughts could make no atonement for him, the fountains of sanctifying grace having ceased to refresh his soul. At most, by an alms given to a beggar whose blessing he fled from, he might hope wearily to win for himself some measure of actual grace. Devotion had gone by the board. What did it avail to pray when he knew that his soul lusted after its own destruction? A certain pride, a certain awe, withheld him from offering to God even one prayer at night though he knew it was in God's power to take away his life while he slept and hurl his soul hellward ere he could beg for mercy. His pride in his own sin, his loveless awe of God, told him that his offence was too grievous to be atoned for in whole or in part by a false homage to the Allseeing and Allknowing.

—Well now, Ennis, I declare you have a head and so has my stick! Do you mean to say that you are not able to tell me what a surd is?

The blundering answer stirred the embers of his contempt of his fellows. Towards others he felt neither shame nor fear. On Sunday mornings as he passed the church door he glanced coldly at the worshippers who stood bareheaded, four deep, outside the church, morally present at the mass which they could neither see nor hear. Their dull piety and the sickly smell of the cheap hair oil with which they had anointed their heads repelled him from the altar they prayed at. He stooped to the evil of hypocrisy with others, sceptical of their innocence which he could cajole so easily.

On the wall of his bedroom hung an illuminated scroll, the certificate of his prefecture in the college of the sodality of the Blessed Virgin Mary. On Saturday mornings when the sodality met in the chapel to recite the little office his place was a cushioned kneeling-desk at the right of the altar from which he led his wing of boys through the responses. The falsehood of his position did not pain him. If at moments he felt an impulse to rise from his post of honour and, confessing before them all his unworthiness, to leave the chapel, a glance at their faces restrained him. The imagery of the psalms of prophecy soothed his barren pride. The glories of Mary held his soul captive: spikenard and myrrh and frankincense, symbolising her royal lineage, her emblems, the late-flowering plant and late-blossoming tree, symbolising the agelong gradual growth of her cultus among men. When it fell to him to read the lesson towards the close of the office he read it in a veiled voice, lulling his conscience to its music.

> *Quasi cedrus exaltata sum in Libanon et quasi cupressus in monte Sion. Quasi palma exaltata sum in Gades et quasi plantatio rosae in Jericho. Quasi uliva speciosa in campis et quasi plantanus exaltata sum juxta aquam in plateis. Sicut cinnamomum et balsamum aromatizans odorem dedi et quasi myrrha electa dedi suavitatem odoris.*

His sin, which had covered him from the sight of God, had led him nearer to the refuge of sinners. Her eyes seemed to regard him with mild pity; her holiness, a strange light glowing faintly upon her frail flesh, did not humiliate the sinner who approached her. If ever he was impelled to cast sin from him and to repent, the impulse that moved him was the wish to be her knight. If ever his soul, re-entering her dwelling shyly after the frenzy of his body's lust had spent itself, was turned towards her whose emblem is the morning star, "bright and musical, telling of heaven and infusing peace," it was when her names were murmured softly by lips whereon there still lingered foul and shameful words, the savour itself of a lewd kiss.

That was strange. He tried to think how it could be but the dusk, deepening in the schoolroom, covered over his thoughts. The bell rang. The master marked the sums and cuts to be done for the next lesson and went out. Heron, beside Stephen, began to hum tunelessly.

> *My excellent friend Bombados.*

Ennis, who had gone to the yard, came back, saying:

—The boy from the house is coming up for the rector.

A tall boy behind Stephen rubbed his hands and said:

—That's game ball. We can scut the whole hour. He won't be in till after half two. Then you can ask him questions on the catechism, Dedalus.

Stephen, leaning back and drawing idly on his scribbler, listened to the talk about him which Heron checked from time to time by saying:

—Shut up, will you. Don't make such a bally racket!

It was strange too that he found an arid pleasure in following up to the end the rigid lines of the doctrines of the church and penetrating into obscure silences only to hear and feel the more deeply his own condemnation. The sentence of Saint James which says that he who offends against one commandment becomes guilty of all had seemed to him first a swollen phrase until he had begun to grope in the darkness of his own state. From the evil seed of lust all other deadly sins had sprung forth: pride in himself and contempt of others, covetousness in using money for the purchase of unlawful pleasures, envy of those whose vices he could not reach to and calumnious murmuring against the pious, gluttonous enjoyment of food, the dull glowering anger amid which he brooded upon his longing, the swamp of spiritual and body sloth in which his whole being had sunk.

As he sat in his bench gazing calmly at the rector's shrewd harsh face his mind wound itself in and out of the curious questions proposed to it. If a man had stolen a pound in his youth and had used that pound to amass a huge fortune how much was he obliged to give back, the pound he had stolen only or the pound together with the compound interest accruing upon it or all his huge fortune? If a layman in giving baptism pour the water before saying the words is the child baptised? Is baptism with a mineral water valid? How comes it that while the first beatitude promises the kingdom of heaven to the poor of heart, the second beatitude promises also to the meek that they shall possess the land? Why was the sacrament of the eucharist instituted under the two species of bread and wine if Jesus Christ be present body and blood, soul and divinity, in the bread alone and in the wine alone? Does a tiny particle of the consecrated bread contain all the body and blood of Jesus Christ or a part only of the body and blood? If the wine change into vinegar and the host crumble into corruption after they have been consecrated, is Jesus Christ still present under the species as God and as man?

—Here he is! Here he is!

A boy from his post at the window had seen the rector come from the house. All the catechisms were opened and all heads bent upon them silently. The rector entered and took his seat on the dais. A gentle kick from the tall boy in the bench behind urged Stephen to ask a difficult question.

The rector did not ask for a catechism to hear the lesson from. He clasped his hands on the desks and said:

—The retreat will begin on Wednesday afternoon in honour of Saint Francis Xavier whose feast day is Saturday. The retreat will go on from Wednesday to Friday. On Friday confession will be heard all the afternoon after beads. If any boys have special confessors perhaps it will be better for them not to change. Mass will be on Saturday morning at nine o'clock and general communion for the whole college. Saturday will be a free day. But Saturday and Sunday being free days some boys might be inclined to think that Monday is a free day also. Beware of making that mistake. I think you, Lawless, are likely to make that mistake.

—I, sir? Why, sir?

A little wave of quiet mirth broke forth over the class of boys from the rector's grim smile. Stephen's heart began slowly to fold and fade with fear like a withering flower.

The rector went on gravely:

—You are all familiar with the story of the life of Saint Francis Xavier, I suppose, the patron of your college. He came of an old and illustrious Spanish family and you remember that he was one of the first followers of Saint Ignatius. They met in Paris where Francis Xavier was professor of philosophy at the university. This young and brilliant nobleman and man of letters entered heart and soul into the ideas of our glorious founder, and you know that he, at his own desire, was sent by Saint Ignatius to preach to the Indians. He is called, as you know, the apostle of the Indies. He went from country to country in the east, from Africa to India, from India to Japan, baptising the people. He is said to have baptised as many as ten thousand idolators in one month. It is said that his right arm had grown powerless from having been raised so often over the heads of those whom he baptised. He wished then to go to China to win still more souls for God but he died of fever on the island of Sancian. A great Saint, Saint Francis Xavier! A great soldier of God!

The rector paused and then, shaking his clasped hands before him, went on:

—He had the faith in him that moves mountains. Ten thousand souls won for God in a single month! That is a true conqueror, true to the motto of our order: *ad majorem Dei gloriam!* A saint who has great power in heaven, remember: power to intercede for us in our grief, power to obtain whatever we pray for if it be for the good of our souls, power above all to obtain for us the grace to repent if we be in sin. A great saint, Saint Francis Xavier! A great fisher of soul!

He ceased to shake his clasped hands and, resting them against his forehead, looked right and left of them keenly at his listeners out of his dark stern eyes.

In the silence their dark fire kindled the dusk into a tawny glow. Stephen's heart had withered up like a flower of the desert that feels the simoom coming from afar.

↓

—*Remember only thy last things and thou shalt not sin for ever*—words taken, my dear little brothers in Christ, from the book of Ecclesiastes, seventh chapter, fortieth verse. In the name of the Father and of the Son and the Holy Ghost. Amen.

Stephen sat in the front bench of the chapel. Father Arnall sat at a table to the left of the altar. He wore about his shoulders a heavy cloak; his pale face was drawn and his voice broken with rheum. The figure of his old master, so strangely rearisen, brought back to Stephen's mind his life at Clongowes: the wide playgrounds, swarming with boys, the square ditch, the little cemetery off the main avenue of limes where he had dreamed of being buried, the firelight on the wall of the infirmary where he lay sick, the sorrowful face of Brother Michael. His soul, as these memories came back to him, became again a child's soul.

—We are assembled here today, my dear little brothers in Christ, for one brief moment far away from the busy bustle of the outer world to celebrate and to honour one of the greatest of saints, the apostle of the Indies, the patron saint also of your college, Saint Francis Xavier. Year after year for much longer than any of you, my dear little boys, can remember or than I can remember the boys of this college have met in this very chapel to make their annual retreat before the feast day of their patron saint. Time has gone on and brought with it its changes. Even in the last few years what changes can most of you not remember? Many of the boys who sat in those front benches a few years ago are perhaps now in distant lands, in the burning tropics or immersed in professional duties or in seminaries or voyaging over the vast expanse of the deep or, it may be, already called by the great God to another life and to the rendering up of their stewardship. And still as the years roll by, bringing with them changes for good and bad, the memory of the great saint is honoured by the boys of his college who make every year their annual retreat on the days preceding the feast day set apart by our Holy Mother the Church to transmit to all the ages the name and fame of one of the greatest sons of catholic Spain.

—Now what is the meaning of this word *retreat* and why is it allowed on all hands to be a most salutory practice for all who desire to lead before God and in the eyes of men a truly Christian life? A retreat, my dear boys, signifies a withdrawal for a while from the cares of our life, the cares of this workaday world, in order to examine the state of our conscience, to reflect on the mysteries of holy religion and to understand better why we are here in this world. During these few days I intend to put before you some thoughts concerning the four last things. They are, as you know from your catechism, death, judgment, hell and heaven. We shall try to understand them fully during these few days so that we may derive from the understanding of them a lasting benefit to our souls. And remember, my dear boys, that we have been sent into this world for one thing and for one thing alone: to do God's holy will and to save our immortal souls. All else is worthless. One thing alone is needful, the salvation of one's soul. What doth it profit a man to gain the whole world if he suffer the loss of his immortal soul? Ah, my dear boys, believe me there is nothing in this wretched world that can make up for such a loss.

—I will ask you therefore, my dear boys, to put away from your minds during these few days all worldly thoughts, whether of study or pleasure or ambition, and to give all your attention to the state of your souls. I need hardly remind you that during the days of the retreat all boys are expected to preserve a quiet and pious demeanour and to shun all loud unseemly pleasure. The elder boys, of course, will see that this custom is not infringed and I look especially to the prefects and officers of the sodality of Our Blessed Lady and of the sodality of the Holy Angels to set a good example to their fellow-students.

—Let us try, therefore, to make this retreat in honour of St. Francis with our whole heart and our whole mind. God's blessing will then be upon all your year's studies. But, above and beyond all, let this retreat be one to which you can look back in after years when, may be, you are far from this college and among very different surroundings, to which you can look back with joy and thankfulness and give thanks to God for having granted you this occasion of laying the first foundation of a pious honourable zealous Christian life. And if, as may so happen, there be at this moment in these benches any poor soul who has had the unutterable misfortune to lose God's holy grace and to fall into grievous sin, I fervently trust and pray that this retreat may be the turning-point in the life of that soul. I pray to God through the merits of His zealous servant Francis Xavier that such a soul may be led to sincere repentance and that the holy communion on St. Francis' day of this year may be a lasting covenant between God and that soul. For just and unjust, for saint and sinner alike, may this retreat be a memorable one.

—Help me, my dear little brothers in Christ. Help me by your pious attention, by your own devotion, by your outward demeanour. Banish from your minds all worldly thoughts, and think only of the last things, death, judgment, hell and heaven. He who remembers these things, says Ecclesiastes, shall not sin for ever. He who remembers the last things will act and think with them always before his eyes. He will live a good life and die a good death, believing and knowing that, if he has sacrificed much in this earthly life, it will be given to him a hundredfold and a thousandfold more in the life to come, in the kingdom without end—a blessing, my dear boys, which I wish you from my heart, one and all, in the name of the Father and of the Son and of the Holy Ghost. Amen!

As he walked home with silent companions a thick fog seemed to compass his mind. He waited in stupor of mind till it should lift and reveal what it had hidden. He ate his dinner with surly appetite and when the meal was over and the grease-strewn plates lay abandoned on the table, he rose and went to the window, clearing the thick scum from his mouth with his tongue and licking it from his lips. So he had sunk to the state of a beast that licks his chaps after meat. This was the end; and a faint glimmer of fear began to pierce the fog of his mind. He pressed his face against the pane of the window and gazed out into the darkening street. Forms passed this way and that through the dull light. And that was life. The letters of the name of Dublin lay heavily upon his mind, pushing one another surily hither and thither with slow boorish insistence. His soul was fattening and congealing into a gross grease, plunging ever deeper in its dull fear into a sombre threatening dusk, while the body that was his stood, listless and dishonoured, gazing out of darkened eyes, helpless, perturbed and human for a bovine god to stare upon.

The next day brought death and judgment, stirring his soul slowly from its listless despair. The faint glimmer of fear became a terror of spirit as the hoarse voice of the preacher blew death into his soul. He suffered its agony. He felt the death-chill touch the extremities and creep onward towards the heart, the film of death veiling the eyes, the bright centres of the brain extinguished one by one like lamps, the last sweat oozing upon the skin, the powerlessness of the dying limbs, the speech thickening and wandering and failing, the heart throbbing faintly and more faintly, all but vanquished, the breath, the poor breath, the poor helpless human spirit, sobbing and sighing, gurgling and rattling in the throat. No help! No help! He—he himself—his body to which he had yielded was dying. Into the grave with it. Nail it down into a wooden box, the corpse. Carry it out of the house on the shoulders of hirelings. Thrust it out of men's sight into a long hole in the ground, into the grave, to rot, to feed the mass of its creeping worms and to be devoured by scuttling plump-bellied rats.

And while the friends were still standing in tears by the bedside the soul of the sinner was judged. At the last moment of consciousness the whole earthly life passed before the vision of the soul and, ere it had time to reflect, the body had died and the soul stood terrified before the judgment seat. God, who had long been merciful, would then be just. He had long been patient, pleading with the sinful soul, giving it time to repent, sparing it yet awhile. But that time had gone. Time was to sin and to enjoy, time was to scoff at God and at the warnings of His holy church, time was to defy His majesty, to disobey His commands, to hoodwink one's fellow men, to commit sin after sin and to hide one's corruption from the sight of men. But that time was over. Now it was God's turn: and He was not to be hoodwinked or deceived. Every sin would then come forth from its lurking-place, the most rebellious against the divine will and the most degrading to our poor corrupt nature, the tiniest imperfection and the most heinous atrocity. What did it avail then to have been a great emperor, a great general, a marvellous inventor, the most learned of the learned? All were as one before the judgment seat of God. He would reward the good and punish the wicked. One single instant was enough for the trial of a man's soul. One single instant after the body's death, the soul had been weighed in the balance. The particular judgment was over and the soul had passed to the abode of bliss or to the prison of purgatory or had been hurled howling into hell.

Nor was that all. God's justice had still to be vindicated before men: after the particular there still remained the general judgment. The last day had come. The doomsday was at hand. The stars of heaven were falling upon the earth like the figs cast by the figtree which the wind has shaken. The sun, the great luminary of the universe, had become as sackcloth of hair. The moon was blood red. The firmament was as a scroll rolled away. The archangel Michael, the prince of the heavenly host, appeared glorious and terrible against the sky. With one foot on the sea and one foot on the land he blew from the archangelical trumpet the brazen death of time. The three blasts of the angel filled all the universe. Time is, time was, but time shall be no more. At the last blast the souls of universal humanity throng towards the valley of Jehosaphat, rich and poor, gentle and simple, wise and foolish, good and wicked. The soul of every human being that has ever existed, the souls of all those who shall yet be born, all the sons and daughters of Adam, all are assembled on that supreme day. And lo, the supreme judge is coming! No longer the lowly Lamb of God, no longer the meek Jesus of Nazareth, no longer the Man of Sorrows, no longer the Good Shepherd, He is seen now coming upon the clouds, in great power and majesty, attended by nine choirs of angels, angels and archangels, principalities, powers and virtues, thrones and dominations, cherubim and seraphim, God Omnipotent, God everlasting. He speaks: and His voice is heard even at the farthest limits of space, even in the bottomless abyss. Supreme Judge, from His sentence there will be and can be no appeal. He calls the just to His side, bidding them enter into the Kingdom, the eternity of bliss, prepared for them. The unjust He casts from Him, crying in His offended majesty: *Depart from me, ye cursed, into everlasting fire which was prepared for the devil and his angels.* O, what agony then for the miserable sinners! Friend is torn apart from friend, children are torn from their parents, husbands from their wives. The poor sinner holds out his arms to those who were dear to him in this earthly world, to those whose simple piety perhaps he made a mock of, to those who counselled him and tried to lead him on the right path, to a kind brother, to a loving sister, to the mother and father who loved him so dearly. But it is too late: the just turn away from the wretched damned souls which now appear before the eyes of all in their hideous and evil character. O you hypocrites, O you whited sepulchres, O you who present a smooth smiling face to the world while your soul within is a foul swamp of sin, how will it fare with you in that terrible day?

And this day will come, shall come, must come; the day of death and the day of judgment. It is appointed unto man to die, and after death the judgment. Death is certain. The time and manner are uncertain, whether from long disease or from some unexpected accident; the Son of God cometh at an hour when you little expect Him. Be therefore ready every moment, seeing that you may die at any moment. Death is the end of us all. Death and judgment, brought into the world by the sin of our first parents, are the dark portals that close our earthly existence, the portals that open into the unknown and the unseen, portals through which every soul must pass, alone, unaided save by its good works, without friend or brother or parent or master to help it, alone and trembling. Let that thought be ever before our minds and then we cannot sin. Death, a cause of terror to the sinner, is a blessed moment for him who has walked in the right path, fulfilling the duties of his station in life, attending to his morning and evening prayers, approaching the holy sacrament frequently and performing good and merciful works. For the pious and believing catholic, for the just man, death is no cause of terror. Was it not Addison, the great English writer, who, when on his deathbed, sent for the wicked young earl of Warwick to let him see how a christian can meet his end. He it is and he alone, the pious and believing christian, who can say in his heart:

> *O grave, where is thy victory?*
> *O death, where is thy sting?*

Every word of it was for him. Against his sin, foul and secret, the whole wrath of God was aimed. The preacher's knife had probed deeply into his disclosed conscience and he felt now that his soul was festering in sin. Yes, the preacher was right. God's turn had come. Like a beast in its lair his soul had lain down in its own filth but the blasts of the angel's trumpet had driven him forth from the darkness of sin into the light. The words of doom cried by the angel shattered in an instant his presumptuous peace. The wind of the last day blew through his mind; his sins, the jewel-eyed harlots of his imagination, fled before the hurricane, squeaking like mice in their terror and huddled under a mane of hair.

As he crossed the square, walking homeward, the light laughter of a girl reached his burning ear. The frail, gay sound smote his heart more strongly than a trumpetblast, and, not daring to lift his eyes, he turned aside and gazed, as he walked, into the shadow of the tangled shrubs. Shame rose from his smitten heart and flooded his whole being. The image of Emma appeared before him and under her eyes the flood of shame rushed forth anew from his heart. If she knew to what his mind had subjected her or how his brutelike lust had torn and trampled upon her innocence! Was that boyish love? Was that chivalry? Was that poetry? The sordid details of his orgies stank under his very nostrils. The soot-coated packet of pictures which he had hidden in the flue of the fireplace and in the presence of whose shameless or bashful wantonness he lay for hours sinning in thought and deed; his monstrous dreams, peopled by apelike creatures and by harlots with gleaming jewel eyes; the foul long letters he had written in the joy of guilty confession and carried secretly for days and days only to throw them under cover of night among the grass in the corner of a field or beneath some hingeless door or in some niche in the hedges where a girl might come upon them as she walked by and read them secretly. Mad! Mad! Was it possible he had done these things? A cold sweat broke out upon his forehead as the foul memories condensed within his brain.

When the agony of shame had passed from him he tried to raise his soul from its abject powerlessness. God and the Blessed Virgin were too far from him: God was too great and stern and the Blessed Virgin too pure and holy. But he imagined that he stood near Emma in a wide land and, humbly and in tears, bent and kissed the elbow of her sleeve.

In the wide land under a tender lucid evening sky, a cloud drifting westward amid a pale green sea of heaven, they stood together, children that had erred. Their error had offended deeply God's majesty though it was the error of two children; but it had not offended her whose beauty "is not like earthly beauty, dangerous to look upon, but like the morning star which is its emblem, bright and musical." The eyes were not offended which she turned upon him nor reproachful. She placed their hands together, hand in hand, and said, speaking to their hearts:

—Take hands, Stephen and Emma. It is a beautiful evening now in heaven. You have erred but you are always my children. It is one heart that loves another heart. Take hands together, my dear children, and you will be happy together and your hearts will love each other.

The chapel was flooded by the dull scarlet light that filtered through the lowered blinds; and through the fissure between the last blind and the sash a shaft of wan light entered like a spear and touched the embossed brasses of the candlesticks upon the altar that gleamed like the battleworn mail armour of angels.

Rain was falling on the chapel, on the garden, on the college. It would rain for ever, noiselessly. The water would rise inch by inch, covering the grass and shrubs, covering the trees and houses, covering the monuments and the mountain tops. All life would be choked off, noiselessly: birds, men, elephants, pigs, children: noiselessly floating corpses amid the litter of the wreckage of the world. Forty days and forty nights the rain would fall till the waters covered the face of the earth.

It might be. Why not?

—*Hell has enlarged its soul and opened its mouth without any limits*—words taken, my dear little brothers in Christ Jesus, from the book of Isaias, fifth chapter, fourteenth verse. In the name of the Father and of the Son and of the Holy Ghost. Amen.

The preacher took a chainless watch from a pocket within his soutane and, having considered its dial for a moment in silence, placed it silently before him on the table.

He began to speak in a quiet tone.

—Adam and Eve, my dear boys, were, as you know, our first parents, and you

459

will remember that they were created by God in order that the seats in heaven left vacant by the fall of Lucifer and his rebellious angels might be filled again. Lucifer, we are told, was a son of the morning, a radiant and mighty angel; yet he fell: he fell and there fell with him a third part of the host of heaven: he fell and was hurled with his rebellious angels into hell. What his sin was we cannot say. Theologians consider that it was the sin of pride, the sinful thought conceived in an instant: *non serviam: I will not serve.* That instant was his ruin. He offended the majesty of God by the sinful thought of one instant and God cast him out of heaven into hell for ever.

—Adam and Eve were then created by God and placed in Eden, in the plain of Damascus, that lovely garden resplendent with sunlight and colour, teeming with luxuriant vegetation. The fruitful earth gave them her bounty: beasts and birds were their willing servants: they knew not the ills our flesh is heir to, disease and poverty and death: all that a great and generous God could do for them was done. But there was one condition imposed on them by God: obedience to His word. They were not to eat of the fruit of the forbidden tree.

—Alas, my dear little boys, they too fell. The devil, once a shining angel, a son of the morning, now a foul fiend came in the shape of a serpent, the subtlest of all the beasts of the field. He envied them. He, the fallen great one, could not bear to think that man, a being of clay, should possess the inheritance which he by his sin had forfeited for ever. He came to the woman, the weaker vessel, and poured the poison of his eloquence into her ear, promising her—O, the blasphemy of that promise!—that if she and Adam ate of the forbidden fruit they would become as gods, nay as God Himself. Eve yielded to the wiles of the arch tempter. She ate the apple and gave it also to Adam who had not the moral courage to resist her. The poison tongue of Satan had done its work. They fell.

—And then the voice of God was heard in that garden, calling His creature man to account: and Michael, prince of the heavenly host, with a sword of flame in his hand, appeared before the guilty pair and drove them forth from Eden into the world, the world of sickness and striving, of cruelty and disappointment, of labour and hardship, to earn their bread in the sweat of their brow. But even then how merciful was God! He took pity on our poor degraded parents and promised that in the fulness of time He would send down from heaven One who would redeem them, make them once more children of God and heirs to the kingdom of heaven: and that One, that Redeemer of fallen man, was to be God's only-begotten Son, the Second Person of the Most Blessed Trinity, the Eternal Word.

—He came. He was born of a virgin pure, Mary the virgin mother. He was born in a poor cowhouse in Judea and lived as a humble carpenter for thirty years until the hour of his mission had come. And then, filled with love for men, He went forth and called to men to hear the new gospel.

—Did they listen? Yes, they listened but would not hear. He was seized and bound like a common criminal, mocked at as a fool, set aside to give place to a public robber, scourged with five thousand lashes, crowned with a crown of thorns, hustled through the streets by the Jewish rabble and the Roman soldiery, stripped of his garments and hanged upon a gibbet and His side was pierced with a lance and from the wounded body of our Lord water and blood issued continually.

—Yet even then, in that hour of supreme agony, Our Merciful Redeemer had pity for mankind. Yet even there, on the hill of Calvary, He founded the Holy Catholic Church against which, it is promised, the gates of hell shall not prevail. He founded it upon the rock of ages and endowed it with His grace, with sacraments and sacrifice, and promised that if men would obey the word of His Church they would still enter into eternal life, but if, after all that had been done for them, they still persisted in their wickedness there remained for them an eternity of torment: hell.

The preacher's voice sank. He paused, joined his palms for an instant, parted them. Then he resumed:

—Now let us try for a moment to realise, as far as we can, the nature of that abode of the damned which the justice of an offended God has called into existence for the eternal punishment of sinners. Hell is a strait and dark and foul smelling prison, an abode of demons and lost souls, filled with fire and smoke. The straitness of this prison house is expressly designed by God to punish those who refused to be bound by His laws. In earthly prisons the poor captive has at least some liberty of movement, were it only within the four walls of his cell or in the gloomy yard of his prison. Not so in hell. There, by reason of the great number of the damned, the prisoners are heaped together in their awful prison, the walls of which are said to be four thousand miles thick: and the damned are so utterly bound and helpless that, as a blessed saint, Saint Anselm, writes in his book on Similitudes, they are not even able to remove from the eye a worm that gnaws it.

—They lie in exterior darkness. For, remember, the fire of hell gives forth no light. As, at the command of God, the fire of the Babylonian furnace lost its heat but not its light so, at the command of God, the fire of hell, while retaining the intensity of its heat, burns eternally in darkness. It is a neverending storm of darkness, dark flames and dark smoke of burning brimstone, amid which the bodies are heaped one upon another without even a glimpse of air. Of all the plagues with which the land of the Pharaohs was smitten one plague alone, that of darkness, was called horrible. What name, then, shall we give to the darkness of hell which is to last not for three days alone but for all eternity?

—The horror of this strait and dark poison is increased by its awful stench. All the filth of the world, all the offal and scum of the world, we are told, shall run there as to a vast reeking sewer when the terrible conflagration of the last day has purged the world. The brimstone, too, which burns there in such prodigious quantity fills all hell with its intolerable stench; and the bodies of the damned themselves exhale such a pestilential odour that as Saint Bonaventure says, one of them alone would suffice to infect the whole world. The very air of this world, that pure element, becomes foul and unbreathable when it has been long enclosed. Consider then what must be the foulness of the air of hell. Imagine some foul and putrid corpse that has lain rotting and decomposing in the grave, a jellylike mass of liquid corruption. Imagine such a corpse a prey to flames, devoured by the fire of burning brimstone and giving off dense choking fumes of nauseous loathsome decomposition. And then imagine this sickening stench, multiplied a millionfold and a millionfold again from the millions upon millions of fetid carcasses massed together in the reeking darkness, a huge and rotting human fungus. Imagine all this and you will have some idea of the horror of the stench of hell.

—But this stench is not, horrible though it is, the greatest physical torment to which the damned are subjected. The torment of fire is the greatest torment to which the tyrant has ever subjected his fellow creatures. Place your finger for a moment in the flame of a candle and you will feel the pain of fire. But our earthly fire was created by God for the benefit of man, to maintain in him the spark of life and to help him in the useful arts whereas the fire of hell is of another quality and was created by God to torture and punish the unrepentant sinner. Our earthly fire also consumes more or less rapidly according as the object which it attacks is more or less combustible so that human ingenuity has even succeeded in inventing chemical preparations to check or frustrate its action. But the sulphurous brimstone which burns in hell is a substance which is specially designed to burn for ever and for ever with unspeakable fury. Moreover our earthly fire destroys at the same time as it burns so that the more intense it is the shorter is its duration: but the fire of hell has this property that it preserves that which it burns and though it rages with incredible intensity it rages for ever.

—Our earthly fire again, no matter how fierce or widespread it may be, is always of a limited extent: but the lake of fire in hell is boundless, shoreless and bottomless. It is on record that the devil himself, when asked the question by a certain soldier, was obliged to confess that if a whole mountain were thrown into the burning ocean of hell it would be burned up in an instant like a piece of wax. And this terrible fire will not afflict the bodies of the damned only from without but each lost soul will be a hell unto itself, the boundless fire raging in its very vitals. O, how terrible is the lot of those wretched beings! The blood seethes and boils in the veins, the brains are boiling in the skull, the heart in the breast glowing and bursting, the bowels a redhot mass of burning pulp, the tender eyes flaming like molten balls.

—And yet what I have said as to the strength and quality and boundlessness of this fire is as nothing when compared to its intensity, an intensity which it has as being the instrument chosen by divine design for the punishment of soul and body alike. It is a fire which proceeds directly from the ire of God, working not of its own activity but as an instrument of divine vengeance. As the waters of baptism cleanse the soul with the body so do the fires of punishment torture the spirit with the flesh. Every sense of the flesh is tortured and every faculty of the soul therewith: the eyes with impenetrable utter darkness, the nose with noisome odours, the ears with yells and howls and execrations, the taste with foul matter, leprous corruption, nameless suffocating filth, the touch with redhot goads and spikes, with cruel tongues of flame. And through the several torments of the senses the immortal soul is tortured eternally in its very essence amid the leagues upon leagues of glowing fires kindled in the abyss by the offended majesty of the Omnipotent God and fanned into everlasting and ever increasing fury by the breath of the anger of the Godhead.

—Consider finally that the torment of this infernal prison is increased by the company of the damned themselves. Evil company on earth is so noxious that the plants, as if by instinct, withdraw from the company of whatsoever is deadly or hurtful to them. In hell all laws are overturned—there is no thought of family or country, of ties, of relationships. The damned howl and scream at one another, their torture and rage intensified by the presence of beings tortured and raging like themselves. All sense of humanity is forgotten. The yells of the suffering sinners fill the remotest corners of the vast abyss. The mouths of the damned are full of blasphemies against God and of hatred for their fellow sufferers and of curses against those souls which were their accomplices in sin. In olden times it was the custom to punish the parricide, the man who had raised his murderous hand against his father, by casting him into the depths of the sea in a sack in which were placed a cock, a monkey and a serpent. The intention of those law-givers who framed such a law, which seems cruel in our times, was to punish the criminal by the company of hurtful and hateful beasts. But what is the fury of those dumb beasts compared with the fury of execration which bursts from the parched lips and aching throats of the damned in hell when they behold in their companions in misery those who aided and abetted them in sin, those whose words sowed the first seeds of evil thinking and evil living in their minds, those whose immodest suggestions led them on to sin, those whose eyes tempted and allured them from the path of virtue. They turn upon those accomplices and upbraid them and curse them. But they are helpless and hopeless: it is too late now for repentance.

—Last of all consider the frightful torment to those damned souls, tempted alike, of the company of the devils. These devils will afflict the damned in two ways, by their presence and by their reproaches. We can have no idea of how horrible these devils are. Saint Catherine of Siena once saw a devil, and she has written that, rather than look again for one single instant on such a frightful monster, she would prefer to walk until the end of her life along a track of red coals. These devils, who were once beautiful angels, have become as hideous and ugly as they once were beautiful. They mock and jeer at the lost souls whom they dragged down to ruin. It is they, the foul demons, who are made in hell the voices of conscience. Why did you sin? Why did you lend an ear to the temptings of friends? Why did you turn aside from your pious practices and good works? Why did you not shun the occasions of sin? Why did you not leave that evil companion? Why did you not give up that lewd habit, that impure habit? Why did you not listen to the counsels of your confessor? Why did you not, even after you had fallen the first or the second or the third or the fourth or the hundredth time, repent of your evil ways and turn to God who only waited for your repentance to absolve you of your sins? Now the time for repentance has gone by. Time is, time was, but time shall be no more! Time was to sin in secrecy, to indulge in that sloth and pride, to covet the unlawful, to yield to the promptings of your lower nature, to live like the beasts of the field, nay worse than the beasts of the field for they, at least, are but brutes and have not reason to guide them: time shall be no more. God spoke to you by so many voices but you would not hear. You would not crush out that pride and anger in your heart, you would not restore those ill-gotten goods, you would not obey the precepts of your holy church nor attend to your religious duties, you would not abandon those wicked companions, you would not avoid those dangerous temptations. Such is the language of those fiendish tormentors, words of taunting and of reproach, of hatred and of disgust. Of disgust, Yes! For even they, the very devils, when they sinned, sinned by such a sin as alone was compatible with such angelical natures, a rebellion of the intellect: and they, even they, the foul devils must turn away, revolted and disgusted, from the contemplation of those unspeakable sins by which degraded man outrages and defiles the temple of the Holy Ghost, defiles and pollutes himself.

—O, my dear little brothers in Christ, may it never be our lot to hear that language! May it never be our lot, I say! In the last day of terrible reckoning I pray fervently to God that not a single soul of those who are in this chapel today may be found among those miserable beings whom the Great Judge shall command to depart for ever from His sight, that not one of us may ever hear ringing in his ears the awful sentence of rejection: *Depart from me, ye cursed, into everlasting fire which was prepared for the devil and his angels!*—

He came down the aisle of the chapel, his legs shaking and the scalp of his head trembling as though it had been touched by ghostly fingers. He passed up the staircase and into the corridor along the walls of which the overcoats and waterproofs hung like gibbeted male-factors, headless and dripping and shapeless. And at every step he feared that he had already died, that his soul had been wrenched forth of the sheath of his body, that he was plunging headlong through space.

He could not grip the floor with his feet and sat heavily at his desk, opening one of his books at random and poring over it. Every word for him! It was true. God was almighty. God could call him now, call him as he sat at his desk, before he had time to be conscious of the summons. God had called him. Yes? What? Yes? His flesh shrank together as it felt the approach of the ravenous tongues of flames, dried up as it felt about it the swirl of stifling air. He had died. Yes. He was judged. A wave of fire swept through his body: the first. Again a wave. His brain began to glow. Another. His brain was simmering and bubbling within the cracking tenement of the skull. Flames burst forth from his skull like a corolla, shrieking like voices:

—Hell! Hell! Hell! Hell! Hell!—

Voices spoke near him:

—On hell.—

—I suppose he rubbed it into you well.—

—You bet he did. He put us all into a blue funk.—

—That's what you fellows want: and plenty of it to make you work.—

He leaned back weakly in his desk. He had not died. God had spared him still. He was still in the familiar world of the school. Mr. Tate and Vincent Heron stood at the window, talking, jesting, gazing out at the bleak rain, moving their heads.

—I wish it would clear up. I had arranged to go for a spin on the bike with some fellows out by Malahide. But the roads must be kneedeep.—

—It might clear up, sir.—

The voices that he knew so well; the common words, the quiet of the classroom when the voices paused and the silence was filled by the sound of softly browsing cattle as the other boys munched their lunches tranquilly lulled his aching soul.

There was still time. O Mary, refuge of sinners, intercede for him! O Virgin Undefiled, save him from the gulf of death!

The English lesson began with the hearing of the history. Royal persons, favourites, intriguers, bishops, passed like mute phantoms behind their veil of names. All had died: all had been judged. What did it profit a man to gain the whole world if he lost his soul? At last he had understood: and human life lay around him, a plain of peace whereon antlike men laboured in brotherhood, their dead sleeping under quiet mounds. The elbow of his companion touched him and his heart was touched: and when he spoke to answer a question of his master he heard his own voice full of the quietude of humility and contrition.

His soul sank back deeper into depths of contrite peace, no longer able to suffer the pain of dread, and sending forth, as she sank, a faint prayer. Ah yes, he would still be spared; he would repent in his heart and be forgiven; and then those above, those in heaven, would see what he would do to make up for the past: a whole life, every hour of life. Only wait.

—All, God! All, all!—

A messenger came to the door to say that confessions were being heard in the chapel. Four boys left the room; and he heard others passing down the corridor. A tremulous chill blew round his heart, no stronger than a little wind, and yet, listening and suffering silently, he seemed to have laid an ear against the muscle of his own heart, feeling it close and quail, listening to the flutter of its ventricles.

No escape. He had to confess, to speak out in words what he had done and thought, sin after sin. How? How?

—Father, I . . .—

The thought slid like a cold shining rapier into his tender flesh: confession. But not there in the chapel of the college. He would confess all, every sin of deed and thought, sincerely: but not there among his school companions. Far away from there in some dark place he would murmur out his own shame: and he besought God humbly not to be offended with him if he did not dare to confess in the college chapel: and in utter abjection of spirit he craved forgiveness mutely of the boyish hearts about him.

Time passed.

He sat again in the front bench of the chapel. The daylight without was already failing and, as it fell slowly through the dull red blinds, it seemed that the sun of the last day was going down and that all souls were being gathered for the judgment.

—*I am cast away from the sight of Thine eyes:* words taken, my dear little brothers in Christ, from the Book of Psalms, thirtieth chapter, twenty-third verse, In the name of the Father and of the Son and of the Holy Ghost. Amen.

The preacher began to speak in a quiet friendly tone. His face was kind and he joined gently the fingers of each hand, forming a frail cage by the union of their tips.

—This morning we endeavoured, in our reflection upon hell, to make what our holy founder calls in his book of spiritual exercises, the composition of place. We endeavoured, that is, to imagine with the senses of the mind, in our imagination, the material character of that awful place and of the physical torments which all who are in hell endure. This evening we shall consider for a few moments the nature of the spiritual torments of hell.

—Sin, remember, is a twofold enormity. It is a base consent to the promptings of our corrupt nature to the lower instincts, to that which is gross and beastlike; and it is also a turning away from the counsel of our higher nature, from all that is pure and holy, from the Holy God Himself. For this reason mortal sin is punished in hell by two different forms of punishment, physical and spiritual.

Now of all these spiritual pains by far the greatest is the pain of loss, so great, in fact, that in itself it is a torment greater than all the others. Saint Thomas, the greatest doctor of the Church, the angelic doctor, as he is called, says that the worst damnation consists in this that the understanding of man is totally deprived of Divine light and his affection obstinately turned away from the goodness of God. God, remember, is a being infinitely good and therefore the loss of such a being must be a loss infinitely painful. In this life we have not a very clear idea of what such a loss must be but the damned in hell, for their greater torment, have a full understanding of that which they have lost and understand that they have lost it through their own sins and have lost it for ever. At the very instant of death the bonds of the flesh are broken asunder and the soul at once flies towards God as towards the centre of her existence. Remember, my dear little boys, our souls long to be with God. We come from God, we live by God, we belong to God: we are His, inalienably His. God loves with a divine love every human soul and every human soul lives in that love. How could it be otherwise? Every breath that we draw, every thought of our brain, every instant of life proceed from God's inexhaustible goodness. And if it be pain for a mother to be parted from her child, for a man to be exiled from hearth and home, for friend to be sundered from friend, O think what pain, what anguish, it must be for the poor soul to be spurned from the presence of the supremely good and loving Creator Who has called that soul into existence from nothingness and sustained it in life and loved it with an immeasurable love. This, then, to be separated for ever from its greatest good, from God, and to feel the anguish of that separation, knowing full well that it is unchangeable, this is the greatest torment which the created soul is capable of bearing, *pœna damni,* the pain of loss.

The second pain which will afflict the souls of the damned in hell is the pain of conscience. Just as in dead bodies worms are engendered by putrefaction so in the souls of the lost there arises a perpetual remorse from the putrefaction of sin, the sting of conscience, the worm, as Pope Innocent the Third calls it, of the triple sting. The first sting inflicted by this cruel worm will be the memory of past pleasures. O what a dreadful memory will that be! In the lake of alldevouring flame the proud king will remember the pomps of his court, the wise but wicked man his libraries and instruments of research, the lover of artistic pleasures his marbles and pictures and other art treasures, he who delighted in the pleasures of the table his gorgeous feasts, his dishes prepared with such delicacy, his choice wines, the miser will remember his hoard of gold, the robber his illgotten wealth, the angry and revengeful and merciless murderers their deeds of blood and violence in which they revelled, the impure and adulterous the unspeakable and filthy pleasures in which they delighted. They will remember all this and loathe themselves and their sins. For how miserable will all those pleasures seem to the soul condemned to suffer in hell-fire for ages and ages. How they will rage and fume to think that they have lost the bliss of heaven for the dross of earth, for a few pieces of metal, for vain honours, for bodily comforts, for a tingling of the nerves. They will repent indeed: and this is the second sting of the worm of conscience, a late and fruitless sorrow for sins committed. Divine justice insists that the understanding of those miserable wretches be fixed continually on the sins of which they were guilty and moreover, as Saint Augustine points out, God will impart to them His own knowledge of sin so that sin will appear to them in all its hideous malice as it appears to the eyes of God Himself. They will behold their sins in all their foulness and repent but it will be too late and then they will bewail the good occasions which they neglected. This is the last and deepest and most cruel sting of the worm of conscience. The conscience will say: You had time and opportunity to repent and would not. You were brought up religiously by your parents. You had the sacraments and graces and indulgences of the church to aid you. You had the minister of God to preach to you to call you back when you had strayed, to forgive you your sins, no matter how many, how abominable, if only you had confessed and repented. No. You would not. You flouted the ministers of holy religion, you turned your back on the confessional, you wallowed deeper and deeper in the mire of sin. God appealed to you, threatened you, entreated you to return to him. O, what shame, what misery! The Ruler of the universe entreated you, a creature of clay, to love Him Who made you and to keep His law. No. You would not. And now, though you were to flood all hell with your tears if you could still weep, all that sea of repentance would not gain for you what a single tear of true repentance shed during your mortal life would have gained for you. You implore now a moment of earthly life wherein to repent: in vain. That time is gone: gone for ever.

—Such is the threefold sting of conscience, the viper which gnaws the very heart's core of the wretches in hell so that filled with hellish fury they curse themselves for their folly and curse the evil companions who have brought them to such ruin and curse the devils who tempted them in life and now mock them in eternity and even revile and curse the Supreme Being Whose goodness and patience they scorned and slighted but Whose justice and power they cannot evade.

—The next spiritual pain to which the damned are subjected is the pain of extension. Man, in this earthly life, though he be capable of many evils, is not capable of them all at once inasmuch as one evil corrects and counteracts another, just as one poison frequently corrects another. In hell, on the contrary, one torment, instead of counteracting another, lends it still greater force: and, moreover, as the internal faculties are more perfect than the external senses, so are they more capable of suffering. Just as every sense is afflicted with a fitting torment so is every spiritual faculty; the fancy with horrible images, the sensitive faculty with alternate longing and rage, the mind and understanding with an interior darkness more terrible even than the exterior darkness which reigns in that dreadful prison. The malice, impotent though it be, which possesses these demon souls is an evil of boundless extension, of limitless duration, a frightful state of wickedness which we can scarcely realise unless we bear in mind the enormity of sin and the hatred God bears to it.

—Opposed to this pain of extension and yet co-existent with it we have the pain of intensity. Hell is the centre of evils and, as you know, things are more intense at their centres than at their remotest points. There are no contraries or admixtures of any kind to temper or soften in the least the pains of hell. Nay, things which are good in themselves become evil in hell. Company, elsewhere a source of comfort to the afflicted, will be there a continual torment: knowledge, so much longed for as the chief good of the intellect, will there be hated worse than ignorance: light, so much coveted by all creatures from the lord of creation down to the humblest plant in the forest, will be loathed intensely. In this life our sorrows are either not very long or not very great because nature either overcomes them by habits or puts an end to them by sinking under their weight. But in hell the torments cannot be overcome by habit, for while they are of terrible intensity they are at the same time of continual variety, each pain, so to speak, taking fire from another and re-endowing that which has enkindled it with a still fiercer flame. Nor can nature escape from these intense and various tortures by succumbing to them for the soul is sustained and maintained in evil so that its suffering may be the greater. Boundless extension of torment, incredible intensity of suffering, unceasing variety of torture—this is what the divine majesty, so outraged by sinners, demands, this is what the holiness of heaven, slighted and set aside for the lustful and low pleasures of the corrupt flesh, requires, this is what the blood of the innocent Lamb of God, shed for the redemption of sinners, trampled upon by the vilest of the vile, insists upon.

—Last and crowning torture of all the tortures of that awful place is the eternity of hell. Eternity! O, dread and dire word. Eternity! What mind of man can understand it? And remember, it is an eternity of pain. Even though the pains of hell were not so terrible as they are yet they would become infinite as they are destined to last for ever. But while they are everlasting they are at the same time, as you know, intolerably intense, unbearably extensive. To bear even the sting of an insect for all eternity would be a dreadful torment. What must it be, then, to bear the manifold tortures of hell for ever? For ever! For all eternity! Not for a year or for an age but for ever. Try to imagine the awful meaning of this. You have often seen the sand on the seashore. How fine are its tiny grains! And how many of those tiny little grains go to make up the small handful which a child grasps in its play. Now imagine a mountain of that sand, a million miles high, reaching from the earth to the farthest heavens, and a million miles broad, extending to remotest space, and a million miles in thickness: and imagine such an enormous mass of countless particles of sand multiplied as often as there are leaves in the forest, drops of water in the mighty ocean, feathers on birds, scales on fish, hairs on animals, atoms in the vast expanse of the air: and imagine that at the end of every million years a little bird came to that mountain and carried away in its beak a tiny grain of that sand. How many millions upon millions of centuries would pass before that bird had carried away even a square foot of that mountain, how many eons upon eons of ages before it had carried away all. Yet at the end of that immense stretch of time not even one instant of eternity could be said to have ended. At the end of all those billions and trillions of years eternity would have scarcely begun. And if that mountain rose again after it had been all carried away and if the bird came again and carried it all away again grain by grain: and if it so rose and sank as many times as there are stars in the sky, atoms in the air, drops of water in the sea, leaves on the trees, feathers upon birds, scales upon fish, hairs upon animals, at the end of all those innumerable risings and sinkings of that immeasurably vast mountain not one single instant of eternity could be said to have ended; even then, at the end of such a period, after that eon of time the mere thought of which makes our very brain reel dizzily, eternity would have scarcely begun.

—A holy saint (one of our own fathers I believe it was) was once vouchsafed a vision of hell. It seemed to him that he stood in the midst of a great hall, dark and silent save for the ticking of a great clock. The ticking went on unceasingly; and it seemed to this saint that the sound of the ticking was the ceaseless repetition of the words: ever, never; ever, never. Ever to be in hell, never to be in heaven; ever to be shut off from the presence of God, never to enjoy the beatific vision; ever to be eaten with flames, gnawed by vermin, goaded with burning spikes, never to be free from those pains; ever to have the conscience upbraid one, the memory enrage, the mind filled with darkness and despair, never to escape; ever to curse and revile the foul demons who gloat fiendishly over the misery of their dupes, never to behold the shining raiment of the blessed spirits; ever to cry out of the abyss of fire to God for an instant, a single instant, of respite from such awful agony, never to receive, even for an instant, God's pardon; ever to suffer, never to enjoy; ever to be damned, never to be saved; ever, never; ever, never. O, what a dreadful punishment! An eternity of endless agony, of endless bodily and spiritual torment, without one ray of hope, without one moment of cessation, of agony limitless in intensity, of torment infinitely varied, of torture that sustains eternally that which it eternally devours, of anguish that everlastingly preys upon the spirit while it racks the flesh, an eternity, every instant of which is itself an eternity of woe. Such is the terrible punishment decreed for those who die in mortal sin by an almighty and a just God.

—Yes, a just God! Men, reasoning always as men, are astonished that God should mete out an everlasting and infinite punishment in the fires of hell for a single grievous sin. They reason thus because, blinded by the gross illusion of the flesh and the darkness of human understanding they are unable to comprehend the hideous malice of mortal sin. They reason thus because they are unable to comprehend that even venial sin is of such a foul and hideous nature that even if the omnipotent Creator could end all the evil and misery in the world the wars, the diseases, the robberies, the crime, the deaths, the murders, on condition that he allowed a single venial sin to pass unpunished, a single venial sin, a lie, an angry look, a moment of wilful sloth, He, the great omnipotent God could not do so because sin, be it in thought or deed, is a transgression of His law and God would not be God if He did not punish the transgressor.

—A sin, an instant of rebellious pride of the intellect, made Lucifer and a third part of the cohorts of angels fall from their glory. A sin, an instant of folly and weakness, drove Adam and Eve out of Eden and brought death and suffering into the world. To retrieve the consequences of that sin the Only Begotten Son of God came down to earth, lived and suffered and died a most painful death, hanging for three hours on the cross.

—O, my dear little brethren in Christ Jesus, will we then offend that good Redeemer and provoke His anger? Will we trample again upon that torn and mangled corpse? Will we spit upon that face so full of sorrow and love? Will we too, like the cruel Jews and the brutal soldiers, mock that gentle and compassionate Saviour Who trod alone for our sake the awful winepress of sorrow? Every word of sin is a wound in His tender side. Every sinful act is a thorn piercing His head. Every impure thought, deliberately yielded to, is a keen lance transfixing that sacred and loving heart. No, no. It is impossible for any human being to do that which offends so deeply the divine Majesty, that which is punished by an eternity of agony, that which crucifies again the Son of God and makes a mockery of Him.

—I pray to God that my poor words may have availed today to confirm in holiness those who are in a state of grace, to strengthen the wavering, to lead back to the state of grace the poor soul that has strayed if any such be among you. I pray to God, and do you pray with me, that we may repent of our sins. I will ask you now, all of you, to repeat after me the act of contrition, kneeling here in this humble chapel in the presence of God. He is there in the tabernacle burning with love for mankind, ready to comfort the afflicted. Be not afraid. No matter how many or how foul the sins if only you repent of them they will be forgiven you. Let no worldly shame hold you back. God is still the merciful Lord who wishes not the eternal death of the sinner but rather that he be converted and live.

—He calls you to Him. You are His. He made you out of nothing. He loved you as only a God can love. His arms are open to receive you even though you have sinned against Him. Come to Him, poor sinner, poor vain and erring sinner. Now is the acceptable time. Now is the hour.

The priest rose and turning towards the altar knelt upon the step before the tabernacle in the fallen gloom. He waited till all in the chapel had knelt and every least noise was still. Then, raising his head, he repeated the act of contrition, phrase by phrase, with fervour. The boys answered him phrase by phrase. Stephen, his tongue cleaving to his palate, bowed his head, praying with his heart.

—*O my God!*—
—*O my God!*—
—*I am heartily sorry*—
—*I am heartily sorry*—
—*for having offended Thee*—

—for having offended Thee—
—and I detest my sins—
—and I detest my sins—
—above every other evil—
—above every other evil—
—because they displease Thee, my God—
—because they displease Thee, my God—
—Who art so deserving—
—Who art so deserving—
—of all my love—
—of all my love—
—and I firmly purpose—
—and I firmly purpose—
—by Thy Holy grace—
—by Thy Holy grace—
—never more to offend Thee—
—never more to offend Thee—
—and to amend my life—
—and to amend my life—

↓

He went up to his room after dinner in order to be alone with his soul: and at every step his soul seemed to sigh: at every step his soul mounted with his feet, sighing in the ascent, through a region of viscid gloom.

He halted on the landing before the door and then, grasping the porcelain knob, opened the door quickly. He waited in fear, his soul pining within him, praying silently that death might not touch his brow as he passed over the threshold, that the fiends that inhabit darkness might not be given power over him. He waited still at the threshold as at the entrance to some dark cave. Faces were there; eyes: they waited and watched.

—We knew perfectly well of course that although it was bound to come to the light he would find considerable difficulty in endeavouring to try to induce himself to try to endeavour to ascertain the spiritual plenipotentiary and so we knew of course perfectly well—

Murmuring faces waited and watched; murmurous voices filled the dark shell of the cave. He feared intensely in spirit and in flesh but, raising his head bravely, he strode into the room firmly. A doorway, a room, the same room, same window. He told himself calmly that those words had absolutely no sense which had seemed to rise murmurously from the dark. He told himself that it was simply his room with the door open.

He closed the door and, walking swiftly to the bed, knelt beside it and covered his face with his hands. His hands were cold and damp and his limbs ached with chill. Bodily unrest and chill and weariness beset him, routing his thoughts. Why was he kneeling there like a child saying his evening prayers? To be alone with his soul, to examine his conscience, to meet his sins face to face, to recall their times and manners and circumstances, to weep over them. He could not weep. He could not summon them to his memory. He felt only an ache of soul and body, his whole being, memory, will, understanding, flesh, benumbed and weary.

That was the work of devils, to scatter his thoughts and overcloud his conscience, assailing him at the gates of the cowardly and sin corrupted flesh: and, praying God timidly to forgive him his weakness, he crawled up on to the bed and, wrapping the blankets closely about him, covered his face again with his hands. He had sinned. He had sinned so deeply against heaven and before God that he was not worthy to be called God's child.

Could it be that he, Stephen Dedalus, had done those things? His conscience sighed in answer. Yes, he had done them, secretly, filthily, time after time and, hardened in sinful impenitence, he had dared to wear the mask of holiness before the tabernacle itself while his soul within was a living mass of corruption. How came it that God had not struck him dead? The leprous company of his sins closed about him, breathing upon him, bending over him from all sides. He strove to forget them in an act of prayer, huddling his limbs closer together and binding down his eyelids: but the senses of his soul would not be bound and, though his eyes were shut fast, he saw the places where he had sinned and, though his ears were tightly covered, he heard. He desired with all his will not to hear nor see. He desired till his frame shook under the strain of his desire and until the senses of his soul closed. They closed for an instant and then opened. He saw.

A field of stiff weeds and thistles and tufted nettlebunches. Thick among the tufts of rank stiff growth lay battered canisters and clots and coils of solid excrement. A faint marsh light struggling upwards from all the ordure through the bristling grey green weeds. An evil smell, faint and foul as the light, curled upwards sluggishly out of the canisters and from the stale crusted dung.

Creatures were in the field; one, three, six: creatures were moving in the field, hither and thither. Goatish creatures with human faces, horny browed, lightly bearded and grey as indiarubber. The malice of evil glittered in their hard eyes, as they moved hither and thither, trailing their long tails behind them. A rictus of cruel malignity lit up greyly their old bony faces. One was clasping about his ribs a torn flannel waistcoat, another complained monotonously as his beard stuck in the tufted weeds. Soft language issued from their spittleless lips as they swished in slow circles round and round the field, winding hither and thither through the weeds, dragging their long tails amid the rattling canisters. They moved in slow circles, circling closer and closer to enclose, to enclose, soft language issuing from their lips, their long swishing tails besmeared with stale shite, thrusting upwards their terrific faces . . .

Help!

He flung the blankets from him madly to free his face and neck. That was his hell. God had allowed him to see the hell reserved for his sins: stinking, bestial, malignant, a hell of lecherous goatish fiends. For him! For him!

He sprang from the bed, the reeking odour pouring down his throat, clogging and revolting his entrails. Air! The air of heaven! He stumbled towards the window, groaning and almost fainting with sickness. At the washstand a convulsion seized him within; and, clasping his cold forehead wildly, he vomited profusely in agony.

When the fit had spent itself he walked weakly to the window and lifting the sash, sat in a corner of the embrasure and leaned his elbow upon the sill. The rain had drawn off; and amid the moving vapours from point to point of light the city was spinning about herself a soft cocoon of yellowish haze. Heaven was still and faintly luminous and the air sweet to breathe, as in a thicket drenched with showers: and amid peace and shimmering lights and quiet fragrance he made a covenant with his heart.

He prayed:

> —He once had meant to come on earth in heavenly glory but we sinned: and then He could not safely visit us but with a shrouded majesty and a bedimmed radiance for He was God. So He came Himself in weakness not in power and He sent thee, a creature in His stead, with a creature's comeliness and lustre suited to our state. And now thy very face and form, dear mother, speak to us of the Eternal; not like earthly beauty, dangerous to look upon, but like the morning star which is thy emblem, bright and musical, breathing purity, telling of heaven and infusing peace. O harbinger of day! O light of the pilgrim! Lead us still as thou hast led. In the dark night, across the bleak wilderness guide us on to our Lord Jesus, guide us home.—

His eyes were dimmed with tears and, looking humbly up to heaven, he wept for the innocence he had lost.

When evening had fallen he left the house and the first touch of the damp dark air and the noise of the door as it closed behind him made ache again his conscience, lulled by prayer and tears. Confess! Confess! It was not enough to lull the conscience with a tear and a prayer. He had to kneel before the minister of the Holy Ghost and tell over his hidden sins truly and repentantly. Before he heard again the footboard of the housedoor trail over the threshold as it opened to let him in, before he saw again the table in the kitchen set for supper he would have knelt and confessed. It was quite simple.

The ache of conscience ceased and he walked onward swiftly through the dark streets. There were so many flagstones on the footpath of that street and so many streets in that city and so many cities in the world. Yet eternity had no end.

He was in mortal sin. Even once was a mortal sin. It could happen in an instant. But how so quickly? By seeing or by thinking of seeing. The eyes see the thing, without having wished first to see. Then in an instant it happens. But does that part of the body understand or what? The serpent, the most subtle beast of the field. It must understand when it desires in one instant and then prolongs its own desire instant after instant, sinfully. It feels and understands and desires. What a horrible thing! Who made it to be like that, a bestial part of the body able to understand bestially and desire bestially? Was that then he or an inhuman thing moved by a lower soul? His soul sickened at the thought of a torpid snaky life feeding itself out of the tender marrow of his life and fattening upon the slime of lust. O why was that so? O why?

He cowered in the shadow of the thought abasing himself in the awe of God Who had made all things and all men. Madness. Who could think such a thought? And, cowering in darkness and abject, he prayed mutely to his angel guardian to drive away with his sword the demon that was whispering to his brain.

The whisper ceased and he knew then clearly that his own soul had sinned in thought and word and deed wilfully through his own body. Confess! He had to confess every sin. How could he utter in words to the priest what he had done? Must, must. Or how could he explain without dying of shame? Or how could he have done such things without shame? A madman! Confess! O he would indeed to be free and sinless again! Perhaps the priest would know. O dear God!

He walked on and on through ill-lit streets, fearing to stand still for a moment lest it might seem that he held back from what awaited him, fearing to arrive at that towards which he still turned with longing. How beautiful must be a soul in the state of grace when God looked upon it with love!

Frowsy girls sat along the curbstones before their baskets. Their dank hair hung trailed over their brows. They were not beautiful to see as they crouched in the mire. But their souls were seen by God; and if their souls were in a state of grace they were radiant to see: and God loved them, seeing them.

A wasting breath of humiliation blew bleakly over his soul to think of how he had fallen, to feel that those souls were dearer to God than his. The wind blew over him and passed on to the myriads and myriads of other souls, on whom God's favour shone now more and now less, stars now brighter and now dimmer, sustained and failing. And the glimmering souls passed away, sustained and failing, merged in a moving breath. One soul was lost; a tiny soul: his. It flickered once and went out, forgotten, lost. The end: black cold void waste.

Consciousness of place came ebbing back to him slowly over a vast tract of time unlit, unfelt, unlived. The squalid scene composed itself around him; the common accents, the burning gasjets in the shops, odours of fish and spirits and wet sawdust, moving men and women. An old woman was about to cross the street, an oilcan in her hand. He bent down and asked her was there a chapel near.

—A chapel, sir? Yes, sir. Church Street chapel.—

—Church?—

She shifted the can to her other hand and directed him: and, as she held out her reeking withered right hand under its fringe of shawl, he bent lower towards her, saddened and soothed by her voice.

—Thank you.—

—You are quite welcome, sir.—

The candles on the high altar had been extinguished but the fragrance of incense still floated down the dim nave. Bearded workmen with pious faces were guiding a canopy out through a side door, the sacristan aiding them with quiet gestures and words. A few of the faithful still lingered praying before one of the side-altars or kneeling in the benches near the confessionals. He approached timidly and knelt at the last bench in the body, thankful for the peace and silence and fragrant shadow of the church. The board on which he knelt was narrow and worn and those who knelt near him were humble followers of Jesus. Jesus too had been born in poverty and had worked in the shop of a carpenter, cutting boards and planing them, and had first spoken of the kingdom of God to poor fisherman, teaching all men to be meek and humble of heart.

He bowed his head upon his hands, bidding his heart be meek and humble that he might be like those who knelt beside him and his prayer as acceptable as theirs. He prayed beside them but it was hard. His soul was foul with sin and he dared not ask forgiveness with the simple trust of those whom Jesus, in the mysterious ways of God, had called first to His side, the carpenters, the fisherman, poor and simple people following a lowly trade, handling and shaping the wood of trees, mending their nets with patience.

A tall figure came down the aisle and the penitents stirred: and, at the last moment glancing up swiftly, he saw a long grey beard and the brown habit of a capuchin. The priest entered the box and was hidden. Two penitents rose and entered the confessional at either side. The wooden slide was drawn back and the faint murmur of a voice troubled the silence.

His blood began to murmur in his veins, murmuring like a sinful city summoned from its sleep to bear its doom. Little flakes of fire fell and powdery ashes fell softly, alighting on the houses of men. They stirred, waking from sleep, troubled by the heated air.

The slide was shot back. The penitent emerged from the side of the box. The farther side was drawn. A woman entered quietly and deftly where the first penitent had knelt. The faint murmur began again.

He could still leave the chapel. He could stand up, put one foot before the other and walk out softly and then run, run, run swiftly through the dark streets. He could still escape from the shame. Had it been any terrible crime but that one sin! Had it been murder! Little fiery flakes fell and touched him at all points, shameful thoughts, shameful words, shameful acts. Shame covered him wholly like fine glowing ashes falling continually. To say it in words! His soul, stifling and helpless, would cease to be.

The slide was shot back. A penitent emerged from the farther side of the box. The near slide was drawn. A penitent entered where the other penitent had come out. A soft whispering noise floated in vaporous cloudlets out of the box. It was the woman: soft whispering cloudlets, soft whispering vapour, whispering and vanishing.

He beat his breast with his fist humbly, secretly under cover of the wooden armrest. He would be at one with others and with God. He would love his neighbour. He would love God Who had made and loved him. He would kneel and pray with others and be happy. God would look down on him and on them and would love them all.

It was easy to be good. God's yoke was sweet and light. It was better never to have sinned, to have remained always a child, for God loved little children and suffered them to come to Him. It was a terrible and a sad thing to sin. But God was merciful to poor sinners who were truly sorry. How true that was! That was indeed goodness.

The slide was shot to suddenly. The penitent came out. He was next. He stood up in terror and walked blindly into the box.

At last it had come. He knelt in the silent gloom and raised his eyes to the white crucifix suspended above him. God could see that he was sorry. He would tell all his sins. His confession would be long, long. Everybody in the chapel would know then what a sinner he had been. Let them know. It was true. But God had promised to forgive him if he was sorry. He was sorry. He clasped his hands and raised them towards the white form, praying with his darkened eyes, praying with all his trembling body, swaying his head to and fro like a lost creature, praying with whimpering lips.

—Sorry! Sorry! O sorry!—

The slide clicked back and his heart bounded in his breast. The face of an old priest was at the grating, averted from him, leaning upon a hand. He made the sign of the cross and prayed of the priest to bless him for he had sinned. Then, bowing his head, he repeated the *Confiteor* in fright. At the words *my most grievous fault* he ceased, breathless.

—How long is it since your last confession, my child?—

—A long time, father.—

—A month, my child?—

—Longer, father.—

—Three months, my child?—

—Longer, father.—

—Six months?—

—Eight months, father.—

He had begun. The priest asked:

—And what do you remember since that time?—

He began to confess his sins: masses missed, prayers not said, lies.

—Anything else, my child?—

Sins of anger, envy of others, gluttony, vanity, disobedience.

—Anything else, my child?—

There was no help. He murmured:

—I . . . committed sins of impurity, father.—

The priest did not turn his head.

—With yourself, my child?—

—And . . . with others.—

—With women, my child?—

—Yes, father.—

—Were they married women, my child?—

He did not know. His sins trickled from his lips, one by one, trickled in shameful drops from his soul festering and oozing like a sore, a squalid stream of vice. The last sins oozed forth, sluggish filthy. There was no more to tell. He bowed his head, overcome.

The priest was silent. Then he asked:

—How old are you, my child?—

—Sixteen, father.—

The priest passed his hand several times over his face. Then, resting his forehead against his hand, he leaned towards the grating and, with eyes still averted, spoke slowly. His voice was weary and old.

—You are very young, my child—he said,—and let me implore of you to give up that sin. It is a terrible sin. It kills the body and it kills the soul. It is the cause of many crimes and misfortunes. Give it up, my child, for God's sake. It is dishonourable and unmanly. You cannot know where that wretched habit will lead you or where it will come against you. As long as you commit that sin, my poor child, you will never be worth one farthing to God. Pray to our mother Mary to help you. She will help you, my child. Pray to Our Blessed Lady when that sin comes into you mind. I am sure you will do that, will you not? You repent of all those sins. I am sure you do. And you will promise God now that by His holy grace you will never offend Him any more by that wicked sin. You will make that solemn promise to God, will you not?—

—Yes, father.—

The old and weary voice fell like sweet rain upon his quaking parching heart. How sweet and sad!

—Do so, my poor child. The devil has led you astray. Drive him back to hell when he tempts you to dishonour your body in that way—the foul spirit who

478

hates Our Lord. Promise God now that you will give up that sin, that wretched wretched sin.—

Blinded by his tears and by the light of God's mercifulness he bent his head and heard the grave words of absolution spoken and saw the priest's hand raised above him in token of forgiveness.

—God bless you, my child. Pray for me.—

He knelt to say his penance, praying in a corner of the dark nave: and his prayers ascended to heaven from his purified heart like perfume streaming upwards from a heart of white rose.

The muddy streets were gay. He strode homeward, conscious of an invisible grace pervading and making light his limbs. In spite of all he had done it. He had confessed and God had pardoned him. His soul was made fair and holy once more, holy and happy.

It would be beautiful to die if God so willed. It was beautiful to live in grace a life of peace and virtue and forbearance with others.

He sat by the fire in the kitchen, not daring to speak for happiness. Till that moment he had not known how beautiful and peaceful life could be. The green square of paper pinned round the lamp cast down a tender shade. On the dresser was a plate of sausages and white pudding and on the shelf there were eggs. They would be for the breakfast in the morning after the communion in the college chapel. White pudding and eggs and sausages and cups of tea. How simple and beautiful was life after all! And life lay all before him.

In a dream he fell asleep. In a dream he rose and saw that it was morning. In a waking dream he went through the quiet morning towards the college.

The boys were all there, kneeling in their places. He knelt among them, happy and shy. The altar was heaped with fragrant masses of white flowers: and in the morning light the pale flames of the candles among the white flowers were clear and silent as his own soul.

He knelt before the altar with his classmates, holding the altar cloth with them over a living rail of hands. His hands were trembling and his soul trembled as he heard the priest pass with the ciborium from communicant to communicant.

—*Corpus Domini nostri.*—

Could it be? He knelt there sinless and timid: and he would hold upon his tongue the host and God would enter his purified body.

—*In vitam eternam. Amen.*—

Another life! A life of grace and virtue and happiness! It was true. It was not a dream from which he would wake. The past was past.

—*Corpus Domini nostri.*—

The ciborium had come to him.

IV

Sunday was dedicated to the mystery of the Holy Trinity, Monday to the Holy Ghost, Tuesday to the Guardian Angels, Wednesday to Saint Joseph, Thursday to the Most Blessed Sacrament of the Altar, Friday to Suffering Jesus, Saturday to the Blessed Virgin Mary.

Every morning he hallowed himself anew in the presence of some holy image or mystery. His day began with an heroic offering of its every moment of thought or action for the intentions of the sovereign pontiff and with an early mass. The raw morning air whetted his resolute piety; and often as he knelt among the few worshippers at the side altar, following with his interleaved prayer book the murmur of the priest, he glanced up for an instant towards the vested figure standing in the gloom between the two candles, which were the old and the new testaments, and imagined that he was kneeling at mass in the catacombs.

His daily life was laid out in devotional areas. By means of ejaculations and prayers he stored up ungrudgingly for the souls in purgatory centuries of days and quarantines and years; yet the spiritual triumph which he felt in achieving with ease so many fabulous ages of canonical penances did not wholly reward his zeal of prayer since he could never know how much temporal punishment he had remitted by way of suffrage for the agonising souls: and, fearful lest in the midst of the purgatorial fire, which differed from the infernal only in that it was not everlasting, his penance might avail no more than a drop of moisture he drove his soul daily through an increasing circle of works of supererogation.

Every part of his day, divided by what he regarded now as the duties of his station in life, circled about its own centre of spiritual energy. His life seemed to have drawn near to eternity; every thought, word and deed, every instance of consciousness could be made to revibrate radiantly in heaven: and at times his sense of such immediate repercussion was so lively that he seemed to feel his soul in devotion pressing like fingers the keyboard of a great cash register and to see the amount of his purchase start forth immediately in heaven, not as a number but as a frail column of incense or as a slender flower.

The rosaries, too, which he said constantly—for he carried his beads loose in his trousers' pockets that he might tell them as he walked the streets—transformed themselves into coronals of flowers of such vague unearthly texture that they seemed to him as hueless and odourless as they were nameless. He offered up each of his three daily chaplets that his soul might grow strong in each of the three theological virtues, in faith in the Father Who had created him, in hope in the Son Who had redeemed him, and in love of the Holy Ghost Who had sanctified him; and this thrice triple prayer he offered to the Three Persons through Mary in the name of her joyful and sorrowful and glorious mysteries.

On each of the seven days of the week he further prayed that one of the seven gifts of the Holy Ghost might descend upon his soul and drive out of it day by day the seven deadly sins which had defiled it in the past; and he prayed for each gift on its appointed day, confident that it would descend upon him, though it seemed strange to him at times that wisdom and understanding and knowledge were so distinct in their nature that each should be prayed for apart from the others. Yet he believed that at some future stage of his spiritual progress this difficulty would be removed when his sinful soul had been raised up from its weakness and enlightened by the Third Person of the Most Blessed Trinity. He believed this all the more, and with trepidation, because of the divine gloom and silence wherein dwelt the unseen Paraclete, Whose symbols were a dove and a mighty wind, to sin against Whom was a sin beyond forgiveness, the eternal, mysterious secret Being to Whom, as God, the priests offered up mass once a year, orbed in the scarlet of the tongues of fire.

The imagery through which the nature and kinship of the Three Persons of the Trinity were darkly shadowed forth in the books of devotion which he read—the Father contemplating from all eternity as in a mirror His Divine Perfections and thereby begetting eternally the Eternal Son and the Holy Spirit proceeding out of Father and Son from all eternity—were easier of acceptance by his mind by reason of their august incomprehensibility than was the simple fact that God had loved his soul from all eternity, for ages before he had been born into the world, for ages before the world itself had existed.

He had heard the names of the passions of love and hate pronounced solemnly on the stage and in the pulpit, had found them set forth solemnly in books, and had wondered why his soul was unable to harbour them for any time or to force his lips to utter their names with conviction. A brief anger had often invested him, but he had never been able to make it an abiding passion and had always felt himself passing out of it as if his very body were being divested with ease of some outer skin or peel. He had felt a subtle, dark and murmurous presence penetrate his being and fire him with a brief iniquitous lust: it, too, had slipped beyond his grasp leaving his mind lucid and indifferent. This, it seemed, was the only love and that the only hate his soul would harbour.

But he could no longer disbelieve in the reality of love since God himself had loved his individual soul with divine love from all eternity. Gradually, as his soul was enriched with spiritual knowledge, he saw the whole world forming one vast symmetrical expression of God's power and love. Life became a divine gift for every moment and sensation of which, were it even the sight of a single leaf hanging on the twig of a tree, his soul should praise and thank the giver. The world for all its solid substance and complexity no longer existed for his soul save as a theorem of divine power and love and universality. So entire and unquestionable was this sense of the divine meaning in all nature granted to his soul that he could scarcely understand why it was in any way necessary that he should continue to live. Yet that was part of the divine purpose and he dared not question its use, he above all others who had sinned so deeply and so foully against the divine purpose. Meek and abased by this consciousness of the one eternal omnipresent perfect reality his soul took up again her burden of pieties, masses and prayers and sacraments and mortifications, and only then for the first time since he had brooded on the great mystery of love did he feel within him a warm movement like that of some newly born life or virtue of the soul itself. The attitude of rapture in sacred art, the raised and parted hands, the parted lips and eyes as of one about to swoon, became for him an image of the soul in prayer, humiliated and faint before her Creator.

But he had been forewarned of the dangers of spiritual exaltation and did not allow himself to desist from even the least or lowliest devotion, striving also by constant mortification to undo the sinful past rather than to achieve a saintliness fraught with peril. Each of his senses was brought under a rigorous discipline. In order to mortify the sense of sight he made it his rule to walk in the street with downcast eyes, glancing neither to right nor left and never behind him. His eyes shunned every encounter with the eyes of women. From time to time also he balked them by a sudden effort of the will, as by lifting them suddenly in the middle of an unfinished sentence and closing the book. To mortify his hearing he exerted no control over his voice which was then breaking, neither sang nor whistled and made no attempt to flee from noise which caused him painful nervous irritation such as the sharpening of knives on the knifeboard, the gathering of cinders on the fireshovel and the twigging of the carpet. To mortify his smell was more difficult as he found in himself no instinctive repugnance to bad odours, whether they were the odours of the outdoor world such as those of dung or tar or the odours of his own person among which he had made many curious comparisons and experiments. He found in the end that the only odour against which his sense of smell revolted was a certain stale fishy stink like that of longstanding urine: and whenever it was possible he subjected himself to this unpleasant odour. To mortify the taste he practised strict habits at table, observed to the letter all the facts of the church and sought by distraction to divert his mind from the savours of different foods. But it was to the mortification of touch that he brought the most assiduous ingenuity of inventiveness. He never consciously changed his position in bed, sat in the most uncomfortable positions, suffered patiently every itch and pain, kept away from the fire, remained on his knees all through the mass except at the gospels, left parts of his neck and face undried so that air might sting them and, whenever he was not saying his beads, carried his arms stiffly at his sides like a runner and never in his pockets or clasped behind him.

He had no temptations to sin mortally. It surprised him, however, to find that at the end of his course of intricate piety and selfrestraint he was so easily at the mercy of childish and unworthy imperfections. His prayers and fasts availed him little for the suppression of anger at hearing his mother sneeze or at being disturbed in his devotions. It needed an immense effort of his will to master the impulse which urged him to give outlet to such irritation. Images of the outbursts of trivial anger which he had often noted among his masters, their twitching mouths, closeshut lips and flushed cheeks, recurred to his memory, discouraging him, for all his practice of humility, by the comparison. To merge his life in the common tide of other lives was harder for him than any fasting or prayer, and it was his constant failure to do this to his own satisfaction which caused in his soul at last a sensation of spiritual dryness together with a growth of doubts and scruples. His soul traversed a period of desolation in which the sacraments themselves seemed to have turned into dried up sources. His confession became a channel for the escape of scrupulous and unrepented imperfections. His actual reception of the eucharist did not bring him the same dissolving moments of virginal self-surrender as did those spiritual communions made by him sometimes at the close of some visit to the Blessed Sacrament. The book which he used for these visits was an old neglected book written by Saint Alphonsus Liguori, with fading characters and sere foxpapered leaves. A faded world of fervent love and virginal responses seemed to be evoked for his soul by the reading of its pages in which the imagery of the canticles was interwoven with the communicant's prayers. An inaudible voice seemed to caress the soul, telling her names and glories, bidding her arise as for espousal and come away, bidding her look forth, a spouse, from Amana and from the mountains of the leopards; and the soul seemed to answer with the same inaudible voice, surrendering herself: *Inter ubera mea commorabitur.*

This idea of surrender had a perilous attraction for his mind now that he felt his soul beset once again by the insistent voices of the flesh which began to murmur to him again during his prayers and meditations. It gave him an intense sense of power to know that he could by a single act of consent, in a moment of thought, undo all that he had done. He seemed to feel a flood slowly advancing towards his naked feet and to be waiting for the first faint timid noiseless wavelet to touch his fevered skin. Then, almost at the instant of that touch, almost at the verge of sinful consent, he found himself standing far away from the flood upon a dry shore, saved by a sudden act of the will or a sudden ejaculation: and, seeing the silver line of the floor far away and beginning again its slow advance towards his feet, a new thrill of power and satisfaction shook his soul to know that he had not yielded nor undone all.

When he had eluded the flood of temptation many times in this way he grew troubled and wondered whether the grace which he had refused to lose was not being filched from him little by little. The clear certitude of his own immunity grew dim and to it succeeded a vague fear that his soul had really fallen unawares. It was with difficulty that he won back his old consciousness of his state of grace by telling himself that he had prayed to God at every temptation and that the grace which he had prayed for must have been given to him inasmuch as God was obliged to give it. The very frequency and violence of temptations showed him at last the truth of what he had heard about the trials of the saints. Frequent and violent temptations were a proof that the citadel of the soul had not fallen and that the devil raged to make it fall.

Often when he had confessed his doubts and scruples, some momentary inattention at prayer, a movement of trivial anger in his soul or a subtle wilfulness in speech or act, he was bidden by his confessor to name some sin of his past life before absolution was given him. He named it with humility and shame and repented of it once more. It humiliated and shamed him to think that he would never be freed from it wholly, however holily he might live or whatever virtues or perfections he might attain. A restless feeling of guilt would always be present with him: he would confess and repent and be absolved, confess and repent again and be absolved again, fruitlessly. Perhaps that first hasty confession wrung from him by the fear of hell had not been good? Perhaps, concerned only for his imminent doom, he had not had sincere sorrow for his sin? But the surest sign that his confession had been good and that he had had sincere sorrow for his sin was, he knew, the amendment of his life.

—I have amended my life, have I not? he asked himself.—

✦

The director stood in the embrasure of the window, his back to the light, leaning an elbow on the brown crossblind, and, as he spoke and smiled, slowly dangling and looping the cord of the other blind, Stephen stood before him, following for a moment with his eyes the waning of the long summer daylight above the roofs or the slow deft movements of the priestly fingers. The priest's face was in total shadow, but the waning daylight from behind him touched the deeply grooved temples and the curves of the skull. Stephen followed also with his ears the accents and intervals of the priest's voice as he spoke gravely and cordially of indifferent themes, the vacation which had just ended, the colleges of the order abroad, the transference of masters. The grave and cordial voice went on easily with its tale, and in the pauses Stephen felt bound to set it on again with respectful questions. He knew that the tale was a prelude and his mind waited for the sequel. Ever since the message of summons had come for him from the director his mind had struggled to find the meaning of the message; and during the long restless time he had sat in the college parlour waiting for the director to come in his eyes had wandered from one sober picture to another around the walls and his mind wandered from one guess to another until the meaning of the summons had almost become clear. Then, just as he was wishing that some unforeseen cause might prevent the director from coming, he had heard the handle of the door turning and the swish of a soutane.

The director had begun to speak of the Dominican and Franciscan orders and of the friendship between Saint Thomas and Saint Bonaventure. The Capuchin dress, he thought, was rather too. . . .

Stephen's face gave back the priest's indulgent smile and, not being anxious to give an opinion, he made a slight dubitative movement with his lips.

—I believe,—continued the director,—that there is some talk now among the Capuchins themselves of doing away with it and following the example of the other Franciscans.—

—I suppose they would retain it in the cloisters?— said Stephen.

—O, certainly,—said the director.—For the cloister it is all right, but for the street I really think it would be better to do away with, don't you?—

—It must be troublesome, I imagine?—

—Of course it is, of course. Just imagine when I was in Belgium I used to see them out cycling in all kinds of weather with this thing up about their knees! It was really ridiculous. *Les jupes,* they call them in Belgium.—

The vowel was so modified as to be indistinct.

—What do they call them?—

—*Les jupes.*—

—O!—

Stephen smiled again in answer to the smile which he could not see on the priest's shadowed face, its image or spectre only passing rapidly across his mind as the low discreet accent fell upon his ear. He gazed calmly before him at the waning sky, glad of the cool of the evening and the faint yellow glow which hid the tiny flame kindling upon his cheek.

The names of articles of dress worn by women or of certain soft and delicate stuffs used in their making brought always to his mind a delicate and sinful perfume. As a boy he had imagined the reins by which horses are driven as slender silken bands and it shocked him to feel at Stradbrooke the greasy leather of harness. It had shocked him, too, when he had felt for the first time beneath his tremulous fingers the brittle texture of a woman's stocking for, retaining nothing of all he read save that which seemed to him an echo or a prophecy of his own state, it was only amid softworded phrases or within rosesoft stuffs that he dared to conceive of the soul or body of a woman moving with tender life.

But the phrase on the priest's lips was disingenuous for he knew that a priest should not speak lightly on that theme. The phrase had been spoken lightly with design and he felt that his face was being searched by the eyes in the shadow. Whatever he had heard or read of the craft of jesuits he had put aside frankly as not borne out by his experience. His masters, even when they had not attracted him, had seemed to him always intelligent and serious priests, athletic and high-spirited prefects. He thought of them as men who washed their bodies briskly with cold water and wore clean cold linen. During all the years he had lived among them in Clongowes and in Belvedere he had received only two pandies and, though these had been dealt him in the wrong, he knew that he had often escaped punishment. During all those years he had never heard from any of his masters a flippant word: it was they who had taught him christian doctrine and urged him to live a good life and, when he had fallen into grievous sin, it was they who had led him back to grace. Their presence had made him diffident of himself when he was a muff in Clongowes and it had made him diffident of himself also while he had held his equivocal position in Belvedere. A constant sense of this had remained with him up to the last year of his school life. He had never once disobeyed or allowed turbulent companions to seduce him from his habit of quiet obedience: and, even when he doubted some statement of a master, he had never presumed to doubt openly. Lately some of their judgments had sounded a little childish in his ears and had made him feel a regret and pity as though he were slowly passing out of an accustomed world and were hearing its language for the last time. One day when some boys had gathered round a priest under the shed near the chapel, he heard the priest say:

—I believe that Lord Macaulay was a man who probably never committed a mortal sin in his life, that is to say, a deliberate mortal sin.—

Some of the boys had then asked the priest if Victor Hugo were not the greatest French writer. The priest had answered that Victor Hugo had never written half so well when he had turned against the church as he had written when he was a catholic.

—But there are many eminent French critics,—said the priest,—who consider that even Victor Hugo, great as he certainly was, had not so pure a French style as Louis Veuillot.—

The tiny flame which the priest's allusion had kindled upon Stephen's cheek had sunk down again and his eyes were still fixed calmly on the colourless sky. But an unresting doubt flew hither and thither before his mind. Masked memories passed quickly before him: he recognised scenes and persons yet he was conscious that he had failed to perceive some vital circumstance in them. He saw himself walking about the grounds watching the sports in Clongowes and eating chocolate out of his cricketcap. Some jesuits were walking round the cycletrack in the company of ladies. The echoes of certain expressions used in Clongowes sounded in remote caves of his mind.

His ears were listening to these distant echoes amid the silence of the parlour when he became aware that the priest was addressing him in a different voice.

—I sent for you today, Stephen, because I wished to speak to you on a very important subject.—

—Yes, sir.—

—Have you ever felt that you had a vocation?—

Stephen parted his lips to answer yes and then withheld the word suddenly. The priest waited for the answer and added:

—I mean have you ever felt within yourself, in your soul, a desire to join the order. Think.—

—I have sometimes thought of it,—said Stephen.

The priest let the blindcord fall to one side and, uniting his hands, leaned his chin gravely upon them, communing with himself.

—In a college like this,—he said at length,—there is one boy or perhaps two or three boys whom God calls to the religious life. Such a boy is marked off from his companions by his piety, by the good example he shows to others. He is looked up to by them; he is chosen perhaps as prefect by his fellow sodalists. And you, Stephen, have been such a boy in this college, prefect of Our Blessed Lady's sodality. Perhaps you are the boy in this college whom God designs to call to Himself.—

A strong note of pride reinforcing the gravity of the priest's voice made Stephen's heart quicken in response.

—To receive that call, Stephen,—said the priest,—is the greatest honour that the Almighty God can bestow upon a man. No king or emperor on this earth has the power of the priest of God. No angel or archangel in heaven, no saint, not even the Blessed Virgin herself has the power of a priest of God: the power of the keys, the power to bind and to loose from sin, the power of exorcism, the power to cast out from the creatures of God the evil spirits that have power over them, the power, the authority, to make the great God of Heaven come down upon the altar and take the form of bread and wine. What an awful power, Stephen!—

A flame began to flutter again on Stephen's cheek as he heard in this proud address an echo of his own proud musings. How often had he seen himself as a priest wielding calmly and humbly the awful power of which angels and saints stood in reverence! His soul had loved to muse in secret on this desire. He had seen himself, a young and silentmannered priest, entering a confessional swiftly, ascending the altarsteps, incensing, genuflecting, accomplishing the vague acts of the priesthood which pleased him by reason of their semblance of reality and of their distance from it. In that dim life which he had lived through in his musings he had assumed the voices and gestures which he had noted with various priests. He had bent his knee sideways like such a one, he had shaken the thurible only slightly like such a one, his chasuble had swung open like that of such another as he turned to the altar again after having blessed the people. And above all it had pleased him to fill the second place in those dim scenes of his imagining. He shrank from the dignity of celebrant because it displeased him to imagine that all the vague pomp should end in his own person or that the ritual should assign to him so clear and final an office. He longed for the minor sacred offices, to be vested with the tunicle of subdeacon at high mass, to stand aloof from the altar, forgotten by the people, his shoulders covered with a humeral veil, holding the paten within its folds or, when the sacrifice had been accomplished, to stand as deacon in a dalmatic cloth of gold on the step below the celebrant, his hands joined and his face towards the people, and sing the chant, *Ite missa est.* If ever he had seen himself celebrant it was as in the pictures of the mass in his child's massbook, in a church without worshippers, save for the angel of the sacrifice, at a bare altar and served by an acolyte scarcely more boyish than himself. In vague sacrificial or sacramental acts alone his will seemed drawn to go forth to encounter reality: and it was partly the absence of an appointed rite which had always constrained him to inaction whether he had allowed silence to cover his anger or pride or had suffered only an embrace he longed to give.

He listened in reverent silence now to the priest's appeal and through the words he heard even more distinctly a voice bidding him approach, offering him secret knowledge and secret power. He would know then what was the sin of Simon Magus and what the sin against the Holy Ghost for which there was no forgiveness. He would know obscure things, hidden from others, from those who were conceived and born children of wrath. He would know the sins, the sinful longings and sinful thoughts and sinful acts, of others, hearing them murmured into his ears in the confessional under the shame of a darkened chapel by the lips of women and of girls: but rendered immune mysteriously at his ordination by the imposition of hands his soul would pass again uncontaminated to the white peace of the altar. No touch of sin would linger upon the hands with which he would elevate and break the host; no touch of sin would linger on his lips in prayer to make him eat and drink damnation to himself not discerning the body of the Lord. He would hold his secret knowledge and secret power, being as sinless as the innocent: and he would be a priest for ever according to the order of Melchisedec.

—I will offer up my mass tomorrow morning, said the director, that Almighty God may reveal to you His holy will. And let you, Stephen, make a novena to your holy patron saint, the first martyr who is very powerful with God, that God may enlighten your mind. But you must be quite sure, Stephen, that you have a vocation because it would be terrible if you found afterwards that you had none. Once a priest always a priest, remember. Your catechism tells you that the sacrament of Holy Orders is one of those which can be received only once because it imprints on the soul an indelible spiritual mark which can never be effaced. It is before you must weigh well, not after. It is a solemn question, Stephen, because on it may depend the salvation of your eternal soul. But we will pray to God together.—

He held open the heavy hall door and gave his hand as if already to a companion in the spiritual life. Stephen passed out on to the wide platform above the steps and was conscious of the caress of mild evening air. Towards Findlater's church a quartette of young men were striding along with linked arms, swaying their heads and stepping to the agile melody of their leader's concertina. The music passed in an instant, as the first bars of sudden music always did, over the fantastic fabrics of his mind, dissolving them painlessly and noiselessly as a sudden wave dissolves the sandbuilt turrets of children. Smiling at the trivial air he raised his eyes to the priest's face and, seeing in it a mirthless reflection of the sunken day, detached his hand slowly which had acquiesced faintly in that companionship.

As he descended the steps the impression which effaced his troubled selfcommunion was that of a mirthless mask reflecting a sunken day from the threshold of the college. The shadow, then, of the life of the college passed gravely over his consciousness. It was a grave and ordered and passionless life that awaited him, a life without material cares. He wondered how he would pass the first night in the novitiate and with what dismay he would wake the first morning in the dormitory. The troubling odour of the long corridors of Clongowes came back to him and he heard the discreet murmur of the burning gas flames. At once from every part of his being unrest began to irradiate. A feverish quickening of his pulses followed and a din of meaningless words drove his reasoned thoughts hither and thither confusedly. His lungs dilated and sank as if he were inhaling a warm moist unsustaining air, and he smelt again the moist warm air which hung in the bath in Clongowes above the sluggish turfcoloured water.

Some instinct, waking at these memories, stronger than education or piety quickened within him at every near approach to that life, an instinct subtle and hostile, and armed him against acquiescence. The chill and order of the life repelled him. He saw himself rising in the cold of the morning and filing down with the others to early mass and trying vainly to struggle with his prayers against the fainting sickness of his stomach. He saw himself sitting at dinner with the community of a college. What, then, had become of that deeprooted shyness of his which had made him loth to eat or drink under a strange roof? What had come of the pride of his spirit which had always made him conceive himself as a being apart in every order?

The Reverend Stephen Dedalus, S.J.

His name in that new life leaped into characters before his eyes and to it there followed a mental sensation of an undefined face or colour of a face. The colour faded and became strong like a changing glow of pallid brick red: Was it the raw reddish glow he had so often seen on wintry mornings on the shaven gills of the priests? The face was eyeless and sourfavoured and devout, shot with pink tinges of suffocated anger. Was it not a mental spectre of the face of one of the jesuits whom some of the boys called Lantern Jaws and others Foxy Campbell?

He was passing at that moment before the jesuit house in Gardiner Street, and wondered vaguely which window would be his if he ever joined the order. Then he wondered at the vagueness of his wonder, at the remoteness of his own soul from what he had hitherto imagined her sanctuary, at the frail hold which so many years of order and obedience had of him when once a definite and irrevocable act of his threatened to end for ever, in time and in eternity, his freedom. The voice of the director urging upon him the proud claims of the church and the mystery and power of the priestly office repeated itself idly in his memory. His soul was not there to hear and greet it and he knew now that the exhortation he had listened to had already fallen into an idle formal tale. He would never swing the thurible before the tabernacle as priest. His destiny was to be elusive of social or religious orders. The wisdom of the priest's appeal did not touch him to the quick. He was destined to learn his own wisdom apart from others or to learn the wisdom of others himself wandering among the snares of the world.

The snares of the world were its ways of sin. He would fall. He had not yet fallen but he would fall silently, in an instant. Not to fall was too hard, too hard: and he felt the silent lapse of his soul, as it would be at some instant to come, falling, falling, but not yet fallen, still unfallen, but about to fall.

He crossed the bridge over the stream of the Tolka, and turned his eyes coldly for an instant towards the faded blue shrine of the Blessed Virgin which stood fowlwise on a pole in the middle of a hamshaped encampment of poor cottages. Then, bending to the left, he followed the lane which led up to his house. The faint sour stink of rotted cabbages came towards him from the kitchen gardens on the rising ground above the river. He smiled to think that it was this disorder, the misrule and confusion of his father's house and the stagnation of vegetable life, which was to win the day in his soul. Then a short laugh broke from his lips as he thought of that solitary farmhand in the kitchen gardens behind their house whom they had nicknamed The Man with the Hat. A second laugh, taking rise from the first after a pause, broke from him involuntarily as he thought of how The Man with the Hat worked, considering in turn the four points of the sky and then regretfully plunging his spade in the earth.

He pushed open the latchless door of the porch and passed through the naked hallway into the kitchen. A group of his brothers and sisters was sitting round the table. Tea was nearly over and only the last of the second watered tea remained in the bottoms of the small glass jars and jampots which did service for teacups. Discarded crusts and lumps of sugared bread, turned brown by the tea which had been poured over them, lay scattered on the table. Little wells of tea lay here and there on the board and a knife with a broken ivory handle was stuck through the pith of a ravaged turnover.

The sad quiet greyblue glow of the dying day came through the window and the open door, covering over and allaying quietly a sudden instinct of remorse in Stephen's heart. All that had been denied them had been freely given to him, the eldest: but the quiet glow of evening showed him in their faces no sign of rancour.

He sat near them at the table and asked where his father and mother were. One answered:

—Goneboro toboro lookboro atboro aboro houseboro.—

Still another removal! A boy named Fallon, in Belvedere, had often asked him with a silly laugh why they moved so often. A frown of scorn darkened quickly his forehead as he heard again the silly laugh of the questioner.

He asked:

—Why are we on the move again, if it's a fair question?—

—Becauseboro theboro landboro lordboro willboro putboro usboro outboro.—

The voice of his youngest brother from the farther side of the fireplace began to sing the air "Oft in the Stilly Night." One by one the others took up the air until a full choir of voices was singing. They would sing so for hours, melody after melody, glee after glee, till the last pale light died down on the horizon, till the first dark nightclouds came forth and night fell.

He waited for some moments, listening, before he too took up the air with them. He was listening with pain of spirit to the overtone of weariness behind their frail fresh innocent voices. Even before they set out on life's journey they seemed weary already of the way.

He heard the choir of voices in the kitchen echoed and multiplied through an endless reverberation of the choirs of endless generations of children: and heard in all the echoes an echo also of the recurring note of weariness and pain. All seemed weary of life even before entering upon it. And he remembered that Newman had heard this note also in the broken lines of Virgil "giving utterance, like the voice of Nature herself, to that pain and weariness yet hope of better things which has been the experience of her children in every time."

↓

He could wait no longer.

From the door of Byron's public-house to the gate of Clontarf Chapel, from the gate of Clontarf Chapel to the door of Byron's public-house, and then back again to the chapel and then back again to the public-house he had paced slowly at first, planting his steps scrupulously in the spaces of the patchwork of the footpath, then timing their fall to the fall of verses. A full hour had passed since his father had gone in with Dan Crosby, the tutor, to find out for him something about the university. For a full hour he had paced up and down, waiting: but he could wait no longer.

He set off abruptly for the Bull, walking rapidly lest his father's shrill whistle might call him back; and in a few moments he had rounded the curve at the police barrack and was safe.

Yes, his mother was hostile to the idea, as he had read from her listless silence. Yet her mistrust pricked him more keenly than his father's pride and he thought

491

coldly how he had watched the faith which was fading down in his soul ageing and strengthening in her eyes. A dim antagonism gathered force within him and darkened his mind as a cloud against her disloyalty: and when it passed, cloud-like, leaving his mind serene and dutiful towards her again, he was made aware dimly and without regret of a first noiseless sundering of their lives.

The university! So he had passed beyond the challenge of the sentries who had stood as guardians of his boyhood and had sought to keep him among them that he might be subject to them and serve their ends. Pride after satisfaction uplifted him like long slow waves. The end he had been born to serve yet did not see had led him to escape by an unseen path: and now it beckoned to him once more and a new adventure was about to be opened to him. It seemed to him that he heard notes of fitful music leaping upwards a tone and downwards a diminishing fourth, upwards a tone and downwards a major third, like triple-branching flames leaping fitfully, flame after flame, out of a midnight wood. It was an elfin prelude, endless and formless; and, as it grew wilder and faster, the flames leaping out of time, he seemed to hear from under the boughs and grasses wild creatures racing, their feet pattering like rain upon the leaves. Their feet passed in pattering tumult over his mind, the feet of hares and rabbits, the feet of harts and hinds and antelopes, until he heard them no more and remembered only a proud cadence from Newman:—

—Whose feet are as the feet of harts and underneath the everlasting arms.—

The pride of that dim image brought back to his mind the dignity of the office he had refused. All through his boyhood he had mused upon that which he had so often thought to be his destiny and when the moment had come for him to obey the call he had turned aside, obeying a wayward instinct. Now time lay between: the oils of ordination would never anoint his body. He had refused. Why?

He turned seaward from the road at Dollymount and as he passed on to the thin wooden bridge he felt the planks shaking with the tramp of heavily shod feet. A squad of Christian Brothers was on its way back from the Bull and had begun to pass, two by two, across the bridge. Soon the whole bridge was trembling and resounding. The uncouth faces passed him two by two, stained yellow or red or livid by the sea, and as he strove to look at them with ease and indifference, a faint stain of personal shame and commiseration rose to his own face. Angry with himself he tried to hide his face from their eyes by gazing down sideways into the shallow swirling water under the bridge but he still saw a reflection therein of their topheavy silk hats, and humble tapelike collars and loosely hanging clerical clothes.

—Brother Hickey.
Brother Quaid.
Brother MacArdle.
Brother Keogh.—

Their piety would be like their names, like their faces, like their clothes; and it was idle for him to tell himself that their humble and contrite hearts, it might be, paid a far richer tribute of devotion than his had ever been, a gift tenfold more acceptable than his elaborate adoration. It was idle for him to move himself to be generous towards them, to tell himself that if he ever came to their gates, stripped of his pride, beaten and in beggar's weeds, that they would be generous towards him, loving him as themselves. Idle and embittering, finally, to argue, against his own dispassionate certitude, that the commandment of love bade us not to love our neighbours as ourselves with the same amount and intensity of love but to love him as ourselves with the same kind of love.

He drew forth a phrase from his treasure and spoke it softly to himself:

—A day of dappled seaborne clouds.—

The phrase and the day and the scene harmonised in a chord. Words. Was it their colours? He allowed them to glow and fade, hue after hue: sunrise gold, the russet and green of apple orchards, azure of waves, the greyfringed fleece of clouds. No, it was not their colours: it was the poise and balance of the period itself. Did he then love the rhythmic rise and fall of words better than their associations of legend and colour? Or was it that, being as weak of sight as he was shy of mind, he drew less pleasure from the reflection of the glowing sensible world through the prism of a language manycoloured and richly storied than from the contemplation of an inner world of individual emotions mirrored perfectly in a lucid supple periodic prose.

He passed from the trembling bridge on to firm land again. At that instant, as it seemed to him, the air was chilled; and looking askance towards the water he saw a flying squall darkening and crisping suddenly the tide. A faint click at his heart, a faint throb in his throat told him once more of how his flesh dreaded the cold infrahuman odour of the sea: yet he did not strike across the downs on his left but held straight on along the spine of rocks that pointed against the river's mouth.

A veiled sunlight lit up faintly the grey sheet of water where the river was embayed. In the distance along the course of the slowflowing Liffey slender masts flecked the sky and, more distant still, the dim fabric of the city lay prone in haze. Like a scene on some vague arras, old as man's weariness, the image of the seventh city of christendom was visible to him across the timeless air, no older nor more weary nor less patient of subjection than in the days of the thingmote.

Disheartened, he raised his eyes towards the slowdrifting clouds, dappled and seaborne. They were voyaging across the deserts of the sky, a host of nomads on the march, voyaging high over Ireland, westward bound. The Europe they had come from lay out there beyond the Irish Sea, Europe of strange tongues and valleyed and woodbegirt and citadelled and of entrenched and marshalled races. He heard a confused music within him as of memories and names which he was almost conscious of but could not capture even for an instant; then the music seemed to recede, to recede, to recede: and from each receding trail of nebulous music there fell always one long-drawn calling note, piercing like a star the dusk of silence. Again! Again! Again! A voice from beyond the world was calling.

—Hello, Stephanos!—

—Here comes The Dedalus!—

—Ao! . . . Eh, give it over, Dwyer, I'm telling you or I'll give you a stuff in the kisser for yourself. . . . Ao!—

—Good man, Towser! Duck him!—

—Come along, Dedalus! Bous Stephanoumenos! Bous Stephaneforos!—

—Duck him! Guzzle him now, Towser!—

—Help! Help! . . . Ao!—

He recognised their speech collectively before he distinguished their faces. The mere sight of that medley of wet nakedness chilled him to the bone. Their bodies, corpsewhite or suffused with a pallid golden light or rawly tanned by the suns, gleamed with the wet of the sea. Their divingstone, poised on its rude supports and rocking under their plunges, and the rough-hewn stones of the sloping breakwater over which they scrambled in their horseplay, gleamed with cold wet lustre. The towels with which they smacked their bodies were heavy with cold seawater: and drenched with cold brine was their matted hair.

He stood still in deference to their calls and parried their banter with easy words. How characterless they looked: Shuley without his deep unbuttoned collar, Ennis without his scarlet belt with the snaky clasp, and Connolly without his Norfolk coat with the flapless sidepockets! It was a pain to see them and a sword-like pain to see the signs of adolescence that made repellent their pitiable nakedness. Perhaps they had taken refuge in number and noise from the secret dread in their souls. But he, apart from them and in silence, remembered in what dread he stood of the mystery of his own body.

—Stephanos Dedalos! Bous Stephanoumenos! Bous Stephaneforos!—

Their banter was not new to him and now it flattered his mild proud sovereignty. Now, as never before, his strange name seemed to him a prophecy. So timeless seemed the grey warm air, so fluid and impersonal his own mood, that all ages were as one to him. A moment before the ghost of the ancient kingdom of the Danes had looked forth through the vesture of the hazewrapped city. Now, at the name of the fabulous artificer, he seemed to hear the noise of dim waves and to see a winged form flying above the waves and slowly climbing the air. What did it mean? Was it a quaint device opening a page of some medieval book of prophecies and symbols, a hawklike man flying sunward above the sea, a prophecy of the end he had been born to serve and had been following through the mists of childhood and boyhood, a symbol of the artist forging anew in his workshop out of the sluggish matter of the earth a new soaring impalpable imperishable being?

His heart trembled; his breath came faster and a wild spirit passed over his limbs as though he were soaring sunward. His heart trembled in an ecstacy of fear and his soul was in flight. His soul was soaring in an air beyond the world and the body he knew was purified in a breath and delivered of incertitude and made radiant and commingled with the element of the spirit. An ecstasy of flight made radiant his eyes and wild his breath and tremulous and wild and radiant his windswept limbs.

—One! Two! . . . Look out!—

—O, Cripes, I'm drownded!—

—One! Two! Three and away!—

—The next! The next!—

—One! . . . Uk!—

—Stephaneforos!—

His throat ached with a desire to cry aloud, the cry of a hawk or eagle on high, to cry piercingly of his deliverance to the winds. This was the call of life to his soul not the dull gross voice of the world of duties and despair, not the inhuman voice that had called him to the pale service of the altar. An instant of wild flight had delivered him and the cry of triumph which his lips withheld cleft his brain.

—Stephaneforos!—

What were they now but the cerements shaken from the body of death—the fear he had walked in night and day, the incertitude that had ringed him round, the shame that had abased him within and without—cerements, the linens of the grave?

His soul had arisen from the grave of boyhood, spurning her graveclothes. Yes! Yes! Yes! He would create proudly out of the freedom and power of his soul, as the great artificer whose name he bore, a living thing, new and soaring and beautiful, impalpable, imperishable.

He started up nervously from the stoneblock for he could no longer quench the flame in his blood. He felt his cheeks aflame and his throat throbbing with song. There was a lust of wandering in his feet that burned to set out for the ends of the earth. On! On! his heart seemed to cry. Evening would deepen above the sea, night fall upon the plains, dawn glimmer before the wanderer and show him strange fields and hills and faces. Where?

He looked northward towards Howth. The sea had fallen below the line of seawrack on the shallow side of the breakwater and already the tide was running out fast along the foreshore. Already one long oval bank of sand lay warm and dry amid the wavelets. Here and there warm isles of sand gleamed above the shallow tide: and about the isles and around the long bank and amid the shallow currents of the beach were lightclad figures, wading and delving.

In a few moments he was barefoot, his stockings folded in his pockets, and his canvas shoes dangling by their knotted laces over his shoulders: and, picking a pointed salteaten stick out of the jetsam among the rocks, he clambered down the slope of the breakwater.

There was a long rivulet in the strand: and, as he waded slowly up its course, he wondered at the endless drift of seaweed. Emerald and black and russet and olive, it moved beneath the current, swaying and turning. The water of the rivulet was dark with endless drift and mirrored the highdrifting clouds. The clouds were drifting above him silently and silently the seatangle was drifting below him; and the grey warm air was still: and a new wild life was singing in his veins.

Where was his boyhood now? Where was the soul that had hung back from her destiny, to brood alone upon the shame of her wounds and in her house of squalor and subterfuge to queen it in faded cerements and in wreaths that withered at the touch? Or, where was he.

He was alone. He was unheeded, happy, and near to the wild heart of life. He was alone and young and wilful and wildhearted, alone amid a waste of wild air and brackish waters and the seaharvest of shells and tangle and veiled grey sunlight and gayclad lightclad figures of children and girls and voices childish and girlish in the air.

A girl stood before him in midstream: alone and still, gazing out to sea. She seemed like one whom magic had changed into the likeness of a strange and beautiful seabird. Her long slender bare legs were delicate as a crane's and pure save where an emerald trail of seaweed had fashioned itself as a sign upon the flesh. Her thighs, fuller and softhued as ivory, were bared almost to the hips where the white fringes of her drawers were like feathering of soft white down. Her slate-blue skirts were kilted boldly about her waist and dovetailed behind her. Her bosom was as a bird's, soft and slight, slight and soft as the breast of some dark-plumaged dove. But her long fair hair was girlish: and girlish, and touched with the wonder of mortal beauty, her face.

She was alone and still, gazing out to sea; and when she felt his presence and the worship of his eyes her eyes turned to him in quiet sufferance of his gaze, without shame or wantonness. Long, long she suffered his gaze and then quietly withdrew her eyes from his and bent them towards the stream, gently stirring the water with her foot hither and thither. The first faint noise of gently moving water broke the silence, low and faint and whispering, faint as the bells of sleep; hither and thither, hither and thither: and a faint flame trembled on her cheek.

—Heavenly God! cried Stephen's soul, in an outburst of profane joy.—

He turned away from her suddenly and set off across the strand. His cheeks were aflame; his body was aglow; his limbs were trembling. On and on and on and on he strode, far out over the sands, singing wildly to the sea, crying to greet the advent of the life that had cried to him.

Her image had passed into his soul for ever and no word had broken the holy silence of his ecstasy. Her eyes had called him and his soul had leaped at the call. To live, to err, to fall, to triumph, to recreate life out of life! A wild angel had appeared to him, the angel of mortal youth and beauty, an envoy from the fair courts of life, to throw open before him in an instant of ecstasy the gates of all the ways of error and glory. On and on and on and on!

He halted suddenly and heard his heart in the silence. How far had he walked? What hour was it?

There was no human figure near him nor any sound borne to him over the air. But the tide was near the turn and already the day was on the wane. He turned landward and ran towards the shore and, running up the sloping beach, reckless of the sharp shingle, found a sandy nook amid a ring of tufted sand knolls and lay down there that the peace and silence of the evening might still the riot of his blood.

He felt above him the vast indifferent dome and the calm processes of the heavenly bodies: and the earth beneath him, the earth that had borne him, had taken him to her breast.

He closed his eyes in the languor of sleep. His eyelids trembled as if they felt the vast cyclic movement of the earth and her watchers, trembled as if they felt the strange light of some new world. His soul was swooning into some new world, fantastic, dim, uncertain as under sea, traversed by cloudy shapes and beings. A world, a glimmer, or a flower? Glimmering and trembling, trembling and unfolding, a breaking light, an opening flower, it spread in endless succession to itself, breaking in full crimson and unfolding and fading to palest rose, leaf by leaf and wave of light by wave of light, flooding all the heavens with its soft flushes, every flush deeper than other.

Evening had fallen when he woke and the sand and arid grasses of his bed glowed no longer. He rose slowly and, recalling the rapture of his sleep, sighed at its joy.

He climbed to the crest of the sandhill and gazed about him. Evening had fallen. A rim of the young moon cleft the pale waste of sky line, the rim of a silver hoop embedded in grey sand: and the tide was flowing in fast to the land with a low whisper of her waves, islanding a few last figures in distant pools.

V

He drained his third cup of watery tea to the dregs and set to chewing the crusts of fried bread that were scattered near him, staring into the dark pool of the jar. The yellow dripping had been scooped out like a boghole, and the pool under it brought back to his memory the dark turfcoloured water of the bath in Clongowes. The box of pawn tickets at his elbow had just been rifled and he took up idly one after another in his greasy fingers the blue and white dockets, scrawled and sanded and creased and bearing the name of the pledger as Daly or MacEvoy.

1 Pair Buskins.

1 D. Coat.

3 Articles and White.

1 Man's Pants.

Then he put them aside and gazed thoughtfully at the lid of the box, speckled with louse marks, and asked vaguely:

—How much is the clock fast now?

His mother straightened the battered alarm clock that was lying on its side in the middle of the mantelpiece until its dial showed a quarter to twelve and then laid it once more on its side.

—An hour and twenty five minutes, she said. The right time now is twenty past ten. The dear knows you might try to be in time for your lectures.

—Fill out the place for me to wash, said Stephen.

—Katey, fill out the place for Stephen to wash.

—Booty, fill out the place for Stephen to wash.

—I can't, I'm going for blue. Fill it out, you, Maggie.

When the enamelled basin had been fitted into the well of the sink and the old washing glove flung on the side of it, he allowed his mother to scrub his neck and root into the folds of his ears and into the interstices at the wings of his nose.

—Well, it's a poor case, she said, when a university student is so dirty that his mother has to wash him.

—But it gives you pleasure, said Stephen calmly.

An ear splitting whistle was heard from upstairs and his mother thrust a damp overall into his hands, saying:

—Dry yourself and hurry out for the love of goodness.

A second shrill whistle, prolonged angrily, brought one of the girls to the foot of the staircase.

—Yes, father?

—Is your lazy bitch of a brother gone out yet?

—Yes, father.

—Sure?

—Hm!

The girl came back, making signs to him to be quick and go out quietly by the back. Stephen laughed and said:

—He has a curious idea of genders if he thinks a bitch is masculine.

—Ah, it's a scandalous shame for you, Stephen, said his mother, and you'll live to rue the day you set your foot in that place. I know how it had changed you.

—Good morning, everybody, said Stephen, smiling and kissing the tips of his fingers in adieu.

The lane behind the terrace was waterlogged and as he went down it slowly, choosing his steps amid heaps of wet rubbish, he heard a mad nun screeching in the nun's madhouse beyond the wall.

—Jesus! O Jesus! Jesus!

He shook the sound out of his ears by an angry toss of his head and hurried on, stumbling through the mouldering offal, his heart already bitten by an ache of loathing and bitterness. His father's whistle, his mother's mutterings, the screech of an unseen maniac were to him now so many voices offending and threatening to humble the pride of his youth. He drove their echoes even out of his heart with an execration: but, as he walked down the avenue and felt the grey morning light falling about him through the dripping trees and smelt the strange wild smell of the wet leaves and bark, his soul was loosed of her miseries.

The rain laden trees of the avenue evoked in him, as always, memories of the girls and women in the plays of Gerhart Hauptmann; and the memory of their pale sorrows and the fragrance falling from the wet branches mingled in a mood of quiet joy. His morning walk across the city had begun; and he foreknew that as he passed the sloblands of Fairview he would think of the cloistral silverveined prose of Newman; that as he walked along the North Strand Road, glancing idly at the windows of the provision shops, he would recall the dark humour of Guido Cavalcanti and smile; that as he went by Baird's stone cutting works in Talbot Place the spirit of Ibsen would blow through him like a keen wind, a spirit of wayward boyish beauty; and that passing a grimy marine dealer's shop beyond the Liffey he would repeat the song by Ben Jonson which begins:

I was not wearier where I lay.

His mind when wearied of its search for the essence of beauty amid the spectral words of Aristotle or Aquinas turned often for its pleasure to the dainty songs of the Elizabethans. His mind, in the vesture of a doubting monk, stood often in shadow under the windows of that age, to hear the grave and mocking music of the lutenists or the frank laughter of waistcoateers until a laugh too low, a phrase, tarnished by time, of chambering and false honour, stung his monkish pride and drove him on from his lurking-place.

The lore which he was believed to pass his days brooding upon so that it had rapt him from the companionship of youth was only a garner of slender sentences from Aristotle's Poetics and Psychology and a *Synopsis Philosophiœ Scholasticœ ad mentem divi Thomœ*. His thinking was a dusk of doubt and selfmistrust, lit up at moments by the lightnings of intuition, but lightnings of so clear a splendour that in those moments the world perished about his feet as if it had been fire consumed: and thereafter his tongue grew heavy and he met the eyes of others with unanswering eyes for he felt that the spirit of beauty had folded him round like a mantle and that in reverie at least he had been acquainted with nobility. But, when this brief pride of silence upheld him no longer, he was glad to find himself still in the midst of common lives, passing on his way amid the squalor and noise and sloth of the city fearlessly and with a light heart.

Near the hoardings on the canal he met the consumptive man with the doll's face and the brimless hat coming towards him down the slope of the bridge with little steps, tightly buttoned into his chocolate overcoat, and holding his furled umbrella a span or two from him like a divining rod. It must be eleven, he thought, and peered into a dairy to see the time. The clock in the dairy told him that it was five minutes to five but, as he turned away, he heard a clock somewhere near him, but unseen, beating eleven strokes in swift precision. He laughed as he heard it for it made him think of McCann; and he saw him a squat figure in a shooting jacket and breeches and with a fair goatee, standing in the wind at Hopkins' corner, and heard him say:

—Dedalus, you're an anti-social being, wrapped up in yourself. I'm not. I'm a democrat: and I'll work and act for social liberty and equality among all classes and sexes in the United States of the Europe of the future.

Eleven! Then he was late for that lecture too. What day of the week was it? He stopped at a newsagent's to read the headline of a placard. Thursday. Ten to eleven, English; eleven to twelve, French; twelve to one, Physics. He fancied to himself the English lecture and felt, even at that distance, restless and helpless. He saw the heads of his classmates meekly bent as they wrote in their notebooks the points they were bidden to note, nominal definitions, essential definitions and examples or dates of birth or death, chief works, a favourable and an unfavourable criticism side by side. His own head was unbent for his thoughts wandered abroad and whether he looked around the little class of students or out of the window across the desolate gardens of the Green an odour assailed him of cheerless cellar damp and decay. Another head than his, right before him in the first benches, was poised squarely above its bending fellows like the head of a priest appealing without humility to the tabernacle for the humble worshippers about him. Why was it that when he thought of Cranly he could never raise before his mind the entire image of his body but only the image of the head and face? Even now against the grey curtain of the morning he saw it before him like the phantom of a dream, the face of a severed head or death-mask, crowned on the brows by its stiff black upright hair as by an iron crown. It was a priestlike face, priestlike in its pallor, in the wide winged nose, in the shadowings below the eyes and along the jaws, priestlike in the lips that were long and bloodless and faintly smiling: and Stephen, remembering swiftly how he had told Cranly of all the tumults and unrest and longings in his soul, day after day and night by night, only to be answered by his friend's listening silence, would have told himself that it was the face of a guilty priest who heard confessions of those whom he had not power to absolve but that he felt again in memory the gaze of its dark womanish eyes.

Through this image he had a glimpse of a strange dark cavern of speculation but at once turned away from it, feeling that it was not yet the hour to enter it. But the night shade of his friend's listlessness seemed to be diffusing in the air around him a tenuous and deadly exhalation; and he found himself glancing from one casual word to another on his right or left in stolid wonder that they had been so silently emptied of instantaneous sense until every mean shop legend bound his mind like the words of a spell and his soul shrivelled up sighing with age as he walked on in a lane among heaps of dead language. His own consciousness of language was ebbing from his brain and tricking into the very words themselves which set to band and disband themselves in wayward rhythms:

> *The ivy whines upon the wall,*
> *And whines and twines upon the wall,*
> *The yellow ivy upon the wall,*
> *Ivy, ivy up the wall.*

Did any one ever hear such drivel? Lord Almighty! Who ever heard of ivy whining on a wall? Yellow ivy: that was all right. Yellow ivory also. And what about ivory ivy?

The word now shone in his brain, clearer and brighter than any ivory sawn from the mottled tusks of elephants. *Ivory, ivoire, avorio, ebur.* One of the first examples that he had learnt in Latin had run: *India mittit ebur;* and he recalled the shrewd northern face of the rector who had taught him to construe the Metamorphoses of Ovid in a courtly English, made whimsical by the mention of porkers and potshreds and chines of bacon. He had learnt what little he knew of the laws of Latin verse from a ragged book written by a Portuguese priest.

> *Contrahit orator, variant in carmine vates.*

The crises and victories and secessions in Roman history were handed on to him in the trite words *in tanto discrimine* and he had tried to peer into the social life of the city of cities through the words *implere ollam denariorum* which the rector had rendered sonorously as the filling of a pot with denaries. The pages of his timeworn Horace never felt cold to the touch even when his own fingers were cold: they were human pages: and fifty years before they had been turned by the human fingers of John Duncan Inverarity and by his brother, William Malcolm Inverarity. Yes, those were noble names on the dusky flyleaf and, even for so poor a Latinist as he, the dusky verses were as fragrant as though they had lain all those years in myrtle and lavender and vervain; but yet it wounded him to think that he would never be but a shy guest at the feast of the world's culture and that the monkish learning, in terms of which he was striving to forge out an esthetic philosophy, was held no higher by the age he lived in than the subtle and curious jargons of heraldry and and falconry.

The grey block of Trinity on his left, set heavily in the city's ignorance like a dull stone set in a cumbrous ring, pulled his mind downward; and while he was

striving this way and that to free his feet from the fetters of the reformed conscience he came upon the droll statue of the national poet of Ireland.

He looked at it without anger: for, though sloth of the body and of the soul
crept over it like unseen vermin, over the shuffling feet and up the folds of the
cloak and around the servile head, it seemed humbly conscious of its indignity. It
was a Firbolg in the borrowed cloak of a Milesian; and he thought of his friend
Davin, the peasant student. It was a jesting name between them, but the young
peasant bore with it lightly:

—Go on, Stevie, I have a hard head, you tell me. Call me what you will.

The homely version of his christian name on the lips of his friend had touched
Stephen pleasantly when first heard for he was as formal in speech with others as
they were with him. Often, as he sat in Davin's rooms in Grantham Street, wondering at his friend's well made boots that flanked the wall pair by pair and
repeating for his friend's simple ear the verses and cadences of others which were
the veils of his own longing and dejection, the rude Firbolg mind of his listener
had drawn his mind towards it and flung it back again, drawing it by a quiet
inbred courtesy of attention or by a quaint turn of old English speech or by the
force of its delight in rude bodily skill—for Davin had sat at the feet of Michael
Cusack, the Gael—repelling swiftly and suddenly by a grossness of intelligence
or by a bluntness of feeling or by a dull stare of terror in the eyes, the terror of soul
of a starving Irish village in which the curfew was still a nightly fear.

Side by side with his memory of the deeds of prowess of his uncle Mat Davin,
the athlete, the young peasant worshipped the sorrowful legend of Ireland. The
gossip of his fellow students which strove to render the flat life of the college significant at any cost loved to think of him as a young fenian. His nurse had taught
him Irish and shaped his rude imagination by the broken lights of Irish myth. He
stood towards the myth upon which no individual mind had ever drawn out a
line of beauty and to its unwieldy tales that divided themselves as they moved
down the cycles in the same attitude as towards the Roman catholic religion, the
attitude of a dull witted loyal serf. Whatsoever of thought or of feeling came to
him from England or by way of English culture his mind stood armed against in
obedience to a password: and of the world that lay beyond England he knew only
the foreign legion of France in which he spoke of serving.

Coupling this ambition with the young man's humour Stephen had often
called him one of the tame geese: and there was even a point of irritation in the
name pointed against that very reluctance of speech and deed in his friend which
seemed so often to stand between Stephen's mind, eager of speculation, and the
hidden ways of Irish life.

One night the young peasant, his spirit stung by the violent or luxurious language in which Stephen escaped from the cold silence of intellectual revolt, had
called up before Stephen's mind a strange vision. The two were walking slowly

towards Davin's rooms through the dark narrow streets of the poorer jews.

—A thing happened to myself, Stevie, last autumn, coming on winter, and I never told it to a living soul and you are the first person now I ever told it to. I disremember if it was October or November. It was October because it was before I came up here to join the matriculation class.

Stephen had turned his smiling eyes towards his friend's face, flattered by his confidence and won over to sympathy by the speaker's simple accent.

—I was away all that day from my own place over in Buttevant—I don't know if you know where that is—at a hurling match between the Croke's Own Boys and the Fearless Thurles and by God, Stevie, that was the hard fight. My first cousin, Fonsy Davin, was stripped to his buff that day minding cool for the Limericks but he was up with the forwards half the time and shouting like mad. I never will forget that day. One of the Crokes made a woeful wipe at him one time with his caman and I declare to God he was within an aim's ace of getting it at the side of his temple. Oh, honest to God, if the crook of it caught him that time he was done for.

—I am glad he escaped, Stephen had said with a laugh, but surely that's not the strange thing that happened you?

—Well, I suppose that doesn't interest you but leastways there was such noise after the match that I missed the train home and I couldn't get any kind of a yoke to give me a lift for, as luck would have it, there was a mass meeting that same day over in Castletownroche and all the cars in the country were there. So there was nothing for it only to stay the night or to foot it out. Well, I started to walk and on I went and it was coming on night when I got into the Ballyhoura Hills, that's better than ten miles from Kilmallock and there's a long lonely road after that. You wouldn't see the sign of a christian house along the road or hear a sound. It was pitch dark almost. Once or twice I stopped by the way under a bush to redden my pipe and only for the dew was thick I'd have stretched out there and slept. At last, after a bend of the road, I spied a little cottage with a light in the window. I went up and knocked at the door. A voice asked who was there and I answered I was over at the match in Buttevant and was walking back and that I'd be thankful for a glass of water. After a while a young woman opened the door and brought me out a big mug of milk. She was half undressed as if she was going to bed when I knocked and she had her hair hanging; and I thought by her figure and by something in the look of her eyes that she must be carrying a child. She kept me in talk a long while at the door and I thought it strange because her breast and her shoulders were bare. She asked me was I tired and would I like to stop the night there. She said she was all alone in the house and that her husband had gone that morning to Queenstown with his sister to see her off. And all the time she was talking, Stevie, she had her eyes fixed on my face and she stood so close to me I could hear her breathing. When I handed her back the mug at last she took my hand to draw me in over the threshold and said: *"Come in and stay the night here. You've no call to be frightened. There's no one in but ourselves. . . ."* I didn't go in, Stevie. I thanked her and went on my way again, all in a fever. At the first bend of the road I looked back and she was standing at the door.

The last words of Davin's story sang in his memory and the figure of the woman in the story stood forth, reflected in other figures of the peasant women whom he had seen standing in the doorways at Clane as the college cars drove by, as a type of her race and of his own, a batlike soul waking to the consciousness of itself in darkness and secrecy and loneliness and, through the eyes and voice and gesture of a woman without guile, calling the stranger to her bed.

A hand was laid on his arm and a young voice cried:

—Ah, gentleman, your own girl, sir! The first handsel today, gentleman. Buy that lovely bunch. Will you, gentleman?

The blue flowers which she lifted towards him and her young blue eyes seemed to him at that instant images of guilelessness; and he halted till the image had vanished and he saw only her ragged dress and damp coarse hair and hoydenish face.

—Do, gentleman! Don't forget your own girl, sir!

—I have no money, said Stephen.

—Buy them lovely ones, will you, sir? Only a penny.

—Did you hear what I said? asked Stephen, bending towards her. I told you I had no money. I tell you again now.

—Well, sure, you will some day, sir, please God, the girl answered after an instant.

—Possibly, said Stephen, but I don't think it likely.

He left her quickly, fearing that her intimacy might turn to gibing and wishing to be out of the way before she offered her ware to another, a tourist from England or a student of Trinity. Grafton Street, along which he walked, prolonged that moment of discouraged poverty. In the roadway at the head of the street a slab was set to the memory of Wolfe Tone and he remembered having been present with his father at its laying. He remembered with bitterness that scene of tawdry tribute. There were four French delegates in a brake and one, a plump smiling young man, held, wedged on a stick, a card on which were printed the words: *Vive l'Irlande!*

But the trees in Stephen's Green were fragrant of rain and the rainsodden earth gave forth its mortal odour, a faint incense rising upward through the mould from many hearts. The soul of the gallant venal city which his elders had told him of had shrunk with time to a faint mortal odour rising from the earth and he knew that in a moment when he entered the sombre college he would be conscious of a corruption other than that of Buck Egan and Burnchapel Whaley.

It was too late to go upstairs to the French class. He crossed the hall and took the corridor to the left which led to the physics theatre. The corridor was dark and silent but not unwatchful. Why did he feel that it was not unwatchful? Was it because he had heard that in Buck Whaley's time there was a secret staircase there? Or was the jesuit house extra-territorial and was he walking among aliens? The Ireland of Tone and of Parnell seemed to have receded in space.

He opened the door of the theatre and halted in the chilly grey light that struggled through the dusty windows. A figure was crouching before the large grate and by its leanness and greyness he knew that it was the dean of studies lighting the fire. Stephen closed the door quietly and approached the fireplace.

—Good morning, sir! Can I help you?—

The priest looked up quickly and said:

—One moment now, Mr. Dedalus, and you will see. There is an art in lighting a fire. We have the liberal arts and we have the useful arts. This is one of the useful arts.—

—I will try to learn it—said Stephen.

—Not too much coal—said the dean—working briskly at his task—that is one of the secrets.—

He produced four candle butts from the side pockets of his soutane and placed them deftly among the coals and twisted papers. Stephen watched him in silence. Kneeling thus on the flagstone to kindle the fire and busied with the disposition of his wisps of paper and candle butts he seemed more than ever a humble server making ready the place of sacrifice in an empty temple, a levite of the Lord. Like a levite's robe of plain linen the faded worn soutane draped the kneeling figure of one whom the canonicals or the bellybordered ephod would irk and trouble. His very body had waxed old in lowly service of the Lord—in tending the fire upon the altar, in bearing tidings secretly, in waiting upon worldlings, in striking swiftly when bidden—and yet had remained ungraced by aught of saintly or of prelatic beauty. Nay, his very soul had waxed old in that service without growing towards light and beauty or spreading abroad a sweet odour of her sanctity—a mortified will no more responsive to the thrill of its obedience than was to the thrill of love or combat his ageing body, spare and sinewy, greyed with a silver-pointed down.

The dean rested back on his hunkers and watched the sticks catch. Stephen, to fill the silence, said:

—I am sure I could not light a fire.—

—You are an artist, are you not, Mr. Dedalus?—said the dean, glancing up and blinking his pale eyes.—The object of the artist is the creation of the beautiful. What the beautiful is is another question.—

He rubbed his hands slowly and drily over the difficulty.

—Can you solve that question now?—he asked.

—Aquinas—answered Stephen—says *pulcra sunt quæ visa placent.*—

—This fire before us—said the dean—will be pleasing to the eye. Will it therefore be beautiful?—

—In so far as it is apprehended by the sight, which I suppose means here esthetic intellection, it will be beautiful. But Aquinas also says *Bonum est in quod tendit appetitus.* In so far as it satisfies the animal craving for warmth fire is a good. In hell, however, it is an evil.—

—Quite so—said the dean—you have certainly hit the nail on the head.—

He rose nimbly and went towards the door, set it ajar and said:

—A draught is said to be a help in these matters.—

As he came back to the hearth, limping slightly but with a brisk step, Stephen saw the silent soul of a jesuit look out at him from the pale loveless eyes. Like Ignatius he was lame but in his eyes burned no spark of Ignatius' enthusiasm. Even the legendary craft of the company, a craft subtler and more secret than its fabled books of secret subtle wisdom, had not fired his soul with the energy of apostleship. It seemed as if he used the shifts and lore and cunning of the world, as bidden to do, for the greater glory of God, without joy in their handling or hatred of that in them which was evil but turning them, with a firm gesture of obedience, back upon themselves: and for all this silent service it seemed as if he loved not at all the master and little, if at all, the ends he served. *Similiter atque senis baculus,* he was, as the founder would have had him, like a staff in an old man's hand, to be leaned on in the road at nightfall or in stress of weather, to lie with a lady's nosegay on a garden seat, to be raised in menace.

The dean returned to the hearth and began to stroke his chin.

—When may we expect to have something from you on the esthetic question?—he asked.

—From me!—said Stephen in astonishment.—I stumble on an idea once a fortnight if I am lucky.—

—These questions are very profound, Mr. Dedalus—said the dean.—It is like looking down from the cliffs of Moher into the depths. Many go down into the depths and never come up. Only the trained diver can go down into those depths and explore them and come to the surface again.—

—If you mean speculation, sir—said Stephen—I also am sure that there is no such thing as free thinking inasmuch as all thinking must be bound by its own laws.—

—Ha!—

—For my purpose I can work on at present by the light of one or two ideas of Aristotle and Aquinas.—

—I see. I quite see your point.—

—I need them only for my own use and guidance until I have done something for myself by their light. If the lamp smokes or smells I shall try to trim it. If it does not give light enough I shall sell it and buy another.—

—Epictetus also had a lamp—said the dean—which was sold for a fancy price after his death. It was the lamp he wrote his philosophical dissertations by. You know Epictetus?—

—An old gentleman—said Stephen coarsely—who said that the soul is very like a bucketful of water.—

—He tells us in his homely way—the dean went on—that he put an iron lamp before a statue of one of the gods and that a thief stole the lamp. What did the philosopher do? He reflected that it was in the character of a thief to steal and determined to buy an earthen lamp next day instead of the iron lamp.—

A smell of molten tallow came up from the dean's candle butts and fused itself in Stephen's consciousness with the jingle of the words, bucket and lamp and lamp and bucket. The priest's voice, too, had a hard jingling tone. Stephen's mind halted by instinct, checked by the strange tone and the imagery and by the priest's face which seemed like an unlit lamp or a reflector hung in a false focus. What lay behind it or within it? A dull torpor of the soul or the dullness of the thunder-cloud, charged with intellection and capable of the gloom of God?

—I meant a different kind of lamp, sir—said Stephen.

—Undoubtedly—said the dean.

—One difficulty—said Stephen—in esthetic discussion is to know whether words are being used according to the literary tradition or according to the tradition of the marketplace. I remember a sentence of Newman's, in which he says of the Blessed Virgin that she was detained in the full company of the saints. The use of the word in the marketplace is quite different. *I hope I am not detaining you.*—

—Not in the least—said the dean politely.

—No, no—said Stephen, smiling—I mean . . . —

—Yes, yes: I see—said the dean quickly—I quite catch the point: *detain.*—

He thrust forward his under jaw and uttered a dry short cough.

—To return to the lamp—he said—the feeding of it is also a nice problem. You must choose the pure oil and you must be careful when you pour it in not to overflow it, not to pour in more than the funnel can hold.—

—What funnel?—asked Stephen.

—The funnel through which you pour the oil into your lamp.—

—That?—said Stephen.—Is that called a funnel? Is it not a tundish?—

—What is a tundish?—

—That. The . . . the funnel.—

—Is that called a tundish in Ireland?—asked the dean.—I never heard the word in my life.—

—It is called a tundish in Lower Drumcondra—said Stephen, laughing—where they speak the best English.—

—A tundish—said the dean reflectively.—That is a most interesting word. I must look that word up. Upon my word I must.—

His courtesy of manner rang a little false, and Stephen looked at the English convert with the same eyes as the elder brother in the parable may have turned on the prodigal. A humble follower in the wake of clamorous conversions, a poor

Englishman in Ireland, he seemed to have entered on the stage of jesuit history when that strange play of intrigue and suffering and envy and struggle and indignity had been all but given through—a late comer, a tardy spirit. From what had he set out? Perhaps he had been born and bred among serious dissenters, seeing salvation in Jesus only and abhoring the vain pomps of the establishment. Had he felt the need of an implicit faith amid the welter of sectarianism and the jargon of its turbulent schisms, six principal men, peculiar people, seed and snake baptists, supralapsarian dogmatists. Had he found the true church all of a sudden in winding up to the end like a reel of cotton some finespun line of reasoning upon insufflation on the imposition of hands or the procession of the Holy Ghost? Or had Lord Christ touched him and bidden him follow, like that disciple who had sat at the receipt of custom, as he sat by the door of some zinc roofed chapel, yawning and telling over his church pence?

The dean repeated the word yet again.

—Tundish! Well now, that is interesting!—

—The question you asked me a moment ago seems to me more interesting. What is that beauty which the artist struggles to express from lumps of earth— said Stephen coldly.

The little word seemed to have turned a rapier point of his sensitiveness against this courteous and vigilant foe. He felt with a smart of dejection that the man to whom he was speaking was a countryman of Ben Jonson. He thought:

—The language in which we are speaking is his before it is mine. How different are the words *home, Christ, ale, master,* on his lips and on mine! I cannot speak or write these words without unrest of spirit. His language, so familiar and so foreign, will always be for me an acquired speech. I have not made or accepted its words. My voice holds them at bay. My soul frets in the shadow of his language.—

—And to distinguish between the beautiful and the sublime—the dean added—to distinguish between moral beauty and material beauty. And to inquire what kind of beauty is proper to each of the various arts. These are some interesting points we might take up.—

Stephen, disheartened suddenly by the dean's firm dry tone, was silent: and through the silence a distant noise of many boots and confused voices came up the staircase.

—In pursuing these speculations—said the dean conclusively—there is, however, the danger of perishing of inanition. First you must take your degree. Set that before you as your first aim. Then, little by little, you will see your way. I mean in every sense, your way in life and in thinking. It may be uphill pedalling at first. Take Mr. Moonan. He was a long time before he got to the top. But he got there.—

—I may not have his talent—said Stephen quietly.

—You never know—said the dean brightly.—We never can say what is in us. I most certainly should not be despondent. *Per aspera ad astra.*—

He left the hearth quickly and went towards the landing to oversee the arrival of the first arts' class.

Leaning against the fireplace Stephen heard him greet briskly and impartially every student of the class and could almost see the frank smiles of the coarser students. A desolating pity began to fall like dew upon his easily embittered heart for this faithful servingman of the knightly Loyola, for this half brother of the clergy, more venal than they in speech, more steadfast of soul than they, one whom he would never call his ghostly father: and he thought how this man and his companions had earned the name of worldlings at the hands not of the unworldly only but of the worldly also for having pleaded, during all their history, at the bar of God's justice for the souls of the lax and the lukewarm and the prudent.

The entry of the professor was signalled by a few rounds of Kentish fire from the heavy boots of those students who sat on the highest tier of the gloomy theatre under the grey cobwebbed windows. The calling of the roll began, and the responses to the names were given out in all tones until the name of Peter Byrne was reached.

—Here!—

A deep base note in response came from the upper tier, followed by coughs of protest along the other benches.

The professor paused in his reading and called the next name:

—Cranly!—

No answer.

—Mr. Cranly!—

A smile flew across Stephen's face as he thought of his friend's studies.

—Try Leopardstown!—said a voice from the bench behind.

Stephen glanced up quickly but Moynihan's snoutish face, outlined on the grey light, was impassive. A formula was given out. Amid the rustling of the notebooks Stephen turned back again and said:

—Give me some paper for God's sake.—

—Are you as bad as that?—asked Moynihan with a broad grin.

He tore a sheet from his scribbler and passed it down, whispering:

—In case of necessity any layman or woman can do it.—

The formula which he wrote obediently on the sheet of paper, the coiling and uncoiling calculations of the professor, the spectrelike symbols of force and velocity fascinated and jaded Stephen's mind. He had heard some say that the old professor was an atheist freemason. Oh, the grey dull day! It seemed a limbo of painless patient consciousness through which souls of mathematicians might wander, projecting long slender fabrics from plane to plane of ever rarer and paler twilight, radiating swift eddies to the last verges of a universe ever vaster, farther and more impalpable.

—So we must distinguish between elliptical and ellipsoidal. Perhaps some of you gentlemen may be familiar with the works of Mr. W. S. Gilbert. In one of his songs he speaks of the billiard sharp who is condemned to play:

> *On a cloth untrue*
> *With a twisted cue*
> *And elliptical billiard balls.*

—He means a ball having the form of the ellipsoid of the principal axes of which I spoke a moment ago.—

Moynihan leaned down towards Stephen's ear and murmured:—What price ellipsoidal balls! chase me, ladies, I'm in the cavalry!—

His fellow student's rude humour ran like a gust through the cloister of Stephen's mind, shaking into gay life limp priestly vestments that hung upon the walls, setting them to sway and caper in a sabbath of misrule. The forms of the community emerged from the gust blown vestments, the dean of studies, the portly florid bursar with his cap of grey hair, the president, the little priest with feathery hair who wrote devout verses, the squat peasant form of the professor of economics, the tall form of the young professor of mental science discussing on the landing a case of conscience with his class like a giraffe cropping high leafage among a herd of antelopes, the grave troubled prefect of the sodality, the plump round headed professor of Italian with his rogue's eyes. They came ambling and stumbling, tumbling and capering, kilting their gowns for leap frog, holding one another back, shaken with deep false laughter, smacking one another behind and laughing at their rude malice, calling to one another by familiar nicknames, protesting with sudden dignity at some rough usage, whispering two and two behind their hands.

The professor had gone to the glass cases on the sidewall, from a shelf of which he took down a set of coils, blew away the dust from many points and, bearing it carefully to the table, held a finger on it while he proceeded with his lecture. He explained that the wires in modern coils were of a compound called platinoid lately discovered by F. W. Martino.

He spoke clearly the initials and surname of the discoverer. Moynihan whispered from behind:

—Good old Fresh Water Martin!—

—Ask him—Stephen whispered back with weary humour—if he wants a subject for electrocution. He can have me.—

Moynihan, seeing the professor bend over the coils, rose in his bench and, clacking noiselessly the fingers of his right hand, began to call with the voice of a slobbering urchin:—Please, teacher! This boy is after saying a bad word, teacher.—

—Platinoid—the professor said solemnly—is preferred to German silver because it has a lower coefficient of resistance by changes of temperature. The platinoid wire is insulated and the covering of silk that insulates it is wound on the ebonite bobbins just where my finger is. If it were wound single an extra current would be induced in the coils. The bobbins are saturated in hot paraffin wax . . .—

A sharp Ulster voice said from the bench below Stephen:

—Are we likely to be asked questions on applied science?—

The professor began to juggle gravely with the terms pure science and applied science. A heavybuilt student, wearing gold spectacles, stared with some wonder at the questioner. Moynihan murmured from behind in his natural voice:

—Isn't MacAlister a devil for his pound of flesh?—Stephen looked down coldly on the oblong skull beneath him overgrown with tangled twinecoloured hair. The voice, the accent, the mind of the questioner offended him and he allowed the offence to carry him towards wilful unkindness, bidding his mind think that the student's father would have done better had he sent his son to Belfast to study and have saved something on the train fare by so doing.

The oblong skull beneath did not turn to meet this shaft of thought and yet the shaft came back to its bowstring: for he saw in a moment the student's whey pale face.

—That thought is not mine—he said to himself quickly.—It came from the comic Irishman in the bench behind. Patience. Can you say with certitude by whom the soul of your race was bartered and its elect betrayed—by the questioner or by the mocker? Patience. Remember Epictetus. It is probably in his character to ask such a question at such a moment in such a tone and to pronounce the word *science* as a monosyllable.—

The droning voice of the professor continued to wind itself slowly round and round the coils it spoke of, doubling, trebling, quadrupling its somnolent energy as the coil multiplied its ohms of resistance.

Moynihan's voice called from behind in echo to a distant bell:

—Closing time, gents!—

The entrance hall was crowded and loud with talk. On a table near the door were two photographs in frames and between them a long roll of paper bearing an irregular tail of signatures. MacCann went briskly to and fro among the students, talking rapidly, answering rebuffs and leading one after another to the table. In the inner hall the dean of studies stood talking to a young professor, stroking his chin gravely and nodding his head.

Stephen, checked by the crowd at the door, halted irresolutely. From under the wide falling leaf of a soft hat Cranly's dark eyes were watching him.

—Have you signed?—Stephen asked.

Cranly closed his long thinlipped mouth, communed with himself an instant and answered:

—*Ego habeo.*—

—What is it for?—

—*Quod?*—

—What is it for?—

Cranly turned his pale face to Stephen and said blandly and bitterly:

—*Per pax universalis.*—

Stephen pointed to the Tsar's photograph and said:

—He has the face of a besotted Christ.—

The scorn and anger in his voice brought Cranly's eyes back from a calm survey of the walls of the hall.

—Are you annoyed?—he asked.

—No—answered Stephen.

—Are you in bad humour?—

—No.—

—*Credo ut vos sanguinarius mendax estis*—said Cranly—*quia facies vostra monstrat ut vos in damno malo humore estis.*—

Moynihan, on his way to the table, said in Stephen's ear:

—MacCann is in tiptop form. Ready to shed the last drop. Brand new world. No stimulants and votes for the bitches.—

Stephen smiled at the manner of this confidence and, when Moynihan had passed, turned again to meet Cranly's eyes.

—Perhaps you can tell me—he said—why he pours his soul so freely into my ear. Can you?—

A dull scowl appeared on Cranly's forehead. He stared at the table where Moynihan had bent to write his name on the roll; and then said flatly:

—A sugar!—

—*Quis est in malo humore*—said Stephen—*ego aut vos?*—

Cranly did not take up the taunt. He brooded sourly on his judgment and repeated with the same flat force:

—A flaming bloody sugar, that's what he is!—

It was his epitaph for all dead friendships and Stephen wondered whether it would ever be spoken in the same tone over his memory. The heavy lumpish phrase sank slowly out of hearing like a stone through a quagmire. Stephen saw it sink as he had seen many another, feeling its heaviness depress his heart. Cranly's speech, unlike that of Davin, had neither rare phrases of Elizabethan English nor quaintly turned versions of Irish idioms. Its drawl was an echo of the quays of Dublin given back by a bleak decaying seaport, its energy an echo of the sacred eloquence of Dublin given back flatly by a Wicklow pulpit.

The heavy scowl faded from Cranly's face as MacCann marched briskly towards them from the other side of the hall.

—Here you are!—said MacCann cheerily.

—Here I am!—said Stephen.

—Late as usual. Can you not combine the progressive tendency with a respect for punctuality?—

—That question is out of order—said Stephen.— Next business.—

His smiling eyes were fixed on a silver wrapped tablet of milk chocolate which peeped out of the propagandist's breast-pocket. A little ring of listeners closed round to hear the war of wits. A lean student with olive skin and lank black hair thrust his face between the two, glancing from one to the other at each phrase and seeming to try to catch each flying phrase in his open moist mouth. Cranly took a small grey handball from his pocket and began to examine it closely, turning it over and over.

—Next business?—said MacCann.—Hom!—

He gave a loud cough of laughter, smiled broadly, and tugged twice at the strawcoloured goatee which hung from his blunt chin.

—The next business is to sign the testimonial.—

—Will you pay me anything if I sign?—asked Stephen.

—I thought you were an idealist—said MacCann.

The gipsylike student looked about him and addressed the onlookers in an indistinct bleating voice.

—By hell, that's a queer notion. I consider that notion to be a mercenary notion.—

His voice faded into silence. No heed was paid to his words. He turned his olive face, equine in expression, towards Stephen, inviting him to speak again.

MacCann began to speak with fluent energy of the Tsar's rescript, of Stead, of general disarmament, arbitration in cases of international disputes, of the signs of the times, of the new humanity and the new gospel of life which would make it the business of the community to secure as cheaply as possible the greatest possible happiness of the greatest possible number.

The gipsy student responded to the close of the period by crying:

—Three cheers for universal brotherhood!—

—Go on, Temple—said a stout ruddy student near him.—I'll stand you a pint after.—

—I'm a believer in universal brotherhood—said Temple, glancing about him out of his dark, oval eyes.—Marx is only a bloody cod.—

Cranly gripped his arm tightly to check his tongue, smiling uneasily, and repeated:

—Easy, easy, easy!—

Temple struggled to free his arm but continued, his mouth flecked by a thin foam:

—Socialism was founded by an Irishman and the first man in Europe who preached the freedom of thought was Collins. Two hundred years ago. He denounced priestcraft, the philosopher of Middlesex. Three cheers for John Anthony Collins!—

A thin voice from the verge of the ring replied:

—Pip! pip!—

Moynihan murmured beside Stephen's ear:

—And what about John Anthony's poor little sister:

> *Lottie Collins lost her drawers;*
> *Won't you kindly lend her yours?*

Stephen laughed and Moynihan, pleased with the result, murmured again:

—We'll have five bob each way on John Anthony Collins.—

—I am waiting for your answer—said MacCann briefly.

—The affair doesn't interest me in the least—said Stephen wearily.—You know that well. Why do you make a scene about it?—

—Good!—said MacCann, smacking his lips.—You are a reactionary, then?—

—Do you think you impress me—Stephen asked—when you flourish your wooden sword?—

—Metaphors!—said MacCann bluntly.—Come to facts.—

Stephen blushed and turned aside. MacCann stood his ground and said with hostile humour:

—Minor poets, I suppose, are above such trivial questions as the question of universal peace.—

Cranly raised his head and held the handball between the two students by way of a peaceoffering, saying:

—*Pax super totum sanguinarium globum.*—

Stephen, moving away the bystanders, jerked his shoulder angrily in the direction of the Tsar's image, saying:

—Keep your icon. If you must have a Jesus, let us have a legitimate Jesus.—

—By hell, that's a good one!—said the gipsy student to those about him—that's a fine expression. I like that expression immensely.—

He gulped down the spittle in his throat as if he were gulping down the phrase and, fumbling at the peak of his tweed cap, turned to Stephen, saying:

—Excuse me, sir, what do you mean by that expression you uttered just now?—

Feeling himself jostled by the students near him, he said to them:

—I am curious to know now what he meant by that expression.—

He turned again to Stephen and said in a whisper:

—Do you believe in Jesus? I believe in man. Of course, I don't know if you believe in man. I admire you, sir. I admire the mind of man independent of all religions. Is that your opinion about the mind of Jesus?—

—Go on, Temple—said the stout ruddy student, returning, as was his wont, to his first idea—that pint is waiting for you.—

—He thinks I'm an imbecile—Temple explained to Stephen—because I'm a believer in the power of mind.—

Cranly linked his arms into those of Stephen and his admirer and said:

—*Nos ad manum ballum jocabimus.*—

Stephen, in the act of being led away, caught sight of MacCann's flushed blunt-featured face.

—My signature is of no account—he said politely.— You are right to go your way. Leave me to go mine.—

—Dedalus—said MacCann crisply—I believe you're a good fellow but you have yet to learn the dignity of altruism and the responsibility of the human individual.—

A voice said:

—Intellectual crankery is better out of this movement than in it.—

Stephen, recognizing the harsh tone of MacAlister's voice, did not turn in the direction of the voice. Cranly pushed solemnly through the throng of students, linking Stephen and Temple like a celebrant attended by his ministers on his way to the altar. Temple bent eagerly across Cranly's breast and said:

—Did you hear MacAlister what he said? That youth is jealous of you. Did you see that? I bet Cranly didn't see that. By hell, I saw that at once.—

As they crossed the inner hall the dean of studies was in the act of escaping from the student with whom he had been conversing. He stood at the foot of the staircase, a foot on the lowest step, his threadbare soutane gathered about him for the ascent with womanish care, nodding his head often and repeating:

—Not a doubt of it, Mr. Hackett! Very fine! Not a doubt of it!—

In the middle of the hall the prefect of the college sodality was speaking earnestly, in a soft querulous voice, with a boarder. As he spoke he wrinkled a little his freckled brow, and bit, between his phrases, at a tiny bone pencil.

—I hope the matric men will all come. The first arts men are pretty sure. Second arts, too. We must make sure of the newcomers.—

Temple bent again across Cranly, as they were passing through the doorway, and said in a swift whisper:

—Do you know that he is a married man? He was a married man before they converted him. He has a wife and children somewhere. By hell, I think that's the queerest notion I ever heard! Eh?—

His whisper trailed off into sly cackling laughter. The moment they were through the doorway Cranly seized him rudely by the neck and shook him, saying:

—You flaming floundering fool! I'll take my dying bible there isn't a bigger bloody ape, do you know, than you in the whole flaming bloody world!—

Temple wriggled in his grip, laughing still with sly content, while Cranly repeated flatly at every rude shake:

—A flaming flaring bloody idiot!—

They crossed the weedy garden together. The president, wrapped in a heavy loose cloak, was coming towards them along one of the walks, reading his office. At the end of the walk he halted before turning and raised his eyes. The students saluted, Temple fumbling as before at the peak of his cap. They walked forward in silence. As they neared the alley Stephen could hear the thuds of the players' hands and the wet smacks of the ball and Davin's voice crying out excitedly at each stroke.

The three students halted round the box on which Davin sat to follow the game. Temple, after a few moments, sidled across to Stephen and said:

—Excuse me, I wanted to ask you do you believe that Jean Jacques Rousseau was a sincere man?—

Stephen laughed outright. Cranly, picking up the broken stave of a cask from the grass at his feet, turned swiftly and said sternly:

—Temple, I declare to the living God if you say another word, do you know, to anybody on any subject I'll kill you *super spottum.*—

—He was like you, I fancy—said Stephen—an emotional man.—

—Blast him, curse him!—said Cranly broadly.—Don't talk to him at all. Sure, you might as well be talking, do you know, to a flaming chamberpot as talking to Temple. Go home, Temple. For God's sake, go home.—

—I don't care a damn about you, Cranly—answered Temple, moving out of reach of the uplifted stave and pointing at Stephen.—He's the only man I see in this institution that has an individual mind.—

—Institution! Individual!—cried Cranly.—Go home, blast you, for you're a hopeless bloody man.—

—I'm an emotional man—said Temple.—That's quite rightly expressed. And I'm proud that I'm an emotionalist.—

He sidled out of the alley, smiling slyly. Cranly watched him with a blank expressionless face.

—Look at him!—he said.—Did you ever see such a go-by-the-wall?—

His phrase was greeted by a strange laugh from a student who lounged against the wall, his peaked cap down on his eyes. The laugh, pitched in a high key and coming from a so muscular frame, seemed like the whinny of an elephant. The student's body shook all over and, to ease his mirth, he rubbed both his hands delightedly, over his groins.

—Lynch is awake—said Cranly.

Lynch, for answer, straightened himself and thrust forward his chest.

—Lynch puts out his chest—said Stephen—as a criticism of life.—

Lynch smote himself sonorously on the chest and said:

—Who has anything to say about my girth?—

Cranly took him at the word and the two began to tussle. When their faces had flushed with the struggle they drew apart, panting. Stephen bent down towards Davin who, intent on the game, had paid no heed to the talk of the others.

—And how is my little tame goose?—he asked.—Did he sign, too?—

Davin nodded and said:—And you Stevie?—

Stephen shook his head.—You're a terrible man, Stevie—said Davin, taking the short pipe from his mouth—always alone.—

—Now that you have signed the petition for universal peace—said Stephen—I suppose you will burn that little copybook I saw in your room.—

As Davin did not answer Stephen began to quote:

—Long pace, fianna! Right incline, fianna! Fianna, by numbers, salute, one, two!—

—That's a different question—said Davin.—I'm an Irish nationalist, first and foremost. But that's you all out. You're a born sneerer, Stevie.—

—When you make the next rebellion with hurley-sticks—said Stephen—and want the indispensable informer, tell me. I can find you a few in this college.—

—I can't understand you—said Davin.—One time I hear you talk against English literature. Now you talk against the Irish informers. What with your name and your ideas . . . are you Irish at all?—

—Come with me now to the office of arms and I will show you the tree of my family—said Stephen.

—Then be one of us—said Davin.—Why don't you learn Irish? Why did you drop out of the league class after the first lesson?—

—You know one reason why—answered Stephen.

Davin tossed his head and laughed.

—Oh, come now—he said.—Is it on account of that certain young lady and Father Moran? But that's all in your own mind, Stevie. They were only talking and laughing.—

Stephen paused and laid a friendly hand upon Davin's shoulder.

—Do you remember—he said—when we knew each other first? The first morning we met you asked me to show you the way to the matriculation class, putting a very strong stress on the first syllable. You remember? Then you used to address the jesuits as father, you remember? I ask myself about you: *Is he as innocent as his speech?*—

—I'm a simple person—said Davin.—You know that. When you told me that night in Harcourt Street those things about your private life, honest to God, Stevie, I was not able to eat my dinner. I was quite bad. I was awake a long time that night. Why did you tell me those things?—

—Thanks—said Stephen.—You mean I am a monster.—

—No—said Davin—but I wish you had not told me.—

A tide began to surge beneath the calm surface of Stephen's friendliness.

—This race and this country and this life produced me—he said.—I shall express myself as I am.—

—Try to be one of us—repeated Davin.—In your heart you are an Irishman but your pride is too powerful.—

—My ancestors threw off their language and took another—Stephen said.—They allowed a handful of foreigners to subject them. Do you fancy I am going

517

to pay in my own life and person debts they made? What for?—

—For our freedom—said Davin.

—No honourable and sincere man—said Stephen—has given up to you his life and his youth and his affections from the days of Tone to those of Parnell but you sold him to the enemy or failed him in need or reviled him and left him for another. And you invite me to be one of you. I'd see you damned first.—

—They died for their ideals, Stevie—said Davin.—Our day will come yet, believe me.—

Stephen, following his own thought, was silent for an instant.

—The soul is born—he said vaguely—first in those moments I told you of. It has a slow and dark birth, more mysterious than the birth of the body. When the soul of a man is born in this country there are nets flung at it to hold it back from flight. You talk to me of nationality, language, religion. I shall try to fly by those nets.—

Davin knocked the ashes from his pipe.

—Too deep for me, Stevie—he said.—But a man's country comes first. Ireland first, Stevie. You can be a poet or mystic after.—

—Do you know what Ireland is?—asked Stephen with cold violence.—Ireland is the old sow that eats her farrow.—

Davin rose from his box and went towards the players, shaking his head sadly. But in a moment his sadness left him and he was hotly disputing with Cranly and the two players who had finished their game. A match of four was arranged, Cranly insisting, however, that his ball should be used. He let it rebound twice or thrice to his hand and struck it strongly and swiftly towards the base of the alley, exclaiming in answer to its thud:

—Your soul!—

Stephen stood with Lynch till the score began to rise. Then he plucked him by the sleeve to come away. Lynch obeyed, saying:

—Let us eke go, as Cranly has it.—

Stephen smiled at this sidethrust.

They passed back through the garden and out through the hall where the doddering porter was pinning up a notice in the frame. At the foot of the steps they halted and Stephen took a packet of cigarettes from his pocket and offered it to his companion.

—I know you are poor—he said.

—Damn your yellow insolence—answered Lynch.

This second proof of Lynch's culture made Stephen smile again.

—It was a great day for European culture—he said—when you made up your mind to swear in yellow.—

They lit their cigarettes and turned to the right. After a pause Stephen began:

—Aristotle has not defined pity and terror. I have. I say . . . —

Lynch halted and said bluntly:

—Stop! I won't listen! I am sick. I was out last night on a yellow drunk with Horan and Goggins.—

Stephen went on:

—Pity is the feeling which arrests the mind in the presence of whatsoever is grave and constant in human sufferings and unites it with the human sufferer. Terror is the feeling which arrests the mind in the presence of whatsoever is grave and constant in human sufferings and unites it with the secret cause.—

—Repeat—said Lynch.

Stephen repeated the definitions slowly.

—A girl got into a hansom a few days ago—he went on—in London. She was on her way to meet her mother whom she had not seen for many years. At the corner of a street the shaft of a lorry shivered the window of the hansom in the shape of a star. A long fine needle of the shivered glass pierced her heart. She died on the instant. The reporter called it a tragic death. It is not. It is remote from terror and pity according to the terms of my definitions.

—The tragic emotion, in fact, is a face looking two ways, towards terror and towards pity, both of which are phases of it. You see I use the word *arrest*. I mean that the tragic emotion is static. Or rather the dramatic emotion is. The feelings excited by improper art are kinetic, desire or loathing. Desire urges us to possess, to go to something; loathing urges us to abandon, to go from something. The arts which excite them, pornographical or didactic, are therefore improper arts. The esthetic emotion (I used the general term) is therefore static. The mind is arrested and raised above desire and loathing.—

—You say that art must not excite desire—said Lynch—I told you that one day I wrote my name in pencil on the backside of the Venus of Praxiteles in the Museum. Was that not desire?—

—I speak of normal natures—said Stephen.—You also told me that when you were a boy in that charming carmelite school you ate pieces of dried cowdung.—

Lynch broke again into a whinny of laughter and again rubbed both his hands over his groins but without taking them from his pockets.

—O, I did! I did!—he cried.

Stephen turned towards his companion and looked at him for a moment boldly in the eyes. Lynch, recovering from his laughter, answered his look from his humbled eyes. The long slender flattened skull beneath the long pointed cap brought before Stephen's mind the image of a hooded reptile. The eyes, too, were reptile-like in glint and gaze. Yet at that instant, humbled and alert in their look, they were lit by one tiny human point, the window of a shrivelled soul, poignant and selfembittered.

—As for that—Stephen said in polite parenthesis—we are all animals. I also am an animal.—

—You are—said Lynch.

—But we are just now in a mental world—Stephen continued.—The desire and loathing excited by improper esthetic means are really not esthetic emotions not only because they are kinetic in character but also because they are not more than physical. Our flesh shrinks from what it dreads and responds to the stimulus of what it desires by a purely reflex action of the nervous system. Our eyelid closes before we are aware that the fly is about to enter our eye.—

—Not always—said Lynch critically.

—In the same way—said Stephen—your flesh responded to the stimulus of a naked statue but it was, I say, simply a reflex action of the nerves. Beauty expressed by the artist cannot awaken in us an emotion which is kinetic or a sensation which is purely physical. It awakens, or ought to awaken, or induces, or ought to induce, an esthetic stasis, an ideal pity or an ideal terror, a stasis called forth, prolonged and at last dissolved by what I call the rhythm of beauty.—

—What is that exactly?—asked Lynch.

—Rhythm—said Stephen—is the first formal esthetic relation of part to part in any esthetic whole or of an esthetic whole to its part or parts or of any part to the esthetic whole of which it is a part.—

—If that is rhythm—said Lynch—let me hear what you call beauty: and, please remember, though I did eat a cake of cowdung once, that I admire only beauty.—

Stephen raised his cap as if in greeting. Then, blushing slightly, he laid his hand on Lynch's thick tweed sleeve.

—We are right—he said—and the others are wrong. To speak of these things and to try to understand their nature and, having understood it, to try slowly and humbly and constantly to express, to press out again, from the gross earth or what it brings forth, from sound and shape and colour which are the prison gates of our soul, an image of the beauty we have come to understand—that is art.—

They had reached the canal bridge and, turning from their course, went on by the trees. A crude grey light, mirrored in the sluggish water, and a smell of wet branches over their heads seemed to war against the course of Stephen's thought.

—But you have not answered my question—said Lynch—What is art? What is the beauty it expresses?—

—That was the first definition I gave you, you sleepy-headed wretch—said Stephen—when I began to try to think out the matter for myself. Do you remember the night? Cranly lost his temper and began to talk about Wicklow bacon.—

—I remember—said Lynch.—He told us about them flaming fat devils of pigs.—

—Art—said Stephen—is the human disposition of sensible or intelligible matter for an esthetic end. You remember the pigs and forgot that. You are a distressing pair, you and Cranly.—

Lynch made a grimace at the raw grey sky and said:

—If I am to listen to your esthetic philosophy give me at least another cigarette. I don't care about it. I don't even care about women. Damn you and damn everything. I want a job of five hundred a year. You can't get me one.—

Stephen handed him the packet of cigarettes. Lynch took the last one that remained, saying simply:

—Proceed!—

—Aquinas—said Stephen—says that is beautiful the apprehension of which pleases.—

Lynch nodded.

—I remember that—he said—*Pulcra sunt quæ visa placent.*—

—He uses the word *visa*—said Stephen—to cover esthetic apprehensions of all kinds, whether through sight or hearing or through any other avenue of apprehension. This word, though it is vague, is clear enough to keep away good and evil, which excite desire and loathing. It means certainly a stasis and not a kinesis. How about the true? It produces also a stasis of the mind. You would not write your name in pencil across the hypothenuse of a rightangled triangle.—

—No,—said Lynch—give me the hypothenuse of the Venus of Praxiteles.—

—Static therefore—said Stephen—Plato, I believe, said that beauty is the splendour of truth. I don't think that it has a meaning but the true and the beautiful are akin. Truth is beheld by the intellect which is appeased by the most satisfying relations of the intelligible: beauty is beheld by the imagination which is appeased by the most satisfying relations of the sensible. The first step in the direction of truth is to understand the frame and scope of the intellect itself, to comprehend the act itself of intellection. Aristotle's entire system of philosophy rests upon his book of psychology and that, I think, rests on his statement that the same attribute cannot at the same time and in the same connexion belong to and not belong to the same subject. The first step in the direction of beauty is to understand the frame and scope of the imagination, to comprehend the act itself of esthetic apprehension. Is that clear?—

—But what is beauty?—asked Lynch impatiently.—Out with another definition. Something we see and like! Is that the best you and Aquinas can do?—

—Let us take woman—said Stephen.

—Let us take her!—said Lynch fervently.

—The Greek, the Turk, the Chinese, the Copt, the Hottentot—said Stephen—all admire a different type of female beauty. That seems to be a maze out of which we cannot escape. I see, however, two ways out. One is this hypothesis: that every physical quality admired by men in women is in direct connexion with the manifold functions of women for the propagation of the species. It may be so. The world, it seems, is drearier than even you, Lynch, imagined. For my part I dislike that way out. It leads to eugenics rather than to esthetic. It leads you out of the maze into a new gaudy lecture room where MacCann, with one hand on *The Origin of Species* and the other hand on the new testament, tells you that you admired the great flanks of Venus because you felt that she would bear you burly offspring and admired her great breasts because you felt that she would give good milk to her children and yours.—

—Then MacCann is a sulphuryellow liar—said Lynch energetically.

—There remains another way out—said Stephen, laughing.

—To wit?—said Lynch.

—This hypothesis—Stephen began.

A long dray laden with old iron came round the corner of sir Patrick Dun's hospital covering the end of Stephen's speech with the harsh roar of jangled and rattling metal. Lynch closed his ears and gave out oath after oath till the dray had passed. Then he turned on his heel rudely. Stephen turned also and waited for a few moments till his companion's ill-humour had had its vent.

—This hypothesis—Stephen repeated—is the other way out: that, though the same object may not seem beautiful to all people, all people who admire a beautiful object find in it certain relations which satisfy and coincide with the stages themselves of all esthetic apprehension. These relations of the sensible, visible to you through one form and to me through another, must be therefore the necessary qualities of beauty. Now, we can return to our old friend saint Thomas for another pennyworth of wisdom.—

Lynch laughed.

—It amuses me vastly—he said—to hear you quoting him time after time like a jolly round friar. Are you laughing in your sleeve?—

—MacAlister—answered Stephen—would call my esthetic theory applied Aquinas. So far as this side of esthetic philosophy extends Aquinas will carry me all along the line. When we come to the phenomena of artistic conception, artistic gestation and artistic reproduction, I require a new terminology and a new personal experience.—

—Of course—said Lynch.—After all Aquinas, in spite of his intellect, was exactly a good round friar. But you will tell me about the new personal experience and new terminology some other day. Hurry up and finish the first part.—

—Who knows?—said Stephen, smiling.—Perhaps Aquinas would understand me better than you. He was a poet himself. He wrote a hymn for Maundy Thursday. It begins with the words *Pange lingua gloriosi*. They say it is the highest glory of the hymnal. It is an intricate and soothing hymn. I like it: but there is no hymn that can be put beside that mournful and majestic processional song, the *Vexilla Regis* of Venantius Fortunatus.—

Lynch began to sing softly and solemnly in a deep bass voice:

> *Inpleta sunt quæ concinit*
> *David fideli carmine*
> *Dicendo nationibus*
> *Regnavit a lingo Deus.*

—That's great!—he said, well pleased.—Great music!—

They turned into Lower Mount Street. A few steps from the corner a fat young man, wearing a silk neckcloth, saluted them and stopped.—Did you hear the results of the exams?—he asked.—Griffin was plucked. Halpin and O'Flynn are through the home civil. Moonan got fifth place in the Indian. O'Shaughnessy got fourteenth. The Irish fellows in Clark's gave them a feed last night. They all ate curry.—

His pallid bloated face expressed benevolent malice and, as he had advanced through his tidings of success, his small fat encircled eyes vanished out of sight and his weak wheezing voice out of hearing.

In reply to a question of Stephen's his eyes and his voice came forth again from their lurking places.

—Yes, MacCullagh and I—he said.—He's taking pure mathematics and I'm taking constitutional history. There are twenty subjects. I'm taking botany too. You know I'm a member of the field club.—

He drew back from the other two in a stately fashion and placed a plump woollen gloved hand on his breast, from which muttered wheezing laughter at once broke forth.

—Bring us a few turnips and onions the next time you go out—said Stephen drily—to make a stew.—

The fat student laughed indulgently and said:

—We are all highly respectable people in the field club. Last Saturday we went out to Glenmalure, seven of us.—

—With women, Donovan?—said Lynch.

Donovan again laid his hand on his chest and said:

—Our end is the acquisition of knowledge.—

Then he said quickly:

—I hear you are writing some essay about esthetics.—

Stephen made a vague gesture of denial.

—Goethe and Lessing—said Donovan—have written a lot on that subject, the classical school and the romantic school and all that. The Laocoon interested me very much when I read it. Of course it is idealistic, German, ultra profound.—

Neither of the others spoke. Donovan took leave of them urbanely.

I must go—he said softly and benevolently—I have a strong suspicion, amounting almost to a conviction, that my sister intended to make pancakes today for the dinner of the Donovan family.—

—Goodbye—Stephen said in his wake.—Don't forget the turnips for me and my mate.—

Lynch gazed after him, his lip curling in slow scorn till his face resembled a devil's mask:

—I think that that yellow pancake eating excrement can get a good job—he said at length—and I have to smoke cheap cigarettes!—

They turned their faces towards Merrion Square and went on for a little in silence.

—To finish what I was saying about beauty—said Stephen—the most satisfying relations of the sensible must therefore correspond to the necessary phases of artistic apprehension. Find these and you find the qualities of universal beauty. Aquinas says: *Ad pulcritudinem tria requiruntur integritas, consonantia, claritas.* I translate it so: Three things are needed for beauty, wholeness, harmony and radiance. Do these correspond to the phases of apprehension? Are you following?—

—Of course, I am—said Lynch.—If you think I have an excrementitious intelligence run after Donovan and ask him to listen to you.—

Stephen pointed to a basket which a butcher's boy had slung inverted on his head.

—Look at that basket—he said.

—I see it—said Lynch.

—In order to see that basket—said Stephen—your mind first of all separates the basket from the rest of the visible universe which is not the basket. The first phase of apprehension is a bounding line drawn about the object to be apprehended. An esthetic image is presented to us either in space or in time. What is audible is presented in time, what is visible is presented in space. But temporal or spatial, the esthetic image is first luminously apprehended as selfbounded and selfcontained upon the immeasurable background of space or time which is not it. You apprehended it as *one* thing. You see it as one whole. You apprehend its wholeness. That is *integritas.*—

—Bull's eye!—said Lynch, laughing—Go on.—

—Then—said Stephen—you pass from point to point, led by its formal lines; you apprehend it as balanced part against part within its limits; you feel the rhythm of its structure. In other words, the synthesis of immediate perception is followed by the analysis of apprehension. Having first felt that it is *one* thing you feel now that it is a *thing.* You apprehend it as complex, multiple, divisible, separable, made up of its parts, the result of its parts and their sum, harmonious. That is *consonantia.*—

—Bull's eye again!—said Lynch wittily.—Tell me now what is claritas and you win the cigar.—

—The connotation of the word—Stephen said—is rather vague. Aquinas uses a term which seems to be inexact. It baffled me for a long time. It would lead you to believe that he had in mind symbolism or idealism, the supreme quality of beauty being a light from some other world, the idea of which the matter was but the shadow, the reality of which it was but the symbol. I thought he might mean that *claritas* was the artistic discovery and representation of the divine purpose in anything or a force of generalization which would make the esthetic image a universal one, make it outshine its proper conditions. But that is literary talk. I

524

understand it so. When you have apprehended that basket as one thing and have then analysed it according to its form and apprehended it as a thing you make the only synthesis which is logically and esthetically permissible. You see that it is that thing which it is and no other thing. The radiance of which he speaks in the scholastic *quidditas,* the *whatness* of a thing. This supreme quality is felt by the artist when the esthetic image is first conceived in his imagination. The mind in that mysterious instant Shelley likened beautifully to a fading coal. The instant wherein that supreme quality of beauty, the clear radiance of the esthetic image, is apprehended luminously by the mind which has been arrested by its wholeness and fascinated by its harmony is the luminous silent stasis of esthetic pleasure, a spiritual state very like to that cardiac condition which the Italian physiologist Luigi Galvani, using a phrase almost as beautiful as Shelley's, called the enchantment of the heart.—

Stephen paused and, though his companion did not speak, felt that his words had called up around them a thought enchanted silence.

—What I have said—he began again—refers to beauty in the wider sense of the word, in the sense which the word has in the literary tradition. In the market place it has another sense. When we speak of beauty in the second sense of the term our judgment is influenced in the first place by the art itself and by the form of that art. The image, it is clear, must be set between the mind or senses of the artist himself and the mind or senses of others. If you bear this in memory you will see that art necessarily divides itself into three forms progressing from one to the next. These forms are: the lyrical form, the form wherein the artist presents his image in immediate relation to himself; the epical form, the form wherein he presents his image in mediate relation to himself and to others; the dramatic form, the form wherein he presents his image in immediate relation to others.—

—That you told me a few nights ago—said Lynch—and we began the famous discussion.—

—I have a book at home—said Stephen—in which I have written down questions which are more amusing than yours were. In finding the answers to them I found the theory of the esthetic which I am trying to explain. Here are some questions I set myself: *Is a chair finely made tragic or comic? Is the portrait of Mona Lisa good if I desire to see it? Is the bust of Sir Philip Crampton lyrical, epical or dramatic? If not, why not?—*

—Why not, indeed?—said Lynch, laughing.

—*If a man hacking in fury at a block of wood*—Stephen continued—*make there an image of a cow, is that image a work of art? If not, why not?—*

—That's a lovely one—said Lynch, laughing again.—That has the true scholastic stink.—

—Lessing—said Stephen—should not have taken a group of statues to write of. The art, being inferior, does not present the forms I spoke of distinguished clearly one from another. Even in literature, the highest and most spiritual art, the forms are often confused. The lyrical form is in fact the simplest verbal vesture of an instant of emotion, a rhythmical cry such as ages ago cheered on the man who pulled at the oar or dragged stones up a slope. He who utters it is more conscious of the instant of emotion than of himself as feeling emotion. The simplest epical form is seen emerging out of lyrical literature when the artist prolongs and broods upon himself as the centre of an epical event and this form progresses till the centre of emotional gravity is equidistant from the artist himself and from others. The narrative is no longer purely personal. The personality of the artist passes into the narration itself, flowing round and round the persons and the action like a vital sea. This progress you will see easily in that old English ballad *Turpin Hero,* which begins in the first person and ends in the third person. The dramatic form is reached when the vitality which has flowed and eddied round each person fills every person with such vital force that he or she assumes a proper and intangible esthetic life. The personality of the artist, at first a cry or a cadence or a mood and then a fluid and lambent narrative, finally refines itself out of existence, impersonalizes itself, so to speak. The esthetic image in the dramatic form is life purified in and reprojected from the human imagination. The mystery of esthetic like that of material creation is accomplished. The artist, like the God of the creation, remains within or behind or beyond or above his handiwork, invisible, refined out of existence, indifferent, paring his fingernails.—

—Trying to refine them also out of existence—said Lynch.

A fine rain began to fall from the high veiled sky and they turned into the duke's lawn, to reach the national library before the shower came.

—What do you mean—Lynch asked surlily—by prating about beauty and the imagination in this miserable God forsaken island? No wonder the artist retired within or behind his handiwork after having perpetrated this country.—

The rain fell faster. When they passed through the passage beside the royal Irish academy they found many students sheltering under the arcade of the library. Cranly, leaning against a pillar, was picking his teeth with a sharpened match, listening to some companions. Some girls stood near the entrance door. Lynch whispered to Stephen:

—Your beloved is here.—

Stephen took his place silently on the step below the group of students, heedless of the rain which fell fast, turning his eyes towards her from time to time. She too stood silently among her companions. She has no priest to flirt with, he thought with conscious bitterness, remembering how he had seen her last. Lynch was right. His mind, emptied of theory and courage, lapsed back into a listless peace.

He heard the students talking among themselves. They spoke of two friends who had passed the final medical examination, of the chances of getting places on ocean liners, of poor and rich practices.

—That's all a bubble. An Irish country practice is better.—

—Hynes was two years in Liverpool and he says the same. A frightful hole he said it was. Nothing but midwifery cases.—

—Do you mean to say it is better to have a job here in the country than in a rich city like that? I know a fellow . . .—

—Hynes has no brains. He got through by stewing, pure stewing.—

—Don't mind him. There's plenty of money to be made in a big commercial city.—

—Depends on the practice.—

—*Ego credo ut vita pauperum est simpliciter atrox, simpliciter sanguinarius atrox, in Liverpoolio.*—

Their voices reached his ears as if from a distance in interrupted pulsation. She was preparing to go away with her companions.

The quick light shower had drawn off, tarrying in clusters of diamonds among the shrubs of the quadrangle where an exhalation was breathed forth by the blackened earth. Their trim boots prattled as they stood on the steps of the colonnade, talking quietly and gaily, glancing at the clouds, holding their umbrellas at cunning angles against the few last raindrops, closing them again, holding their skirts demurely.

And if he had judged her harshly? If her life were a simple rosary of hours, her life simple and strange as a bird's life, gay in the morning, restless all day, tired at sundown? Her heart simple and wilful as a bird's heart?

⚘

Towards dawn he awoke. O what sweet music! His soul was all dewy wet. Over his limbs in sleep pale cool waves of light had passed. He lay still, as if his soul lay amid cool waters, conscious of faint sweet music. His mind was waking slowly to a tremulous morning knowledge, a morning inspiration. A spirit filled him, pure as the purest water, sweet as dew, moving as music. But how faintly it was inbreathed, how passionlessly, as if the seraphim themselves were breathing upon him! His soul was waking slowly, fearing to awake wholly. It was that windless hour of dawn when madness wakes and strange plants open to the light and the moth flies forth silently.

An enchantment of the heart! The night had been enchanted. In a dream or vision he had known the ecstacy of seraphic life. Was it an instant of enchantment only or long hours and years and ages?

The instant of inspiration seemed now to be reflected from all sides at once from a multitude of cloudy circumstances of what had happened or of what might have happened. The instant flashed forth like a point of light and now from cloud on cloud of vague circumstance confused form was veiling softly its afterglow. O! In the virgin womb of the imagination the word was made flesh. Gabriel the seraph had come to the virgin's chamber. An afterglow deepened within his spirit, whence the white flame had passed, deepening to a rose and ardent light. That rose and ardent light was her strange wilful heart, strange that no man had known or would know, wilful from before the beginning of the world: and lured by that ardent roselike glow the choirs of the seraphim were falling from heaven.

Are you not weary of ardent ways,
Lure of the fallen seraphim?
Tell no more of enchanted days.

The verses passed from his mind to his lips and, murmuring them over, he felt the rhythmic movement of a villanelle pass through them. The roselike glow sent forth its rays of rhyme; ways, days, blaze, praise, raise. Its rays burned up the world, consumed the hearts of men and angels: the rays from the rose that was her wilful heart.

Your eyes have set man's heart ablaze
And you have had your will of him.
Are you not weary of ardent ways?

And then? The rhythm died away, ceased, began again to move and beat. And then? Smoke, incense ascending from the altar of the world.

Above the flame the smoke of praise
Goes up from ocean rim to rim
Tell no more of enchanted days.

Smoke went up from the whole earth, from the vapoury oceans, smoke of her praise. The earth was like a swinging swaying censer, a ball of incense, an ellipsoidal ball. The rhythm died out at once; the cry of his heart was broken. His lips began to murmur the first verses over and over; then went on stumbling through half verses, stammering and baffled; then stopped. The heart's cry was broken.

The veiled windless hour had passed and behind the panes of the naked window the morning light was gathering. A bell beat faintly very far away. A bird twittered; two birds, three. The bell and the bird ceased: and the dull white light spread itself east and west, covering the world, covering the roselight in his heart.

Fearing to lose all, he raised himself suddenly on his elbow to look for paper and pencil. There was neither on the table; only the soup plate he had eaten the rice from for supper and the candlestick with its tendrils of tallow and its paper socket, singed by the last flame. He stretched his arm wearily towards the foot of the bed, groping with his hand in the pockets of the coat that hung there. His fingers found a pencil and then a cigarette packet. He lay back and, tearing open the packet, placed the last cigarette on the window ledge and began to write out the stanzas of the villanelle in small neat letters on the rough cardboard surface.

Having written them out he lay back on the lumpy pillow, murmuring them again. The lumps of knotted flock under his head reminded him of the lumps of knotted horsehair in the sofa of her parlour on which he used to sit, smiling or serious, asking himself why he had come, displeased with her and with himself, confounded by the print of the Sacred Heart above the untenanted sideboard. He saw her approach him in a lull of the talk and beg him to sing one of his curious songs. Then he saw himself sitting at the old piano, striking chords softly from its speckled keys and singing, amid the talk which had risen again in the room, to her who leaned beside the mantelpiece a dainty song of the Elizabethans, a sad and sweet loth to depart, the victory chant of Agincourt, the happy air of Greensleeves. While he sang and she listened, or feigned to listen his heart was at rest but when the quaint old songs had ended and he heard again the voices in the room he remembered his own sarcasm: the house where young men are called by their christian names a little too soon.

At certain instants her eyes seemed about to trust him but he had waited in vain. She passed now dancing lightly across his memory as she had been that night at the carnival ball, her white dress a little lifted, a white spray nodding in her hair. She danced lightly in the round. She was dancing towards him and, as she came, her eyes were a little averted and a faint glow was on her cheek. At the pause in the chain of hands her hand had lain in his an instant, a soft merchandise.

—You are a great stranger now.—

—Yes. I was born to be a monk.—

—I am afraid you are a heretic.—

—Are you much afraid?—

For answer she had danced away from him along the chain of hands, dancing lightly and discreetly, giving herself to none. The white spray nodded to her dancing and when she was in shadow the glow was deeper on her cheek.

A monk! His own image started forth a profaner of the cloister, a heretic Franciscan, willing and willing not to serve, spinning like Gherardino da Borgo San Donnino, a lithe web of sophistry and whispering in her ear.

No, it was not his image. It was like the image of the young priest in whose company he had seen her last, looking at him out of dove's eyes, toying with the pages of her Irish phrasebook.

—Yes, yes, the ladies are coming round to us. I can see it every day. The ladies are with us. The best helpers the language has.—

—And the church, Father Moran?—

—The church too. Coming round too. The work is going ahead there too.

Don't fret about the church.—

Bah? he had done well to leave the room in disdain. He had done well not to salute her on the steps of the library. He had done well to leave her to flirt with her priest, to toy with a church which was the scullery-maid of christendom.

Rude brutal anger routed the last lingering instant of ecstasy from his soul. It broke up violently her fair image and flung the fragments on all sides. On all sides distorted reflections of her image started from his memory: the flower girl in the ragged dress with damp coarse hair and a hoyden's face who had called herself his own girl and begged his handsel, the kitchen-girl in the next house who sang over the clatter of her plates, with the drawl of a country singer, the first bars of *By Killarney's Lakes and Fells,* a girl who had laughed gaily to see him stumble when the iron grating in the footpath near Cork Hill had caught the broken sole of his shoe, a girl he had glanced at, attracted by her small ripe mouth as she passed out of Jacob's biscuit factory, who had cried to him over her shoulder:

—Do you like what you seen of me, straight hair and curly eyebrows?—

And yet he felt that, however he might revile and mock her image, his anger was also a form of homage. He had left the classroom in disdain that was not wholly sincere, feeling that perhaps the secret of her race lay behind those dark eyes upon which her long lashes flung a quick shadow. He had told himself bitterly as he walked through the streets that she was a figure of the womanhood of her country, a batlike soul waking to the consciousness of itself in darkness and secrecy and loneliness, tarrying awhile, loveless and sinless, with her mild lover and leaving him to whisper of innocent transgressions in the latticed ear of a priest. His anger against her found vent in coarse railing at her paramour, whose name and voice and features offended his baffled pride: a priested peasant, with a brother a policeman in Dublin and a brother a potboy in Moycullen. To him she would unveil her soul's shy nakedness, to one who was but schooled in the discharging of a formal rite rather than to him, a priest of the eternal imagination, transmuting the daily bread of experience into the radiant body of everliving life.

The radiant image of the eucharist united again in an instant his bitter and despairing thoughts, their cries arising unbroken in a hymn of thanksgiving.

> *Our broken cries and mournful lays*
> *Rise in one eucharistic hymn*
> *Are you not weary of ardent ways?*
> *While sacrificing hands upraise*
> *The chalice flowing to the brim*
> *Tell no more of enchanted days.*

He spoke the verses aloud from the first lines till the music and rhythm suffused his mind, turning it to quiet indulgence; then copied them painfully to feel them the better by seeing them; then lay back on his bolster.

The full morning light had come. No sound was to be heard: but he knew that all around him life was about to awaken in common noises, hoarse voices, sleepy prayers. Shrinking from that life he turned towards the wall, making a cowl of the blanket and staring at the great overblown scarlet flowers of the tattered wallpaper. He tried to warm his perishing joy in their scarlet glow, imaging a roseway from where he lay upwards to heaven all strewn with scarlet flowers. Weary! Weary! He too was weary of ardent ways.

A gradual warmth, a languorous weariness passed over him, descending along his spine from his closely cowled head. He felt it descend and, seeing himself as he lay, smiled. Soon he would sleep.

He had written verses for her again after ten years. Ten years before she had worn her shawl cowlwise about her head, sending sprays of her warm breath into the night air, tapping her foot upon the glassy road. It was the last tram; the lank brown horses knew it and shook their bells to the clear night in admonition. The conductor talked with the driver, both nodding often in the green light of the lamp. They stood on the steps of the tram, he on the upper, she on the lower. She came up to his step many times between their phrases and went down again and once or twice remained beside him forgetting to go down and then went down. Let be! Let be!

Ten years from that wisdom of children to his folly. If he sent her the verses? They would be read out at breakfast amid the tapping of eggshells. Folly indeed! Her brothers would laugh and try to wrest the page from each other with their strong hard fingers. The suave priest, her uncle, seated in his armchair would hold the page at arm's length, read it smiling and approve of the literary form.

No, no: that was folly. Even if he sent her the verses she would not show them to others. No, no: she could not.

He began to feel that he had wronged her. A sense of her innocence moved him almost to pity her, an innocence he had never understood till he had come to the knowledge of it through sin, an innocence which she too had not understood while she was innocent or before the strange humiliation of her nature had first come upon her. Then first her soul had begun to live as his soul had when he had first sinned: and a tender compassion filled his heart as he remembered her frail pallor and her eyes, humbled and saddened by the dark shame of womanhood.

While his soul had passed from ecstasy to languor where had she been? Might it be, in the mysterious ways of spiritual life, that her soul at those same moments had been conscious of his homage? It might be.

A glow of desire kindled again his soul and fired and fulfilled all his body. Conscious of his desire she was waking from odorous sleep, the temptress of his villanelle. Her eyes, dark and with a look of languor, were opening to his eyes. Her nakedness yielded to him, radiant, warm odorous and lavish limbed, enfolded

531

him like a shining cloud, enfolded him like water with a liquid life: and like a cloud of vapour or like waters circumfluent in space the liquid letters of speech, symbols of the element of mystery, flowed forth over his brain.

Are you not weary of ardent ways,
Lure of the fallen seraphim?
Tell no more of enchanted days.

Your eyes have set man's heart ablaze
And you have had your will of him.
Are you not weary of ardent ways?

Above the flame the smoke of praise
Goes up from ocean rim to rim.
Tell no more of enchanted days.

Our broken cries and mournful lays
Rise in one eucharistic hymn.
Are you not weary of ardent ways?

While sacrificing hands upraise
The chalice flowing to the brim.
Tell no more of enchanted days.

And still you hold our longing gaze
With languorous look and lavish limb!
Are you not weary of ardent ways?
Tell no more of enchanted days.

↓

What birds were they? He stood on the steps of the library to look at them, leaning wearily on his ashplant. They flew round and round the jutting shoulder of a house in Molesworth Street. The air of the late March evening made clear their flight, their dark darting quivering bodies flying clearly against the sky as against a limp hung cloth of smoky tenuous blue.

He watched their flight; bird after bird: a dark flash, a swerve, a flutter of wings. He tried to count them before all their darting quivering bodies passed: Six, ten, eleven: and wondered were they odd or even in number. Twelve, thirteen: for two came wheeling down from the upper sky. They were flying high and low but ever round and round in straight and curving lines and ever flying from left to right, circling about a temple of air.

He listened to the cries: like the squeak of mice behind the wainscot: a shrill twofold note. But the notes were long and shrill and whirring, unlike the cry of vermin, falling a third or a fourth and trilled as the flying beaks clove the air. Their cry was shrill and clear and fine and falling like threads of silken light unwound from whirring spools.

The inhuman clamour soothed his ears in which his mother's sobs and reproaches murmured insistently and the dark frail quivering bodies wheeling and fluttering and swerving round an airy temple of the tenuous sky soothed his eyes which still saw the image of his mother's face.

Why was he gazing upwards from the steps of the porch, hearing their shrill twofold cry, watching their flight? For an augury of good or evil? A phrase of Cornelius Agrippa flew through his mind and then there flew hither and thither shapeless thoughts from Swedenborg on the correspondence of birds to things of the intellect and of how the creatures of the air have their knowledge and know their times and seasons because they, unlike man, are in the order of their life and have not perverted that order by reason.

And for ages men had gazed upward as he was gazing at birds in flight. The colonnade above him made him think vaguely of an ancient temple and the ash-plant on which he leaned wearily of the curved stick of an augur. A sense of fear of the unknown moved in the heart of his weariness, a fear of symbols and por-tents, of the hawklike man whose name he bore soaring out of his captivity on osier woven wings, of Thoth, the god of writers, writing with a reed upon a tablet and bearing on his narrow ibis head the cusped moon.

He smiled as he thought of the god's image, for it made him think of a bottle-nosed judge in a wig, putting commas into a document which he held at arm's length and he knew that he would not have remembered the god's name but that it was like an Irish oath. It was folly. But was it for this folly that he was about to leave for ever the house of prayer and prudence into which he had been born and the order of life out of which he had come?

They came back with shrill cries over the jutting shoulder of the house, flying darkly against the fading air. What birds were they? He thought that they must be swallows who had come back from the south. Then he was to go away? for they were birds ever going and coming, building ever an unlasting home under the eaves of men's houses and ever leaving the homes they had built to wander.

> *Bend down your faces, Oona and Aleel,*
> *I gaze upon them as the swallow gazes*
> *Upon the nest under the eave before*
> *He wander the loud waters.*

A soft liquid joy like the noise of many waters flowed over his memory and he felt in his heart the soft peace of silent spaces of fading tenuous sky above the waters, of oceanic silence, of swallows flying through the seadusk over the flowing waters.

A soft liquid joy flowed through the words where the soft long vowels hurtled noiselessly and fell away, lapping and flowing back and ever shaking the white bells of their waves in mute chime and mute peal and soft low swooning cry; and he felt that the augury he had sought in the wheeling darting birds and in the pale space of sky above him had come forth from his heart like a bird from a turret quietly and swiftly.

Symbol of departure or of loneliness? The verses crooned in the ear of his memory composed slowly before his remembering eyes the scene of the hall on the night of the opening of the national theatre. He was alone at the side of the balcony, looking out of jaded eyes at the culture of Dublin in the stalls and at the tawdry scenecloths and human dolls framed by the garish lamps of the stage. A burly policeman sweated behind him and seemed at every moment about to act. The catcalls and hisses and mocking cries ran in rude gusts round the hall from his scattered fellow students.

—A libel on Ireland!—

—Made in Germany—

—Blasphemy!—

—We never sold our faith!—

—No Irish woman ever did it!—

—We want no amateur atheist.—

—We want no budding buddhists.—

A sudden swift hiss fell from the windows above him and he knew that the electric lamps had been switched on in the reader's room. He turned into the pillared hall, now calmly lit, went up the staircase and passed in through the clicking turnstile.

Cranly was sitting over near the dictionaries. A thick book, opened at the frontispiece, lay before him on the wooden rest. He leaned back in his chair, inclining his ear like that of a confessor to the face of the medical student who was reading to him a problem from the chess page of a journal. Stephen sat down at his right and the priest at the other side of the table closed his copy of *The Tablet* with an angry snap and stood up.

Cranly gazed after him blandly and vaguely. The medical student went on in a softer voice:

—Pawn to king's fourth.—

—We had better go, Dixon—said Stephen in warning.—He has gone to complain.—

Dixon folded the journal and rose with dignity, saying:

—Our men retired in good order.—

—With guns and cattle—added Stephen, pointing to the titlepage of Cranly's book on which was written *Diseases of the Ox*.

As they passed through a lane of the tables Stephen said:

—Cranly, I want to speak to you.—

Cranly did not answer or turn. He laid his book on the counter and passed out, his well shod feet sounding flatly on the floor. On the staircase he paused and gazing absently at Dixon repeated:

—Pawn to king's bloody fourth.—

—Put it that way if you like—Dixon said.

He had a quiet toneless voice and urbane manners and on a finger of his plump clean hand he displayed at moments a signet ring.

As they crossed the hall a man of dwarfish stature came towards them. Under the dome of his tiny hat his unshaven face began to smile with pleasure and he was heard to murmur. The eyes were melancholy as those of a monkey.

—Good evening, gentlemen—said the stubble grown monkeyish face.

—Warm weather for March—said Cranly.—They have the windows open upstairs.—

Dixon smiled and turned his ring. The blackish monkey puckered face pursed its human mouth with gentle pleasure and its voice purred:

—Delightful weather for March. Simply delightful.—

—There are two nice young ladies upstairs, captain, tired of waiting—Dixon said.

Cranly smiled and said kindly:

—The captain has only one love: sir Walter Scott. Isn't that so, captain?—

—What are you reading now, captain?—Dixon asked.—*The Bride of Lammermoor?*—

—I love old Scott—the flexible lips said—I think he writes something lovely. There is no writer can touch sir Walter Scott.—

He moved a thin shrunken brown hand gently in the air in time to his praise and his thin quick eyelids beat often over his sad eyes.

Sadder to Stephen's ear was his speech: a genteel accent, low and moist, marred by errors: and, listening to it, he wondered was the story true and was the thin blood that flowed in his shrunken frame noble and come of an incestuous love?

The park trees were heavy with rain and rain fell still and ever in the lake, lying grey like a shield. A game of swans flew there and the water and the shore beneath were fouled with their greenwhite slime. They embraced softly impelled by the grey rainy light, the wet silent trees, the shield like witnessing lake, the swans. They embraced without joy or passion, his arm about his sister's neck. A grey woollen cloak was wrapped athwart her from her shoulder to her waist: and her fair head was bent in willing shame. He had loose redbrown hair and tender shapely strong freckled hands. Face? There was no face seen. The brother's face was bent upon her fair rain fragrant hair. The hand freckled and strong and shapely and caressing was Davin's hand.

He frowned angrily upon his thought and on the shrivelled mannikin who had called it forth. His father's gibes at the Bantry gang leaped out of his memory. He held them at a distance and brooded uneasily on his own thought again. Why were they not Cranly's hands? Had Davin's simplicity and innocence stung him more secretly?

He walked on across the hall with Dixon, leaving Cranly to take leave elaborately of the dwarf.

Under the colonnade Temple was standing in the midst of a little group of students. One of them cried:

—Dixon, come over till you hear. Temple is in grand form.—

Temple turned on him his dark gipsy eyes.

—You're a hypocrite, O'Keeffe—he said.—And Dixon is a smiler. By hell, I think that's a good literary expression.—

He laughed slily, looking in Stephen's face, repeating:

—By hell, I'm delighted with that name. A smiler.—

A stout student who stood below them on the steps said:

—Come back to the mistress, Temple. We want to hear about that.—

—He had, faith—Temple said.—And he was a married man too. And all the priests used to be dining there. By hell, I think they all had a touch.—

—We shall call it riding a hack to spare the hunter—said Dixon.

—Tell us, Temple—O'Keeffe said—how many quarts of porter have you in you?—

—All your intellectual soul is in that phrase, O'Keeffe—said Temple with open scorn.

He moved with a shambling gait round the group and spoke to Stephen.

—Did you know that the Forsters are the kings of Belgium?—he asked.

Cranly came out through the door of the entrance hall, his hat thrust back on the nape of his neck and picking his teeth with care.

—And here's the wiseacre—said Temple.—Do you know that about the Forsters?—

He paused for an answer. Cranly dislodged a fig seed from his teeth on the point of his rude toothpick and gazed at it intently.

—The Forster family—Temple said—is descended from Baldwin the First, king of Flanders. He was called the Forester. Forester and Forster, are the same name. A descendant of Baldwin the First, captain Francis Forster, settled in Ireland and married the daughter of the last chieftan of Clanbrassil. Then there are the Blake Forsters. That's a different branch.—

—From Baldhead, king of Flanders.—Cranly repeated, rooting again deliberately at his gleaming uncovered teeth.

—Where did you pick up all that history?—O'Keeffe asked.

—I know all the history of your family too—Temple said, turning to Stephen.

—Do you know what Giraldus Cambrensis says about your family?—

—Is he descended from Baldwin too?—asked a tall consumptive student with dark eyes.

—Baldhead—Cranly repeated, sucking at a crevice in his teeth.

—*Pernobilis et pervetusta familia*—Temple said to Stephen.

The stout student who stood below them on the steps farted briefly. Dixon turned towards him saying in a soft voice.

—Did an angel speak?

Cranly turned also and said vehemently but without anger:

—Goggins, you're the flamingest dirty devil I ever met, do you know.—

—I had it on my mind to say that—Goggins answered firmly.—It did no one any harm, did it?—

—We hope—Dixon said suavely—that it was not of the kind known to science as a *paulo post futurum.*—

—Didn't I tell you he was a smiler?—said Temple, turning right and left.— Didn't I give him that name?—

—You did. We're not deaf—said the tall consumptive.

Cranly still frowned at the stout student below him. Then, with a snort of disgust, he shoved him violently down the steps.

—Go away from here—he said rudely.—Go away, you stinkpot. And you are a stinkpot.—

Goggins skipped down on to the gravel and at once returned to his place with good humour. Temple turned back to Stephen and asked:

—Do you believe in the law of heredity?—

—Are you drunk or what are you or what are you trying to say?—asked Cranly, facing round on him with an expression of wonder.

—The most profound sentence ever written—Temple said with enthusiasm—is the sentence at the end of the zoology. Reproduction is the beginning of death.—

He touched Stephen timidly at the elbow and said eagerly:

—Do you feel how profound that is because you are a poet?—

Cranly pointed his long forefinger.

—Look at him!—he said with scorn to the others—Look at Ireland's hope!—

They laughed at his words and gesture. Temple turned on him bravely, saying:

—Cranly, you're always sneering at me. I can seen that. But I am as good as you any day. Do you know what I think about you now as compared with myself?—

—My dear man—said Cranly urbanely—you are incapable, do you know, absolutely incapable of thinking.—

—But do you know—Temple went on—what I think of you and of myself compared together?—

—Out with it, Temple!—the stout student cried from the steps.—Get it out in bits!—

Temple turned right and left, making sudden feeble gestures as he spoke.

—I'm a ballocks—he said, shaking his head in despair—I am and I know am. And I admit it that I am.—

Dixon patted him lightly on the shoulder and said mildly:

—And it does you every credit, Temple.—

—But he—Temple said, pointing to Cranly—he is a ballocks, too, like me. Only he doesn't know it. And that's the only difference, I see.—

A burst of laughter covered his words. But he turned again to Stephen and said with a sudden eagerness:

—That word is a most interesting word. That's the only English dual number. Did you know?—

—Is it?—Stephen said vaguely.

He was watching Cranly's firm featured suffering face, lit up now by a smile of false patience. The gross name had passed over it like foul water poured over an old stone image, patient of injuries: and, as he watched him, he saw him raise his hat in salute and uncover the black hair that stood up stiffly from his forehead like an iron crown.

She passed out from the porch of the library and bowed across Stephen in reply to Cranly's greeting. He also? Was there not a slight flush on Cranly's cheek? Or had it come forth at Temple's words? The light had waned. He could not see.

Did that explain his friend's listless silence, his harsh comments, the sudden intrusions of rude speech with which he had shattered so often Stephen's ardent wayward confessions? Stephen had forgiven freely for he had found this rudeness also in himself. And he remembered an evening when he had dismounted from a borrowed creaking bicycle to pray to God in a wood near Malahide. He had lifted up his arms and spoken in ecstasy to the sombre nave of the trees, knowing that he stood on holy ground and in a holy hour. And when two constabulary men had come into sight round a bend in the gloomy road he had broken off his prayer to whistle loudly an air from the last pantomime.

He began to beat the frayed end of his ashplant against the base of a pillar. Had Cranly not heard him? Yet he could wait. The talk about him ceased for a moment: and a soft hiss fell again from a window above. But no other sound was in the air and the swallows whose flight had followed with idle eyes were sleeping.

She had passed through the dusk. And therefore the air was silent save for one soft hiss that fell. And therefore the tongues about him had ceased their babble. Darkness was falling.

Darkness falls from the air.

A trembling joy, lambent as a faint light, played like a fairy host around him. But why? Her passage through the darkening air or the verse with its black vowels and its opening sound, rich and lutelike?

He walked away slowly towards the deeper shadows at the end of the colonnade, beating the stone softly with his stick to hide his revery from the students whom he had left: and allowed his mind to summon back to itself the age of Dowland and Byrd and Nash.

Eyes, opening from the darkness of desire, eyes that dimmed the breaking east. What was their languid grace but the softness of chambering? And what was their shimmer but the shimmer of the scum that mantled the cesspool of the court of a slobbering Stuart. And he tasted in the language of memory ambered wines, dying fallings of sweet airs, the proud pavan: and saw with the eyes of memory kind gentlewomen in Covent Garden wooing from their balconies with sucking mouths and the pox fouled wenches of the taverns and young wives that, gaily yielding to their ravishers, clipped and clipped again.

The images he had summoned gave him no pleasure. They were secret and enflaming but her image was not entangled by them. That was not the way to think of her. It was not even the way in which he thought of her. Could his mind then not trust itself? Old phrases, sweet only with a disinterred sweetness like the fig seeds Cranly rooted out of his gleaming teeth.

It was not thought nor vision, though he knew vaguely that her figure was passing homeward through the city. Vaguely first and then more sharply he smelt her body. A conscious unrest seethed in his blood. Yes, it was her body he smelt: a wild and languid smell: the tepid limbs over which his music had flowed desirously and the secret soft linen upon which her flesh distilled odour and a dew.

A louse crawled over the nape of his neck and, putting his thumb and forefinger deftly beneath his loose collar, he caught it. He rolled its body, tender yet brittle as a grain of rice, between thumb and finger for an instant before he let it fall from him and wondered would it live or die. There came to his mind a curious phrase from Cornelius a Lapide which said that the lice born of human sweat were not created by God with the other animals on the sixth day. But the ticking of the skin of his neck made his mind raw and red. The life of his body, ill clad, ill fed, louse eaten, made him close his eyelids in a sudden spasm of despair: and in the darkness he saw the brittle bright bodies of lice falling from the air and turning often as they fell. Yes; and it was not darkness that fell from the air. It was brightness.

Brightness falls from the air.

He had not even remembered rightly Nash's line. All the images it had awakened were false. His mind bred vermin. His thoughts were lice born of the sweat of sloth.

He came back quickly along the colonnade towards the group of students. Well then let her go and be damned to her! She could love some clean athlete who washed himself every morning to the waist and had black hair on his chest. Let her.

Cranly had taken another dried fig from the supply in his pocket and was eating it slowly and noisily. Temple sat on the pediment of a pillar, leaning back, his cap pulled down on his sleepy eyes. A squat young man came out of the porch, a leather portfolio tucked under his armpit. He marched towards the group, striking the flags with the heels of his boots and with the ferrule of his heavy umbrella. Then, raising the umbrella in salute, he said to all:

—Good evening, sirs.—

He struck the flags again and tittered while his head trembled with a slight nervous movement. The tall consumptive student and Dixon and O'Keeffe were speaking in Irish and did not answer him. Then, turning to Cranly, he said:

—Good evening, particularly to you.—

He moved the umbrella in indication and tittered again. Cranly, who was still chewing the fig, answered with loud movements of his jaws.

—Good? Yes. It is a good evening.—

The squat student looked at him seriously and shook his umbrella gently and reprovingly.

—I can see—he said—that you are about to make obvious remarks.—

—Um—Cranly answered, holding out what remained of the half chewed fig and jerking it towards the squat student's mouth in sign that he should eat.

The squat student did not eat it but, indulging his special humour, said gravely, still tittering and prodding his phrase with his umbrella:

—Do you intend that . . .—

He broke off, pointed bluntly to the munched pulp of the fig and said loudly:

—I allude to that.—

—Um—Cranly said as before.

—Do you intend that now—the squat student said—as *ipso facto* or, let us say, as so to speak?—

Dixon turned aside from his group, saying:

—Goggins was waiting for you, Glynn. He has gone round to the Adelphi to look for you and Moynihan. What have you there?—he asked, tapping the portfolio under Glynn's arm.

—Examination papers—Glynn answered.—I give them monthly examinations to see that they are profiting by my tuition.—

He also tapped the portfolio and coughed gently and smiled.

—Tuition!—said Cranly rudely.—I suppose you mean the barefooted children that are taught by a bloody ape like you. God help them!—

He bit off the rest of the fig and flung away the butt.

—I suffer little children to come unto me—Glynn said amiably.

—A bloody ape—Cranly repeated with emphasis—and a blasphemous bloody ape!—

Temple stood up and, pushing past Cranly addressed Glynn:

—That phrase you said now—he said—is from the new testament about suffer the children to come to me.—

—Go to sleep again, Temple—said O'Keeffe.

—Very well, then—Temple continued, still addressing Glynn—and if Jesus suffered the children to come why does the church send them all to hell if they die unbaptised? Why is that?—

—Were you baptised yourself, Temple?—the consumptive student asked.

—But why are they sent to hell if Jesus said they were all to come?—Temple said, his eyes searching Glynn's eyes.

Glynn coughed and said gently, holding back with difficulty the nervous titter in his voice and moving his umbrella at every word:

—And, as you remark, if it is thus I ask emphatically whence comes this thusness.—

—Because the church is cruel like all old sinners—Temple said.

—Are you quite orthodox on that point, Temple?—Dixon said suavely.

—Saint Augustine says that about unbaptised children going to hell—Temple answered—because he was a cruel old sinner too.—

—I bow to you—Dixon said—but I had the impression that limbo existed for such cases.—

—Don't argue with him, Dixon—Cranly said brutally. —Don't talk to him or look at him. Lead him home with a sugan the way you'd lead a bleating goat.—

—Limbo!—Temple cried.—That's a fine invention too. Like hell.—

—But with the unpleasantness left out—Dixon said.

He turned smiling to the others and said:

—I think I am voicing the opinions of all present in saying so much.—

—You are—Glynn said in a firm tone.—On that point Ireland is united.—

He struck the ferrule of his umbrella on the stone floor of the colonnade.

—Hell—Temple said.—I can respect that invention of the grey spouse of Satan. Hell is Roman, like the walls of the Romans, strong and ugly. But what is limbo?—

—Put him back into the perambulator, Cranly—O'Keeffe called out.

Cranly made a swift step towards Temple, halted, stamping his foot, crying as if to a fowl:

—Hoosh!—

Temple moved away nimbly.

—Do you know what limbo is?—he cried.—Do you know what we call a notion like that in Roscommon?—

—Hoosh! Blast you!—Cranly cried, clapping his hands.

—Neither my arse nor my elbow!—Temple cried out scornfully—And that's what I call limbo.—

—Give us that stick here—Cranly said.

He snatched the ashplant roughly from Stephen's hand and sprang down the steps: but Temple, hearing him move in pursuit, fled through the dusk like a wild creature, nimble and fleet footed. Cranly's heavy boots were heard loudly charging across the quadrangle and then returning heavily, foiled and spurning the gravel at each step.

His step was angry and with an angry abrupt gesture he thrust the stick back into Stephen's hand. Stephen felt that his anger had another cause, but feigning patience, touched his arm slightly and said quietly:

—Cranly, I told you I wanted to speak to you. Come away.—

Cranly looked at him for a few moments and asked:

—Now?—

—Yes, now—Stephen said—We can't speak here. Come away.—

They crossed the quadrangle together without speaking. The bird call from Siegfried whistled softly followed them from the steps of the porch. Cranly turned: and Dixon, who had whistled, called out:

—Where are you fellows off to? What about that game, Cranly?—

They parleyed in shouts across the still air about a game of billiards to be played in the Adelphi hotel. Stephen walked on alone and out into the quiet of Kildare Street opposite Maple's hotel he stood to wait, patient again. The name of the hotel, a colourless polished wood, and its colourless front stung him like a glance of polite disdain. He stared angrily back at the softly lit drawingroom of the hotel in which he imagined the sleek lives of the patricians of Ireland housed in calm. They thought of army commissions and land agents: peasants greeted them along the roads in the country: they knew the names of certain French dishes and gave orders to jarvies in highpitched provincial voices which pierced through their skintight accents.

How could he hit their conscience or how cast his shadow over the imaginations of their daughters, before their squires begat upon them, that they might breed a race less ignoble than their own? And under the deepened dusk he felt the thoughts and desires of the race to which he belonged flitting like bats, across the dark country lanes, under trees by the edges of streams and near the pool mottled bogs. A woman had waited in the doorway as Davin had passed by at night and, offering him a cup of milk, had all but wooed him to her bed: for Davin had the mild eyes of one who could be secret. But him no woman's eyes had wooed.

His arm was taken in a strong grip and Cranly's voice said:

—Let us eke go.—

They walked southward in silence. Then Cranly said:

—That blithering idiot, Temple! I swear to Moses, do you know, that I'll be the death of that fellow one time.—

But his voice was no longer angry and Stephen wondered was he thinking of her greeting to him under the porch.

They turned to the left and walked on as before. When they had gone on so far for some time Stephen said:

—Cranly, I had an unpleasant quarrel this evening.—

—With your people?—Cranly asked.

—With my mother.—

—About religion?—

—Yes—Stephen answered.

After a pause Cranly asked:

—What age is your mother?—

—Not old—Stephen said.—She wishes me to make my easter duty.—

—And will you?—

—I will not—Stephen said.

—Why not?—Cranly said.

—I will not serve—answered Stephen.

—That remark was made before—Cranly said calmly.

—It is made behind now—said Stephen hotly.

Cranly pressed Stephen's arm, saying:

—Go easy, my dear man. You're an excitable bloody man, do you know.—

He laughed nervously as he spoke and, looking up into Stephen's face with moved and friendly eyes, said:

—Do you know that you are an excitable man?—

—I daresay I am—said Stephen, laughing also.

Their minds, lately estranged, seemed suddenly to have been drawn closer, one to the other.

—Do you believe in the eucharist?—Cranly asked.

—I do not—Stephen said.

—Do you disbelieve then?—

—I neither believe in it nor disbelieve in it—Stephen answered.

—Many persons have doubts, even religious persons, yet they overcome them or put them aside—Cranly said.—Are your doubts on that point too strong?—

—I do not wish to overcome them—Stephen answered.

Cranly, embarrassed for a moment, took another fig from his pocket and was about to eat it when Stephen said:

—Don't, please. You cannot discuss this question with your mouth full of chewed fig.—

Cranly examined the fig by the light of a lamp under which he halted. Then he smelt it with both nostrils, bit a tiny piece, spat it out and threw the fig rudely into the gutter. Addressing it as it lay, he said:

—Depart from me, ye cursed, into everlasting fire!—

Taking Stephen's arm, he went on again and said:

—Do you not fear that those words may be spoken to you on the day of judgment?—

—What is offered me on the other hand?—Stephen asked.—An eternity of bliss in the company of the dean of studies?—

—Remember—Cranly said—that he would be glorified.—

—Ay—Stephen said somewhat bitterly—bright agile, impassible and, above all, subtle.

—It is a curious thing, do you know—Cranly said dispassionately—how your mind is supersaturated with the religion in which you say you disbelieve. Did you believe in it when you were at school? I bet you did.—

—I did—Stephen answered.

—And were you happier then?—Cranly asked softly—happier than you are now, for instance?—

—Often happy—Stephen said—and often unhappy. I was someone else then.—

—How someone else? What do you mean by that statement?—

—I mean—said Stephen—that I was not myself as I am now, as I had to become.—

—Not as you are now, not as you had to become—Cranly repeated.—Let me ask you a question. Do you love your mother?—

Stephen shook his head slowly.

—I don't know what your words mean—he said simply.

—Have you never loved anyone?—Cranly asked.

—Do you mean women?—

—I am not speaking of that—Cranly said in a colder tone.—I ask you if you ever felt love towards anyone or anything.—

Stephen walked on beside his friend, staring gloomily at the footpath.

—I tried to love God—he said at length.—It seems now I failed. It is very difficult. I tried to unite my will with the will of God instant by instant. In that I did not always fail. I could perhaps do that still . . . —

Cranly cut him short by asking:

—Has your mother had a happy life?—

—How do I know?—Stephen said.

—How many children had she?—

—Nine or ten—Stephen answered.—Some died.—

—Was your father. . . . —Cranly interrupted himself for an instant: and then said:—I don't want to pry into your family affairs. But was your father what is called well-to-do? I mean when you were growing up?—

—Yes—Stephen said.

—What was he?—Cranly asked after a pause.

Stephen began to enumerate glibly his father's attributes.

—A medical student, an oarsman, a tenor, an amateur actor, a shouting politician, a small landlord, a small investor, a drinker, a good fellow, a storyteller, somebody's secretary, something in a distillery, a taxgatherer, a bankrupt and at present a praiser of his own past.—

Cranly laughed, tightening his grip on Stephen's arm, and said:

—The distillery is damn good.—

—Is there anything else you want to know?— Stephen asked.

—Are you in good circumstances at present?—

—Do I look it?—Stephen asked bluntly.

—So then—Cranly went on musingly—you were born in the lap of luxury.—

He used the phrase broadly and loudly as he often used technical expressions as if he wished his hearer to understand that they were used by him without conviction.

—Your mother must have gone through a good deal of suffering—he said then.—Would you not try to save her from suffering more even if . . .or would you?—

—If I could—Stephen said—that would cost me very little.—

—Then do so—Cranly said.—Do as she wishes you to do. What is it for you? You disbelieve in it. It is a form: nothing else. And you will set her mind at rest.—

He ceased and, as Stephen did not reply, remained silent. Then, as if giving utterance to the process of his own thought, he said:

—Whatever else is unsure in this stinking dunghill of a world a mother's love is not. Your mother brings you into the world, carries you first in her body. What do we know about what she feels? But whatever she feels, it, at least, must be real. It must be. What are our ideas or ambitions? Play. Ideas! Why, that bloody bleating goat Temple has ideas. MacCann has ideas too. Every jackass going the roads thinks he has ideas.—

Stephen, who had been listening to the unspoken speech behind the words, said with assumed carelessness:

—Pascal, if I remember rightly, would not suffer his mother to kiss him as he feared the contact of her sex.—

—Pascal was a pig—said Cranly.

—Aloysius Gonzaga, I think, was of the same mind—Stephen said.

—And he was another pig then—said Cranly.

—The church calls him a saint—Stephen objected.

—I don't care a flaming damn what anyone calls him—Cranly said rudely and flatly.—I call him a pig.—

Stephen, preparing the words neatly in his mind, continued:

—Jesus, too, seems to have treated his mother with scant courtesy in public but

Suarez a jesuit theologian and Spanish gentleman, has apologised for him.—

—Did the idea ever occur to you—Cranly asked—that Jesus was not what he pretended to be?—

—The first person to whom that idea occurred—Stephen answered—was Jesus himself.—

—I mean—Cranly said, hardening in his speech—did the idea ever occur to you that he was himself a conscious hypocrite, what he called the jews of his time, a white sepulchre? Or, to put it more plainly, that he was a blackguard?—

—That idea never occurred to me—Stephen answered.—But I am curious to know are you trying to make a convert of me or a pervert of yourself?—

He turned towards his friend's face and saw there a raw smile which some force of will strove to make finely, significant.—

Cranly asked suddenly in a plain sensible tone:—Tell me the truth. Were you at all shocked by what I said?—

—Somewhat—Stephen said.

—And why were you shocked—Cranly pressed on in the same tone—if you feel sure that our religion is false and that Jesus was not the son of God?—

—I am not at all sure of it—Stephen said.—He is more like a son of God than a son of Mary.—

—And is that why you will not communicate—Cranly asked—because you are not sure of that too, because you feel that the host, too, may be the body and blood of the son of God and not a wafer of bread? And because you fear that it may be?—

—Yes—Stephen said quietly—I feel that and I also fear it.—

—I see.—Cranly said.

Stephen, struck by his tone of closure, reopened the discussion at once by saying:

—I fear many things: dogs, horses, firearms, the sea, thunderstorms, machinery, the country roads at night.—

—But why do you fear a bit of bread?—

—I imagine—Stephen said—that there is a malevolent reality behind those things I say I fear.—

—Do you fear then—Cranly asked—that the God of the Roman catholics would strike you dead and damn you if you made a sacrilegious communion?—

—The God of the Roman catholics could do that now—Stephen said.—I fear more than that the chemical action which would be set up in my soul by a false homage to a symbol behind which are massed twenty centuries of authority and veneration.—

—Would you—Cranly asked—in extreme danger commit that particular sacrilege? For instance, if you lived in the penal days?—

—I cannot answer for the past—Stephen replied.—Possibly not.—

—Then—said Cranly—you do not intend to become a protestant?—

—I said that I had lost the faith—Stephen answered—but not that I had lost selfrespect. What kind of liberation would that be to forsake an absurdity which is logical and coherent and to embrace one which is illogical and incoherent?—

They had walked on towards the township of Pembroke and now, as they went on slowly along the avenues, the trees and the scattered lights in the villas soothed their minds. The air of wealth and repose diffused about them seemed to comfort their neediness. Behind a hedge of laurel a light glimmered in the window of a kitchen and the voice of a servant was heard singing as she sharpened knives. She sang, in short broken bars,

Rosie O'Grady—

Cranly stopped to listen, saying:

—*Mulier cantat.—*

The soft beauty of the Latin word touched with an enchanting touch the dark of the evening, with a touch fainter and more persuading than the touch of music or of a woman's hand. The strife of their minds was quelled. The figure of woman as she appears in the liturgy of the church passed silently through the darkness: a white robed figure, small and slender as a boy, and with a falling girdle. Her voice, frail and high as a boy's, was heard intoning from a distant choir the first words of a woman which pierce the gloom and clamour of the first chanting of the passion:

—*Et tu cum Jesu Galilœo eras.—*

And all hearts were touched and turned to her voice, shining like a young star, shining clearer as the voice intoned the proparoxyton and more faintly as the cadence died.

The singing ceased. They went on together, Cranly repeating in strongly stressed rhythm the end of the refrain:

> *And when we are married,*
> *O, how happy we'll be*
> *For I love sweet Rosie O'Grady*
> *And Rosie O'Grady loves me.*

—There's real poetry for you—he said.—There's real love.—

He glanced sideways at Stephen with a strange smile and said:

—Do you consider that poetry? Or do you know what the words mean?—

—I want to see Rosie first—said Stephen.

—She's easy to find—Cranly said.

His hat had come down on his forehead. He shoved it back: and in the shadow of the trees Stephen saw his pale face, framed by the dark, and his large dark eyes. Yes. His face was handsome: and his body was strong and hard. He had spoken of a mother's love. He felt then the sufferings of women, the weaknesses of their bodies and souls: and would shield them with a strong and resolute arm and bow his mind to them.

Away then: it is time to go. A voice spoke softly to Stephen's lonely heart, bidding him go and telling him that his friendship was coming to an end. Yes; he would go. He could not strive against another. He knew his part.

—Probably I shall go away—he said.

—Where?—Cranly asked.

—Where I can—Stephen said.

—Yes—Cranly said.—It might be difficult for you to live here now. But is it that makes you go?—

—I have to go—Stephen answered.

—Because—Cranly continued—you need not look upon yourself as driven away if you do not wish to go or as a heretic or an outlaw. There are many good believers who think as you do. Would that surprise you? The church is not the stone building nor even the clergy and their dogmas. It is the whole mass of those born into it. I don't know what you wish to do in life. Is it what you told me the night we were standing outside Harcourt Street station?—

—Yes—Stephen said, smiling in spite of himself at Cranly's way of remembering thoughts in connexion with places.—The night you spent half an hour wrangling with Doherty about the shortest way from Sallygap to Larras.—

—Pothead!—Cranly said with calm contempt.—What does he know about the way from Sallygap to Larras? Or what does he know about anything for that matter? And the big slobbering washingpot head of him!—

He broke out into a loud long laugh.

—Well?—Stephen said.—Do you remember the rest?—

—What you said, is it?—Cranly asked.—Yes, I remember it. To discover the mode of life or of art whereby your spirit could express itself in unfettered freedom.—

Stephen raised his hat in acknowledgment.

—Freedom!—Cranly repeated.—But you are not free enough yet to commit a sacrilege. Tell me would you rob?—

—I would beg first—Stephen said.

—And if you got nothing, would you rob?—

—You wish me to say—Stephen answered—that the rights of property are provisional and that in certain circumstances it is not unlawful to rob. Everyone would act in that belief. So I will not make you that answer. Apply to the jesuit theologian Juan Mariana de Talavera who will also explain to you in what circumstances you may lawfully kill your king and whether you had better hand him his poison in a goblet or smear it for him upon his robe or his saddlebow. Ask me rather would I suffer others to rob me or, if they did, would I call down upon them what I believe is called the chastisement of the secular arm?—

—And would you?—

—I think—Stephen said—it would pain me as much to do as to be robbed.—

—I see—Cranly said.

He produced his match and began to clean the crevice between two teeth. Then he said carelessly:

—Tell me, for example, would you deflower a virgin?—

—Excuse me—Stephen said politely—is that not the ambition of most young gentlemen?—

—What then is your point of view?—Cranly asked.

His last phrase, sour smelling as the smoke of charcoal and disheartening, excited Stephen's brain, over which its fumes seemed to brood.

—Look here, Cranly—he said.—You have asked me what I would do and what I would not do. I will tell you what I will do and what I will not do. I will not serve that in which I no longer believe, whether it call itself my home, my fatherland or my church: and I will try to express myself in some mode of life or art as freely as I can and as wholly as I can, using for my defence the only arms I allow myself to use, silence, exile and cunning.—

Cranly seized his arm and steered him round so as to lead back towards Lesson Park. He laughed almost slyly and pressed Stephen's arm with an elder's affection.

—Cunning indeed!—he said.—Is it you? You poor poet, you!—

—And you made me confess to you—Stephen said, thrilled by his touch—as I have confessed to you so many others things, have I not?—

—Yes, my child—Cranly said, still gaily.

—You made me confess the fears that I have. But I will tell you also what I do not fear. I do not fear to be alone or to be spurned for another or to leave whatever I have to leave. And I am not afraid to make a mistake, even a great mistake, a lifelong mistake and perhaps as long as eternity too.—

Cranly, now grave again, slowed his pace and said:

—Alone, quite alone. You have no fear of that. And you know what that word means? Not only to be separate from all others but to have not even one friend.—

—I will take the risk—said Stephen.

—And not to have any one person—Cranly said—who would be more than a friend, more even than the noblest and truest friend a man ever had.—

His words seemed to have struck some deep chord in his own nature. Had he spoken of himself, of himself as he was or wished to be? Stephen watched his face for some moments in silence. A cold sadness was there. He had spoken of himself, of his own loneliness which he feared.

—Of whom are you speaking?—Stephen asked at length.—

Cranly did not answer.

↓

March 20. Long talk with Cranly on the subject of my revolt.

He had his grand manner on. I supple and suave. Attacked me on the score of love for one's mother. Tried to imagine his mother: cannot. Told me once, in a moment of thoughtlessness, his father was sixty-one when he was born. Can see him. Strong farmer type. Pepper and salt suit. Square feet. Unkempt grizzled beard. Probably attends coursing matches. Pays his dues regularly but not plentifully to Father Dwyer of Larras. Sometimes talks to girls after nightfall. But his mother? Very young or very old? Hardly the first. If so, Cranly would not have spoken as he did. Old then. Probably, and neglected. Hence Cranly's despair of soul: the child of exhausted loins.

March 21, morning. Thought this in bed last night but was too lazy and free to add it. Free, yes. The exhausted loins are those of Elizabeth and Zacchary. Then he is the precursor. Item: he eats chiefly belly bacon and dried figs. Read locusts and wild honey. Also, when thinking of him, saw always a stern severed head or death mask as if outlined on a grey curtain or veronica. Decollation they call it in the fold. Puzzled for the moment by saint John at the Latin gate. What do I see? A decollated precursor trying to pick the lock.

March 21, night. Free. Soul free and fancy free. Let the dead bury the dead. Ay. And let the dead marry the dead.

March 22. In company with Lynch followed a sizable hospital nurse. Lynch's idea. Dislike it. Two lean hungry greyhounds walking after a heifer.

March 23. Have not seen her since that night. Unwell? Sits at the fire perhaps with mamma's shawl on her shoulders. But not peevish. A nice bowl of gruel? Won't you now?

March 24. Began with a discussion with my mother. Subject: B.V.M. Handicapped by my sex and youth. To escape held up relations between Jesus and Papa against those between Mary and her son. Said religion was not a lying-in hospital. Mother indulgent. Said I have a queer mind and have read too much. Not true. Have read little and understood less. Then she said I would come back to faith because I had a restless mind. This means to leave church by backdoor of sin and re-enter through the skylight of repentance. Cannot repent. Told her so and asked for sixpence. Got threepence.

Then went to college. Other wrangle with little round head rogue's eye Ghezzi. This time about Bruno the Nolan. Began in Italian and ended in pidgin English. He said Bruno was a terrible heretic. I said he was terribly burned. He agreed to this with some sorrow. Then gave me recipe for what he calls *ristollo alla bergamasca*. When he pronounces a soft *o* he protrudes his full carnal lips as if he kissed the vowel. Has he? And could he repent? Yes, he could: and cry two round rogue's tears, one from each eye.

Crossing Stephen's, that is, my Green, remembered that his countrymen and not mine had invented what Cranly the other night called our religion. A quartet of them, soldiers of the ninetyseventh infantry regiment, sat at the foot of the cross and tossed up dice for the overcoat of the crucified.

Went to library. Tried to read three reviews. Useless. She is not out yet. Am I alarmed? About what? That she will never be out again.

Blake wrote:

> *I wonder if William Bond will die,*
> *For assuredly he is very ill.*

Alas, poor William!

I was once at a diorama in Rotunda. At the end were pictures of big nobs. Among them William Ewart Gladstone, just then dead. Orchestra played *O, Willie, we have missed you.*

A race of clodhoppers!

March 25, morning. A troubled night of dreams. Want to get them off my chest.

A long curving gallery. From the floor ascend pillars of dark vapours. It is peopled by the images of fabulous kings, set in stone. Their hands are folded upon their knees in token of weariness and their eyes are darkened for the errors of men go up before them for ever as dark vapours.

Strange figures advance as from a cave. They are not as tall as men. One does not seem to stand quite apart from another. Their faces are phosphorescent, with darker streaks. They peer at me and their eyes seem to ask me something. They do not speak.

March 30. This evening Cranly was in the porch of the library, proposing a problem to Dixon and her brother. A mother let her child fall into the Nile. Still harping on the mother. A crocodile seized the child. Mother asked it back. Crocodile said all right if she told him what he was going to do with the child, eat it or not eat it.

This mentality, Lepidus would say, is indeed bred out of your mud by the operation of your sun.

And mine? Is it not too? Then into Nile mud with it!

April 1. Disapprove of this last phrase.

April 2. Saw her drinking tea and eating cakes in Johnston's, Mooney and O'Brien's. Rather, lynx eyed Lynch saw her as we passed. He tells me Cranly was invited there by brother. Did he bring his crocodile? Is he the shining light now? Well, I discovered him. I protest I did. Shining quietly behind a bushel of Wicklow bran.

April 3. Met Davin at the cigar shop opposite Findlater's church. He was in a black sweater and had a hurley stick. Asked me was it true I was going away and why. Told him the shortest way to Tara was *via* Holyhead. Just then my father came up. Introduction. Father, polite and observant. Asked Davin if he might offer him some refreshment. Davin could not, was going to a meeting. When we came away father told me he had a good honest eye. Asked me why I did not join a rowing club. I pretended to think it over. Told me then how he broke

Pennyfeather's heart. Wants me to read law. Says I was cut out for that. More mud, more crocodiles.

April 5. Wild spring. Scudding clouds. O life! Dark stream of swirling bog-water on which apple trees have cast down their delicate flowers. Eyes of girls among the leaves. Girls demure and romping. All fair or auburn: no dark ones. They blush better. Houp-la!

April 6. Certainly she remembers the past. Lynch says all women do. Then she remembers the time of her childhood—and mine if I was ever a child. The past is consumed in the present and the present is living only because it brings forth the future. Statues of women, if Lynch be right, should always be fully draped, one hand of the woman feeling regretfully her own hinder parts.

April 6, later. Michael Robartes remembers forgotten beauty and, when his arms wrap her round, he presses in his arms the loveliness which has long faded from the world. Not this. Not at all. I desire to press in my arms the loveliness which has not yet come into the world.

April 10. Faintly, under the heavy night, through the silence of the city which has turned from dreams to dreamless sleep as a weary lover whom no caresses move, the sound of hoofs upon the road. Not so faintly now as they come near the bridge: and in a moment as they pass the darkened windows the silence is cloven by alarm as by an arrow. They are heard now far away, hoofs that shine amid the heavy night as gems, hurrying beyond the sleeping fields to what journey's end— what heart?—bearing what tidings?

April 11. Read what I wrote last night. Vague words for a vague emotion. Would she like it? I think so. Then I should have to like it also.

April 13. That tundish has been on my mind for a long time. I looked it up and find it English and good old blunt English too. Damn the dean of studies and his funnel! What did he come here for to teach us his own language or to learn it from us. Damn him one way or the other!

April 14. John Alphonsus Mulrennan has just returned from the west of Ireland. European and Asiatic papers please copy. He told us he met an old man there in a mountain cabin. Old man had red eyes and short pipe. Old man spoke Irish. Mulrennan spoke Irish. Then old man and Mulrennan spoke English. Mulrennan spoke to him about universe and stars. Old man sat, listened, smoked, spat. Then said:

—Ah, there must be terrible queer creatures at the later end of the world.—

I fear him. I fear his redrimmed horny eyes. It is with him I must struggle all through this night till day come, till he or I lie dead, gripping him by the sinewy throat till . . . Till what? Till he yield to me? No. I mean him no harm.

April 15. Met her today point blank in Grafton Street. The crowd brought us together. We both stopped. She asked me why I never came, said she had heard all sorts of stories about me. This was only to gain time. Asked me, was I writing poems? About whom? I asked her. This confused her more and I felt sorry and mean. Turned off that valve at once and opened the spiritual-heroic refrigerating apparatus, invented and patented in all countries by Dante Alighieri. Talked rapidly of myself and my plans. In the midst of it unluckily I made a sudden gesture of a revolutionary nature. I must have looked like a fellow throwing a handful of peas up into the air. People began to look at us. She shook hands a moment after and, in going away, said she hoped I would do what I said.

Now I call that friendly, don't you?

Yes, I liked her today. A little or much? Don't know. I liked her and it seems a new feeling to me. Then, in that case, all the rest, all that I thought I thought and all that I felt I felt, all the rest before now, in fact . . . O, give it up, old chap! Sleep it off!

April 16. Away! Away!

The spell of arms and voices: the white arms of roads, their promise of close embraces and the black arms of tall ships that stand against the moon, their tale of distant nations. They are held out to say: We are alone—come. And the voices say with them: We are your kinsmen. And the air is thick with their company as they call to me, their kinsman, making ready to go, shaking the wings of their exultant and terrible youth.

April 26. Mother is putting my new secondhand clothes in order. She prays now, she says, that I may learn in my own life and away from home and friends what the heart is and what it feels. Amen. So be it. Welcome, O life! I go to encounter for the millionth time the reality of experience and to forge in the smithy of my soul the uncreated conscience of my race.

April 27. Old father, old artificer, stand me now and ever in good stead.

THE END

Dublin, 1904
Trieste, 1914

THOMAS J. CLARKE, et al.

PROCLAMATION OF THE EASTER RISING OF 1916

*On April 24, 1916, more than 1,000 Irish citizens led by representatives
of three revolutionary organizations (the Irish Republican Brotherhood,
the Irish Volunteers, and the Irish Citizen Army), seized the General
Post Office in Dublin. Their proclamation, signed by seven leaders of
the Rising, was read to the crowd and posted all over the city. The seven
signers, who included amongst them three established poets—Patrick
Pearse, Thomas MacDonagh, and Joseph Plunkett—were executed the
following month.*

THE PROVISIONAL GOVERNMENT OF THE IRISH REPUBLIC
TO THE PEOPLE OF IRELAND

IRISHMEN AND IRISHWOMEN: In the name of God and of the dead generations
from which she receives her old tradition of nationhood, Ireland, through us,
summons her children to her flag and strikes for her freedom.

Having organised and trained her manhood through her secret revolutionary
organisation, the Irish Republican Brotherhood, and through her open military
organisations, the Irish Volunteers and the Irish Citizen Army, having patiently
perfected her discipline, having resolutely waited for the right moment to reveal
itself, she now seizes that moment, and, supported by her exiled children in
America and by gallant allies in Europe, but relying in the first on her own
strength, she strikes in full confidence of victory.

We declare the right of the people of Ireland to the ownership of Ireland, and
to the unfettered control of Irish destinies, to be sovereign and indefeasible. The
long usurpation of that right by a foreign people and government has not extinguished the right, nor can it ever be extinguished except by the destruction of the

Irish people. In every generation the Irish people have asserted their right to national freedom and sovereignty; six times during the past three hundred years they have asserted it in arms. Standing on that fundamental right and again asserting it in arms in the face of the world, we hereby proclaim the Irish Republic as a Sovereign Independent State, and we pledge our lives and the lives of our comrades-in-arms to the cause of its freedom, of its welfare, and of its exaltation among the nations.

The Irish Republic is entitled to, and hereby claims, the allegiance of every Irishman and Irishwoman. The Republic guarantees religious and civil liberty, equal rights and equal opportunities to all its citizens, and declares its resolve to pursue the happiness and prosperity of the whole nation and of all its parts, cherishing all the children of the nation equally, and oblivious of the differences carefully fostered by an alien government, which have divided a minority from the majority in the past.

Until our arms have brought the opportune moment for the establishment of a permanent National Government, representative of the whole people of Ireland and elected by the suffrages of all her men and women, the Provisional Government, hereby constituted, will administer the civil and military affairs of the Republic in trust for the people.

We place the cause of the Irish Republic under the protection of the Most High God, Whose blessing we invoke upon our arms, and we pray that no one who serves that cause will dishonour it by cowardice, inhumanity, or rapine. In this supreme hour the Irish Nation must, by its valour and discipline and by the readiness of its children to sacrifice themselves for the common good, prove itself worthy of the august destiny to which it is called.

SIGNED ON BEHALF OF THE PROVISIONAL GOVERNMENT,

THOMAS J. CLARKE
SEAN MACDIARMADA, THOMAS MACDONAGH
P. H. PEARSE, EAMONN CEANNT
JAMES CONNOLLY, JOSEPH PLUNKETT

POEMS

The mystical poet, playwright, and painter AE (George William Russell) was a close friend of W. B. Yeats. "Salutation" honors the men and women of the Easter Rising of 1916. "Immortality" first appeared in AE's collection, The Earth Breath *(1897).*

SALUTATION

Written for those who took part in the 1916 Rebellion

Your dream had left me numb and cold
But yet my spirit rose in pride,
Re-fashioning in burnished gold
The images of those who died,
Or were shut in the penal cell—
Here's to you, Pearse, your dream, not mine,
But yet the thought—for this you fell—
Turns all life's water into wine.

I listened to high talk from you,
Thomas MacDonagh, and it seemed
The words were idle, but they grew
To nobleness, by death redeemed.
Life cannot utter things more great
Than life can meet with sacrifice,
High words were equalled by high fate,
You paid the price. You paid the price.

The hope lives on, age after age,
Earth with her beauty might be won
For labor as a heritage—
For this has Ireland lost a son,
This hope into a flame to fan
Men have put life by with a smile.
Here's to you, Connolly, my man,
Who cast the last torch on the pile.

Here's to the women of our race
Stood by them in the fiery hour,
Rapt, lest some weakness in their blood
Rob manhood of a single power—
You, brave as such a hope forlorn,
Who smiled through crack of shot and shell,
Though the world look on you with scorn,
Here's to you, Constance,[1] in your cell.

Here's to you, men I never met,
But hope to meet behind the veil,
Thronged on some starry parapet
That looks down upon Inisfail,
And see the confluence of dreams
That clashed together in our night,
One river born of many streams
Roll in one blaze of blinding light!

IMMORTALITY

We must pass like smoke or live within the spirit's fire;
For we can no more than smoke unto the flame return
If our thought has changed to dream, our will unto desire,
    As smoke we vanish though the fire may burn.

Lights of infinite pity star the grey dusk of our days:
Surely here is soul: with it we have eternal breath:
In the fire of love we live, or pass by many ways,
    By unnumbered ways of dream to death.

---

[1] Countess de Markievicz, one of the leaders of the Rising

558

FROM
THE INFORMER

The following excerpt, taken from the beginning of Liam O'Flaherty's best novel, The Informer *(1925), describes the workings of Gypo Nolan's mind after he is sought out by his fellow revolutionary and closest friend, Francis McPhillip, who has been on the run for six months after killing a union official.*

MCPHILLIP SAT DOWN AT THE opposite side of the table. He did not speak and he did not express recognition by any sign or movement of his body. But he knew the man quite well. They were bosom friends. The man was Gypo Nolan, McPhillip's companion during the strike of farm-labourers, when McPhillip had killed the secretary of the Farmers' Union. Gypo Nolan had once been a policeman in Dublin, but he had been dismissed owing to a suspicion at Headquarters that he was in league with the Revolutionary Organization and had given information to them relative to certain matters that had leaked out. Since then he had been an active member of the Revolutionary Organization and had always acted with Francis Joseph McPhillip, so that they were known in revolutionary circles as the "Devil's Twins."

"Well, Gypo," said McPhillip at last, "how is things?"

McPhillip's voice was cracked and weak, but it had a fierce sincerity that gave it immense force, like the force in the chirping of a tiny bird whose nest is being robbed.

"Did ye leave them messages I gave ye?" he continued after a moment, during which he gasped for breath. "I didn't hear anythin' from home since I saw ye that evenin' I had to take to the hills. What's doin', Gypo?"

Gypo stared in silence for several moments, breathing slowly, with open mouth and distended eyes. He never spoke. Then he made a strange sound, like a suppressed exclamation, in his throat. He slowly cut a large potato in four pieces with his knife. He transferred one piece to his mouth on the tip of his knife. He began to chew slowly. Then he stopped chewing suddenly and spoke. It was a deep thunderous voice.

"Where the divil did ye come from, Frankie?" he said.

"It don't matter where I come from," cried McPhillip in an irritated tone, "I got no time to waste passin' the compliments o' the season. I came in here to get wise to all the news. Tell us all ye knew. First, tell me . . . wait a minute. How about them messages? Did ye deliver them? Don't mind that grub. Man alive, are ye a savage or what? Here I am with the cops after me for me life an' ye go on eatin' yer spuds. Lave down that damn knife or I'll plug ye. Come on, I'm riskin' me life to come in here and ask ye a question. Get busy an' tell me all about it."

Gypo sighed easily and wiped his mouth with the back of his right sleeve. Then he put his knife on the table and swallowed his mouthful.

"Ye were always a cranky fellah," he growled, "an' ye don't seem to be improvin', with the spring weather. I'll tell ye if ye hold on a minute. I delivered yer messages, to yer father an' mother and to the Executive Committee. Yer ol' man gev me dog's abuse and drov' me outa the house, an' he cursed ye be bell, book an' candle light. Yer mother followed me out cryin' an' put half a quid into me hand to give to ye. I had no way o' findin' ye an' I was hungry mesel', so I spent it. Well——"

McPhillip interrupted with a muttered curse. Then he was seized with a fit of coughing. When the fit was over, Gypo went on.

"Well," continued Gypo. "Ye know yersel' what happened with the Executive Committee. They sent a man out to tell ye. I wouldn't mind them sendin' a letter to the papers sayin' they had nothin' to do with the strike. It ud only be all swank anyway, an' who cares? But I declare to Christ they near had me plugged when I went in to report. Commandant Gallagher was goin' to send down men to plug ye too, but lots o' the other fellahs got around him and he didn't. Anyway I was fired out o' the Organization as well as yersel', although ye know yersel', Frankie, that I had nothin' to do with firin' that shot. An'——"

"What the——" began McPhillip angrily, rapping the table; but again he began to cough. Gypo went on without taking notice of the coughing.

"The police arrested me, but they could find no evidence, so they gev me an awful beatin' and threw me out. I ben wanderin' around since without a dog to lick me trousers, half starvin'!"

"What do I want to know about the Executive Committee?" grumbled McPhillip angrily, recovering his breath. "I don't want to hear anything about executive committees or revolutionary organizations, me curse on the lot o' them. I want to hear about me father an' mother. What about 'em, Gypo?"

Gypo expanded his thick under lip and stared at McPhillip with distended eyes. His eyes seemed to hold an expression of sadness in their dim recesses, but it was hard to say. The face was so crude and strong that the expression that might be termed sadness in another face was mere wonder in his. For the first time he had noticed the pallor of McPhillip's face, the hectic flush, the fits of coughing, the jerky movements and the evident terror in the eyes that used to be so fearless.

"Frankie," cried Gypo in his deep, slow, passionless voice, "yer sick. Man alive, ye look as if ye were dyin'."

McPhillip started and looked about him hurriedly as if he expected to see death there behind his back waiting to pounce upon him.

"Have a bite," continued Gypo, "'twill warm ye up."

At the same time he himself began to eat again fiercely, like a great strong animal, tackling the solitary meal of its day. The large red hands with just stumps of fingers held the knife and fork so ponderously that those frail instruments seemed to run the danger of being crushed, like some costly thing picked up on the tip of an elephant's trunk. But McPhillip did not follow the invitation. He looked angrily at the food for several seconds with wrinkled forehead, as if he were trying to remember what it was and what it was for, and then he spoke again.

"I know I'm dyin', Gypo, an' that's why I came in. I got the consumption." Gypo started. He was struck at that moment by an insane and monstrous idea. "I came in to get some money from me mother. An' I wanted to see her before I die. Good God, it was awful, Gypo, out there on them hills all the winter, with me gun in me hand night an' day, sleeping in holes on the mountains, with the wind blowin' about me all night, screechin' like a pack o' devils, an' every blast o' them winds spoke with a man's voice, an' I lyin' there listenin' to them. Good God——"

Again he began to cough and he had to stop. Gypo was not listening to him. He had not heard a word. A monstrous idea had prowled into his head, like an uncouth beast straying from a wilderness into a civilized place where little children are alone. He did not hear McPhillip's words or his coughing, although the monstrous idea was in relation to McPhillip.

"So I said to mesel', that I might as well chance me arm be comin' into town as lyin' out there, starvin' to death with the cold an' hunger an' this cough. So I came along here to see ye, Gyp, first, so as to get a bead on what's doin'. Have they got a guard on the house?"

"Divil a guard," replied Gypo suddenly, and then he started and stretched out his right hand towards McPhillip with a little exclamation. His eyes were wild and his mouth was wide open like the mouth of a man looking at a spectre. Gypo's mind was looking at that uncouth ogre that was prowling about in his brain.

McPhillip leaned across the table. Gradually, his eyes narrowed into an intense stare of ferocity. His lips curled up and his forehead wrinkled. He began to tremble.

"What is it, Gypo?" he hissed. "Tell me, Gyp, or I'll . . ." He made a rapid movement with the wrist of the hand that clutched his automatic. "The cops are after me, Gyp, an' I'm dyin', so I don't mind how I use the twenty-four rounds I got left. I've notched their noses so they can make a quare hole. There's one for mesel' too." He shuddered as if at the thought of a tender pleasure. Then he scowled fiercely and half drew the butt of his pistol from his pocket. His voice was almost inaudible. "Tell me the truth about how things stand without any jig actin' or I'll plug ye."

He glared at Gypo, his hand on his pistol, his right arm rigid to the shoulder, ready to draw the gun and fire in one movement. Gypo stared him in the eyes without any emotion, either of fear or of surprise. With the nail of his right fore-finger he abstracted a string of meat from between two teeth. He spluttered with his lips and then he shrugged his shoulders. The spectre had suddenly gone out of his mind without his being able to make head or tail of it.

"No use talkin' like that to me, Frankie," he murmured lazily. "The only rea-son why I didn't want to say anythin' was because I didn't like to . . ." Again the ghoulish thing came into his mind and he stopped with a start. But almost imme-diately he continued in a forced voice. He was beginning to be ashamed of that spectre as if he had already given way to the horrid suggestions it made, although he did not at all comprehend those suggestions. "I didn't like to maybe send ye into harm's way. Ye see, I don't know if there's a guard on ye father's house or if there's not. I generally knock around Titt Street, but I haven't been near No. 44 since that night I went there with yer message an' yer ol' man told me never to darken his door again. There may be a guard on it or there may be no guard on it. But if I told ye there wasn't and ye went there and got nabbed, ye know——"

"What are ye drivin' at, Gypo?" growled McPhillip suspiciously.

"Nothin' at all," said Gypo with a great deep laugh. "But it's how ye've come in on me so sudden, an' I don't know right what I'm talkin' about. Ye see, I'm all mixed up for the last six months, wanderin' around here, without a mate that ud give me a tanner for a flop if I were to die o' the cold lyin' in O'Connell's Street with a foot o' frost on the ground. They——"

"Oh, shut up about yersel' an' the frost an' tell us somethin'."

"Now don't get yer rag out, Frankie. I was comin' to that. I was comin' to it, man. They held me up in the street the other day and had a long talk about ye. They're after ye yet all right. Sergeant McCartney an' another fellah from Sligo was there. That Detective-Sergeant McCartney is a bad lot. Huh, he's a rascal, an' no goin' behind a wall to say it. He swore to me that he'd get ye dead or alive. 'I wouldn't care much for yer job then,' says I to him, just like that, an' he gave me an eye that ud knock ye stiff."

"He says he's goin' to get me, did he?" murmured McPhillip dreamily. Suddenly his mind seemed to wander away and he lost interest in his present surroundings. His eyes rested vacantly on the table, about a foot away to the right.

Gypo looked hurriedly at the spot upon which McPhillip's eyes were fixed. He saw nothing. He looked back again at McPhillip's face and wrinkled up his forehead. Then he made a noise in his throat and began to eat once more with great rapidity. He breathed on his food, to cool it, as he put it into his jaws. He made noises.

McPhillip stared at the table for a long time. His right hand toyed nervously with the butt of his pistol. His left hand rapped the table. Then a strange sparkle came into his eyes. He laughed suddenly. It was a strange laugh. It made Gypo start.

"What's the matter, Frankie?" he asked in a terrified voice.

"Nothin' at all," said McPhillip, shaking himself. "Gimme something' t' eat."

He began to eat ravenously, using his penknife as a knife and fork. He had not eaten for a long time. He did not taste the food but gulped it down at a great speed.

Gypo ate also, but he kept staring at McPhillip while he ate. Every time his wandering little eyes reached McPhillip's eyes they narrowed and became very sharp. Then he would roll his tongue around in his cheek and make a sucking sound.

At last McPhillip stopped eating. He wiped his penknife on his trousers and put it into his pocket.

"Gypo," he said slowly, "are there any cops watchin' our house, the old man's place in Titt Street?"

Gypo shook his head three times in reply. His mouth was full. Then he swallowed his mouthful, he put his fork to his forehead and set to thinking.

"Lemme see," he said at last. "Yeh. They had two cops watchin' the place until after Christmas. Then they took 'em off. They didn't put any on since as far as I know, but I believe that a fellah goes around there now an' again to make inquiries. O' course they might have secret-service men on it as well. God only knows who's givin' information to the Government now, an' who isn't. Ye never know who yer talkin' to. I never in me life saw anythin' like it. Tell ye what, Frankie, the workin' class is not worth fightin' for. They think yer gone to the United States, but all the same it might be dangerous goin' down there now. I'm sorry I have no money to give ye, so as ye could——"

"Where the divil did ye get all the gab?" cried McPhillip suddenly, looking suspiciously at Gypo. "I never knew ye to let out all that much talk in a day, or maybe a whole week. Are ye goin' to the university now in yer spare time or what ails ye?"

McPhillip began to rap the table again. There was silence. Gypo nonchalantly transferred the scraps from his plate to his mouth on the flat of his knife. When the plate was completely cleaned up he rattled the knife and fork on to it. Then he stuck out his massive chest and rubbed his palms along it.

Suddenly McPhillip swore and jumped to his feet. He stood, as if in a dream, looking at the table for several moments. Gypo watched his face, with his little tufted eyebrows quivering. At the same time he cleaned his teeth with his left thumb-nail. At last McPhillip drew in a deep breath through his teeth, making a noise as if he were sucking ice.

"Right," he said, with his eyes still on the table. "My ould fellah is at home now, is he?"

"Yes," said Gypo. "I saw him yesterday. He was over in the 'Pool on a job, but he's back this fortnight. I think he's workin' on a new house out in Rathmines."

"Right," said McPhillip again. Then he raised his eyes, looking at Gypo fiercely and smiled in a curious fashion. "See ye again, Gypo, unless the cops get me."

As he spoke he seemed to think of something. His face quivered and darkened. Then he shrugged his shoulders and laughed outright. He nodded twice and turned on his heel. He strode hurriedly out of the room.

Gypo looked after him for a long time without moving. He had finished cleaning his teeth. He just stared at the door through which McPhillip had disappeared. Then gradually his mind began to fill with suggestions. His forehead wrinkled up. His body began to fidget. At last he jumped to his feet. He collected the plate, the knife and fork and the salt. He walked into the passage and put them in a locker, which was provided by the management for the lodgers. The locker did not belong to Gypo. He had no locker because he was merely a casual lodger since he had no regular income to pay for a bed by the week. The locker belonged to a carter of Gypo's acquaintance. Gypo had seen the man put his next-day's dinner in the locker and go away without turning the key. Gypo knew also that the man would not be back until ten o'clock that night. So he took the dinner.

He placed the things in the locker and walked away casually. He sat on the corner of a seat in one of the alcoves. He rummaged in the pockets of his dungarees and collected several minute scraps of cigarettes. He carefully unrolled the scraps, collecting all the tobacco in the palm of his right hand. Then he begged a cigarette paper from an old man who sat beside him. The old man had none and said so with an angry curse. Gypo wrinkled his forehead and sniffed as if he were smelling the old man. Then he turned to a young man who passed and requested a cigarette paper. The young man halted and supplied one grudgingly. Gypo took the paper in silence, without a word or a nod of thanks. He rolled his cigarette and lit it at the gas jet. Then he sat down again, crossed his legs, let his body go limp and began to smoke.

His ears seemed to stick out very far, as he lay back limply in the seat, in the half-darkness of the corridor.

For a minute the odour and the taste of the tobacco held him in a state of enjoyment. He did not think either of the fact that he had no bed for the night or of his meeting with McPhillip. Then gradually his forehead began to wrinkle and furrow. His little tufted eyebrows began to twitch. When he pulled at his cigarette his face was enshrouded in a bright glow and the humps on his face stood out, glistening and smooth. He began to shift about in his seat. First he uncrossed his legs. Then he crossed them again. He began to tap his knee with his right hand. He sighed. His cigarette wore out until it was burning his lips without his becoming aware of the fact. Then he spluttered it out of his mouth on to his chest and he jumped to his feet.

He stood looking at the ground with his hands deep in his trousers pockets. He seemed to be deep in thought, but he was not thinking. At least there was no concrete idea fixed in his mind. Two facts rumbled about in his brain, making that loud primeval noise, which is the beginning of thought and which tired people experience when the jaded brain has spun out the last threads of its energy. There were two facts in his brain. First, the fact of his meeting with McPhillip. Second, the fact of his having no money to buy a bed for the night.

These two facts stood together in an amorphous mass. But he could not summon up courage to tackle them and place them in proper juxtaposition and reason out their relationship. He just stood looking at the ground.

Then a drunken bookmaker's clerk named Shanahan brushed against him. He stepped aside with a muttered oath. He pulled one hand from his pocket to strike, with the fingers extended in the shape of a bird's claw. Shanahan, doubled up in the middle by the helplessness of intoxication, stared at Gypo with blue eyes that had gone almost completely red. Gypo turned away with a shrug of his shoulders. At any other time he would gladly have availed himself of this opportunity of begging a shilling from Shanahan. Shanahan was always good for the loan of a shilling when he was drunk. A shilling would procure Gypo a bed for the night and leave a little for a light breakfast in the morning. Ten minutes ago, a *rencontre* of this sort would have been a godsend to Gypo. But now, those two cursed facts stood in his brain, making him unconscious of everything else.

He walked out of the House and up the lane towards the B—— Road.

He walked with his hands deep in his pockets, slowly, with his thighs brushing on the insides as he walked. He seemed to haul his big boots after him, bringing them as near the ground as possible. His hips moved up and down as his feet went forward. His eyes were on the ground. His lips were distended outwards. His little torn, brown, slouch hat was perched incongruously on the top of his head, much too small for his large square skull, with the brim turned up closely all around. When a squall of wind, laden with little sharp hailstones, struck him across the face and body, his clothes puffed out and he curled up his short stubby nose in an angry grin.

He was looking into the window of a saddler's shop in Dame Street, when the relationship between the two facts became known to him. He was looking at a pair of bright spurs and his face contorted suddenly. His eyes bulged as if he were taken with a fit of terror. He looked about him suspiciously, as if he were about to steal something for the first time. Then he rushed away hurriedly. He moved through lanes and alleyways to the river. He crossed the street to the river wall. He leaned his elbows on the wall and spat into the dark water. With his chin resting on his arms, he stood perfectly still, thinking.

He was contemplating the sudden discovery that his mind had made, about the relationship between his having no money for a bed and his having met Francis Joseph McPhillip, who was wanted for murder in connection with the farm-labourers' strike at M—— in the previous October. A terrific silence reigned within his head.

Now and again he looked around him with a kind of panting noise. He snorted and smelled the air and screwed up his eyes. Then he leaned over the wall again and rested his chin on his crossed hands. He was that way for half an hour. Then at last he drew himself up straight. He stretched his arms above his head. He yawned. He stuck his hands in his trousers pockets. He stared at the ground. Then with his eyes on the ground he walked away at the same slouching pace as before.

He crossed the river and traversed a maze of side streets, with his eyes always on the ground, until he reached the corner of a dark side street, that had a bright lamp hanging over a doorway, half-way down on the right-hand side. That was a police-station. He stared at the lamp with his eyes wide open for several moments. Almost a minute. Then he said "Huh" out loud. Then he looked around him cautiously on all sides.

The street was empty. Rain drizzled slowly. He examined the street, the warehouses on his side of the street, the blank wall on the other side. Then his eyes came back to the bright lamp that hung above the door of the police-station. He sighed deeply and began to walk slowly, ever so slowly and ponderously, towards the lamp.

He walked up the steps, steadily, one at a time, making a loud noise. He kicked the swing door open with his foot without taking his hands out of his pockets. In the hallway, a constable in a black, cone-shaped, night helmet stood facing him, pulling on his gloves. Gypo halted and stared at the constable.

"I have come to claim the twenty pounds reward offered by the Farmers' Union for information concerning Francis Joseph McPhillip," he said in a deep, low voice.

↓

At thirty-five minutes past seven Francis Joseph McPhillip shot himself dead while trying to escape from No. 44 Titt Street, his father's house. The house had been surrounded by Detective-Sergeant McCartney and ten men. Hanging by his left hand from the sill of the back-bedroom window on the second floor, McPhillip put two bullets into McCartney's left shoulder. While he was trying to fire again, his left hand slipped and lost its hold. The pistol muzzle struck the edge of the sill. The bullet shot upwards and entered McPhillip's brain through the right temple.

When they picked him out of the orange box in the back garden where he fell, he was quite dead.

FROM
TWENTY YEARS A-GROWING
A NIGHT IN THE INISH

Maurice O'Sullivan's memoir Twenty Years A-Growing *(1933) recounts his childhood on Ireland's Great Blasket, a Gaelic-speaking island off the Atlantic coast. "A Night in the Inish" describes a delightful fishing expedition to a neighboring island circa 1914.*

THE MONTH OF SAMHAIN[1] is the time when there does be a rush for pollock in the Island.

One fine day when the ground was hard with frost, with a little air of wind from the east and a fragrant smell from the sea, I wandered out of the house and stood a while thinking. The sea-birds were flying around in quest of fish. There were thrushes in plenty hard by and they fleeing before the cold. It was of the life of the birds I was thinking and the passing of the tide from the strand.

After a while another thought struck me and I made my way to the house of Pádrig O'Dála. Pádrig was before me at the door, gazing south-east, humming a tune.

"A fine day, Pádrig."

"It is, thanks be to God, and a good day on the sea."

I went inside the house and who would be there but Paddy Tim.

"It is a fresh day, Paddy."

"Ah, it is not so fresh yet, and that the goats would eat it."[2]

Pádrig came in.

"Do you know what I was thinking?" said he. "That it would be a good day to go fishing for pollock on the Wild Bank."

"And spend the night in the Inish?" said I, delighted.

"I dare say we will do that," said Pádrig, "but get ready now and don't delay."

The Wild Bank lies to the south-east of Inish-vick-ilaun, a good way out in the Bay. It is a reef under water where the sea sweeps and breaks in bad weather, and it has a great name among the old men for fish.

We were across the Great Sound now, and there's no doubt but it would delight a sick man at that time to be looking north and south at the sea-birds hunting over the wild sea. Soon we saw a guillemot a little way off to the south with her young chick behind her. Above them was a great black-backed gull and he swooping down at the chick. Every time he swooped the chick would dive and go astray on him; and every time the chick came up again, the gull would make another swoop.

"Musha, isn't the gull a treacherous bird?" said Pádrig O'Dála.

"Not at all," said Paddy Tim. "Isn't it trying to fill his belly he is, and isn't it the same thing you are trying to do yourself with the pollock on the Wild Bank to the south?"

"Och, that's talk in the air," said Pádrig.

"Why so? Isn't the guillemot herself watching for something to put in her belly and isn't it the same way with the gull? Upon my word, I see no more treachery in him than there is in yourself."

I was not giving much ear to their talk but watching the gull swooping down, and the poor mother doing her best to defend her own. In the end the gull made another swoop and caught the chick by the tail. With that the mother flew at him, and you never saw such a tussle as there was between the two birds until at last the gull had to let go. Then the chick dived under water and the mother after it. Faith, thought I, they are after making a fool of the gull. And away he flew west over the waves.

We were making the Inish by this time and my heart beating like a watch with delight, for I was never yet up in the island. "It is growing late," said Pádrig. "The best thing we can do is to go ashore for the night and we can rise with the sparrow's chirp in the morning."

I looked west towards the island. The sea was like glass for smoothness, little fish playing on the top of the water, the sun going down behind the Narrow Sound and throwing its golden beams on the Foze Rocks which looked like a castle of gold on the horizon, shining with a supernatural light.

"Musha, Pádrig," said I, "isn't it a beautiful sight that is around and about us?"

"I swear," said he, turning to me with a laugh, "I don't know is it on myself or not, but as soon as I clear the Horse's Mouth westward it seems as if a cloud rises from my heart. Maybe it is because I was born in the Inish."

"In my opinion," said Paddy, "even if you were born above on the Muilcheann, you would love it."

The word was not out of his mouth when I heard from the island a noise which took an echo out of the coves: Gurla-gu-hu-hu-golagón! gurla-gu-hu-hu-golagón!

My heart leapt, for it is often before I had heard that spirits were to be seen and fairy music to be heard above in the Inish.

"What is it, Pádrig?" said I tremulously.

"Row on," said he with a laugh, "and you will soon see what it is."

We rowed on, our eyes on the strand, and soon we heard it again: Gurla-gu-hu-hu-golagón!

"Look in now, and keep your eyes on the shingle."

I looked in and what did I see but up to forty seals stretched at full length, sunning themselves on the strand. Pádrig let out a roar. They raised their heads. Then away with them as hard as they could go to the water. Not a spot of the strand but was hidden by the spouts of foam they sent up into the sky; and when we were within ten yards of the strand, not a seal was to be seen, the sea still again, save only the rings they had left in their wake. I looked down through the water. I could see the bottom clearly and the seals rushing out below.

"Oh, Lord, Pádrig, isn't it a marvellous speed they have?"

"It is no wonder, my boy. Did you never hear the saying: Sturgeon, ling, or seal, the three swiftest fish in the sea?"

We went in on to the shingle. I looked up at the cliff above my head as is the habit of a stranger when he comes to a foreign land. When we had the curragh on the stays and our gear in order for the night, I strolled away, wandering, taking heed of everything around me.

In the course of my ramblings I found a black stone and some old names cut into it. I could not count all that were on it, but this is the one that put the greatest wonder on me: "W. W. Wilson, Jan. 1630."

I called Pádrig: "Devil take it, would you believe there is a name here which has been made for two hundred and eighty-four years?"

"Och, my pity for your head, did I not see a man from Dublin once who found a name above in the churchyard which was made a thousand years ago?"

"Better still," said I, and at that moment a verse came into my head and I recited it to Pádrig:

> The trout lives in the stream,
> The duck lives on the pool,
> The blossom lives on the tree,
> But lives not the hand that wrote.

"Indeed, my boy," said Pádrig, looking at me between the eyes, "there is a power of nonsense inside your head."

We turned our faces up into the island and climbed an old path through the cliff. There was a beautiful view. The Teeracht with its little white houses lay behind us to the north. Over in the west, nine miles away, were the Foze Rocks, and nothing to be seen beyond them but the sky like a great shining wall, and the sun descending big and round into the sea. Over to the east was the Bay of Dingle and a melancholy look coming over the hills with the fall of night.

We moved on together, up to our knees in the long grass. Soon I saw the house above me at the foot of a little hill with fine fields around it. We had three dogs with us, and with their ears cocked they ran off before us through the island. Hundreds of rabbits were to be seen making hurriedly for the warrens, running past as thick as ants, ears back, tails up, and the eyes starting out of their heads in terror of the dogs. In a few moments the whole island was in confusion—the sheep running wild, the goat fleeing for its life, the birds screaming across the fields northwards to the lonely reefs. What wonder! When did they last see a man of this world? I thought of Robinson Crusoe when he landed on just such an island. What would he not have given to be a goat when he saw a herd of them running together and he without a companion!

The delight in my heart was growing as I came nearer to the mystery of the island. But I grew sad as I thought of all who had ever lived there, making a livelihood for themselves like the wild goats, and not one of them alive today.

Two of the dogs came running up to us, each with a rabbit across his mouth. They threw them down at our feet, and then made off again.

"Oh, Pádrig, aren't the dogs well taught?"

"Upon my word," said he, feeling the rabbits, "there is fat on these. Have you a knife?"

I gave him mine and he soon had the guts out of them.

We walked on again but had not gone far when we saw the dogs running back with two more rabbits. "Faith," said I, "if they keep this up, we'll have spoils tomorrow."

When we came to the ditch of the field outside the house, a start was taken out of me. I stopped and listened. I hear it, said I in my own mind, the sweetest music I ever heard. I heard it again. My heart leapt. "Pádrig!" said I, "do you hear anything?"

He looked at me and listened. "I swear by the devil," said he, lifting his cap and scratching his head, "that all who ever died in the island are above in the house making sport."

I did not doubt him on account of the reputation of the place for fairies and a shudder ran up from my little toe to the roots of my hair.

Pádrig looked at me again. He was smiling. "Did you never hear of a petrel?"

"I did not."

"That is a petrel now."

"Where?"

"It is inside the ditch."

I listened again, and true enough for him I could hear it clearly now, the sweetest song ever heard by mortal ear. I would have spent the whole evening listening to it but for Pádrig making fun of me.

We went up to the house—a little, low hut with a felt roof, ruins in plenty around, weed and nettles growing among them. We went inside. It was nice and clean, the walls whitened with lime, and a little room below. I went down to the room, to see two rabbits scampering away through a hole they had made in the wall. Pádrig came down and threw a curse at them when he saw the hole.

I looked up at the walls which were covered in cobwebs and a picture of Moses as black as soot. I took it down, but could not read what was written on it. "I suppose, Pádrig, this is here since you were born?"

"It is, and for ages before me. Let us go out now and cut some fine dry fern for the night."

Not far from the house we came upon fern in plenty growing as high as ourselves. We began tearing it out, and soon each of us had gathered the makings of a good bed. We left it to dry at the bottom of the house and went in. One of us kindled a fire, another went to draw water, another swept out the floor—each at his own task. I opened two of the rabbits and hung the other two outside the door on a nail.

We soon got the look of a hearth on the place, the lamp alight, a fine glowing fire put down and sending out warmth through the house. We sat down to dinner, and a savoury dinner it was—a fine stew of rabbits and plenty of soup.

When we had eaten our fill: "Faith," said Pádrig, "I had better go out now and lay twenty traps or so, and maybe we will have another dozen of rabbits tomorrow."

In half an hour he was back again. "It is as well for us now to bring in the fern," said he, "for we have need of a stretch."

We soon had our beds made, each in his own corner, and stretched ourselves out after the weariness of the day.

"Don't be sleepy in the morning," said Pádrig, "for the quaybach[3] is the very devil for the rabbits. Musha," said he again, stretched back contentedly in the fern with his pipe in his mouth, "it's many the day I spent here in my youth with ne'er a care nor a trouble in the world, and I tell you there was abundance here then as for milk in plenty and butter. My father had twelve cows here at one time and it's many the firkin he sold at the market. But, my sorrow! look at it today—nothing but ferns and nettles."

Before long we fell asleep. About two o'clock I awoke. There was nothing but darkness and the sound of the other two snoring. I was seized with fear when I saw where I was, thinking of all I had ever heard about the fairies. The moonlight was pouring through the window. How envious I was of the other two snoring peacefully in the dead of night! As I lay thinking, what did I see but a human hand passing across the window and taking up the two rabbits I had hung on the nail.

I leapt up and tried to scream, but the tongue swelled in my mouth. I could see him clearly now. He had a horn-peaked cap and the clothes of a sailor. I could hear his footsteps outside as he went away with the rabbits. "Oh, Lord," I cried, "save me from the fairies!"

I got up somehow and went over to Pádrig and gave him a kick which lifted him clean out of the fern.

"What ails you?" said he, looking up in the moonlight.

"Oh, oh, Pádrig, it is someone I saw outside the window going off with the rabbits."

"Musha, my pity for your brass head," said he, stretching back again into the fern.

I lay down once more and at last I fell into a light doze. How long I was asleep I do not know, but when I awoke Pádrig was calling me:

"Oh, Lord," said he, "the bright day is here."

"It is not. It is only the light of the moon."

He went down to call Paddy Tim: "Paddy! Paddy!"

"Hm," mumbled Paddy at last.

"You had better stay here, Paddy, till the two of us go drawing the traps, and let you have the breakfast ready before us when we return."

"Hm, hm!" said Paddy, stretching back again.

"What were the delusions that came on you last night?" said Pádrig as he lit the lamp.

"Upon my word, they were no delusions at all, but the man was there in his own shape and I'll bet anything you like that the rabbits are not on the nail now."

"Arra, man," said he, turning to me when he had the lamp alight, "don't you know that no one dead would take the rabbits?"

"I don't know, but alive or dead, he took them."

"And where is the living man on this island?"

"Isn't that the whole matter?" I was getting a sort of courage now that the lamp was lit.

"Go out now and see if the rabbits are there still."

"Upon my word I will not, but go yourself for I have had enough of it."

As he reached the door he struck something heavy with his foot. "What the devil is this?" said he, stooping to pick it up. "Arra, your soul to the devil, it is a big tin of tobacco. Faith, Maurice, you were right. The rabbits are gone. A sailor must have come ashore and taken them, and, look, what did he do but slip a tin of tobacco under the door, as is the custom with them?"

We started out to draw the traps. The moon was moving slowly among the stars above and throwing a silver glitter on the sea through the Bay of Dingle to the east; bright points of light in the dew, which lay heavy on the grass; a dead calm on the sea and not a breath from the sky; grass and fern up to our knees and a sound like a whirlwind sweeping through the fern from the rabbits running through it with the dogs pursuing them; an odd cry from the heron with the fairness of the night; the petrel with her own song; cóch-cóch-cóch! from the black-backed gull across the island to the north; meggy-geg-geg! from the goats among the rocks; baa-baa! from a sheep in the distance; and the seal not forgetting his own olagón in the gullies far below.

We were now across the field to the south and we as light-hearted as any rabbit in the island. We heard a cry from a gull, then another, as if they were closing around something.

"Och, bad cess to them, they have the rabbits eaten," said Pádrig, leaping over a rock and I after him, ever and ever, till we came to the first trap where we found two of them tearing a rabbit asunder. "Hucs, hucs, hucs!" he cried as he drew near them. Off they flew to perch on the top of a rock near by, crying cág-cág!

They hadn't done much damage to the rabbit. We drew it out; then away with us as fast as we could by the Rock's Foot to the east and then by the Spring Meadow to the south, drawing one trap after another and a rabbit in every one of them.

Away with us again to Bird Cove in the west, till we came to the head of the Cove, and there we heard the olagón from the seals on the shingle below. Anyone who had no knowledge of them would think that the living and dead were gathered there. We sat down for a while listening, the moon shining in on us.

"I wonder, Pádrig," said I, his back to me, lighting his pipe, "would you believe that those are men under magic?"

"I have heard it, and upon my word I would believe it for they are just like old women keening. Och," says he leaping up, "the strand does not wait for milking-time."

Away he went and I after him, my heart out on the palm of my hand for I had a dozen rabbits on my back, and I could not keep up with him. Only that was not the trouble, but the island was full of holes covered with fern, the way it was often when I put out my foot I would go down a hole up to my hip and then away with me on the crown of my head and the rabbits on top of me. I was blind out, down a hole and down a hole, till at last I became so out of humour I wished the island and the rabbits to the old fellow. I had no view of Pádrig and was drowned in sweat, and I did not know east from west. I sat down, dropped my pack of rabbits on a clump of grass, threw off my cap and wiped my brow. Well, said I to myself, I am alone at last, and I might as well have taken it softly from the beginning.

I looked round. There was nobody to me or from me, and I knew not on what side of the island I had stopped. I was listening to the different cries of the birds and watching the dew sparkling in the moonlight, rabbits darting by me to the east and to the west and making black paths through the dew. Some lines of "The Midnight Court" came into my mind, and with the delight in my heart I recited them aloud:

> 'Twas my wont to wander beside the stream
> On the soft green sward in the morning beam,
> Where the woods lie thick on the mountain-side,
> Without trouble or care what might betide.[4]

After a while I got up. I wonder am I long here, said I. Pádrig will think I have fallen over the cliff. I threw my pack over my back. I looked east and I looked west. God send me on the right road, I prayed. Where is the house now? And where is Pádrig?

I went on among the rocks, stooping low and thinking again of all who ever died in the island, and the more I thought the more afraid I became. Isn't it a strange thing I cannot think of anything else to scatter those terrible thoughts out of my mind? I would try and fail. I was glancing into every hollow in the rocks for fear there would be anyone from the other world within. Then I heard a couple of coughs such as you might hear from an old man.

My heart leapt. I stopped. There I stood poised on one foot, like the man long ago when the wind and the sun tried to see who would strip the coat from him and he standing without a stir in the middle of the road. I remained in the same posture, my two eyes thrust into a dark hole, for it seemed to me that it was out of that hole the coughing came. As I watched, a cold shiver ran through me the way I was trembling from head to heel.

Then I heard the coughing again, loud and strong. I could stand it no longer and let out a roar. When the thing within heard me, out he came with a rush, and when I saw the big white mass making towards me from the hole I let out one shout and fell out of my standing on the clump. Just as I fell I saw what it was— a big wether belonging to Pádrig O'Dála, and away he went down the hill at a gallop. "Ah, musha," cried I when I got back my speech, "may the big fellow take the head from your scroggle if it isn't fine the way you are after putting the yellow terror on me!"

I stood up and looked around. Look now, said I, woe to the man without patience. And it is my firm opinion that it is thus ghosts are made for many on this island, for, for my own part, I have seen two apparitions in one night.

I put my pack on my back again and off I went. I had not got over my fright. I was still weak, but I swore to myself, whatever else I would see, it would not trouble me.

Before long I heard a hand-whistle, and my heart leapt again. Listening carefully I heard another, nearer this time. It is Pádrig in search of myself, said I, putting a finger in my mouth and whistling in reply.

"Where are you?" called his voice.

"I am here," said I in the height of my head; "where is yourself?"

"I am at the Hollow of the Eagles," cried the voice.

"Och, God be with me," said I, "where is the Hollow of the Eagles?"

He shouted again: "Where's yourself?"

"The devil I know where I am," I cried. "I'm going astray."

"Do you see the Teeracht?" he cried hoarsely.

"I do not, but I see the Foze."

"Don't stir, so, till I find you."

I sat down on a clump, exhausted. Soon he was above me.

"Come up," said he. "The devil take you, where are you all the night?"

"Arra, man, I had to make shift for myself when I couldn't keep up with you."

"Faith, I thought you were up at the house long ago but when I went up myself you were not there before me."

"I will be there soon enough." But not a word did I say about the sheep for fear he would be mocking me for ever.

We went up to the house, to find Paddy Tim still fast asleep. I gave him a kick in the side. He leapt up, looked around, and rubbed his eyes. "Are ye come since?" says he.

"Arra, man, aren't we after walking the four corners of the island?"

"It must be day, so."

"Not yet," said Pádrig, "but near it."

I put down a fire and went out to get water from the well. The windows of the day were now opening in the east, the moon sinking west of the Foze, and the red light of the sun rising over the Macgillicuddy Reeks and so westward across the Bay of Dingle, the light of day quenching the light of night.

I returned home, put the water in the kettle, and hung it over the fire. Then the thought struck me to walk out and see the churchyard. I had long wanted to see it and now was my time for it while the kettle was boiling.

It was only three hundred yards from the house. I soon found it, in nice order, and beside it an old chapel. Standing above the ruin was a cross, looking very ancient, my hand's length of moss on every stone. Look how even the stone grows old! It is said that a priest is buried there from the time when there was persecution on the clergy, though there is a great change on the world today, praise on high to the Eternal Father!

It was a lovely morning; steam rising from grass and fern as the sun drew up the dew; the goat, the sheep, and the birds stretching themselves after the sleep of night.

When I had examined the churchyard, I went into the chapel—four feet of a doorway going in and a place for an altar in the wall made out of a fine, firm block of stone. I noticed many names cut here and there into the stones. Everyone who had ever visited the place had left his name behind. Among them I found some old writing of which I could make nothing. I was working away at it and spending my mind on it when I heard a hand-whistle. Faith, said I, I have spent the day and to say that they are calling me; and off I went at a run back to the house.

The other two were eating their breakfast before me.

"It seems," said Pádrig as I came in, "that you are running wild in the island."

"Do you know what happened? I came across an old writing in the chapel and I was trying to read it, but I could make nothing of it."

"Oh, I know where that is," said he, pouring out the tea.

"The devil, I thought no one had ever found it but myself."

"Ho, ho!" said he, turning to Paddy Tim, "hear what he says! I remember," he went on, turning to me again, "when I was but ten years old, a great scholar came here from England in search of old writings, and ne'er a stone nor a rock did he leave without examining it, and after all his examining he did not find the writing you are speaking of now. Then myself and my sister, who is in America now, we went with him one day around the island and we said to each other that we had better show it to him. So we brought him up to the place, and I tell you he was delighted to get it. There he was with big glasses on his eyes working away at it till he had taken down every word, and when he had finished he put his hand in his pocket, and gave each of us a shilling."

"Well now, wasn't he a kind man?"

"Faith, I think he was the most decent gentleman ever I saw," said Pádrig, filling his pipe.

"I suppose," said Paddy Tim, "it was the shilling made the decent man of him."

"Upon my word it was not, then, for he was decent in every way. But do you know how long it is since that writing was made?"

"I do not."

"Guess."

"A century?"

"No."

"Three centuries," said Paddy Tim, spitting on the floor.

"Twelve centuries," said Pádrig.

"And how would you know that?" said Paddy Tim.

"Arra, man, isn't that the date below?"

After a while I wandered out again and there is no doubt but it was a heart-lifting day. I looked east between me and the Great Sound. The sea was black with birds, some settled on the water, others diving, and their sweet music passing through my ears.

When I was tired with the sight of my eyes I went in again. "Faith, men," said I, "it looks as if we will have a good day's fishing on the Wild Bank."

"We had better be moving off so, in the name of God," said Pádrig, rising from the table and clearing away the things.

We went down to the strand. Soon we had turned our faces to the Island and our backs to the Wild Bank, myself in the bows, the other two putting the lines in order, the sea like glass and flotsam in plenty floating on its surface.

"Do you know now," said Pádrig, with a glance to the bows, "what is the landmark you would take to be on the Wild Bank?"

"Wait now," said I, bending on my head and thinking, for I had often heard that landmark from my grandfather. At last I thought of it and raised my head.

"I have it, Pádrig. It is the Bank of the Gardens of the Mouth across the White Cleft."

"Quite right."

"But I am no wiser for that, because I don't know where is the Bank of the Gardens of the Mouth, nor the White Cleft either."

"You are in a muddle so, but I will tell you now where they are," said he, stretching his finger straight to the north. "Do you see that cleft in the back of Inish-na-Bró? That is the White Cleft. And about two miles straight to the north from there is a reef which they call the Bank of the Gardens of the Mouth."

"I understand."

"Be rowing on now, and as soon as you see that reef straight over the White Cleft, you are on the Wild Bank."

"Faith," said I, putting out the oars, "there is no limit to knowledge."

I was the paddler of the curragh, so I had my two eyes fixed on the horizon beyond Inish-na-Bró the way I would see the reef. I was rowing on slowly, ever and ever, till I saw clearly the Bank of the Gardens of the Mouth across the White Cleft.

"Now," said I with a shout of joy, "put out the lines, and, by God, it looks like fish."

It did, too, at that time, with all the guillemots, razor-bills, sea-ravens and kittiwakes dipping themselves in pursuit of fish, and now and then the leap of a pollock would send up a spurt of foam which sparkled in the sun the way it would put stars on my eyes. Pádrig stood up, drew out his pipe, and lighted it. I was paddling slowly round the reef, each of the others with a pair of lines out and they watching.

Soon there was a pull at one of Pádrig's lines. He began to draw, but could make no headway.

"That is no pollock, I'm thinking," said I.

"The devil a pollock," said he, "but a seal, and it will make two halves of my line."

At times it would come fine and easy and Pádrig would make a grimace, trying to keep hold of it. He was working away at it, ever and ever, till at last we could see it through the water—a big, bright eel as long as the curragh.

"The devil take you, Paddy," said I, "have the hook ready for it."

Paddy Tim took up the hook, put it neatly into the gills and hauled in the eel.

"Faith, it is a fine fish," said Pádrig, laughing for joy.

"It appears that the fish you would catch here is worth calling a fish," said Paddy Tim.

At that moment he got up quickly from the thwart for there was another fish on his own line. He began to draw, a sharp look in his eye, for fear it would get away.

"Easy, Paddy!" says Pádrig. "Back her, Maurice," says he again softly, the way you would think he was afraid to speak up lest the fish would hear him. Paddy was drawing away and panting for breath, ever and ever, till at last he landed it into the curragh—the finest pollock I ever saw.

In the end of all, the boat was down to the gunwale with fish. Then the tide turned and never a bite after it. So we turned our faces homewards, well satisfied with the hunting of the day.

There was a nice puff of wind from the west. "I suppose the sail would take us east, Pádrig?"

"No doubt. Why wouldn't it? Haul it up."

We took in the oars and I soon had the mast up and threw the jib-sheet to Paddy. I hauled up the sail to the top mast and she slipped away to the east.

We were seated at our ease without a trouble or a care in the world, though there is seldom such a thing on a man of the sea. It was a comfortable time—the boat down to gunwale with fine pollock, not a touch of stress on us as we made for home, but the curragh moving east and ploughing the sea before her, we pulling at our pipes and talking and discussing the affairs of the world.

↓

[1] November

[2] Glas, "fresh," also means "green"

[3] Great black-backed gull

[4] Percy Usher's translation. "The Midnight Court" is a long poem by Brian Merriman, a Clare poet of the early nineteenth century

SEAN O'CASEY

I WANNA WOMAN

This lively story of the sexual desperation of a transplanted Irishman in London appeared in Sean O'Casey's Windfalls *(1934), a collection of poems, plays, and stories.*

JACK AVREEN WAS WAITING FOR a girl to come and have a light little supper with him in his flat. Between half-past eight and nine she was to arrive, and it was now a quarter to nine. Any minute she might be here now, tossing all his emotions into a hot and exquisite whirl of uncertain anticipations. The packed bud of anticipation might burst into a rich-coloured realisation tonight if he wasn't careful enough. It wanted a little careful handling, that was all. A girl didn't come along to a man's flat for nothing. Sit down calmly together and sing hymns? Not damn well likely. He would have to move cannily tonight, though. Bring her along gradually. A hasty movement might frighten her and spoil everything. It would be maddening if she fought shy of it again. Like the night a week ago when she was with him here, and he hurried the pace on too suddenly. Everything was going grand, and if he only had had the patience to spread the final fuss over another half-hour or so, he'd have got her sure—but no, he must try to rush things, and in ten minutes she had her hat on saying she'd have to go, and biding him an agitated good-night. Then for a week he had to bring her to a theatre, to meals in public restaurants, and to walk respectfully and respectably with her till he had subdued her timidity into coming again to his flat for a light supper and an hour or so of secluded companionship. She was a Catholic and that made it more difficult, though it shouldn't, for plenty of Catholics were hot stuff. But Catholic or no Catholic, if he couldn't get her going this time, he'd just shunt her off finally about her business. She went too far altogether without going far enough. It was a bit thick to applaud desire till it was a passion ready to overthrow everything, and then to expect a sudden thought of shyness or fear to trim it down to a cool-centred flame of torturing self-control. Pandering to passion, playing with passion, and then asking passion to behave itself. She wouldn't get him to stop so easily this time. When he saw that passion had filled her with a wild, throbbing, and delicious confusion he would go on determinedly and exact a full and perfect satisfaction out of her. She could even do a faint if she liked; that wouldn't lure him into any frightened, pitiful, or conscientious withdrawal. In fact a faintness would make the job easier. When she weakened with emotion, that was the time to hammer a job on her. So long as she didn't start to yell. That would make everything impossible. He remembered the last time she was with him here how she started to yell when he tried to show her how nice she'd look lying down stretched out on the divan. The roars of her . . . let me up . . . let me up . . . let me up! Pretence, the whole of it. Imagine a girl, even a Catholic, living in London all her life not knowing her way about. The idea was stillborn. He would carry on this time if only she didn't start to yell. Then he'd have to put the brake on, for he couldn't afford to let the people in the other flats hear a girl yelling in his room. He didn't want to have a cloud of witnesses to the thing he wanted to do. But he didn't think there was any real risk of a yell tonight. Even though she did yell the last time there were signs that she was beginning to get into her stride. She came, if she came at all, expecting things to happen, and she had no reason to grumble if she wasn't disappointed. Besides there was the present he had bought for her nestling up on the mantel-shelf in its satin-lined casket: a twenty-guinea gold and jewelled wristlet watch which was worth something more than a kiss. A big expense, he thought, but she was worth it. . . . Oh, she was fairer than the evening air clad in the beauty of a thousand stars. . . . Not quite so wonderful as that, but she was fair, and he was mad for her.

Everything was ready, and everything was waiting for her. The room was aglow with the heat from a blazing fire. Everything whispered encouragement to, and tolerance of, the solace of sex enjoyment. Food, fruit, and flowers; light glowing softly through amber shades; the bottle of wine offering exhilaration; cushions coyly clamouring for the vivid conclusion of passion. And all would contribute to, and form, a happy harmony, hiding in softness and colour the savageness and sadness born in the energy and ecstasy of the sex encounter.

After they had taken supper they could sit down courageously and cozily on the divan. He wouldn't force or even press her to take any wine, but if she would take a glass or two, all the better. After a little while he would place the watch around her wrist . . . and listen to her cries of admiration . . . he would kiss and kiss her while he was looking quietly to see how her things were fastened . . . then fondle some of them open here and there . . . so that when the right moment paused in front of him, a little struggle, sweet and rapid, would be a sweet beginning of a sweeter end.

He glanced around the room to see that everything was in order. To see that there was nothing that could even delicately interfere with the plans or the excited emotions of the evening. There now; look at it, look at it, look at it! He had overlooked the print of Lochner's picture of the Crucifixion, hanging on the wall so that when she was lying on the divan, it would be staring her in the face . . . that gruesome, beautiful, tranquil, primitive expression of the last terrible act of the Passion. . . . To the right on the Cross the stark, wasted figure of Jesus with the look of predestined, agonising resignation on His tortured, peaceful face. . . . Three wondering, funny-looking angels, fluttering like little birds in the air, each with a tiny chalice in tiny hands; two of them catching in the tiny cups the blood that trickled from the nailwounds in His hands; the third gathering in the cup the blood that streamed from His wounded side. . . . Mary Magdalene, dressed in brown and modified purple, kneeling at the foot of the Cross, the train of her gown sweeping around a bare skull and a bare bone. . . . To the left of the picture, the rich purple-mantled St. John supporting the fainting, black-gowned figure of the Saviour's Mother. . . . Behind, the peaceful features of a valley, with a narrow, curving, swift-flowing brook in its bosom. . . . And high up in the background, to the left, on a tiny indication of a road, the little figure of a soldier marching up and down on guard.

That picture would have to come down and be hidden away for a while. It was bound to be a disturbing element. Once let it catch her eye, and superstitious fear would make her briskly button up all her secrets, and fend her back into a condition of agitated and implacable primness. Besides he wouldn't feel perfectly comfortable himself, now that his attention had hovered around it. Something strange and sorrowful would be there contesting silently everything they said, everything they did. It must come down and be set aside. Perhaps that very picture was the influence that stood in the way on previous occasions when she was here, and was ready apparently to go the whole hog, and then suddenly became hard and denying. . . . Curious that it never occurred to him before. He extended his hand to take it from the wall, and withdrew it again. He wished the picture had never been where it was. . . . He felt a chill thrill at the thought of removing it. Was he getting superstitious too? He laughed softly and deridingly at the thought. . . . It was pitiful that this silly feeling of nervousness should dart through him. . . . He wasn't a Catholic or even a Christian, so down, down you come. He turned his head a little aside, and pressing his lips together, he lifted the picture from the wall, smiling, to rebuke his infirmity of sudden fear, went into another room quietly and deliberately, and placed the picture behind a bookcase there. Returning, he sat down, lighted a cigarette, and puffed and puffed, and waited tremulously. She was twenty minutes behind her time now, and that wasn't promising. She really was a provoking little bitch. Between eight-thirty and nine—that was what she had written to him, and have a nice little supper ready for his little darling. Well, the supper was here, but where was the little darling? And at the end of the letter that she wouldn't be later than nine-fifteen, so if she wasn't with him by nine-twenty, he needn't wait, for she wouldn't be coming. . . . Nine-twenty now, and she wasn't here. . . . One thing certain—if she didn't come tonight, she had seen the last of him. He toyed with the flowers in the vase on the table; he read the label on the bottle of wine; he put some more coal on the fire; he crossed to the window, pulled the curtains aside and looked out on to the street; he pulled the curtains back, returned to his seat by the fire and smoked furiously. . . . A quarter to ten, by God, and she hadn't come. If she wasn't coming, couldn't she phone, and not keep him waiting this way for her? Or if she was afraid of reproaches if she phoned, couldn't she at least send a telegram? He took a little book mechanically, opened it and began to read a few lines. . . . "Critics have referred to Monet as being of Norman birth, when as a fact his mother was of a Lyons family, and the artist was born in Paris. . . ." Happy Paris, happy Monet. . . . Lucky fellows these artists who could make a high hill of dainty, fragrant garments stripped from pretty women. . . . If he were a sculptor or a painter or something of that kind, this jade wouldn't be keeping him waiting like this, time nipping into his anticipations of delight with uncertainty and misgiving. . . . Still she might come yet. . . . Many things in London might delay her. . . . The traffic . . . a bad jam. . . . Ticking of the clock getting on his nerves. . . . He'd just wait patiently a little longer, then if she didn't come he'd seek a compensation down in Piccadilly. . . . Ten times the little clock on the mantelpiece struck. . . . He sat like a stone listening, puffed up with rage and disappointment. The clock stopped striking and resumed its laughing tick, tick, tick. He sat there still as a stone. . . . He saw his maid come in, leave a small tray of things on the table beside him, and heard her say "Cup of tea" while he was "wyting" . . . "didn't look as if she'd come tonight . . . wot a shime, and things so nice and comfy. . . ." He sat there still as a stone, sick and hot with rage and disappointment. . . . His mind went forth savagely and sought her out; his hands went round her throat and he shook her and shook her. Perhaps it was just as well. . . . What fools men were to lacerate their senses with these delicious and dangerous emotions. . . . He sipped his tea with a stiff, set face, and nibbled his toast, while his hands in imagination circled her throat and shook and shook and shook her. . . . He would go out and take a long walk, a swift walk, a furious walk, and sweat all his longing and disappointment out of him. . . . He put on his heavy coat and wrapped a muffler round his neck. . . . His eye fell on the little blue box on the mantelpiece, and snapping it open he fixed the gold and jewelled watch round his wrist. . . . She had missed something, anyhow, by not coming to him. . . . Then he descended the stairs and passed out into the street. She could come now if she liked. . . . Hoped she would. Price of her to come and find him out. . . .

Here was a taxi coming up the street. . . . No, but she might be in it. . . . He'd peep as it passed. Damn fellows allowed to drive too quickly. Couldn't snatch a glimpse of whoever was in it, he flashed past so fast. . . . Dangerous speed altogether. He'd go back a little just to see if it stopped at his place. . . . Wouldn't go back though if she was in it. . . . No demeaning himself that way. Damned taxi had flown past his place. Might have known it couldn't have been she.

He tightened again his loosened emotions, and walked swiftly, never lowering the quickness of his pace till he came into sight of a glow in the near distance that told him he was coming into the colour-lighted sprightliness of Piccadilly Circus. Pausing at the corner by Swan and Edgar's, he looked on at the streaming, hurrying, pleasure-seeking, prettily dressed, neatly dressed, snappily dressed hordes that surged along and around, that crossed and passed and crossed again in all the curious, bewildering, merging and rejecting jugglery of human life and movement. The circle of life streamed round and round, moving off the Circle down Shaftesbury Avenue, towards Leicester Square, or up Regent Street. Long, lithe limousines, purring confidently, joining in the orgy of movement, slipped by with a majestic glide, passing superciliously the perky little two-seaters that raced vehemently alongside for a while, then shamedly dropped behind and followed afar off with a cringe in their perkiness. Bull-bodied taxis, graceless, assertive, self-absorbed, facing forward, ignoring all the wheels around them, nosing boldly up to the front of a traffic jam, standing still or rushing along, ever determinedly minding their own particular business. Buses, big and red-faced, abrim with strength, bullying their rumbling way through the traffic, trumpeted around corners with engine-whir and horn-hoot. And all this streamed in, rushed round, and poured out within a blazing halo of lights, rich blue, light blue, purple, bright red, pale red, rich green, light green, mauve, yellow, and orange, flashing, dimming, vanishing, moving slowly, whirling fast, rippling down yellow, rippling up green, gliding across to the left red, gliding purple across to the right, making an endless flow and ebb of animated colour. Over opposite, a steady, dignified, silvery yellow glow told that a Cochran Revue had a home there. The name of an actress that carried a terrible load of loveliness about with her blazed imperiously in golden lights on the breast of Shaftesbury Avenue. Over to the right, on a great broad space, a shower of red, yellow, and green stars, flanked by zigzagging, curving lines of red and green, merged into a huge, gorgeously flamed announcement of an unction of beer in flashing yellow, changing in a moment to half green and half yellow; then all yellow again, with a crimson strip in the centre of each letter; then the upper half became red and the lower half remained yellow; then it was entirely red; then all green; then the upper half red and the lower half green, then it became all yellow again, to vanish in darkness and give place again in a few moments to the shower of red, yellow, and green stars that recommenced its cycle of announcement. On the wall of a restaurant in brilliant colours were the orange sunbright blue sea and emerald-green trees of some resort in Southern Europe. The whole place flamed with the gaudy gusto of advertisement.

But he hadn't come here to look at the lights, he hadn't come here to look at the lights. He came to get a woman. But the woman must be something worth while to compensate him for what he had missed. He hummed softly to himself:

I wanna woman, oh, bo, I wanna woman,
With wavy hair and time to spare to banish care,
I wanna woman, I wanna wanna woman, wanna woman.
That's always gay, doesn't pray; for last hours o' night, first hours
o' day;
I wanna woman, I wanna woman.
That'll say, oh gee, my guy, you know the way; now my clothes
are astray, you know the way, my guy; oh gee,
I wanna woman, I wanna wanna woman . . . today!

He watched a man coming towards him with a placard hanging over his breast looped over his shoulders to another hanging down his back. He read the one in front, "The wages of Sin is Death." He looked at the face of the man passing and saw there a sign of severe, sodden, and enviously imagined sanctity. He watched him, moving quietly and obstinately onward, mingling with the crowd, looking to neither the right nor the left, carrying his holy placard glorified with the reflected glow of the vanishing, reappearing, gleaming, twisting, rippling, coloured lights of the Circus. Nobody took the slightest notice of this wandering herald of heaven. He wondered—oh that wasn't a bad little bird that passed; face just a little bit too coarse though—at the curious sensations different people sought to bring them pleasure. Churches were old-fashioned. Hanging on still to pulpits and placards. No novelty in them now; what was wanted were Stations of the Cross in coloured electric lights. Ireland's one-up there, for, in Dublin, he remembered seeing a statue of the Blessed Virgin with a ring of coloured electric bulbs around her head for a halo. Unbecoming thoughts for a man on a mission like his, so he crossed the Circus and wandered down Piccadilly towards Leicester Square, humming softly to himself:

I wanna woman, I wanna woman,
For first hours o' day, last hours o' night,
I wanna, wanna, wanna woman.

He kept watching out keenly for a suitable bit of skirt. They were streaming past him, many giving him an inquiring and desirous glance as they went by. No, thank you, he wouldn't have any of those. They were all so common, so coarse, and so obvious. He wanted just a little elegance of manner and a saucy reticence that surrendered with a sad, sham charm what it was paid for and had to give. These were rare among birds, for their life muddied their manners as well as their bodies.

He passed into a bright patch of coloured light on the pavement flowing from a window display of green, black, crimson, and yellow dresses. Glancing casually at the richer light and colour in the window, he saw a woman leaving it and walking off in the opposite direction. Pretty, dressed in a smartly-made tailored suit, covered by a fur coat that reached to the hem of the skirt, short enough to show the full knee when she took a step forward; a delicious helmet hat of modest red made a sweet frame for her face. His indifference flaming into excited interest, he swung round, said "Sorry" to a man he bumped into, and hurriedly walked after her. Was she one? Hard to say. She seemed to have an elegance and taste in dress, and a gracefulness in walk that few tarts had, but there still seemed to be something about her that suggested the possibility of hire. He'd walk on quickly, get in front of her, stop at a shop window, and eye her as she passed. He went by her rapidly, walked on in front for a few moments, stopped at a shop window, watching her sideways as she came along. His heart beat a little faster as he saw first the right, then the left leg from the knee down issuing out of the narrow sweep of her neatly-tailored frock. Trim, and he loved them trim, and with this bird everything else seemed to be in coy conformity with the pretty legs. He wheeled around as she came level with him, and looked longingly and inquiringly at her, but she apparently took no notice and walked on. This was disappointing, and made things doubtful. Was she one, or was she not? She was worth following for a while, and if she only would turn down one of the quieter streets, he'd tighten up to her, and ask her how she felt towards the world. Wouldn't be nice to get a choke-off in a crowd, so he'd wait a quieter chance to find out if her clothes came off easily. He hadn't the courage yet to go up and say "Good evening" and chance it. She might be waiting for some man to do the clicking quietly. Some birds were like that—only out occasionally to add a little week-end tail to their wages; or, those that were a little new at the game, still frightened and shy. If he wasn't quick some johnny was bound to nip in and she'd be snapped up before his eyes just because he hadn't enough of the pure stuff in him to Charleston up to her and whisper, "Say, kid, you'd look nicer with a little less on; oh, you'd look a lot nicer with a lot less on. . . ." Damn this leisurely moving crowd that was hindering his efforts to keep close to her. He could see in the distance the little soft red hat dodging forward, in and out through the people, apparently with ease and certainty, while every man and every woman that came toward him seemed to plonk themselves right in front of his face, and then begin to dodge the wrong way to get by. He hurried and twisted as cleverly as he could. She was a lovely bird, and he'd willingly bury four or even five quid under the world-forgetting trickeries of a night with her. There was the soft little red hat crossing Wardour Street. He'd hurry, reach her, walk side by side and get it over before his halting hesitation lost her. . . .

Now he was caught in a crowd gathered at the edge of the path gaping greedily at something that probably wasn't worth a flickering thought, coming up Wardour Street. . . . Oh, procession of people singing something like a hymn. . . .

Church Parade. Leader carrying a cross. . . . Lift the cross higher, brother. . . . Choir in white surplices and black cassocks with heads reverently bent over their hymn-books. Jammed here now for at least three minutes and the soft little red hat getting farther and farther away. . . . Why do the authorities shut their eyes to this sort of wandering, maundering, philandering missionary mania holding up regular and necessary traffic? My God, listen to them:

> Lord in this Thy Mercy's day, ere it pass for aye away
> On our knees we fall and pray.

No use, gentlemen; no one in Piccadilly has the slightest intention of falling on his knees. . . . She'd be miles away before he'd get himself out of this mess. . . . Hurry up, hurry up; get along, please. . . .

> Holy Jesus grant us tears, fill us with heart-searching fears
> Ere that awful doom appears.

Soft, sloppy, winding, creeping, crawling, snaily, snobby, snarling bastards dividing him from all the heart-quickening gifts beneath the red hat, the tailored suit, and the silk stockings. . . . Oh, if he were a savage how he'd like to jump in and spear a hundred percent of them. . . . Not a sign of her now. That procession had crossed the hunt and saved the quarry. He breathed deeply in disappointment and rancour. And they did this sort of thing out of their love for men. Annoying thing to come up against and mingle with his present mood. Even if he did manage to get into touch with her again, things wouldn't feel so comfortable, for he knew the hymn by heart, and here it was maliciously humming in his mind, blunting the innocence of his eagerness. She might be anywhere now. . . . Grant us tears . . . fill us with heart-searching fears. . . . No use of looking any longer. . . . To go home is best. . . . Nothing in skirts could interest him now till he'd forgotten a little about the girl in the soft red hat. A peach. . . . No doubt about it, he'd missed a peach. . . . Lord in this Thy Mercy's day, ere it pass for aye away. . . . Bakerloo, from Piccadilly to Baker Street, and then a bus to Swiss Cottage. . . . On our knees we fall and pray. . . . It was just twelve anyhow, and only the "Pros" that time has tossed a lot paraded now. . . . Strange, determinedly sliding movement of the escalators. . . . Wonder how the procession would look coming up or going down one of them. . . . Keep time and step off together, please. . . . Trains going west . . . that was his platform . . . empty carriage . . . drowse to Baker Street. . . . When eyes are closed curious feeling runs through body with the gentle, rumbling shake in the movement of a tube train. . . . Feeling of motion and of rest . . . Oxford Circus. . . . Two more stations. . . . Somebody coming in . . . sitting opposite him. . . . Woman . . . see so by shoes. Some uninteresting looking old cow or young heifer not worth noticing. . . . Keep his eyes closed. . . . Regent's Park. . . . Next stop. . . . Nothing

586

exciting in the night after all his hope. . . . Procession spoilt everything. . . . Procession spoilt sport. . . . Perhaps it was just as well to get a check now and again. Thoughtless compliance with the complaints of sex was bound to overbalance his nervous system, and that wouldn't do at all. He was almost glad now that the procession had poked its way between him and his desire to make a fool of himself. He wouldn't feel that seething sense of remorse that invariably followed a night with a new woman; the dead, revolting dissatisfaction of deliriously misspent energy and passion; the miserable surge of emptiness that followed the feat of giving too much for a short enjoyment. He could rest and go to sleep without the soul-nagging sense of sex weariness. Perhaps this would be the first step towards a stronger self-directed life, of decided and persistent effort towards self-control. Back to a virtuous bed. . . . Good bed; better bed; best bed.

Baker Street . . . oh hell, don't stir. . . . Fur coat, tailored suit, and soft red hat sitting opposite. Damn fool keep eyes closed. Where's she getting. . . . Passing Marylebone. Oh, that was a cute glance. . . . Measuring up his naughtiness. Opening her fur coat. Too hot in here, dearie. Good sign; wants to show her legs. . . . Passing Warwick Avenue. . . . She's a peach, boys, she's a peach. . . . A sense of uncomfortable fullness made his heart beat faster. . . . He lighted a cigarette, and his hand shook. . . . His nerves were tingling again. . . . Oh, gee, my guy, you know the way, now my clothes are astray, you know the way, my guy, oh gee, you wanna wannna wanna woman. . . . Getting out at Maida Vale. . . . So was he, you bet. . . . Along the passages to the lift. . . . He feverishly paid his excess fare from Baker Street to Maida Vale to the attendant, watching her from the other end of the lift. Anyhow, she knew that he was interested in her. She had seen him look at her with suggestion in his eyes, and had shown no annoyance. Indeed, she had sent him glances that seemed to venture an invitation. The lift doggedly moved upwards, came to the road-level, the gates crashed open, and they passed out into the street. If she hopped off quickly now, all was over, but if she went on slowly the thing promised fruit. The street was quiet and restful, animated only by an odd taxi cruising past. Up in the sky, in the northwest shone The Plow and in the northeast sparkled The Lyra. . . . She went along slowly. His mouth that had dried twitched a little, and his heart beat unpleasantly as he hurried on and walked by her side. . . . "Good evening," he murmured nervously. She gave a slow, careless glance at him, and continued to walk on slowly. . . . "The air is very clear tonight," he went on, "and the stars are remarkably plain. . . ."

She turned her head to him, smiled and said, "What are you doing with yourself at this time of night?"

He stammered a little as he murmured, "Oh, just taking a stroll round about thoughtlessly."

"You passed me in Piccadilly," she asked, "didn't you?"

"Yes," he said, "I think that I did see you somewhere in Piccadilly."

She's very cool about it all, he thought; she must be a bird after all.

"Well, now that you've seen me again," she said, "do you fancy me as much as ever?"

She was a Pro then, so he'd have to be carefully indifferent, for the more desire he showed, the higher would be the fee. So he kept silent.

"You'd like to come up to my flat and have a drink or a cup of tea, wouldn't you?" she asked.

"Yes, I wouldn't mind," he answered.

"I'm afraid if I let you come you might want to be naughty, would you, my dear?" she asked smilingly.

"I might, you never know," he answered.

"If I let you come, and was very nice to you, you'd give me a little present, darling?"

"Oh, of course," he replied.

"How much?"

"Two pounds," he murmured.

"You're not out to spend much!" she said disdainfully, hastening away from him. "Cheerio, darling!"

He hurried after her and said, "Don't run away, dear; let's talk together for a minute or two. There's no necessity to rush off in a rage."

"I'm not in a rage, dear," she said, "but I don't let myself be man-mauled for two quid. Go back to Piccadilly and you'll get lots of girls ready to accommodate themselves to your idea of generosity."

He was fascinated; she was a rare bird, and he didn't want to lose her, but he wanted to get his pleasure as cheaply as possible.

"How much do you want then, to let me go home and make a fuss of you?" he asked.

"Five pounds, at least," she said.

"That's a lot of money for a few hours. I'll give you four," he bargained.

"Five, dear, or there's nothing doing. If you fancied me so much, and followed me so long, I'm worth a fiver."

He walked beside her pondering, fingering in his pocket one note from another and counting thoughtfully. . . . One . . . two . . . three . . . four . . . five . . . six . . . seven . . . and a ten-bob note.

"Oh, be a sport," she said encouragingly, "and I'll give you a right good time."

"All right," he answered. "I'll give the fiver."

Stopping at a house of flats, she took a key from her bag, opened the hall door, ascended to the first floor, where she rang a bell; the door of the flat was opened by a maid who gave him a quick, furtive look as they entered. She brought him into a sitting-room, quietly and comfortably furnished with easy-chairs and lounges. Some ordinary landscapes were on the walls, and on the mantelpiece were two large photographs of pretty women pictured in a state of saucy and semi-nudity. She pulled brilliantly green curtains that were on the window closer together as she said to him: "Take off your coat, dear, and make yourself at home."

To the right of the fireplace were six shelves filled with books. Spicy, naughty, and nonsensical, the lot of them, he thought.

"Tilly," she called to the maid, "bring me and my gentleman friend some tea and biscuits."

She took off her fur coat and soft red hat, and sat down in one of the easy-chairs before the fire, crossing one leg over the other. "Nice to be sitting before a fire on a cold night like this," she said as she sipped her tea.

"Nothing better," he said, "with a pretty girl waiting to be nice to you."

"And with a man that wants to be naughty," she added.

"I see," he said, "you're interested in books."

"Just a little," she answered, glancing at the shelves. "They pass in a pleasant way many a dull hour."

"Who's your favorite writer?" he asked.

"I've none," she said. "I like Hardy, France, and Dostoevsky a lot."

"Dostoevsky's one of the Russian fellows," he said; "don't know how anyone could be interested in such a writer, though I haven't read him myself."

"If you haven't, how do you know?" she asked.

"I know from those that tried to read him," he said, "that he's a terrible writer."

"Yes," she admitted, "he is, sometimes . . . terrible."

"Who's the johnny that wrote all the books you have covered in green?"

"Balzac," she said. "Wonderful writer. Never read his *Poor Relations? Madame Marneffe, Baron Hulot,* and *Cousin Pons*—far greater than his better known *Père Goriot.* Powerful realism, and pathetic, remorseless imagination."

"Come over here," he said, "and sit beside me; I don't want to be bothered about Balzac just now."

She got up out of the chair, smiled, lifted her skirt a little, danced over to him, and sat down by his side on the settee. She put an arm round his neck, kissed him quick and cooed into his face, the suggestive look in her eyes hardening a little.

"Now, darling," she whispered, "what about my little present? Not nice to talk about it, but it's best to get all the nasty things over at once."

"Oh, I'll give it to you all right," he said.

"I know, but I might as well have it now."

"You won't trust me?" he asked peevishly.

"I know you're a sport," she said, "but it's just as well to get it over and done with before we begin to amuse ourselves."

He took the notes from his pocket with a serious, half-timid sigh, and handed her five, saying, "Here you are, five of the best and brightest."

She quickly and gently caught hold of his hand, and with a confident smile said, "The ten-bob note as a little present for the maid, dear."

"Oh, now you've had enough out of me," he protested.

"I always get a present for the maid," she insisted; "she's a dear woman, and I never forget to ask for a little tip for her. . . . Go on, don't spoil things now by a mean refusal of such a small thing; we're getting on so nicely together."

And the ten-shilling note was pulled gently from his hand, added to the five, and all were locked away in a drawer of a cabinet that stood quietly and expectantly close to the window. Then she removed her skirt, coat, and blouse, pulled loose the ribbons threading the shoulders of her caminickers, showing her breasts, animatedly sat beside him, put her arm round him, and murmured, "Now, darling, don't you like me a lot better with a little less on?"

He abandoned himself to the surge of desire that swept through him. He caught her in his arms and tried to bend her back on the settee. With a sour laugh she freed herself, crossed the room, and opened a door opposite.

"Come into the bedroom, dear," she said, "where we'll have plenty of room."

What a fool he had been to stop so long with her. It was maddening to have to stay on here in bed beside her, after having got all that he wanted. She had fallen asleep, while he was still awake listening to the ticking of the little clock at the other end of the room, thinking and cursing deeply in his mind about the weariness and waste of affection, energy, and money that made this honeycomb a bitterness and a loathing to him. He sat up in bed and winked his eyes several times to press the heaviness out of them. The first glimpse of a cold dawn was trickling in through the green curtains that covered the window. The room that had looked so full of nimbly dancing promises of pleasure was now filled with a sickly sense of weariness, and seemed to be stuffy with the breath of dead things. He moved as far away as possible from his companion, and looked down at her sleeping there with her bare breasts, tossed hair, and partly open mouth. Attractiveness had ceased to meddle with her now. He felt a wish to beat till he bruised the breasts that he had fiercely fondled only a few hours ago. Tear and rend them for the ruin of tiredness and silent agony of remorse that they had helped to bring upon him. Lying here for three hours he had been trying to deafen himself to his thoughts, and put away the memories that had stormed his mind before he had bargained with this unashamed whore that now lay asleep and naked beside him. . . . The procession that had cut across his path and the hymn they had been singing. . . . "Holy Jesus grant us tears, fill us with heart-searching fears. . . ." Keep it out, keep it out. . . . I wanna woman, I wanna woman, with wavy hair, to banish care, I wanna woman . . . keep it out, keep it out. . . .

She had felt him moving and was murmuring drowsily, "Lie down, sweetie; cold coming in under clothes, and I've nothing on . . . lie down, sweetie."

He plunged down into the bed again, and roughly pushed away a leg of hers that had wandered over near him. "Not so rough, dear," she murmured.

What vice-armored souls these women had. But perhaps it was better if one wanted to be anything, to be that thing right out. Wallowing grandly in her own shame. Let the light of dawn but mount a little higher up and he'd slide from bed, and dress and leave this place of poisoned satisfaction.

Her eyes opened a little and a peculiar, spiteful smile darkened them, and her hand began to fondle him. "Keep that damned hand quiet," he said, as he jerked it away with a savage and resentful movement.

"Sweetie doesn't want pretty Alice any more," she murmured, giving his cheek a malicious caress.

"I'm going out of this," he said surlily, getting out of bed and beginning to creep shiveringly into his clothes. Glancing in the glass he saw himself hollow-eyed, hair-tossed, with his chin darkened where his beard was beginning to show strongly.

She sat up sleepily, resting on her elbow, took a card from a drawer in a bed-side table, held it out to him and said, "Card, dear, double ten double nine Berkeley. You might like to ring me up some evening."

Paying no attention to her, he tugged on his heavy coat, pulled on his hat, wrapped his muffler round his neck, glanced at the cabinet where his five pounds ten were stored, and said, "I'm off now, good-bye."

She snuggled down in the bed, pulled the clothes warmly round her shoulders and under her chin, and murmured, "Don't make a noise, dear, to wake the maid . . . she's such a dear woman, and I'm very fond of her . . . close the street door after you as gently as you can. . . . Cheerio, darling."

It was cold and damp coming into the air of the street. Leaving that whore warmly nested in her bed, too. He was done with women for a long time. He kept his head bent as he slouched sleepily homewards. The exhaustion of the night was letting this dampness into his marrow. Ding, dong, ding, dong, dell. . . . Some damn church bell ringing for some damn service. Waste of time. . . . Never keep people from making fools of themselves. . . . Ding, dong, dell, sinners sent to hell, to clothe their pain in an everlasting yell; so cease to do evil, learn to do well; ding, dong, ding, dong, ding, dong, dell. . . . Palpitating nonsense, these bells.

He opened the door of his flat, and let himself shivering in. He would sleep till about five in the evening, then he would have a warm bath, a brandy and soda, a good dinner, and he would feel a lot better. He stripped to his shirt, and let his clothes slide from him in a heap on the floor. He slipped his pajamas on over his shirt. Must be getting on for eight, now. . . . He bent his arm to look at his wrist. . . . Jesus, he had left the wristlet watch in the house of the whore! He didn't—he couldn't—have stuck it in one of his pockets. . . . He rummaged fiercely in the pockets of his trousers. . . . No, and he flung them savagely back on the floor. . . . His coat? He rummaged through the pockets of the coat . . . no, and he flung it down again on the floor. . . . He remembered . . . he had put it down on the little table beside the bed, and had forgotten it was there in his eagerness to get away from the place. . . . Oh, the idiot, the fool, the ape, to forget to take it up and put it on when he was leaving. Oh, what a stinkingly stupid thing to do. . . . What did he want to bring it out with him for? And he had no idea of the street or the house, only that they were somewhere in Maida Vale. . . . He had hurried away noticing nothing. . . . Wouldn't take her card even. . . . Hadn't the least idea of her telephone number. . . . A big-brained idiot, that's what he was. . . . She had been well paid for her favors—five pounds ten and a wristlet watch and bangle worth twenty guineas. . . . She was laughing at him now . . . and fitting it on. . . . Pity it couldn't turn to steel and stop the circulation of her blood. . . . He turned down the clothes and stormed into bed. As he lay down his eye caught sight of Lochner's Crucifixion hanging again on the wall over his bed. . . . The blasted maid of his couldn't keep from ferreting around. . . . Fished it out from behind the bookcase and replaced it on the wall. . . . Frantic to meddle with everything. . . . Mocking him there with its tale of tragedy. . . . Take him weeks now to recover from the shock of his stupidity. He pressed himself down on the bed in a rush of rage. His head throbbed with the nerve-rack of his loss. Forget it and sleep. . . . That's all he could do . . . sleep and forget it. . . . He lay silent. . . . The telephone bell rang, rang . . . rang. He snapped down the receiver and bellowed, "Hello? yes, this is Mr. Avreen. . . . Yes, it's Jack. . . . No, you can't come tonight. . . . I'll be engaged till long after midnight. . . . If you long to see me, why didn't you come last night? Explain . . . yes it will need some explanation. . . . Angry? why of course I'm angry. No, I won't post the watch to you, or see you tonight either. . . . Must go now to keep an appointment." And he firmly and angrily replaced the receiver. . . . Then he gathered the clothes tightly around him, closed his eyes, and quivered in a mad medley of thoughts. This was the crowning of his foolishness. He stiffened with repressed and remorseful rage. . . . The telephone bell rang . . . and rang . . . and rang. . . . Ringing me again, he thought; well, let her ring.

A faint trickling beam of light from a timid rising sun crept in through the window and spread over the picture of the Crucifixion, showing wanly to the right the figure of Christ hanging on the Cross, the three funny little black-robed angels with tiny chalices in tiny hands catching the blood that dripped from hands and side; Mary Magdalene, in her brown and purple robes, kneeling at the foot of the Cross; to the left the crimson-mantled St. John supporting the fainting Mother; the brook swiftly flowing through the peaceful valley, and away in the dim distance, the little figure of a careless soldier marching up and down on guard.

And he tightened his teeth together, cursed deeply and lay still, as the telephone bell rang . . . rang . . . rang.

FROM
AT SWIM-TWO-BIRDS

*No mere excerpt (or even two) from Flann O'Brien's brilliant 1939
novel can accurately represent* At Swim-Two-Birds, *and the book is
almost impossible to describe without first-hand experience. At its simplest, the story is that of a young college student who prefers his bed
above any other place, and writes in many different genres until all of
his characters join together, revolt, and then outlandishly carry on the
stories themselves. One might say that in* At Swim-Two-Birds *O'Brien
encapsulates, then mocks, all of Irish literature.*

*The first excerpt introduces the narrator's theory of the novel, as
explained to Brinsley, a friend who visits him as he recovers from a
three-day hangover. In the second excerpt the characters—or "suitable
existing puppets," to use O'Brien's phrase—have broken free from their
narrator's control and are telling a tall Irish folktale.*

O N THE EVENING OF THE THIRD day, a friend of mine, Brinsley, was
admitted to my chamber. He bore miscellaneous books and papers. I
complained on the subject of my health and ascertained from him that
the weather was inimical to the well-being of invalids. . . . He remarked that there
was a queer smell in the room.

Description of my friend: Thin, dark-haired, hesitant; an intellectual Meath-
man; given to close-knit epigrammatic talk; weak-chested, pale.

I opened wide my windpipe and made a coarse noise unassociated with the
usages of gentlemen.

I feel very bad, I said.

By God you're the queer bloody man, he said.

I was down in Parnell Street, I said, with the Shader Ward, the two of us drinking pints. Well, whatever happened me, I started to puke and I puked till the eyes nearly left my head. I made a right haimes of my suit. I puked till I puked air.

Is that the way of it? said Brinsley.

Look at here, I said.

I arose in my bed, my body on the prop of an elbow.

I was talking to the Shader, I said, talking about God and one thing and another, and suddenly I felt something inside me like a man trying to get out of my stomach. The next minute my head was in the grip of the Shader's hand and I was letting it out in great style. O Lord save us. . . .

Here Brinsley interposed a laugh.

I thought my stomach was on the floor, I said. Take it easy, says the Shader, you'll be better when you get that off. Better? How I got home at all I couldn't tell you.

Well you did get home, said Brinsley.

I withdrew my elbow and fell back again as if exhausted by my effort. My talk had been forced, couched in the accent of the lower or working classes. Under the cover of the bed-clothes I poked idly with a pencil at my navel. Brinsley was at the window giving chuckles out.

Nature of chuckles: Quite, private, averted.

What are you laughing at? I said.

You and your book and your porter, he answered.

Did you read that stuff about Finn, I said, that stuff I gave you?

Oh, yes, he said, that was the pig's whiskers. That was funny all right.

This I found a pleasing eulogy. The God-big Finn. Brinsley turned from the window and asked me for a cigarette. I took out my "butt" or half-spent cigarette and showed it in the hollow of my hand.

That is all I have, I said, affecting a pathos in my voice.

By God you're the queer bloody man, he said.

He then brought from his own pocket a box of the twenty denomination, lighting one for each of us.

There are two ways to make big money, he said, to write a book or to make a book.

It happened that this remark provoked between us a discussion on the subject of Literature—great authors living and dead, the character of modern poetry, the predilections of publishers and the importance of being at all times occupied with literary activities of a spare-time or recreative character. My dim room rang with the iron of fine words and the names of great Russian masters were articulated with fastidious intonation. Witticisms were canvassed, depending for their utility on a knowledge of the French language as spoken in the medieval times. Psycho-analysis was mentioned—with, however, a somewhat light touch. I then tendered an explanation spontaneous and unsolicited concerning my own work, affording an insight as to its aesthetic, its daemon, its argument, its sorrow and its joy, its darkness, its sun-twinkle clearness.

Nature of explanation offered: It was stated that while the novel and the play were both pleasing intellectual exercises, the novel was inferior to the play inasmuch as it lacked the outward accidents of illusion, frequently inducing the reader to be outwitted in a shabby fashion and caused to experience a real concern for the fortunes of illusory characters. The play was consumed in wholesome fashion by large masses in places of public resort; the novel was self-administered in private. The novel, in the hands of an unscrupulous writer, could be despotic. In reply to an inquiry, it was explained that a satisfactory novel should be a self-evident sham to which the reader could regulate at will the degree of his credulity. It was undemocratic to compel characters to be uniformly good or bad or poor or rich. Each should be allowed a private life, self-determination and a decent standard of living. This would make for self-respect, contentment and better service. It would be incorrect to say that it would lead to chaos. Characters should be interchangeable as between one book and another. The entire corpus of existing literature should be regarded as a limbo from which discerning authors could draw their characters as required, creating only when they failed to find a suitable existing puppet. The modern novel should be largely a work of reference. Most authors spend their time saying what has been said before—usually said much better. A wealth of references to existing works would acquaint the reader instantaneously with the nature of each character, would obviate tiresome explanations and would effectively preclude mountebanks, upstarts, thimbleriggers and persons of inferior education from an understanding of contemporary literature. Conclusion of explanation.

That is all my bum, said Brinsley.

↓

That was always one thing, said Shanahan wisely, that the Irish race was always noted for, one place where the world had to give us best. With all his faults and by God he has plenty, the Irishman can jump. By God he can jump. That's one thing the Irish race is honoured for no matter where it goes or where you find it— jumping. The world looks up to us there.

We were good jumpers from the start, said Furriskey.

It was in the early days of the Gaelic League, said Lamont. This Sergeant Craddock was an ordinary bloody bobby on the beat, down the country somewhere. A bit of a bags, too, from what I heard. One fine morning he wakes up and is ordered to proceed if you don't mind to the Gaelic League Sports or whatever it was that was being held in the town that fine spring Sunday. To keep his eye open for sedition do you know and all the rest of it. All right. In he marches to do his duty, getting the back of the bloody hand from the women and plenty of guff from the young fellows. Maybe he was poking around too much and sticking his nose where it wasn't wanted. . . .

I know what you mean, said Shanahan.

Anyway, didn't he raise the dander of the head of the house, the big man, the head bottle-washer. Up he came to my cool sergeant with his feathers ruffled and his comb as red as a turkeycock and read out a long rigmarole in Irish to your man's face.

That'll do you, says the sergeant, keep that stuff for them that wants it. I don't know what you're saying, man.

So you don't know your own language, says the head man.

I do, says the sergeant, I know plenty of English.

Your man then asks the sergeant his business in Irish and what he's doing there in the field at all.

Speak English, says the sergeant.

So be damned but your man gets his rag out and calls the sergeant a bloody English spy.

Well maybe he was right, said Furriskey.

Shh, said Shanahan.

But wait till I tell you. The sergeant just looked at him as cool as blazes.

You're wrong, says he, *and I'm as good a man as you or any other man,* says he.

You're a bloody English bags, says your man in Irish.

And I'll prove it, says the sergeant.

And with that your man gets black in the face and turns his back and walks to the bloody platform where all the lads were doing the Irish dancing with their girls, competitions of one kind and another, you know. Oh it was all the fashion at one time, you were bloody nothing if you couldn't do your Walls of Limerick. And here too were my men with the fiddles and the pipes playing away there at the reels and jigs for further orders. Do you know what I mean?

Oh I know what you're talking about all right, said Shanahan, the national music of our country, Rodney's Glory, the Star of Munster and the Rights of Man.

The Flogging Reel and Drive the Donkey, you can't beat them, said Furriskey.

That's the ticket, said Lamont. Anyway, didn't your man get into a dark corner with his butties till they hatched out a plan to best the sergeant. All right. Back went your man to the sergeant, who was taking it easy in the shade of a tree.

You said a while ago, says your man, that you were a better man than any man here. Can you jump?

I can not, says the sergeant, but I'm no worse than the next man.

We'll see, says your man.

Now be damned but hadn't they a man in the tent there from the county Cork, a bloody dandy at the long jump, a man that had a name, a man that was known in the whole country. A party by the name of Bagenal, the champion of all Ireland.

God that was a cute one, said Furriskey.

A very cute one. But wait till I tell you. The two of them lined up and a hell of a big crowd gathering there to watch. Here was my nice Bagenal as proud as a bloody turkey in his green pants, showing off the legs. Beside him stands another man, a man called Craddock, a member of the polis. His tunic is off him on the grass but the rest of his clothes is still on. He is standing as you find him with his blue pants and his big canal-barges on his two feet. I'm telling you it was something to look at. It was a sight to see.

I don't doubt it, said Shanahan.

Yes. Well Bagenal is the first off, sailing through the air like a bird and down in a shower of sand. What was the score?

Eighteen feet, said Furriskey.

Not at all man, twenty-two. Twenty-two feet was the jump of Bagenal there and then and by God the shout the people gave was enough to make the sergeant puke what was inside him and plenty more that he never swallowed.

Twenty-two feet is a good jump any day, said Shanahan.

After the cheering had died down, said Lamont, my man Bagenal strolls around and turns his back on the sergeant and asks for a cigarette and starts to blather out of him to his friends. What does my sergeant do, do you think, Mr. Shanahan.

I'm saying nothing, said knowing Shanahan.

By God you're a wise man. Sergeant Craddock keeps his mouth shut, takes a little run and jumps twenty-four feet six.

Do you tell me that! cried Furriskey.

Twenty-four feet six.

I'm not surprised, said Shanahan in his amazement, I'm not surprised. Go where you like in the wide world, you will always find that the Irishman is looked up to for his jumping.

Right enough, said Furriskey, the name of Ireland is honoured for that.

Go to Russia, said Shanahan, go to China, go to France. Everywhere and all the time it is hats off and a gra-ma-cree to the Jumping Irishman. Ask who you like they'll all tell you that. The Jumping Irishman.

It's a thing, said Furriskey, that will always stand to us—jumping.

A BASH
IN THE TUNNEL

*Flann O'Brien's newspaper pieces (usually published using the name
"Myles na Gopaleen") also made him famous. This "rant" from 1951
investigates the nature of the Irish artist, in particular James Joyce. The
title refers to a story told to O'Brien in a bar—"bash" meaning an
extended session of drinking.*

JAMES JOYCE WAS AN ARTIST. He has said so himself. His was a case of Ars
gratia Artis. He declared that he would pursue his artistic mission even if the
penalty was as long as eternity itself. This appears to be an affirmation of belief
in Hell, therefore of belief in Heaven and in God.

A better title for this article might be: "Was Joyce Mad?" By Hamlet, Prince
of Denmark. Yet there is a reason for the present title.

Some thinkers—all Irish, all Catholic, some unlay—have confessed to discerning a resemblance between Joyce and Satan. True, resemblances there are.
Both had other names, the one Stephen Dedalus, the other Lucifer; the latter
name, meaning "Maker of Light," was to attract later the ironical gloss "Prince of
Darkness!" Both started off very well under unfaultable teachers, both were very
proud, both had a fall. But they differed on one big, critical issue. Satan never
denied the existence of the Almighty; indeed he acknowledged it by challenging
merely His primacy. Joyce said there was no God, proving this by uttering various blasphemies and obscenities and not being instantly struck dead.

A man once said to me that he hated blasphemy, but on purely rational
grounds. If there is no God, he said, the thing is stupid and unnecessary. If there
is, it's dangerous.

Anatole France says this better. He relates how, one morning, a notorious agnostic called on a friend who was a devout Catholic. The devout Catholic was drunk and began to pour forth appalling blasphemies. Pale and shocked, the agnostic rushed from the house. Later, a third party challenged him on this incident.

"You have been saying for years that there is no God. Why then should you be so frightened at somebody else insulting this God who doesn't exist?"

"I still say there is no God. But that fellow thinks there is. Suppose a thunderbolt was sent down to strike him dead. How did I know I wouldn't get killed as well? Wasn't I standing beside him?"

Another blasphemy, perhaps—doubting the Almighty's aim. Yet it is still true that all true blasphemers must be believers.

What is the position of the artist in Ireland?

Shortly before commencing to assemble material for this essay, I went into the Bailey in Dublin to drink a bottle of stout and do some solitary thinking. Before any considerable thought had formed itself, a man—then a complete stranger—came, accompanied by his drink, and stood beside me: addressing me by name, he said he was surprised to see a man like myself drinking in a pub.

My pub radar screen showed up the word "toucher." I was instantly much on my guard.

"And where do you think I should drink?" I asked. "Pay fancy prices in a hotel?"

"Ah, no," he said. "I didn't mean that. But any time I feel like a good bash myself, I have it in the cars. What will you have?"

I said I would have a large one, knowing that his mysterious reply would entail lengthy elucidation.

"I needn't tell you that that crowd is a crowd of bastards," was his prefatory exegesis.

Then he told me all. At one time his father had a pub and grocery business, situated near a large Dublin railway terminus. Every year the railway company invited tenders for the provisioning of its dining cars, and every year the father got the contract. (The narrator said he thought this was due to the territorial proximity of the house, with diminished handling and cartage charges.)

The dining cars (hereinafter known as "the cars") were customarily parked in remote sidings. It was the father's job to load them from time to time with costly victuals—eggs, rashers, cold turkey and whiskey. These cars, bulging in their lonely sidings with such fabulous fare, had special locks. The father had the key, and nobody else in the world had authority to open the doors until the car was part of a train. But my informant had made it his business, he told me, to have a key too.

"At that time," he told me, "I had a bash once a week in the cars."

One must here record two peculiarities of Irish railway practice. The first is a chronic inability to "make up" trains in advance, i.e., to estimate expected passenger traffic accurately. Week after week a long-distance train is scheduled to be five passenger coaches and a car. Perpetually, an extra 150 passengers arrive on the departure platform unexpectedly. This means that the car must be detached, a passenger coach substituted, and the train despatched foodless and drinkless on its way.

The second peculiarity—not exclusively Irish—is the inability of personnel in charge of shunting engines to leave coaches, parked in far sidings, alone. At all costs they must be shifted.

That was the situation as my friend in the Bailey described it. The loaded dining cars never went anywhere, in the long-distance sense. He approved of that. But they were subject to endless enshuntment. That, he said, was a bloody scandal and a waste of the taxpayers' money.

When the urge for a "bash" came upon him, his routine was simple. Using his secret key, he secretly got into a parked and laden car very early in the morning, penetrated to the pantry, grabbed a jug of water, a glass and a bottle of whiskey and, with this assortment of material and utensil, locked himself in the lavatory.

Reflect on that locking. So far as the whole world was concerned the car was utterly empty. It was locked with special, unprecedented locks. Yet this man locked himself securely within those locks.

Came the dawn—and the shunters. They espied, as doth the greyhound the hare, the lonely dining car, mute, immobile, deserted. So they coupled it up and dragged it to another siding at Liffey Junction. It was there for five hours but ("that crowd of bastards," i.e., other shunters) it was discovered and towed over to the yards behind Westland Row Station. Many hours later it was shunted on to the tail of the Wexford Express but later angrily detached owing to the unexpected arrival of extra passengers.

"And are you sitting in the lavatory drinking whiskey all the time?" I asked.

"Certainly I am," he answered, "what the hell do you think lavatories in trains is for? And with the knees of me trousers wet with me own whiskey from the jerks of them shunter bastards!"

His resentment was enormous. Be it noted that the whiskey was not in fact his own whiskey, that he was that oddity, an unauthorized person.

"How long does a bash in the cars last?" I asked him.

"Ah, that depends on a lot of things," he said. "As you know, I never carry a watch." (Exhibits cuffless, hairy wrist in proof.) "Did I ever tell you about the time I had a bash in the tunnel?"

He had not—for the good reason that I had never met him before.

"I seen meself," he said, "once upon a time on a three-day bash. The bastards took me out of Liffey Junction down to Hazelhatch. Another crowd shifted me into Harcourt Street yards. I was having a good bash at this time, but I always try to see, for the good of me health, that a bash doesn't last more than a day and night. I know it's night outside when it's dark. If it's bright it's day. Do you follow me?"

"I think I do."

"Well, I was about on the third bottle when this other shunter crowd come along—it was dark, about eight in the evening—and nothing would do them only bring me into the Liffey Tunnel under the Phoenix Park and park me there. As you know I never use a watch. If it's bright, it's day. If it's dark, it's night. Here was meself parked in the tunnel opening bottle after bottle in the dark, thinking the night was a very long one, stuck there in the tunnel. I was three-quarters way into the jigs when they pulled me out of the tunnel into Kingsbridge. I was in bed for a week. Did you ever in your life hear of a greater crowd of bastards?"

"Never."

"That was the first and last time I ever had a bash in the tunnel."

Funny? But surely there you have the Irish artist? Sitting fully dressed, innerly locked in the toilet of a locked coach where he has no right to be, resentfully drinking somebody else's whiskey, being whisked hither and thither by anonymous shunters, keeping fastidiously the while on the outer face of his door the simple word ENGAGED!

I think the image fits Joyce; but particularly in his manifestation of a most Irish characteristic—the transgressor's resentment with the nongressor.

A friend of mine found himself next door at dinner to a well-known savant who appears in *Ulysses*. (He shall be nameless, for he still lives.) My friend, making dutiful conversation, made mention of Joyce. The savant said that Ireland was under a deep obligation to the author of Joyce's *Irish Names of Places*. My friend lengthily explained that his reference had been to a different Joyce. The savant did not quite understand, but ultimately confessed that he had heard certain rumours about the other man. It seemed that he had written some dirty books, published in Paris.

"But you are a character in one of them," my friend incautiously remarked.

The next two hours, to the neglect of wine and cigars, were occupied with a heated statement by the savant that he was by no means a character in fiction, he was a man, furthermore he was alive and he had published books of his own.

"How can I be a character in fiction," he demanded, "if I am here talking to you?"

That incident may be funny, too, but its curiosity is this: Joyce spent a lifetime establishing himself as a character in fiction. Joyce created, in narcissus fascination, the ageless Stephen. Beginning with importing real characters into his books, he achieves the magnificent inversion of making them legendary and fictional. It is quite preposterous. Thousands of people believe that there once lived a man named Sherlock Holmes.

Joyce went further than Satan in rebellion.

Two characters who confess themselves based on Aquinas: Joyce and Maritain.

In *Finnegans Wake*, Joyce appears to favour the Vico theory of inevitable human and recurring evolution-theocracy: aristocracy: democracy: chaos.

AE referred to the chaos of Joyce's mind.

That was wrong, for Joyce's mind was indeed very orderly. In composition he used coloured pencils to keep himself right. All his works, not excluding *Finnegans Wake*, have a rigid classic pattern. His personal moral and family behaviours were impeccable. He seems to have deserved equally with George Moore the sneer about the latter—he never kissed, but told.

What was really abnormal about Joyce? At Clongowes he had his dose of Jesuit casuistry. Why did he substitute his home-made chaosistry?

It seems to me that Joyce emerges, through curtains of salacity and blasphemy, as a truly fear-shaken Irish Catholic, rebelling not so much against the Church but against its near-schism Irish eccentricities, its pretence that there is only one Commandment, the vulgarity of its edifices, the shallowness and stupidity of many of its ministers. His revolt, noble in itself, carried him away. He could not see the tree for the woods. But I think he meant well. We all do, anyway.

What is *Finnegans Wake*? A treatise on the incommunicable night-mind? Or merely an example of silence, exile and punning?

Some think that Joyce was at heart an Irish dawn-bursting romantic, an admirer of de Valera, and one who dearly wished to be recalled to Dublin as an ageing man to be crowned with a D. Litt. from the national and priest-haunted university. This is at least possible, if only because it explains the preposterous "aesthetic" affectations of his youth, which included the necessity for being rude to his dying mother. The theme here is that a heart of gold was beating under the artificial waistcoat. Amen.

Humour, the handmaid of sorrow and fear, creeps out endlessly in all Joyce's works. He uses the thing in the same way as Shakespeare does but less formally, to attenuate the fear of those who have belief and who genuinely think that they will be in hell or in heaven shortly, and possibly very shortly. With laughs he palliates the sense of doom that is the heritage of the Irish Catholic. True humour needs this background urgency: Rabelais is funny, but his stuff cloys. His stuff lacks tragedy.

Perhaps the true fascination of Joyce lies in his secretiveness, his ambiguity (his polyguity, perhaps?), his leg-pulling, his dishonesties, his technical skill, his attraction for Americans. His works are a garden in which some of us may play. All that we can claim to know is merely a small bit of that garden.

But at the end, Joyce will still be in his tunnel, unabashed.

THE
MAD LOMASNEYS

Eighteen-year-old Rita Lomasney has great amounts of personal style, according to her most sophisticated friend, Ned Lowry, although her family just finds her odd. In this Frank O'Connor story from 1944, the sorting out of Rita's love life takes on an epic quality.

NED LOWRY AND RITA LOMASNEY had, one might say, been lovers from childhood. The first time they had met was when he was fourteen and she a year or two younger. It was on the North Mall on a Saturday afternoon, and she was sitting on a bench under the trees; a tall, bony string of a girl with a long, obstinate jaw. Ned was a studious young fellow in a blue and white college cap, thin, pale, and spectacled. As he passed he looked at her owlishly and she gave him back an impudent stare. This upset him—he had no experience of girls—so he blushed and raised his cap. At that she seemed to relent.

"Hello," she said experimentally.

"Good afternoon," he replied with a pale smile.

"Where are you off to?" she asked.

"Oh, just up the dike for a walk."

"Sit down," she said in a sharp voice, laying her hand on the bench beside her, and he did as he was told. It was a lovely summer evening, and the white quay walls and tall, crazy, claret-colored tenements under a blue and white sky were reflected in the lazy water, which wrinkled only at the edges and seemed like a painted carpet.

"It's very pleasant here," he said complacently

"Is it?" she asked with a truculence that startled him. "I don't see anything very pleasant about it."

"Oh, it's very nice and quiet," he said in mild surprise as he raised his fair eyebrows and looked up and down the Mall at the old Georgian houses and the

605

nursemaids sitting under the trees. "My name is Lowry," he added politely.

"Oh, are ye the ones that have the jeweler's shop on the Parade?" she asked.

"That's right," replied Ned with modest pride.

"We have a clock we got from ye," she said. "'Tisn't much good of an old clock either," she added with quiet malice.

"You should bring it back to the shop," he said in considerable concern. "It probably needs overhauling."

"I'm going down the river in a boat with a couple of chaps," she said, going off at a tangent. "Will you come?"

"Couldn't," he said with a smile.

"Why not?"

"I'm only left go up the dike for a walk," he said complacently. "On Saturdays I go to Confession at St. Peter and Paul's, then I go up the dike and back the Western Road. Sometimes you see very good cricket matches. Do you like cricket?"

"A lot of old sissies pucking a ball!" she said shortly. "I do not."

"I like it," he said firmly. "I go up there every Saturday. Of course, I'm not supposed to talk to anyone," he added with mild amusement at his own audacity.

"Why not?"

"My mother doesn't want me to."

"Why doesn't she?"

"She comes of an awfully good family," he answered mildly, and but for his gentle smile she might have thought he was deliberately insulting her. "You see," he went on gravely in his thin, pleasant voice, ticking things off on his fingers and then glancing at each finger individually as he ticked it off—a tidy sort of boy— "there are three main branches of the Hourigan family: the Neddy Neds, the Neddy Jerrys, and the Neddy Thomases. The Neddy Neds are the Hayfield Hourigans. They are the oldest branch. My mother is a Hayfield Hourigan, and she'd have been a rich woman only for her father backing a bill for a Neddy Jerry. He defaulted and ran away to Australia," he concluded with a contemptuous sniff.

"Cripes!" said the girl. "And had she to pay?"

"She had. But, of course," he went on with as close as he ever seemed likely to get to a burst of real enthusiasm, "my grandfather was a well-behaved man. When he was eating his dinner the boys from the National School in Bantry used to be brought up to watch him, he had such beautiful table manners. Once he caught my uncle eating cabbage with a knife and he struck him with a poker. They had to put four stitches in him after," he added with a joyous chuckle.

"Cripes!" the girl said again. "What did he do that for?"

"To teach him manners," Ned said earnestly.

"He must have been dotty."

"Oh, I wouldn't say so," Ned exclaimed in mild surprise. Everything this girl said came as a shock to him. "But that's why my mother won't let me mix with other children. On the other hand, we read a good deal. Are you fond of reading, Miss—I didn't catch the name."

"You weren't told it," she said, showing her claws. "But if you want to know, it's Rita Lomasney."

"Do you read much, Miss Lomasney?"

"I couldn't be bothered."

"I read all sorts of books," he said enthusiastically. "And as well as that, I'm learning the violin from Miss Maude on the Parade. Of course, it's very difficult, because it's all classical music."

"What's classical music?" she asked with sudden interest.

"*Maritana* is classical music," he replied eagerly. He was a bit of a puzzle to Rita. She had never before met anyone with such a passion for handing out instruction. "Were you at *Maritana* in the opera house, Miss Lomasney?"

"I was never there at all," she said curtly.

"And *Alice Where Art Thou* is classical music," he added. "It's harder than plain music. You see," he went on, composing signs in the air, "it has signs on it like this, and when you see the signs, you know it's after turning into a different tune, though it has the same name. Irish music is all the same tune and that's why my mother won't let us learn it."

"Were you ever at the opera in Paris?" she asked suddenly.

"No," said Ned. "I was never in Paris. Why?"

"That's where you should go," she said with airy enthusiasm. "You couldn't hear any operas here. The staircase alone is bigger than the whole opera house here."

It seemed as if they were in for a really informative conversation when two fellows came down Wyse's Hill. Rita got up to meet them. Lowry looked up at them and then rose too, lifting his cap politely.

"Well, good afternoon," he said cheerfully. "I enjoyed the talk. I hope we meet again."

"Some other Saturday," said Rita.

"Oh, good evening, old man," one of the two fellows said in an affected drawl, pretending to raise a top hat. "Do come and see us soon again."

"Shut up, Foster!" Rita said sharply. "I'll give you a puck in the gob."

"Oh, by the way," Ned said, coming back to hand her a number of the *Gem* which he took from his coat pocket, "you might like to look at this. It's not bad."

"Thanks, I'd love to," she said insincerely, and he smiled and touched his cap again. Then with a polite and almost deferential air he went up to Foster. "Did you say something?" he asked.

Foster looked as astonished as if a kitten had suddenly got on its hind legs and challenged him to fight.

"I did not," he said, and backed away.

"I'm glad," Ned said, almost purring. "I was afraid you might be looking for trouble."

It came as a surprise to Rita as well. Whatever opinion she might have formed of Ned Lowry, fighting was about the last thing she would have associated him with.

The Lomasneys lived in a house on Sunday's Well, a small house with a long, sloping garden and a fine view of the river and city. Harry Lomasney, the builder, was a small man who wore gray tweed suits and soft collars several sizes too big for him. He had a ravaged brick-red face with keen blue eyes, and a sandy, straggling mustache with one side going up and the other down, and his workmen said you could tell his humor by the side he pulled. He was nicknamed "Hasty Harry." "Great God!" he fumed when his wife was having her first baby. "Nine months over a little job like that! I'd do it in three weeks if I could only get started." His wife was tall and matronly and very pious, but her piety never got much in her way. A woman who had survived Hasty would have survived anything. Their eldest daughter, Kitty, was loud-voiced and gay and had been expelled from school for writing indecent letters to a boy. She had copied the letters out of a French novel but she failed to tell the nuns that. Nellie was placider and took more after her mother; besides, she didn't read French novels.

Rita was the exception among the girls. There seemed to be no softness in her. She never had a favorite saint or a favorite nun; she said it was soppy. For the same reason she never had flirtations. Her friendship with Ned Lowry was the closest she ever got to that, and though Ned came regularly to the house, and the pair of them went to the pictures together, her sisters would have found it hard to say whether she cared any more for him than she did for any of her girl acquaintances. There was something in her they didn't understand, something tongue-tied, twisted, and unhappy. She had a curious raw, almost timid smile as though she felt people desired no better sport than hurting her. At home she was reserved, watchful, almost mocking. She could listen for hours to her mother and sisters without once opening her mouth, and then suddenly mystify them by dropping a well-aimed jaw-breaker—about classical music, for instance—before relapsing into a sulky silence; as though she had merely drawn back the veil for a moment on depths in herself which she would not permit them to explore.

After taking her degree, she got a job in a convent school in a provincial town in the west of Ireland. She and Ned corresponded and he even went to see her there. He reported at home that she seemed quite happy.

But this didn't last. A few months later the Lomasney family were at supper one evening when they heard a car stop, the gate squeaked, and steps came up the long path to the front door. Then came the sound of a bell and a cheerful voice from the hall.

"Hullo, Paschal, I suppose ye weren't expecting me?"

"'Tis never Rita!" said her mother, meaning that it was but that it shouldn't be.

"As true as God, that one is after getting into trouble," Kitty said prophetically.

The door opened and Rita slouched in, a long, stringy girl with a dark, glowing face. She kissed her father and mother lightly.

"Hullo," she said. "How's tricks?"

"What happened you?" her mother asked, rising.

"Nothing," replied Rita, an octave up the scale. "I just got the sack."

"The sack?" said her father, beginning to pull the wrong side of his mustache. "What did you get the sack for?"

"Give me a chance to get something to eat first, can't you?" Rita said laughingly. She took off her hat and smiled at herself in the mirror over the mantelpiece. It was a curious smile as though she were amused by the spectacle of what she saw. Then she smoothed back her thick black hair. "I told Paschal to bring in whatever was going. I'm on the train since ten. The heating was off as usual. I'm frizzled."

"A wonder you wouldn't send us a wire," said Mrs. Lomasney as Rita sat down and grabbed some bread and butter.

"Hadn't the tin," replied Rita.

"Can't you tell us what happened?" Kitty asked brightly.

"I told you. You'll hear more in due course. Reverend Mother is bound to write and tell ye how I lost my character."

"But what did you do, child?" her mother asked placidly. Her mother had been through all this before, with Hasty and Kitty, and she knew God was very good and nothing much ever happened.

"Fellow that wanted to marry me," said Rita. "He was in his last year at college, and his mother didn't like me, so she got Reverend Mother to give me the push."

"And what has it to do with Reverend Mother?" Nellie asked indignantly. "What business is it of hers?"

"That's what I say," said Rita.

But Kitty looked suspiciously at her. Rita wasn't natural; there was something wild about her, and this was her first real love affair. Kitty just couldn't believe that Rita had gone about it the same as anyone else.

"Still, I must say you worked pretty fast," she said.

"You'd have to in that place," said Rita. "There was only one possible man in the whole village and he was the bank clerk. We called him 'The One.' I wasn't there a week when the nuns ticked me off for riding on the pillion of his motorbike."

"And did you?" asked Kitty.

"I never got the chance, girl. They did it to every teacher on principle to give

609

her the idea that she was well watched. I only met Tony Donoghue a fortnight ago—home after a breakdown."

"Well, well, well!" her mother exclaimed without rancor. "No wonder his poor mother was upset. A boy that's not left college yet! Couldn't ye wait till he was qualified anyway?"

"Not very well," said Rita. "He's going to be a priest."

Kitty sat back with a superior grin. Of course, Rita could do nothing like anyone else. If it wasn't a priest it would have been a Negro, and Rita would have made theatre of it in precisely the same deliberate way.

"A what?" asked her father, springing to his feet.

"All right, don't blame me!" Rita said hastily. "It wasn't my fault. He told me he didn't want to be a priest. It was his mother was driving him into it. That's why he had the breakdown."

"Let me out of this," said her father, "before I—"

"Go on!" Rita said with tender mockery (she was very fond of her father). "Before you what?"

"Before I wish I was a priest myself," he snarled. "I wouldn't be saddled with a family like I am."

He stumped out of the room, and the girls laughed. The idea of their father as a priest appealed to them almost as much as the idea of him as a mother. Hasty had a knack of stating his grievances in such a way that they inevitably produced laughter. But Mrs. Lomasney did not laugh.

"Reverend Mother was perfectly right," she said severely. "As if it wasn't hard enough on the poor boys without girls like you throwing temptation in their way. I think you behaved very badly, Rita."

"All right, if you say so," Rita said shortly with a boyish shrug of her shoulders, and refused to answer any more questions.

After her supper she went to bed, and her mother and sisters sat on in the front room discussing the scandal. Someone rang and Nellie opened the door.

"Hullo, Ned," she said. "I suppose you came up to congratulate us on the good news?"

"Hullo," Ned said, smiling with his mouth primly shut. With a sort of automatic movement he took off his coat and hat and hung them on the rack. Then he emptied the pockets with the same thoroughness. He hadn't changed much. He was thin and pale, spectacled and clever, with the same precise and tranquil manner, "like an old Persian cat," as Nellie said. He read too many books. In the last year or two something seemed to have happened him. He didn't go to Mass any longer. Not going to Mass struck all the Lomasneys as too damn clever. "What good news?" he added, having avoided any unnecessary precipitation.

"You didn't know who was here?"

"No," he replied, raising his brows mildly.

"Rita!"

"Oh!" The same tone. It was part of his cleverness not to be surprised at any-thing.

"She's after getting the sack for trying to run off with a priest," said Nellie.

If Nellie thought that would shake him she was mistaken. He merely tossed his head with a silent chuckle and went in, adjusting his pince-nez. For a fellow who was supposed to be in love with her since they were kids, he behaved in a very peculiar manner. He put his hands in his trouser pockets and stood on the hearth with his legs well apart.

"Isn't it awful, Ned?" Mrs. Lomasney asked in her deep voice.

"Is it?" Ned purred, smiling.

"With a priest?" cried Nellie.

"Now, he wasn't a priest, Nellie," said Mrs. Lomasney reprovingly. "'Tis bad enough as it is without making it any worse."

"Suppose you tell me what happened," suggested Ned.

"But we don't know, Ned," cried Mrs. Lomasney. "You know what that one is like in one of her sulky fits. Maybe she'll tell you. She's up in bed."

"I'll try," said Ned.

Still with his hands in his pockets, he rolled after Mrs. Lomasney up the thickly carpeted stairs to Rita's little bedroom on top of the house. She left him on the landing and he paused for a moment to look out over the river and the lighted city behind it. Rita, wearing a pink dressing-jacket, was lying with one arm under her head. By the bed was a table with a packet of cigarettes she had been using as an ashtray. He smiled and shook his head reprovingly at her.

"Hullo, Ned," she cried, reaching him a bare arm. "Give us a kiss. I'm quite kissable now."

He didn't need to be told that. He was astonished at the change in her. Her whole bony, boyish face seemed to have gone mawkish and soft and to be lit up from inside. He sat on an armchair by the bed, carefully pulling up the bottoms of his trousers, then put his hands in his trouser pockets again and sat back with crossed legs and shoulders slightly hunched.

"I suppose they're all in a floosther downstairs?" Rita asked with amusement.

"They seem a little excited," said Ned with bowed head cocked a little side-ways, looking like a wise old bird.

"Wait till they hear the details and they'll have something to be excited about," said Rita grimly.

"Why?" he asked mildly. "Are there details?"

"Masses of them," said Rita. "Honest to God, Ned, I used to laugh at the glamor girls in the convent. I never knew you could get like that about a fellow. It's like something busting inside you. Cripes, I'm as soppy as a kid!"

"And what's the fellow like?" Ned asked curiously.

611

"Tony Donoghue? His mother had a shop in the Main Street. He's decent enough, I suppose. I don't know. He kissed me one night coming home. I was furious. I cut the blooming socks off him. Next evening he came round to apologize. I never got up or asked him to sit down or anything. I suppose I was still mad with him. He said he never slept a wink. 'Didn't you?' said I. 'It didn't trouble me much.' Bloody lies, of course. 'I did it because I was fond of you,' says he. 'Is that what you told the last one too?' said I. Then he got into a wax too. Said I was calling him a liar. 'And aren't you?' said I. Then I waited for him to hit me, but, begor, he didn't, and I ended up sitting on his knee. Talk about the Babes in the Wood! First time he ever had a girl on his knee, he said, and you know how much of it I did."

They heard a step on the stairs and Mrs. Lomasney smiled benevolently at them both round the door.

"I suppose 'tis tea Ned is having?" she asked in her deep voice.

"No, I'm having the tea," said Rita. "Ned says he'd sooner a drop of the hard tack."

"Oh, isn't that a great change, Ned?" cried Mrs. Lomasney.

"'Tis the shock," Rita explained lightly, throwing him a cigarette. "He didn't think I was that sort of girl."

"He mustn't know much about girls," said Mrs. Lomasney.

"He's learning now," said Rita.

When Paschal brought up the tray, Rita poured out tea for Ned and whiskey for herself. He made no comment. Things like that were a commonplace in the Lomasney household.

"Anyway," she went on, "he told his old one he wanted to chuck the Church and marry me. There was ructions, of course. The people in the shop at the other side of the street had a son a priest. She wanted to be as good as them. So away with her up to Reverend Mother, and Reverend Mother sends for me. Did I want to destroy the young man's life and he on the threshold of a great calling? I told her 'twas they wanted to destroy him. I asked her what sort of priest Tony would make. Oh, 'twas a marvellous sacrifice, and after it he'd be twice the man. Honest to God, Ned, the way that woman went on, you'd think she was talking about doctoring an old tomcat. I told her that was all she knew about Tony, and she said they knew him since he was an altar boy in the convent. 'Did he ever tell you how he used to slough the convent orchard and sell the apples in town?' says I. So then she dropped the Holy Willie stuff and told me his ma was after getting into debt to put him in for the priesthood, and if he chucked it, he'd never be able to get a job at home to pay it back. Three hundred quid! Wouldn't they kill you with style?"

"And what did you do then?" asked Ned with amusement.

"I went to see his mother."

"You didn't!"

"I did. I thought I might work it with the personal touch."

"You don't seem to have been very successful."

"I'd as soon try the personal touch on a traction engine, Ned. That woman was too tough for me altogether. I told her I wanted to marry Tony. 'I'm sorry,' she said; 'you can't.' 'What's to stop me?' said I. 'He's gone too far,' says she. 'If he was gone farther it wouldn't worry me,' says I. I told her then what Reverend Mother said about her being three hundred pounds in debt and offered to pay it back to her if she let him marry me."

"And had you the three hundred?" Ned asked in surprise.

"Ah, where would I get three hundred?" she replied ruefully. "And she knew it too, the old jade! She didn't believe a word I said. After that I saw Tony. He was crying; said he didn't want to break his mother's heart. As true as God, Ned, that woman had as much heart as a traction engine."

"Well, you seem to have done it in style," Ned said approvingly as he put away his teacup.

"That wasn't the half of it. When I heard the difficulties his mother was making, I offered to live with him instead."

"Live with him?" asked Ned. Even he was startled.

"Well, go away on holidays with him. Lots of girls do it. I know they do. And, God Almighty, isn't it only natural?"

"And what did he say to that?" asked Ned curiously.

"He was scared stiff."

"He would be," said Ned, wrinkling up his nose and giving his superior little sniff as he took out a packet of cigarettes.

"Oh, it's all very well for you," Rita cried, bridling up. "You may think you're a great fellow, all because you read Tolstoy and don't go to Mass, but you'd be just as scared if a girl offered to go to bed with you."

"Try me," Ned said sedately as he lit her cigarette for her, but somehow the notion of suggesting such a thing to Ned only made her laugh.

He stayed till quite late, and when he went downstairs the girls and Mrs. Lomasney fell on him and dragged him into the sitting room.

"Well, doctor," said Mrs. Lomasney, "how's the patient?"

"Oh, I think the patient is coming round nicely," said Ned.

"But would you ever believe it, Ned?" she cried. "A girl that wouldn't look at the side of the road a fellow was at, unless 'twas to go robbing orchards with him. You'll have another drop of whiskey?"

"I won't."

"And is that all you're going to tell us?" asked Mrs. Lomasney.

"Oh, you'll hear it all from herself."

"We won't."

"I dare say not," he said with a hearty chuckle, and went for his coat.

"Wisha, Ned," said Mrs. Lomasney, "what'll your mother say when she hears it?"

"'All *quite* mad,'" said Ned, sticking his nose in the air and giving an exaggerated version of what Mrs. Lomasney called "his Hayfield sniff."

"The dear knows, I think she's right," she said with resignation, helping him with his coat. "I hope your mother doesn't notice the smell of whiskey from your breath," she added dryly, just to show him that she couldn't be taken in, and then stood at the door, looking up and down, as she waited for him to wave from the gate.

"Ah," she sighed as she closed the door behind her, "with the help of God it might be all for the best."

"If you think he's going to marry her, I can tell you now he's not," said Kitty. "I'd like to see myself trying it on Bill O'Donnell. He'd have my sacred life. That fellow only enjoys it."

"Ah, God is good," her mother said cheerfully, kicking a mat into place. "Some men might like that."

Inside a week Kitty and Nellie were sick to death of the sight of Rita round the house. She was bad enough at the best of times, but now she just brooded and mooned and snapped the head off you. In the afternoons she strolled down the dike and into Ned's little shop, where she sat on the counter, swinging her legs and smoking, while Ned leaned against the side of the window, tinkering at the insides of a watch with some delicate instrument. Nothing seemed to rattle him. When he had finished work, he changed his coat and they went out to tea. He sat at the back of the teashop in a corner, pulled up the legs of his trousers, and took out a packet of cigarettes and a box of matches, which he placed on the table before them with a look that almost commanded them to stay there and not get lost. His face was pale and clear and bright, like an evening sky when the last light has drained from it.

"Anything wrong?" he asked one evening when she was moodier than usual.

"Just fed up," she said, thrusting out her jaw.

"What is it?" he asked gently. "Still fretting?"

"Ah, no. I can get over that. It's Kitty and Nellie. They're bitches, Ned; proper bitches. And all because I don't wear my heart on my sleeve. If one of them got a knock from a fellow she'd take two aspirins and go to bed with the other one. They'd have a lovely talk—can't you imagine? 'And was it then he said he loved you?' I can't do that sort of stuff. And it's all because they're not sincere, Ned. They couldn't be sincere."

"Remember, they have a long start on you," Ned said smiling.

"Is that it?" she asked without interest. "They think I'm batty. Do you?"

"I've no doubt that Mrs. Donoghue, if that's her name, thought something of the sort," replied Ned with a tightlipped smile.

"And wasn't she right?" asked Rita with sudden candor. "Suppose she'd agreed to take the three hundred quid, wouldn't I be in a nice pickle? I wake in a sweat whenever I think of it. I'm just a blooming chancer, Ned. Where would I get three hundred quid?"

"Oh, I dare say someone would have lent it to you," he said with a shrug.

"They would like fun. Would you?"

"Probably," he said gravely after a moment's thought.

"Are you serious?" she whispered earnestly.

"Quite."

"Cripes," she gasped, "you must be very fond of me."

"It looks like it," said Ned, and this time he laughed with real heartiness, a boy's laugh of sheer delight at the mystification he was causing her. It was characteristic of Rita that she should count their friendship of years as nothing, but his offer of three hundred pounds in cash as significant.

"Would you marry me?" she asked frowningly. "I'm not proposing to you, only asking," she added hastily.

"Certainly," he said, spreading out his hands. "Whenever you like."

"Honest to God?"

"Cut my throat."

"And why didn't you ask me before I went down to that kip? I'd have married you then like a shot. Was it the way you weren't keen on me then?"

"No," he replied matter-of-factly, drawing himself together like an old clock preparing to strike. "I think I've been keen on you as long as I know you."

"It's easily seen you're a Neddy Ned," she said with amusement. "I go after mine with a scalping knife."

"I stalk mine," said Ned.

"Cripes, Ned," she said with real regret, "I wish you'd told me sooner. I couldn't marry you now."

"No?"

"No. It wouldn't be fair to you."

"Isn't that my look-out?"

"It's my look-out now." She glanced around the restaurant to make sure no one was listening and then went on in a dry voice, leaning one elbow on the table. "I suppose you'll think this is all cod, but it's not. Honest to God, I think you're the finest bloody man I ever met—even though you do think you're an atheist or something," she added maliciously with a characteristic Lomasney flourish in the cause of Faith and Fatherland. "There's no one in the world I have more respect for. I think I'd nearly cut my throat if I did something you really disapproved of—I don't mean telling lies or going on a skite," she added hastily, to prevent misunderstandings. "They're only gas. Something that really shocked you is what I mean. I think if I was tempted to do anything like that I'd ask myself: 'What would that fellow Lowry think of me now?'"

"Well," Ned said in an extraordinary quiet voice, squelching the butt of his cigarette on his plate, "that sounds to me like a very good beginning."

"It is not, Ned," she said sadly, shaking her head. "That's why I say it's my look-out. You couldn't understand it unless it happened to yourself; unless you fell in love with a girl the way I fell in love with Tony. Tony is a scut, and a cow-ardly scut, but I was cracked about him. If he came in here now and said: 'Come on, girl, we're going to Killarney for the weekend,' I'd go out and buy a night-dress and toothbrush and be off with him. And I wouldn't give a damn what you or anybody thought. I might chuck myself in the lake afterwards, but I'd go. Christ, Ned," she exclaimed, flushing and looking as though she might burst into tears, "he couldn't come into a room but I went all mushy inside. That's what the real thing is like."

"Well," Ned said sedately, apparently not in the least put out—in fact, looking rather pleased with himself, Rita thought—"I'm in no hurry. In case you get tired of scalping them, the offer will still be open."

"Thanks, Ned," she said absent-mindedly, as though she weren't listening.

While he paid the bill, she stood in the porch, doing her face in the big mirror that flanked it, and paying no attention to the crowds, coming homeward through streets where the shop windows were already lit. As he emerged from the shop she turned on him suddenly.

"About that matter, Ned," she said, "will you ask me again, or do I have to ask you?"

Ned just refrained from laughing outright. "As you like," he replied with quiet amusement. "Suppose I repeat the proposal every six months."

"That would be the hell of a long time to wait if I changed my mind," she said with a thoughtful scowl. "All right," she said, taking his arm. "I know you well enough to ask you. If you don't want me by that time, you can always say so. I won't mind."

Ned's proposal came as a considerable comfort to Rita. It bolstered up her self-esteem, which was always in danger of collapse. She might be ugly and unedu-cated and a bit of a chancer, but the best man in Cork—the best in Ireland, she sometimes thought—wanted to marry her, even after she had been let down by another man. That was a queer one for her enemies! So while her sisters made fun of her, Rita considered the situation, waiting for the best possible moment to let them know she had been proposed to and could marry before either of them if it suited her. Since her childhood Rita had never given anything away without extracting the last ounce of theatrical effect from it. She would tell her sisters, but not before she could make them sick with the news.

That was a pity, for it left Rita unaware that Ned, whom she respected, was far from being the only one who liked her. For instance, there was Justin Sullivan, the lawyer, who had once been by way of being engaged to Nellie. He hadn't become engaged to her, because she was as slippery as an eel, and her fancy finally lit on a solicitor called Fahy whom Justin despised with his whole heart and soul as a lightheaded, butterfly sort of man. But Justin continued to visit the house as a friend of the girls. There happened to be no other house that suited him half as well, and besides he knew that sooner or later Nellie would make a mess of her life with Fahy, and his services would be required.

Justin, in other words, was a sticker. He was a good deal older than Rita, a tall, burly man with a broad face, a brow that was rising from baldness as well as brains, and a slow, watchful ironic air. Like many lawyers, he tended to conduct conversation as though the person he was speaking to were a hostile witness who had either to be coaxed into an admission of perjury or bullied into one of mental deficiency. When Justin began, Fahy simply clutched his head and retired to sit on the stairs. "Can't anyone shut that fellow up?" he would moan with a martyred air. Nobody could. The girls shot their little darts at him, but he only brushed them aside. Ned Lowry was the only one who could even stand up to him, and when the pair of them argued about religion, the room became a desert. Justin, of course, was a pillar of orthodoxy. "Imagine for a moment," he would declaim in a throaty rounded voice that turned easily to pomposity, "that I am Pope." "Easiest thing in the world, Justin," Kitty assured him. He drank whiskey like water, and the more he drank, the more massive and logical and orthodoxly Catholic he became.

At the same time, under his truculent air he was exceedingly gentle, patient, and understanding, and disliked the ragging of Rita by her sisters.

"Tell me, Nellie," he asked one night in his lazy, amiable way, "do you talk like that to Rita because you like it, or because you think it's good for her?"

"How soft you have it!" Nellie cried. "We have to live with her. You haven't."

"That may be my misfortune, Nellie," said Justin with a broad smile.

"Is that a proposal, Justin?" asked Kitty shrewdly.

"Scarcely, Kitty," said Justin. "You're not what I might call a good jury."

"Better be careful or you'll have her dropping in on your mother, Justin," Kitty said maliciously.

"Thanks, Kitty," Rita said with a flash of cold fury.

"I hope my mother would have sufficient sense to realize it was an honor, Kitty," Justin said severely.

When he rose to go, Rita accompanied him to the hall.

"Thanks for the moral support, Justin," she said in a low voice, and then threw her overcoat over her shoulders to go as far as the gate with him. When he opened the door they both stood and gazed about them. It was a moonlit night; the garden, patterned in black and silver, sloped to the quiet roadway, where the gas lamps burned with a dim green light, and in the farther walls gateways shaded by black trees led to flights of steps or to steep-sloping avenues which led to moonlit houses on the river's edge.

"God, isn't it lovely?" Rita said in a hushed voice.

"Oh, by the way, Rita," he said, slipping his arm through hers, "that was a proposal."

"Janey Mack, they're falling," she said, giving his arm a squeeze.

"What are falling?"

"Proposals."

"Why? Had you others?"

"I had one anyway."

"And did you accept it?"

"No," Rita said doubtfully. "Not quite. At least, I don't think I did."

"You might consider this one," Justin said with unusual humility. "You know, of course, that I was very fond of Nellie. At one time I was very fond of her indeed. You don't mind that, I hope. It's all over and done with now, and there are no regrets on either side."

"No, Justin, of course I don't mind. If I felt like marrying you I wouldn't give it a second thought. But I was very much in love with Tony too, and that's not all over and done with yet."

"I know that, Rita," he said gently. "I know exactly what you feel. We've all been through it." If he had left it at that everything might have been all right, but Justin was a lawyer, which meant that he liked to keep things absolutely ship-shape. "But that won't last forever. In a month or two you'll be over it, and then you'll wonder what you saw in that fellow."

"I don't think so, Justin," she said with a crooked little smile, not altogether displeased to be able to enlighten him on the utter hopelessness of her position. "I think it will take a great deal longer than that."

"Well, say six months, even," Justin went on, prepared to yield a point to the defense. "All I ask is that in one month or six, whenever you've got over your regrets for this—this amiable young man" (momentarily his voice took on its familiar ironic ring), "you'll give me a thought. I'm old enough not to make any more mistakes. I know I'm fond of you, and I feel pretty sure I could make a success of my end of it."

"What you really mean," said Rita, keeping her temper with the greatest difficulty, "is that I wasn't in love with Tony at all. Isn't that it?"

"Not quite," Justin said judiciously. Even if he'd had a serenade as well as the moonlight and the girl, it couldn't have kept him from correcting what he considered to be a false deduction. "I've no doubt you were very much attracted by this—this clerical Adonis; this Mr. Whatever-his-name-is, or that at any rate you thought you were, which in practice comes to the same thing, but I also know that that sort of thing, though it's painful enough while it lasts, doesn't last very long."

"You mean yours didn't, Justin," Rita said tartly.

"I mean mine or anybody else's," Justin said pompously. "Because love—the only sort of thing you can really call love—is something that comes with experience. You're probably too young yet to know what the real thing is."

As Rita had only recently told Ned that he didn't yet know what the real thing was, she found this rather hard to stomach.

"How old would you say you'd have to be?" she asked viciously. "Thirty-five?"

"You'll know soon enough—when it hits you," said Justin.

"Honest to God, Justin," she said, withdrawing her arm and looking at him with suppressed fury, "I think you're the thickest man I ever met."

"Good night, my dear," said Justin with perfect good humor, and he raised his cap and took the few steps to the gate at a run.

Rita stood gazing after him with folded arms. At the age of eighteen to be told that there is anything you don't know about love is like a knife in your heart.

Kitty and Nellie grew so tired of her moodiness that they persuaded her mother that the best way of distracting her mind was to find her another job. A new environment was also supposed to be good for her complaint, so Mrs. Lomasney wrote to her sister who was a nun in England, and the sister found her work in a convent there. Rita let on to pay no attention, though she let Ned see something of her resentment.

"But why England?" he asked wonderingly.

"Why not?" replied Rita challengingly.

"Wouldn't any place nearer do you?"

"I suppose I wouldn't be far enough away from them."

"But why not make up your own mind?"

"I'll probably do that too," she said with a short laugh. "I'd like to see what's in theirs first though."

On Friday she was to leave for England, and on Wednesday the girls gave a farewell party. This, too, Rita affected to take no great interest in. Wednesday was the half-holiday, and it rained steadily all day. The girls' friends all turned up. Most were men: Bill O'Donnell of the bank, who was engaged to Kitty; Fahy, the solicitor, who was Justin's successful rival for Nellie; Justin himself, who simply could not be kept out of the house by anything short of an injunction; Ned Lowry, and a few others. Hasty soon retired with his wife to the dining room to read the evening paper. He said all his daughters' young men looked exactly alike and he never knew which of them he was talking to.

Bill O'Donnell was acting as barman. He was a big man, bigger even than

Justin, with a battered boxer's face and a Negro smile, which seemed to well up from depths of good humor with life rather than from any immediate contact with others. He carried on loud conversations with everyone he poured out drink for, and his voice overrode every intervening tête-à-tête, and challenged even the piano, on which Nellie was vamping music-hall songs.

"Who's this one for, Rita?" he asked. "A bottle of Bass for Paddy. Ah, the stout man! Remember the New Year's Day in Bandon, Paddy? Remember how you had to carry me up to the bank in evening dress and jack me up between the two wings of the desk? Kitty, did I ever tell you about that night in Bandon?"

"Once a week for the past five years, Bill," said Kitty philosophically.

"Nellie," said Rita, "I think it's time for Bill to sing his song. 'Let Me Like a Soldier Fall,' Bill!"

"My one little song!" Bill said with a roar of laughter. "My one and only song, but I sing it grand. Don't I, Nellie? Don't I sing it fine?"

"Fine!" agreed Nellie, looking up at his big, beaming moonface shining at her over the piano. "As the man said to my mother, 'Finest bloody soprano I ever heard.'"

"He did not, Nellie," Bill said softly. "You're making that up. . . . Silence please!" he shouted joyously, clapping his hands. "Ladies and gentlemen, I must apologize. I ought to sing something like Tosti's 'Good-bye,' but the fact is, ladies and gentlemen, that I don't know Tosti's 'Good-bye.'"

"Recite it, Bill," said Justin amiably.

"I don't know the words of it either, Justin," said Bill. "In fact, I'm not sure if there's any such song, but if there is, I ought to sing it."

"Why, Bill?" Rita asked innocently. She was wearing a long black dress that threw up the unusual brightness of her dark, bony face. She looked happier than she had looked for months. All the evening it was as though she were laughing to herself.

"Because 'twould be only right, Rita," said Bill with great melancholy, putting his arm about her and drawing her closer to him. "You know I'm very fond of you, don't you, Rita?"

"And I'm mad about you, Bill," said Rita candidly.

"I know that, Rita," he said mournfully, pulling at his collar as though to give himself air. "I only wish you weren't going, Rita. This place isn't the same without you. Kitty won't mind my saying that," he added with a nervous glance at Kitty, who was flirting with Justin on the sofa.

"Are you going to sing your blooming old song or not?" Nellie asked impatiently, running her fingers over the keys.

"I'm going to sing now in one minute, Nellie," Bill said ecstatically, stroking Rita fondly under the chin. "I only want Rita to know the way we'll miss her."

"Damn it, Bill," Rita said, snuggling up to him with her dark head on his chest, "if you go on like that I won't go at all. Tell me, would you really prefer me not to go?"

"I would prefer you not to go, Rita," he replied, stroking her cheeks and eyes. "You're too good for the fellows over there."

"Oh, go on doing that," she said hastily, as he dropped his hand. "It's gorgeous, and you're making Kitty mad jealous."

"Kitty isn't jealous," Bill said fondly. "Kitty is a lovely girl and you're a lovely girl. I hate to see you go, Rita."

"That settles it, Bill," she said, pulling herself free of him with a determined air. "I simply couldn't cause you all that suffering. As you put it that way, I won't go."

"Won't you, just?" said Kitty with a grin.

"Now, don't worry your head about it anymore, Bill," said Rita briskly. "It's all off."

Justin, who had been quietly consuming large whiskeys, looked round lazily.

"Perhaps I ought to have mentioned," he boomed, "that the young lady has just done me the honor of proposing to me and I've accepted her."

Ned Lowry, who had been enjoying the scene between Bill and Rita, looked at him for a moment in surprise.

"Bravo! Bravo!" cried Bill, clapping his hands with childish delight. "A marriage has been arranged and all the rest of it—what? I must give you a kiss, Rita. Justin, you don't mind if I give Rita a kiss?"

"Not at all, not at all," replied Justin with a lordly wave of his hand. "Anything that's mine is yours, old man."

"You're not serious, Justin, are you?" Kitty asked incredulously.

"Oh, I'm serious all right," said Justin. "I'm not quite certain whether your sister is. Are you, Rita?"

"What?" Rita asked as though she hadn't heard.

"Serious," repeated Justin.

"Why?" asked Rita. "Trying to give me the push already?"

"We're much obliged for the information," Nellie said ironically as she rose from the piano. "Now, maybe you'd oblige us further and tell us does Father know."

"Hardly," said Rita coolly. "It was only settled this evening."

"Well, maybe 'twill do with some more settling by the time Father is done with you," Nellie said furiously. "The impudence of you! How dare you! Go in at once and tell him."

"Keep your hair on, girl," Rita advised with cool malice and then went jauntily out of the room. Kitty and Nellie began to squabble viciously with Justin. They were convinced that the whole scene had been arranged by Rita to make them look ridiculous, and in this they weren't very far out. Justin sat back and began to enjoy the sport. Then Ned Lowry struck a match and lit another ciga-

621

rette, and something about the slow, careful way in which he did it drew every-one's attention. Just because he was not the sort to make a fuss, people realized from his strained look that his mind was very far away. The squabble stopped as quickly as it had begun and a feeling of awkwardness ensued. Ned was too old a friend of the family for the girls not to feel that way about him.

Rita returned, laughing.

"Well?" asked Nellie.

"Consent refused," growled Rita, bowing her head and pulling the wrong side of an imaginary mustache.

"What did I say?" exclaimed Nellie, but without rancor.

"You don't think it makes any difference?" Rita asked dryly.

"I wouldn't be too sure of that," said Nellie. "What else did he say?"

"Oh, he hadn't a notion who I was talking about," Rita said lightly. "'Justin who?'" she mimicked. "'How the hell do you think I can remember all the young scuts ye bring to the house?'"

"Was he mad?" asked Kitty with amusement.

"Hopping."

"He didn't call us scuts?" asked Bill in a wounded tone.

"Oh, begor, that was the very word he used, Bill," said Rita.

"Did you tell him he was very fond of me the day I gave him the tip for Golden Boy at the Park Races?" asked Justin.

"I did," said Rita. "I said you were the stout block of a fellow with the brown hair that he said had the fine intelligence, and he said he never gave a damn about intelligence. He wanted me to marry the thin fellow with the specs. 'Only bloody gentlemen that comes to the house.'"

"Is it Ned?" cried Nellie.

"Who else?" said Rita. "I asked him why he didn't tell me that before and he nearly ate the head off me. 'Jesus Christ, girl, don't I feed ye and clothe ye? Isn't that enough without having to coort for ye as well? Next thing, ye'll be asking me to have a few babies for ye.' Anyway, Ned," she added with a crooked, almost malicious smile, "you can always say you were Pa's favorite."

Once more the attention was directed to Ned. He put his cigarette down with care and sprang up with a broad smile, holding out his hand.

"I wish you all the luck in the world, Justin," he said.

"I know that well, Ned," boomed Justin, catching Ned's hand in his own two. "And I'd feel the same if it was you."

"And you too, Miss Lomasney," Ned said gaily.

"Thanks, Mr. Lowry," she replied with the same crooked smile.

Justin and Rita got married, and Ned, like all the Hayfield Hourigans, behaved in a decorous and sensible manner. He didn't take to drink or break the crockery or do any of the things people are expected to do under the circumstances. He gave them a very expensive clock as a wedding present, went once or twice to visit them and permitted Justin to try and convert him, and took Rita to the pictures when Justin was away from home. At the same time he began to walk out with an assistant in Halpin's; a gentle, humorous girl with a great mass of jet-black hair, a snub nose, and a long, pointed melancholy face. You saw them everywhere together.

He also went regularly to Sunday's Well to see the old couple and Nellie, who wasn't yet married. One evening when he called, Mr. and Mrs. Lomasney were at the chapel, but Rita was there, Justin being again away. It was months since she and Ned had met; she was having a baby and very near her time; and it made her self-conscious and rude. She said it made her feel like a yacht that had been turned into a cargo boat. Three or four times she said things to Ned which would have maddened anyone else, but he took them in his usual way, without resentment.

"And how's little Miss Bitch?" she asked insolently.

"Little Miss who?" he asked mildly.

"Miss—how the hell can I remember the names of all your dolls? The Spanish-looking one who sells the knickers at Halpin's."

"Oh, she's very well, thanks," Ned said primly.

"What you might call a prudent marriage," Rita went on, all on edge.

"How's that, Rita?"

"You'll have the ring and the trousseau at cost price."

"How interested you are in her!" Nellie said suspiciously.

"I don't give a damn about her," Rita with a shrug. "Would Senorita What's-her-name ever let you stand godfather to my footballer, Ned?"

"Why not?" Ned asked mildly. "I'd be delighted, of course."

"You have the devil's own neck to ask him after the way you treated him," said Nellie. Nellie was interested; she knew Rita and knew that she was in one of her emotional states, and was determined on finding out what it meant. Ordinarily Rita, who also knew her sister, would have delighted in thwarting her, but now it was as though she wanted an audience.

"How did I treat him?" she asked with amusement.

"Codding him along like that for years, and then marrying a man that was twice your age."

"Well, how did he expect me to know?"

Ned rose and took out a packet of cigarettes. Like Nellie he knew that Rita had deliberately staged the scene and was on the point of telling him something. She was leaning very far back in her chair and laughed up at him while she took a cigarette and waited for him to light it.

"Come on, Rita," he said encouragingly. "As you've said so much you might as well tell us the rest."

"What else is there to tell?"

"What you had against me."

"Who said I had anything against you? Didn't I distinctly tell you when you asked me to marry you that I didn't love you? Maybe you thought I didn't mean it."

He paused for a moment and then raised his brows.

"I did," he said quietly.

She laughed.

"The conceit of that fellow!" she said to Nellie, and then with a change of tone: "I had nothing against you, Ned. This was the one I had the needle in. Herself and Kitty were forcing me into it."

"Well, the impudence of you!" cried Nellie.

"Isn't it true for me?" Rita said sharply. "Weren't you both trying to get me out of the house?"

"We weren't," Nellie replied hotly, "and anyway that has nothing to do with it. It was no reason why you couldn't have married Ned if you wanted to."

"I didn't want to. I didn't want to marry anyone."

"And what changed your mind?"

"Nothing changed my mind. I didn't care about anyone, only Tony, but I didn't want to go to that damn place, and I had no alternative. I had to marry one of you, so I made up my mind that I'd marry the first of you that called."

"You must have been mad," Nellie said indignantly.

"I felt it. I sat at the window the whole afternoon, looking at the rain. Remember that day, Ned?"

He nodded.

"The rain had a lot to do with it. I think I half hoped you'd come first. Justin came instead—an old aunt of his was sick and he came for supper. I saw him at the gate and he waved to me with his old brolly. I ran downstairs to open the door for him. 'Justin,' I said, grabbing him by the coat, 'if you still want to marry me, I'm ready.' He gave me a dirty look—you know Justin! 'Young woman,' he said, 'there's a time and place for everything.' And away with him up to the lavatory. Talk about romantic engagements! Damn the old kiss did I get off him, even!"

"I declare to God!" said Nellie in stupefaction.

"I know," Rita cried, laughing again over her own irresponsibility. "Cripes, when I knew what I was after doing I nearly dropped dead."

"Oh, so you came to your senses?" Nellie asked ironically.

"What do you think? That's the trouble with Justin; he's always right. That fellow knew I wouldn't be married a week before I didn't give a snap of my fingers for Tony. And me thinking my life was over and that was that or the river! God, the idiots we make of ourselves over men!"

"And I suppose 'twas then you found out you'd married the wrong man?" Nellie asked.

"Who said I married the wrong man?" Rita asked hotly.

"I thought that was what you were telling us," Nellie said innocently.

"You get things all wrong, Nellie," Rita replied shortly. "You jump to conclusions too much. If I did marry the wrong man I wouldn't be likely to tell you— or Ned Lowry either."

She looked mockingly at Ned, but her look belied her. It was plain enough now why she wanted Nellie as an audience. It kept her from admitting more than she had to admit, from saying things which, once said, might make her own life impossible. Ned rose and flicked his cigarette ash into the fire. Then he stood with his back to it, his hands behind his back, his feet spread out on the hearth.

"You mean if I'd come earlier you'd have married me?" he asked quietly.

"If you'd come earlier, I'd probably be asking Justin to stand godfather to your brat," said Rita. "And how do you know but Justin would be walking out the senorita, Ned?"

"Then maybe you wouldn't be quite so interested whether he was or not," said Nellie, but she didn't say it maliciously. It was now only too plain what Rita meant, and Nellie was sorry for her.

Ned turned and lashed his cigarette savagely into the fire. Rita looked up at him mockingly.

"Go on!" she taunted him. "Say it, blast you!"

"I couldn't," he said bitterly.

A month later he married the senorita.

MY
OEDIPUS COMPLEX

This child's-eye view of life with father is both heartwarming (without a hint of sentimentality) and laugh-out-loud funny. At the same time "My Oedipus Complex" (1950) offers a brilliant example of a technical virtuoso at the height of his skill, especially in terms of narrative voice and point of view (has there ever been a more unreliable narrator than little Larry?).

FATHER WAS IN THE ARMY all through the war—the first war, I mean—so, up to the age of five, I never saw much of him, and what I saw did not worry me. Sometimes I woke and there was a big figure in khaki peering down at me in the candlelight. Sometimes in the early morning I heard the slamming of the front door and the clatter of nailed boots down the cobbles of the lane. These were Father's entrances and exits. Like Santa Claus he came and went mysteriously.

In fact, I rather liked his visits, though it was an uncomfortable squeeze between Mother and him when I got into the big bed in the early morning. He smoked, which gave him a pleasant musty smell, and shaved, an operation of astounding interest. Each time he left a trail of souvenirs—model tanks and Gurkha knives with handles made of bullet cases, and German helmets and cap badges and button-sticks, and all sorts of military equipment—carefully stowed away in a long box on top of the wardrobe, in case they ever came in handy. There was a bit of the magpie about Father; he expected everything to come in handy. When his back was turned, Mother let me get a chair and rummage through his treasures. She didn't seem to think so highly of them as he did.

The war was the most peaceful period of my life. The window of my attic faced southeast. My mother had curtained it, but that had small effect. I always woke with the first light and, with all the responsibilities of the previous day melted, feeling myself rather like the sun, ready to illumine and rejoice. Life never seemed so simple and clear and full of possibilities as then. I put my feet out from under the clothes—I called them Mrs. Left and Mrs. Right—and invented dramatic situations for them in which they discussed the problems of the day. At least Mrs. Right did; she was very demonstrative, but I hadn't the same control of Mrs. Left, so she mostly contented herself with nodding agreement.

They discussed what Mother and I should do during the day, what Santa Claus should give a fellow for Christmas, and what steps should be taken to brighten the home. There was that little matter of the baby, for instance. Mother and I could never agree about that. Ours was the only house in the terrace without a new baby, and Mother said we couldn't afford one till Father came back from the war because they cost seventeen and six. That showed how simple she was. The Geneys up the road had a baby, and everyone knew they couldn't afford seventeen and six. It was probably a cheap baby, and Mother wanted something really good, but I felt she was too exclusive. The Geneys' baby would have done us fine.

Having settled my plans for the day, I got up, put a chair under the attic window, and lifted the frame high enough to stick out my head. The window overlooked the front gardens of the terrace behind ours, and beyond these it looked over a deep valley to the tall, red-brick houses terraced up the opposite hillside, which were all still in shadow, while those at our side of the valley were all lit up, though with long strange shadows that made them seem unfamiliar; rigid and painted.

After that I went into Mother's room and climbed into the big bed. She woke and I began to tell her of my schemes. By this time, though I never seem to have noticed it, I was petrified in my nightshirt, and I thawed as I talked until, the last frost melted, I fell asleep beside her and woke again only when I heard her below in the kitchen, making the breakfast.

After breakfast we went into town; heard Mass at St. Augustine's and said a prayer for Father, and did the shopping. If the afternoon was fine we either went for a walk in the country or a visit to Mother's great friend in the convent, Mother St. Dominic. Mother had them all praying for Father, and every night, going to bed, I asked God to send him back safe from the war to us. Little, indeed, did I know what I was praying for!

One morning, I got into the big bed, and there, sure enough, was Father in his usual Santa Claus manner, but later, instead of uniform, he put on his best blue suit, and Mother was as pleased as anything. I saw nothing to be pleased about, because, out of uniform, Father was altogether less interesting, but she only beamed, and explained that our prayers had been answered, and off we went to Mass to thank God for having brought Father safely home.

The irony of it! That very day when he came in to dinner he took off his boots and put on his slippers, donned the dirty old cap he wore about the house to save him from colds, crossed his legs, and began to talk gravely to Mother, who looked anxious. Naturally, I disliked her looking anxious, because it destroyed her good looks, so I interrupted him.

"Just a moment, Larry!" she said gently.

This was only what she said when we had boring visitors, so I attached no importance to it and went on talking.

"Do be quiet, Larry!" she said impatiently. "Don't you hear me talking to Daddy?"

This was the first time I had heard those ominous words, "talking to Daddy," and I couldn't help feeling that if this was how God answered prayers, he couldn't listen to them very attentively.

"Why are you talking to Daddy?" I asked with as great a show of indifference as I could muster.

"Because Daddy and I have business to discuss. Now, don't interrupt again!"

In the afternoon, at Mother's request, Father took me for a walk. This time we went into town instead of out the country, and I thought at first, in my usual optimistic way, that it might be an improvement. It was nothing of the sort. Father and I had quite different notions of a walk in town. He had no proper interest in trams, ships, and horses, and the only thing that seemed to divert him was talking to fellows as old as himself. When I wanted to stop he simply went on, dragging me behind him by the hand; when he wanted to stop I had no alternative but to do the same. I noticed that it seemed to be a sign that he wanted to stop for a long time whenever he leaned against a wall. The second time I saw him do it I got wild. He seemed to be settling himself forever. I pulled him by the coat and trousers, but, unlike Mother who, if you were too persistent, got into a wax and said: "Larry, if you don't behave yourself, I'll give you a good slap," Father had an extraordinary capacity for amiable inattention. I sized him up and wondered would I cry, but he seemed to be too remote to be annoyed even by that. Really, it was like going for a walk with a mountain! He either ignored the wrenching and pummelling entirely, or else glanced down with a grin of amusement from his peak. I had never met anyone so absorbed in himself as he seemed.

At teatime, "talking to Daddy" began again, complicated this time by the fact that he had an evening paper, and every few minutes he put it down and told Mother something new out of it. I felt this was foul play. Man for man, I was prepared to compete with him any time for Mother's attention, but when he had it all made up for him by other people it left me no chance. Several times I tried to change the subject without success.

"You must be quiet while Daddy is reading, Larry," Mother said impatiently.

It was clear that she either genuinely liked talking to Father better than talking to me, or else that he had some terrible hold on her which made her afraid to admit the truth.

"Mummy," I said that night when she was tucking me up, "do you think if I prayed hard God would send Daddy back to the war?"

She seemed to think about that for a moment.

"No, dear," she said with a smile. "I don't think he would."

"Why wouldn't he, Mummy?"

"Because there isn't a war any longer, dear."

"But, Mummy, couldn't God make another war, if He liked?"

"He wouldn't like to, dear. It's not God who makes wars, but bad people."

"Oh!" I said.

I was disappointed about that. I began to think that God wasn't quite what he was cracked up to be.

Next morning I woke at my usual hour, feeling like a bottle of champagne. I put out my feet and invented a long conversation in which Mrs. Right talked of the trouble she had with her own father till she put him in the Home. I didn't quite know what the Home was but it sounded the right place for Father. Then I got my chair and stuck my head out of the attic window. Dawn was just breaking, with a guilty air that made me feel I had caught it in the act. My head bursting with stories and schemes, I stumbled in next door, and in the half-darkness scrambled into the big bed. There was no room at Mother's side so I had to get between her and Father. For the time being I had forgotten about him, and for several minutes I sat bolt upright, racking my brains to know what I could do with him. He was taking up more than his fair share of the bed, and I couldn't get comfortable, so I gave him several kicks that made him grunt and stretch. He made room all right, though. Mother waked and felt for me. I settled back comfortably in the warmth of the bed with my thumb in my mouth.

"Mummy!" I hummed, loudly and contentedly.

"Sssh! dear," she whispered. "Don't wake Daddy!"

This was a new development, which threatened to be even more serious than "talking to Daddy." Life without my early-morning conferences was unthinkable.

"Why?" I asked severely.

"Because poor Daddy is tired."

This seemed to me a quite inadequate reason, and I was sickened by the sentimentality of her "poor Daddy." I never liked that sort of gush; it always struck me as insincere.

"Oh!" I said lightly. Then in my most winning tone: "Do you know where I want to go with you today. Mummy?"

"No, dear," she sighed.

"I want to go down the Glen and fish for thornybacks with my new net, and then I want to go out to the Fox and Hounds, and—"

"Don't-wake-Daddy!" she hissed angrily, clapping her hand across my mouth.

But it was too late. He was awake, or nearly so. He grunted and reached for the matches. Then he stared incredulously at his watch.

"Like a cup of tea, dear?" asked Mother in a meek, hushed voice I had never heard her use before. It sounded almost as though she were afraid.

"Tea?" he exclaimed indignantly. "Do you know what the time is?"

"And after that I want to go up the Rathcooney Road," I said loudly, afraid I'd forget something in all those interruptions.

"Go to sleep at once, Larry!" she said sharply.

I began to snivel. I couldn't concentrate, the way that pair went on, and smothering my early-morning schemes was like burying a family from the cradle.

Father said nothing, but lit his pipe and sucked it, looking out into the shadows without minding Mother or me. I knew he was mad. Every time I made a remark Mother hushed me irritably. I was mortified. I felt it wasn't fair; there was even something sinister in it. Every time I had pointed out to her the waste of making two beds when we could both sleep in one, she had told me it was healthier like that, and now here was this man, this stranger, sleeping with her without the least regard for her health!

He got up early and made tea, but though he brought Mother a cup he brought none for me.

"Mummy," I shouted, "I want a cup of tea, too."

"Yes, dear," she said patiently. "You can drink from Mummy's saucer."

That settled it. Either Father or I would have to leave the house. I didn't want to drink from Mother's saucer; I wanted to be treated as an equal in my own home, so, just to spite her, I drank it all and left none for her. She took that quietly, too.

But that night when she was putting me to bed she said gently:

"Larry, I want you to promise me something."

"What is it?" I asked.

"Not to come in and disturb poor Daddy in the morning. Promise?"

"Poor Daddy" again! I was becoming suspicious of everything involving that quite impossible man.

"Why?" I asked.

"Because poor Daddy is worried and tired and he doesn't sleep well."

"Why doesn't he, Mummy?"

"Well, you know, don't you, that while he was at the war Mummy got the pennies from the Post Office?"

"From Miss MacCarthy?"

"That's right. But now, you see, Miss MacCarthy hasn't any more pennies, so Daddy must go out and find us some. You know what would happen if he couldn't?"

"No," I said, "tell us."

"Well, I think we might have to go out and beg for them like the poor old woman on Fridays. We wouldn't like that, would we?"

"No," I agreed. "We wouldn't."

"So you'll promise not to come in and wake him?"

"Promise."

Mind you, I meant that. I knew pennies were a serious matter, and I was all against having to go out and beg like the old woman on Fridays. Mother laid out all my toys in a complete ring round the bed so that, whatever way I got out, I was bound to fall over one of them.

When I woke I remembered my promise all right. I got up and sat on the floor and played—for hours, it seemed to me. Then I got my chair and looked out the attic window for more hours. I wished it was time for Father to wake; I wished someone would make me a cup of tea. I didn't feel in the least like the sun; instead, I was bored and so very, very cold! I simply longed for the warmth and depth of the big featherbed.

At last I could stand it no longer. I went into the next room. As there was still no room at Mother's side I climbed over her and she woke with a start.

"Larry," she whispered, gripping my arm very tightly, "what did you promise?"

"But I did, Mummy," I wailed, caught in the very act. "I was quiet for ever so long."

"Oh, dear, and you're perished!" she said sadly, feeling me all over. "Now, if I let you stay will you promise not to talk?"

"But I want to talk, Mummy," I wailed.

"That has nothing to do with it," she said with a firmness that was new to me. "Daddy wants to sleep. Now, do you understand that?"

I understood it only too well. I wanted to talk, he wanted to sleep—whose house was it, anyway?

"Mummy," I said with equal firmness, "I think it would be healthier for Daddy to sleep in his own bed."

That seemed to stagger her, because she said nothing for a while.

"Now, once for all," she went on, "you're to be perfectly quiet or go back to your own bed. Which is it to be?"

The injustice of it got me down. I had convicted her out of her own mouth of inconsistency and unreasonableness, and she hadn't even attempted to reply. Full of spite, I gave Father a kick, which she didn't notice but which made him grunt and open his eyes in alarm.

"What time is it?" he asked in a panic-stricken voice, not looking at Mother but at the door, as if he saw someone there.

"It's early yet," she replied soothingly. "It's only the child. Go to sleep again. . . . Now, Larry," she added, getting out of bed, "you've wakened Daddy and you must go back."

This time, for all her quiet air, I knew she meant it, and knew that my principal rights and privileges were as good as lost unless I asserted them at once. As she lifted me, I gave a screech, enough to wake the dead, not to mind Father. He groaned.

"That damn child! Doesn't he ever sleep?"

"It's only a habit, dear," she said quietly, though I could see she was vexed.

"Well, it's time he got out of it," shouted Father, beginning to heave in the bed. He suddenly gathered all the bedclothes about him, turned to the wall, and then looked back over his shoulder with nothing showing only two small, spiteful, dark eyes. The man looked very wicked.

To open the bedroom door, Mother had to let me down, and I broke free and dashed for the farthest corner, screeching. Father sat bolt upright in bed.

"Shut up, you little puppy!" he said in a choking voice.

I was so astonished that I stopped screeching. Never, never had anyone spoken to me in that tone before. I looked at him incredulously and saw his face convulsed with rage. It was only then that I fully realized how God had codded me, listening to my prayers for the safe return of this monster.

"Shut up, you!" I bawled, beside myself.

"What's that you said?" shouted Father, making a wild leap out of the bed.

"Mick, Mick!" cried Mother. "Don't you see the child isn't used to you?"

"I see he's better fed than taught," snarled Father, waving his arms wildly. "He wants his bottom smacked."

All his previous shouting was as nothing to these obscene words referring to my person. They really made my blood boil.

"Smack your own!" I screamed hysterically. "Smack your own! Shut up! Shut up!"

At this he lost his patience and let fly at me. He did it with the lack of conviction you'd expect of a man under Mother's horrified eyes, and it ended up as a mere tap, but the sheer indignity of being struck at all by a stranger, a total stranger who had cajoled his way back from the war into our big bed as a result of my innocent intercession, made me completely dotty. I shrieked and shrieked, and danced in my bare feet, and Father, looking awkward and hairy in nothing but a short gray army shirt, glared down at me like a mountain out for murder. I think it must have been then that I realized he was jealous too. And there stood Mother in her nightdress, looking as if her heart was broken between us. I hoped she felt as she looked. It seemed to me that she deserved it all.

From that morning out my life was a hell. Father and I were enemies, open and avowed. We conducted a series of skirmishes against one another, he trying to steal my time with Mother and I his. When she was sitting on my bed, telling me a story, he took to looking for some pair of old boots which he alleged he had left behind him at the beginning of the war. While he talked to Mother I played loudly with my toys to show my total lack of concern. He created a terrible scene one evening when he came in from work and found me at his box, playing with his regimental badges, Gurkha knives and button-sticks. Mother got up and took the box from me.

"You mustn't play with Daddy's toys unless he lets you, Larry," she said severely. "Daddy doesn't play with yours."

For some reason Father looked at her as if she had struck him and then turned away with a scowl.

"Those are not toys," he growled, taking down the box again to see had I lifted anything. "Some of those curios are very rare and valuable."

But as time went on I saw more and more how he managed to alienate Mother and me. What made it worse was that I couldn't grasp his method or see what attraction he had for Mother. In every possible way he was less winning than I. He had a common accent and made noises at his tea. I thought for a while that it might be the newspapers she was interested in, so I made up bits of news of my own to read to her. Then I thought it might be the smoking, which I personally thought attractive, and took his pipes and went round the house dribbling into them till he caught me. I even made noises at my tea, but Mother only told me I was disgusting. It all seemed to hinge round that unhealthy habit of sleeping together, so I made a point of dropping into their bedroom and nosing round, talking to myself, so that they wouldn't know I was watching them, but they were never up to anything that I could see. In the end it beat me. It seemed to depend on being grown-up and giving people rings, and I realized I'd have to wait.

But at the same time I wanted him to see that I was only waiting, not giving up the fight. One evening when he was being particularly obnoxious, chattering away well above my head, I let him have it.

"Mummy," I said, "do you know what I'm going to do when I grow up?"

"No, dear," she replied. "What?"

"I'm going to marry you," I said quietly

Father gave a great guffaw out of him, but he didn't take me in. I knew it must only be pretense. And Mother, in spite of everything, was pleased. I felt she was probably relieved to know that one day Father's hold on her would be broken.

"Won't that be nice?" she said with a smile.

"It'll be very nice," I said confidently. "Because we're going to have lots and lots of babies."

"That's right dear," she said placidly. "I think we'll have one soon, and then you'll have plenty of company."

I was no end pleased about that because it showed that in spite of the way she gave in to Father she still considered my wishes. Besides, it would put the Geneys in their place.

It didn't turn out like that, though. To begin with, she was very preoccupied—

I supposed about where she would get the seventeen and six—and though Father took to staying out late in the evenings it did me no particular good. She stopped taking me for walks, became as touchy as blazes, and smacked me for nothing at all. Sometimes I wished I'd never mentioned the confounded baby—I seemed to have a genius for bringing calamity on myself.

And calamity it was! Sonny arrived in the most appalling hullabaloo—even that much he couldn't do without a fuss—and from the first moment I disliked him. He was a difficult child—so far as I was concerned he was always difficult—and demanded far too much attention. Mother was simply silly about him, and couldn't see when he was only showing off. As company he was worse than useless. He slept all day, and I had to go round the house on tiptoe to avoid waking him. It wasn't any longer a question of not waking Father. The slogan now was "Don't-wake-Sonny!" I couldn't understand why the child wouldn't sleep at the proper time, so whenever Mother's back was turned I woke him. Sometimes to keep him awake I pinched him as well. Mother caught me at it one day and gave me a most unmerciful flaking.

One evening, when Father was coming in from work, I was playing trains in the front garden. I let on not to notice him; instead, I pretended to be talking to myself, and said in a loud voice: "If another bloody baby comes into this house, I'm going out."

Father stopped dead and looked at me over his shoulder.

"What's that you said?" he asked sternly.

"I was only talking to myself," I replied, trying to conceal my panic. "It's private."

He turned and went in without a word. Mind you, I intended it as a solemn warning, but its effect was quite different. Father started being quite nice to me. I could understand that, of course. Mother was quite sickening about Sonny. Even at mealtimes she'd get up and gawk at him in the cradle with an idiotic smile, and tell Father to do the same. He was always polite about it, but he looked so puzzled you could see he didn't know what she was talking about. He complained of the way Sonny cried at night, but she only got cross and said that Sonny never cried except when there was something up with him—which was a flaming lie, because Sonny never had anything up with him, and only cried for attention. It was really painful to see how simpleminded she was. Father wasn't attractive, but he had a fine intelligence. He saw through Sonny, and now he knew that I saw through him as well.

One night I woke with a start. There was someone beside me in the bed. For one wild moment I felt sure it must be Mother, having come to her senses and left Father for good, but then I heard Sonny in convulsions in the next room, and Mother saying: "There! There! There!" and I knew it wasn't she. It was Father. He was lying beside me, wide awake, breathing hard and apparently as mad as hell.

After a while it came to me what he was mad about. It was his turn now. After turning me out of the big bed, he had been turned out himself. Mother had no consideration now for anyone but that poisonous pup, Sonny. I couldn't help feeling sorry for Father. I had been through it all myself, and even at that age I was magnanimous. I began to stroke him down and say: "There! There!" He wasn't exactly responsive.

"Aren't you asleep either?" he snarled.

"Ah, come on and put your arm around us, can't you?" I said, and he did, in a sort of way. Gingerly, I suppose, is how you'd describe it. He was very bony but better than nothing.

At Christmas he went out of his way to buy me a really nice model railway.

THE DEMON LOVER

This sinister (and now classic) tale, published in 1946, is set against an evacuated and bombed-out World War II London, where a woman comes to the terrifying realization that her past is about to catch up with her.

TOWARDS THE END OF HER day in London Mrs. Drover went round to her shut-up house to look for several things she wanted to take away. Some belonged to herself, some to her family, who were by now used to their country life. It was late August; it had been a steamy, showery day: at the moment the trees down the pavement glittered in an escape of humid yellow afternoon sun. Against the next batch of clouds, already piling up ink-dark, broken chimneys and parapets stood out. In her once familiar street, as in any unused channel, an unfamiliar queerness had silted up; a cat wove itself in and out of railings, but no human eye watched Mrs. Drover's return. Shifting some parcels under her arm, she slowly forced round her latchkey in an unwilling lock, then gave the door, which had warped, a push with her knee. Dead air came out to meet her as she went in.

The staircase window having been boarded up, no light came down into the hall. But one door, she could just see, stood ajar, so she went quickly through into the room and unshuttered the big window in there. Now the prosaic woman, looking about her, was more perplexed than she knew by everything that she saw, by traces of her long former habit of life—the yellow smoke-stain up the white marble mantelpiece, the ring left by a vase on the top of the escritoire; the bruise in the wallpaper where, on the door being thrown open widely, the china handle had always hit the wall. The piano, having gone away to be stored, had left what looked like claw-marks on its part of the parquet. Though not much dust had seeped in, each object wore a film of another kind; and, the only ventilation being the chimney, the whole drawing-room smelled of the cold hearth. Mrs. Drover put down her parcels on the escritoire and left the room to proceed upstairs; the things she wanted were in a bedroom chest.

She had been anxious to see how the house was—the part-time caretaker she shared with some neighbours was away this week on his holiday, known to be not yet back. At the best of times he did not look in often, and she was never sure that she trusted him. There were some cracks in the structure, left by the last bombing, on which she was anxious to keep an eye. Not that one could do anything—

A shaft of refracted daylight now lay across the hall. She stopped dead and stared at the hall table—on this lay a letter addressed to her.

She thought first—then the caretaker *must* be back. All the same, who, seeing the house shuttered, would have dropped a letter in at the box? It was not a circular, it was not a bill. And the post office redirected, to the address in the country, everything for her that came through the post. The caretaker (even if he *were* back) did not know she was due in London today—her call here had been planned to be a surprise—so his negligence in the manner of this letter, leaving it to wait in the dusk and the dust, annoyed her. Annoyed, she picked up the letter, which bore no stamp. But it cannot be important, or they would know . . . She took the letter rapidly upstairs with her, without a stop to look at the writing till she reached what had been her bedroom, where she let in light. The room looked over the garden and other gardens: the sun had gone in; as the clouds sharpened and lowered, the trees and rank lawns seemed already to smoke with dark. Her reluctance to look again at the letter came from the fact that she felt intruded upon—and by someone contemptuous of her ways. However, in the tenseness preceding the fall of rain she read it: it was a few lines:

> Dear Kathleen: You will not have forgotten that today is our anniversary, and the day we said. The years have gone by at once slowly and fast. In view of the fact that nothing has changed, I shall rely upon you to keep your promise. I was sorry to see you leave London, but was satisfied that you would be back in time. You may expect me, therefore, at the hour arranged. Until then . . .
>
> K.

Mrs. Drover looked for the date: it was today's. She dropped the letter on to the bed-springs, then picked it up to see the writing again—her lips, beneath the remains of lipstick, beginning to go white. She felt so much the change in her own face that she went to the mirror, polished a clear patch in it and looked at once urgently and stealthily in. She was confronted by a woman of forty-four, with eyes starting out under a hat-brim that had been rather carelessly pulled down. She had not put on any more powder since she left the shop where she ate her solitary tea. The pearls her husband had given her on their marriage hung loose round her now rather thinner throat, slipping in the V of the pink wool jumper her sister knitted last autumn as they sat round the fire. Mrs. Drover's most normal expression was one of controlled worry, but of assent. Since the birth of the third of her little boys, attended by a quite serious illness, she had had an intermittent muscular flicker to the left of her mouth, but in spite of this she could always sustain a manner that was at once energetic and calm.

Turning from her own face as precipitately as she had gone to meet it, she went to the chest where the things were, unlocked it, threw up the lid and knelt to search. But as rain began to come crashing down she could not keep from looking over her shoulder at the stripped bed on which the letter lay. Behind the blanket of rain the clock of the church that still stood struck six—with rapidly heightening apprehension she counted each of the slow strokes. "The hour arranged . . . My God," she said, "*what* hour? How should I . . . ? After twenty-five years . . ."

The young girl talking to the soldier in the garden had not ever completely seen his face. It was dark; they were saying goodbye under a tree. Now and then—for it felt, from not seeing him at this intense moment, as though she had never seen him at all—she verified his presence for these few moments longer by putting out a hand, which he each time pressed, without very much kindness, and painfully, on to one of the breast buttons of his uniform. That cut of the button on the palm of her hand was, principally what she was to carry away. This was so near the end of a leave from France that she could only wish him already gone. It was August 1916. Being not kissed, being drawn away from and looked at intimidated Kathleen till she imagined spectral glitters in the place of his eyes. Turning away and looking back up the lawn she saw, through branches of trees, the drawing-room window alight: she caught a breath for the moment when she could go running back there into the safe arms of her mother and sister, and cry: "What shall I do, what shall I do? He has gone."

Hearing her catch her breath, her fiancé said, without feeling: "Cold?"

"You're going away such a long way."

"Not so far as you think."

"I don't understand?"

"You don't have to," he said. "You will. You know what we said."

"But that was—suppose you—I mean, suppose."

"I shall be with you," he said, "sooner or later. You won't forget that. You need do nothing but wait."

Only a little more than a minute later she was free to run up the silent lawn. Looking in through the window at her mother and sister, who did not for the moment perceive her, she already felt that unnatural promise drive down between her and the rest of all human kind. No other way of having given herself could have made her feel so apart, lost and foresworn. She could not have plighted a more sinister troth.

Kathleen behaved well when, some months later, her fiancé was reported missing, presumed killed. Her family not only supported her but were able to praise her courage without stint because they could not regret, as a husband for her, the man they knew almost nothing about. They hoped she would, in a year or two, console herself—and had it been only a question of consolation things might have gone much straighter ahead. But her trouble, behind just a little grief, was a complete dislocation from everything. She did not reject other lovers, for these failed to appear: for years she failed to attract men—and with the approach of her thirties she became natural enough to share her family's anxiousness on this score. She began to put herself out, to wonder; and at thirty-two she was very greatly relieved to find herself being courted by William Drover. She married him, and the two of them settled down in this quiet, arboreal part of Kensington: in this house the years piled up, her children were born and they all lived till they were driven out by the bombs of the next war. Her movements as Mrs. Drover were circumscribed, and she dismissed any idea that they were still watched.

As things were—dead or living the letter-writer sent her only a threat. Unable, for some minutes, to go on kneeling with her back exposed to the empty room, Mrs. Drover rose from the chest to sit on an upright chair whose back was firmly against the wall. The desuetude of her former bedroom, her married London home's whole air of being a cracked cup from which memory, with its reassuring power, had either evaporated or leaked away, made a crisis—and at just this crisis the letter-writer had, knowledgeably, struck. The hollowness of the house this evening cancelled years on years of voices, habits and steps. Through the shut windows she only heard rain fall on the roofs around. To rally herself, she said she was in a mood—and for two or three seconds shutting her eyes, told herself that she had imagined the letter. But she opened them—there it lay on the bed.

On the supernatural side of the letter's entrance she was not permitting her mind to swell. Who, in London, knew she meant to call at the house today? Evidently, however, this had been known. The caretaker, *had* he come back, had had no cause to expect her: he would have taken the letter in his pocket, to forward it, at his own time, through the post. There was no other sign that the caretaker had been in—but, if not? Letters dropped in at doors of deserted houses do not fly or walk to tables in halls. They do not sit on the dust of empty tables with the air of certainty that they will be found. There is needed some human hand— but nobody but the caretaker had a key. Under circumstances she did not care to consider, a house can be entered without a key. It was possible that she was not alone now. She might be being waited for, downstairs. Waited for—until when? Until "the hour arranged." At least that was not six o'clock: six has struck.

She rose from the chair and went over and locked the door.

The thing was, to get out. To fly? No, not that: she had to catch her train. As a woman whose utter dependability was the keystone of her family life she was not willing to return to the country, to her husband, her little boys and her sister, without the objects she had come up to fetch. Resuming work at the chest she set about making up a number of parcels in a rapid, fumbling-decisive way. These, with her shopping parcels, would be too much to carry; these meant a taxi—at the thought of the taxi her heart went up and her normal breathing resumed. I will ring up the taxi now; the taxi cannot come too soon: I shall hear the taxi out there running its engine, till I walk calmly down to it through the hall. I'll ring up— But no: the telephone is cut off . . . She tugged at a knot she had tied wrong.

The idea of flight . . . He was never kind to me, not really. I don't remember him kind at all. Mother said he never considered me. He was set on me, that was what it was—not love. Not love, not meaning a person well. What did he do, to make me promise like that? I can't remember— But she found that she could.

She remembered with such dreadful acuteness that the twenty-five years since then dissolved like smoke and she instinctively looked for the weal left by the button on the palm of her hand. She remembered not only all that he said and did but the complete suspension of *her* existence during that August week. I was not myself—they all told me so at the time. She remembered—but with one white burning blank as where acid has dropped on a photograph: *under no conditions* could she remember his face.

So, wherever he may be waiting, I shall not know him. You have no time to run from a face you do not expect.

The thing was to get to the taxi before any clock struck what could be the hour. She would slip down the street and round the side of the square to where the square gave on the main road. She would return in the taxi, safe, to her own door, and bring the solid driver into the house with her to pick up the parcels from room to room. The idea of the taxi driver made her decisive, bold: she unlocked her door, went to the top of the staircase and listened down.

She heard nothing—but while she was hearing nothing the passé air of the staircase was disturbed by a draught that travelled up to her face. It emanated from the basement: down there a door or window was being opened by someone who chose this moment to leave the house.

The rain had stopped; the pavements steamily shone as Mrs. Drover let herself out by inches from her own front door into the empty street. The unoccupied houses opposite continued to meet her look with their damaged stare. Making towards the thoroughfare and the taxi, she tried not to keep looking behind. Indeed, the silence was so intense—one of those creeks of London silence exaggerated this summer by the damage of war—that no tread could have gained on hers unheard. Where her street debouched on the square where people went on living, she grew conscious of, and checked, her unnatural pace. Across the open end of the square two buses impassively passed each other: women, a perambulator, cyclists, a man wheeling a barrow signalized, once again, the ordinary flow of life. At the square's most populous corner should be—and was—the short taxi rank. This evening, only one taxi—but this, although it presented its blank rump, appeared already to be alertly waiting for her. Indeed, without looking round the driver started his engine as she panted up from behind and put her hand on the door. As she did so, the clock struck seven. The taxi faced the main road: to make the trip back to her house it would have to turn—she had settled back on the seat and the taxi *had* turned before she, surprised by its knowing movement, recollected that she had not "said where." She leaned forward to scratch at the glass panel that divided the driver's head from her own.

The driver braked to what was almost a stop, turned round and slid the glass panel back: the jolt of this flung Mrs. Drover forward till her face was almost into the glass. Through the aperture driver and passenger, not six inches between them, remained for an eternity eye to eye. Mrs. Drover's mouth hung open for some seconds before she could issue her first scream. After that she continued to scream freely and to beat with her gloved hands on the glass all round as the taxi, accelerating without mercy, made off with her into the hinterland of deserted streets.

THE
O'FAOLAINS

↯

SEAN AND JULIA O'FAOLAIN have more than a family name in common. Sean, born in county Cork, the son of a police constable, was originally called John Francis Whelan, but he Gaelicized his name in response to the ruthless English response to the 1916 Easter Rising by Irish nationalists. An active member of the IRA for several years in the 1920s, O'Faolain studied at Harvard College for three years before returning to Ireland to teach and write. The often lyrical short stories that soon established his reputation deal with a variety of subjects, from politics to the church, but generally feature a sense of frustration at small-town provincialism and life's limitations (his work is often compared to Chekhov's). Years later, O'Faolain's daughter, Julia, born in 1932, began writing her own short stories about Ireland, characterizing its society as beset by hypocrisy and sexual repression. The styles of the two O'Faolains differ, and their emphases vary, but father and daughter seem to have been in general agreement about the social and psychological problems that characterize the Irish version of the human condition.

SEAN O'FAOLAIN

THE MAN WHO INVENTED SIN

The narrator of "The Man Who Invented Sin" looks back at the summer of 1920, a time he spent in the mountains learning the Irish language, while sharing close quarters with two monks and two nuns. O'Faolain's atmospheric 1947 story witnesses the narrator's delight at the burgeoning friendship between the young monks and nuns as they drop some of the limitations of religious life and begin to behave like anybody else. That is, until a disapproving curate intervenes with suspicions that may or may not be unfounded.

IN OUR YOUTH WHEN WE USED to pour into the mountains to learn Irish, places that were lonely and silent for the rest of the year became full of gaiety during the summer months. Every day there were picnics and expeditions; every night there were dances, moonlight boating parties, sing-songs in the cottages. The village street became a crowded promenade; its windows never went black before one in the morning; the pub was never empty. Where once you could have been utterly alone half a mile off the road, in the bog or up the mountain, you could not now be sure of privacy anywhere. If you went up the mountain to bathe naked in some tiny loch you might suddenly see a file of young students like Alpineers coming laughing down on you over the next scarp; you might turn the corner of a lonely mountain-pass courting your girl and burst upon a bevy of nuns sedately singing choruses among the rocks—for every kind of teacher, laymen and women, nuns, priests and monks were encouraged in those years to come out into the hills.

How we all got accommodation I do not know. The priests took lodgings in the villages. The monks and nuns purchased derelict houses which had been abandoned by the landlords after the Revolution. The people gave up their best rooms to the rest of us, turned lofts into dormitories, one or two even set up second-hand bell tents. One July, so stifling was the house where I stayed—six at least to every room—that I used to take a rug every night and climb into the high hay in the barn; and there were always four or five like me who preferred to be bitten by the ticks and wakened early by the birds and the mountain air than to be half-suffocated in feather-beds under the baking slates. By the end of the month, however, I got so tired of digging the little crab-like ticks from under my skin that I moved two miles out the road to a place called Ryder's, a small house on the lower lake, which usually took nobody at all. Indeed, only by great cajoling did I persuade Mrs. Ryder to take me in. My only fear, then, was that I might be lonely. But before she knew what had happened Mrs. Ryder had not merely one lodger but five, for with the beginning of August the monks' hostel overflowed, and the nuns' hostel overflowed, and she had to take in two of the monks and two of the nuns.

There was nothing remarkable about my fellow-students, except, perhaps, that little Sister Magdalen was so dainty and gay and spirited that it seemed a shame to lock her away from the world in a convent. Sister Crysostom was tall, delicate, with big hands and a blotchy skin, and she walked with her toes turned in. She was a bit of a Miss Prim, and I think she had been chosen as companion for Sister Magdalen because she was so prim. Brother Virgilius was a countryman with a powerful frame and a powerful voice, round red cheeks, and no nerves, and why he had chosen to be a monk was hard to understand. It seemed to me that he would have made a better farmer than a teacher. However, I found that he was a fine hurler and I am sure the boys loved him for his natural ways. Brother Majellan was very different, a gentle, apple-cheeked man with big glasses, a complexion like a girl, teeth as white as a hound's, and soft, beaming eyes. He was an intelligent, sensitive man. I took to him immediately.

At first we saw very little of one another. They had their principal meal at their own hostels, were studying most of the day, and the only time we all met was in the evenings, when we sat in the little garden and passed discreet remarks across the path about politics or the weather; or, if there was rain, we would meet in the drawing-room where there was a turf fire, and talk of the day's lessons. They kept convent hours, were off to their rooms by nine at the latest, and long before I rose were gone down to the village to morning Mass. That year, however, the weather broke suddenly in the middle of August so that we found ourselves in the drawing-room almost every evening, over our notebooks and dictionaries and grammars. We had, by then, become like travellers on a long railway-journey who have broken the silence and are beginning to chat companionably. We might still sit silent for, say, a quarter of an hour, but then somebody would say something and we would all get going. One night for instance, Majellan lifted his eager, earnest, doggy eyes, and said:

"Sister Magdalen, how do you pronounce the word which I call *cearrbhach*?"

"Oh, Brother Majellan," she laughed, shocked at herself, entertained by her own folly, "I am afraid I do not even know what the word means!"

Virgilius clapped his two big countryman's paws together and roared out laughing.

"Sister Magdalen, I'm surprised at you! I'm surprised at you! Not know the word *cearrbhach*? It means a card-player or a gambler."

"And is that what is means? *Cearrbhach*." And she pronounced the guttural word as daintily as if it rhymed with *peruke*.

She was a city-girl and had never before heard Irish spoken by anybody but city-people.

"No! You're not saying it right at all. You're too ladylike about it. Say it the way the people say it. *This* way."

"I see." And again the dainty pronunciation like *peruke*. "Like that?"

"Listen, Sister. I'll show you the way to talk Irish. If you'll pardon the expression, make a great big shpit inside in your mouth and gurgle it. Like this, Carrrwoochhhk."

Crysostom immediately protested.

"Please, Brother Virgilius! If we cannot speak our own language like ladies let us not speak it at all."

"But," from Majellan, "that really is the way the people speak. It is a guttural language. Like German."

"Not Bavarian German. It is true that the Prussians . . ."

And off they went into a heated argument—the sort of argument we were always having in those days, about whether Ireland must always be a peasant country, and what other countries had achieved, and Virgilius, who hated arguments, blew out his lips and looked gloomily at his two big feet stretched out before him, and Majellan and Magdalen got so excited that Crysostom had to stop it with her usual: "Sister, I really think it is our hour to retire."

One day at the College, as we called the sunbaked tin building where we studied from ten to one, we were asked to write an essay on a proverb to which the nearest Saxon equivalent is "The Child is Father to the Man." I remember, that evening, how the mists lifted from the hills, and the sun began to raise gentle wisps of steam from the rocks, and the trout were leaping from a lake as blue as the patches of sky between the dissolving clouds. We spread newspapers on the two damp garden seats, and as we discussed the proper Irish terms to be used, the four of them began, without noticing it, to speak of their own childhood; where they had been born, where they went to school, and so on. Sister Magdalen sucked the end of her silver pencil and said:

"I know the Gaelic for "I was born," that is *Do rugadh mé*. And the place— Templemore. Of course, that is *An Teampall Mór*. The Great Temple. Or the big church. Though the Lord knows there's no big temple in Templemore." She sighed. Then she cocked her head suddenly. "I suppose you were never in Templemore, Brother Majellan? But, sure, why would you! It's an out-of-the-way little place."

Crysostom tapped my fingers irritably with her pencil. I was idly pulling a fuchsia flower to pieces:

"How would you say that, Sister?"

"Which? What? What was it you said, Sister Crysostom?"

" 'It's an out-of-the-way little place.' You see I want to say that, too. I was born in a small little place like Templemore."

"Where was that?" asked Virgilius idly. He had been staring solemnly at the fuchsia that I threw into his lap.

"Kilfinnane," said Crysostom, "in County Limerick."

At once Virgilius whirled and slapped her thigh.

"Yerrah, Crysostom, do you mean to tell me that you come from Kilfinnane!"

"Brother!" And she held his arm excitedly. "Do you know Kilfinnane?"

"Do I know my own father? Wasn't I born just below in Kilmallock? Oh, wisha, then, 'tis many the fine Sunday I took the old bicycle out to Kilfinnane hunting hares behind the rath. If you come from Kilfinnane you must surely know the rath?"

"The rath is on our land!"

"Ah, no?"—in a huge childish delight.

"Often and often I stood on the rath and looked down at the smoke of the train coming into Kilmallock—in and out of the woods—the little white smoke. And I could watch it again for another half an hour after it left Kilmallock, puffing away down towards Cork."

"I well believe you! It's a wonderful view. They say you can see six counties?"

"For a whole hour," she remembered. "The little white smoke. I used to wonder who might be in it, and would I ever travel away in it myself."

"Didn't I go every night to meet it at the station and gather the Dublin papers, for my uncle kept a paper shop in the Main Street? The Cork train we called it. Majellan, you're a Corkman, aren't you?"

Majellan was not listening to us. He was gazing across the darkening lake whose headlands were faint as smoke.

"My father," said Sister Magdalen thoughtfully, "was a doctor. I know how to say that, too. My mother died when I was fourteen . . . I was a lone child . . . My father married a second time."

Majellan kept staring over the lake. She said something about a notebook and flitted indoors. I got tired of listening to Virgilius and Crysostom and got up to go to the dance. It was only then I noticed that Majellan and Magdalen were in the hall. She was dabbing her eyes with his big red handkerchief.

When I came back from the dance the half moon had vaporized the moist land with a melancholy, filmy light. The house was black and silent.

I think it was Virgilius who first began to play pitch-and-toss along the garden path, and it was that evening that Magdalen called Majellan "Jelly." I came on them laughing over the game, which Brother Virgilius was trying to teach to the other three. Brother Majellan was, by then, calling Sister Magdalen "Maggie," Crysostom naturally became "Crissy," and Virgilius, of course, joined Jelly as "Jilly." How they laughed over that! I crowned the night for them by taking them up to the drawing-room piano and teaching them all a song with a chorus:

"Bab Eró 'gus O mo mhíle grá."

And Crissy so surprised us by the strength and sweetness of her voice that at the end Virgilius clapped his hands and shouted, "I wouldn't doubt you, Crissy. I knew you had it in you," and made her sing the song again alone. As she sang we heard a clear echo: it was a boating party out on the lake. They took up the chorus and gave it back to her until they faded around a headland still singing.

"But you know," gurgled Magdalen, "I really don't know what it all means. Can you translate it for me, Jelly?"

"No trouble at all," said Majellan. "It is a young fellow singing a song to his lady and this is what he says."

As he translated he gradually blushed redder and redder, and Virgilius winked at the big, rolling eyes of Magdalen, and her rounded little mouth, just ready to burst into laughter. When Majellan stuck his head right out through the window to look at the lake Magdalen burst. Crysostom said: "I really think, Sister, it is our hour to retire."

"Jelly," said Virgilius, when they were gone, "you big gom! You have as much sense as a child of two."

When monks and nuns quarrel, I found, they seem to be astonished and shocked rather than angry: like children who have bumped against a door or a calf who has tried his first nettle. Grown men would have ended it with a curse or a clout. I escaped down to the kitchen to practise my Irish on Mrs. Ryder. She was baking a cake, and humming *Bab Eró . . .* Her cousin, who was the clerk in the Post Office, was sitting on the settle. She asked me which had the lovely voice. Mrs. Ryder said her house was blessed.

"The creatures! Isn't it grand to hear them enjoying themselves? Four saints I have in the house."

"Only four?" I protested.

"What time did *you* come in last night?" she asked, and the conversation became exuberantly coarse.

The next evening too, was exquisitely silent. The tiny trout-splashes could be heard clearly, and the cattle lying on the dry strand across the water chewing the cud. We were all upstairs, I playing the piano, Virgilius seated in the open window singing and beating time with a silver tankard that young Ryder won in a tug-of-war, Jelly and Maggie trying to waltz, and when Crissy was not laughing at poor Jelly's efforts to learn the steps she, too, was singing, at *Bab Eró*, like a blackbird. The music must have carried a long way over the water.

The door was slashed open with a bang that made the piano hum, and there was our local curate's black barrel of a body blocking the opening: for though he was not more than twenty-five—I believe it was his first parish—he was very fat. He was also pompous and cocksure. In the College we called him Lispeen, which is the Irish for a frog. For that second it was as if a camera-reel stopped dead—the tankard held in the air, the two dancers like a waxworks, and Crissy with her mouth open.

"Glory be to God," he moaned. "So I have been informed correctly." (It was only after that I thought of the postmistress on the settle the night before; you might as well talk to a microphone as to a postmistress.) "To think that this kind of thing has been going on under my nose for weeks." He let his voice fall solemnly, even secretively. "Unknown to anybody!" He roared then: "To think I cannot go for a summer walk to read my office without hearing this kind of caterwauling!" His voice fell again. "If Martin Luther could only see this! What's your name?" he stabbed at Crissy. She had turned as pale as her coif.

"Sissster Cryssossostom, father."

"And your name, Sister?"

"My name is Sister Mary Magdalen," said Maggie, very dignified and entirely self-possessed, and looking very angry.

"Well-named," he growled. I saw Jelly grow red with fury. "Go to your rooms, please. I'll talk to these gentlemen." With a scornful emphasis on the last word.

They fluttered out obediently, Magdalen with her head in the air, Crysostom with terror in her eyes. Majellan turned on him. I held his arm. He was only a monk, and no match for a curate in his own parish.

"You had no right, father, to talk to the sisters like that."

The curate swelled.

"Are you daring to answer me back, young man?"

Majellan's voice shook but he held his ground.

"We are doing no harm."

Even Virgilius spoke up, though more respectfully—he knew the power before him.

"Sure we were only having a bit of sing-song, father?"

The curate gasped, melodramatically—I swear he had taken a prize for elocution at his seminary—then dropped into a wonderful tone of sarcasm.

"Only having a bit of a sing-song? *Only* having a bit of a sing-song? Well, well!" He put his stick behind him like a shooting-stick and teetered back and fro on it. He was very sure of himself. "Perhaps, gentlemen, we think that we are back in the days of the Reformation?" Then he did his roar again. "Singing? Dancing? Drinking?" He whirled his stick and cracked the tankard.

Virgilius stared into the tankard, and sighed: "Shweepstake Tickets."

That sent the blood to Lispeen's forehead.

"I'll talk to you young bucks in the morning when I've had a word with your Superior. Good evening to you."

The door slammed. We heard him go downstairs. His voice boomed in the kitchen at the Ryders. Then we saw his shadow passing across the paling sheen of the lake.

"The bosthoon," hissed Majellan.

"Jelly," moaned Virgilius, who had seized the situation at once, "we're for the long drop!"

With that we stole down the corridor and tapped at the sisters' doors and conferred in a huddle, and Virgilius and Crysostom blamed Majellan for speaking back but Magdalen said, "You were quite right, Brother. He is no gentleman." But Crysostom kept pulling her fingers and looking at each of us in turn. She knew, too, how all this would appear back in the city where the Bishop and their Superiors would say, "What is this! Nuns and monks living in the same house? Dancing together? Singing choruses? Playing pitch-and-toss out in the garden? And what's all this about *a tankard?*"

Magdalen said next morning that she heard Crysostom crying late into the night.

Actually nothing at all happened. Old Ryder and the Parish Priest between them must have put a stop to the curate's gallop. After all curates come and curates go but parish priests, like the brook, go on for ever. But the story spread, and the students gathered round the four to comfort and encourage them, and of evenings people started to walk out to Ryder's and, in spite of Sister Crysostom's warnings and tremors, we began to have regular concerts in the garden. The four even began to go out on surreptitious boating-parties, and the bed-at-nine rule gradually became bed-at-ten, and even bed-at-eleven, until they were soon having as happy a time as anybody. Or should have, if their consciences were at ease. But were they? For, looking back at it now, I think I understand what had occurred. The Serpent had come into the garden with the most wily of temptations. He had said, "How dare you eat this apple?" And straightaway they began to eat it. They swallowed the last morsel of their apple the night before they were due to return to the city, perhaps for a lifetime, among the smelly slums about their schools.

We were moody that evening in the garden.

"I suppose this will be the last time we'll see the moon on the lake," said Sister Magdalen.

But the moon would not be up until after eleven, and a fairy-wind in the reeds, ruffling the stars in the water into a fuzz, meant that even then there might be a clouded night.

"Our bus goes at seven," said Sister Crysostom. "When does yours go, Brother Virgilius?"

By anticipation they were already becoming formal with one another.

"Half-past seven," said Brother Virgilius.

"Who'll walk as far as the lake?" suggested Brother Majellan.

They went down the white road. Autumn was coming already. A white mist hung low over the river. The lake was dim as a ghost. They stood at the edge of it and looked at the low hills beyond.

"Sure, we can be looking forward to next year," said Brother Virgilius cheerfully.

"If there are any summer courses next year," murmured Sister Magdalen.

The soft sound of oars was heard and a boat appeared out on the water. The people in it were singing quietly; a last boating-party. It was one of those big, barge-like boats built for excursion parties, and there must have been twenty people in it, crushed shoulder to shoulder. Majellan hailed them and they approached and when they invited the four out for a row even Crissy hardly demurred. The presence of the two monks and the two nuns seemed to cheer them up, for as they rowed away towards the narrows, making for the upper lake, the songs became louder and more merry. The lights of the village overflowed into the lake. Promenaders there heard them and sang back. Doubtless the curate heard them, too, and thanked God they would all be gone in the morning.

Time ceases to exist on a lake: every fisherman knows that. Somebody said that the moon would be up at eleven and would light them home. Crissy whispered to Maggie that that would be very late, and what would happen if some message came from the Hostel? But Maggie hushed her passionately, and Virgilius cried, "Let the last night be the longest."

It was much later than eleven before they got through the narrows—the old barge stuck there as it always did. Then the grey mountain slowly swelled up like a ghost against the spreading moon, and the whole land became black and white. On the bright side of the land the white cottages shone under their tarry roofs, and on the dark hills their scattered yellow lights invited us home. It became cold on the water. Rowing back against the current was a slow business. Heavy drops of phosphorescence fell from the blades. Presently a voice said, "It is near twelve, lads, put your backs into it." Now they were not singing at all; nor did they sing again until they saw the remaining village lights—only one or two left now. And they did not sing Irish songs, which are nearly all melancholy, but old music-hall songs like *Daisy, Daisy*, and *The Girls You Can't Forget*, and *I'm One of the Knuts of Barcelona*. The barge was not much more than twelve feet from the shore when they saw, clear in the moonlight, the black figure standing on the causeway. Majellan yelled, "Backwater!" The barge slewed around.

"I suppose, my dear ladies and gentlemen, that it does not matter to you that you are keeping the whole village awake?"

Nobody replied. The rowers set off for the opposite shore. The two brothers turned up their coat collars to hide their Roman collars. The two nuns hid their guimps and coifs with borrowed coats. Everybody was feeling cross and tired. As they neared the far shore the same black figure awaited them. He had raced round by the bridge, and gone leaping over heather and bog-pool.

"You won't land here tonight until I have the name of every person on that boat!"

The midnight mountains cried back, "On-that-boat."

The boat pushed off again and in mid-lake they held a conference: for even lay-teachers do not like falling out with a priest. And the four religious? There was only one thing to do. It was easy to disguise Majellan and Virgilius: caps for black hats, and the Roman collars ripped off. The nuns had to remove guimps, and cowls, put on kerchiefs and pin up their skirts. Then the boat again rowed to the landing-place, the men crushed around the priest arguing loudly, and the rest ran. In five minutes he was alone on the causeway. At his feet he saw a white object on the stones: a nun's starched guimp. As he looked at it he trembled like a dog.

He was no longer alone by the moon-flooded lake. He was roaring in the pulpit, holding up the guimp: he was in the Bishop's Palace quietly unfolding a pale linen object out of brown paper: he was in the Parish Priest's sitting-room and the white thing lay between them on the table: he was knocking at Ryder's door—yes, even if it was nearly one o'clock in the morning. He might have done all these things if, when he got back to his cottage, there was not a sick-call before him, and he had to get out his car and drive at once three and a half miles into the heart of the hills. Half an hour later he was tearing back. He had been hoaxed. The window of his cottage was open. The guimp was gone. It was the one good deed I did for my four friends.

I was awakened by the supernaturally bright light: it was not the sunrise: it was the sinking moon. My watch showed me that it was barely turned five o'clock. Dew and mist were all around the silent house: the lake was frosty; the sky pallid. The trees were weighted with sleep. Only the ceaseless mountain-stream and the deceived birds made a sweet noise. Below in the garden, by the wooden gate, stood Majellan and Magdalen, talking . . .

I never saw Magdalen again; I never saw Virgilius again; I never saw Crysostom again.

That was nineteen hundred and twenty, and not for twenty-three years did I meet Majellan. He was, of course, still a monk, and will always be: he was greying, and a little stooped, and much thinner. His eager, doggy eyes lit up for me: until I began to joke about those days, and then the light faded. I asked him about the others, and he told me that Virgilius was now a Principal somewhere. He had not heard of the two nuns since that night on the lake.

"Ah!" I sighed. "Great days! But nobody wants to learn the language now. The mountains are empty."

"Yes. The mountains are empty."

"What a shame!"

"Mind you," he said, after a moment. "I'm not sure that I altogether approve of young people going out to these places. I hope I'm not being puritanical or anything like that, but . . . well, you know the sort of thing that goes on there."

I was so shocked that I could not reply for a moment.

"But, surely, it's all very harmless?"

He shook his head seriously.

"Maybe. You *never* know."

I said something idle. Then I asked him did he go out there at all nowadays.

"That was our last year."

"I hope it wasn't any trouble with your superiors?" I asked anxiously.

"Oh, nothing like that. No. It was just . . ." He looked away. Then he said over his shoulder, "I didn't much want to, really." Then he looked at me, and in a little gush of confidence he said, "You mightn't understand it, now! But it's not good to take people out of their rut. I didn't enjoy that summer."

I said I understand that. After a few more words, we parted. He smiled, said he was delighted to see I was looking so well, and went off, stooping his way back to his monastery in the slum.

By coincidence, two hours later, I found myself side by side with Lispeen, looking into a bookshop window. He was scarcely changed, except for a faint brush of grey at each ear; he wore a tall silk hat and carried a silver-headed umbrella. When I spoke to him and he turned, the sunset struck his rosy face and lit the sides of his hat so that they glowed and shone. With difficulty I brought his mind back to those years, but when I did he greeted me as heartily as if I was his best friend, and laughed so merrily at the memory of those old days that I almost expected him to clap me on the back.

"Of course, you know," he confided, with wide eyes, "they were only children. Such innocents!" He laughed at the thought of the innocents. "Of course, I *had* to frighten them!" And he laughed again, and then threw up his head and said heigh-ho in a big sigh. Then he shook my hand, and beamed at me, told me I was looking grand, and went his cheerful way. He bowed benevolently to every respectful salute along the glowing street, and when he did his elongated shadow waved behind him like a tail.

A POT OF
SOOTHING HERBS

It's the 1960s, and Dublin is swinging every bit as much as London. In "A Pot of Soothing Herbs" (1968), twenty-one-year-old virgin Sheila attends a wild party, anxious to finally reel in the recalcitrant Aidan.

I'D LIKE TO MAKE THIS BRIEF, but I doubt if I shall. Like my friends, I talk a great deal. *Why* is probably going to become clear from this letter. (Is it a letter? That too may become clear.) The depressing thing about our talk is that it is not about activity. It is about talk. I'm told the Irish were always that way—given to word-games since the sixth century. It is typical of us too to say "the Irish" instead of "I": a way of running for tribal camouflage. I am trying to be honest here, but I can't discard our usual rituals. In a way, that would be more dishonest. It would mean trying to talk like someone else: like some of my friends, sheep in monkeys' clothing, who chatter cynically all day in pubs, imitating the tuneful recusancy of a Brendan Behan while knowing damn well all the while that they'd tar and feather anyone who seriously threatened the comfortable values of the Irish Republican Middle Classes. Not that anyone is likely to. We're a modest, solid little oligarchy. The bloodshot eyes of our drunks are the pinkest things about us. So we can be smug. And in a way we are. And in a way we aren't. The collective memory ripples in our sky like a damp, nostalgic flag. A red flag. Our parents didn't work their way up selling underwear or sweat out their fantasy for scholarships. They fought—they meant to fight—a social revolution. Even now, they can still find a frondeur's rage in the dregs of their third double whiskey. Of course, you might see that happen anywhere. I've caught flickers of it in the *bien-pensant* French families with which I've stayed *au pair*—we have, you see, all the habits. I've had the traditional advantages—but with us a whole class is prone. My mother's college-day memories are of raids, curfews, and dancing in mountain farmhouses with irregular soldiers who were sometimes shot a few hours after

655

the goodnight kiss. She once carved up an ox and served it in sandwiches to a retreating procession of civil-war rebels. She has the track of a Black and Tan bullet in her thigh and spent a brief spell in prison. My father and all my friends' fathers have the same memories. Even the nuns in school had nonconformist quirks, traces of a deviated radicalism which crept with heady irrelevance into the conventional curriculum. We've never known what to do with it. When our parents sing their old marching songs and thrill to images they won't pass on to us—scenes from those haylofts, for instance, where the young men hid and their girl couriers rested after long bicycle rides—we, with our blood pumping to their tunes, neat and shy in the deep clasp of their armchairs, finger our cocktail glasses and feel faintly silly. They mock us. "Yerrah, ye missed it!" they say, their vowels broadening reminiscently. "I have to pity the young today. . . ." They return to the Eden of memory. It is as if sex, in Ireland, were the monopoly of the over-fifties.

And why should it be? an outsider might ask. Why *do* we sit there listening to them like envious paralytics? Why has it taken me this long to get to sex if that is what I want to talk about? If I knew, I wouldn't be telling this ridiculous story. It wouldn't have happened in the first place. If I were talking now instead of writing, the rush of my breath would be noticeable, a faint bravado at having taken even such a gingerly hold on the matter. I suppose it would be clear then that I am a virgin, a twenty-one-year-old virgin, which is something I usually try to conceal from foreigners. From the Irish I couldn't—and besides it's nothing to want to conceal here. *"Mon petit capital"* (as Robert, my disappointed French beau of last June, called it) is really just that in Holy Catholic Ireland. Though it's not that I wouldn't like to disperse it secretly, feed my cake to the pigeons and have it too. But? Oh, a lot of impalpables. For one thing, I'm mechanically very ignorant. I've read *Ulysses* carefully and the *Complete Rabelais* and *Fanny Hill* and a number of other promising and disappointing books, but I don't quite know how humans make love. In the convent we didn't study biology and my mother's explanations when my brother was born were unclear. When I add that contraceptives—*whatever* they are—are unavailable in Ireland and that *three* of my mother's maids ended in the Magdalene Homes with illegitimate babies, I think I've stated the most tangible reason for my hesitation.

I imagine the girls in my group are even more ignorant than I am. Of course, if one did emancipate herself she would conceal the fact with all her might, so it's hard to tell. Maeve may have "gone rather far"—our favorite euphemism—with her French escort in Paris last summer. I know I went further with mine than I'd been before. I would probably have trusted to his precautions and slept with him if I'd liked him better. But there's where the residual native romanticism—my grand-opera morality—hamstrings me like a mucky umbilical cord. And I abominate it!

For my degree, I chose all the periods and poets who worked with their eye on the object: brisk Gallic *gaillards* of the sixteenth century, late Latin sensualists whose tight rhythms leave no room for drool, eighteenth-century types like N. de Lenclos or Ch. de Laclos whose *Liaisons* I've studied as a chess player studies old strategies. And then after all that and hours defending Mme. de Merteuil to Maeve, who can't see that hers was the only response to a phony society like ours, I pull away from Robert when he moors the boat under a bush in the Bois—what more setting did I want anyway?—and asks: *"Eh bien, tu as envie ou pas?"* *"Non,"* I said. He was the most beautiful creature I'd ever seen—casual, well-tailored, amusing. *"Menteuse!"* The boat rocked under us as he slid his hands all over me and I felt liquids racing within me, tides quivering down my spine and along the soles of my feet, and I wondered when I must stop him before he got too excited to be stopped. This is one of our great anxieties which I discuss constantly with Maeve. Can they—men—really not control themselves? I don't mean Irish men, because they don't seem to have any needs at all. Or they're queer. Aidan is queer. And I need hardly add that I don't know precisely what that means, either. I wonder how much precision matters? I mean anatomical precision. It's curious how abstract the most reputedly bawdy French writers are when you get right down to trying to understand details from them. Maybe if I'd read classics instead I'd have learned more by now. Because I can't ask anyone. I'm twenty-one and it seems ridiculous. I'll probably learn in practice if someone I like enough to satisfy my disgusting romanticism ever does try to sleep with me. I go round in a constant state of excitement. I wonder does everybody? Maeve says she doesn't, but I think she's a liar. When I'm in a crowd, on the bus, say, and something touches me—often it turns out to be a shopping basket or a dog—I get violent sensations of liquids running inside me. Everywhere: the back of my knees, my breasts. Sometimes I can hardly stand up. Then if I see Aidan it becomes almost unbearable. Usually I do see him from a bus, and often, even if it's the rush hour and I've had to queue for forty minutes to get on it, I get off and dash round the block just so that I can pass him by casually and say, "Hullo, Aidan." "Hullo," he says with his furtive smile, and rushes off with his head bent. He has a long white face and has neither the poise nor the class, the looks or the taste of Robert. He's unsure of himself, bad-tempered, and with a chip on his shoulder. All that. I enjoy saying this about him. It's true, and I say it not so much to try and deceive people about my feelings for him—Maeve has probably told everyone anyway, so there wouldn't be much use—but simply because I like to talk about him. He seems tormented, and this—romanticism again—I'm afraid I enjoy. I know his torment comes from something quite ignoble like the fact that his family probably live in a slum. We've deduced this from his always insisting on being set down at Merrion Square when he gets a lift home, which is about a mile from his postal address.

It suddenly occurs to me, seeing the ingredients of my love set down on paper, that they look like the ingredients for hate, or as if I were insincere and didn't *want* sex at all and so chose to fall for a queer, or were masochistic, or reacting against my class or some such oddity. It would no doubt be easy for some dab to erect theories like this which it would be hard for me to deny. One can never prove things, anyway, which is what makes them rather dull. I only know that I am attracted where I sense tensions and dissatisfactions—I prefer the fat, panting Hamlet to Hotspur—and that it was the grace and *easiness* of Robert's approach that turned me away from him. This may seem to contradict what I said earlier about liking the eighteenth century; I would answer that one can choose one's intellectual polestar but not the way one's bowels jump.

I am usually rude to Aidan. It is the one form of intimacy open to me. I think he's aware of this. I also think he likes me and that the reason he doesn't invite me out is simply that he has no money. Though as a matter of fact he once did invite me. We met uncomfortably on the canal bridge where our bus routes cross. It was damp and we walked along the towpath while he talked allusively of Rimbaud. I don't know whether this is his technique with businessmen in pubs who like listening to a University boy, or whether it was intended as an oblique confession of queerness—though if he thought that necessary he underrates the grape-vine. He talked French the whole time, saying, *"C'est difficile, c'est difficile!"* and giving me the *vous*. Then suddenly he rushed me into Mooney's. "Jesus! A drink!" He paid, which must make me one of the only people ever to have got a drink out of him— hardly a consoling distinction. Still, I went home feeling less miserable than someone who doesn't know Dublin might think. I'm used to Irish dates. For one thing, he had given me to understand that he was not a virgin, and I had hopes of him— and had until this past Saturday.

I wish there were someone whose advice I could ask about *that*. Not Maeve's. And priests make me sad with their good-housekeeping morality. ("Now you wouldn't," says our PP on the subject of matrimony, "if you were giving someone a present, want it to be chipped or cracked?") So I am writing this down and maybe I shall send it to Aidan. Why not? Or to Robert, whom I shall probably be seeing at Easter. (Actually, I know I shall do neither, but one has to pretend if the writing is to be a vent. Besides, I might.)

Since Saturday I've been feeling like a shaken thundersheet. What is bad is not the hollow sensation itself but the importance I find myself attributing to it, the way the mind gets subordinated to the belly and I take my bloody blood throbs for telepathic messages: Morse tattoos from some friendly *deus ex machina*— Aidan? ha!—who is going to solve my troubles without my having to take any responsibility. This feeding on fancy must do something to the brain. (Do Irish women ever recover?) Even writing this I am ridiculously expectant. I *must* lay out the facts.

Saturday? Maeve and I went to Enda O'Hooey's. He was giving a party together with Simon FitzSimons and had asked the two of us to come early and help. We accepted. A party is a party, and I knew that Aidan was to come later. It was the usual thing. While we made sandwiches, the men talked and we giggled appropriately from time to time or said: "You're terrible!" or: "Don't make me laugh!" Half mechanical, half ironical. They talked about their families (Enda's was away for the weekend), pretending to deride them; boasting. Simon comes from a line of Castle-Catholics—pre-revolutionary collaborators, which gives his gentility seniority over ours—and he talked about *that*. Enda's father made his money in children's prayer books with pastel celluloid bindings. He got a monopoly from the Republican government in return for *his* father's having been hanged by the British—which is the bit of family past which Enda prefers to remember. The O'Hooeys own an enormous eighteenth-century house with a rather tarty nineteen-sixtyish bathroom on the ground floor, fitted, including the lavatory bowl, in bright baby-pink. It was while Enda was regaling us in the drawing-room with a doggerel ballad on his grandfather's death that Maeve broke this lavatory bowl. How she did I don't know, unless it was made from celluloid left over from the prayer-book bindings. Once broken, the ensuing fuss left us feeling flighty for the rest of the evening. It is not the sort of misdemeanor that a girl of our set feels comfortable about confessing to her host. If Maeve had broken a decanter or something of that sort she would have insisted on paying. We are sticklers about money. Unfortunately, we are sticklers too about taboo words, and "lavatory" tops the list. So Maeve, who couldn't think of an acceptable euphemism, was in a fix. She stayed for a while in the bathroom drinking whiskey and laughing at herself in the mirror, then dashed into the drawing room and began hissing at me in French: "*Ecoute, Sheila, j'ai cassé le cabinet, le water, la machin, le . . . enfin tu me comprends!*" This embarrassed me. I calculated quickly that (a) she would not confess; (b) Enda might suspect me of breaking the thing; (c) I might as well encourage her nervousness in the hope that this would give the men a clue as to where, eventually, to lay the blame. So I teased her, whipping her, and by the way myself, into a state of hilarious idiocy. "*N'y touchez pas,*" Maeve yelled, "*elle est brisée,*" and cackled untunefully—to the obvious annoyance of Simon, who had been trying to set the atmosphere for a little mild necking before the arrival of other guests. When he tried to cuddle her, Maeve—she doesn't like him, anyway—let out a screech. "I'm mortified!" she called, and began to hop about waving a beer-glass full of whiskey. "Am I positively repulsive to her?" Simon asked me in earnest distress.

By the time Aidan came we were so lightheaded that, with most unnatural aplomb, I kissed him on the cheek and told him what had happened. It charmed him since he rather dislikes Enda, and our amusement cut out the need we usually feel to spar. "Come into the kitchen," he said. Aidan always gravitates toward kitchens. I felt promoted and physically tranquil, which often happens when I am with someone who attracts me.

We went on talking French, which was a help. It gives one a feeling of detachment. We managed to laugh a lot, too, and were warming agreeably toward each other—I had always known he liked me really, else why would I like him? A half-hour later, as we began to talk of some place to which we could go on, the back door opened, letting in a stream of cold air and a crowd of gate-crashers to interrupt us. "Will yez look who's here—Aidan!" Red-faced from wind and drink, they arrived like pantomime demons with jovial, fake brogues and gushes of pestilential breath. "A friendly face!" said the same crasher, although Aidan's face had actually relapsed to its driest and prissiest detachment; his furtive grin was back, stuck across it like sticking-plaster. Being queer, he has whole sets of acquaintances outside the college crowd, and he is at pains to keep each apart from the other. It occurred to me, too, that he might not like it to be thought in certain circles that he shows interest in women. "Who's giving this bloody party anyway?" yelled the crashers, gargling their consonants, drunken and pretending to be more so. An older crowd than we, they had not bothered to bring the usual gift of liquor. Aidan appeared to be savoring a sedate interior joke. The old empty feeling had come over me. I have had such practice in controlling disappointment that I freeze it before it gets started, only recognizing it in the vacancy of my own grin. "Any drink?" a crasher asked the absent Aidan. "Remember what Whistler said? I drink to make my hosts seem witty?" Feeling I must be embarrassing him, I turned away from Aidan. As I did so I noticed that among the arrivals, though in her containment very much apart from them, was Claudia Rain. She is a tall, bee-blonde creature with stemlike neck and wrists and immense, painted, Byzantine eyes. One of those slightly monstrous females whose beauty is disputable but, to those who recognize it, overwhelming. She had always impressed me, though I had only seen her before across streets—the exhalations from damp lounge bars. She is a fable round town: the sort who strikes young girls' mothers as "a common tart" and the girls themselves as a creature of daring, both gallant and *galante*. I lend her figure when I read Proust to Odette de Crécy and prefer her for peopling Yeats's poems to the fuzzy-haired photos of Maud Gonne. She manages to project an image that is both exotic and sedate. She is English but has, as they say, "been around." She arrived in town first with Rory MacMourragh— who met her when he was sculpting in Vienna—and is still officially with him, although she has picked and dropped half the emancipated males of Dublin in the eighteen months since she came.

"Aidan, my dear!" She dived on him with a swish of expensively eccentric clothes. "Your horrid little friend, the host, is threatening to throw us out. Come and restrain him. He's ringing the *gardaí*." She said *gardaí* in Gaelic as we never would, an English concession which might be mocking or punctilious. The artificial pipe of her voice surprised me at first, but after a second I decided it was not affected, merely strange. Aidan muttered some excuse, gave me a mean, little grin, and trotted after her. He had not introduced us. I was furious. Did he think her too strong meat for me? I stood sipping my drink, staring in sulky wonder at the sottish men with whom she had arrived. What did such a splendid creature want with them? In a second or two she was back. She had begun unknotting the vast nest of hair which she wears, wound like a family-sized brioche, on top of her head. Suddenly she poured it over the face of one of the sots who was sitting on a chair drinking stout—*not,* I noticed, Rory MacMourragh. The man laughed and grabbed at her. She evaded him.

"Will you look at that one?" said Maeve, who had staggered in without my noticing her, although she was easy enough to pick out with her royal blue taffeta and Coral Glow lipstick. She had become dishevelled and tarty to an extent to which I could not imagine the English girl ever being reduced.

"You *have* been drinking!" I observed. There was a bleary patina, a kind of sweaty bloom, over her make-up which was dissolving her face in a pointillist glow. "My mirror," I thought sourly, looking at her; "the drunken, rat-tailed virgin."

Maeve took no notice of my remark. She was staring sagely at Claudia. "*They* say," she stated, "that she's nympho!"

"Well, a damn good thing for *them* if she is!" I snapped. "Given what the rest of us are!"

Maeve giggled, swaying on her spike heels. "Enda has taken down his grand-father's gun," she confided excitedly. "The one hanging over the mirror. He keeps threatening Aidan with it and all the crashers."

"Are guns dangerous after three generations?" I asked. "Not that it would be loaded." But I was annoyed with myself for even listening to Maeve. She is like a maidservant, always trying to frighten and excite herself with stories. I stared at the gores in the English girl's tweed skirt. They limbered the flow of it until it achieved some of the swirl of a dancer's dress. She was moving off again now, sup-ple inside it as a paper streamer.

"I've heard," Maeve muttered, "that Rory MacMourragh likes Aidan. They say," she went on with typical Dublin mime of lowered voice and furtive eye which advertises to a room of twenty that you're saying something scandalous, "that *she* has him so tormented that he's taken to the men. . . ." Maeve's sour breath was so close now I could feel its warmth horribly on my cheek and upper lip. "They say," and she dug her angular elbow into me with the rough gesture of country grandparents (it will take the convent schools a few more generations to lay *those* ghosts), "that her mother was a kind of kept woman until the end when the father married her! *He's* a peer, you know."

I was beginning to feel mortally tired. Standing and the issueless excitement of earlier in the evening had left me limp. "I'm going to see what *is* happening in front," I announced.

"That's right," Maeve said approvingly. "Keep an eye on Aidan!"

"Are you coming?" I asked with distaste.

"No," Maeve answered loudly. "I can't face Enda!" She raised her glass at me as I left. "I'm too mortified," she shouted, and smiled intriguingly at the men around her.

In the front room, among the usual Dublin mixture of Georgian antiques bought by lot and Dunlopillo upholstering, Enda was still posturing with the gun. "My grandfather shot sixteen men with this," he said. "Isn't that a poem by Willy Yeats?" someone inquired. Enda's mouth was drawn down, his movements heavy. "Don't provoke me now," he begged with ponderous politeness. "I might feel it my duty to shoot."

I saw Aidan standing in the listless little group of onlookers, drinking Enda's whiskey. I went into the library. Rory MacMourragh was lying on a couch. He got up.

"An apparition," he said.

"Yes," I agreed, "and as brief." I turned back.

"Do you hate this party?" he asked. "Will you come home with me?"

"No," I said. "I'm waiting for Aidan."

"Are you in love with Aidan?"

"Yes."

"He's no good for you," said MacMourragh—who is, I should add, disturbingly attractive with an eighteenth-century Irish face, black curls, square jaw, and a sculptor's heft.

"I suppose I know that," I admitted.

MacMourragh caught my arm, and fixed his black eyes lengthily on mine. It's a trick I've had played on me before by men, but it always disconcerts me. His ease was of a quality different from Robert's. I imagined that I could sense reserves of controlled violence here, but this may have been suggested by stories I'd heard of his fights over Claudia. He is Anglo-Irish, of a different *pâte* to the natives. "You're probably thinking that Claudia went off with that sot Hennessey," Rory went on. "And you're doing a division sum in your head. Stop it. I'm not offering you a fraction of anything. Besides, calculations are so dreary!" He was still fixing me with both eyes. I did not want to flinch, but was aware that if anyone came in we would look rather absurd, and laughed to give myself a countenance. I did not want to break away from him, either, and the tides within me which had ebbed and curdled earlier in the evening were back, hammering at my temples and impeding my usual spate of words. I tried to laugh as unconsentingly as possible. "Come," said Rory. I stopped laughing. We faced each other in silence for several moments. It was then that I noticed someone watching us. Aidan was slouching in the door, whiskey glass still in hand, looking ridiculously censorious. The tides turned sickeningly. "Aidan!" Rory called easily. "You hide your friends from each other. But you're in time to make amends! I don't know this young lady's name yet."

"I shall *not* introduce you," said Aidan, loping toward us. "And I want you to keep away from this girl!" He straddled the fireplace, leaning back, surveying us down the slope of his nose. His absurdity was warming me to him until I remembered what Maeve had said about his liking Rory. Or was it Rory liking him? Which? Either way, *that* little element turned me into a piece of camouflage in the triangle, a fig-leaf, a cache-sexe. I sat dejectedly down in an armchair. Rage, despair, and my own fatal ignorance had me again by the groin. What an evening!

I was scarcely surprised, and anyway indifferent, when Enda came rushing in with his gun, yelling that he was giving no more parties. "Fine thanks I get!" He had got rid of the other guests, he told us, "before they did any more damage! They broke the bloody jakes!" he explained. "Bogmen! God knows what they're used to. I don't know what my mother will say!" He seemed near tears.

"I wouldn't be surprised," Rory suggested, "if it was that sot Hennessey."

"He's a gurrier," stated Enda. "Yez are all low-bred gurriers! Get out of my house!" I stood up. "You stay here, Sheila," Enda commanded. "I invited you out tonight and I'm responsible to your father."

"Oh, shut up, Enda!"

"I won't let you out of my sight," he bullied. "That pair of gurriers might take advantage of you. You don't know what you're up against. You're an innocent girl!"

This low cut roused me. "I'm going," I said. "I'm getting out of here." I went to look for my coat. It was the last one left in the bedroom except for Maeve's.

She herself had evidently passed out, for she was stretched across the bed, blowsier than ever, with powder spilled all down one side of her skirt. But even now she lay in a neat, convent-girl attitude, with clasped hands and crossed ankles.

When I left the bedroom the men were still threatening each other in the hall. I couldn't make out how drunk or serious they might be, so I skittered down the basement stairs and out the side door into the garden. By the time I reached the gate Aidan was with me. Then the other two appeared, and it looked as though Enda was not going to let us out. He stood with his back to the gate, waving the gun again and talking about his responsibilities.

"I'll shoot," he threatened. "I'll telephone your father, Sheila!"

"Enda, if you do that. . . ."

"They'll take advantage of you," he pleaded. "I can't stand by . . . Sheila, *I* asked you out this evening!"

This sad little appeal, coming after his rambunctious threats, might have moved me if he had been less drunk. But he was an unappetizing sight: mouth caked with the black lees of Guinness, sparse, pale stubble erupting on his chin, and a popped button on his chest revealing the confirmation medal underneath. Besides, I had never given Enda any reason to suppose I took him seriously. "Don't be childish, Enda," I said.

He lifted the gun as if to strike me. Rory snatched it. "Steady, now, fellow, steady! Remember that old Irish hero, Cuchulain, whose weapon used to get out of control and had to be put in a pot of soothing herbs? I think that's what *we* need here." And he planted the gun, barrel down, in one of Enda's mother's geranium pots. "Come on, now, good chap! Let us pass." He pushed Enda easily and gently out of the way, and the three of us went out the gate. The last I saw of Enda was through the railing. He was sitting on the ground weeping and muttering about "insensitivity" and his grandfather.

It was rather a miserable little incident, but in an odd way it made the three of us friendlier toward each other, which was a good thing as it turned out that neither Aidan nor I had the money to take taxis back to our opposite suburbs. Rory had no money either, and Claudia had taken their car.

"You'd better spend the night in my studio," he said. "That seems the best solution."

"What about Claudia?"

"She won't be back tonight!"

So we walked down Pembroke Road, Leeson Street, and the Green, singing the song about Enda's grandfather. There wasn't much for us to talk about and it hasn't a bad tune. When we got to the studio, Rory kicked over a milk bottle and began swearing, which diverted any embarrassment I might have felt. Who did seem embarrassed was Aidan. He kept whispering to me behind his hand that he was responsible for this and would never forgive himself and that I needn't be afraid. When Rory suggested that we all three get into the large and only bed, Aidan began twittering like a nun.

"Don't worry, don't worry," he kept telling me.

"I'm *not* worried," I said bitterly.

Rory yawned. "I'm sleepy. I'll sleep on the outside." He pulled off his trousers and climbed in. Aidan began pulling cushions about until he had a sort of barricade all down one side of the bed. Then he climbed in on Rory's side of this, fully dressed, and motioned me into the little furrow between the cushions and wall.

I took off my dress and climbed in in my slip. In the dark I tried to fix a couple of pin curls so that my hair wouldn't be straight as a stick in the morning. Then I lay staring at the light which was beginning to dilute the studio window and at the pattern formed by paper scraps pasted over broken panes. A rubber plant, which I remembered seeing in some of Rory's sketches of Claudia in the Grafton Gallery, complicated the design, giving it a live, animal, and foreign savor, reminding me that this was a studio: a place of freedom, alchemy, and secret intuitions. I almost expected the air to affect me as I lay there breathing it. The men had fallen silent and the only communication was when Rory passed across an egg-saucepan full of water. "Take a swig," he said. "The old malt dries the throat." Then there was more isolating silence. When Aidan's hand burrowed under the barricade toward mine, it was so obviously a fraternal grip that I couldn't presume on it. Besides, if I pressed or bit it, wouldn't he think this was from fear? And could I be sure that I wouldn't be afraid if one of them were to make a move?

In the middle of these wonderings the light snapped on. Aidan pulled the sheet over my head and the delicate, piping voice of Claudia Rain produced a four-letter word. "To think," she followed it up, "that I should come home to this! You have a virgin in my bed. A tight little virgin! And I could have had a passionate night with Louie Hennessey! I left him to come home to you," she called loudly to Rory, while Aidan's hand clamped over my mouth. "You clod! Get that virgin out of my bed! I won't have virgins in my bed! Damn you! Unblooded virgins!"

"Put a sock in it, Claudia!" Aidan growled. Rory said nothing and I, even if Aidan hadn't got both hands, like metal hooks, on me now, was too paralysed with embarrassment to stir from under my sheet.

I could hear Claudia moving roughly around the room and lay in terror of a physical attack. "I could have had a passionate night," she repeated.

"Come and lie with me, then," Rory's voice coaxed. "Come on, sweetie!"

"I don't want *you!*" Claudia's accents were more and more cultured, British, and musical. "I want Aidan. I want to make love with Aidan. His virgin won't mind, will she?"

"Shut *up,*" yelled Aidan. "Can't you shut her up, Rory?"

"Come on," said Rory, "I'll give it to you, sweetie, let me give it to you."

"I want Aidan. You'll never get another chance, Aidan!"

"Shut your filthy mouth, Claudia!" said Aidan, whose hands were kneading me ferociously in his rage.

"Well, make love with your virgin, then," Claudia suggested. "I won't have you lying there masturbating unhealthily in my bed."

Aidan nearly throttled me in his fury. Rory apparently got hold of Claudia, because the light went out and heavings of the mattress took the place of talk. After a while even that stopped and after another while Aidan cautiously released me, even uncovering my head so that I could breathe a bit and see the window, which had grown paler, and the rubber plant, which was greyer now and more three-dimensional than before. It must have been about three or four in the morning. Astonishing, I fell asleep.

I woke up to find sun streaming across my face and that it was eleven o'clock by my watch. The others were still asleep. I crept off the bed and dressed fast and furtively. I wanted to confront them from as poised a position as possible. In the bathroom I found pots of make-up with which I constructed for myself as understated and elegant a face as their tones permitted. Then I mooched about the studio, observing the odd appeal of things whose uses had got confused. I found food tangled up in some piles of scrap iron and the skeleton of a sheep. As there didn't seem to be much else to do, I got breakfast and brought it in on a tray. Claudia had been woken up by my clatter and had, to my relief, put on a very *Harper's Bazaar* dressing-gown.

"Good morning," she said. "How sweet of you. Let's eat it on the bed. There are bits of plaster and junk on the table."

We smiled at each other over cups of tea and boiled eggs and, when the men sat up, the four of us had a session as formal and sedate as any old county figures nodding their hats together in the Shelbourne Lounge. When he'd finished, Rory sprawled back on his pillow.

"Let's drive out to the country," he suggested. "Let's visit Crazy Shaughnessy, the bird-man in Glencree. You'll like him," he told me, "and I'm sure he'll like you. I'm going to do a bust of Sheila," he told Claudia. "She has a fine neck." Claudia agreed.

Were they being *too* sweet? I wondered. But they seemed spontaneous and I felt more relaxed than I ever do, almost as if I'd come to terms with my wretched state or as if its acknowledgment had in some way exorcised it. "I'd love to," I said. "But I'll have to ring my parents. They'll think I spent the night with Maeve, but even so they'll be expecting me back by now."

"The phone's broken," Rory told me. "But we can call in on them on our way to Glencree. Don't worry. We'll be out of here in a jiffy."

But it was another two hours before we managed to seat ourselves in Rory's ancient and elegant car. It was a tall, black, angular affair and Claudia, in unfashionably long hobble skirt and Ferragamo shoes, emphasized its antiquity. I wondered how consciously she planned her effects. The drive was convivial. The men sang, quoted, joked. Claudia smoked and I was happy in a way I never had been before and can't explain. It was as if their ease and freedom were communicable and everything was now going to be very simple for me. I was still careless as the wind when we turned in our drive and I saw my parents in their Sunday clothes, standing on the steps with their missals in their hands. "Wait a second," I told the others, "I'll just tell them I'm not lunching and be back."

My mother's outraged abuse was like a foreign language to me at first. I didn't understand. When I did I turned back to the others—I was still sufficiently attuned to them to know I needn't put a face on things—and asked them to go. "I can't come," I said. As they drove off my mother's words and sentiments began to assume impact.

"Consorting," I heard her say, "consorting with . . . bringing to the house . . . a filthy little whore like that! And where did you spend the night? Maeve's mother rang up. She's beside herself. Maeve hasn't been home all night. And you can imagine how we felt! Where is your self respect? Your values? . . ." And on and on.

I screamed at her, which was stupid as I like her a lot and she may be honest.

I'm not sure. I don't, I realize, understand her at all, but she *does* get hurt. I think of the wild youth she had and the erotic books she enjoys and has let me read and I am utterly confused. Because of course I prefer not to think of my parents as consciously hypocritical. And, worst of all, I can feel the comfortable depression of my familiar groove ready to receive me again, and as nothing *actual*—goddamn it and damn me for being as vulgarly physical as they are—happened last night, maybe I am back where I began. Maybe nothing snapped—or mentally ever will. Maybe I am as unfree as ever. Maybe too I have ruined myself with Rory and Claudia and maybe Rory and Claudia are a mirage and next time I see them she will strike *me* as a "common little tart"? Or perhaps all this is irrelevant and I am just suffering from blood-pressure or something—though, my God, I am physically and mentally in a state and this bloody letter is doing me no good at all . . .

FROM

THE FIRE IN THE DUST

The events of Francis MacManus's brilliant and somber novel, The
Fire in the Dust *(1950), center around the Golden family, who have
just relocated to a small Irish town after living abroad. The Goldens'
worldliness causes them to stand out, and only a few of the townspeo-
ple, including teenager Larry Hackett, a wholesome and levelheaded
classmate of Stephen Golden, will tolerate their differences. In this
excerpt, Larry visits the Golden house for the first time, and meets
Stephen's sister, Maria, who causes him great discomfort.*

THAT FIRST SERENE SATURDAY afternoon in the house in Bridge Street has
colored every memory I have of Stevie and Maria Golden, and of the
child Joan, as amber glass tints sunlight. Their features are fixed under old
honey-colored varnish, as it were: their mutual private fun is preserved in a translu-
cent innocence; they share likeness through a harmony of diverse, lively, happy
gestures. What harm but the picture is false. Nothing of them was ever so smooth.

I heard their laughter through the open letter box, and it was distant, tinkling
and cloistered. I wasn't expected. Stevie was up out of bed, sitting in a bright blue
dressing-gown with a rug around his legs in the sunny conservatory at the rear,
overlooking the garden, the orchard and the tree-shaded river; Mr. Golden was
out strolling—with an eye towards a building site for a house, Stevie said; and it
was Maria who opened the door.

"You must be Stephen's friend," she said emphasizing the word "friend" flatteringly. "Aren't you? Do please come in." She reached out and took my right
hand and drew me in, and she was still smiling with the memory of whatever fun
they had been having in the conservatory. I had imagined her a girl, a creature in
plaits, long-legged and precocious like Stevie; and when he had said she was
beautiful, and intimated that she was only a few years older than he, I had not

known what he meant. I just couldn't see her that way. Not this young woman, brown-haired, her complexion dark as a gypsy's, high-breasted, and as sure of herself as a mother, who made me so foolishly shy. She wore a cotton frock, printed with tiny red flowers, that was fitted close to her skin, and the skirt of it was, in that old fashion, well above the knees: just the kind of thing to make Miss Dreelin disapprove. "Come along to Stephen," she said. Then, as she handed me along the hallway that was all color with prints and pictures, she sang out: "Stephen! Stephen! A visitor." The conservatory was littered with books, magazines and drawing paper. "You never told me, Stephen," she protested, "that your friend was a young man."

"What did you think he was?" Stevie drawled. "A horse?" He was being grown-up. "Hello, old man. Leave him go, Maria. He's blushing. She's a tease, Larry."

"Silly, Stephen, he's not a schoolboy, I mean," she retorted. Then, linking her arm in mine, she sat us down on a cushioned bench. "Thank Heavens, it's a man. Now tell me, what was that brother of mine doing? He got himself a cold. What red hair you have, Larry! I may call you Larry, please. It's lovely here, isn't it? Look at the river down there, beyond the apple trees. I've been trying to paint it. Stephen says I make it look too tropical." She swung out a foot, sandaled and shapely, towards water-color sketches spread across the red tiles of the floor. None of them was finished, and while she talked inconsequentially, I thought it was just like her to flit from one view of the river to another. There were other unfinished sketches, too, a shuffled bundle of them lying along the cushions beside me—John's Bridge, Greene's Bridge, the Castle, the Parade—all familiar places but all transformed, or rather, translated into high violent color and romantic carelessness that evaded the signs of age and decay. Did the old city really look like that to her? Wasn't there much of herself, and something of him, too, in the selection of the highest colors and the brightest light? At least, I could see nothing on all the paper on the floor that returned to me the somber, tarnished, silvery, smoky tenderness of the ancient trees, the river dark but clear after the flood, the old pocked limestone walls, mossed and lichened and topped with grass and weeds, and motleyed with weather-tints. Yet, I could see something else which was disturbing. Maria's sketches, with their bright greens and yellows and oranges, brilliant blues and even touches of scarlet, were what I desired the town to be, in my few moments of daydreaming. There was adventure in her colors, but protest as well. Her unoccupied vitality was in the bold strokes. Beauty had brightened dully familiar things with a tropical ripeness, and suddenly I realized that the beauty was there.

"He doesn't like your daubs," Stevie drawled. He was turning the pages of a magazine.

"No?" she questioned, squeezing my arm against her side. Her full breast was against my arm, her face was close, and I saw the decorously laid on lipstick and the faint transparent down on her upper lip. All the little whips of my conscience began to crackle, and instantly I became mulish. She looked into my eyes boldly but ironically, as if sure of every pulse of the effect she was working. "Look at me," she urged. "Tell me truthfully. You don't like my daubs?" She shook her head. Her hair spun out and brushed my face. I tried gently at first, then crudely, to disengage my arm.

"Who learned you?" I growled.

She smiled at my grammar—so I thought. Her overbright eyes were malicious. "Learned!"

"They say 'learned' here sometimes, Maria," said Stevie. "And I do think you should let the fellow's arm go. You're overwhelming him."

She let my arm free. "My God," she exclaimed, "he's blushing. Larry, Larry, you're not a schoolboy."

"He goes to school," Stevie said. "So do I, by the way. Now, where's Joan?"

She leaned across me to look through the glass down into the garden. The conservatory was warm. Near her, the air seemed warmer, and I could smell face-powder and a faint fresh scent. I leaned back and pretended to look. A child, a little girl in a pink frock—I caught by one glance—was toddling waist deep in the new grass beneath the apple trees with something in her hands that sparkled in the sun. Then, Maria ran, crying, "The little devil. It's a broken bottle."

I stood up to watch her and I became aware that my forehead and back were prickly with perspiration.

"Well," said Stevie, after a few moments, "what do you think of my sister?"

"Sure I don't know her more than a few minutes."

He guffawed. "But what's your first impression?"

"Oh, all right."

"Don't commit yourself too deeply. She teased you a bit, didn't she?"

"Not much."

"Fibber! You should see your face."

He stared at me thoughtfully and he said: "We're probably different to most people you know, Larry. I suppose we must be. Maria is full of fun. I wish, though, she wouldn't tease."

"It was a queer kind of teasing," I blurted.

He frowned. "Queer! Queer!" I knew he was translating our idiom into terms that would bring its meaning closer to his mind; and I didn't want that, because I knew I had said the wrong thing. He had gone quite pale and hard-eyed. "Queer! What do you mean, Hackett? There's a suggestion in that I don't like. Something wicked."

"I'm not used to it, that's all," I replied stubbornly. But I was overwhelmed with doubt as to whether I hadn't misconstrued Maria's grasp of my arm and the pressure of her breast and the mocking amusement of her mouth.

"By God!" Stevie murmured. He threw the rug aside from his feet and trod across the floor to me, seeing nothing but me, perhaps not even me. "Own up to it, Hackett."

To make it worse, I said, "Well, I'm sorry."

He confronted me. His fingers were wrapped into useless, inexpert fists. He would hit me, I thought, and they would break off like pipe-stems against my face. Seeing them close and wavering across my eyes, I wondered how on earth he had suffered the lolloping he had received in school; and more than that, I wondered how he who rejected every cocky challenge to fight had come to be stamping his slippered feet with rage. But he didn't hit me. He dropped his fists, eased off his panting breath into a long-drawn sigh, and muttered, "I'm being an ass."

"I could break you up."

He returned to his chair and rearranged the rug around his legs. "I wasn't thinking of that," he returned calmly. "What you said wasn't your fault, I suppose. It wasn't just Maria in particular. Or you in particular either. I expect," he continued loftily, "I'd find the same sort of dislike in any fellow for any . . . No! It's not dislike. Do you remember how you behaved in Mrs. Costello's house when you were undressing? You stood there, stiff as a . . ."

"I don't know what you're gassing about. And I don't want to know either."

"She is a lovely woman, isn't she? Papa tells me she's coming here. It'll be marvelous for Maria. She'll be able to get out more and have some sort of life."

"God, you're an old man. Katie Costello is coming all right. She promised my mother she would."

"Well," he laughed, "the old man apologizes for losing his temper."

"Forget about it. I haven't a notion what was up with you."

"Truly not?"

I shook my head.

"I must be careful, then," he smiled.

He raised himself to look down to the garden. Maria stood below under the trees, lifting the child to pluck at leaves and blossom, and I could hear their shrill chatter through the open door.

"Who's Joan?" I asked. "Is she your sister? She looks only a baby."

He was examining a photograph in a magazine. "No," he said casually. "She's not my sister. She's a child Papa adopted."

"An orphan?"

He stared too long at the picture before replying: "Yes, I suppose she's an orphan."

Maria came up the steps, carrying Joan, nuzzling her neck with her nose, tickling her till she screamed. The child was like a doll—pink and white of skin, pearly teeth, dainty little hands, a frilly frock. Maria was absorbed in play with her, and presently, as she looked across and appeared to remember me, she called out: "Look, Joan. Over there. That's Stephen's friend."

672

The child wobbled towards me, held out her hands and tried to climb to my lap. I lifted her. Suddenly she pulled my hair and laughed. "Larry, she's taking to you," Maria said, seating herself beside me. "It's your hair. It's funny hair, Joanie. Funny hair."

"Fire," cried the child. "Fire."

Maria ran her fingers through my hair and let her arm rest on my shoulders. "Joanie, we have a man in the house. Not grumpy Stephen. Have you a big kiss for him?"

"Two kisses."

I wriggled uneasily under the warmth and the weight of Maria's side and kept my face averted from hers. The child blobbed me on the cheek again and again with her moist doll's mouth.

"And one for me?" said Maria.

I swung my shoulders away so that she was almost behind my back. "Chuck this," I protested. "I'm not some kind of idiot."

The child looked around, confused, her round little face solemn, and then Maria swept her from me to the floor, saying, "I'll take it myself then."

"Watch out," Stevie warned. "Don't do it, Maria."

She held my face firmly between her palms and before I could jerk free, she had kissed me on the mouth with an exact, slightly prolonged pressure of her lips. Neither she nor Stevie, nor perhaps even myself, could understand the little thing that happened then. I slapped one of her wrists hard, thrust her away, and backed off against the wall. She cried out with the pain, pulled herself up from the cushions to which she had been toppled, and began to rub her wrist and stare up at me in astonishment. I stared back, fuming, trying to find an apology for my brutality in the scent, the powder, the lipstick, the short cotton frock, until a little more provocation would have made me shout that she was a bad woman.

Do I recall that little incident correctly? I wonder. The world has changed so much since then—but not *that* much—I wonder if I can remember my side of that unspoken violent colloquy between Maria Golden and myself. She rubbed her smarting wrist and tried to join the pain to the playful kiss, but only I could join them with an infinity of echoes from prayers and sermons and exhortations and pastorals and pamphlets. I felt wretched. I looked across to Stevie for help.

"I say, Maria," he smiled, "Larry couldn't help that."

"It was quite vicious."

"Could you help it, Larry?"

I mumbled.

"It's not my idea of fun," she said coldly.

"You shouldn't tease, Maria."

The child had begun to swing out of one of my arms. She was calling me "Lally, Lally." I lifted her up, swung her and put her down, and then she asked with upstretched arms and stamping feet to be lifted again.

"You're not really very tame, are you?" Maria inquired.

"I think I'll be going now, Stevie."

"Not so soon?"

"I'm no good with girls."

"Don't go," Maria said. "We mustn't be silly. We're going to have some tea presently. Play with Joan. She likes you." On her way into the kitchen, she smiled back and held up her red-marked wrist for me to see: "You're the only man who ever did that to me!"

"No more teasing," Stevie warned. "Here, Larry," he complained, "don't look so sad. It's all over. She deserved it. Take this deck-chair. Come over here, Joan, and Larry will show you some pictures. That's the little woman."

The child walked gravely to stand at my knee. I could imagine mothers in the town comparing her with their own children and saying that she was spoiled, too forward, old-fashioned, or even that she was only a little fairy of a thing. She put her hands on mine and peered into my face impishly—like Stevie when he was quizzical, like Maria when she was teasing me. "Do you know," I said, "Joan is a bit like both of you? She might be one of the family."

"And isn't she one of the family?"

"Yes. But I mean . . ."

"Children have ears, Larry."

"I get you," I replied, stung by his tact. The old man, I thought. The bloody old man, sitting there in his dressing-gown. "Sit on my knee, Joan."

She climbed up eagerly and began to go through the contents of my breast pocket: a pen, pencils, scraps of paper and the remains of a rosary beads which she dismembered. "Joanie," Stevie called. "How would you like an uncle? Will we make Larry an honorable uncle? Uncle Larry. Sounds all right. Say Uncle Larry!"

"No," she squeaked. "No. No. Grumpy Stephen." She shook her little fists mischievously.

Stevie growled in imitation of some wild animal and advanced, crouching, from the chair. She was familiar with the game, for she slipped from my knee and ran from him, and then, pretending to be savagely angry, he squinted his eyes inwardly till the whites showed, bulged his tongue into a sausage between his teeth, and whirled his arms. She toddled to me again after a round of the conservatory, gripped my neck and hid her face on my shoulder, saying, "Save me, Nuncle Lally, save me." I swung her to my back and trotted in front of Stevie, just out of reach of his gently clawing hands. The game was a release: the old man become a boy, and I—what did I become? I remember that I wished Maria back from the house, and that she too were playing and fooling. The dust exploded up from our tramping feet till the layers of sunlight were alive with circulating golden crumbs. Maria's drawings flapped and sidled across the floor from the draughty swirl of Stevie's dressing-gown, and the prodigal colors, tropic glimpses of a town that never existed, stained the air with running dyes. I let Joan fall into Stevie's arms. She thrust him from her, crying in mock terror, "Nuncle Lally, Lally." She was tousled like a golliwog, and her skimpy pink dress had worked its way up under her arms. Stevie tossed her back, and as I held her, she was plucked from me and I was pushed aside.

"You savages," said Maria.

"We won't hurt her," Stevie protested.

"You ass."

"We won't hurt her," I said. "Honest, Maria."

"Again, Nuncle Lally. Again."

"Oh, Maria, what's all this fuss about?"

"School for you on Monday, Stephen. No more malingering."

"Of course, Maria. But really, we were very careful. Don't be silly."

"Silly, am I? You say so! Come, Joanie, look at your dress and your hair. Silly? Oh, go away, Stephen. How could you? You poor little child. You're scratched on the arm."

"Please, Maria. Don't be angry," Stephen pleaded. "Joan liked it all. Didn't she, Larry?"

"You hurt her, you mule." His sister changed before my eyes from a girl into a dark, head-shaking, foreign-looking woman who quivered and stamped her sandaled feet, and twisted a virago's red mouth in ferocity. "Go away. Upstairs at once and change your clothes. I'm sick of you hanging about the house. I'm sick of living like a half-nun. Waiting on you. Waiting on Papa. You know all the trouble I've had with her since she was born. And all this pretense! Who are we fooling? Who?"

"Oh!" Stevie sighed, hanging his head. "I'm sorry. But you shouldn't say that, Maria."

"Do something," she stamped. "Dress yourself properly . . ."

Stevie was about to interrupt but he changed his mind and without looking at me, slipped into the house. Maria ignored me, too. She hugged the child in her arms and snuggled her, tidied her dress and rearranged the ribbon on her hair. Her hands were trembling so that she had to make the bow twice.

"I'm sorry," I said. "We were only playing."

She shrugged and kept her face averted. I began to move to the doorway that led to the kitchen and the hallway when she looked up for a moment, and I saw that her eyes had softened and that tears had spread in them like a lens till the thread-like veins of the eyeballs appeared magnified. The change of mood was more disconcerting than her outburst.

"Nuncle Lally, Nuncle Lally," said the child. "Come back." The moods were all one to her.

"Forgive me," Maria said. "I'm afraid I have a temper. I can't be like Stephen. They say I'm impulsive. Mother used to be the same. Stay, Larry, or we'll feel miserable. Joanie wants you." She contemplated me for a few seconds and added: "You're only a boy and somehow you're more human, more of a man than Stephen."

"That's not right."

"I'm not teasing. Oh, you suspect me of pulling your leg again. Will you promise me something?"

"It all depends."

"You're as wary as a lawyer, aren't you? Will you please forget anything I said. We're a very excitable family."

The child fidgeted. "Play again, Lally," she appealed.

"See! You're one of the family already. Now, Uncle, take care of her and we'll have some tea. Supper and bed for you, Joanie. You promise me, Larry, don't you?"

"But what am I to promise?"

I hoped my face didn't reveal too much of what I felt as I put that question. I half knew the answer but I evaded, not from politeness or tact, of which I had little, but because I hadn't fully appreciated the natural disguised relationship of the child to her, and of the effect of that relationship on Stevie. Mr. Golden didn't enter my mind. I wasn't curious about his feelings.

"It doesn't matter," said Maria gruffly.

Still watching me sharply, she stroked the child's hair. The combing slide of her fingers, well cared for and not quite as slender as Stevie's, ushered out the slow procession of her thoughts; and her face settled into a repose that gave no clue to her animal vitality or her passion. What she said, or rather whispered with easy breathing, drifted down the air like the motes of sunny dust. Perhaps it was this repose of her features and the quietness of her voice that color my memory of her as with the amber sunlight. "You may not wish to be friends with us any more," she said. "We haven't made your first visit too happy." Joan rested against her knees, wondering with wide eyes. "If you don't wish to be a friend, well, don't. You're old enough to know your own mind." She was withdrawing further from me, as it were, showing her firm womanly maturity, her toughness of mind before a raw, troubled boy. "But Stephen needs friends, young friends like yourself, to keep him from becoming old too soon. If you care to help Stephen, we'll be glad." She let her hands fall and released the child who toddled to pick up from beneath the table a little dish scummed with the muddied washings of the water-color brushes.

The evening was falling level with the orchard, the trees along the river bank, the boathouse at the far side, and the houses. That was the town I knew. I can still recall how my mind returned eagerly to the familiarity of it with a mild shock of relief. A clock, muffled by the depths of the house, chimed four. I had been with the Goldens for an hour only, and yet it stretched like years in a foreign place, marked out and prolonged with innumerable incidents to which one would never become adjusted.

DANTE . . . BRUNO .
VICO . . JOYCE

In 1928 Samuel Beckett met James Joyce in Paris, where Beckett had gone to study after college and Joyce was in the midst of his Work in Progress, *eventually to be published as* Finnegans Wake. *Beckett's resulting essay is an appreciation (not a systematic explication—this essay is the source of Beckett's noted aphorism that "Literary criticism is not bookkeeping") of the philosophical and stylistic influences of Dante Alighieri, Giordano Bruno, and Giambattista Vico on the* Work. *(The inconsistent punctuation of the title indicates the centuries between the periods when each figure flourished.) His perceptions of how Bruno's idea of relativistic realities, Vico's vision of history as a cyclical flow, and Dante's concept of language as a thing in itself all influenced Joyce's writing are impressive, but no more so than the visible workings of Beckett's own muscular intellect and his distinctive, dynamic use of language.*

THE DANGER IS IN THE neatness of identifications. The conception of Philosophy and Philology as a pair of nigger minstrels out of the Teatro dei Piccoli is soothing, like the contemplation of a carefully folded ham-sandwich. Giambattista Vico himself could not resist the attractiveness of such coincidence of gesture. He insisted on complete identification between the philosophical abstraction and the empirical illustration, thereby annulling the absolutism of each conception—hoisting the real unjustifiably clear of its dimensional limits, temporalizing that which is extratemporal. And now here am I, with my handful of abstractions, among which notably: a mountain, the coincidence of contraries, the inevitability of cyclic evolution, a system of Poetics, and the prospect of self-extension in the world of Mr. Joyce's *Work in Progress*. There is the temptation to treat every concept like "a bass dropt neck fust in till a bung crate," and make a really tidy job of it. Unfortunately such an exactitude of application would imply distortion in one of two directions. Must we wring the neck of a certain system in order to stuff it into a contemporary pigeon-hole, or modify the dimensions of that pigeon-hole for the satisfaction of the analogymongers? Literary criticism is not bookkeeping.

↯

Giambattista Vico was a practical roundheaded Neapolitan. It pleases Croce to consider him as a mystic, essentially speculative, *"disdegnoso dell' empirismo."* It is a surprising interpretation, seeing that more than three-fifths of his *Scienza Nuova* is concerned with empirical investigation. Croce opposes him to the reformative materialistic school of Ugo Grozio, and absolves him from the utilitarian preoccupations of Hobbes, Spinoza, Locke, Bayle and Machiavelli. All this cannot be swallowed without protest. Vico defines Providence as: *"una mente spesso diversa ed alle volte tutta contraria e sempre superiore ad essi fini particolari che essi uomini si avevano proposti; dei quali fini ristretti fatti mezzi per servire a fini più ampi, gli ha sempre adoperati per conservare l'umana generazione in questa terra."* What could be more definitely utilitarianism? His treatment of the origin and functions of poetry, language and myth, as will appear later, is as far removed from the mystical as it is possible to imagine. For our immediate purpose, however, it matters little whether we consider him as a mystic or as a scientific investigator; but there are no two ways about considering him as an *innovator*. His division of the development of human society into three ages: Theocratic, Heroic, Human (civilized), with a corresponding classification of language: Hieroglyphic (sacred), Metaphorical (poetic), Philosophical (capable of abstraction and generalization), was by no means new, although it must have appeared so to his contemporaries. He derived this convenient classification from the Egyptians, via Herodotus. At the same time it is impossible to deny the originality with which he applied and developed its implications. His exposition of the ineluctable circular progression of Society was completely new, although the germ of it was contained in Giordano Bruno's treatment of identified contraries. But it is in Book 2, described by himself as *"tutto il corpo . . . la chiave maestra . . . dell' opera,"* that appears the unqualified originality of his mind; here he evolved a theory of the origins of poetry and language, the significance of myth, and the nature of barbaric civilization that must have appeared nothing less than an impertinent outrage against tradition. These two aspects of Vico have their reverberations, their reapplications—without, however, receiving the faintest explicit illustration—in *Work in Progress*.

It is first necessary to condense the thesis of Vico, the scientific historian. In the beginning was the thunder: the thunder set free Religion, in its most objective and unphilosophical form—idolatrous animism: Religion produced Society, and the first social men were the cave-dwellers, taking refuge from a passionate Nature: this primitive family life receives its first impulse towards development from the arrival of terrified vagabonds: admitted, they are the first slaves: growing stronger, they exact agrarian concessions, and a despotism has evolved into a primitive feudalism: the cave becomes a city, and the feudal system a democracy: then an anarchy: this is corrected by a return to monarchy: the last stage is a tendency towards interdestruction: the nations are dispersed, and the Phoenix of Society arises out of their ashes. To this six-termed social progression corresponds a six-termed progression of human motives: necessity, utility, convenience, pleasure, luxury, abuse of luxury: and their incarnate manifestations: Polyphemus, Achilles, Caesar and Alexander, Tiberius, Caligula and Nero. At this point Vico applies Bruno—though he takes very good care not to say so—and proceeds from rather arbitrary data to philosophical abstraction. There is no difference, says Bruno, between the smallest possible chord and the smallest possible arc, no difference between the infinite circle and the straight line. The maxima and minima of particular contraries are one and indifferent. Minimal heat equals minimal cold. Consequently transmutations are circular. The principle (minimum) of one contrary takes its movement from the principle (maximum) of one another. Therefore not only do the minima coincide with the minima, the maxima with the maxima, but the minima with the maxima in the succession of transmutations. Maximal speed is a state of rest. The maximum of corruption and the minimum of generation are identical: in principle, corruption is generation. And all things are ultimately identified with God, the universal monad, Monad of monads. From these considerations Vico evolved a Science and Philosophy of History. It may be an amusing exercise to take an historical figure, such as Scipio, and label him No. 3; it is of no ultimate importance. What is of ultimate importance is the recognition that the passage from Scipio to Caesar is as inevitable as the passage from Caesar to Tiberius, since the flowers of corruption in Scipio and Caesar are the seeds of vitality in Caesar and Tiberius. Thus we have the spectacle of a human progression that depends for its movement on individuals, and which at the same time is independent of individuals in virtue of what appears to be a preordained cyclicism. It follows that History is neither to be considered as a formless structure, due exclusively to the achievements of individual agents, nor as possessing reality apart from and independent of them, accomplished behind their backs in spite of them, the work of some superior force, variously known as Fate, Chance, Fortune, God. Both these views, the materialistic and the transcendental, Vico rejects in favour of the rational. Individuality is the concretion of universality, and every individual action is at the same time superindividual. The individual and the universal cannot be considered as distinct from each other. History, then, is not the result of Fate or Chance—in both cases the individual would be separated from his product—but the result of a Necessity that is not Fate, of a Liberty that is not Chance (compare Dante's "yoke of liberty"). This force he called Divine Providence, with his tongue, one feels, very much in his cheek. And it is to this Providence that we must trace the three institutions common to every society: Church, Marriage, Burial. This is not Bossuet's Providence, transcendental and miraculous, but immanent and the stuff itself of human life, working by natural means. Humanity is its work in itself. God acts on her, but by means of her. Humanity is divine, but no man is divine. This social and historical classification is clearly adapted by Mr. Joyce as a structural convenience—or inconvenience. His position is in no way a philosophical one. It is the detached attitude of Stephen Dedalus in *Portrait of the Artist* . . . who describes Epictetus to the Master of Studies as "an old gentleman who said that the soul is very like a bucketful of water." The lamp is more important than the lamp-lighter. By structural I do not only mean a bold outward division, a bare skeleton for the housing of material. I mean the endless substantial variations on these three beats, and interior intertwining of these three themes into a decoration of arabesques—decoration and more than decoration. Part 1 is a mass of past shadow, corresponding therefore to Vico's first human institution, Religion, or to his Theocratic age, or simply to an abstraction—Birth. Part 2 is the lovegame of the children, corresponding to the second institution, Marriage, or to the Heroic age, or to an abstraction—Maturity. Part 3 is passed in sleep, corresponding to the third institution, Burial, or to the Human age, or to an abstraction—Corruption. Part 4 is the day beginning again, and corresponds to Vico's Providence, or to an abstraction—Generation. Mr. Joyce does not take birth for granted, as Vico seems to have done. So much for the dry bones. The consciousness that there is a great deal of the unborn infant in the lifeless octogenarian, and a great deal of both in the man at the apogee of his life's curve, removes all the stiff interexclusiveness that is often the danger in neat construction. Corruption is not excluded from Part 1 nor maturity from Part 3. The four "lovedroyd curdinals" are presented on the same plane—"his element curdinal numen and his enement curdinal marrying and his epulent curdinal weisswasch and his eminent curdinal Kay o' Kay!" There are numerous references to Vico's four human institutions—Providence counting as one! "A good clap, a fore wedding, a bad wake, tell hell's well": "their weatherings and their marryings and their buryings and their natural selections": "the lightning look, the birding cry, awe from the grave, ever-flowing on our times": "by four hands of forethought the first babe of reconcilement is laid in its last cradle of hume sweet hume."

Apart from this emphasis on the tangible conveniences common to Humanity, we find frequent expressions of Vico's insistence on the inevitable character of every progression—or retrogression: "The Vico road goes round to meet where terms begin. Still onappealed to by the cycles and onappalled by the recourses, we feel all serene, never you fret, as regards our dutyful cask. . . . before there was a man at all in Ireland there was a lord at Lucan. We only wish everyone was as sure of anything in this watery world as we are of everything in the newlywet fellow that's bound to follow. . . ." "The efferfresh-painted livy in beautific repose upon the silence of the dead from Pharoph the next first down to ramescheckles the last bust thing." "In fact, under the close eyes of the inspectors the traits featuring the chiaroscuro coalesce, their contrarieties eliminated, in one stable somebody similarly as by the providential warring of heartshaker with housebreaker and of dramdrinker against freethinker our social something bowls along bumpily, experiencing a jolting series of prearranged disappointments, down the long lane of (it's as semper as oxhousehumper) generations, more generations and still more generations"—this last a case of Mr. Joyce's rare subjectivism. In a word, here is all humanity circling with fatal monotony about the Providential fulcrum—the "convey wheeling encirculing abound the gigantig's lifetree." Enough has been said, or at least enough has been suggested, to show how Vico is substantially present in the *Work in Progress*. Passing to the Vico of the Poetics we hope to establish an even more striking, if less direct, relationship.

Vico rejected the three popular interpretations of the poetic spirit, which considered poetry as either an ingenious popular expression of philosophical conceptions, or an amusing social diversion, or an exact science within the research of everyone in possession of the recipe. Poetry, he says, was born of curiosity, daughter of ignorance. The first men had to create matter by the force of their imagination, and "poet" means "creator." Poetry was the first operation of the human mind, and without it thought could not exist. Barbarians, incapable of analysis and abstraction, must use their fantasy to explain what their reasons cannot comprehend. Before articulation comes song; before abstract terms, metaphors. The figurative character of the oldest poetry must be regarded, not as sophisticated confectionary, but as evidence of a poverty-stricken vocabulary and of a disability to achieve abstraction. Poetry is essentially the antithesis of Metaphysics: Metaphysics purge the mind of the senses and cultivate the disembodiment of the spiritual; Poetry is all passion and feeling and animates the inanimate; Metaphysics are most perfect when most concerned with universals; Poetry, when most concerned with particulars. Poets are the sense, philosophers the intelligence of humanity. Considering the Scholastics' axiom: *"niente è nell'intelletto che prima non sia nel senso,"* it follows that poetry is a prime condition of philosophy and civilization. The primitive animistic movement was a manifestation of the *"forma poetica dello spirito."*

His treatment of the origin of language proceeds along similar lines. Here again he rejected the materialistic and transcendental views; the one declaring that language was nothing but a polite and conventional symbolism; the other, in desperation, describing it as a gift from the Gods. As before, Vico is the rationalist, aware of the natural and inevitable growth of language. In its first dumb form, language was gesture. If a man wanted to say "sea," he pointed to the sea. With the spread of animism this gesture was replaced by the word: "Neptune." He directs our attention to the fact that every need of life, natural, moral and economic, has its verbal expression in one or other of the 30,000 Greek divinities. This is Homer's "language of the Gods." Its evolution through poetry to a highly civilized vehicle, rich in abstract and technical terms, was as little fortuitous as the evolution of society itself. Words have their progressions as well as social phases. "Forest-cabin-village-city-academy" is one rough progression. Another: "mountain-plain-riverbank." And every word expands with psychological inevitability. Take the Latin word: "Lex."

1.   Lex = Crop of acorns.
2.   Ilex = Tree that produces acorns.
3.   Legere = To gather.
4. Aquilex = He that gathers the waters.
5.   Lex = Gathering together of peoples, public assembly.
6.   Lex = Law.
7.   Legere = To gather together letters into a word, to read.

The root of any word whatsoever can be traced back to some prelingual symbol. This early inability to abstract the general from the particular produced the Type-names. It is the child's mind over again. The child extends the names of the first familiar objects to other strange objects in which he is conscious of some analogy. The first men, unable to conceive the abstract idea of "poet" or "hero," named every hero after the first hero, every poet after the first poet. Recognizing this custom of designating a number of individuals by the names of their prototypes, we can explain various classical and mythological mysteries. Hermes is the prototype of the Egyptian inventor: so for Romulus, the great law-giver, and Hercules, the Greek hero: so for Homer. Thus Vico asserts the spontaneity of language and denies the dualism of poetry and language. Similarly, poetry is the foundation of writing. When language consisted of gesture, the spoken and written were identical. Hieroglyphics, or sacred language, as he calls it, were not the invention of philosophers for the mysterious expression of profound thought, but the common necessity of primitive peoples. Convenience only begins to assert itself at a far more advanced stage of civilization, in the form of alphabetism. Here Vico, implicitly at least, distinguishes between writing and direct expression. In such direct expression, form and content are inseparable. Examples are the medals of the Middle Ages, which bore no inscription and were a mute testimony to the feebleness of conventional alphabetic writing: and the flags of our own day. As with Poetry and Language, so with Myth. Myth, according to Vico, is neither an allegorical expression of general philosophical axioms (Conti, Bacon), nor a derivative from particular peoples, as for instance the Hebrews or Egyptians, nor yet the work of isolated poets, but an historical statement of fact, of actual contemporary phenomena, actual in the sense that they were created out of necessity by primitive minds, and firmly believed. Allegory implies a threefold intellectual operation: the construction of a message of general significance, the preparation of a fabulous form, and an exercise of considerable technical difficulty in uniting the two, an operation totally beyond the reach of the primitive mind. Moreover, if we consider the myth as being essentially allegorical, we are not obliged to accept the form in which it is cast as a statement of fact. But we know that the actual creators of these myths gave full credence to their face-value. Jove was no symbol: he was terribly real. It was precisely their superficial metaphorical character that made them intelligible to people incapable of receiving anything more abstract than the plain record of objectivity.

Such is a painful exposition of Vico's dynamic treatment of Language, Poetry and Myth. He may still appear as a mystic to some: if so, a mystic that rejects the transcendental in every shape and form as a factor in human development, and whose Providence is not divine enough to do without the cooperation of Humanity.

On turning to the *Work in Progress* we find that the mirror is not so convex. Here is direct expression—pages and pages of it. And if you don't understand it, Ladies and Gentlemen, it is because you are too decadent to receive it. You are not satisfied unless form is so strictly divorced from content that you can comprehend the one almost without bothering to read the other. The rapid skimming and absorption of the scant cream of sense is made possible by what I may call a continuous process of copious intellectual salivation. The form that is an arbitrary and independent phenomenon can fulfil no higher function than that of stimulus for a tertiary or quartary conditioned reflex of dribbling comprehension. When Miss Rebecca West clears her decks for a sorrowful deprecation of the Narcissistic element in Mr. Joyce by the purchase of 3 hats, one feels that she might very well wear her bib at all her intellectual banquets, or alternatively, assert a more noteworthy control over her salivary glands than is possible for Monsieur Pavlov's unfortunate dogs. The title of this book is a good example of a form carrying a strict inner determination. It should be proof against the usual volley of cerebral sniggers: and it may suggest to some a dozen incredulous Joshuas prowling around the Queen's Hall, springing their tuning-forks lightly against finger-nails that have not yet been refined out of existence. Mr. Joyce has a word to say to you on the subject: "Yet to concentrate solely on the literal sense or even the psychological content of any document to the sore neglect of the enveloping facts themselves circumstantiating it is just as harmful; etc." And another: "Who in his heart doubts either that the facts of feminine clothiering are there all the time or that the feminine fiction, stranger than the facts, is there also at the same time, only a little to the rere? Or that one may be separated from the other? Or that both may be contemplated simultaneously? Or that each may be taken up in turn and considered apart from the other?"

Here form *is* content, content *is* form. You complain that this stuff is not written in English. It is not written at all. It is not to be read—or rather it is not only to be read. It is to be looked at and listened to. His writing is not *about* something;

683

it is that something itself. (A fact that has been grasped by an eminent English novelist and historian whose work is in complete opposition to Mr. Joyce's.) When the sense is sleep, the words go to sleep. (See the end of *Anna Livia*.) When the sense is dancing, the words dance. Take the passage at the end of Shaun's pastoral: "To stirr up love's young fizz I tilt with this bridle's cup champagne, dimming douce from her peepair of hide-seeks tight squeezed on my snowybreasted and while my pearlies in their sparkling wisdom are nippling her bubblets I swear (and let you swear) by the bumper round of my poor old snaggletooth's solidbowel I ne'er will prove I'm untrue to (theare!) you liking so long as my hole looks. Down." The language is drunk. The very words are tilted and effervescent. How can we qualify this general esthetic vigilance without which we cannot hope to snare the sense which is for ever rising to the surface of the form and becoming the form itself? St. Augustine puts us on the track of a word with his *"intendere,"* Dante has: *"Donne ch'avete intelletto d'amore,* and *"Voi che, intendendo, il terzo ciel movete"*; but his *"intendere"* suggests a strictly intellectual operation. When an Italian says to-day *"Ho inteso,"* he means something between *"Ho udito"* and *"Ho capito,"* a sensuous untidy art of intellection. Perhaps "apprehension" is the most satisfactory English word. Stephen says to Lynch: "Temporal or spatial, the esthetic image is first luminously apprehended as selfbounded and selfcontained upon the immeasurable background of space or time which is not it . . . You apprehend its wholeness." There is one point to make clear: the Beauty of *Work in Progress* is not presented in space alone, since its adequate apprehension depends as much on its visibility as on its audibility. There is a temporal as well as a spatial unity to be apprehended. Substitute "and" for "or" in the quotation, and it becomes obvious why it is as inadequate to speak of "reading" Work in Progress as it would be extravagant to speak of "apprehending" the work of the late Mr. Nat Gould. Mr. Joyce has desophisticated language. And it is worth while remarking that no language is so sophisticated as English. It is abstracted to death. Take the word "doubt": it gives us hardly any sensuous suggestion of hesitancy, of the necessity for choice, of static irresolution. Whereas the German "Zweifel" does, and, in lesser degree, the Italian "dubitare." Mr. Joyce recognizes how inadequate "doubt" is to express a state of extreme uncertainty, and replaces it by "in twosome twiminds." Nor is he by any means the first to recognize the importance of treating words as something more than mere polite symbols. Shakespeare uses fat, greasy words to express corruption: "Duller shouldst thou be than the fat weed that rots itself in death on Lethe wharf." We hear the ooze squelching all through Dickens's description of the Thames in *Great Expectations*. This writing that you find so obscure is a quintessential extraction of language and painting and gesture, with all the inevitable clarity of the old inarticulation. Here is the savage economy of hieroglyphics. Here words are not the polite contortions of 20th century printer's ink. They are alive. They elbow their way on to the page, and glow and blaze and fade and disappear. "Brawn is my name and broad is my nature and I've breit on my brow and all's right with every feature and I'll brune this bird or Brown Bess's bung's gone bandy." This is Brawn blowing with a light gust through the trees or Brawn passing with the sunset. Because the wind in the trees means as little to you as the evening prospect from the Piazzale Michelangiolo—though you accept them both because your non-acceptance would be of no significance, this little adventure of Brawn means nothing to you—and you do not accept it, even though here also your non-acceptance is of no significance. H. C. Earwigger, too, is not content to be mentioned like a shilling-shocker villain, and then dropped until the exigencies of the narrative require that he be again referred to. He continues to suggest himself for a couple of pages, by means of repeated permutations on his "normative letters," as if to say: "This is all about me, H. C. Earwigger: don't forget this is all about me!" This inner elemental vitality and corruption of expression imparts a furious restlessness to the form, which is admirably suited to the purgatorial aspect of the work. There is an endless verbal germination, maturation, putrefaction, the cyclic dynamism of the intermediate. This reduction of various expressive media to their primitive economic directness, and the fusion of these primal essences into an assimilated medium for the exteriorization of thought, is pure Vico, and Vico, applied to the problem of style. But Vico is reflected more explicitly than by a distillation of disparate poetic ingredients into a synthetical syrup. We notice that there is little or no attempt at subjectivism or abstraction, no attempt at metaphysical generalization. We are presented with a statement of the particular. It is the old myth: the girl on the dirt track, the two washerwomen on the banks of the river. And there is considerable animism: The mountain "abhearing," the river puffing her old doudheen. (See the beautiful passage beginning: "First she let her hair fall down and it flussed.") We have Type-names: Isolde—any beautiful girl: Earwigger—Guinness's Brewery, the Wellington monument, the Phoenix Park, anything that occupies an extremely comfortable position between the two stools. Anna Livia herself, mother of Dublin, but no more the only mother than Zoroaster was the only oriental stargazer. "Teems of times and happy returns. The same anew. Ordovico or viricordo. Anna was, Livia is, Plurabelle's to be. Northmen's thing made Southfolk's place, but howmultyplurators made eachone in person." Basta! Vico and Bruno are here, and more substantially than would appear from this swift survey of the question. For the benefit of those who enjoy a parenthetical sneer, we would draw attention to the fact that when Mr. Joyce's early pamphlet *The Day of Rabblement* appeared, the local philosophers were thrown into a state of some bewilderment by a reference in the first line to "The Nolan." They finally succeeded in identifying this mysterious individual with one of the obscurer ancient Irish kings. In the present work he appears frequently as "Browne & Nolan," the name of a very remarkable Dublin Bookseller and Stationer.

To justify our title, we must move North, *"Sovra'l bel fiume d'Arno alla gran villa"* . . . Between "colui per lo cui verso—il meonio cantor non è più solo" and the "still to-day insufficiently malestimated notesnatcher, Shem the Penman," there exists considerable circumstantial similarity. They both saw how worn out and threadbare was the conventional language of cunning literary artificers, both rejected an approximation to a universal language. If English is not yet so definitely a polite necessity as Latin was in the Middle Ages, at least one is justified in declaring that its position in relation to other European languages is to a great extent that of mediaeval Latin to the Italian dialects. Dante did not adopt the vulgar out of any kind of local jingoism nor out of any determination to assert the superiority of Tuscan to all its rivals as a form of spoken Italian. On reading his *De Vulgari Eloquentia* we are struck by his complete freedom from civic intolerance. He attacks the world's Portadownians: *"Nam quicumque tam obscenae rationis est, ut locum suae nationis delitosissimum credat esse sub sole, huic etiam proe cunctis propriam volgare licetur, idest maternam locutionem. Nos autem, cui mundus est patria . . . etc."* When he comes to examine the dialects he finds Tuscan: *"turpissimum . . . fere omnes Tusci in suo turpiloquio obtusi . . . non restat in dubio quin aliud sit vulgare quod quaerimus quam quod attingit populus Tuscanorum."* His conclusion is that the corruption common to all the dialects make it impossible to select one rather than another as an adequate literary form, and that he who would write in the vulgar must assemble the purest elements from each dialect and construct a synthetic language that would at least possess more than a circumscribed local interest: which is precisely what he did. He did not write in Florentine any more than in Neapolitan. He wrote a vulgar that *could* have been spoken by an ideal Italian who had assimilated what was best in all the dialects of his country, but which in fact was certainly not spoken nor ever had been. Which disposes of the capital objection that might be made against this attractive parallel between Dante and Mr. Joyce in the question of language, i.e. that at least Dante wrote what was being spoken in the streets of his own town, whereas no creature in heaven or earth ever spoke the language of *Work in Progress*. It is reasonable to admit that an international phenomenon might be capable of speaking it, just as in 1300 none but an inter-regional phenomenon could have spoken the language of the Divine Comedy. We are inclined to forget that Dante's literary public was Latin, that the form of his Poem was to be judged by Latin eyes and ears, by a Latin Esthetic intolerant of innovation, and which could hardly fail to be irritated by the substitution of *"Nel mezzo del cammin di nostra vita"* with its "barbarous" directness for the suave elegance of: *"Ultima regna canam, fluido contermina mundo,"* just as English eyes and ears prefer: "Smoking his favourite pipe in the sacred presence of ladies" to "Rauking his flavourite turfco in the smukking precincts of lydias." Boccaccio did not jeer at the *"piedi sozzi"* of the peacock that Signora Alighieri dreamed about.

I find two well made caps in the *"Convivio,"* one to fit the collective noodle of the monodialectical arcadians whose fury is precipitated by a failure to discover "innoce-free" in the concise Oxford Dictionary and who qualify as the "ravings of a Bedlamite" the formal structure raised by Mr. Joyce after years of patient and inspired labour: *"Questi sono da chiamare pecore e non uomini; chè se una pecora si gittasse da una ripa di mille passi, tutte l'altre le adrebbono dietro; e se una pecore a per alcuna cagione al passare d'una strada salta, tutte le altre saltano, eziando nulla veggendo da saltare. E io ne vidi già molte in un pozzo saltare, per una che dentro vi salto, forse credendo di saltare un muro."* And the other for Mr. Joyce, biologist in words: *"Questo* (formal innovation) *sarà luce nuova, sole nuovo, il quale sorgerà ore l'usato tramonterà e darà luce a coloro che sono in tenebre e in oscurità per lo usato sole che a loro non luce."* And, lest he should pull it down over his eyes and laugh behind the peak, I translate *"in tenebre e in oscurità"* by "bored to extinction." (Dante makes a curious mistake speaking of the origin of language, when he rejects the authority of Genesis that Eve was the first to speak, when she addressed the Serpent. His incredulity is amusing: *"inconvenienter putatur tam egregium humani generis actum, vel prius quam a viro, foemina profluisse."* But before Eve was born, "the animals were given names by Adam," the man who "first said goo to a goose." Moreover it is explicitly stated that the choice of names was left entirely to Adam, so that there is not the slightest Biblical authority for the conception of language as a direct gift of God, any more than there is any intellectual authority for conceiving that we are indebted for the "Concert" to the individual who used to buy paint for Giorgione.)

We know very little about the immediate reception accorded to Dante's mighty vindication of the "vulgar," but we can form our own opinions when, two centuries later, we find Castiglione splitting more than a few hairs concerning the respective advantages of Latin and Italian, and Poliziano writing the dullest of dull Latin Elegies to justify his existence as the author of *"Orfeo"* and the *"Stanze."* We may also compare, if we think it worth while, the storm of ecclesiastical abuse raised by Mr. Joyce's work, and the treatment that the Divine Comedy must certainly have received from the same source. His Contemporary Holiness might have swallowed the crucifixion of *"lo sommo Giove,"* and all it stood for, but he could scarcely have looked with favour on the spectacle of three of his immediate predecessors plunged head-foremost in the fiery stone of Malebolge, nor yet the identification of the Papacy in the mystical procession of Terrestrial Paradise with a *"puttana sciolta."* The *"De Monarshia"* was burnt publicly under Pope Giovanni XXII at the instigation of Cardinal Beltrando and the bones of its author would have suffered the same fate but for the interference of an influential man of letters, Pino della Tosa. Another point of comparison is the preoccupation with the significance of numbers. The death of Beatrice inspired nothing less than a highly complicated poem dealing with the importance of the number 3 in her life.

Dante never ceased to be obsessed by this number. Thus the poem is divided into three Cantiche, each composed of 33 Canti, and written in terza rima. Why, Mr. Joyce seems to say, should there be four legs to a table, and four to a horse, and four seasons and four Gospels and four Provinces in Ireland? Why twelve Tables of the Law, and twelve Apostles and twelve months and twelve Napoleonic marshals and twelve men in Florence called Ottolenghi? Why should the Armistice be celebrated at the eleventh hour of the eleventh day of the eleventh month? He cannot tell you because he is not God Almighty, but in a thousand years he will tell you, and in the meantime must be content to know why horses have not five legs, nor three. He is conscious that things with a common numerical characteristic tend towards a very significant inter-relationship. This preoccupation is freely translated in his present work, see the "Question and Answer" chapter, and the Four speaking through the child's brain. They are the four winds as much as the four Provinces, and the four Episcopal Sees as much as either.

A last word about the Purgatories. Dante's is conical and consequently implies culmination. Mr. Joyce's is spherical and excludes culmination. In the one there is an ascent from real vegetation—Ante-Purgatory, to ideal vegetation—Terrestrial Paradise: in the other there is no ascent and no ideal vegetation. In the one, absolute progression and a guaranteed consummation: in the other, flux—progression or retrogression, and an apparent consummation. In the one movement is unidirectional, and a step forward represents a net advance: in the other movement is non-directional—or multi-dimensional, and a step forward is, by definition, a step back. Dante's Terrestrial Paradise is the carriage entrance to a Paradise that is not terrestrial: Mr. Joyce's Terrestrial Paradise is the tradesmen's entrance on to the sea-shore. Sin is an impediment to movement up the cone, and a condition of movement round the sphere. In what sense, then, is Mr. Joyce's work purgatorial? In the absolute absence of the Absolute. Hell is the static lifelessness of unrelieved viciousness. Paradise the static lifelessness of unrelieved immaculation. Purgatory a flood of movement and vitality released by the conjunction of these two elements. There is a continuous purgatorial process at work, in the sense that the vicious circle of humanity is being achieved, and this achievement depends on the recurrent predomination of one of two broad qualities. No resistance, no eruption, and it is only in Hell and Paradise that there are no eruptions, that there can be none, need be none. On this earth that is Purgatory, Vice and Virtue—which you may take to mean any pair of large contrary human factors—must in turn be purged down to spirits of rebelliousness. Then the dominant crust of the Vicious or Virtuous sets, resistance is provided, the explosion duly takes place and the machine proceeds. And no more than this; neither prize nor penalty; simply, a series of stimulants to enable the kitten to catch its tail. And the partially purgatorial agent? The partially purged.

DANTE AND
THE LOBSTER

Samuel Beckett's More Pricks Than Kicks *(1934) is a volume of ten stories (including this one) involving a man named Belacqua Shuah who veers between contemplation of the most rarefied intellectual issues and the bizarre occurrences of his daily life. The flavor of Joyce's* Ulysses *infiltrates this early work, but Beckett's characteristic commitment to the power of language and his use of apparent banalities to articulate the most profound themes is already evident here.*

IT WAS MORNING AND BELACQUA was stuck in the first of the canti in the moon. He was so bogged that he could move neither backward nor forward. Blissful Beatrice was there, Dante also, and she explained the spots on the moon to him. She shewed him in the first place where he was at fault, then she put up her own explanation. She had it from God, therefore he could rely on its being accurate in every particular. All he had to do was to follow her step by step. Part one, the refutation, was plain sailing. She made her point clearly, she said what she had to say without fuss or loss of time. But part two, the demonstration, was so dense that Belacqua could not make head or tail of it. The disproof, the reproof, that was patent. But then came the proof, a rapid shorthand of the real facts, and Belacqua was bogged indeed. Bored also, impatient to get on to Piccarda. Still he pored over the enigma, he would not concede himself conquered, he would understand at least the meanings of the words, the order in which they were spoken and the nature of the satisfaction that they conferred on the misinformed poet, so that when they were ended he was refreshed and could raise his heavy head, intending to return thanks and make formal retraction of his old opinion.

He was still running his brain against this impenetrable passage when he heard midday strike. At once he switched his mind off its task. He scooped his fingers under the book and shovelled it back till it lay wholly on his palms. The *Divine Comedy* face upward on the lectern of his palms. Thus disposed he raised it under his nose and there he slammed it shut. He held it aloft for a time, squinting at it angrily, pressing the boards inwards with the heels of his hands. Then he laid it aside.

He leaned back in his chair to feel his mind subside and the itch of this mean quodlibet die down. Nothing could be done until his mind got better and was still, which gradually it did and was. Then he ventured to consider what he had to do next. There was always something that one had to do next. Three large obligations presented themselves. First lunch, then the lobster, then the Italian lesson. That would do to be going on with. After the Italian lesson he had no very clear idea. No doubt some niggling curriculum had been drawn up by someone for the late afternoon and evening, but he did not know what. In any case it did not matter. What did matter was: one, lunch; two, the lobster; three, the Italian lesson. That was more than enough to be going on with.

Lunch, to come off at all, was a very nice affair. If his lunch was to be enjoyable, and it could be very enjoyable indeed, he must be left in absolute tranquillity to prepare it. But if he were disturbed now, if some brisk tattler were to come bouncing in now big with a big idea or a petition, he might just as well not eat at all, for the food would turn to bitterness on his palate, or, worse again, taste of nothing. He must be left strictly alone, he must have complete quiet and privacy, to prepare the food for his lunch.

The first thing to do was to lock the door. Now nobody could come at him. He deployed an old *Herald* and smoothed it out on the table. The rather handsome face of McCabe the assassin stared up at him. Then he lit the gas-ring and unhooked the square flat toaster, asbestos grill, from its nail and set it precisely on the flame. He found he had to lower the flame. Toast must not on any account be done too rapidly. For bread to be toasted as it ought, through and through, it must be done on a mild steady flame. Otherwise you only charred the outside and left the pith as sodden as before. If there was one thing he abominated more than another it was to feel his teeth meet in a bathos of pith and dough. And it was so easy to do the thing properly. So, he thought, having regulated the flow and adjusted the grill, by the time I have the bread cut that will be just right. Now the long barrel-loaf came out of its biscuit-tin and had its end evened off on the face of McCabe. Two inexorable drives with the bread-saw and a pair of neat rounds of raw bread, the main elements of his meal, lay before him, awaiting his pleasure. The stump of the loaf went back into prison, the crumbs, as though there were no such thing as a sparrow in the wide world, were swept in a fever away, and the slices snatched up and carried to the grill. All these preliminaries were very hasty and impersonal.

It was now that real skill began to be required, it was at this point that the average person began to make a hash of the entire proceedings. He laid his cheek against the soft of the bread, it was spongy and warm, alive. But he would very soon take that plush feel off it, by God but he would very quickly take that fat white look off its face. He lowered the gas a suspicion and plaqued one flabby slab plump down on the glowing fabric, but very pat and precise, so that the whole resembled the Japanese flag. Then on top, there not being room for the two to do evenly side by side, and if you did not do them evenly you might just as well save yourself the trouble of doing them at all, the other round was set to warm. When the first candidate was done, which was only when it was black through and through, it changed places with its comrade, so that now it in its turn lay on top, done to a dead end, black and smoking, waiting till as much could be said of the other.

For the tiller of the field the thing was simple, he had it from his mother. The spots were Cain with his truss of thorns, dispossessed, cursed from the earth, fugitive and vagabond. The moon was that countenance fallen and branded, seared with the first stigma of God's pity, that an outcast might not die quickly. It was a mix-up in the mind of the tiller, but that did not matter. It had been good enough for his mother, it was good enough for him.

Belacqua on his knees before the flame, poring over the grill, controlled every phase of the broiling. It took time, but if a thing was worth doing at all it was worth doing well, that was a true saying. Long before the end the room was full of smoke and the reek of burning. He switched off the gas, when all that human care and skill could do had been done, and restored the toaster to its nail. This was an act of dilapidation, for it seared a great weal in the paper. This was hooliganism pure and simple. What the hell did he care? Was it his wall? The same hopeless paper had been there fifty years. It was livid with age. It could not be disimproved.

Next a thick paste of Savora, salt and Cayenne on each round, well worked in while the pores were still open with the heat. No butter, God forbid, just a good foment of mustard and salt and pepper on each round. Butter was a blunder, it made the toast soggy. Buttered toast was all right for Senior Fellows and Salvationists, for such as had nothing but false teeth in their heads. It was no good at all to a fairly strong young rose like Belacqua. This meal that he was at such pains to make ready, he would devour it with a sense of rapture and victory, it would be like smiting the sledded Polacks on the ice. He would snap at it with closed eyes, he would gnash it into a pulp, he would vanquish it utterly with his fangs. Then the anguish of pungency, the pang of the spices, as each mouthful died, scorching his palate, bringing tears.

But he was not yet all set, there was yet much to be done. He had burnt his offering, he had not fully dressed it. Yes, he had put the horse behind the tumbrel.

He clapped the toasted rounds together, he brought them smartly together like cymbals, they clave the one to the other on the viscid salve of Savora. Then he wrapped them up for the time being in any old sheet of paper. Then he made himself ready for the road.

Now the great thing was to avoid being accosted. To be stopped at this stage and have conversational nuisance committed all over him would be a disaster. His whole being was straining forward towards the joy in store. If he were accosted now he might just as well fling his lunch into the gutter and walk straight back home. Sometimes his hunger, more of mind, I need scarcely say, than of body, for this meal amounted to such a frenzy that he would not have hesitated to strike any man rash enough to buttonhole and baulk him, he would have shouldered him out of his path without ceremony. Woe betide the meddler who crossed him when his mind was really set on this meal.

He threaded his way rapidly, his head bowed, through a familiar labyrinth of lanes and suddenly dived into a little family grocery. In the shop they were not surprised. Most days, about this hour, he shot in off the street in this way.

The slab of cheese was prepared. Separated since morning from the piece, it was only waiting for Belacqua to call and take it. Gorgonzola cheese. He knew a man who came from Gorgonzola, his name was Angelo. He had been born in Nice but all his youth had been spent in Gorgonzola. He knew where to look for it. Every day it was there, in the same corner, waiting to be called for. They were very decent obliging people.

He looked sceptically at the cut of cheese. He turned it over on its back to see was the other side any better. The other side was worse. They had laid it better side up, they had practised that little deception. Who shall blame them? He rubbed it. It was sweating. That was something. He stooped and smelt it. A faint fragrance of corruption. What good was that? He didn't want fragrance, he wasn't a bloody gourmet, he wanted a good stench. What he wanted was a good green stenching rotten lump of Gorgonzola cheese, alive, and by God he would have it.

He looked fiercely at the grocer.

"What's that?" he demanded.

The grocer writhed.

"Well?" demanded Belacqua, he was without fear when roused, "is that the best you can do?"

"In the length and breadth of Dublin" said the grocer "you won't find a rottener bit this minute."

Belacqua was furious. The impudent dogsbody, for two pins he would assault him.

"It won't do" he cried "do you hear me, it won't do at all. I won't have it." He ground his teeth.

The grocer, instead of simply washing his hands like Pilate, flung out his arms in a wild crucified gesture of supplication. Sullenly Belacqua undid his packet and slipped the cadaverous tablet of cheese between the hard cold black boards of the toast. He stumped to the door where he whirled round however.

"You heard me?" he cried.

"Sir" said the grocer. This was not a question, nor yet an expression of acqui-escence. The tone in which it was let fall made it quite impossible to know what was in the man's mind. It was a most ingenious riposte.

"I tell you" said Belacqua with great heat "this won't do at all. If you can't do better than this" he raised the hand that held the packet "I shall be obliged to go for my cheese elsewhere. Do you mark me?"

"Sir" said the grocer.

He came to the threshold of his store and watched the indignant customer hobble away. Belacqua had a spavined gait, his feet were in ruins, he suffered with them almost continuously. Even in the night they took no rest, or next to none. For then the cramps took over from the corns and hammer-toes, and carried on. So that he would press the fringes of his feet desperately against the end-rail of the bed or, better again, reach down with his hand and drag them up and back towards the instep. Skill and patience could disperse the pain, but there it was, complicating his night's rest.

The grocer, without closing his eyes or taking them off the receding figure, blew his nose in the skirt of his apron. Being a warm-hearted human man he felt sympathy and pity for this queer customer who always looked ill and dejected. But at the same time he was a small tradesman, don't forget that, with a small tradesman's sense of personal dignity and what was what. Thruppence, he cast it up, thruppence worth of cheese per day, one and a tanner per week. No, he would fawn on no man for that, no, not on the best in the land. He had his price.

Stumbling along by devious ways towards the lowly public where he was expected, in the sense that the entry of his grotesque person would provoke no comment or laughter, Belacqua gradually got the upper hand of his choler. Now that lunch was as good as a fait accompli, because the incontinent bosthoons of his own class, itching to pass on a big idea or inflict an appointment, were seldom at large in this shabby quarter of the city, he was free to consider items two and three, the lobster and the lesson, in closer detail.

At a quarter to three he was due at the school. Say five to three. The public closed, the fishmonger reopened, at half-past two. Assuming then that his lousy old bitch of an aunt had given her order in good time that morning, with strict injunctions that it should be ready and waiting so that her blackguard boy should on no account be delayed when he called for it first thing in the afternoon, it would be time enough if he left the public as it closed, he could remain on till the last moment. Benissimo. He had half-a-crown. That was two pints of draught anyway and perhaps a bottle to wind up with. Their bottled stout was particularly excellent and well up. And he would still be left with enough coppers to buy a *Herald* and take a tram if he felt tired or was pinched for time. Always assuming, of course, that the lobster was all ready to be handed over. God damn these trades-men, he thought, you can never rely on them. He had not done an exercise but that did not matter. His Professoressa was so charming and remarkable. Signorina Adriana Ottolenghi! He did not believe it possible for a woman to be more intelligent or better informed than the little Ottolenghi. So he had set her on a pedestal in his mind, apart from other women. She had said last day that they would read *Il Cinque Maggio* together. But she would not mind if he told her, as he proposed to, in Italian, he would frame a shining phrase on his way from the public, that he would prefer to postpone the *Cinque Maggio* to another occasion. Manzoni was an old woman, Napoleon was another. *Napoleone di mezza calzetta, fa l'amore a Giacominetta.* Why did he think of Manzoni as an old woman? Why did he do him that injustice? Pellico was another. They were all old maids, suf-fragettes. He must ask his Signorina where he could have received that impres-sion, that the 19th century in Italy was full of old hens trying to cluck like Pindar. Carducci was another. Also about the spots on the moon. If she could not tell him there and then she would make it up, only too gladly, against the next time. Everything was all set now and in order. Bating, of course, the lobster, which had to remain an incalculable factor. He must just hope for the best. And expect the worst, he thought gaily, diving into the public, as usual.

Belacqua drew near to the school, quite happy, for all had gone swimmingly. The lunch had been a notable success, it would abide as a standard in his mind. Indeed he could not imagine its ever being superseded. And such a pale soapy piece of cheese to prove so strong! He must only conclude that he had been abusing himself all these years in relating the strength of cheese directly to its greenness. We live and learn, that was a true saying. Also his teeth and jaws had been in heaven, splinters of vanquished toast spraying forth at each gnash. It was like eating glass. His mouth burned and ached with the exploit. Then the food had been further spiced by the intelligence, transmitted in a low tragic voice across the counter by Oliver the improver, that the Malahide murderer's petition for mercy, signed by half the land, having been rejected, the man must swing at dawn in Mountjoy and nothing could save him. Ellis the hangman was even now on his way. Belacqua, tearing at the sandwich and swilling the precious stout, pondered on McCabe in his cell.

The lobster was ready after all, the man handed it over instanter, and with such a pleasant smile. Really a little bit of courtesy and goodwill went a long way in this world. A smile and a cheerful word from a common working-man and the face of the world was brightened. And it was so easy, a mere question of muscu-lar control.

"Lepping" he said cheerfully, handing it over.

"Lepping?" said Belacqua. What on earth was that?

"Lepping fresh, sir" said the man, "fresh in this morning."

Now Belacqua, on the analogy of mackerel and other fish that he had heard described as lepping fresh when they had been taken but an hour or two previously, supposed the man to mean that the lobster had very recently been killed.

Signorina Adriana Ottolenghi was waiting in the little front room off the hall, which Belacqua was naturally inclined to think of rather as the vestibule. That was her room, the Italian room. On the same side, but at the back, was the French room. God knows where the German room was. Who cared about the German room anyway?

He hung up his coat and hat, laid the long knobby brown-paper parcel on the hall-table, and went prestly in to the Ottolenghi.

After about half an hour of this and that obiter, she complimented him on his grasp of the language.

"You make rapid progress" she said in her ruined voice.

There subsisted as much of the Ottolenghi as might be expected to of the person of a lady of a certain age who had found being young and beautiful and pure more of a bore than anything else.

Belacqua, dissembling his great pleasure, laid open the moon enigma.

"Yes" she said "I know the passage. It is a famous teaser. Off-hand I cannot tell you, but I will look it up when I get home."

The sweet creature! She would look it up in her big Dante when she got home. What a woman!

"It occurred to me" she said "apropos of I don't know what, that you might do worse than make up Dante's rare movements of compassion in Hell. That used to be" her past tenses were always sorrowful "a favourite question."

He assumed an expression of profundity.

"In that connexion" he said "I recall one superb pun anyway: *'qui vive la pietà quando è ben morta . . .'*"

She said nothing.

"Is it not a great phrase?" he gushed.

She said nothing.

"Now" he said like a fool "I wonder how you could translate that?"

Still she said nothing. Then:

"Do you think" she murmured "it is absolutely necessary to translate it?"

Sounds as of conflict were borne in from the hall. Then silence. A knuckle tambourined on the door, it flew open and lo it was Mlle. Glain the French instructress, clutching her cat, her eyes out on stalks, in a state of the greatest agitation.

"Oh" she gasped "forgive me. I intrude, but what was in the bag?"

"The bag?" said the Ottolenghi.

Mlle. Glain took a French step forward.

"The parcel" she buried her face in the cat "the parcel in the hall."

Belacqua spoke up composedly.

"Mine" he said, "a fish."

He did not know the French for lobster. Fish would do very well. Fish had been good enough for Jesus Christ, Son of God, Saviour. It was good enough for Mlle. Glain.

"Oh" said Mlle. Glain, inexpressibly relieved, "I caught him in the nick of time." She administered a tap to the cat. "He would have tore it to flitters."

Belacqua began to feel a little anxious.

"Did he actually get at it?" he said.

"No no" said Mlle. Glain "I caught him just in time. But I did not know" with a blue-stocking snigger "what it might be, so I thought I had better come and ask."

Base prying bitch.

The Ottolenghi was faintly amused.

"Puisqu'il n'y a pas de mal . . ." she said with great fatigue and elegance.

"Heureusement" it was clear at once that Mlle. Glain was devout "heureusement."

Chastening the cat with little skelps she took herself off. The grey hairs of her maidenhead screamed at Belacqua. A devout, virginal blue-stocking, honing after a penny's worth of scandal.

"Where were we?" said Belacqua.

But Neapolitan patience has its limits.

"Where are we ever?" cried the Ottolenghi "where we were, as we were."

Belacqua drew near to the house of his aunt. Let us call it Winter, that dusk may fall now and a moon rise. At the corner of the street a horse was down and a man sat on its head. I know, thought Belacqua, that that is considered the right thing to do. But why? A lamplighter flew by on his bike, tilting with his pole at the standards, jousting a little yellow light into the evening. A poorly dressed couple stood in the bay of a pretentious gateway, she sagging against the railings, her head lowered, he standing facing her. He stood up close to her, his hands dangled by his sides. Where we were, thought Belacqua, as we were. He walked on gripping his parcel. Why not piety and pity both, even down below? Why not mercy and Godliness together? A little mercy in the stress of sacrifice, a little mercy to rejoice against judgment. He thought of Jonah and the gourd and the pity of a jealous God on Nineveh. And poor McCabe, he would get it in the neck at dawn. What was he doing now, how was he feeling? He would relish one more meal, one more night.

His aunt was in the garden, tending whatever flowers die at that time of year. She embraced him and together they went down into the bowels of the earth, into the kitchen in the basement. She took the parcel and undid it and abruptly the lobster was on the table, on the oilcloth, discovered.

"They assured me it was fresh" said Belacqua.

Suddenly he saw the creature move, this neuter creature. Definitely it changed its position. His hand flew to his mouth.

"Christ!" he said "it's alive."

His aunt looked at the lobster. It moved again. It made a faint nervous act of life on the oilcloth. They stood above it, looking down on it, exposed cruciform on the oilcloth. It shuddered again. Belacqua felt he would be sick.

"My God!" he whined "it's alive, what'll we do?"

The aunt simply had to laugh. She bustled off to the pantry to fetch her smart apron, leaving him goggling down at the lobster, and came back with it on and her sleeves rolled up, all business.

"Well" she said "it is to be hoped so, indeed."

"All this time" muttered Belacqua. Then, suddenly aware of her hideous equipment: "What are you going to do?" he cried.

"Boil the beast" she said, "what else?"

"But it's not dead" protested Belacqua "you can't boil it like that."

She looked at him in astonishment. Had he taken leave of his senses?

"Have sense" she said sharply, "lobsters are always boiled alive. They must be." She caught up the lobster and laid it on its back. It trembled. "They feel nothing" she said.

In the depths of the sea it had crept into the cruel pot. For hours, in the midst of its enemies, it had breathed secretly. It had survived the Frenchwoman's cat and his witless clutch. Now it was going alive into scalding water. It had to. Take into the air my quiet breath.

Belacqua looked at the old parchment of her face, grey in the dim kitchen.

"You make a fuss" she said angrily "and upset me and then lash into it for your dinner."

She lifted the lobster clear of the table. It had about thirty seconds to live.

Well, thought Belacqua, it's a quick death, God help us all.

It is not.

FROM
WAITING FOR GODOT

This "tragicomedy in 2 acts" was originally written in French in 1948, and subsequently translated into English by the author. Waiting for Godot has been variously interpreted by critics as a modern morality play, an existential cry of pain, and classic absurdist theater. The following excerpt supports all these positions.

VLADIMIR. Did you ever read the Bible?

ESTRAGON. The Bible . . . [*He reflects.*] I must have taken a look at it.

VLADIMIR. Do you remember the Gospels?

ESTRAGON. I remember the maps of the Holy Land. Coloured they were. Very pretty. The Dead Sea was pale blue. The very look of it made me thirsty. That's where we'll go, I used to say, that's where we'll go for our honeymoon. We'll swim. We'll be happy.

VLADIMIR. You should have been a poet.

ESTRAGON. I was. [*Gesture towards his rags.*] Isn't that obvious?
  Silence.

VLADIMIR. Where was I . . . How's your foot?

ESTRAGON. Swelling visibly.

VLADIMIR. Ah yes, the two thieves. Do you remember the story?

ESTRAGON. No.

VLADIMIR. Shall I tell it to you?

ESTRAGON. No.

VLADIMIR. It'll pass the time. [*Pause.*] Two thieves, crucified at the same time as our Saviour. One—

ESTRAGON. Our what?

VLADIMIR. Our Saviour. Two thieves. One is supposed to have been saved and the other . . . [*he searches for the contrary of saved*] . . . damned.

ESTRAGON. Saved from what?

VLADIMIR. Hell.

ESTRAGON. I'm going.

He does not move.

VLADIMIR. And yet . . . [*pause*] . . . how is it—this is not boring you I hope—how is it that of the four Evangelists only one speaks of a thief being saved. The four of them were there—or thereabouts—and only one speaks of a thief being saved. [*Pause.*] Come on, Gogo, return the ball, can't you, once in a way?

ESTRAGON [*with exaggerated enthusiasm*]. I find this really most extraordinarily interesting.

VLADIMIR. One out of four. Of the other three two don't mention any thieves at all and the third says that both of them abused him.

ESTRAGON. Who?

VLADIMIR. What?

ESTRAGON. What's all this about? Abused who?

VLADIMIR. The Saviour.

ESTRAGON. Why?

VLADIMIR. Because he wouldn't save them.

ESTRAGON. From hell?

VLADIMIR. Imbecile! From death.

ESTRAGON. I thought you said hell.

VLADIMIR. From death, from death.

ESTRAGON. Well what of it?

VLADIMIR. Then the two of them must have been damned.

ESTRAGON. And why not?

VLADIMIR. But one of the four says that one of the two was saved.

ESTRAGON. Well? They don't agree and that's all there is to it.

VLADIMIR. But all four were there. And only one speaks of a thief being saved. Why believe him rather than the others?

ESTRAGON. Who believes him?

VLADIMIR. Everybody. It's the only version they know.

ESTRAGON. People are bloody ignorant apes.

He rises painfully, goes limping to extreme left, halts, gazes into distance off with his hand screening his eyes, turns, goes to extreme right, gazes into distance. Vladimir watches him, then goes and picks up the boot, peers into it, drop sit hastily.

VLADIMIR. Pah!

He spits. Estragon moves to center, halts with his back to auditorium.

ESTRAGON. Charming spot. [*He turns, advances to front, halts facing auditorium.*] Inspiring prospects. [*He turns to Vladimir.*] Let's go.

VLADIMIR. We can't.

ESTRAGON. Why not?

VLADIMIR. We're waiting for Godot.

ESTRAGON [*despairingly*]. Ah! [*Pause.*] You're sure it was here?

VLADIMIR. What?

ESTRAGON. That we were to wait.

VLADIMIR. He said by the tree. [*They look at the tree.*] Do you see any others.

ESTRAGON. What is it?

VLADIMIR. I don't know. A willow.

ESTRAGON. Where are the leaves?

VLADIMIR. It must be dead.

ESTRAGON. No more weeping.

VLADIMIR. Or perhaps it's not the season.

ESTRAGON. Looks to me more like a bush.

VLADIMIR. A shrub.

ESTRAGON. A bush.

VLADIMIR. A—. What are you insinuating? That we've come to the wrong place?

ESTRAGON. He should be here.

VLADIMIR. He didn't say for sure he'd come.

ESTRAGON. And if he doesn't come?

VLADIMIR. We'll come back to-morrow.

ESTRAGON. And then the day after to-morrow.

VLADIMIR. Possibly.

ESTRAGON. And so on.

VLADIMIR. The point is—

ESTRAGON. Until he comes.

VLADIMIR. You're merciless.

ESTRAGON. We came here yesterday.

VLADIMIR. Ah no, there you're mistaken.

ESTRAGON. What did we do yesterday?

VLADIMIR. What did we do yesterday?

ESTRAGON. Yes.

VLADIMIR. Why . . . [*Angrily.*] Nothing is certain when you're about.

ESTRAGON. In my opinion we were here.

VLADIMIR [*looking round*]. You recognize the place?

ESTRAGON. I didn't say that.

VLADIMIR. Well?

ESTRAGON. That makes no difference.

VLADIMIR. All the same . . . that tree . . . [*turning towards auditorium*] that bog . . .

ESTRAGON. You're sure it was this evening?

VLADIMIR. What?

ESTRAGON. That we were to wait.

VLADIMIR. He said Saturday. [*Pause.*] I think.

ESTRAGON. You think.

VLADIMIR. I must have made a note of it. [*He fumbles in his pockets, bursting with miscellaneous rubbish.*]

ESTRAGON [*very insidious*]. But what Saturday? And is it Saturday? Is it not rather Sunday? [*Pause.*] Or Monday? [*Pause.*] Or Friday?

VLADIMIR [*looking wildly about him, as though the date was inscribed in the landscape*]. It's not possible!

ESTRAGON. Or Thursday?

VLADIMIR. What'll we do?

ESTRAGON. If he came yesterday and we weren't here you may be sure he won't come again to-day.

VLADIMIR. But you say we were here yesterday.

ESTRAGON. I may be mistaken.

JAMES JOYCE'S WORLD & LETTERS OF JAMES JOYCE

This entertaining piece by poet and critic Louis MacNeice reviews two books on James Joyce: Patricia Hutchins's James Joyce's World *and* Letters of James Joyce, *edited by Stuart Gilbert. Appearing originally in the November 1957 issue of* London Magazine, *it was later reprinted, with the footnotes that appear here, in* Selected Literary Criticism of Louis MacNeice, *edited by Alan Heuser.*

JAMES STEPHENS, QUOTED BY Miss Hutchins, said of *Finnegans Wake:* "This book is not written in prose, it is written in speech . . . speech moves at the speed of light, prose moves at the speed of the alphabet."[1] So to catch their Joyce as it flies is a hard task for his interpreters. Shaw, Yeats, and Joyce, all three Irish and, in their quite different ways, only too adept at word-play, were three gigantic cranks. But they all were quick on the laugh and it seems an irony that their works should now be at the mercy of the evergrowing tribes of humourless scholars, of Quintilian G. Grinder on his campus or little Plucky Jim making red bricks without straw in the hope they will add up to a doctorate. At this rate June 16 will soon be not Bloomsday but Boresday.[2] Joyce wrote in a letter to his grandson (see Mr. Gilbert's collection): "The devil mostly speaks a language of his own called Bellsybabble which he makes up himself as he goes along but when he is very angry he can speak quite bad French very well though some who have heard him say that he has a strong Dublin accent."[3] Neither Jim nor Grinder can really understand this accent—like many a stranger to Dublin they cannot tell the wind in the reeds from the tongue in the cheek—and so they dehydrate Joyce, destroying both the devil and the child in him.

I do not include either Mr. Gilbert (who knew Joyce) or Miss Hutchins (who didn't) in this condemnation, but both their new books are disappointing. Miss Hutchins's is less interesting than her earlier *James Joyce's Dublin,* which it inevitably overlaps (where else was his world anyway?), and even the photographs in it are duller than those in the earlier book, such as Noel Moffett's intriguing and apposite sand patterns; while Mr. Gilbert, who in 1930 published, with Joyce's approval, a fascinating study of *Ulysses,* appears, in editing these letters which are most of them themselves pretty dull, a halfhearted and inattentive editor, labouring less from love than because he is stuck in a groove. Both these books make sticky reading. Joyce's letters, like Yeats's, are largely concerned with royalties, book reviews, etc.—many of them are written to his patroness Harriet Shaw Weaver[4]—and are often formal and stiff; as with Yeats, decades of acquaintance could not bring him down to Christian names. The redeeming moments are those of arrogance, as when at the age of nineteen he writes to Ibsen, or of playfulness as in several letters to Frank Budgen. As for Miss Hutchins, too much of her book is irrelevant conjecture, as when she writes about Joyce's stay in Bognor where he was toiling at *Work in Progress* (the italics that follow are mine): "*If* he asked his daughter . . . the name of the big red house on the corner, and she told him it was a House of Rest for Women, he *probably* gave his short laugh and asked her if there wasn't one next door for weary writers." Nor is it illuminating to have every building described, in Zurich or Paris, that Joyce, a chronic nomad, ever stayed in for a week or two. Miss Hutchins probably enjoyed this paper chase but Solomon had the right word for it.

Still let us be grateful for the crumbs. It is interesting to learn from Miss Hutchins that the youthful Joyce used to play charades, dressing up for instance as Carmen, and also liked a game which was a play on place names, e.g. "Harold's Cross because Terenure" (Terry knew her); and that at the same period he always asked in the Irish National Library for *The Illustrated London News.* The books an author read are usually more revealing than the houses he lived in and I am glad that Miss Hutchins, in a footnote, details the periodicals Joyce bought during two months in 1929: "*The Baker and Confectioner, Boy's Cinema, The Furniture Record, Poppy's Paper, The Schoolgirl's Own, Woman, Woman's Friend, Justice of the Peace, The Hairdressers' Weekly.*" Still better are some of the rare declarations she quotes from the master's lips, e.g. "I hate generalities" (take note, all jargoneers and boreocrats) or the magnificent "If *Ulysses* isn't fit to read, life isn't worth living."[5] But it must be remembered that Joyce, like T. S. Eliot, is a paradox; both have drawn on colloquial speech—and Joyce at least is a master of written dialogue—but both remain essentially literary and neither of them could be described as a sparkling conversationalist. Which is why Dr. Richard Best, onetime National Librarian of Ireland, said to me of Joyce—and he said the same of Synge: "I didn't think he was important; you see, he had no conversation." It is an irony that the greatest celebrant of Dublin should have been so lacking in the Dubliner's most famous virtue or vice.

Mr. Gilbert's collection of letters also contains its memorable sentences. Joyce writes in 1902, still under age, to Lady Gregory: "I have found no man yet with a faith like mine."[6] To Grant Richards about *Dubliners* in 1906: "I believe that in composing my chapter of *moral* (italics mine) history in exactly the way I have composed it I have taken the first step towards the spiritual liberation of my country."[7] In 1917 to Ezra Pound: "Unfortunately, I have very little imagination."[8] In 1919 to Harriet Shaw Weaver on *Ulysses:* "I confess that it is an extremely tiresome book but it is the only book which I am able to write at present."[9] And to Frank Budgen on the chapter of parodies in *Ulysses:* "As I told you a catchword is enough to set me off."[10] And to Miss Weaver again in 1921: "I have not read a work of literature for several years. My head is full of pebbles and rubbish and broken matches and lots of glass picked up 'most everywhere.'"[11] And there is a very interesting explanation, to Budgen, of the last episode in *Ulysses* and its four cardinal points: "It begins and ends with the female word *yes.*"[12] And, beginning his yet stranger experiments, he parodies "St. Patrick's Breastplate": "Complications to right of me, complications to left of me, complex on the page before me, perplex in the pen beside me, duplex in the meandering eyes of me, stuplex in the face that reads me."[13] There is also a commentary—"just forty-seven times as long as the text"—on a very short passage of *Finnegans Wake.*[14] These letters bring out his dedication and his innocence, his formality and his inconsequence (he admits that his sympathy with Vico was heightened because he too, unlike most Italians, feared thunderstorms). When he writes to his family there is also a tenderness. Above all, though he was never "engagé" and appears to have loathed Irish politics, like all politics, there is the regional fixation; at the age of fifty-five he writes from Paris: "But every day in every way I am walking along the streets of Dublin."[15] Or, as he put it in one of his last puns, "the Finn again wakes."[16] Joyce's own work will be waking when his scholiasts have all gone to sleep—if they are not asleep already over their typewriters.

$\downarrow$

[1] In a broadcast of readings from *Finnegans Wake* (1939), Jan. 1947, cited by Hutchins, 221-1.

[2] Bloomsday, 16 June 1904, is the day on which the action of *Ulysses* (1922) is set; its anniversary has been widely celebrated by Joyceans.

[3] Postscript to letter, 10 Aug. 1936, to Stephen Joyce: *Letters,* ed. Gilbert (1957, corr. 1966), 387. Vols. II and III of Joyce's *Letters* were edited by Richard Ellmann (1966).

[4] Editor of the *Egoist* 1914-19 who published Joyce's *A Portrait of the Artist as a Young Man* as a serial and as a book (1916, 1917), as well as the early episodes of *Ulysses.* She helped issue *Ulysses* as a book, was a source of funds over many years, and became Joyce's literary executrix; yet Miss Weaver did not appreciate *Finnegans Wake.* See Jane Lidderdale and Mary Nicholson, *Dear Miss Weaver: Harriet Shaw Weaver 1876-1961* (1970), *passim.*

[5] Hutchins, 149 and 139.

[6] Letter, Nov. 1902: *Letters,* ed. Gilbert, 53.

[7] Letter, 20 May 1906: op. cit., 62-3.

[8] Letter, 9 April 1917: ibid., 101.

[9] Letter, 20 July 1919: ibid., 128.

[10] Letter, Michaelmas 1920: ibid., 147; on episode 15, "Circe" (or "nighttown"), *not* episode 14, "Oxen of the Sun" (parodies).

[11] Letter, 24 June 1921: *Letters,* 167.

[12] Letter, 16 Aug. 1921: ibid., 170.

[13] Letter, 16 Nov. 1924, to Harriet Shaw Weaver: ibid., 222.

[14] Commentary "Twilight of Blindness Madness Descends on Swift"—Letter, 23 Oct. 1928, to Harriet Shaw Weaver: ibid., 273-4.

[15] Letter, 6 Aug. 1937, to Constantine P. Curran: ibid., 395.

[16] Letter, 8 Feb. 1940, to Frank Budgen: ibid., 408.

FROM
BORSTAL BOY

In Part One of Brendan Behan's classic prison memoir, the sixteen-year-old member of the IRA's 2nd Battalion, Dublin Brigade, awaits trial after his arrest in Liverpool for possession of bomb-making chemicals and detonators. The brave young prisoner becomes accustomed to the machinations of life inside, but is furious and hurt over his excommunication from the church. On the brighter side, Behan is given two precious books a week, and he also truly enjoys his jail cuisine.

FRIDAY, IN THE EVENING, the landlady shouted up the stairs:
"Oh God, oh Jesus, oh Sacred Heart. Boy, there's two gentlemen to see you."

I knew by the screeches of her that these gentlemen were not calling to enquire after my health, or to know if I'd had a good trip. I grabbed my suitcase, containing Pot. Chlor, Sulph Ac, gelignite, detonators, electrical and ignition, and the rest of my Sinn Fein conjuror's outfit, and carried it to the window. Then the gentlemen arrived.

A young one, with a blonde, Herrenvolk head and a B.B.C. accent shouted, "I say, greb him, the bestud."

When I was safely grabbed, the blonde one gave me several punches in the face, though not very damaging ones. An older man, in heavy Lancashire speech, told him to leave me alone, and to stop making a —— of himself. . . . There were now two or three others in the room, and this old man was the sergeant and in charge of the raid.

He took some Pot Chlor and sugar out of the case, put it in the empty fireplace and lit it with a match. It roared into flame and filled the room with smoke. He nodded to me and I nodded back.

Saxonhead and another, a quiet fellow, had me gripped by the arms.

"Got a gun, Paddy?" asked the sergeant.

"If I'd have had a gun you wouldn't have come through that door so shagging easy."

He looked at me and sighed, as if I had said nothing, or as if he had not heard me.

"Turn him over," he told the quiet one.

Blondie began to search me with violence.

"No, not you," said the sergeant, "Vereker."

Vereker searched me, quietly, and, even along the seams of my flies, with courtesy.

"Lift your arms up over your head. Put your leg up. Thank you."

From an inside pocket he took my money, a forged travel permit, and a letter which happened to be written in Irish.

It was from a boy in Dublin who was sick in bed and wanted me to come and see him. He was a dreary bastard in any language, and I, a good-natured and affectionate boy, found him distressing to meet and embarrassing to avoid. I would have a good excuse for not meeting him for some time to come.

The blonde studied the Gaelic writing over Vereker's shoulder.

Disgusted, he turned to me and shouted, "You facquing bestud, how would you like to see a woman cut in two by a plate-glass window?"

I would have answered him on the same level—Bloody Sunday, when the Black and Tans attacked a football crowd in our street; the massacre at Cork; Balbriggan; Amritsar; the R.A.F. raids on Indian villages. I had them all off, and was expecting something like this. But the sergeant said in a reasonable tone:

"Well, Paddy, there are people gathered round this house, and I don't think they mean you any good." He laughed a bit. "But take no heed of them. We'll get you to the Assizes all right. Safe and sound."

Vereker released my arm and went to the window. "Uniformed men are making them move along."

The sergeant told Blondie to let me go.

"We'll sit here a while," he said, sitting on the side of the bed, grunting. He pointed, and I came over and sat beside him.

"I wish to Christ I was your age, Paddy, I'd have something better to do than throwing bombs around. How old are you?"

"I'm sixteen, and I'll be seventeen in February."

"So they sent you over here, you silly little twirp, while the big shots are in America, going around spouting and raking in the dollars and living on the fat of the land."

Sean Russell, Chief of Staff of the I.R.A., was in the United States.

Vereker offered me a cigarette.

"Maybe he'd like one of his own. Give him them back. They'll take them off him soon enough in the Bridewell."

He lit a pipe and Vereker and I smoked cigarettes. Blondie stood and did not smoke or say anything.

The sergeant pointed his pipe at the case. "You're a silly lot of chaps, going on with this lot. You don't even know why you're bloody well doing it. It's supposed to be about Partition. About the Six Counties. Well, I've interviewed a lot of your fellows, and God blind old Reilly if one of them could even name the bloody things. Not all six, they couldn't. Go on, now, you. The whole six, mind."

I began. "Antrim, Armagh."

The sergeant counted on his fingers. "Right, that's two you've got."

"Down, Derry, and Fermanagh and . . ."

"Right, five you got. Come on, the last one."

"Down, Derry, and Fermanagh and . . . and . . ."

"There you are, Paddy, what did I tell you?" He shook his head triumphantly.

I left out County Tyrone, for he was a nice old fellow.

After a while Vereker had another look through the window and said that we could go, that there weren't so many people outside the house.

The sergeant undid the buttons of my pants, and I held them up with my hands in my pockets, going down the stairs.

Outside, as we got in the car, a few people shouted:

"String the bastard up. Fughing Irish shit-'ouse."

It was an Orange district, but I think some of them were Liverpool-Irish, trying to prove their solidarity with the loyal stock.

In the car the sergeant said: "That landlady of yours won't have a window left in her house tonight. They'll probably give the lodger a kicking and all."

That was the least of my worries. The landlady was a mean woman from the Midlands. I don't mean that coming from the Midlands caused her meanness. You'll get good people from there, or from any airt or part of the world, but if Cockneys or a Siamese are mean or decent, they'll be mean or decent in a Cockney or a Siamese way.

This landlady was mean and as barren as a bog. Her broken windows would be a judgement on her for the cheap sausages and margarine she poisoned her table with, for she was only generous with things that cost little in cash, locking hall doors at night time and kneeling down to say the rosary with the lodger and her sister, who always added three Hail Marys for holy purity and the protection of her person and modesty, so that you would think half the men in Liverpool were running after her, panting for a lick of her big buck teeth.

The lodger was a big thick from an adjacent bog. After the prayers for purity he had one of his own: that God would grant unto him strength and perseverance to abstain from all alcoholic drinks and to mortify the appetite, so gross a cause of insult to the most loving heart of Jesus, by partaking, but sparingly even, of innocent liquid refreshments such as tea, lemonade, herb beer, ginger pop, and cocoa.

The lodger had to say this every night, for he was a member of the Sacred Thirst, and went to their meetings on Friday night, directly after leaving the Post Office and putting his money in the Savings Bank. But the landlady told us that it would do us no harm to say it with him.

On the back of the hall door was a picture of the Sacred Heart, saying: "God is here. Stand firm."

"Yes," said the sergeant, "I shouldn't be surprised if they leave that house a wreck."

I was brought to the C.I.D. headquarters in Lime Street. In accordance with instructions, I refused to answer questions. I agreed to make a statement, with a view to propaganda for the cause. It would look well at home, too. I often read speeches from the dock, and thought the better of the brave and defiant men that made them so far from friends or dear ones.

"My name is Brendan Behan. I came over here to fight for the Irish Workers' and Small Farmers' Republic, for a full and free life, for my countrymen, North and South, and for the removal of the baneful influence of British Imperialism from Irish affairs. God save Ireland."

"Here, what's this about small farmers? It's your statement, Paddy, and you can put what you bloody well like in it, but I never seen a small farmer, Irish or English; they're all bloody big fellows with bulls' 'eads on 'em, from eating bloody great feeds and drinking cider."

The left-wing element in the movement would be delighted, and the others, the craw-thumpers, could not say anything against me, because I was a good Volunteer, captured carrying the struggle to England's doorstep—but they would be hopping mad at me giving everyone the impression that the I.R.A. was Communistic.

The "God Save Ireland" bit made me feel like the Manchester Martyrs, hanged amidst the exulting cheers of fifty-thousand fair-play merchants, and crying out with their last breath:

> "God save Ireland," cried the heroes,
> "God save Ireland," cry we all;
> "Whether on the scaffold high,
> Or the battle field we die,
> Sure what matter when for Ireland dear we fall."

Blondie took the statement and looked at me with as much savagery as he could muster. I looked back at him, and he looked back to my statement.

> Girt around by cruel foes,
> Still their courage proudly rose

As they thought of them that loved them far and near,
Of the millions true and brave
O'er the stormy ocean's wave,
And our friends in Holy Ireland, ever dear. . . .

And all the people at home would say, reading the papers, "Ah sure, God help poor Brendan, wasn't I only talking to him a week ago?" "By Jasus, he was a great lad all the same, and he only sixteen."

And Shiela would be sorry she did not let me thread her, the night we walked the canal.

Her cousin had been sentenced to fifteen years under an assumed name in England, and she was taking me up to his mother that I might break the news.

Shiela, when I tried her up against a telegraph pole on the canal bank, said that I should be ashamed of myself, and I a Volunteer, and especially at a time like that.

My statement was taken down, and I signed it. Again they asked me questions which I refused to answer.

I was a bit surprised to hear a chief inspector refer to "——ing old Roger Casement." At home Casement was regarded as a Republican saint. Rory, my eldest brother, was named after him.

They gave me tea. Vereker said I was a well-read chap, and told me in a whisper that he himself did the competitions in *John O'London's Weekly*.

"Well, Paddy," said the sergeant, "we're taking you to Dale Street lock-up now. It's not going to be too nice there, but we'll have you in court Monday morning and you'll most likely be shifted to Walton in the afternoon. You'll get a proper bed there, with sheets. Come along, son."

Dale Street was not so good. The station sergeant was an ignorant class of an animal; he took my cigarettes and my matches away from me, and told me he hoped I would get twenty years.

The sergeant and Vereker waved good night to me from the day-room, and I caught a last glimpse of them before I was taken along a dark passage and down a stair, where we stopped outside an open door.

A policeman said, "This do, Sergeant?"

"Yes, shove the bastard in there. Hope he chokes during the ——ing night."

I went to the door.

"Eh, not so fast. Take off them bloody shoes"

I thought they were going to beat me up, and wanted me barefoot, so that I would be less well able to defend myself.

"Come on, off with them."

I bent slowly, my back to the wall, and undid my laces.

"Come on, look sharp. Don't keep us here all night, you sloppy Irish mick."

I removed my shoes and left them at the cell door.

"Now, off with your jacket; undo your braces and give them to me."

I gave them to him.

"You might decide to 'ang yourself in the night. Not that that would be any loss. Now get in that cell and if I 'ear one peep out of you during the night, we'll come down 'ere and we'll murder you."

I went into the cell, holding my trousers up and carrying my jacket, shuffling slowly.

"Come on, get in there before I have to put my boot in your arsehole."

They banged the door and went off up the stairs, their keys jangling in the distance. I looked around me. Bare concrete walls and floor. The door was a massive piece of timber and steel. The window was high up in the wall, below ground level and looking on to another wall. A bare electric bulb, over the door, shone through wire grating.

The bed was a wooden bench with a pillow of the same material, but I had three blankets.

I lay down, wrapped myself in the blankets, but the pillow was too much for me. I reversed, putting my feet on the pillow, with my head resting on my jacket. The pillow was too hard for my feet, and it strained my ankles, keeping them there. Then I wanted to use the lavatory. It was in a corner from the door. I stood over it, my bare toes on the cold concrete floor. As I stood, waiting over the lavatory, I heard a church bell peal in the frosty night, in some other part of the city. Cold and lonely it sounded, like the dreariest noise that ever defiled the ear of man. If you could call it a noise. It made misery mark time.

I got back on my bench, coiled myself up, so that my feet avoided the wooden pillow, in some comfort, and realized my doom. Even if I got away with a few years only, on account of my age, it was for ever. It wasn't even possible that Monday should come, when at least I'd get a walk up the stairs. The clock was not made that would pass the time between now and Monday morning. It was like what we were told about the last day, "Time is, time was, time is no more." And Jesus Christ, even now, I was only locked up ten minutes.

I put my mind on other things. It was at least and at last permissible to a man in my position.

Then I settled myself more comfortably and wondered if anyone else had done it in the same position. I didn't like to mention them by name, even in my mind. Some of them had left the cell for the rope or the firing squad. More pleasantly tired, from the exercise, I fell asleep.

Waking, I felt the hardness of my resting-place. I didn't wonder where I was. I knew that all right. I looked up at the grey light, through the barred windows, and remembered it better. A blunt and numbing pain it is, to wake up in a cell for the first time. I consoled myself, comparing it to the greater horror, surprise and indignation of a condemned man waking up the morning of his execution.

I lay for a while, and wondered if they would take me to court this morning.

Maybe I'd be shifted to prison in the afternoon.

There were noises of key-jangling and door-banging. I hoped they would open my door. Even if they were distributing nothing better than kicks or thumps, I'd prefer not to be left out, in my cold shroud of solitude. Fighting is better than loneliness.

He was coming down my way. He was at the door, looking in the spy-hole. Come in, we know your knock. For Jesus' sake, mister, don't go away without a word. Have a heart.

He turned the key in the lock, and, standing in the open door, said: "Come on, out of it. Down for a wash. Look sharp."

A big lump of a man and friendly, without caring much one way or the other.

"Can't keep you'ands easy. What 'ave you been pinching now, eh?"

"I haven't been pinching anything."

He noticed my accent, and the friendliness left his voice.

"Oh, you're the bastarding I.R.A. man was lifted in Everton last night." He was regretting the friendliness of his first remarks. "Going to put bombs in the new battleships in Cammell Lairds, was you?" He shouted down the passage. "Larry, come down and see your bleedin' countryman."

Another constable came and stood in the doorway of the cell. An elderly man, with a long Irish upper lip.

He shouted straight away, "By Jasus, we didn't do in half enough of you during the Trouble."

He had a heavy Munster accent, with an English one mixed into it. Probably, he had helped to murder people with the Black and Tans during the Trouble, and was afraid to stop in his own country or go near it since. I had him weighed up, all right.

I stood holding my trousers, and spoke up to him, "I wasn't born the time of the Trouble."

His voiced screeched into the falsetto of hysterical laughter or rage. "But I got my share of them, and as for you, you bloody swine, I know what I'd do with you."

I looked up into his glaring red face, and shouted, myself:

"By Jasus, and they chased you out it, anyway. You haven't stopped running yet."

"Be the living Lord Jesus," he roared, aiming a blow at me.

The English turnkey intervened.

"Now, Larry, don't 'eed the dirty little ——er. 'E's not worth a kick in the arse-'ole."

He turned on me, stern, indignant. "Get on down to that wash-house and wash your bleedin' neck."

Out of consideration for the other one, I suppose, he omitted the traditional jibe about Irish dirt.

I went down to the wash-house, if not in good humor, at least feeling more alive.

There were four bowls, all in use. A very old, or very down-and-out man, was replacing brown paper inside his shirt. A young man, in a bottle-green suit and a look of stupid conceit, was surveying his finger-nails. There was a boy in sailor's uniform, a little older than I, but lighter built.

I took my place behind him, innocently admiring the back of his neck.

The turnkey was in the passage, giving consoling chat to the Irish constable.

The sailor turned round. He had brown hair and long dark eyelashes. He rubbed his chin, and smiled.

"Could do with a rasp, mate," he said importantly. "Been here three days now. They won't let you have your bleedin' razor."

"I only came in last night," said I, rubbing my chin, "I'm not so bad." I had shaved four times in my life.

"You Irish?"

I nodded.

"Well, there's a lot of blokes round our way are Irish. Went to R.C. school and all, they did. We all used to sing Irish songs. Confidentially," he lowered his voice, "I don't like these Lancashire blokes myself. Bloody lot of swede-bashers. I'm from Croydon. Know where that is, Paddy?"

"Of course I do. It's in London, where the airport is."

"That's it. Smashing place it is and all, Croydon. Not like this hole. I was picked up here for some screwing jobs. Here and in Manchester—another bloody graveyard. But some good screwing jobs to be done round there. What are you in for, Pad? Boozer battle or something?"

"No, I'm in over the I.R.A. Explosives."

"Are you——!"

"I am, though."

"Straight up?"

"Straight up."

"Cor, you won't half cop it for that lot." There was no hostility in his voice but almost concern. "Fix that vest, will you, Pad? Just shove it down a bit."

He turned round, and I shoved down an inch of his vest that was showing above his blouse. "There is a bit of soap behind your ear."

He handed me a towel and I wiped, carefully, the back of his ears.

"Thanks, Paddy."

The three others were finished and had lit cigarettes. The old man held a butt straight in front of his nose, staring into the smoke. The turnkey shoved in three others. He did not seem to mind the smoking. I remarked on this to the sailor.

"It's got bugger all to do with him," he said. "You can smoke your head off in here if you got any snout or the money to buy it. You can buy scoff, your break-fast, dinner and tea, chocolate. Any perishing thing. Except drink or a bit of crumpet, I suppose."

"They took my cigarettes and matches away from me."

"Oh well, Pad," he said, seriously, "it might be different for you. Being I.R.A., like. It's a sort of 'igh treason, isn't it." But then, more cheerfully, "But —— 'em all, china, you can have some of mine."

I turned from the wash-bowl, protesting.

"Yes, you bloody will. I'll give you three snout, a card of matches, and a packet of chewing gum. I got stacks of that. And 'ave you got anything to read?"

"No, I haven't."

"Well, I'll give you last week's *News of the World*." He took it out of his pocket. "Though maybe you saw that one?"

I said I hadn't seen that issue. I had never read the *News of the World* in my life. I was only forty-eight hours left Ireland, and it had been banned there since I was four years old. I thanked him again, and turned to finish my wash.

"Your hands are wet, Paddy. I'll shove them in your sky-rocket for you."

I gave myself a final rinse, bent over the bowl. He put his hands in my trousers pocket.

"No bottle, Paddy, that one's got an 'ole in it."

He tried the other side. "That's all right. I'll shove the snout, matches, and chewing gum in here."

I turned from the bowl, drying myself.

"And I'll put the paper inside your shirt, so's as that old bastard of a grass-'opper won't tumble it." He put the *News of the World* next my skin, putting his hand round me. "He won't tumble it there, Paddy, under your jacket."

"Thanks, kid," said I.

"That's all right, kid. And, Paddy, my name is Charlie."

"Thanks, Charlie."

"That's all right, kid. And if I get any more stuff today, I'll work you a bit of snout, and chocolate, maybe, tomorrow. And I'll tell you what, Paddy," he said, eagerly, "I know Irish songs. I'll sing you one when we get back to the flowery. Those other geezers are going to court today. All except you and me. We'll wait till the copper takes them to court. I'm on the landing over you. You'll hear me all right. I'll have my lips to the spy-hole."

The door of the wash-house was unlocked, and the big turnkey came in. "Right, all you shower. Puffed, powdered and shaved for his worship?"

The prisoners laughed and marched out behind him, and he locked up each one as he came to the cell door.

"'Bye, Pad," whispered Charlie. He tipped me with his elbow, and went into his cell.

"I'll put a double lock on you," said the screw. "You London blokes are so leery. Regular bloody lot of 'Oudinis, down there."

I was left on my own.

"Now, Guy Fawkes, lead on to the dungeons."

I went down the stairs.

"Plenty of accommodation 'ere. You've got an 'ole suite of rooms to yourself."

I said nothing.

"And I bet you ain't satisfied. That's the Irish, all over. Never done cribbing."

He opened the door. "And fold up them bloody blankets. You ain't sleeping with the pigs now, you know."

I collected my breath to speak without stammering. "I don't know if that sort of abuse is provided for in the regulations, but, what's more to the point, I want some breakfast, and if I can't order it from outside I'm quite sure you'll have to provide me with something."

There; it was done. I looked up at him. I'd often heard my father and uncles say that this matter of speaking worked wonders during the Trouble, soldiers, police, and warders being for the most part an ignorant body of men. But, then, that was a long time ago and the whole of Ireland was in arms against England and the sympathy of the world behind her. I watched his face, steadily keeping my anxiety out of my own eyes. But though he opened his mouth to roar, I knew, relieved, that he was a little bit puzzled.

"You'll order sweet fanny adams from outside, and never you mind the regulations, I'll regulate you, and give you a thick ear for your breakfast, if I get any more of your lip. Don't come the sea-lawyer 'ere. And, you ——ing little bastard, you'll 'ave respect for Constable 'Oulihan and all."

—— you and Constable Houlihan, said I, in my own mind, and to the turnkey, "And I'll complain to the magistrate about your bad language." Now, you poxy looking ballocks, see what you make of that.

His wattles flamed in anger, and he banged the door and went off heavily up the iron stairs.

I thought it better not to smoke till he went to the court. I put a bit of chewing gum in my mouth and walked up and down chewing in rhythm with my footsteps. Three chews a step. An advantage of my dungeon was that there was no one underneath to object to my walking overhead. Not that I'd have felt upset about disturbing him, but I'd heard a frightening shout from someone above to someone on the upper landings: "Hey, you rotten bastard, for Christ's sake, kip in. Hey, you up there, get on your bloody bench and lay there, you ——ing ——." Thanks be to God, there was nothing under me, only Australia, and I could take my morning walk in peace and dignity.

I heard steps on the stairs and stopped in mid-floor. They were coming down to me. Jesus, maybe I should not have said that about the regulations—or, worse still, told that old whore's melt that I was going to report him to the magistrate for his bad language.

They were in the passage. They could easily kill you. Say you cut up rough. It had happened before. Who could give a fish's tit about you over here?

At home it would be all right if you were there to get the credit of it. Give us back the mangled corpse of our martyr. Drums muffled, pipes draped, slow march. When but a lad of sixteen years a felon's cap he wore, God rest you, Frankie Doherty, Ireland's cross you proudly bore.

But the mangling would have to be gone through first.

The key was in the door. Into Thy Hands I commended my spirit, Lord Jesus, receive my soul. The door opened. The turnkey stood, with a prisoner who carried three slices of bread and a mug of cocoa.

"'Ere's your bloody breakfast. ——ing sight more than you deserve."

I took it and would have thanked him if he had waited. It was just as well he didn't. I'd have nearly kissed him in relief.

❧

They were going to court. The doors above were being opened and people were walking about.

I sat cross-legged on my bench, in some contentment, with my breakfast between my knees. The bread was thinly scraped with margarine. Previous occupants of the cell had only thought the cocoa good enough for decorating the walls with; but hunger is a good sauce, and I ate and drank, and opened my *News of the World* luxuriously, and read a consoling item. A magistrate of Hull had himself been sentenced to two years for offences against girls of eleven and thirteen, daughters of an unemployed man. The magistrate used to give them free vegetables from his greengrocer's shop. The older girl was noticed by her schoolteacher to be pregnant.

In Somerset, some farm labourers in a cider house fell upon one of their number, stripped him naked, poured paraffin on him, and set him alight.

When I'd finished my breakfast, I lit one of my Players' Weights and lay back to study the cross-word.

Then I heard singing. A young, clear baritone, not long in use.

> "Oh, the days of the Kerry dancing,
>   Oh, the ring of the piper's tune,
>   Oh, for one of those hours of gladness,
>   Gone, alas, like our youth too soon. . . ."

I noticed Charlie's accent. How he sang, "dawncing," and "pipah," but he had his mouth to the spy-hole all right. I got every word.

Everyone, except Charlie and I, being gone to court, it was very quiet.

The morning is always a good time. Till about eleven o'clock, when it begins to feel its age.

I was anxious about the lavatory. The seat was in a corner, in full view of the spy-hole. I wasn't shy in camp with the Fianna, or in the Tech. An apprentice sitting on the bowl would call over another boy to give him a light of a cigarette. Or pretend to be an old fellow after a night's porter and shout out, "One of yous, which of yous, some of yous, any of yous, for Jasus' sake, come over here, and squeeze me head." But if a master or building trade instructor came they'd shut over the door and be quiet till he left. I didn't like the idea of using the lavatory and that old John Bull's bastard of a copper looking in at me, so now was the time, while he was away at court with the others.

I sat reading the paper, ready to hide it behind the seat if I heard footsteps on the stairs. The serial was a full page. Not Hemingway or Liam O'Flaherty, I thought, settling myself in comfort, and inclining my head to condescension. It was entitled, "No Star is Lost," and was a lot less interesting than the rest of the paper.

"Hey, Paddy."

—— you, Charlie, said I in my own mind, I'm not finished yet.

He shouted again.

All right, I'll be there in a minute.

The serial would do nicely, only ads. about lost relations on the back. I pulled the chain, and went to the spy-hole.

"Hello, Charlie."

"Hello, Paddy, that you?"

Who, in Jasus' Name, do you think it could be?

"Like that song, Paddy?"

"Smashing, china." I speak it like a native, English, in two days and a bit.

Our voices echoed through the lonely Bridewell.

"You sing one, Paddy. An Irish song."

"In Irish?"

"Yes, 'Mother Machree' or 'Galway Bay.'"

—— "Mother Machree" and "Galway Bay." I'll sing a song I learned at school. Ireland crying for the Bonnie Prince, not that him or his old fellow or anyone belonging to him ever did anything for us, but it was a good song.

> "A bhuachail aoibhinn, aluinn-ó
> Ba leathan do chroí, is ba dheas do phóg . . .
> . . . beautiful, lightsome, awesome boy,
> Wide was your heart, and mild was your eye,
> My sorrow without you, for ever I'll cry,
> . . . Is go dteíghidh tú, a mhuírnín, slán,
> Walk my love, walk surely.

White as new lime, your thighs and hips,
Your clustering hair, and your sweet-bitten lips,
My last blaze of strength would die well in
                                    their kiss. . . .
Is go dteíghidh tú, a mhuírnín, slán,
Walk my love, walk surely. . . ."

"Good old Paddy, but I couldn't understand it. Give us 'Kevin Barry.'"
I sang up, slowly and mournfully, through the lonely corridors:

". . . And before he faced the hangman,
                            in his dreary prison cell,
British soldiers tortured Barry,
Just because he would not tell,
The names of his companions,
And other things they wished to know,
'Turn informer and we'll free you,'
But Kevin proudly, answered, 'No' . . .
. . . Just a lad of eighteen summers,
Yet, no one can deny,
That as he marched to death that morning,
He proudly held his head on high. . . ."

When the prisoners came back from the court I heard them shouting to each other. Some had been remanded, and others, on minor charges, had been sentenced to short terms. They all seemed anxious to get up to the jail before dinner. The food there, it seemed, was better than what we got here. Jesus judge the food that could be worse.

About two o'clock I heard the Black Maria back into the yard, and they were taken off, and the Bridewell was quiet again.

After a while I heard Charlie's door opened and shut again, and they came down my stairs. The door opened, and the turnkey handed me my dinner; three dirty and half-rotten potatoes on an enamel plate, two slices of dry bread, and a mug of water.

I looked at the plate.

"What's the matter?" said the turnkey, "off your grub or something? You're bloody good soldiers and no mistake. 'Up the Republic,' and 'Long live old Ireland,' when you're outside a Scotty Road boozer on Saturday night, but you don't be long cracking up after a few hours in the old digger, do you? What'll you feel like after twenty year? That's if you're lucky, and they don't 'ang you. That scoff is good enough for you. Better than you got at 'ome, in 'ungry Ireland. ——ing 'erring and an 'ot potato."

I took the plate and mug, and he banged the door and went off.

719

I walked up and down in the cold light. It was already beginning to fade grey-ly from the window. I looked at the plate on the bench, and took a drink of the water. It made me colder, and the cold was gathering water in my eyes, and to try and warm myself or tire myself, I walked up and down a bit more, giving the plate an odd glance on my return journey from the wall towards the door. At last I sat down and ate the lot.

I had another chew of gum, a drink of water, and a smoke, and, revived, wrapped up in the blankets. Till it was time for walking till evening.

But there was an unexpected bit of diversion in the afternoon. In the middle of a walk I was taken to a room upstairs to be photographed. It was a different policeman opened my door, and this one said nothing to me one way or another.

The photographer was a young man with a pin head and a little moustache. He was wearing a sports coat and flannels. I could not imagine him laughing or being excited but at a cricket match.

In the hope of conversation I asked him the time. But he didn't answer and seemed to be professionally impregnable in his silence.

"Your head this way." He hung a wooden label round my neck with the words "I.R.A." and a number and my name chalked on it. I supposed this was like the pictures one sees of wanted men, and was interested in it, apart from wishing that I was wanted.

"Now, sideways."

Sideways yourself, and take a running jump at yourself. Might put a bit of life into you.

When he was finished with me, I was brought back to the cell and walked up and down and drank water and urinated to pass the time.

The turnkey brought me a mug of cocoa, and my three slices of bread, and, sitting cross-legged on the bench, I pulled a blanket over my shoulders and had my supper. The light was switched on, and I fixed my bed and got into it. In the height of luxury, and hoping the turnkey would not come back, I lit a butt and read the half of the *News of the World* I had rationed for the evening.

"Good night, Paddy, good night."

It was cold to jump out on those flags, but Charlie had got out. He was stand-ing there, waiting, his face to the spy-hole in his shirt, and his bare legs as far as his thighs pink with the cold.

I jumped out in my shirt, and put my lips to the spy-hole.

"Good night, Charlie."

"Night, Pad."

Lying in bed, I could hear the trams far away in the distance. Turning the cor-ners heavily, and gathering speed for the hills.

I used to hear them back in Dublin on the Northside when I was small, lying in bed, avoiding the eye of the Sacred Heart in the picture on the far wall. The house we lived in was a great lord's town house before it was a tenement, and there was a big black Kilkenny marble fireplace before my bed. If the souls in Purgatory really came back, it was out of there they would come. A Hail Mary was all right, but there was more comfort in the sound of the trams. There were lights and people on them. Old fellows, a bit jarred and singing, and fellows leaving their mots home to Drumcondra after the pictures.

The night was broken with shouts and thumps, curses and drunken singing. Some of the other prisoners shouted, "Shah-rap, you baa-a-stad," in their English accents, but I think they were only shouting to show that they had the privilege of shouting and being on the side of the turnkey at the same time. I didn't mind the noise and the singing. It made me feel as if I was not altogether removed from Saturday nights. And I had the whole of Sunday to get through, and to have a bit of extra sleeping to do would be like having money in the bank.

In the wash-house Charlie and I met amongst the others. I was delighted to see him, and he was glad to see me. I don't know why he should not have been there. But I smiled with relief when I saw he was. We got bowls beside each other, and while we washed he said that those bastards didn't half make a bloody row last night. I agreed with him and said there was one bastard over me sang the theme song over and over again, that's if you could call it singing. It was more like a death rattle.

Charlie said the turnkey had not brought him any more cigarettes or papers, though he had ordered them first thing yesterday morning, but he could let me have a butt and a bit of chewing gum. I refused, saying that I still had two snout left and a bit of gum, and was all right. He had brought down a paper for me, and I told him that was all I wanted. I put it in my shirt, and we said we'd see each other going to court in the morning, and after that we'd be shoved up to the nick together.

On the way back he tipped me with his elbow before going into his cell, and muttered, "Cheerio, Pad"; and I went downstairs and was locked in my own cell and lay looking up at the window, till breakfast came round.

I wondered if they had Mass in this place. It would be great to hear an Irish accent, except Constable Houlihan's, and I felt more in a humour for the religion of my fathers than if I were outside and at home.

But they did not say anything about it, and, when the turnkey brought my breakfast, neither did I. He was quiet this morning, and I thought it best to let the hare sit.

↓

Not that we were not reminded of Sunday in another way.

The bells of a hundred churches crashed and banged on my ears all morning.

It was not so bad then, because I like the morning time, and the day did not begin to get gloomy till the light faded from the sky in the afternoon. Then the bells began again, and in defenceless misery I bore them.

I could not even walk, but sat huddled on the bed in my blankets, with tears in my mind and in my heart, and wishing I could wake up and find out that I had only been dreaming this, and could wake up at home, and say, well, that's how it would be if you were pinched in England, and not attend any more parades, and drop out of the I.R.A. and attend more to my trade, and go out dancing or something, and get married; and if, watching an Easter Sunday parade and listening to the crash of drums and scream of the pipes as the four battalions of the Dublin Brigade went into the slow march and gave "eyes left," as they passed the G.P.O. with their banners lowered, and the crowds either side of O'Connell Street baring their heads, I felt my blood go to my scalp—then I could always remind myself of the time I dreamt I was captured in Liverpool, and bring my blood back to my feet.

Dreams were often sent to warn people about the troubles they were likely to bring on themselves if they didn't alter their ways. Outside, I didn't think of such things, or, if I did, it was only to laugh at them; but here it seemed very likely that such things would happen and that it was better to be quiet and good; and here being good meant not being a Republican. Even Casement, that the loyalists at home respected (every paper, including the *Irish Times* and the *Independent*, joined in the demand for the return of his remains, and W. B. Yeats wrote a poem about it: "The Ghost of Roger Casement is knocking on the Door"), was abused, and called "——ing old Roger Casement" by the chief inspector on Friday night.

Well, I was beginning to see the justice of that. He could do that here; and we could abuse the old Famine Queen at home, or the Black and Tans; and every man to it in his own country. And then to come over here and plant bombs in it, you couldn't expect them to love people for that. But, only to wake up and take the dream for the warning. Or to get out, anyway. Jesus, even to be let free and never to be let home again. Apart from anything else, wouldn't it save them money? Yes, that was a way of looking at it. Maybe, if I recognized the court and pleaded guilty, or said someone gave me the stuff to mind and I didn't know what was in it till I got it back to my room, they might only deport me.

I heard steps on the stairs and the turnkey opened my door and brought me up the lighted passageway. My shoes and socks and braces were there, laid out on the floor.

"Put them on," said he.

I will begod, sir, thanking you. Maybe something great was going to happen. Maybe they were going just to send me home, and say, "Stop out of here, in future." Oh, and God knows I would, and thankful.

"Follow me; there's someone wants to see you upstairs."

I kept up with him quickly and was shown into a room. My sergeant was there, and Vereker, who smiled at me. The sergeant winked, and pointed to a third man. A tallish, well-dressed man, and with a good appearance. The thin lips of an Englishman, and that was all right too—wasn't it his country, to have any kind of lips he liked?

"This is Mr. O'Sullivan, Brendan," said the sergeant.

Better again, he called me "Brendan," and the gentleman in the good clothes was Irish—maybe from the St. Vincent de Paul Society or something, to bring me home. He smiled, even, a little, and said: "I'm an Irishman, the same as you. I'm from Cork."

"O'Sullivan's a Cork name, sir," said I.

"So it is," said he, "but what kind of a name is Behan?"

"It's a very Irish name, sir. Literary family once prominent in South Leinster, Irish form, 'Ó Beacháin' from 'beach' a bee, meaning one who keeps bees, Anglicé, 'Behan, Beggan, Beegan.' It's in *Sloinnte Gael agus Gall*. That's Irish, sir. *The Names of the Irish and the Norman*, it is in English, sir. Maybe you don't read Irish, but the English is on the opposite page. Your own name is there too, sir."

"I don't read Irish, Behan, nor do I speak it. A lot of good it would do me if I did. What good is it anywhere outside Ireland?"

"Well, in Nova Scotia, sir, in Cape Breton, it's the only language they use. They publish a daily paper in Gaelic."

"That's Scotch Gaelic—a different language, different altogether."

I knew it wasn't. The principal difference in saying "it is" was that they said "Thá" and we said "tá," but it wouldn't do to act the know-all, or to downface the gentleman. "I suppose you're right, sir, when you come to think of it."

"How old are you, Behan?"

"I'm sixteen, sir."

"I suppose you realize you can go to jail for the best part of your life over this business. The last crowd sentenced in London got a hundred years' penal servitude between five of them. Twenty years each. The sixth arrested with them is lying under sentence of death in Birmingham. For a cowardly murder."

"It was no murder," said I, off the tip of my tongue.

"It was no murder?" His lips tightened in anger. "To put a bomb in a crowded street and kill five innocent people?" His indignation got the better of him, and his voice grated and his accent changed. "You bloody little bastard!" he shouted, and rose his hand to strike me, as if he couldn't restrain himself, ground his teeth, and came forward. "I'll give you murder!"

The sergeant restrained him with Vereker, and both of them looked reproachfully at me. I lowered my eyes and moved back a pace.

Mr. O'Sullivan grunted as they held him, "Let me go, ca-an't you." His face was terrible to watch, the eyes bulging in anger from behind his glasses. "Uh," said he.

"Now, now, Inspector," said the sergeant to pacify him.

"All right, Sergeant, all right," said Mr. O'Sullivan, in an easier tone. They took their hands from him, and he spoke to me more evenly.

"Don't you come that stuff here, Behan. You're not with your murder-gang pals in Dublin or Belfast, now."

"Right, sir," I said in a low voice, and a little bit dazed, wondering what to say that wouldn't start him off again. "I only meant, sir, that that man had nothing to do with it."

He looked at me incredulously, and Vereker and the sergeant sighed and shook their heads in my direction.

"I mean, sir, I mean——" I stammered.

"You mean that you are saying that the Birmingham police officers got an innocent man sentenced to death? Is that what you mean, Behan? Is it? Answer me." His voice rose again, and the sergeant and Vereker moved towards him, but he waved them aside. "Answer me," he added in a lower tone.

I swallowed some spit and tried to collect my utterance. "I mean, sir, there may have been a mistake, sir——"

"The English police, Behan, make no mistakes. In Birmingham—or Liverpool."

"The man was arrested in London, with those other five fellows, and was in the custody of Scotland Yard before the bomb exploded in Coventry—an hour before."

I got ready to shrink back, but he did not move.

"You seem to know a lot about it, Behan; maybe you were in that little operation, as you soldiers of the Irish Republic term your murders. How do you know all this?"

"I read it in the papers, sir, in English papers."

"You were in England, then, when it happened?"

"No, sir, I was in Ireland, at home, but you can buy English papers in Dublin, sir."

"I see; it's a pity you didn't learn a bit more sense from them." He spoke very reasonably, and I breathed more easily. Then he put his hand in his pocket and took out a packet of cigarettes. He offered them to the sergeant and to Vereker, and then passed them to me. "Have one," he said.

"Thank you, sir," said I.

Vereker struck a match and passed lights round.

"Listen, Behan," said the inspector; "you're only a boy, and your leaders are safe home in Ireland, or in America. We don't want to be hard on you, but the only one that can help you is yourself. You need not consider other people; they're not considering you. But if you tell us where we can lay our hands on more of this stuff in England, we'll go and get it, and there'll be no questions asked or answered on one side or the other."

"I don't know where is any other stuff in England, sir."

"You're sure?"

"Certain, sir. The I.R.A. does not let me into all its secrets."

"Never mind that. If you did know, would you help us find it?"

"Well, as I don't know where to tell you to find it, that does not matter, does it? I mean, I could tell you a lie and say I would, and then, for that again, if I did know I might not—and what difference would it make?"

"Do you know much about the organization of the I.R.A. in Ireland? In Belfast?"

"Very little, sir."

"How much?"

"Nothing that would be worth your while hearing about, sir."

"We're the best judges of that. How much do you know of the I.R.A. in Dublin? Who are the members of G.H.Q., as you call it?"

"I know something, of course, of the I.R.A. in Dublin, but," I smiled, "I'm not a G.H.Q. man."

"Nobody said you were. And take the grin off your face. This is a serious matter, more serious for you than for anybody in this room."

"Yes, sir."

"Who gave you this stuff?"

"I didn't know his name, sir."

"Who gave you the money you were found with, gave you your ticket, and your forged travel permit? I suppose you don't know that either?"

I said nothing.

"Listen, Behan, if you're afraid of what will happen to you when you go home, I can tell you this. If you help us, we can look after you. I'm sorry for you, in a way. You're only a foolish boy meddling in things that don't concern you. You owe these people nothing. They sent you over here, and now you have to face the music, not them. Now, you know plenty about the I.R.A. organization in Ireland. You've been connected with it since you could walk—you didn't get much chance, really—and you can be of assistance to us. You won't be the cause of anyone being arrested, because we can't make arrests in Ireland, but you'll help us in stopping this business, and, as I say, we'll look after you. You're a young man, not even that yet. We'll send you to the Colonies, Canada, maybe, put you on the boat with money in your pocket."

He looked at me. "Well?"

I looked at him, and something told me that he was not going to jump at me any more. I was glad of that.

"I can't help you, sir."

"You mean you won't. However, you've a long time to go till the Assizes. Think it over when you're up in Walton, and when you change your mind let me know. I'll be up there, right away."

He nodded to the sergeant and Vereker, and we went out, to the top of the stairs. The turnkey came up, and Vereker smiled at me. "Good night, men," said I.

"Good night, Paddy," said Vereker.

"Good night, you bloody young fool," said the sergeant. I followed the turnkey down the stairs, till we came to the cell door.

"Get them boots and braces off," said the turnkey, "before you go in there."

Before I bent to untie my laces, I put the cigarette into my mouth to take a draw of it.

The turnkey put up his hand, and grabbed it from my mouth. "What's all this 'ere," he shouted, "who told you you could smoke? Who gave you that?"

"The inspector," said I, "Mr. O'Sullivan."

"I don't care who gave it to you," said the turnkey, and flung it from him into the darkness, "and get them boots and braces off."

I took off my shoes and braces, and went into the cell. My cocoa was lying there and it was not too cold. I had my supper, and walked around for a bit, in some humour. I sang a bit of a song, at the top of my voice:

> "Over hill, and through sands, shall I fly for thy weal,
>   Your holy delicate, white hands, shall girdle me with steel,
>   At home, in your emerald bower, from morning's dawn, till e'en,
>   You'll think of me, my flower of flowers, my dark Rosaleen,
>   My own Rosaleen,
>   You'll think of me, through daylight's hours,
>   My virgin flower, my flower of flowers,
>   My dark Rosaleen.
>   But the earth shall run red, with redundance of blood,
>   And the earth shall rock beneath thy tread,
>   And flame wrap hill and wood,
>   And gun-peal, and slogan cry, wake many a glen serene,
>   E'er you shall fade, e'er you shall die, my dark Rosaleen,
>   My own Rosaleen,
>   My judgement hour must first be nigh,
>   E'er you shall fade, e'er you shall die,
>   My dark Rosaleen. . . ."

"Good old Paddy," I heard Charlie shout from above.

I went to the spy-hole.

"We're getting out of this drum in the morning anyway, Paddy," he shouted.

"Right, Charlie, smashing, ain't it?"

But in the morning I was brought away on my own, in a police car. I wondered whether they had a special court for the I.R.A. till we got to our destination and

I was brought into a room and put in with a dozen little boys and girls.

There was a boy of about twelve sitting beside me, smoking a cigarette which he put away every time the door opened.

"Like a bash?" he asked.

"I would," said I, "very much."

He took a packet from his blazer pocket and handed me a crumpled cigarette.

"Thanks a lot," said I. "But what's this place?"

"It's the juvenile court, ain't it?" said he.

I was glad in a way. They could hardly give you twenty years' penal servitude here, but on the other hand, it seemed a funny place for a Republican Army man to be tried.

"It's for anyone under seventeen," said the boy.

Well, that was why Charlie was gone to some other place. He was three months older than I, and a couple of weeks over seventeen.

I was brought before the court, and a lady on the bench told me politely enough that they had no power to try me on that charge in their court, and that, therefore, I was being sent over to the magistrates' court.

At the magistrates' court, it was a much more important business.

The police solicitor asked if they would try the case in camera, and the magistrate asked me if I had any objection.

I said I had, and that it was supposed to be a principle of justice that it be done in public.

Apart from anything else, I wanted my people at home to know where I was, to send me some papers or cigarettes, and to see that at least I was not done in at Walton Prison. Already there were stories at home of the warders having incited the convicts to attack our fellows on the exercise yard in Dartmoor. I did not want to die or be beaten silly, unknownst to anyone that would care a damn about me. But I did not say this to the magistrate, only the bit about justice being public.

He smiled at me, and so did other people in the court, and said that the police felt that it would hamper them, and give information to certain parties, if the case were not in camera; and in camera it was. I was remanded for a week, when he assured me the proceedings would be "as public as one would wish."

The sergeant came round to me afterwards and I asked him if he had a cigarette, and he had none on him, but went back to the police solicitor, who gave him ten Capstan for me, and I stuck one in my gob before I got rightly out of the court, and he told me for Christ's sake to wait till I got into the cells, or did I want to have them all sacked and get everyone in trouble as well as myself?

And in the cell, I saw, was Charlie, with the other prisoners waiting to go up to Walton Jail.

I took out the packet of Capstan, and we lit up and smoked, as Charlie said, "like lords' bastards."

Later in the afternoon, we were brought up to the day-room, and fell into line to have our possessions marked off and signed for. A policeman put them in a leather satchel.

When they had finished with me, the turnkey said, "That's the lot, and keep a tight eye to this bleedin' Irish patriot 'ere."

I looked at him steadily.

"And take that look off your face."

"That's all right, Constable," said the one with the satchel, "'e's going some-where now, where they'll kick 'is arse into good manners."

I sat beside Charlie. Opposite us, in the Black Maria, was a red-haired boy of my own age, and a small man with a broken nose, a cauliflower ear, and a begrudging look. He was going up for kicking his wife. He was not unfriendly, and told me his name was Donohoe. I said that by a coincidence that was my mother's name. It was not her name, but civility costs nothing.

The noise of the traffic, as we passed through the city, was a sad sound. It is impossible to see anything out of the Black Maria. There are slits along the top, but only for ventilation. Donohoe and the red-haired boy argued about the places they thought we were passing.

"We're going through such a street. I can hear so-and-so's mill whistle."

"No, you can't. We're on such a road. That's not such a whistle, it's such another one's horn."

Charlie and I looked at each other in boredom, but said nothing, only listened with respect when Donohoe gave his opinion.

"There," said Ginger, "what did I tell you? We're going up such a street; I can hear the railway yard."

"No," said Donohoe, "that ain't the railway yard."

Before Donohoe could say what it was the Black Maria pulled up with a crash that nearly threw us off our seats.

We could hear the driver arguing with someone on the road. He turned in his cab, and shouted into the policeman: "Bleeding bastard there, ran straight across me, I've a good mind to get him a summons. ——ing coal lorry."

The policeman turned to us. "Could have killed the lot of us."

Ginger said, "——ing bus drivers."

Donohoe said, "Was a coal lorry."

"Well, coal lorries. Think they own the bloody road."

We were patently delighted with each other, and all we'd suffered under this coal lorry driver, and the policeman cocked his head sympathetically, while Ginger told a story about a coal lorry he nearly saw knocking down a woman with a pram, and Charlie said it was the same in London with these bastards. I said that in Dublin they were notorious.

The policeman listened with judicious attention, and only turned the deaf ear when I mentioned Dublin. When I had returned humbly to silence, he was friendly and voluble with the others, and I at least was permitted to listen.

Yes, he agreed, we might have been killed, and some of the drivers nowadays should never have been let behind a wheel.

As far as the jail gate, we considered the position. Till the van pulled up, and the policeman closed up again. Ginger said the driver of the Black Maria must have been a good man, to pull up in time. The policeman said:

"When I open this door, hop out and stand in line in the yard, till I tell you. And no talking."

"We know that," said Donohoe, the begrudger. And to give him his due, they were the first and only words he addressed to the policeman.

We got out, and stood in the front yard of the prison. The outside gate closed on us. As it swung to, I saw the bit of road outside. There was an old man going past, shoving a handcart before him, his breath steaming on the cold air. As he looked in, I suppose he said to himself, "You're never bad, but you could be worse," and pushed on in better heart.

It was a cold raw evening, and the light leaving the sky, wondering how it ever got into it.

The big main door of the prison had a decoration over it. A snake in chains. Crime, strangled by the law. I knew what it meant. There was a similar piece of sculpture over Kilmainham Prison. I had often passed it with my father, taking me for a walk on Sunday mornings. It was where he had first seen me, from his cell window, during the Civil War. I was born after he was captured, and when I was six weeks old my mother brought me up to the jail and held me up, on the road outside, for him to see from the cell window.

A warder came over and chatted with the policeman.

Charlie whispered to me, wondering if we would get anything to eat.

The warder turned on us. "Hey, you, cut out that nattering. You're in prison, now, and if you don't want to begin with a dose of bread and water keep your mouth shut."

We were brought to an annexe of the prison; a single-storied building. Inside, a warder, wearing a white coat, stood by a desk, calling out names. As each name was called, the policeman took our possessions from his satchel, the warder listed them, and we signed the list, in our turn. When this was finished, the policeman went off, the warder and he smiling cordial farewells to each other.

"Now," said the warder, "if you've anything in your pockets, turn 'em out."

I turned out my pockets. Except the one I had the cigarettes in, the Capstans I got off the sergeant.

"Will you turn 'em over, Mr. 'Olmes?" said the warder to another.

Mr. Holmes turned us over. He found a bit of shoelace on Charlie.

"Want to practise sailors' knots or something?"

Charlie said nothing.

"Why did you not hand it over?"

"I didn't know."

"You didn't know—what?"

"I didn't know it was any harm."

Mr. Holmes roared, "You didn't know it was any harm—what?"

"Oh, I didn't know, sir. Sir, I didn't know, sir, sorry, sir."

The other warder came down, and looked at Charlie. "Remember when you speak to Mr. 'Olmes in future, you'll 'ave respect and haddress 'im properly."

"Or," said Mr. Holmes, "any other hofficer of the service, as Mr. Whitbread will tell you."

Mr. Holmes and Mr. Whitbread looked at each other, fine-featured.

Mr. Holmes searched Donohoe, and found a piece of paper in his pocket. The begrudger looked at him.

"You won't want that, you know," said Mr. Holmes. "We give you toilet paper, 'ere."

"I know all about what you give 'ere," said Donohoe.

Mr. Holmes passed on to me. Oh dear dilapidated Jesus, why did I keep those bastarding Capstans?

He passed his hands over me and came to them in some excitement. "What 'ave we got 'ere, eh? What? What 'ave we 'ere?—Mr. Whitbread, sir."

Mr. Whitbread came down and stood with Mr. Holmes in front of me. Mr. Holmes held up the cigarettes, and Mr. Whitbread looked at them.

"'Oo 'ad this little lot, then, Mr. 'Olmes?" asked Mr. Whitbread, who had just seen them taken from my pocket.

"This one 'ere, sir." He spoke into my face. "Tell Mr. Whitbread your name, you."

"Behan, sir."

I put my first name first. In moments of stammering it's easier to pronounce.

"Tell Mr. Whitbread your Christian name," said Mr. Holmes.

"Maybe you don't 'ave any Christian names in Ireland," said Mr. Whitbread.

"Br-Br-Br-Brendan Behan, sir."

"Yes, Behan," said Mr. Whitbread, quietly, looking at his list, "I've got you 'ere all right. I.R.A. man, ain't you? Don't like us much over 'ere, do you, Behan? Pity, you know, seeing as you're going to spend a long, long time with us. About twenty years. That's what the last lot got at Manchester, wasn't it? And you was going to blow us all up, Behan? Weren't you, Behan?" My name seemed strange to me, the way he said it. "Weren't you, Behan?" He shouted into my face. "Weren't you?"

"Answer Mr. Whitbread, Behan," said Mr. Holmes reproachfully.

"Not much of the old rebel in you now, Behan, is there? Thought you blokes would 'ave brought over your ox-guns with you," said Mr. Whitbread. "Do you know what an ox-gun is, Behan? It's what they 'ave in Ireland for shooting bull-shit out of."

He looked at the others. Mr. Holmes laughed, and the ginger boy, and Charlie's face was serious and troubled till he looked away from me and laughed with the rest.

"And 'old up your 'ead, when I speak to you."

"'Old up your 'ead, when Mr. Whitbread speaks to you," said Mr. Holmes.

I looked round at Charlie. His eyes met mine and he quickly lowered them to the ground.

"What are you looking round at, Behan? Look at me."

Young Cuchulainn, after the battle of the ford of Ferdia, on guard the gap of Ulster, with his enemies ringed round him, held his back to a tree and, supported by it, called on the gods of death and grandeur to hold him up till his last blood flowed.

I looked at Mr. Whitbread. "I am looking at you," I said.

"You are looking at Mr. Whitbread—what?" said Mr. Holmes.

"I am looking at Mr. Whitbread."

Mr. Holmes looked gravely at Mr. Whitbread, drew back his open hand, and struck me on the face, held me with his other hand and struck me again.

My head spun and burned and pained and I wondered would it happen again. I forgot and felt another smack, and forgot, and another, and moved, and was held by a steadying, almost kindly hand, and another, and my sight was a vision of red and white and pity-coloured flashes.

"You are looking at Mr. Whitbread—what, Behan?"

I gulped and got together my voice and tried again till I got it out. "I, sir, please, sir, I am looking at you, I mean, I am looking at Mr. Whitbread, sir."

"Well, Behan," said Mr. Whitbread, "now you've learnt that lesson, remember this: We've only three sorts of tobacco 'ere. Three Nuns—none today, none tomorrow, and none the day after."

The others laughed, Mr. Holmes, the ginger boy, and Charlie looking away from me. All except Donohoe, still begrudgingly eyeing the wall.

"Understand that, Behan?"

My face burned and I searched my aching head for my voice.

"Answer Mr. Whitbread, Behan."

"Yes—sir. Yes. Mr. Whitbread."

"Don't you forget it."

"No, Mr. Whitbread, no, sir."

He stood away from me, and gave us all his attention, pointing to each one a cubicle.

"Go in there and take off all your clothes."

Each of us went into a cubicle and he signalled a prisoner in grey clothes, who shut the doors.

It was a tiny place, not the size of a dwarf's coffin, with nothing but a wooden shelf to sit on, too small to stretch my legs in. I hoped in Christ this was not a place they kept people any length of time, and stripped.

The door of the spy-hole lifted and an eye appeared. I put my hands over my crotch, and sat shivering.

"Got your clothes off?" The prisoner in grey opened the door, and threw me a towel and a book. He was a short, tubby man; smiling, he looked me all over while he collected my clothes. "You'll only be here a couple of hours. There aren't many receptions today."

A warder shouted, Tubby winked, smiled, shut the door and went off.

The book was a volume of *Punch* for the twenties. Many of the drawings had to do with Ireland, and Irishmen, drawn with faces like gorillas, shooting Black and Tans who were all like the pictures of Harry Wharton you'd see in the school stories, usually in the back. I found it interesting, and there was easy two hours of pictures and reading if I took it carefully.

Charlie, in the next cubicle, slowly tapped on the wall. A bit timid, I thought. I tapped back, lively, and he answered with a more confident, a reassured rally of his knuckles.

Then I read on, in peace, till it was too dark and I could not even make out the illustrations. Besides, I was frozen with the cold.

At last the doors were opened, and we stepped out, holding our towels round us.

The fat prisoner led us to the baths, gave each one a compartment, and closed over the half-door.

Warm and soapy, I lay studying myself. I thought it would be pleasant to die, just there; weary of the struggle, to slip out of it.

But I stood up to soap my legs and looked over the half-door across at Charlie. He was rubbing his chest and under his arms. He smiled over at me. The red-haired boy in the next cubicle winked and smiled, too.

Tubby went round the cubicles, looking in at us.

"O.K., Paddy? Like me to go in and wash your back?"

I smiled. "No, thanks."

He laughed comfortably, and went over and said something to Charlie, who indignantly told him to bugger off.

This made him laugh the more, and in great spirits he went into Ginger's cubicle. There were splashes and Ginger stood up again and put up his fists, "Give over, you dirty old bastard."

The warder shouted down to be silent, or he would do this and that. Tubby shouted back to enquire whether we were all remands wearing our own clothes. The warder said we were. Except for Behan and Millwall. This was Charlie. He was a sailor, Tubby explained, and the King's uniform can't be worn in the nick, only when he'd be going down to court.

The bath had so far revived me that I told Tubby that Behan wasn't a sailor, and why couldn't I have my own clothes like any other unconvicted prisoner?

He told this to the warder, who said I wasn't fit to be in the sailors, or even in the other Services, nor fit to wear the King's uniform one way or another, and that if I gave any more lip he would shove me into chokey, ballock-naked, wearing sweet fugh-all.

Tubby came back, mock serious, with shirts and underpants, putting them on Charlie's door and on mine.

I asked him to turn on the cold water for me to finish off with. He said I must be fughing mad, weather like this.

"I thought the cold tub was the hall-mark of an English gentleman," said I.

"They're fughing fed for it. They don't do it on skilly and sea-pie."

I was glad of a few minutes' chat, and asked him what was sea-pie.

"You'll see it often, before you go to Borstal. Sea-pie today, see fugh-all tomorrow."

He laughed himself into a black knot over this. I'd to wait to ask him another question.

The police had told me that I would get twenty years. Borstal was for kids. Would I only stay there till I was old enough for a man's prison?

"'Course you won't get twenty years. Don't 'eed those fughing bastards. They can't give you a lagging. You're too young. Can't do nothing but send you to Borstal for three years, and you won't do all that if you keep your nose clean. I'd send you to a fughing nut-'ouse, I would, and all your fughing I.R.A. mates with you. I'd 'ave your brains tested. We 'ad some of your blokes 'ere."

I asked him who they were. Most of them were Northerners, from Belfast or Derry, but one was a Dubliner called Jerry Gildea and I knew him well. I was trained with him in an old castle the I.R.A. had taken over at Killiney, near Bernard Shaw's cottage, looking away out over the Irish Sea. Shaw said that no man was ever the same after seeing it at dawn or sunset. You could sing that if there was an air to it. I know a good many besides himself that are not the same after seeing it, and some of them hung or shot, or gone mad, or otherwise unable to tell the difference.

Jerry Gildea was a clerk in Guinness's brewery, and had volunteered to "go active in England" for the period of his annual summer holidays. A fast whip over *via* the L.M.S., a time bomb planted in a railway or an incendiary package in a dock warehouse, and back to the office. "Have a nice hols., Mr. G.?" Smiles, little do you know. "Yes, quite nice, Miss X, thank you. Shall we do file Y., this morning?" Later on, when the history of that epoch came to be revealed . . . begod, there's many a man became a T.D. for less.

But the inscrutable ways of the Lord being what they are, the first day he was in Liverpool an incendiary primer exploded in his pocket, and he walking up Dale Street, and with half his face burned off, he was savaged and nearly lynched by the populace, who apparently disapproved of having the kip burned about their ears. The accident happened just in time for the Autumn Assizes, and when the period of his holiday was over, he had been had up, tried, and weighed off with fifteen stretch under the assumed name of Clarence Rossiter.

(The I.R.A. mostly used Norman names that could be Irish or English, like D'Arcy, Reynolds, or Dillon. But some of them picked names for themselves. I knew a Connemara man who christened himself Thomas de Quincey. He could barely speak English.)

Jerry Gildea's mother, meanwhile, thought her darling boy was sunning himself and refreshing himself to invoice some more porter barrels in the coming year. When we read the news in the Dublin evening papers I was detailed to break the news to his mother that the Clarence Rossiter who had so bravely defied the might of an Empire that day at Liverpool Assizes, and drawn fifteen years for his trouble, was her son, Jerry, and that there would be a vacant stool in Guinness's counting house for some time to come.

His cousin escorted me to the house. A lovely girl, just a few months older than myself. My weight, in fact, if I could screw up my courage to try.

I did, going up the canal, against a telegraph pole, but it was no dice. She wasn't having any just then, and I have a stammer, and it made me worse and more nervous when I'd to meet the old woman.

I felt that if Shiela had let me, I'd have been so strong in myself that I could have split rocks with a kick, but she didn't and I was nervous and not very able to meet anyone, or break the news to Mrs. Gildea.

When we met the old woman, she wanted to make us tea, and all to that effect, but I made some excuse to refuse. She didn't even know that Jerry was in the movement at all.

"M-m-m-mrs. G-gildea," I began. "Y-y-your son, J-j-jerry, w-w-was——"

In the manner most exasperating to stammerers, she proceeded to help me out.

"Ah, sure, God help us. Take your time, son. My son, Jerry, was——?"

"H-h-h-h-he w-was——"

"He was delayed by the boat, was he? Ah, sure you could expect that this time of the year. I'm told the crowds of the world does be in the Isle of Man."

"H-h-he w-was——"

"Nice place, too, and a nice class of people, be all accounts. Talk Irish and all, some of them. More nor I could do. Though the cats doesn't have any tails."

"He was s-s-s-sen-sen——"

"God knows they must be the queer-looking beasts. Still, everyone to their fancy, as the old one said when she kissed the ass."

I caught her by the sleeve, beseeching.

"He-he-he w-w-was s-sent——"

"God help you, and such a nice, nice boy, too. Maybe, it'd be God's Holy Will that you'd grow out of it. Sure, you're not finished growing yet."

"He-he-he w-was sentenced——"

"Sentenced?"

I got it out with a rush. Now or never. "To fif-fifteen years in Liverpool to-to-today."

"Sweet mother of Jesus, comfort me this night," said Mrs. Gildea, and collapsed in a weakness.

"Don't you go believing anything a copper tells you," said Tubby. "It's their business, putting the wind up you when they ain't being sweet to you. Like fughing parsons, they are. You'll go to Borstal, and you'll 'ave a kip-in time, with football, concerts, swimming. Maybe you'll be sent to Portland, where I was. Drake 'Ouse, I was in. Good old Drake," he sighed wistfully. "You might even be sent to one of these open Borstals. You give your word of honour not to scarper, and there's no lock on the dormitory door, even."

He looked over at Charlie.

"He'll probably go to Borstal and all. Want to watch his ring, though. Hey, Jack," he shouted to Charlie, "ever 'ad a length of bo'sun's whistle? Any old three-badge stoker ever shown you the golden rivet."

Charlie stood, holding the towel to himself, proud and fierce. "I'll show you a knee in the balls."

Tubby laughed and gave us the rest of our prison clothes.

"'Ere you are, young prisoners. Y.P. brown jacket, shorts, shoes, stockings and belt. Bloody 'ikers' outfit. Though you won't 'ike far in it."

"Like a bleedin' Boy Scout," said Charlie, putting on his shorts.

"Well," said Tubby, "just get bent over there, and do your good deed for the day."

Charlie bit his lip in temper.

"Don't mind me, kid," said Tubby. "I just can't 'elp taking the piss. Still, there's no 'arm in me. Just a bit of clean fun."

The warder shouted at him.

"Right, sir," he shouted. "Be right along, sir," adding in a lower tone, "You shit-'ouse."

He turned to me. "Ever 'ear of the screw married the prostitute? 'E dragged 'er down to 'is own level." He exploded, laughing at his own remark, and took a moment to uncrease his face into becoming gravity. "Right, sir. Just coming, sir."

He turned to us and said, "Right, you receptions, 'op along."

We were marched back to the cubicles, and locked in them again. I read some more *Punch* till Tubby came round and shoved in an aluminum can of cocoa, and cob of bread with a piece of cheese the size of an oxo cube, but very nice with one

735

bit of the bread, which was all I could eat. Tubby seemed glad to collect all our left-over bread when he came round again.

"I'll take your can, now, Paddy, and that bit of bread. This time next week you'll be offering me a Player for that much. And now, we're 'aving some more mannyquin parade. Get your clothes off again and put that round you." He threw in a sheet and went off with the can and the bread. I did not begrudge it to him. He was a friendly sort of chap, even to me.

I took my clothes, and looked down at myself. My legs were glowing from the bath, and my hairs were curling and still a bit damp, and laziness and heat were coming back into my crotch after the cold water, and even when I bent forward there was no more than a crinkle on my belly. Jesus, it must be the terrible thing to get fat, I thought. Porter it was that fattened people in my own family, and it would be a hard thing not to drink porter with every other decent man, and maybe stand filling your pipe with your back to the counter, and maybe talk of the time you were in jail in England, still that day was a good bit from us yet, but so thank God was the day of old age. I rapped into Charlie, and he rapped back, real lively, with a smooth rally of his knuckles.

They opened the doors and we were lined up outside the doctor's.

"You three Y.P.s stand together," said the screw to me and Charlie and Ginger. We shuffled over together in our sheets. It suited us.

Donohoe stood with some other men prisoners, and their bent old legs and twisted buniony toes on a line, the way, I thought, looking from the smooth neatness of Charlie, and Ginger and me, that God would have a lot to do forgiving Himself for sentencing us all that would live long enough, to get like that.

I was marched before the doctor and stood to attention before him as best I could, in my bare feet and holding up my sheet.

He sat in civilian clothing behind a desk, looked down at a form and up at me. He was a dark man, not very old, and very hard in an English way that tries to be dignified and a member of a master race that would burn a black man alive or put a pregnant woman out the side of the road in the interests of stern duty. Looking at him, I thought of the war, and hoped themselves and the Germans would keep at it.

"What's this, Mr. Paine," he asked the medical orderly.

"This," said Mr. Paine, "is an I.R.A. man, Doctor." Then to me, and almost in the same breath, "Leave off the sheet and let the doctor look at you, Behan."

I let the sheet fall and stood naked. I felt puny and weak and miserable, standing there before them and different from when I was with Charlie or Ginger. My hands moved over to cover my lonely bush of hairs as they looked me up and down.

"You don't call that a man, Mr. Paine?" said the doctor, from his desk.

736

"The best the I.R.A. can do, Doctor. Scrapings of the man-power barrel, I suppose."

The doctor came from behind the desk, and put a stethoscope to my chest and back, and put his hands under my balls, and made me cough. Then he sat me on a chair and tapped my knees. All this, I thought, was civil of him, for all his Herrenvolk looks, and when he asked me whether I was sick or not, I replied, "I'm great, thank you!"

"I don't care whether you're great or not," he said sternly.

"Just answer the doctor," said Mr. Paine, "he hasn't the time for any of your old blarney."

The doctor set his lips and spoke through them, like an English officer in a film about the Khyber Pass. "It is my duty to look after the health of the prisoners here, even yours, Behan, or whatever your name, but I'll stand for no familiarity, particularly from you. Understand, Behan?"

"Yes, sir, I mean yes, Doctor."

"Come to attention when you address the doctor," said Mr. Paine.

I looked anxiously round for my sheet.

"Jump to it," shouted Mr. Paine.

I brought my two bare heels together and took my hands off my crotch and brought them to my side, and stood, naked, to attention.

Afterwards I heard the screws talk about the doctor and what a good man he was, and overworked, and he did go round looking like Lionel Barrymore, and sighing like the doctor in *The Citadel*, but I never heard of him actually doing anything for anyone. The prisoners said that he gave a man two aspirins for a broken leg, but that it was not really viciousness, only stupidity, and anyway, if he wasn't a prison doctor he'd have to go in the Forces.

When I got away from the doctor, I was sent to the reception screws to be weighed and have my height taken. I had to take my sheet off for this, and then I was searched. I had to lift my arms above my head, while the screw looked me all over. He put his hands through my hair, looking for cigarettes, though my hair was still damp from the bath, and, lastly, made me bend over while he held open my back passage with his fingers and looked up there, with a pencil torch. I had heard of this personal search in Fenian times, in a book by Tom Clarke, when he got fifteen years for the bombing campaign of the eighties, but I did not know before what it meant. It was a normal part of prison routine and the screw did it with the usual appearance of British official detachment. I noticed that he only searched Charlie and Ginger and me like this and did not bother with Donohoe, the begrudger, or the other adult prisoners.

Then we put our clothes on and at last were ready for the walk to our cells. I did not know what they would be like. Maybe, I hoped, they would be like the cells you see on the pictures, with two or three bunks—I wouldn't have minded being with Charlie and Ginger—and bars up the side, where you could look out and see the fellows on the other side of the cell block.

We walked through darkness, and doors were unlocked and locked after us, and we stood in a huge, high hall, dimly lit, gloomy and full of a heavy smell of well-washed stuffiness. It was like walking away from the world and back into the times of Charles Dickens. I was thinking about this and had not heard the screw tell us to halt, till he shouted, "You, boy, where do think you're going?" I stopped and he said no more, but made us stand in the circle at the end of the wing.

Charlie and Ginger and I were stood together and Donohoe and the other adult prisoners were marched off, I'm happy to say. I could their feet echoing on the iron stairs and the light being switched on and the doors of the cells banged to.

Then Charlie and Ginger and I were marched on again, till we came to a far wing, and there was more door unlocking, and we were told to stand in the circle. Here we were given our kit—pillowcases containing sheets and a towel and comb and a handkerchief, and cell cards. In the dim light I could see that Charlie's was white, Ginger's was yellow, and mine red; C. of E., Nonconformist, and Catholic, which they called "R.C."

We were walked in darkness through the hall, and first Ginger was called to stand to the door of his cell. Ginger moved around a bit. He could see no cell; neither could Charlie nor I for the matter of that. But the screw switched on a light and we could see a peep coming from the wall in front of us. Then the screw turned a key, and we were looking into the cell.

My Jesus, my heart fell into my boots. It was like a white-washed hole in the wall, like a tomb up in Glasnevin.

"Come on, get in and get your bed made down," said the screw; "don't keep us 'ere all bloody night."

Ginger nodded to us as well as he could and went inside. The screw took the door, slammed it over, then re-locked it, as if the door, which was really a piece of the wall, was not secure enough as it was, and walked Charlie and me upstairs to the next landing. He took the card from Charlie and stuck it into a slot beside the door and locked him up. Then it was my turn. We stopped at another place and he switched on the light, and opened the door. I stepped inside and he slammed the door behind me, rose the cover over the little spy-hole in the door, and looked at me again, and re-locked it, and went off down the stairs in padded shoes.

I looked round me. I could walk five paces down from the door to under the window, which was too high in the wall, even if there was anything better than Liverpool to be seen or heard over the wall. There was a table and a chair, and a mirror, and a chamber-pot, and some bedboards, a mattress, and blankets. The floor was made of slate, and there were also the rules to be read. I decided they were better than nothing, and when I had the bed made on the boards, it was all right. I got in between the sheets, and, though it was only a few inches off the floor, when I took up the rules and started to read them, I felt as comfortable as ever I did in my life. I was dead tired after that plank thing, or hand-carved couch in Dale Street, and was drowsy and falling off to sleep when I heard the cover of the spy-hole being moved.

"You all right, there?"

"Smashing, mate," said I in gratitude.

"What do you mean 'mate,'" said the voice from the door; "where the bloody 'ell do you think you are—'*mate,*'" he spat, vicious and indignant; "and what do you think you're on, putting those notices on the floor, eh?"

"I was only having a read of them, sir" said I, sitting up anxiously in my comfortable bed.

"Read them where they're supposed to be read, on the wall, not on the floor. Come on, get up and put 'em back."

"Yes, sir," said I, got up quickly, in my shirt, hung the rules back on the wall, slipped quickly back into bed, lay there breathing quietly till the screw dropped the cover of my spy-hole and went on to the next cell.

I lay in the dark, and heard the sounds of outside, dim and mournful, away over the walls in the distance. A church bell rang out on the frosty air, and I got further down into the warm bed. Eight o'clock, it rang out. I'd have thought it was later than that, much later. It seemed like a year since I came from the court, but the bed was warm and comfortable after the bath, and I was tired after that Dale Street, and I was soon asleep, and half-eating the sleep till I got so far down into it I was unconscious.

⋎

Mornings, we were awakened at six and slopped out, throwing the contents of the chamber-pot into the bucket brought round by the prisoner appointed to this position. There was competition for the job because the same man brought round the breakfast and might nick a bit buckshee for himself. I nearly got sick looking at it, but the screws shouted briskly, "Come on, sling it in, look sharp," and if he was a decent screw he might even say, "I've got to get my breakfast, too, you know."

Then we went down to the recess with an enamel jug and got water for washing. There was only one lavatory on each landing, and it was impossible to get in and use it, with another thirty or forty fellows queueing for water for washing, and rinsing round the bottom of the chamber-pots to get out what had not gone into the big slop bucket. Some of the orderlies did get using the lavatories after they had emptied the slop bucket and while they waited on the breakfast to come up from the kitchen, and it was considered a great thing, because it gave the cell a chance of freshening itself a little during breakfast-time, with an empty pot.

The breakfast consisted of a tin of porridge with an ounce of sugar, six ounces of bread, and a tiny pat of margarine.

Our two landing screws, of whom we saw one or the other first thing in the morning, were Johnston and Mooney. These were in charge of the Young Prisoners because they had special qualifications in Y.P. training. Johnston had been twelve years in the Scots Guards and Mooney had been middle-weight champion of India.

Johnston was cross-eyed. In the Guards they are made to wear their hats over their heads. It makes them keep their heads erect. Because if they don't, they won't see where they are going. He was over six foot, tall and lean.

Mooney was a chesty barrel of a man. He gave us P.T. every morning, in a Lancashire accent. He was a Catholic, "R.C." they called it. Catholic warders were the worst. Irish Catholics, worst of all. They showed their loyalty to the King and Empire by shouting at me and abusing me a bit more than the others. The next worst were the Scotch and Welsh. The Cockney warders were very rare, and the least vicious of all.

One warder, who looked very young, with red cheeks and a happy rough North of England accent, used to smile and whisper "Up the Republic," whenever he was on the locking or unlocking of the doors. Once or twice he gave me an extra slice of bread. He had an English name and I heard the other fellows say that he came from Durham, but maybe his mother was Irish, or his wife, or maybe he was just a decent man that didn't give a God's curse. You find an odd one everywhere.

All the time it was cold and black. In the morning the slate floor was freezing cold, and over the whole huge wing was a cold smell of urine and bad air, like a refrigerated lavatory.

It seemed to me the English were very strong on washing and cold, but not so much on air and cleanliness. Like the well-tubbed and close-shaven looks of the screws—cruel and foul-spoken, but always precise and orderly.

When breakfast was eaten, I had to clean the cell, or wash it. Every morning the bedboards and table and chair had to be scrubbed and the black slate floor rubbed with soap to make it blacker still. We were issued with two big bars of soap a week. It was the only thing we were not short of, and when the morning's cleaning was over, the blankets and sheets laid out for inspection, and the bed-board and plate and mug laid out in a special way on the newly scrubbed table, there was a shine on the cell furniture and the black glistening newly soaped floor and a heavy smell of human excrement over the place that would make you respect the stern fishy eye and the stiff thin lip and the steady and high-purposed gaze of Englishmen doing their duty.

When all was ready for inspection you could have the morning bowel movement. Not before. Business before pleasure.

Unless it was a Chief's inspection. In that case you would have to wait a couple of hours, as no one could leave their cell, even to empty a chamber-pot, until he had gone round. Only once did it happen that a bloke couldn't stick it out and used the pot during breakfast-time. He had finished the porridge and tea and bread, and his stomach was loaded. The breakfast was the most likely meal to do this, because it was the only one that filled you. The dinner and supper were safe enough, and even if you did want to use the pot, you could as much as you liked, and empty it after dinner, or leave it in the cell till morning after supper.

This bloke couldn't stick it out this morning, anyway, and used the pot after eating his breakfast. The screw, when he opened the door and your man tried to get down to the recess to empty it, nearly died of shock and horror. Here was a prisoner with no pot to be laid out for inspection, and the Chief an ex-Navy man, so particular. He let the fellow go down the landing to try and smuggle it into the recess, and empty and clean the pot, but the P.O. was looking up from the bottom of the wing and let a bark up to the screw as to where that man thought he was going with that pot, before the Chief came round, and the fellow had to go back.

The screw got out of it as best he could by making it up with the medical orderly to say the man had medicine the day before. But it was a narrow thing for the screw, and the other screw, the medical orderly, was heard by a prisoner to say that he couldn't take the can back if it happened again.

The prisoner was a Channel Islander, from a place called Peter's Port, and the screw said he'd bloody soon cure him of his dirty French habits.

The screws were forever telling each other they wouldn't take the can back. They hated each other's guts and all with good cause, but never gave us the satisfaction of hearing them saying anything abusive to each other, only an odd dirty look or a mutter. They shouted, "mister" and "sir" to each other all day. When a prisoner left their party or when they were telling another screw at the far end of the wing that prisoners were being sent down to them, they would shout, "One on to you, sir," and "one off, mister." When the Principal Officer passed they would come to attention, so rigid with respect that you'd nearly think they'd burst from keeping themselves tight. When the Chief passed through, which was more seldom, they shouted even louder and got even tighter, and when the Governor came through the wing, they shouted so loud, "Ill Kirr-ect, sir," so loudly and tightened up so much till he'd passed on, that I wondered what was left for a Prison Commissioner if he passed through—they'd have dropped dead from tightening their guts to attention and forcing a thinner but more concentrated "Ill Kirr-ect, sir," from between their thin lips.

On my first morning, I was brought down to the end of the wing to see the Governor. He had an office in each wing, on the left-hand side, looking towards the end, where the P.O. stood and looked out from his kiosk. This wing office of the Governor was a sort of vice-regal apartment in each of the halls of the prison.

His real office was somewhere in the main hallway of the prison, but only very important people were ever allowed or brought there—like a murderer coming back after being sentenced to death, who would be allowed to sign for his property and that there, instead of going through the reception where the other prisoners coming back from the court would see him. As regards his bath, they would give him a bath during the time he was waiting to be topped, all on his own, with a screw to turn off the water and turn on the water, maybe late at night, when nobody else would be going there.

The morning after I came in I got up and folded my blankets, and did out my cell, and ate my breakfast, and used the chamber-pot and slopped out with the rest, but was not opened up with the others when they went down to work. I thought it was something to do with being Irish and that, and in a way I was not displeased but a little bit frightened, till they came to my cell and opened the door and told me to put on my tie, for I was for the Governor.

I went down and stood with Charlie and some other fellows outside the office. The other fellows were wearing shorts and were Y.P.s the same as us, but they looked very old to me. There were three of them and all of them looked as if they shaved at least three times a week. I was hoping to God I wouldn't be left among fellows the like of that, because apart from being big, they did not look too friendly. But Charlie and I and Ginger stood together, happy enough, and listened to the whispering of the others. They were there for extra letters and one fellow was there about a visit from his wife but they said we would all have to wait till the Governor was finished with some fellows that were being had up over having snout. One fellow was a remand but had brought in a butt, a dog-end they called it, off exercise, when he was supposed to throw it in the bucket which was there for that purpose; and another fellow, a convicted prisoner, had been caught with a dog-end which this remand had brought in for him the day before, and which the remand fellow had told about when they caught him and asked him was he bringing in the dog-ends for himself or somebody else.

When the two fellows were brought out of their cells and rushed into the Governor's office to be tried and sentenced, the other Y.P.s that were waiting with Charlie and Ginger and me just laughed and said they'd get Number One, the both of them. They whispered their laugh, but seemed really to enjoy it because they thought it was funny to be punished. For somebody else to be. They seemed to think the screws were better men than themselves, because they could do these things and get fellows put on bread and water and stand up in the circle when the Governor was gone and they were done saluting him, and bend their knees, belch, break wind, yawn, and shout at some fellow they caught talking a bit extra at his work, when he was supposed to be only asking for a loan of a scissors. The prisoners thought the screws were comedians when they caught some fellows like these two merchants and got them to inform on one another and then gave them both solitary confinements. They had a slang term for informing. "Shopping," they called it. A nation of shoppers, and if that's the way they would treat one another, my Jesus, what would they do to me?

My name was shouted at last and I was rushed before the Governor. I was told to stand to the mat, state my registered number, name, age, and religious denomination.

I stood to attention and said, "Behan, sir, sixteen years, Catholic." I did not know my number, but the screw standing beside the desk shouted it for me.

"Be-han, Bren-dan, three five oh one, sixteen years, Y.P., remand, R.C." Then he said "sir" to show he had finished.

The Governor was a desiccated-looking old man, in tweed clothes and wearing a cap, as befitted his rank of Englishman, and looking as if he would ride a horse if he had one. He spoke with some effort, and if you did not hear what he was saying you'd have thought, from his tone, and the sympathetic, loving, and adoring looks of the screw, P.O., and Chief, that he was stating some new philosophical truth to save the suffering world from error.

"You-re—er—remanded—er—till Friday—er—I see—er. See—er—that you behave yourself—er—here and give no—er—trouble to my officers—er." At this point the officers looked sternly, and almost reproachfully, at me, and so intense was their grateful look towards the feeble old face of the Governor that I almost expected them to raise an exultant shout of *"Viva il Papa!"* "If you give— er—us trouble—er—we'll win—er . . . we'll win all the time." The officers' faces set in determination with him. "We can—er—make it—er—very—er—bad for you—er, it's—er—all the same—er—to us, and—er—it's up—er—to you, whatever—er—way you—er—want it."

I was marched out and told to wait outside. We were to see our clergymen and I was looking forward to meeting the priest. Maybe he would be an Irishman, and it would be like water in the desert to hear a friendly Irish voice again.

But the screw put me back in my cell while the others went to see the Protestant chaplain. The priest would not be in till Monday.

I was disappointed but thought that it would make a break in Monday morning, and this was Friday, so after tomorrow I would have Mass to look forward to on Sunday morning, and after the visit to the priest I would be well into the week till I went down to the court on Friday, and that would be that week over.

After a little while I was opened up again from my cell and brought down to the hall of the wing where we sat on our chairs in silent rows, about sixty of us, sewing mailbags. The class instructor, they called the screw who went round showing the prisoners how to do the bags, and examined them or complained about the bad work when it was more or less than four stitches to the inch. That seemed to be the important thing, and most necessary for salvation.

He came over to me and sat down on a chair beside me and showed me how to wax the thread and put it through the canvas with the palm, which was a leather band with a thimble in the middle to save the skin of the palms, though sometimes even the most expert had to shove the needle through the canvas with the forefingers and thumbs, which in most of the prisoners were scarred like the hands or arms of drug addicts with the needle marks you would read about.

On Saturday afternoon we were locked up from twelve-thirty. The screw gave us a half-hour's exercise from twelve o'clock and remarked that it was handier than taking us out for exercise after dinner. It got the whole lot finished early, he said, and we could be left in our cells till morning. We all nodded our heads, and quickly, in agreement with him. It seemed the right thing to want to be locked up in your cell over the week-end, and I even felt my own head nodding when the screw said it was better to get the exercise over with so that we would not have to be opened up again after dinner.

So locked up we were, and Charlie and I and Ginger smiled at each other, so that the others would not know that we were not used to being locked in a cell from half past twelve on Saturday morning till slop-out at seven Sunday morning, and in we went. The dinner was old potatoes, cold, and a slice of bully beef and a piece of bread. This was always the Saturday dinner and I heard a screw saying that it was like that to give the cook a chance to get off, and after all he wanted a rest, too, and when he said that we all nodded our heads, and were glad the screw was so nice and civil as to say it to us.

↓

After breakfast on Sunday, I heard the C. of E.s being fell in and marched off to their chapel, and later I heard the strains of hymn-singing coming from a distance. I walked impatiently and happily up and down the cell, washed and with my hair combed, and wearing my tie, a brown piece of canvas, but still it fitted in with my brown frieze jacket and my brown shorts. I was waiting for our own turn to go to Mass, but the singing of the C. of E.s was good to listen to. They sang a hymn to the tune of *Deutschland Uber Alles*, which surprised me a little bit, till I remembered that the British Royal Family were all Germans and spoke German in their own palaces.

Then our own cells were opened up, and Mooney the screw stood in the hall, and shouted, "R.C.s fall in for morning service, bring your prayer books and your 'ymn books." I had not seen the priest yet, so I had no prayer book or hymn book.

But I did not want any prayer book to follow the Mass. That was the same the whole world over, from one end of it to another.

I had been extra religious when a kid, and the day I made my First Communion I had prayed to God to take me, as Napoleon prayed, when I would

744

go straight to Heaven. I was a weekly communicant for years after, and in spasms, especially during Lent, a daily one. Then I had difficulties, when I was thirteen or so, with myself and sex, and with the Church because they always seemed to be against the Republicans. My father had been excommunicated in 1922 with thousands of others, and so had De Valera, and the Bishops were always backing the shooting and imprisoning of I.R.A. men. I had been for the Republicans in Spain; and it seemed the Church was always for the rich against the poor. But I had never given up the Faith (for what would I give it up for?) and now I was glad that even in this well-washed smelly English hell-hole of old Victorian cruelty, I had the Faith to fall back on. Every Sunday and holiday, I would be at one with hundreds of millions of Catholics, at the sacrifice of the Mass, to worship the God of our ancestors, and pray to Our Lady, the delight of the Gael, the consolation of mankind, the mother of God and of man, the pride of poets and artists, Dante, Villon, Eoghan Ruadh O Sullivan, in warmer, more humorous parts of the world than this nineteenth-century English lavatory, in Florence, in France, in Kerry, where the arbutus grows and the fuchsia glows on the dusty hedges in the soft light of the summer evening. "*Deorini De*"—"The Tears of God"—they called the fuchsia in Kerry, where it ran wild as a weed. "*Lachryma Christi*"—"The Tears of Christ"—was a Latin phrase, but in future I would give Him less reason for tears, and maybe out of being here I would get back into a state of grace and stop in it—well, not stop out of it for long intervals—and out of evil, being here, good would come.

I fell in with the rest and noticed that there were a great number, more than half those I'd seen sewing mailbags in the hall, going to our chapel.

Nobody spoke, of course, but everyone seemed happy, and smiled a bit kindly at each other, like going on a factory outing, for even the screws seemed a bit relaxed and only said, "Straighten your tie, lad," "Tie up your laces, there, boy," and "You put down for an 'aircut, Crapp, Tuesday, like a bloody poet going round there, you are," and we even laughed a bit, quietly.

We marched into the chapel and it was like any church at home, only for a wooden notice-board with numbers on it for the hymns. I'd seen such things in pictures of England. But everything else, the tabernacle, the lamp, the candles, and the stations of the Cross around the walls, were the very exact same as at home, and when the priest came out, genuflected, and began the prayers before Mass, I blessed myself and happily whispered my prayers with him.

The Acts of Faith, Hope, and Charity and the Act of Contrition. . . . "Oh, my God, I am heartily sorry for having offended Thee" . . . so I was too. . . . "Who art worthy of all my love . . ." and that was the truth, and I promised "never more to offend Thee and to amend my life" . . . and I would and maybe here I could get closer to God, and I was sorry it was only in a place like this you appreciated Him, but that's the way with human beings, and He'd know our weakness, and I'd make it up to Him, when I got outside, just to show that it wasn't only as a Friend in need I wanted Him.

The chapel held about four hundred men. The very front rows were occupied by forty thin, haggard and frightened men and boys. They sat apart from each other and kept their eyes fixed straight ahead of them on the altar.

These were the prisoners from the punishment cells, from chokey, where they were on bread and water, Number One Diet, and others of them on Number Two Diet, bread and water for breakfast and evening meal, with a mixture of porridge and potatoes for their midday meal. They were in solitary confinement twenty-four hours of the twenty-four, and this was their only diversion during their time in chokey. They were doing from three days to six months. I noticed half a dozen Y.P.s amongst them, dressed in shorts and coat, the same as the rest of us Y.P.s. They sat apart from each other and apart from the other chokey merchants, at the end of the front bench nearest the door.

The priest was a fat man, and looked reassuringly like a country parish priest at home that you'd see going to a greyhound meeting and wouldn't be afraid to have his ball of malt of an evening.

The server was a little thin miserable-looking Englishman.

I had often heard people at home, who had been to England, saying that you could tell an Irishman on the streets even if you were not personally acquainted with him.

I was beginning to be able to do this, and the priest looked like an Irishman and I was very anxious to meet him in the morning. I would be consoled by the sound of his voice, and whole Faith was a consolation, and I'd often heard the old people say that it was only in time of trouble we appreciated the Faith, and it was the truth—you could say, it was the God's truth.

I had often been impatient with the Church because the Bishops attacked the movement, but still it was like being let to the warmth of a big turf fire this cold Sunday morning to hear the words of love and consolation:

> "There in Thine Ear, all trustfully,
>   We tell our tale of misery,
>   Sweet Sacrament of Love, sweet Sacrament of Love."

Then we went back to our cells and waited till the Methodists came out of service, when we all went out to exercise together. Charlie and Ginger and I marched round behind each other, and even got in a few words of conversation on the way through the passageway from the exercise yard to the wing.

There was a great smell of dinner and the screws shouted, "Come on, hurry up, the quicker you get in your cells, the quicker we get the dinner," and happily we clattered up the iron stairs and into our cells.

They came with the dinner, and it was roast meat with baked potatoes and bread and cabbage, and I smiled at the screw, taking it from him at the door, and he gave me a knife and fork, too, from a box of them he had, and I slammed out my door and sat down to the dinner. I nearly spoke to it and said, "Dinner, I shall never forget you," and I didn't forget it either and never will.

It was cold sitting on the chair, after my dinner. I thought about dinners. Maybe, in a way, the best one was the pork and beans, though it did not taste as good as the Sunday one, with big lumps of pork fat in it, but it filled you better. You were not let make down your bed and lie on it till the bell went at eight o'clock, but Lord Jesus, I was perished with the cold. I sat on my chair facing the door and pulled my mailbag up over my legs, and put my hands down my shirt. Not too far down, though (save that for tonight), and besides it would be dangerous if a screw looked in the spy-hole at me. Not that that was against the rules—at least I hadn't heard it was—and even if the screws mentioned it, it was in a joke; but it would be embarrassing to have them see you, and they would more nor likely jeer the heart out of you for the rest of time. I wished I had something to read, though. At least, thanks be to God, the R.C.s got another service on Sundays. We'd be going to Benediction shortly, where the C. of E.s and the Methodists would be left in their cells. Poor bastards, the ministers were too bloody lazy to come in and disturb themselves by getting up from the fire this cold evening. But I had always heard of the priests and their devotion to duty (even Protestants gave into it) in the first war—priests like Father Willie Doyle, S.J., and Father Patrick Bergin that were killed along with the troops.

Sure enough, at about three o'clock I heard the doors being opened on the ground floor, and the screw coming up the stairs and he opened the door of a fellow opposite I had seen at Mass in the morning. I had left the spy-hole cover up before I came into the cell at dinner-time and I could see the boy opposite stretching himself contentedly and yawning, standing in the doorway.

My own door was unlocked and the screw said, "Stand to your door," and went on, opening the doors of the other R.C.s, anywhere he saw a red cell card.

Then he called us down to the ground floor. We straightened our ties and marched off to the chapel. I could see some of the other spy-holes and the glint of an eye looking out, wistfully, I suppose.

There was the same crowd in the chapel, only there were no chokey fellows. Us Y.P.s sat in the two front seats instead.

The little rat-faced severe-looking one was lighting the candles when we came in. The fellow beside me, a pale boy from Birkenhead, said the server was doing a five stretch for rape.

There you are again, said I to myself, our Church is not for hypocrites, it's for sinners as well as saints, and one mortal sin is as good or as bad as another, whether it was against the Sixth and Ninth Commandment or the Fifth or Tenth.

Ratface was about the ugliest server I'd ever seen, and a real cup-of-tea Englishman with a mind the width of his back garden that'd skin a black man, providing he'd get another to hold him, and send the skin 'ome to mum, but Our Lord would be as well pleased with him if he was in a state of grace as He'd be with St. Stanislaus Kostka, the boy Prince of Poland, and race or nationality did not enter into the matter, either, one way or another.

We sang the Benediction hymns, and I had the fellows in my seat and behind me looking at me. The screw looked at me from where he knelt at the end of the seat. I'm a good singer, but you wouldn't know whether the screw was vexed or pleased by my voice rising over the rest. But rise it I did, and fugh the begrudgers:

> "... *et antiqum documentum, novo ce dat ritui.*
> *Salus honor virtus quo que sit et Benedictio....*"

Ratface swung the thurible with a will, till there was a cloud of incense you could hide yourself and go asleep in, and when it died down a bit the priest began the Divine Praises:

> "Blessed be God, Blessed be His Holy Name, Blessed be Jesus Christ, true God and true Man, Blessed the Name of Jesus.... Blessed be the Name of Mary, Blessed be Her Holy and Immaculate Conception.... Blessed be God in His Angels and in His Saints...."

I was a bit disappointed to notice that the priest had an English accent of the "Haw, old-boy" type, but maybe he had to speak like that to make himself understood, and anyway wasn't it English people he was ministering to?

And no matter what accent he had, wasn't there yet another pleasant surprise in store for us, when the Benediction finished?

The priest went in off the altar carrying the Monstrance and attended by Ratface, but even then they didn't bring us back to the cells.

The screws put the lights on, so that it looked real cosy in the chapel, and everyone looked round them a bit, and the screws never said anything but just gently rebuked an odd one that wasn't satisfied but had to start whispering too. And then the priest came out on the altar wearing only his soutane and biretta casually on the back of his poll and a Sunday newspaper under his arm.

Everyone's face lit up and he began to read the football results and make an odd joke about them, about Burnley and Everton and Liverpool, and the prisoners tittered and had to laugh aloud sometimes at his jokes, and even the screws couldn't repress a grin themselves, much less have anyone up for laughing.

And after that he went in, smiling himself at us, and we marched back, happy and still smiling at some of the things he said, and clattered up the stairs in the dark to our cells where the lights were on in each open door, welcoming us, and the orderlies came round with the supper, the cocoa, the bread, the margarine, and the cube of cheese, and I settled down contented over my steaming mug on the table, waiting for the bell at eight o'clock when I would make down my bed and go asleep.

There was a black dark frost outside and the cocoa was smashing and warm. It was now four o'clock and the biggest part of the week-end punched in, thanks be to God.

On Monday morning we woke and it was almost a merry noise after the long week-end, though us R.C.s had a right to be thankful for our two services on Sunday.

I could hear the doors opening and shutting, and coming nearer and nearer, and I stood with my pot ready till it would be my turn and I could get rid of it.

Everyone tried to get a couple of shits in the daytime and during the time they were sewing bags, and only use the pot for pissing in, but it was not so easy when we only got out of the cell for a half-hour between Saturday noon and Monday morning, so most fellows had to use their pots for everything and the smell this Monday morning was so foul that I felt myself getting sick, when the door was opened, though I suppose my own cell added its quota to the general stench. I emptied my pot into the brimming bucket and joined the queue at the recess to rinse it clean at the tap. I met Charlie there, and while we waited we had a bit of a chat.

Everyone seemed to want to wait on everyone else so as they could whisper a bit longer.

"We get a smoke this morning, Paddy, and all," Charlie whispered. "We fall out, a geezer told me, with the other remands, and exercise smoking, going round the ring."

"Come out of that recess, come on, 'urry up, get moving there," the screw shouted.

"See you later, Pad," whispered Charlie, waving his free hand and running up the landing with his pot.

When I came back to my cell there was a bucket of water, a dirty black mat for kneeling on, a scrubber and a bar of soap.

"Take that in," said the screw, passing my door, "and scrub your furniture and floor, and soap your floor when you've dried it. I want that furniture as white as snow, and the floor as black as soot—got that?"

"Yes, sir," and I ventured a smile in honour of the poetry of the soot and the snow, but the screw meant it as serious wisdom, and only nodded.

"Take it in, then, and get crackin'."

The breakfast came round before I had started and I ate it, and then, God of war, did I want a crap. I squatted down anyway, and used the pot. There was a lid thing for it and when I finished I put it on, and started to scrub the furniture; bedboards, table, chair, and wash-hand stand, and then started on the slate floor, to wash it first, and dry, and then I got on my knees and soaped it, and had to move the chamber-pot out of my way, like some covered dish of disgust.

When I had finished, the cell had the smell of shit and soap—the first smell I was conscious of, when I came into the reception, the smell of a British jail.

I finished my washing and made up the bed, putting the bedboard on its side against the wall, the mattress lying with it, and the bedclothes draped over it, blanket, sheet, blanket, sheet, blanket, the cover lying the length of the top of the mattress and board and the pillow on top. The table at the side, with my plate and mug flanked by my knife, the tin toy one we used except when we had meat for our dinner like Sunday, and got a real knife and fork issued to us for the duration of the meal. I laid my spoon the other side of the plate and mug, and if I said so, myself, it looked real neat.

When the screw opened the door I looked at it, not ashamed of it.

He looked round him for a minute, and then at me. It was Mooney, the short, chesty, Catholic one.

"What the bloody 'ell do you think that is, eh?" he snarled at me. "Come on, lad, come on, why isn't your pot laid out, with the cover off, eh?"

"I'm—I'm after using it, sir."

"You're aaaf-ther using et," he spoke in a mock Irish accent.

Johnston, the long skinny Birkenhead bastard, appeared in the doorway, "What's to do now, Mr. Mooney?"

"This feller 'ere was to clean out his cell and leave it ready for inspection and 'e 'asn't even got 'is pot clean and laid out. 'I'm aaafther using et,' 'e says. I suppose I can tell that to the Chief and all when 'e comes round. ''E's af-ther using it, sir.'"

"Stick 'is bloody 'ead in it," said Johnston, and indignantly, "don't stand there, you dirty Irish pig," he roared at me, "it's swine like you turn a good officer wicked. 'Ow can 'e be 'alf decent with bastards like you trying to get everyone in the shit? Come on." He got me by the neck and shook me. "Come on, get bloody well down to the recess and clean out that bloody pot of yours, get on with it!" He nearly flung me across the cell. I gathered the pot and cover and went down to the recess with it, emptied it, and cleaned it under the tap.

Coming back along the landing, I could see the glint of an eye from behind an odd spy-hole. They'd have been looking out wondering what the row was, and thankful that it wasn't them was involved.

Mooney locked me in the cell again, and I laid the pot in its proper place. The table was at the right side of the cell as you looked in. On it was my plate, flanked, as I said, by my tin knife and my spoon, and with my salt cellar at the back of my mug. On the left side, standing against the wall, was my mattress, and, lying against it, my bedboard with the bedclothes laid out along it. In the middle was my mat, rolled up to show there was nothing in the line of dust or dirt concealed under it. My mailbag of the cell task lay on top of that, with my needle, palm, and scissors laid out on top of that again. My chair was behind the mat, and in the centre of all. My basin laid upside down on the seat, to show that it contained no dirty water, and my chamber-pot at one of its front legs, lying on its side, clean and decent for all to see, and at the other leg, to match it, the cover. I laid out my carpet slippers against the rung of the chair.

These were made out of pieces of old cloth, and were supposed to save you making noise on the head of the fellow in the cell under you, when you were walking up and down.

But after you'd been in a day or two, you had no time to walk up and down, because you were doing your cell task, and in any event, you got used to sitting on your stool, staring at the wall, and having a bit of a read now and again. The staring at the wall saved your library book, because only two a week were issued and the only fellow who couldn't read more than that in the time he was in his cell would be a fellow that wasn't able to read at all.

I had no books yet, so I'd been staring at the wall any time I was not in bed, or sewing the side of my mailbag, so I had not worn my carpet slippers.

The screw opened my cell with others after breakfast, and shouted at me: "What bloody way 'ave you your kit laid out? Get that bloody lot into shape before I come back or I'll get really angry with you—you sloppy Irish bastard." He went off fuming to the next door.

I was miserable enough to myself, looking around hopelessly at the cell. I had washed it and laid out the stuff as best I could, and I was hopelessly looking at it, for I could do nothing else for the reason that I didn't know what else to do.

But when I heard him coming back, after he's finished unlocking the doors, I bent over the bedboard and fumbled with the sheets and blankets, so as to be doing something, and not just standing there. He came back, and looked in the open door at me. "You're a reception, and waiting for the R.C. priest, so you won't be going down to work anyway, but before the Chief comes, by Christ, if you haven't got that lot straightened out"—he reached over and caught me by the hair—"get on with it, you bastard, don't stand there looking at it!"

I was frightened and fumbled around with the bedclothes another bit, till I got hopeless and didn't know what I was doing.

"Christ!" said the screw, and I really thought I was for it, expecting a blow. I stood there with the bedclothes in my hand. He went out on the landing and shouted to someone. I sighed to myself, and waited.

God's help is never farther from the door, for the next thing was Charlie was in the cell with me, and the screw was showing him. "Your cell is not extra good, but it's better than this Irish pig's pigsty, and you know how to make your bed up. Well, show 'im, and try and get some shape on this bloody lot before 'e goes down for the R.C. priest. You're a reception, aren't you? And you're for the doctor, aren't you?"

Charlie began helping me with the blankets and laying them out.

And a bad time was turned into a grand one, for he left Charlie there and went off.

We looked at each other, and smiled.

"This is a bit of all right, Pad, n't it?" said Charlie.

"Handy enough," said I. "That's an awful whore's melt, that screw, Charlie."

"He is and all, china, there's nothing the matter with your cell furniture, the way it's laid out. It's just like it says on the card there—but the bedclothes could do with a bit of straightening out. But the screws just find fault with everyone. It's like in the Glass'ouse, they give a geezer a toothbrush and an eggcupful of soapy water and tell him to scrub the lawn, it's just to be bastards, that's all. Then he don't like Irishmen, that screw. According to what he was saying"—he lowered his voice—"Pad, they got the dead needle for you, Pad, the screws; and, Pad, some"—he spoke as if embarrassed at having to mention something shameful— "some of the blokes don't fancy you neither." He spoke in his serious, concerned, boy's voice, and I felt older, and spoke to him reassuringly.

"They can go and fugh themselves, Charlie, I didn't expect anyone to lay down a red carpet for me if I was pinched over here."

"I don't care, Paddy, if you were in the I.R.A. or what you were bleedin' in. You're my china, Paddy."

I looked into his serious eyes and smiled. "I know that, Charlie."

He smiled. "That's stright-up, Pad."

The screw came back. "You should be finished now."

"Yes, sir," said Charlie, "I've just shown 'im." He turned round to the screw.

The screw looked at us sharply. "Well, get back to your own cell, you, we've no married quarters 'ere."

Charlie blushed and bit his lip. "Yes, sir," said he, and without looking at me went on back to his own cell.

"You get your tie on and be ready for the R.C. priest," he said to me, and banged out my door.

I stood by my mat, not wanting to walk on the clean black floor, with my tie on and waiting to be called. I also decided I wanted to piss and it seems to be always times like that when they can't that people want to. I was there a half-hour or so, when I heard the screw down below calling for "Bee-hann."

The screw on the landing came running up, opened the door, looked at me, and told me to hurry down and get fell in for the priest.

There was a small queue for him outside the doctor's room, and I fell in and waited happily. Every time a boy came out, a screw came out with a list and called a name till at last he called "3501 Behan," and I smiled and willingly hurried to his side. "Go inside and stand to attention, feet to the mat."

I ran, and came smartly to attention at the mat, looking at the priest.

It was the same man, a stout block of a man, God bless him, that had said Mass. He was a bit bald and wearing glasses. I smiled at him and said, "Good morning, Father."

"When are you going to give up this business?" His two eyes glared at me from behind his glasses, and his accent was that of someone who had got a better chance in life, as they'd call it, than their parents. It was the accent of O'Sullivan, detective-inspector from Cork—the Irish peasant's son trying to imitate the Lancashire lad's son whose dad 'as made a bit o' brass.

I shivered and hadn't been expecting this, but now it happened that this priest, too, was part of Walton Prison, I wasn't surprised. Tom Clarke saw Dr. Gallagher in Portland with his lips a mess of raw meat, streaming blood where he had gone mad and started to chew glass.

He told the priest, and the priest told him to mind his own business. The priest had a bad name amongst Irish Republican prisoners, even the most pious of them.

"Haven't you any manners, Behan?"

"Answer Father Lane, Behan," said the screw, who had shut the door and was standing beside me.

"I don't know what business you're talking about, Father," said I.

"You know all right—your membership of this murder gang—the I.R.A."

"The I.R.A. is not a murder gang, Father," said I. Grip tight and hold on, said Tom Clarke. I'd do my best. Clarke held on for fifteen years, and lived to fight the bastards on more equal terms in Easter Week.

"Don't answer Father Lane back, you——" With difficulty the screw held back the low expletive, in deference to the man of God. The screw took a step half-towards me, but the priest put up his hand.

"It's all right, Mr. Millburn," he sighed, and they nodded to each other sympathetically. "Cardinal Hinsley and the Hierarchy of England have issued pastorals denouncing the I.R.A., and while you're here I cannot let you come to the altar, unless you tell me once and for all that you're giving up having anything to do with this gang."

His small eyes looked up at me, and his mouth closed tight in authority.

"Why should the Bishops of England be supposed to have the right to dictate about politics to an Irishman, Father?" I asked, as steadily as I could.

Mr. Millburn looked angry and indignant towards me, but the priest held up his patient hand. "The Bishops of Ireland have denounced the I.R.A., Behan, time and time again, even early this year. The Church has always been Ireland's best friend, in Ireland, here in England, and all over the world. I must inform you that your own clergy and Hierarchy have excommunicated the I.R.A. You are automatically excommunicated till you repent of your sin in being a member of it and promise God in confession to sever all connection with it. Surely you can't set yourself up against the Bishops, an ignorant lad against educated men, who have spent their lifetime studying these matters?"

"I didn't spend a lifetime studying theology, but I know that the Church was always against Ireland and for the British Empire."

Mr. Millburn again looked angry, but the priest looked wise and tolerant, and indicated that I might continue.

"With no disrespect to you, Father. A synod of Irish bishops held at Drumceatt in 1172 decided that any Irishman that refused to acknowledge the King of England as his ruler was excommunicated. That was only three years after the Normans landed and held only a bit of country not the size of the County Louth, the smallest of the Thirty-two Counties. The O'Neills in Ulster even after the Reformation had to threaten to the Pope that they would burn the Catholic Archbishop of Armagh, Richard Creagh, out of the Cathedral if he didn't take Queen Elizabeth's soldiers out of it. In 'Ninety-eight weren't the rebels excommunicated and wasn't Father John Murphy, that was burned alive by the yeomen, excommunicated? Didn't Archbishop Troy issuing pastorals condemning the 'Ninety-eight men, and didn't he have prayers offered up in thanksgiving when poor Robert Emmet was captured?"

"Look here, you," said the screw, Mr. Millburn, and Father Lane looked angry, through his little eyes, but a bit surprised. But I didn't care now. Me blood was up and me country in me knuckles.

"Didn't they condemn the men of 'Forty-eight and tell the people to give up their crops and die of the hunger in the ditches at home, with the grass-juice running green from the dead mouth of a mother clutching a live infant——!"

"Here, you," began the priest, in a gathering roar, but I might as well throw the hammer after the hatchet.

"Weren't the Fenians excommunicated, and didn't the Catholic chaplains in Portland and Chatham join with the rest of the warders in driving Dr. Gallagher mad with torture when the Fenians were doing their solitary confinement in Tom Clarke's time?"

Mr. Millburn glared at me in amazed anger. The priest swallowed his temper and tried to speak, but rage got the better of him and he could only signal to the screw to take me out. But, be Christ, I wasn't done yet. Before Millburn reached for me, I said to the priest right into his seething little eyes: "And excommunication is nothing new to the I.R.A. Didn't yous excommunicate De Valera and ten thousand others in 1922? Didn't Bishop Cohalan of Cork excommunicate the I.R.A. and support the Black and Tans before that? Wasn't——" Millburn grabbed me but I finished what I had to say, eyes blazing and my heart in my ears—to hell with you, you fat bastard, and to hell with England and to hell with

Rome, up the Republic, lurry him he's no relation, the greasy fat bastard trying to show himself a Limey gent with the rest of the screws. "Wasn't my own father excommunicated and him in Kilmainham Prison in 'Twenty-two?"

"Get out, you swine," said Mr. Millburn and threw me out of the priest's office. But I was quiet now. I had said what I wanted to say and would go peaceably to my cell. If I was let. But I wasn't.

"Mister Mooney," said Mr. Millburn to Mr. Mooney, who hurried up the wing from where the rest of the Young Prisoners were sitting in rows sewing their mailbags. In indignation, "This—Irish swine—insulting—the priest——" Mr. Mooney nodded, shocked, and hit me a blow in the face, without taking his attention from Mr. Millburn, and Mister Johnston came up as they shoved me towards the stairs leading up to the landing, and they told him, Mister Millburn and Mister Mooney, "This—Irish—insulted priest—bloody bastard"—not the priest, me, and Mister Johnston, though not a Catholic, but a Protestant and wouldn't bloody well stand for that all the same, insulting any clergyman, any priest even, and especially Father Lane, decent man beloved by all and spending his time working for the prisoners. "You fughing shit-house, we'll teach you 'ow to be'ave, you dirty Irish fugh-pig," and, grunt and push, I fell a couple of times on the iron steps on the way up to the landing. "Wait till we get you up there in the cell— now by Christ we'll—ge-eh-t up, there, you bastard, you Irish ——!"

They took me to the cell, and beat me in the face, slaps but not punches. The punches they gave me in the ribs, in the kidneys, and once or twice they hit me across the face with a bunch of keys, but concentrated mostly on the guts and a few kicks in my arse, when they sent me sprawling across the room and shouted all the time about killing me, and insulting the priest and me a half-starved Irish bastard, and they'd give me I.R.A., and the cell was in disorder with the bed-boards and bedclothes scattered all over the place, and then they shouted at me to clear that bloody mess up and get that lot straightened out and went off banging the door locked, and left me alone, thank Jesus, and still breathing, though heavily, and getting back into breathing practice.

I fumbled around the cell as best I could. I had left the jug full of water in the cell in the morning and I took the liberty of bathing my face with the cold water, and had a look in the mirror when I was finished. My face was not too bad, nothing noticeable, though my lip was cut on the inside where I got the blow of the bunch of keys, and I could feel the blood going down my throat and sickening me. I was also now being sickened, and a cold clammy sweat was coming out on my hands and on my forehead now in delayed action for the fright I hadn't had time to have when they were dragging me up the stairs and belting me in the cell. I wiped the sweat off, too, and then got a kind of sick bilious headache, and I wanted to have a shit, and so I did in quick time on the pot and wiped myself and had the cover on and was up and about again in no time, when the door opened and a prisoner and a screw stood in the doorway. They had a parcel of books, and the prisoner handed me two and wrote my name on a card.

"Don't go swopping them now, you," said the library screw. He had a Cockney accent and was a long, cadaverous-looking man with glasses. "Unless you want to 'ave a little trip down to chokey."

I took the two books in my hand. "I will not, sir," said I, "and thanks very much."

I spoke so fervently that he looked at me as he spoke. "Don't thank me, thank the Lord. You're an Irishman, ain't you? I can tell by your brogue. I got a book about Ireland. Remind me about it or ask for it by writing on your slate for me when we come round Tuesday next week. Write on it, 'Please leave *The Life Savers*, the Irish book.'"

The prisoner was a small, rat-faced man like a twin brother of the altar-boy. Maybe they had a supply of these merchants for library and altar work, all in for rape. But he nodded kindly to me, and I said, in his direction as well as in the screw's, "Thank you very much, and I'll leave you the note if I don't see you."

"Right, Paddy," said the librarian, and "Right, Paddy," said the prisoner, and the prisoner I noticed banged out my door and I turned to lay the books on the table. Better than a dozen of stout it was to see them there, the books.

It didn't look like there was going to be anything more about this morning, and I could have a read tonight, resting my bruises for a bit before the lights were put out, and, happy, I looked at the books and looked forward to the night, for all my mouth was raw and bleeding still a bit and painful on the inside, and my kidneys, if that's the things you have on your sides, were sore and maybe this bit of a belting they got would be a contributory cause of my early death in the years to come, but sure what matter of that? One thing at a time, and I looked forward to my read, and it was decent of that old fellow to call me "Paddy" and say he'd give me a book about Ireland, though I never heard of anything called *The Life Savers*. Maybe it was one of those banned books by Joyce or one of those fellows, in which case all the better as the old one said when she was told that there was no tea but only porter.

In any event I should have a read, and a read every week, and a kind of payday to look forward to when they changed the books; and, thinking these thoughts, I had the cell, between bedclothes and all, laid out and tidied up, and I gave myself another rub with the cold fresh water and had a look at myself in the mirror and I looked all right, except my mouth was a bit bloody with a thin red line around the edge of it, but I wiped that off too and then let myself have a look at the books.

It's a queer world, God knows, but the best we have to be going on with.

↓

One of the books was *Under the Greenwood Tree* by Thomas Hardy, and the other was the life of General Booth, the founder of the Salvation Army. I looked at them a good bit, over and over, but did not open them except to look at the fly-leaves. I was standing on one leg leaning on the table and looking at them, without using up as much as a page of either one. I didn't notice time, till I heard them coming round with the dinner. A great smell it had too, coming nearer and nearer, till they came to my door and opened it the same as they did everyone else's and I took the dinner in; and in the afternoon I was opened up with the rest and got down and emptied and cleaned the chamber-pot and went out and sewed mail-bags with the rest till four o'clock when they locked us up for the night, and gave us our supper till the night was in and the day over, and divil a much the matter with me, everything all right, thanks be to God and His Blessed Mother, only for my mouth being still a bit raw when I sipped my mug of cocoa—but I didn't mind that, looking forward to getting into my bed, being warm, unharmed, and with a book to read.

I was feeling my inside lip with my tongue, and being careful not to eat on it, when the spy-hole cover was lifted, and a voice said, "Ahst ad tha cuckoo, Paddy lad?"

This was a Young Prisoner called Brown. He was a nice decent little round ball of a fellow about eighteen, and went round with the scoff and was an orderly. Everyone liked him, and called him Browny, and he smiled all the time, going about his work, and even the screws didn't seem to mind. He came from some old bog road part of Lancashire, and I think they liked him as a bit of Old England (for the English are very nationalistic). They smiled when Browny spoke in his funny dialect to them, and some of them even answered him in the same way, taking him off in a friendly fashion. He was a bit of a pet with every-one, and I think the screws looked upon his lingo in somewhat the same way as in Ireland they'd look upon the Irish of a lad from the Gaeltacht, in a tender smil-ing approving sort of way.

He was a good little fellow anyway, and I held my mug of cocoa up for him to see, and smiled in the direction of his eye and said, "I've had my cocoa, thanks, Browny."

The eye winked and said: "That's a good lad, Paddy. Ah'll see thee tomorra; g'neet, lad."

"Good night, Browny," said I, and he scarpered off down the landing.

The bells out in the city rang a quarter to five, and I sat with the cocoa and bread and cheese hot inside me till five o'clock, when I started my cell task.

I had to side three mailbags, and it was easy enough to do, now that I had done a few days at it (not that I was a natural sewer), and I was looking forward to *Under the Greenwood Tree*, when I would be done; so I was fairly quick and when the bags were finished I shoved my chair back from the door a bit and turned into the table, stuck my legs in the mailbag, pulled it up tight about me, and when I opened the book on the table I put my hands down under the bag and was warm all over, though the air of the winter night was black cold and blunt as metal.

The lad going home in the late Christmas Eve, and singing the bar of a song for himself:

> "With the rose and the lily, and the daffodown dilly,
> The lads and the lassies a sheep-shearing go."

I tried not to read any more than my ration. There were two hundred pages in the book—that was about thirty a night. The life and times of General William Booth wouldn't be much use. I had read a bit about him in a "Penguin" by St. John Ervine, a North of Ireland man who was manager of the Abbey Theatre when my uncle was property man there. He was in favour of the Salvation Army, but he said their enemies accused them of groping for Jesus in the dark. This book, though, didn't look it would have anything like that in it. Still, it would do for having an odd look at it the week-end, and I could save a bit of *Under the Greenwood Tree* on it. It would be better than nothing, like my father's song about the small potatoes in the time of the Famine:

> Oh, the praties they were small over here,
> Oh, the praties they were small over here,
> Oh, the praties they were small, but we ate them skin and all,
> They were better than fugh-all, over here.

We all used to laugh, only my mother, who said it was a disgrace and a shame to be making game of the poor people that died in Black Forty-Seven and the dead mothers that were found with the green grass-juice trickling from the sides of their mouths and the babies crying and tugging at their dry breasts.

But honest to Jesus, you'd have to laugh at my old fellow, and he put in bits like that into national songs, and it was all equal to him, he'd nearly put them into hymns, only he was never much where they'd be singing any.

He was a great fiddler and so was my uncle, my mother's brother, who had a fiddle presented to him by the prisoners in Ballykinlar Internment Camp for writing the National Anthem. My mother was a good singer, and my stepbrother's aunts were pianists, and great nights we had in their big house on the North Circular Road. I could see my old man with the fiddle, standing beside the piano, and Aunt Emily playing the piano and this book in a way reminded me of them. All these old West of England men, with the cider barrel and mead and meat and cheese.

It was like that at home only, strange to say, we were all city people and these were countrymen. But even their speech when they said "carrel" and "traypsing and rambling about" was like Dublin speech.

And they went round playing their carols in the bright frosty night, and I had to go on reading after page thirty and up to forty to where it was Christmas Day and they were having the Tranter's party that night; I couldn't miss that, so when the bell went I got into bed and read on, warm and enjoying myself, and Dick, the lad that was singing the song at the beginning, is trying to get off his mark with the new school-teacher, a nice little mot of seventeen or eighteen and just my own weight, if it went to that, and everyone is drinking and singing, till they come to the part where they're going to dance and I had to read on there, too, promising myself that I would read only fifteen pages tomorrow night, and make it up with fifteen of the Booth book, which more than likely would not be so quickly read, and the Tranter got the wife up to face him, in the dance.

"Reuben," says she, "was always such a hot man," and she no way ashamed of it, and maybe she ought. It put me in mind of my mother and father, and he getting her up to take the floor in "Haste to the Wedding," and the two of them singing:

> 'Twas beyond at Macreddin, at Owen Doyle's Weddin',
> The lads got the pair of us out for a reel,
> Says I, "Boys, excuse us," says they, "Don't refuse us,"
> "I'll play nice and aisy," says Larry O'Neill,
> I looked at me woman, the song she was hummin',
> Was ould as the hills so I gave her a *póg*
> 'Twas like our ould courtin', half-serious half-sportin',
> When Molly was young and hoops were in vogue. . . .
>
> Says herself to meself, "We're as good as the rest,"
> Says herself to meself, "Sure we're better nor gold,"
> Says herself to meself, "You're as wild as the rest of them,"
> "Kathy," says I, "sure we're time enough old. . . ."

The next morning I was brought before the Governor and told that I could use the money that had been found on me to buy food, cigarettes, and papers.

But I knew no one in Liverpool to get me the food, and the Staff did not want to help me to get food (they thought they were treating me well enough in letting me buy cigarettes and papers, and according to the Governor they were not required even to do that—"to fetch and carry for me," he said).

I was glad to be let have a paper, and I put down for the *Daily Herald*. I asked for *Reynolds News* for Sunday, and the Governor said I could not have *Reynolds News* which was not an approved paper but I might have the *News of the World* which was.

Years and years ago, when I was a child, my father used to get the *News of the*

World, and said it was for the sheet music on the back he bought it. I used to wonder why he laughed, and why my mother said, half-laughing in spite of herself, that he was a terrible man, because it was banned at home, before I could read, and I only saw it once or twice in the Tech when some fellow sneaked it out of his house where it had been posted from England, and on building jobs I saw it an odd time.

It was a very interesting paper, mostly about *that*, and I had enjoyed Charlie's copy in the Bridewell, and I was looking forward to seeing it every Sunday; with that and the *Daily Herald*, and a smoke every day, my standard of living was going up with a bang.

That day I started the life of Reilly, as you might say.

I went to work as usual in the wing on the bottom floor, sitting on my chair in line with the other prisoners. Then the screw called out "Remands and awaiting trials for smoking," and I fell in behind Charlie and the other remands and we went out to the yard.

We fell in in front of a cabinet, and when the screw unlocked it there was a drawer in it with a number corresponding to each cell in the Y.P. wing. There was a drawer with "C.2.26" on it and in it were kept my cigarettes.

The screw struck a match, and we each went up in turn to get a light. Then he warned us not to try bringing a butt into the wing, and that if we did we'd get Number One. "And no talking," he shouted; "now get spread out."

We walked round the ring in single file, smoking like lords' bastards till the frosty air had a great smell of smoke in it, and a kind of an outside smell.

For fifteen minutes or so we walked around and then an orderly came to the gate from inside the prison carrying a bucket. The screw opened the gate and he came out and left the bucket on the steps and stood beside it.

The screw then called us up, and in turn we dropped our dog-ends into the bucket. We marched back again to our seats in the hall and took up our sewing again, while the screw went off down with the orderly carrying the bucket to the recess, where it would be thrown down the lavatory and the chain pulled out by the screw.

Twelve o'clock was not long coming round and I had my paper to read. When I got up to my cell, there it was waiting for me on the table. It was great to see such a thing, although it was a lonely thing in a way to be reading only about things and places I neither knew nor cared about. But it was something to read, and secondly it saved the *Greenwood Tree*, and it couldn't be denied that it was a great and a notable thing to be able to sit there with the day's paper spread out while I leant over my dinner. I could see myself getting through all this, even through a long sentence, and still coming out alive and kicking, even though at the very least I would be over twenty years of age. Still, there were Young Prisoners here that were twenty-three, for I'd seen it on their cell cards, and they looked it.

There were three of them that were fairly old. Two of them were Licence Revokes, fellows who had been in Borstal, and released on licence and brought back to the nick. Dale and James. Dale was a big, Spanish-looking fellow and he told me one day, and I sitting near him, that he was Liverpool-Irish and that his mother was from Westport, County Mayo. He was a bad bastard for all that, and told me in a hurry that he didn't like Irish people, that he was an Englishman himself, and that Irishmen came over to Liverpool to work for scab wages.

I tried to whisper to him in an urgent stammer that that was wrong, that the wages of a Dublin building worker, painter, plumber, carpenter, bricklayer were the highest in Europe, as they were for bakers and printers and most other trades, and that the wages in Liverpool in the painting trade were so low that a fourth-year apprentice in Dublin or Cork or Belfast or Derry or Limerick who would get a bigger rate per hour.

He didn't listen but turned on me and, as if I had done something on him and he was only restraining himself from giving me a belt, he said, half aloud, "Just shag off, you Killarney bastard, or I'll 'it you."

The screw looked down and said angrily, "What's to-do down there?"

"It's this Irish bastard, sir," said Dale, "'e keeps talking all the time—I just told 'im 'e'd get me in trouble."

I looked up at the screw and was trying to tell that Dale had spoken to me first, telling me that his mother was from Westport, County Mayo, and that I didn't care where she was from, nor was I asking any of these bastards to be Irish, but I couldn't, and anyway the screw looked down at me and shouted in a more even and venomous way than he had before:

"I'm just about browned off with you, you gabby Irish bastard. Move over your chair there and get on with it. I shan't warn you again, I shan't. I've warned you before and this is the last time."

I moved over my chair and kept my head down so as the others looking at me couldn't see my red face, but I looked up again when I had my face set right and went on sewing the canvas, staring straight ahead. I could see from the corner of my eyes fellows in the rows in front of me, letting on to reach for their wax or their scissors on the ground beside them so as they could give a quick glance at me from under their arm. I just stared ahead and hated, fixing my eyes on the British coat of arms on a fire-extinguisher on the wall behind the screw.

And for the rest of that morning and other mornings following, I sat by myself on the edge of the row and kept my head down and was ready when the time was up to get my chair and go up to my cell without having anything to do with anyone.

But Dale was promoted, when another fellow got sentenced, to go on the table. James went with him.

On the table they collected the work for the screw when it was finished and they could call him to reject the work if they didn't like it. On siding the seams of the canvas, which was what I was at, the stitches were four to an inch. I was not a very good sewer, but after a week I was able to do it properly, and God knows there was little enough to it, but every time I went to the table to give up finished work they called the screw and he gave it back to me and called me a "stupid Irish bastard." Dale laughed at this a lot, and so did James.

Then I stopped bringing up my finished work, and kept it beside me, waiting for the day the instructor would come round and collect it, but then when I went up for another canvas Dale said I couldn't have another one till I brought up some finished work.

I went back to my chair and sat down. Dale and James were jeering at me, and calling me names in a low tone of voice that only the other fellows at the back rows could hear, and they were looking at me and laughing, too.

Jesus, if they'd only let me sit there and sew away, I could be looking down at the canvas and watching my stitches and seeing them four to an inch, and passing the time myself by thinking about Ireland and forgetting even where I was, and, Jesus, wasn't that little enough to ask? What harm would I be doing them? If any of them was in Mountjoy, say, and I was there with a crowd of Dublin fellows, I wouldn't mess them about, honest to Jesus Christ I wouldn't, no matter what they were in for. And that James, that was a proper white-livered whore's melt.

He had whitey-coloured hair and a sharp little nose, and though he was about twenty and maybe a little bigger than myself, I was not afraid of him. I couldn't say that I was not afraid of Dale because I was. He was a big well-set-up man and James only trailed after him, like a bully's labourer. But, by Jesus for that again, if I was afraid of the engine-driver I was not afraid of the oil-rag. No, be Jesus, and I twisted the palm round in my hand. I'll James you, you foxy-faced drippings of a cankered ——, you poxy bastarding whoor's melt, I put it to myself, and thought it worth it to hit him a belt, but; when all is said and done, I was but sixteen and he was a grown man and had come through Borstal institutions, mostly, I would say, by sucking up to bullying big bollixes the likes of James, not by letting his backstraps down—he was too ugly for that, but maybe some of these bastards would get a bit of a drop. I was no country Paddy from the middle of the Bog of Allen to be frightened to death by a lot of Liverpool seldom-fed bastards, nor was I one of your wrap-the-green-flag-round-me junior Civil Servants that came into the I.R.A. from the Gaelic League, and well ready to die for their country any day of the week, purity in their hearts, truth on their lips, for the glory of God and the honour of Ireland. No, be Jesus, I was from Russell Street, North Circular Road, Dublin, from the Northside where, be Jesus, the likes of Dale wouldn't make a dinner for them, where the whole of this pack of Limeys would be scruff-hounds would be et, bet, and threw up again—et without salt. I'll James you, you bastard.

Then the smile had to fade and the joke was rejected and the gentleness refused, never a better nor my own sweet self, and it wasn't off the stones I licked it. The old fellow would beat the best of them round our way and him only my height now, though fully grown a hell of a long time. James, be Jesus, prepare to meet thy Jesus. And I just stood up, held up a bag and said, "Finished work," and the screw nodded, though I hadn't said "sir" because I hadn't time.

I walked up to the table and stood there till James stood up. That was as well; it would never have done if it had been Dale that stood up. It was James, and I held out the bag to him.

"Finished work," said I.

"Oh, is it?" He put on his sneer, too thick to notice any difference in me. He looked at it in great annoyance, no less, but glad, as I saw by his lips settling for more sneering, to have another bit of diversion at my expense. The more fool you, you bastard, said I in my own mind. He looked at me and took up the bag. "What's to do with you? You Irish bastard, that's one of them you 'aven't done right. 'Ere, take it back and do it again, cop."

He flung the bag in my face, and Dale laughed, and so did the fellows turning round in their seats, pleasurably, as when the curtain rises on a play.

I took the bag and laid it on the table and looked sorrowfully at James, miserably like Oliver Twist, to meekly and hopelessly enquire: "Please, oh please I did nothing to you. Why are you so cruel to me?"

I led with my right and came up with my left, but my open palm with the metal thimble, right up into James' face. He went down and tried to hold his face down and I caught him by the hair with my right hand and held back his face while I rammed him in the face with my palm, the metal one I mean, and his blood was pouring over my hand, and the screw came rushing down; but I was more afraid of Dale, who'd got up from his seat, and I pulled James still by the hair farther down the table so as the screw would get me before Dale could get over the table and give me a few belts, free gratis and for nothing, saying he was stopping Young Prisoner Behan from taking the life of James, Young Prisoner.

And, dear dilapidated Jasus, was I going well at it till the screw caught me and pulled me off James and he went blinded and moaning and holding his hand to his face and the pouring blood.

He went round in a circle of blood, and it dripping from him, holding his hands to his face and moaning words and music.

The screw came down and I thought he was going to start battering me there and then, but he didn't. Johnston, the long skinny ex-Guardsman it was, and he looked at me from his coffin face, and said quietly, "Stand there a minute, you," then he turned and shouted down the wing to a screw who was going round searching the cells, "Here a moment, Mr. Thorne, will you, sir?"

The screw, Thorne, came running when he saw the cut of James.

"Been a bit of bother 'ere, Mister Johnston?"

Johnston nodded and said, "Will you take James over to the hospital while I take Behan up to his cell?"

"Right, come on, lad," said Thorne to James, "and take your 'and from your eyes, if you don't want to trip over yourself and do yourself some more damage. You are a proper bloody mess, as it is."

I stood and waited for Johnston to bring me up to my cell. He was waiting for a few more screws to come up and give me a battering, and for the P.O. to come up and supervise it, I supposed, but I didn't care. I had a look with great satisfaction at the other bastards sitting in their seats and looking round at me. There was no laughing or grinning or jeering or jibing with them now, the shower of shit.

I caught Charlie looking down at me and he gave me a kind of a good-bye look, sad and friendly. That cheered me up a bit, and I looked back at him as much as to say: "It'll be O.K., kid. I'll be seeing you again, won't be both returned for trial to the Assizes till the end of January, and that's still nearly two months away. They'd never give me that much Number One."

I supposed wrong about the battering, too. Johnston just took me to my cell and said, "I suppose you know you'll be for the Governor in the morning, Behan?"

"Yes, sir," said I.

He nodded and shut the door, and I heard him taking my cell card out of the holder outside to make the report. Then he went back down the stairs.

I was delighted, thinking of James, and him going round a walking advertisement to the other bastards to leave me alone.

I took my book and started celebrating with a bit of a read extra. I might as well read as much as I could because they'd more nor likely take it away from me in the morning anyway.

Bejasus, and no one could say that Dick Dewy wasn't getting every chance of a running leap at Fancy Day. He brings over her furniture up to the new house where she's to set up as the village school-teacher; and there he was sitting on his hunkers trying to get the fire going till she'd make the first cup of tea in the house; but by the way they were "Yes, Mr. Dewying" and "Do you think so, Miss Daying?" they'd be there till the Lord would call them before he'd get down to introducing Fagan. And a bed and all in the house.—I heard tell the bed was a gift, far and wide in front of the standy-up job. Bobby Hamill, on our corner, got married to Gloria Carmody when he was only sixteen, and he said there was no comparison. I was sorry over that. That I regretted, and if the judge was to get up at the Assizes and say, "You silly young eedgit, you're not going to get a chance of chasing a mot now till you're no longer a youth, and you can pull your wire now till we let you out," and it's a very well-known sociological class of a phenomenon that, after a long number of years in the nick, men coming out are not able to do anything else. God between us and all harm.

Ah, but Dick wasn't as green as he was cabbage-looking. "Dick, Dick, kiss me and let go instantly—here's somebody coming!"—it's me, Brendan Behan, 3501, H.M. Prison, Liverpool, Vol. Brendan Behan, 2nd Battalion, Dublin Brigade, Irish Republican Army. But I didn't, only started thinking about my cocoa and cheese tonight, maybe the last meal I'd eat for a while, and a man needed all his strength in the times that were in it. Not to be thinking of things like *that*.

In the morning I was left locked up when the others went down to work and until they went out to exercise.

Then the screws shouted "Behan" and rushed up to my door and opened it and said, "Quick, you, put on your tie," though I already had it on, and we rushed down the stairs to the bottom floor and up to the Governor's office, where the Chief looked out at us, the P.O. flung open the door and shouted, "Stand to the mat, and state your full name, number, age, religion, and sentence."

I went in and stood to the mat, and said, "Behan, Brendan, sir, three five oh one, age sixteen, Roman Catholic, awaiting trial."

The old Governor sank back in his chair and didn't look up, but read a sheet of paper in front of him.

Johnston stood, cleared his throat and looked at the P.O., and the P.O. looked at the Chief, and the Chief looked at the Governor, and this time he nodded his old head, and Johnston read off a paper about my assaulting James; and when the P.O. nodded to the Chief and the Chief nodded back to the P.O., the P.O. looked at the Governor, who looked up slowly and said:

"You—er—heard that—er, Behan? That charge that the officer has just read?"

"I did, sir," said I, with my hands at the seams of my trousers and looking manly, admitting my fault to this tired old consul, weary from his labors amongst the lesser breeds, administering the King's justice equal and fairly to wild Irish and turbulent Pathan, teaching fair play to the wily Arab and a sense of sportsmanship to the smooth Confucian. In my ballocks, said I in my own mind, you George-Arliss-headed fughpig, dull scruffy old creeping Jesus, gone past the Bengal Lancer act now back to where you started, like a got-up gentleman with his Curragh cap. Bejasus, any decent horse would drop dead from the shame if he managed to get up on its back. "I did, sir."

He screwed up his keen eyes, which you'd know had been used to gazing over wide open spaces from the gate to the hang-house and said: "There is no need to call the other prisoner. I would warn you that for this offence I could have you charged in the magistrates' court, and I must take this opportunity of warning you that if this assault had been carried out on one of my officers"—the Chief, P.O., and Johnston, the screw, gathered themselves up off the sands of the desert and looked at him, proud and grateful, and looked at me—"or even a lesser sort of violence offered them, you would most certainly have been flogged."

I looked at him and merely nodded, to show my commiseration with him for the trouble I gave him in belting James, but also my horror, at the thoughts of doing anything so awful as striking or offering to strike one of his officers. I had no wish to commit suicide, and secondly I wasn't fed for it.

The old Rider Haggard head of him shook, and he said, "I sentence you to——" What the vicious old cur would have sentenced me to, I'll never know, for the Chief leaned forward to tell him that I was going to court the day after tomorrow. The Governor nodded and said, "And remember this is only a warning to you——"

I nodded my head and looked at him as earnestly as I could. I'll go straight, Gov., strike me pink if I don't.

"——to one day's cellular confinement, one day's deprivation of mattress, and one day's Number One diet."

Well, good old Rudyard, what an escape, I'd be out and about in three days' time. I looked at him and moved my Adam's apple or where it should have been, to thank that good old man—for bugger all. But the Chief roared and the P.O. opened the door, and the screw shouted to me to about-turn, and I was marched off at a hell of a lick up the stairs and back along the landing to my cell.

"Now," said Johnston, "go inside and take out your cell furniture, your table, chair, wash-stand, wash-bowl, jug, knife, spoon, plate, mug, mattress, bedboard, everything except your chamber-pot, and leave them on the landing outside your cell. Come on, boy, look sharp."

I brought them out, one after another. Johnston was not hostile, and even helped me drag out the mattress and bedboards. My two books were on the shelf, and I had a great hope he would not ask for them. He didn't, but when I had everything else out of the cell, he said: "Now, take off your stockings, your shoes, your belt, your tie and your jacket, and put them outside here. You can take back your slippers and wear them."

"Thank you, sir," said I.

Johnston said nothing; only nodded.

I went into the cell and he banged the door, put another card over my ordinary card, pulled down the cover of the spy-hole which I had left open on purpose to have a window on the world and a view of the two doors within my range on the landing opposite, and went off down the stairs.

Then I settled down to my Number One and solitary. Number One, I knew, was eight ounces of bread and a pint of water, and I wondered when I would get it. Would they give it to me at dinner-time, for the rest of the day, or would they leave it till supper-time? The next day I knew I was off the diet, but still on the deprivation of mattress, but the day after I would not give a God's curse, because the solitary would be the only thing, and that would not mean a lot because I was going down to the court, and I would have my mattress back that night.

And I still had *Under the Greenwood Tree*, not to mind the book about the old Salvation Army sawdust pocket.

I walked up and down in my slippers and was not in a bad humour, but whistling softly to myself the songs that many an Irishman had whistled or whispered to himself in those kips. And I'd have sung it out and not given a God's curse for no one, only they might hear me, and it was better to be defiant in a quiet sort of a way. These sportsmen would be serious men if it came to kicking the shit out of you. A desperate thing for the Germans or the Russians or the Fuzzie-Wuzzies to do as much to one of theirs, and a crime against humanity, but a far different thing it looked to them to do the same to someone else—and you couldn't blame them. Everyone has their own way of looking at things and you couldn't blame them for taking a favourable view of their own kicking once they were kicking you in their country and not they being kicked by someone else in someone else's. But still a little whistle was in order, once I kept it low.

> In boyhood's bloom and manhood's pride,
> Foredoomed by alien laws,
> Some on the scaffold proudly died,
> For Holy Ireland's cause;
> And brothers say, Shall we, today,
> Unmoved by cowards stand,
> While traitors shame and foes defame,
> The Felons of our Land. . . .

By Jesus, I could hear the blokes being marched in, dismissed, and then sent hurrying up the stairs, and rattling along the landings, and their doors being banged out, one after another. And I could smell, oh, Jesus, I could smell the dinner.

Would they ever give me my bread and water, now? No, the boards went past me; I could hear them; so another bar of the whistle was indicated, to keep my heart up.

That it may choke you, you shower of bastards!

> Some in the convict's dreary cell,
> Have found a living tomb,
> And some unseen untended fell
> Within the dungeon's gloom,
> But what care we, although it be
> Trod by a ruffian band,
> God bless the clay where rest today
> The Felons of our Land. . . .

The dinners went past me, I could smell. Wasn't it the great pity that the fellow that was doing the suffering couldn't be where the singing was to get the benefit of it. Mother of Christ, wasn't there a thousand places between Belfast and Bantry Bay where a fellow would be stuffed with grub, not to mind doused in porter, if he could only be there and here at the same time? But I suppose that would be like to trying to get a drink at your own funeral. Make way there, you with the face, and let in the man that's doing jail for Ireland, and suffering hunger and abuse, let him up to the bar there. Oh, come up at once, the publican would say, what kind of men are you at all? Have you no decency of spirit about you, that wouldn't make way for one of the Felons of our Land? Come on, son, till herself gives you this plate of bacon and cabbage, and the blessings of Jasus on you, and on everyone like you. It's my own dinner I'm giving you, for you were not expected and you amongst that parcel of white-livered, thin-lipped, paper-waving, key-rattling hangmen. And, come on; after your dinner there's a pint to wash it down, aye, and a glass of malt if you fancy it. Give us up a song there. Yous have enough of songs out of yous about the boys that faced the Saxon foe, but, bejasus, when there's one of them here among you, the real Ally Daly, the real goat's genollickers, yous are silent at the tomb. Sing up, yous whores gets.

> Side by side for the cause when our forefathers battled,
> When our hills never echoed the tread of the slave,
> On many a green field where the leaden hail rattled,
> Through the red gap of glory, they marched to the grave,
> But we who inherit their name and their spirit,
> March 'neath the banner of liberty then,
> Give them back blow for blow,
> Pay them back woe for woe.
> Out and make way for the Bold Fenian Men. . . .

" 'Ello—'ere, Paddy."

I turned on my heel to the spy-hole. It was Browny.

"I'll 'ave your cob and your water up shortly, Paddy."

I smiled in the direction of the spy-hole. "Good man, Browny, thanks."

When all the dinners had been given out and all the doors were locked, my door was opened, and Browny came in, with my bread and water. It was the usual two-tiered aluminium diet can with solids in the top shallow can, and liquids in the bottom long can. In this case a cob of bread and a pint of water.

"'Ere you are, Paddy, lad," said Browny in his soft voice. "It's not much, but it'll keep your guts together till tea-time."

"Do I get more then?" I asked.

"'Course you do," said Browny. "There's eight ounces of bread in that, and you get a six-ounce cob tonight, and a four-ounce in the morning for your breakfast. Then your Number One is up."

"Only for the mattress and the solitary!"

"He'll give you your mattress all right tonight, and you're out then at dinner-time tomorrow and all's well again."

"I thought it was three days—one day's Number One, one without the mattress, and one in solitary."

"Nay, you silly feller," said Browny, "'tis all one day. Pad, I 'ear screw coming back. I'll slip along landing later this afternoon and 'ave a bit of chat to cheer y'up like, if I can make it. I 'ear 'im coming." He gave his soft smile and winked, and went off down the landing.

Johnston came up and looked in round the cell. "Got everything?" he asked.

"Yes, sir," said I, holding my can and my cob of bread.

He nodded, banged out the door and went off down the landing.

I had nothing to sit on but my mat, so I sat there and broke the crust of my cob of bread. It was a new one, and, washed down with the cup of water, I wasn't long finishing it. It was great to think, I thought, that I would be getting more bread at supper-time, and that the whole thing was over tomorrow. I had only two more meals of bread and water before I went back on ordinary diet. It was well worth it, to give that James bastard a trimming, though for that again I hoped he wouldn't be needled enough or have guts enough to go for me over it. But then I knew that was not likely to worry me much, for it couldn't last long. The screws would see to that. The only thing to be afraid of was him coming at me all of a sudden, like I did at him. And I'd look out for that. Get my chair in against the wall, when we were at labour, and keep a good yard round the exercise yard as we walked round the ring.

I got up and did not wipe the crumbs off me, but gathered them and went for a bit of a walk up and down the cell in my slippers, thinking about Ireland and the suffering for her and all the starvation—in particular of Terence MacSwiney, seventy-eight days with no scoff at all, and my own father on hunger strike with ten thousand others in the internment camps during the Civil War, but that was a different thing, with ten thousand others. MacSwiney had the eyes of the world on him, and knew that it must be driving these bastards mad from the publicity it was getting. They were up and offering him every conceivable delicacy, chicken, ham, turkey, roast pork, steak, oh for the love of Jesus, give over, me mouth is watering.

If Johnston came up and said, "Here you are, sing two lines of 'God Save the King' and I'll give you this piece of round steak," would I take it? Would I what? Jesus, Mary and Joseph, he'd be a lucky man that I didn't take the hand and all off him.

And sing a High Mass, never mind a couple of lines of "God Save the King," for it, aye or for the half of it.

After I stopped for a minute or two and allowed myself a bit of a read at *Under*

769

the Greenwood Tree, and had a look at the bit early on where they have a Christmas carol, I started to put an air to it. That's a thing we're all very well able to do in my family. On my mother's side, my uncle was one of the best song-writers in the country, and one of the best known, and others of them were in the variety business, so it wouldn't take me long looking at a poem or a song to put an air to it.

So I put the air of the "Famine Song" to this carol, my situation being more like Famine than like Christmas:

> Remember Adam's fall,
>   O thou Man:
> Remember Adam's fall,
>   From Heaven to hell.
> Remember Adam's fall;
>   How he hath condemned all,
> In hell perpetual
>   There for to dwell. . . .

So I was walking up and down the cell humming this carol of Thomas Hardy's, and I never felt the time going till I heard the cell doors being opened and the cans being left out—door open, clang can, door open, clang can, and then a bit of walking up and down to and from the recess with their pots and the water they had washed their plates and knife and spoon with, and the screw shouting, "Stand to your doors," and they getting ready to go down to work for the afternoon, and I had my humming over by this time and my face serious again because it does not look the thing not to look unhappy in the nick, especially and they going to the trouble of putting you on Number One.

The screw then opened my door, and Browny came in for my containers.

"'Ow goes it, Pad?" he smiled. "You'll be getting a dinner tomorrow. A good one and all, beans and bacon."

I looked sad at the water. "I'll finish that water, Browny, in case I get thirsty later."

Browny laughed. "You can 'ave all the water you want, Paddy. Wait till I tell screw!" He spoke to the screw, who came up and looked in. It was a big old Cockney. He wasn't small and wiry the way they are supposed to be, but he wasn't a bad old bastard for all that.

"You can 'ave all the bleedin' water that's in the tap. Go dahn, Browny, and fetch 'im up that diet can full!" He muttered in the door: "Water. No one's deprivin' you, Taffy."

"Paddy he is, sir," said Browny, "from Ireland."

"Well, Paddy or Taffy or Jock is all bleedin' one to me. Go down and get him the bleedin' water."

Browny came back and left me the diet can, the long bottom part, full of water, and I said, "Thank you, Browny," and, "Thank you, sir," to the screw.

He just said, "Don't thank me, thank the Lord," and gave a bit of a laugh and banged out the door.

I drank a sup of the water when I heard them gone off down the stairs. I was going to have a walk up and down again till it was time to have a piss, and in that way make a break in the time till they came round with my tea-time bread and water. I had nothing to sit on, only the mat, and it was cold, with no jacket on, only my shirt, shorts, stockings, and slippers. It was dark and bleak and the bit of sky I could see was a dirty grey and that nearly dark, with a dead cold.

I walked up and down, and went back to putting an air to the whole carol and getting the other verses off by heart. I did, too.

> Remember God's goodnesse,
> O thou Man:
> Remember God's goodnesse,
> His promise made.
> Remember God's goodnesse;
> He sent His Son sinlesse
> Our ails for to redress;
> Be not afraid!

I had a few drinks of water and pissed three times, and walked up and down, and though the cold was sharp, I'd have been colder if I'd not kept walking up and down. The light was dying, but not the day, more was the pity: the cold, black, hungry day stretched forward, and it was only four o'clock when the night came down and the cell was in pitch darkness.

Then I heard the chairs being shoved back and the fellows coming up the stairs from exercise. At least, I sighed, it was a good thing about getting another bit of bread at tea-time. But, Jesus, it was cold and dark, and my mind even was gone numb from the cold, and I couldn't think myself away any more for this December day. But I did another turn and walk up the floor to keep things going some way.

"Paddy!"

There was a whisper at the spy-hole and I rushed over to it.

Charlie had the cover up and his mouth to the glass.

"Hello, Charlie," I whispered, "how are you?"

"Not bad, kid, and yourself?"

"All right."

"I'd 'ave worked some scoff to you, but I couldn't get near when Brown was bringing your bread and water."

"I know that, kid. I'll take the will for the deed."

"Old James ain't 'alf carved up. Those bastards will be dead frit of you. They won't take no liberties when you come out. James got seven stitches."

"That was a pity—a pity he didn't get seventy bloody stitches."

Charlie's lip parted in a smile at the spy-hole glass. "You're a lad, Paddy, you are. See you tomorrow, kid."

"'Bye, Charlie."

He whispered soft against the glass of the spy-hole, his lips close to it. "'Bye, Paddy," then put his eye to it, winked, and slipped down the landing towards his own cell.

So I walked up and down again with more spring in my heel, and when Browny came with my four-ounce cob, the screw let me go down to the recess, where I used the lavatory, emptied my pot, and refilled my diet can with water for the night. Which meant that I would not have to shit in the cell, a thing to be feared between half past four in the afternoon and seven the next morning.

The screw switched my light on and I walked up and down, feeling better, while I ate my bread and took a drink of the water.

At eight o'clock the screw came and opened my door and, Jesus be praised, told me to take in my bed.

I got in the boards and mattress and blanket, and he banged out the door.

When I had the bed made down and got into it, wasn't as I as good as anyone, tired from the walking and warm after the cold, and my day's chokey over me only for the breakfast, but, sure, wouldn't I appreciate the beans and bacon all the more?

I celebrated with a read of the book. I was well on to the end of it now, but I decided it was worth being reckless for once and read on, warm and happy, where they are all at the wedding and poor Thomas Leaf, an amádan, comes up and asks to be let in to the hooley. "I washed and put on a clane shirt," says Leaf, pleading like, not to be kept out of the diversion.

"Let the poor bastard in," says the Tranter, "he's a bit silly-looking but I never heard he was in jail." Sure, if he was itself, there was as good as ever he was in it.

But they let him anyway, and he tells a story, about a man that got a pound and then he got another pound and another one and another till, before Jesus, he had a thousand pound and such a half-arsed class of a story I never heard, but sure he was doing his best to oblige the company, and I fell asleep.

In the morning I ate my four-ounce cob and drank some water, and waited till dinner-time for the end of my sentence. I walked up and down the cell and was thinking of my beans and bacon when, at eleven o'clock or so, the screw came, opened my door and told me to bring in my furniture and put on my clothes. He asked me if I wanted to slop out and I went down and emptied the pot and had a shit in the recess, as I was there, and got a basin of water.

The screw banged out the door and I had a wash after I had put back my furniture. It was only when I had to put out the furniture that I noticed how desolate the cell was without it.

At dinner-time I heard them marching in and clattering up the iron stairs and the next thing was the screw coming round with my *Daily Herald*, and in a minute or two I smelt the dinner, and heard the doors being opened again.

This time my door was opened like anyone else's and Browny handed me a hot diet can, with a grand smell off it.

"There you are, Paddy, lad." He smiled like you'd think it was himself was getting it. The screw banged out the door and I put it on the table, and spread my *Daily Herald* back of my plate along the wall and got into my beans and bacon.

The beans and bacon were in the bottom long can of the diet cans and there was a cob of bread in the top shallow part. I ate it well, and it was salty and thick, and I drank more water after it.

I thought of going down to work after my dinner in the hall with the others. I did not think James would have the guts to say anything to me nor did I think that Dale would have the decency to do anything to me on James' behalf. Not for fear of me, but for fear of the screws. They would not be acting for love of me, but simply to keep the law. The others, Scouse bastards, would be frit of me, Charlie said, and that was a relief. Bigger and better I.R.A. men than I had got very bad kickings in Dartmoor and Parkhurst when they were there in very small numbers, so it was no harm at all, at all, but a good investment of a day's Number One to scare these sportsmen.

I washed up my plate and tin knife and spoon, and was ready when they came round and opened my door for my descent to the hall.

I went down the stairs carrying my chair and got in a little before the rest, to a place beside the wall, where I could see all round me and where there was no one sitting in front of me.

Dale came on down the stairs and passed me, but didn't take much heed of me one way or another, beyond a look.

Then up the wing came James all dressed in white.

He had a bandage plastered to his cheek, and the two of his eyes were bruised and discoloured, I was happy to see. He looked over at where I was sitting, and I looked back, to be as good as what he was and not lose my hard-earned advantage.

Then he looked away from me and sat down beside Dale, at his usual place at the table.

Then the others came down and sat in their rows, and what happens but Charlie comes and puts his chair beside me.

"'Ello, Pad." He smiled and whispered.

"Good on you, Charlie," said I, "sit down. You're welcome."

So the afternoon passed from two till a quarter past four, and we working off the one-hank of waxed end, and I was content enough, and better again when Charlie reminded me we were both for court in the morning.

I had *Under the Greenwood Tree* finished, but after doing my bit of stitching I had another look at the carol and muttered it to myself, and hummed it till the bell went and I got into bed and read over it again till they put the lights out, and I lay in the dark, happy and thinking about my trip to court in the morning, though too excited about it to go asleep till well after an hour, for I heard nine o'clock strike on the church bells in the city.

In the morning I was rushed down the stairs with my kit, my sheets and my towel and handkerchief, and told to stand at the foot of the stairs. I waited in line for the others. Two were fellows that were going out after doing a six months' and a nine months' sentence, three were going to court, in Birkenhead and Preston; and there was Charlie and Ginger and myself going to court in Liverpool.

We came out of the reception in our own clothes, and stood at the Black Maria which was drawn up in the yard. But I was not put into this but brought away from Charlie and Ginger outside the gate and put into a police car on my own.

I was driven down to Dale Street, Bridewell, and locked in a cell there to wait for the court, but it was not like being there the first night I was brought in.

My sergeant came down and gave me a cigarette and introduced me to a chief inspector.

The chief inspector brought me out right into the street and, it dazes me to tell it, through the crowds and into a snack bar where he bought me a pork pie and a cup of tea.

He was called Chief Inspector Haines, and after I finished the tea and the pork pie we had another cup of tea and I smoked two cigarettes.

He told me he was in charge of my case, and then I remembered him. He was the one that did not like Roger Casement. I did not refer to this, however, and we hardly mentioned my case at all. He certainly did not ask for information. I think he gave me the tea and the pie and the bit of a walk up the city because he was a decent man. That it may be before him.

He brought me back to Dale Street and then I was taken out of my cell again and brought up to the court. The judge remanded me for another week and I was brought back to the cells.

In my cell I still had a smoke and walked up and down like a gent. Then others were brought down and I could hear doors opening and being banged locked, and Charlie shouted to Ginger and they both shouted to me, and we passed a couple of hours smoking and shouting till they came up and put us in the Black Maria, to bring us back to the nick.

Charlie and Ginger and I were three chinas in the wagon and two other new kids even asked us what it was like in Walton, and though Charlie told them they'd bloody well find out when they got up there and nodded to Ginger and me, and we three nodded like old soldiers together at the new kids, I told them that it wouldn't be too bad, they'd get used to it.

And this time when the fat orderly came round the baths even Charlie laughed at his jokes and he gave us a bit of bread each off what the new receptions couldn't eat, and when we came back to the wing, dark and black as it was to us, it wasn't so dark or so frightening as it was to the new kids.

In the morning we saw the doctor and the Governor and the priest, like the other receptions, but they didn't delay us long. The Governor didn't even glance up at me. He only said, "Remanded again." And I said, "Yes, sir," and went out. The doctor was just as brief, and the priest didn't even glance at me, but nodded his head in a surly fashion, and then I went back to sit with the others sewing, my chair against the wall and Charlie sitting beside me.

The days were the same except Friday night, when the R.C.s had a religious instruction in the doctor's room. This was at half past five in the night and everyone looked forward to it. Despite being excommunicated, I half-hoped I would be let go to it, and, sure enough, when they unlocked the doors on Friday night they unlocked mine with the others.

"Right, bring down your chair to the doctor's room," said the screw without looking at me but going on to open the next door where he'd see a red card.

I brought my chair down, and when I went to the doctor's room, there was a blazing fire in the grate, and the fellows all sitting with happy smiling faces round it. They moved their chairs back, quite friendly even to me, and a weedy-looking man with a mournful face came in. I heard the fellows say he was from the Liverpool Archdiocesan Legion of Mary.

I sat with the rest looking up at him and delighted to be there, and saying that maybe the priest wasn't such a bad old sort after all, and was only trying to do what he thought right, when a hand tapped me on the shoulder and a screw spoke to me.

"Take your chair and get back up to your cell, Behan," said he.

I looked at him and he said, "Come on, look sharp, and get up when I tell you."

I saw the others looking at me, took up my chair, put my head down so as they couldn't see my face, and went quickly from the room.

When I got into the wing I saw the priest looking into the room. I looked at him, stared at him, as I went past.

"Get on," said the screw.

I went up the stairs and into my cell, and the screw banged out the door and went off down the stairs.

I sat down on the chair and leaned my head in my hands. I felt like crying for the first time in years, for the first time since I was a kid of four or five. I had often prayed after Mass at home that God would not let me lose the Faith. I thought of Sister Monica, the old nun that prepared me for my first Confession and Communion and Confirmation, and Father Campbell, the old priest in Gardiner Street that I went to Confession to, and Christmas numbers of the little holy books we used to have at home. Never, never no more.

It was all ballocks.

One of the Fenian prisoners said the things you missed most in jail were babies, dogs, and fires.

Wasn't I the soft eedgit all the same, to expect anything more off that fat bastard of a druid? Weren't the priests famous for backing up the warders even the time of the Fenians? When Dr. Gallagher was driven mad in Chatham Prison.

But I wouldn't always be inside, and if I could do the like of Father Lane an ill turn in my turn, by Jesus and I'd be the boy to do it.

Let them come to me some time at home with their creeping Jesus old gab, I'd say to them: what about this night in Walton Jail, you bastards?

Twice more Charlie and Ginger and I went down. We enjoyed the run down, and the smoking in the cells and in the Black Maria coming back, and telling new blokes what it was like, and being welcomed by the fat bloke in the reception and slipping him a dog-end and getting a bit of extra bread off him that the receptions couldn't eat, and looking over at each other and laughing as we soaped ourselves in the bath standing up, and then lying down full length in it, and resting ourselves, and coming up and going straight into kip, till at last we were all returned for trial at Liverpool Assizes, and it was the week before Christmas and we had six weeks to wait, till the first week in February.

The librarian was not an undecent sort, and brought me books by Dickens that I had asked for. It was not much good asking for modern authors because they did not have any. It was my belief they bought the books for the prison by weight. I once got a *Chums* annual for 1917 and a Selfridge's furniture catalog for my nonfiction or educational book. But when I explained to the librarian that I could not read the Selfridge's furniture catalog and that I had had the *Chums* before, which was not true, he changed them for me. He gave *The Mayor of Casterbridge* by Hardy and *The Moonstone* by Wilkie Collins.

"Irishman, eh, Paddy? Ever 'ear of Michael Collins?" asked the screw. Michael Collins gave my mother a five-pound note on O'Connell Bridge, a few months before I was born, when my father was locked up by his government. But I didn't tell the screw that. I only smiled, and nodded. "And this 'ere book—by an Irishman—Ballock is 'is name—must say they got funny names in your country, Paddy—well I couldn't find *The Life Savers* so I brought you another one of 'is."

I thanked him and when I was locked up, had a look at the book. It was by

Shan F. Bullock. "Shan," I supposed, was some gammy way of spelling "Seán"—
like Shaun and Shane. But it was Irish all right.

"Aw, ay," said he and slouched up wiping the wet from his hand on his cor-
duroys; "aw, ay; it'll follow ye safe to Clogheen anyhow. Good-bye and God speed
you!"

At home on the corner of the North Circular Road we used to make a jeer of
that Abbey Theatre bogman talk. "Oh, woman of the roads, be not putting it on
me now." "With your long arm, and your strong arm, be after pulling me a pint
of porther."

But I was delighted to read it here, in this old kip.

The book was short stories and called *Ring o' Rushes*, and was all about the
North of Ireland. The other book, when I got it, which I did, was called not *The
Life Savers* but *The Loughsiders*.

I went out every day and Charlie and Ginger and I walked behind each other
at smoking exercise, and worked near each other at labour. I got my paper every
day and the *News of the World* on Sundays. James said nothing to me (his face was
a bit scarred where it was completely healed), and neither did anyone else say anything to me. I was brought once more to the instruction on Friday night, but it
was a mistake again and I was brought back to my cell, and then I saw a notice in
the office at the top of the wing saying that 3501 Behan was not to attend the R.C.
religious instruction on Friday nights. I still went to Mass and Benediction on
Sundays because it was compulsory and because it passed the time.

The smoking was the big part of the day.

We remands and awaiting trials were called out from the others, the convicted
boys, who looked at us, licking their lips, and sometimes signalled us to try and
bring in a butt for them.

This was nearly impossible. Though a couple of times Charlie and I got in a
little dimp for Browny. He was out of his mind for a smoke all the time. But it
was very dangerous and difficult.

Sometimes, though, we succeeded in breaking a bit off the top of a cigarette,
and then, instead of getting a light off the screw, we got our light off one of the
boys who was already lit, put the bit we'd broken off in our handkerchief and had
the end of the cigarette to hand up when we had it smoked. These butts were put
in a bucket of water, which, when we were finished exercise, was brought into the
wing and flushed down the lavatory. Sometimes the cistern did not flush properly
and the butts floated back on the surface.

Dale's cell was just beside this recess and it was understood that he got these
butts. He was the daddy of the wing and what he claimed was his. He collected
these butts when we finished labour and put them on the sill of the window
where there was a little hole, and left them there to dry.

Sometimes if a fellow went to fall out in the middle of labour, after the screw had emptied the dog-end bucket into the lavatory, and saw them floating, he would whisper to Dale when he came back, and Dale would fall out himself a minute or two later and go down and collect them and put them out to dry.

The orderly on the bottom floor used to watch out for the screw leading in the bloke with the bucket and he'd nip in and flush the lavatory, and slip out again, so that when the screw came up, and told the prisoner to empty the butt bucket into the lavatory and flush the chain, the cistern would be empty. Sometimes the screw would come back and flush it when it had refilled but, for that again, he'd sometimes leave it go with the butts floating there. Then the orderly would nip down and tell Dale and might be rewarded with one himself when the butts were dried. In any event Dale was the daddy, and blokes would like to be doing things for him, to keep on the right side of him.

One morning Dale's butts were knocked off. When he got down to the window and put his finger out of the hole they were not there. The word went round the mailbag class as we worked, and everyone shivered a bit. I was even glad that I was a remand and that Charlie was one. Everyone wondered who'd taken the dog-ends.

The orderly came down from his cleaning to whisper and swear before Jesus as he stood at Dale's table, letting on to be sweeping up bits of canvas, that he did not and he knew not.

I had a good idea who did. There were four orderlies who were working in the wing all day; one on each of the four landings. The only one of them that did much wandering in a general way was Browny, and the day before when Charlie and I told him we were sorry we hadn't been able to nick a bit off a cigarette for him at remands smoking exercise, he only smiled and said it was all right, thanks, that he'd got a bit of snout.

Where did he get it? I looked over at Dale's glowering face, when I stooped to pick up a bit of wax-end, and shivered a bit myself. Poor Browny. It could be worse. It could be me. But still, poor little Browny. He was like a little Teddy Bear, and as innocent.

When we finished at four o'clock I saw Dale pack up his things at the table very quickly and go up the iron stairs to our landing. I went up the stairs just after him. I always made to get locked up in the cell since I had the bundle with James, but I thought too that I might have a chance of warning Browny that Dale was going to put it on him, but I was too late.

I heard a commotion from the recess, and I heard Browny's voice, pleading and then crying. I stood with my chair and my cell-task canvas and didn't know which to do first, but went on to my own cell and left in my chair and canvas and wax-end, and then came down towards the recess; and before I got there I saw Dale come quickly down the landing towards the stairs.

I went into the recess and it was dark and I couldn't see Browny, but then I heard his moans coming from the lavatory, from behind the half-door. I swung it open and there he was, trying to lift his head out of the lavatory bowl. His shorts were all slashed to ribbons and covered in blood.

Ah, Mother of Jesus, I was sorry I went up first with my chair and canvas to my cell, that I had gone up there first and not come down and done something to save him. That was the time he was carved up, and I didn't come down, but waited till I'd left my chair into my cell because I was afraid I'd be carved up. There's a fearless rebel for you.

I lifted him, put my arms under him, and carried him out to the head of the stairs, where the screw would see me without having to shout for him, or interfere in the matter any more than I could help.

Johnston came up the stairs and we carried him to the doctor's room and laid him on the couch, face downwards.

We took off the seat of his pants in blood-soaked strips and the blood still pouring from him.

He kept his hand over his face and moaned. It was trying to protect his face he was, and stuck it in the lavatory, and Dale just slashed away with a razor blade wherever he could.

When the medical orderly arrived and took over, Johnston asked me what I knew about it.

I said I knew nothing; I heard screaming, ran down to the recess and saw Brown lying there moaning.

Johnston nodded and said he would see about that, whether I was telling the truth. The others were all in their cells, locked up for the night, and he came outside with me and saw me go up the stairs into my cell and bang out my door.

The next morning I was brought before the Governor as a witness.

Dale was standing in front of the desk and it was easy to see that the night had not passed easily over him.

I still swore holes through pewter pots that I had not seen the attack on Browny, and knew nothing about it beyond finding him with his head in the lavatory pan and his backside all blood.

The Chief Officer, from the far side of the desk, nodded to the Governor and roared at me to get out. I marched outside and waited till I was told I was not required any more and sent back to my place sewing mailbags.

Later we all looked up and from under our eyes saw Dale marching between two screws down to the punishment cells.

Johnston came back in charge of the mailbags, and after the Governor had gone we heard thumps and moans coming faintly from below stores, from chokey.

The Principal Officer, a thin wafer-shaven man, erect, slim and spotless and beribboned, turned his old eyes to Johnston, cocked his ear to the moaning with the air of a connoisseur, smiled and murmured appreciatively, "Someone getting a clean shirt, Mr. Johnston?"

A clean shirt was the beating they sometimes gave a prisoner beginning his punishment. They told him to strip and then when he had his clothes half-off, they would accuse him of resisting the search, beat him, baton him on the kidneys, and on the thighs.

Our P.O. was most feared. Now that he was no longer young and active enough to lead the fray, he waited till the prisoner was stripped naked by the other screws. Then he would catch him by the ballocks and twist and pull on them. Putting his weight and swinging down out of them, not abusing the prisoner or angry but rather the reverse, grunting and saying softly, "All right, all right, now, it will be over in a minute." Grunting and perspiring with the effort. "There, there, it will soon be over."

It usually was—the bloke passing out. They never hit a prisoner on the face, but on the rest of him which would only be seen by the prison doctor. Extras such as our P.O.'s performance were reserved for people with a good long bit of time to do. Even if the prisoner was ruptured, nobody would know, except prison officials, warders, prison doctors, and clergymen.

The moaning from below grew fainter, and then stopped. The P.O. smiled, and the prisoners smiled to see the old man in such good humour.

James smiled at his new companion on the table.

During the morning, Johnston called down to me, "Paddy, come up and collect a letter."

I smiled and was as delighted to be called "Paddy" as to get the letter.

Charlie and Ginger and I went out with the others to smoking exercise.

Charlie got his light off mine and I reddened it to give him a better light, and he looked up at me, smiled and said, "Thanks, Pad."

"That's O.K., kid," said I, and when we marched round, I went behind him studying the back of his head where the hair finished on the smoothness of his neck.

↓

Now I began to get letters from Ireland wishing me a "happy Christmas."

It was coming up to that in a hurry.

There was a blizzard in Christmas week and on the Saturday afternoon, when I was sitting in my cell after exercise trying to keep myself warm with my legs in a mailbag. They served the supper early on Saturday, at three-thirty sometimes, and you would be in two minds about it. It was great to get it as soon as possible because you were ravenously hungry, not to mind cold, but for that again it meant that by seven o'clock you were starving again, and by eight you were that bad that it was hard to sleep.

There were some blokes that didn't read much or didn't know how to, and they passed the time as long as there was any light at all in the sky looking out their windows. They had to stand up on their table to do this, the window being that high that they couldn't have seen out of it otherwise.

If the screw sneaked round in his slippers and caught them, they might get a report and a day or two on Number One. But most of the screws did not bother much and sometimes the prisoners at the windows carried on shouted conversations with each other.

Some of the prisoners would interrupt these conversations by shouting, "Can't you blokes never quit nattering?" as if they were genuinely annoyed by people shouting, which I do not believe they were. Even when I was reading myself, I enjoyed the noise of voices, and listened sometimes to the conversations. It saved a couple of pages of book anyway.

I never went in for conversation myself, even with Charlie, who was only beside me because my accent stuck out and the others would shout, "Kip in, you dirty Irish bastard," as they did once or twice.

Besides, if I had a book at all, I'd sooner read.

Sometimes two chinas from the same district or town would start off a conversation and get really into it, and as they knew the same places and even the same people, it was worth listening to.

But then some fellows was sure to shout out, "Kip in there, you bastards," in angry tone, and the conversation would be spoiled and end up in an exchange of abuse with the interrupter. "Kip in yourself, you bloody puff," one of the conversationalists would shout and the interrupter would answer, "I'll do you, you bastard, at exercise, see if I don't, you shit-'ouse."

"Get stuffed, you bloody puff."

Compliments pass when the quality meet.

The interrupter would be only shouting to hear his own voice and also there were prisoners who seemed to delight in hearing of other prisoners being punished, and would shout as if they agreed with the silence rule. In another way it was a safe way of breaking the silence.

The rows carried on from the windows were never even remembered when we all came out again, to work or exercise.

This blizzard went on all during Christmas week, and on Saturday the place was under a deep fall of snow and we could not use the exercise yards.

We were glad of this because it was torture to walk round with only a jacket and shorts.

We were wondering up to this what we might get for Christmas, and some fellows thought we might get a concert or something but we began to understand that it would be nothing but a hell of a long week-end. There was to be duff on Christmas Day, but that did not make up for a week-end of one Saturday, a Sunday, a Christmas Day, and a Stephen's Day, all days when we would be deprived of getting down to work in the hall, which to us was like a busy street in the city with people going up and down to governor's and doctor's, and doors with people going up and down, and fellows coming in and going out to court and being brought up before the Governor and down to chokey and fellows being called to the doctor, and you could look up from your sewing and, provided you didn't start talking, there was no law against you enjoying all this, and a bit of noise of doors opening, and screws shouting, "One away, sir," "Two on to you, sir," unlike these dreary four days, which stretched in front of us like a jail sentence, as a person might say outside.

They only gave us half our usual exercise time, walking round the landings, and then we were locked up for the day, at dinner-time. The dinner was the usual Saturday's dinner, a piece of bully beef, which we liked, two cold, bad potatoes, and a piece of bread.

I ate mine. The potatoes and bread didn't go well together, so I ate the potatoes first, and then put the piece of bully beef on the bread and ate that with a drink of water.

It was dark in the cell, and after I washed up, I sat at the table and listened to what few noises there were going on. The fellows had not got up to the windows yet, because a screw was going round the R.C.s' cells and seeing if they wanted to go to Confession.

I'd have like to have gone on account of Christmas-time, even apart from the walk with the other blokes to the chapel, but being excommunicated I could not.

Nearly all the others went, and the screw came round to all the cells with red cards, and when he came to mine he looked in and said, "Going to Confession?" but then he recognized me and muttered something and went off to the next cell with a red card at it.

That fat bastard of a priest. I chewed my lips to myself when I heard the others all going down the stairs like free men.

Then the blokes got up to the windows.

It was too dark to read and, anyway, I wanted to save all the reading I could for these four days, and there was a bit of white light in the sky and the snow coming, and I decided the screws might be a bit easy on us even if they caught us, it being the day before Christmas Eve, so I pulled over my table and got up.

And as well that I did.

Our Chief Officer, the stocky cruel-faced turkey-toed bastard, walks out with his glare and his strut, looking round and down at the snow, and up at the windows, five tiers of them in a square round the yard, in dead silence, and he knowing we were looking at him, and he glaring up at the barred windows, and some near me, though they must have known he could not have seen them at that distance, got down in fear. But I did not, thank God that I did not, and those that got down must have been cutting their throats a minute later, for the next thing is, the Chief Officer, with his red-faced glare and his strut, walks clean off the steps and into six foot of snow.

He floundered and was lost in it, there was even hope he'd smother in it, and oh, Jesus, what a shout went up from all the windows. What delight, what joy, and as a bonus on it, didn't the old bastard, when he struggled up a step, shake his fists in anger and fall down again, and the boys roared from the windows so that the screws came rushing out, thinking we'd all broken loose, and they shouted at us to get down from the windows, even as they helped the Chief up, covered in snow, and brushing himself while we roared, till the screws came rushing into the wings and round the landings, and we jumped down double-quick before they'd look in our spy-holes and catch us.

I sat down again at my table, and was thankful to God and His Blessed Mother for this.

If I had gone to Confession, I'd have missed it, and I was consoled. God never closes one door but He opens another, and if He takes away with His right hand, He gives it back with His left, and more besides.

The next day we went to Mass and had our exercise walking round the landings, and had our usual Sunday dinner, which was good, and the fellows talked a lot up at the windows but the screws did not bother them, and they talked away till they heard the supper coming round at half three.

It was even a bit earlier than usual, I heard an orderly saying to give the screws a chance to get off early.

The R.C.s had no Benediction in the evening on account of having it the next day, and it made that Sunday a bit long.

I got a bit hungry at six o'clock or so and drank some water and walked up and down till eight o'clock, when I went to bed with the bell.

I had a bit of a read till they put the lights out, and then, thinking that at least half the four days were over, went asleep.

I met Charlie in the recess and we wished each other a "happy Christmas."

All the blokes wished each other a "happy Christmas," quiet-like so as the screws wouldn't hear them talking; it would not do to go too far on Christmas morning.

We banged out our doors and washed ourselves, waiting for the breakfast being brought up.

When they came to my door, I heard one of them saying that I was an R.C. and would not be getting my breakfast till after church service. This was on account of most of the R.C.s going to Communion, and I was going to say out through the spy-hole that I was not going and was to get my breakfast in the usual way, when I heard the screw saying to the orderly that I was not allowed to go to anything like that and that I was getting my breakfast with the rest.

He opened my door and asked, "You're not for Communion, are you?"

"No, sir," said I.

"Well, 'ere's your breakfast then!" He was a nice old bloke for that morning anyway and added, "Anyway, Paddy, you get your scoff now and don't 'ave to wait an hour and 'alf for it."

I took it from him and thanked him and he banged out the door. I always like breakfasts and I always like mornings, and the old screw trying to be nice to me and put me in good humour.

When we R.C.s fell in for Mass, the boy beside me whispered that we would see Dale that morning. Be God and so we will, said I to myself, sitting up with the chokey blokes in front, and I heard the boys saying along the line that he would be there to be seen and we'd see how the chokey was affecting him.

We marched out of the wing and had to cross a yard but the snow was glittering white in the sunshine and the sky was blue.

We went in our seats and sat down while the rest of the chapel filled up. At the back of us were old men and younger ones, doing every sort of sentence from seven days to fifteen years, and they all kind of smiled at each other, for it being Christmas.

When all the other seats were filled up and five or six hundred men in the chapel, the chokey merchants were marched into the very front seats and separated from the ones behind them by an empty row. They were all on either Number One, bread and water; or Number Two, bread and water with porridge and potatoes at midday. They had been in chokey, some of them, for five months, and some of them had not been out of the punishment cells to Mass during that time. They seemed to appreciate being brought out today, and looked neither to right nor left as they came in but sat right down and looked straight ahead at the altar.

All the prisoners looked white by comparison with the screws, but these prisoners from chokey were Persil white by comparison with the other prisoners.

The Y.P. gave each other tiny nudges when we picked out Dale amongst the other prisoners from chokey. He seemed to have forgotten us, or how he'd sat back in the seat previous Sundays, and just looked straight in front like the others from chokey.

The priest came out and the chokey prisoners were the first and quickest on their knees. We all got down to it, and knelt till the sermon, when we stood for the gospel and sat down to listen to the priest.

He started off telling us that the greeting was not peace and goodwill to men on earth, but peace on earth to men of goodwill, and went on to say that Christmas was a time of prayer as well as a time for enjoying yourself.

"It is not for us, as it is for thoughtless people outside the Church, or for those who have forgotten the very significance of Christ's Mass, just a time for feasting, a mere Bank Holiday. True, we rejoice, as Christians should, at the birth of our Divine Lord, and welcome Him, with the gifts of a good confession and communion, as did the Three Kings of the East. I mean they welcomed Him with gifts, too. Not with the Sacraments, which were yet to be instituted, but with gifts. I use the word in its symbolic sense. And while not as the lantern-jawed Calvinist, that tried to eradicate from this England of ours the very memory of the feast, that generation of gloom, as the great Chesterton called them. Himself, Chesterton, a great man in all senses of the word, a fat man, jolly in God, as sound a judge of beer as he was of theology. We make rejoicing, and think with love all the time even as we break the crackling of the goose, even as we savour the tender white meat of the turkey."

The chokey merchants in the front seats never took their eyes off the priest, and he looked kindly back at us all, and went on with the sermon.

"As we pour the sauce over that homely symbol of our own dear Christian land, the plum pudding, heavy, dark, rich and laden rarely with fruits of sunnier climes, Spain usually, and Italy, and while we enjoy the wine, as Christians should for, as I think it was Belloc remarked, it was given us in the first miracle, and liqueurs are to this day made by Carthusians, Dominicans, Benedictines and if I may mention, in this our own dear land, at Buckfast, the monks make a good wine, but," here he smiled and we smiled with him, "in accordance with what I suppose is the traditionally more austere tradition of this, called by William Shakespeare, whom, as you know, lived and died in the Old Faith, 'sceptered isle' for medicinal purposes only. Or as we pour ourselves a foaming glass of ale, and draw on our cigar——"

The prisoners drew their breath in unison with the preacher, and some of the fellows on punishment swallowed and rubbed their mouths with the back of their hands.

"——we do so, remembering the great love God bore us, love that brought down this day to Mary ever blessed Virgin, conceived without sin, and to Joseph, her most chaste spouse, a little child to die for our salvation on a wooden cross, nailed and crucified to show His love for us."

He looked serious here and we looked serious with him.

"Love as deep as the deepest ocean, as wide as the farthest horizon. Many of you have been mariners and you know how wide that is."

We all looked round, and the screws did too at prisoners nodding in agreement all over the chapel, even some of the chokey prisoners nodded. They didn't nod to the rest of us, but only to each other, who had been mariners, and up at the priest, who nodded back, and went on with the sermon.

"A tender love, a forgiving love, the love of a father for his children, the love of brother for brother, and in that spirit and in that love, to those of you who are of goodwill, I wish a holy and happy Christmas."

The organ struck up a hymn, then, and we all joined in:

> "See amid the winter's snow,
> Born for us, on earth below,
> See the tender Lamb appear,
> Promised from eternal year."

The chokey merchants left the chapel first, filing out of the door, looking neither right nor left, for their morning bread and water. The rest of us waited until they were gone and then we went back to our wings.

It was still very cold and the snow heavy on the ground but bright and clean to look at, just for the minute we were marching across the yard to our wing.

We got our smoking exercise in the end of the wing away from the others. There had been rumours that everyone was getting five Woodbines to smoke that day, the convicted and all, but when the convicted saw us remands and awaiting trials being called away to smoke separate from them they knew that they were getting no smoke.

I walked round behind Charlie, and we smiled at each other, and when he got a chance to whisper he said that maybe next month we'd have been weighed off at the Assizes and be in Borstal.

Well, we had the Assizes to look forward to. It was a big day out, sometimes a couple of days, if your case went on, or if you were not called the first day, and you got tea and bully sandwiches. Sometimes they made a kind of a pasty made with the bully and it was called Sessions Pie.

Yes. I smiled a bit and whispered to Charlie that from this good day it would be getting better, instead of worse, and we could smell the dinner coming up, and it smelt great.

It was as good as its smell. Usually the screw shouted out, "Bang out your doors" the minute we took the diet can off the tray, but this day I took my diet can into the cell, put it on the table, and banged out the door.

In the top shallow tier of the can were three lovely golden-brown roasted potatoes with chopped green vegetable and in the long part was roast meat, a piece of Yorkshire pudding, at least that's what I though it was, and gravy, and all roasting hot with steam running in pearls down the side of the can.

I was looking at it with delight and already had it eaten with my eyes when the screw came back to the cell.

"Don't you want your duff?"

He turned to someone else on the landing outside and said, "Paddy, 'ere, 'e doesn't want 'is duff," and went to walk off.

"I do, I do," I shouted, and hoping to Christ he would not go off.

But he'd only been joking, and opened the door. It was the old Cockney, and there was a great smell of beer off him. He smiled as he handed me my duff and poured custard on it from a ladle.

"There you are, Paddy. That'll put 'air on your chest. We was forgetting all about you, we was." He smiled again and nodded to the orderly to take up the tray and can of custard.

"A happy Christmas to you, sir," said I, on an impulse of liking.

He looked at me for a second and then said, "And the same to you, son, and many of 'em."

I banged out the door and got out the dinner on the plate. It lay hot and lovely, the roast potatoes, the Yorkshire pudding, the chopped greens and the meat, and a big piece of bread to pack up with, and it wasn't long before I had it finished, and the plate clean (not that I left anything on it) for the duff and custard.

And then the door opened again and the screw gave me the *News of the World*. I'd forgotten that the day before was Sunday. He just threw it in the cell to me, and banged out the door again.

Ah, better again, said I to myself, opening the paper, this is making a good day yet.

But after I heard the bells of the city strike three I knew we were not getting any more exercise, and I put down the paper to save a bit of a read for the night. It was getting too dark to read anyway, so I put down the paper and thought I'd walk up and down for a bit. But it was so cold that I didn't want to take off my shoes, so I just sat there crouched up on the chair leaning on the table, hugging into myself to get a bit of heat.

They brought round the supper about a quarter to four and it warmed me up for a while, and I decided I'd go to bed, for they'd hardly come round now till eight o'clock. I lay in bed after I'd eaten my supper and drunk my cocoa, and was warm, anyway.

I thought of home and my family sitting round the fire in Dublin, where there were forty hearths that would welcome me but, to tell the truth, I only thought of them because I thought it was what I should do, in my situation; and it was only for a moment I went on thinking of them, and then I came back here to my cell in the cold, and at least they had put the light on at tea-time so I had another read of the *News of the World*, but the light was in my eyes, and it was cold on my arms outside the blankets, so I put the paper down, and my hands inside the bed-clothes, and must have fallen asleep, for the next thing I remember was doors opening and being banged out and prisoners shouting.

Jesus, they must be making all the fellows get up till eight o'clock, I thought, and that maybe the bastards would report me to the Governor if I was caught in bed. The screw whoever he was was coming nearer and, by Christ, the fellows were getting very defiant all of a sudden, shouting and cursing: "Fugh off, you rotten bastard." . . . "Fugh off . . ."

Jesus, what was happening? I struggled, standing on the cold slate floor, to get my shorts on. I'd never get the bed up in time. But if the others were ballocking the screw, I'd be as good as the rest anyway.

Charlie's door I heard being banged, and he shouting, "Arn . . . you bastard . . ." and then my own door opened.

Christ, what's this? A small, rat-faced screw never said yes, aye, or no about the bed being made down or anything else, but he handed me an envelope and looked at me, with little nervous eyes, and banged out the door and went on to the next cell.

I opened the envelope and found in it a card. It was not personally addressed to me but to "a prisoner," and wished me a happy and holy Christmas and blessings in the New Year from the General of the Salvation Army.

"Ah, you bastard," I shouted after the screw, "stuff you and him," just in time to hear the next fellow let a roar and a string of curses after the screw, while he went on his rounds delivering his greetings.

Nearly every cell that he threw a card into he got shouts and curses from it in return, a thing I had never heard in Walton before, but sweet Jesus, the dirty little bastard, was it coming to make a jeer of us altogether he was?

I put the General's Christmas card convenient to where I'd be using it in the morning and got back into bed again.

For there was no reason to believe that that screw would be coming back to get us out of bed, barring he was coming back to case us all for the Governor in the morning, so fugh him and his happy Christmas. I'd have committed a sin with myself, only I was too indignant to get my mind concentrated, so I just lay in bed and fell asleep again.

The next day, Stephen's Day, or Boxing Day as they called it here, we had no church services but, in compensation I suppose, we had work in the afternoon, and went down and sewed mailbags in the hall together, till at four o'clock just as any other day. So went into our cells that night and ate our supper and drank our cocoa, glad to know that this bloody Christmas lark was over, and next day was an ordinary day, with blokes going up and down to court and all.

And the next day was an ordinary day like any other, and we passed on to New Year's Day without noticing it.

New Year's Day everyone was in great humour for one reason and another. Some of the convicted because they could say "I'm going out this year," others because they could say "I'm going out next year," and Charlie and I were glad because we would be going down to the Assizes and be in Borstal in a few weeks' time.

One of the L.R.s was a fellow called Littlewood. He had been in chokey since shortly after Charlie and Ginger came into the nick, and we had no chance of seeing him till the day after New Year's Day when he came up.

I had often heard the others talk about him.

Dale, or that other bastard, James, or any of the other L.R.s, if they were asked what it was like in Borstal, they'd try to frighten us with stories of what the screws would do to us, and worse still, with stories of the way receptions were "salted," with their shorts taken down and all manner of stuff rubbed on or poured over them.

Littlewood didn't tell us anything like that. We had a great chat with him, on bath-day, the week he came back to the wing.

Littlewood was twenty and married. We thought he was as old as the Hills of Tullow. The screw hated him because, in a quiet way, he mucked them about. He had been in jails all his life and didn't like coppers or screws.

He started knocking off because he had no work, and then, even when there was, he didn't like work, never having had the habit of it. Dale and James and the other L.R.s were kind of afraid of him and they would try and speak to him but he'd only smile and make no answer.

Dale came back up from chokey the day after Littlewood and didn't look any the better of it. It was too good for him to be looking, the bastard, if he looked twice as well. He wasn't finished with the charge of slashing Browny. It would be brought up when he went before the commissioner about his Borstal Licence being revoked. He and James got together again at the table, but had not got so much impudence and making little of the rest of us, as before.

Charlie and Ginger and I were getting used to the nick and as leery as anyone, now, but we listened to Littlewood with interest when he told us about Borstal, in the bath-house.

"Littlewood, can you talk in Borstal?" he was asked.

"'Course you can talk in Borstal. Talk your bleeding 'ead off if you want." Except, he said, for the Silent Hour, when you had to sit in the dining hall reading a book or writing a letter, or else doing nothing but be quiet. Littlewood laughed and said that even at this period you could shove your head in your hands and think about the last bit of crumpet you had outside. That was, he added, if any us pink arses had ever had a bit, which he doubted.

Littlewood laughed again. I suppose because he was married at sixteen and had two children. He had been put in chokey for throwing a can of porridge at a screw that got leery with him, but to the rest of the prisoners, especially the younger ones like Charlie and Ginger and me, he was always decent and good-humoured.

Towards the end of January, there was an appeal by the two Irishmen that had been sentenced to death at Birmingham before Christmas. I knew the man that had planted the bomb and it was neither of the men that had been sentenced. But that would not matter very much to the English. The men that had most to do with it were back home in Ireland, but all would happen would be that the judge would say that all prejudice must be put out of your mind to the jury and after informing the men in the dock that they were getting justice in England the like of which you would get no place else, they would be sentenced to death, as they were.

I could see the logic of saying to any I.R.A. man, "You may not be the one that planted this bomb, but you have planted others and anyway you are all in this conspiracy together and if we can't get the ones that caused this explosion you'll bloody well do as well as the next, whether you knew they were going to let this bomb off at such a time and at such a place or not."

I could see the logic of it, even if they applied it to myself, which God forbid— I considered my present ration of suffering quite adequate—but where any country might do that—and the Irish in the Civil War had no room to talk about death sentences—only England would shove on all this old insulting hypocrisy and tell you in the next breath that they were desperately careful that every foreigner the world over should know that justice had been done according to law.

Their appeal was dismissed and the screws were more bare-faced than the judges.

"We're going to top those two bastards in Birmingham all right," said Johnston one morning when he opened my door.

I didn't answer him. The prisoner carrying the slop bucket came up behind him.

"You know—your two pals," said Johnston. "Old Pierry will give them harps and shamrocks." He looked round at the orderly and laughed. "Another martyr for old Ireland—eh?"

I just emptied my slop in the bucket and stared straight into the prisoner's eyes. He was a fellow called Shaw from Cheshire and I know he didn't fancy me much, so I stared at him for a minute, daring him more or less to join in a free laugh with Johnston. But the bastard didn't, but just looked down and said nothing.

The belting I gave James was the best day's work I'd ever done. These grey days of the New Year were getting longer and brighter and I was like a man gaining money with each day that brought me towards the spring, towards the Assizes and towards Borstal, where I would get leave to talk, work in the fields, and see the sun and the sky.

I was getting more independent of the shouts of the screws, and they were getting more used to me, and the prisoners were easy in their mind that if they got it up for me too much, I'd carve them up just as quick as I did James.

James now got nearly polite to me, though his face was scarred faintly from where I'd caught him with the palm, and I was polite enough to him when I had to go to the table.

Dale sat with him just as before and said nothing to me either. He was a quiet man since he came out of chokey and was waiting now for the Borstal

Commissioner who would take his attack on Browny into account when he appeared before him to see about finishing his licence period.

Browny we had not seen since. He was still over in the hospital and would be there till he went to Chester Assizes. He was already returned as recommended for Borstal and when he was formally sentenced he would be transferred straight from the hospital to Borstal.

I sewed on at work-time and we had started to go out in the yard for our exercise. Charlie and I were contented enough, and so was Ginger. But to save myself trouble and not embarrass Charlie, I kept my head down these last days of January and did not say much, or put myself forward in any way.

Since the appeals of the two men at Birmingham had been refused there was a lot on the papers about it. It was on my *Daily Herald* and on the *News of the World*. They had begun sending the Irish papers from home, but I got a couple with mention of the condemned men and then they stopped.

There was a great agitation in Ireland, with marching and demonstrations, and in America the Irish were furious and had asked Roosevelt to intervene. But here they were regarded as worse than murderers and it was the best of my play to keep easy and say nothing.

The screws started at me about them, and saying that every I.R.A. bastard should get the rope, that it was too good for them, and that they should be given out to the people of Coventry. The screws began saying, too, that the lags in Dartmoor had kicked the shit out of I.R.A. men, and were nearly telling the prisoners here that they would not mind if they gave me a kicking.

So I looked round me carefully at exercise in case they'd jump on me and give a kicking, and Charlie still walked in front or behind me, though they said things an odd time to him, too, and not very choice things either, but as much as to say that there was more in it than us just being chinas. He just walked round near me and at smoking exercise smiled quietly at me when we went for a light. Ginger said nothing one way or another.

There was one thing. That I was safe inside the wing. Old Dodd the P.O. would never let them give me a kicking. Not because for the pain it would cause me but for the pleasure it would give them.

On the 29th of January we were brought down to the Assizes. There was a whole crowd of us in a bus, handcuffed and chained, on two long chains that ran the length of the bus. Ginger and Charlie and I were in a back seat squeezed up together. I was wearing the blue suit I'd been arrested in, and Ginger was wearing his sports coat and flannels and Charlie was wearing his sailor's uniform. He looked real grown-up and more sure of himself in it. I suppose we all did in our ordinary clothes. The shorts in the Y.P wing made us look like kids, like Boy Scouts.

One of the grown-up prisoners heard my accent and asked if I knew Mountjoy Jail in Dublin. I said that I knew plenty that had been in it, but had never been there myself. This man was Irish, and said he knew some of our blokes in the jail. I thought he was friendly but then he said: "A miserable lot of bastards. They had plenty of snout and scoff but never gave us poor bleeders any of it. They wouldn't parade with the ordinary prisoners—thought they were too good for us."

I did not believe what he said about the I.R.A. prisoners not giving any cigarettes to the others, for it was notoriously well known that they were very generous in that way and, in fact, it had been argued by the Minister for Justice in debates in the Dail that their generosity to the other prisoners with tobacco was an excuse for not letting the politicals have any.

As an Irishman I'm quite sure he understood their position in demanding separate treatment from ordinary prisoners. I was certain he was only saying these things to keep in with the other prisoners and with the screws, and so as they would not hold it against him for being an Irishman.

I turned back to Charlie and Ginger and didn't answer him or have anything further to say to him. I could understand why he didn't want to suffer for Ireland or the I.R.A., but I did not see why the yellow-born bastard should use me as a sort of sounding board for his hunker-sliding to the English.

In the coach it was like an excursion. The screws gave out their cigarettes to the prisoners, and even gave me a packet of twenty Gold Flake out of my property. We smoked and talked as the coach went down to the city. The screws smoked with the adult prisoners and gave them lights, and were as friendly as a crowd of men on a building job or in a factory.

They didn't address any remarks to us Y.P.s, but let us smoke and we talked amongst each other. I talked to Charlie and Ginger.

Nobody was saying anything to me one or another till this shoneen—Irish bastard brought it up about the I.R.A. Then the screws and the adult prisoners began talking about the two men under sentence of death at Birmingham and all found it a great point of agreement that they should be hanged, and every other I.R.A. prisoner with them. I pretended not to take this as a personal matter and said nothing but went on talking to Charlie and Ginger. Ginger went on talking to me, as well as Charlie.

"Bloody lot of murderers," said one of the Y.P.s. I looked over to see who it was and saw it was Shaw. He was a shrivelled-up-looking bastard from outside Birkenhead and was appearing on different charges at two Assizes, this one at Liverpool and another at Chester Castle. The principal charge against him was stealing his dead mother's insurance money. I saw it in the *News of the World* that his aunt said that he put his hand on the corpse and swore he had not touched it. "You're lucky you're not down in Birmingham with your pals, Paddy," he said across to me.

You skinny-looking whore's melt, said I, in my own mind, Jesus look down on you, if I ever get you in a place where I can give you a kicking. All the other prisoners looked over at me and one old fellow angrily said: "Woman cut in 'alf. I'd give 'em bloody bombs, the Irish bastards, I would."

He glared at me with his mad old eyes, but I said nothing. Shaw, though, I promised myself, I'd be like God, and pay my debts without money, with a good kick up in the balls, for a beginning, what they called in the slums at home a Ringsend uppercut.

The other prisoners and the screws all looked round at me and, for a moment or so, I did not like it and wished they'd get back to their own conversations, and forget about me, and so they did, for the next thing was the coach pulled up in the middle of the city and we were told to get out. God's help is never farther than the door.

We were in a big square, and were being brought across to the building opposite—a big place like the Four Courts at home, but not so genuine—more Victorian than Georgian. Like everything else in Liverpool, I'd say.

They got us out and marched us across the square to the court. The ground was covered in dirty snow and the people stopped to have a look at us, some of them coming nearer across to the middle of the road to get a better look—two lines of prisoners on two chains.

The prisoners gave out about the crowd as we trudged into a doorway in the base of the building and down a long tunnel with bare electric bulbs lighting it. I didn't mind about the people looking once they were not looking at me specially as an I.R.A. man, but I suppose it would be different if you were a local of the place and someone that knew was to see you going over the street on a chain, to the court to be tried for robbing or rape. Anyway, the best thing about it was that it kept them off the subject of I.R.A. men and hanging and beating-up.

We were locked in the cells but in two lots together. The grown-up prisoners in one cell and the Y.P.s in another. Charlie and Ginger and I stood talking in a corner and someone said we were not going to be tried that day. Well, I had not thought the judge would get through the whole lot in the one day but I thought he would make a start and, taking the shortest cases at the beginning, might try me amongst the first. It would not mean I would go to Borstal any the quicker, but maybe the other prisoners were wrong, and I might get sent down for about fourteen years, p.s. The screws said I would, and though I'd sooner believe Littlewood or the little fat prisoner in the Reception, both of whom said I could only get Borstal on account of my age, how did I know, maybe, that they were wrong and the screws right, and that I would get fourteen stretch? But at least if I did I'd be along with some of our own fellows.

I'd like to know anyway, to be out of pain, one way or another, and I was a bit ashamed in a way that I was worried over going to p.s. for fourteen years or to Borstal for three and ashamed, too, because it was not really the length of the sentence that worried me—for I had always believed that if a fellow was in the I.R.A.

at all he should be prepared to throw the handle after the hatchet, die dog or shite the licence—but that I'd sooner be with Charlie and Ginger and Browny in Borstal than with my own comrades and countrymen any place else. It seemed a bit disloyal to me, that I should prefer to be with boys from English cities than with my own countrymen and comrades from Ireland's hills and glens.

But no one had really expected the judge to do much business that day and we were not disappointed. At about four o'clock we were chained and taken out of the cells and brought through the tunnel and back up the steps to our coach. We stood together in the shadow of St. George's Hall and it was great for a minute even to stand there and hear the traffic and see the darkened cars and buses move slowly through the black-out, and feel the thousands of free people about us, going home for their tea, or maybe in for a quick one into the pub, warm and bright behind the darkness.

It was sad too, and for the moment we all stood together, united in sadness, in the dark cold night.

Then the door was opened and we got back into the coach and the prisoners had a quick smoke, though this time the screws did not light up, but gave orders to put out them bloody dog-ends when we came to the corner of Walton Road.

We waited for the Assizes; we counted the days. We were all for Borstal. That we knew and we listened only half believing to the whispers of Littlewood on the way to the bath on Wednesdays, or going to the exercise yard, turning the corner of the next wing, and for a moment out of the screw's sight. These were the times for questions and Littlewood was well interrogated.

The screw would shout automatically when we passed round the corner from his sight: "Hey, cut out that nattering in front. What do you bastards think you're on, eh?"

Get stuffed, you old bastard. We'll have another few words on the way back.

"Right, lead on to the yard. Get spaced out there and cut out that whispering. Come along there, well behind each other. You, there, come off his neck. Get spaced out. And not a bloody word from you, unless you want to go before the Governor in the morning. He'll give you something to bleedin' natter about. Quiet."

Round and round in the cold. Dear Jesus, except for this bit of a whisper on the way there and back going round the corner of "D" wing, you'd be better off in your cell. Where you could freeze on the slate floor, in shorts and thin shirts and jackets that were only good for creating a draught up your back. The hands were the worst. Round and round, slip your hands in under your belt. Warm against your stomach. Over your Jesus it's shrivelled to nothing.

"Hey, you, take your hands off your brains. Come on, give over nursing it. That's what has you looking so bloody dossy. Get them hands out of them belts, and swing 'em up."

All right for you, you big-bellied bastard. Standing up there on the steps in your fughing overcoat, muffled up to the cap.

Charlie is ahead of me and smiles as he goes round on the bends. There are three Polish kids and they smile at me too. Charlie looks cold but rosy-cold like an English boy in a soap advertisement. The Poles are refugees because they are Jewish. Out of the frying-pan into the refrigerator. They look frozen. But then for that again, Warsaw is north of Liverpool and they must have been in worse winters than this. But then, for that again, I suppose, they were fed for it. The biggest Jewish boy is about nineteen, and has an ugly strong face. The next fellow is a stocky, hardy-looking youth and I'd have said he was the toughest of them. One of the Y.P.s said something insulting to him, and though he could neither understand English or reply in that language, he gave the English fellow a look as good as a summons and yon Englishman looked away first. The third, and youngest Jewish boy, is slim with a jaunty head of close black curls and blue eyes like a garsun from Connemara.

He smiles but the poor biggest fellow is frozen blue. I suppose it's because he's more face than the other two.

Ah, well, God is good and His Mother is very decent, and it won't be long before the three of yous are burning your bellies beneath the sun of David.

The buildings on the four sides of us are like a sooty grey monster with five rows of eyes. They say that at night time with the lights on in the cells the jail looks like a set of huge tram cars.

↓

I got paper for the purpose of preparing my defence and wrote on it:

> My lord and gentlemen, it is my privilege and honour today, to stand, as so many of my countrymen have done, in an English court, to testify to the unyielding determination of the Irish people to regain every inch of our national territory and to give expression to the noble aspirations for which so much Irish blood has been shed, so many brave and manly hearts have been broken, and for which so many of my comrades are now lying in your jails.

Outside the doctor's one morning I met another Irishman. He was from Monaghan and I am ashamed to say that he might have been from the moon as from Monaghan for all I had in common with him, outside of being for Ireland, against England. By God he was that, all right. Callan was his name and he was a mad Republican. Not that he was in over the I.R.A. but was in over his own business, which was stealing an overcoat from Sir Harry Lauder's car outside the Maghull Alhambra. He gave out to me from between set lips about the two men that were under sentence of death in Birmingham.

But in two months Walton Jail had made me very anxious for a truce with the British. I had come to the conclusion, not only that everything I had ever read or heard in history about them was true, but that they were bigger and crueler bastards than I had taken them for, lately. Because with tyrants all over Europe, I had begun to think that maybe they weren't the worst after all but, by Jesus, now I knew they were, and I was not defiant of them but frightened.

> Pay them back, blow for blow, give them back woe for woe,
> Out and make way for the Bold Fenian Men.

Yes, but for Christ's sake not here. Not here where they could get you kicked to death for a Woodbine, or an extra bit of bread, if they didn't want the trouble of doing you in more officially.

This goddamned Callan though nearly seemed to like the idea of being a martyr. He had been to the great annual procession to Wolfe Tone's grave at Bodenstown, County Kildare. I had marched there myself, first as a Fianna boy, since I was able to walk, and later in the I.R.A., and more often than Callan, but I had to admit that he had the order of the parade and the drill off all right. Except that he gave a whole impression of the procession while we were walking round the exercise yard, I'd have enjoyed it.

He was able to roar in a whisper. When we'd go on the exercise yard, he'd start: "First Cork Brigade, fall in, by the left! Belfast Number One Brigade! Quick march Third Tipperary Brigade, by the left! Third Battalion, Dublin Brigade, South County Battalion, Dublin Number Two, dress by the right, eyes left Clan na Gael contingent Camp Number One, New York City . . ." By the time the screw was standing on the steps and scratching his head and wondering where the muttered roars were coming from, Callan had finished drilling the entire Irish Republican movement from the thirty-two counties of Ireland, Boston, New York, Liverpool, and London and had them on the march to Tone's grave, to the stirring scream of the war-pipes, proceeding from the side of his mouth.

He did it so well that the others started marching round the exercise yard in step to his piping, even despite themselves.

> Proudly the note of the trumpet is sounding,
> Loudly the war cry arise on the gale,
> Swiftly the steed by Lough Swilly is bounding,
> To join the thick squadrons by Saimear's green Vale,
> On! every mountaineer, stranger to fright and fear!
> Rush to the standard of dauntless Red Hugh!
> Bonnoght and gallowglass, rush from your mountain pass,
> On for old Erin, O'Donnell abu!

He didn't sing the words of course but made a noise like the pipes playing them that went like this:

Burp burp buh burp burp bee burp burp beh burp burp, ur
ur uh hur hur deh dur dur duh dur,
Birp birp bih birp birp bir birp birp bih birp birp.

which went just to a steady sensible marching noise, till he got to a frenzied screech of the pipes at the end:

. . . Miaow aow aow aow aow aow, miaow yaow yaow
aow, haow yaow,
Yaow aow aow aow aow, yaow aow haow yaow yaow!

For a time the screw stood on the steps in amazement looking round and straining his ears to catch the faint but rhythmic and persistent drone of Callan's piping. Then he screwed up his eyes and spoke through his teeth.

"'Oo's making that bleedin' noise, eh?"

We all looked around to show him our mouths and to show it wasn't us. Callan did too, and I was the only one to know that it was him was making the noise, and I wouldn't have known it but I'd already heard his preliminary drilling and ordering of the troops.

The other prisoners were terrified of getting into trouble over the noise and would have stopped whoever was doing it double quick, and Callan or me quicker than anyone, but his mouth never moved. It's ventriloquism Callan should have gone in for, in place of patriotism and overcoat-robbing.

The others did not know in the name of God where the noise was coming from, and were getting as worried about it as the screw.

He was doing his nut, standing up there on the steps. He stared at each face in turn, in a quiet frenzy, but still the piping went on. He came down off his steps and stood on the edge of the ring as we passed him, and looked into each face.

Callan came up in his turn and just stared quietly and passed on after the others. I was following and opened my mouth so that at least he'd be certain it wasn't me. . . . The piping had ceased, and the screw went back on his steps, and the piping started again, resolute, though quiet. The screw stared about him, and cocked his ears to see if he was imagining the noise, and then nodded his head slowly and looked about him in horror. We looked at him in horror, Callan looking at him in horror, even while he went on with the march.

Then the screw fixed his eyes on one of us. I hoped to the dear Christ it wasn't me. He took a run down the steps, and Callan stopped his music. The screw came forward and I ducked with the rest. He made a dive on a boy from Glasgow that had hardly ever been heard to open his mouth in the place, even to ask you to pass the wax-end at labour.

"Aaarh, you Scotch bastard. Want to play your bleedin' bagpipes, do you?"

He caught a hold of poor Jock and beat him up the steps, to the gate, where he shouted through the bars for the screw on duty inside in the wing to come and take control of Jock.

"Playing the bleedin' bagpipes through 'is bleedin' teeth, 'e was."

The other screw gave the usual reproachful look one screw gave when you were accused of having talked or broken any rule while in charge of another screw. As much as to ask how could you find it in your heart to do anything that would make life difficult for such a good kind man. Then he gave Jock a routine blow into the face and took him by the scruff of the neck, and nodded reassuringly to the exercise screw as much as to say that he wouldn't let these bastards take advantage of his good nature.

When Jock had been dragged off to his cell to await the Governor, the screw came from the gate and stood on the steps, shaking his head with satisfaction, while we all, myself included, more shame to me, breathed easier, and plodded round in our less martial and more resigned gait.

And then, in despair, because we couldn't help it, our steps tramped in unison and our backs straightened and our heads went up. Callan was at it again. This time it was drums and trumpets that blared discreetly out the side of his mouth, as he crashed into the old Republican march with a warning roll of the drums:

> Burump de dumpiddy dum, burump de dumpiddy dum,
> Step together, boldly tread, firm each foot, erect each head,
> Fixed in front be every glance, forward! at the word
> > advance!
>
> Noise befits neither hall nor camp,
> Eagles soar on silent feather,
> Proud sight, left! right! steady boys, steady boys!
> > and step together!
>
> Steady boys! and step together!
> Bardiddly bardiddly bar bar bar bar!

The screw looked down at us and said the exercise was over and all inside, and up to our cells. While we passed him on the steps into the wing, he kept his ears cocked to each prisoner's face. But Callan was not as green as he was Irish and we broke off and went into our cells without his musical accompaniment, though I thought when we halted in the Y.P. wing before falling out that he was going to shout in a whisper, "Irish Republican Army, dismiss!"

Safely in the cell I was pleased with Callan's performance. I had never seen anyone get the better of the screws before. It was hard luck on poor Jock, though.

If it had been one of the English bastards I wouldn't have cared a God's curse, except for Charlie or Ginger, of course.

In the first week of February, the snow was over and there were birds of some dirty colour singing on the window-sills. But, whatever their colour, we were glad of them. They were like the spring and a change from the pigeons that sat grunting on the windows all during the winter.

The First of February is the first day of spring and the ninth is my birthday. And the old saying had it, "If we live through the winter the divil wouldn't kill us in summer."

Well, I was after living through the winter and on the ninth I would be seventeen.

The First of February is St. Bridget's day. She was from the County Kildare and is called the Mary of the Gael, being very beautiful and a great friend to the poor.

Raftery had a song about the springtime and it went, "Anois, teacht an Erraigh, beidh an la dul chun sineadh. . . ."

> Now, in the springtime, the day's getting longer,
> On the feast of Saint Bridget, up my sail will go,
> And I'll not delay, but my step getting stronger,
> Till I stand once again in the Plains of Mayo . . .

Every day except Sunday, Charlie would be saying that we might be going to the Assizes that day.

On my paper it said that the two men sentenced to death at Birmingham were to be hanged on the seventh. On Ash Wednesday.

The screw started again to make jeering remarks about them. So did some of the prisoners. Dale didn't nor James. I'd given the latter bastard something to cure him the time I belted him but I could see the pair of them were delighted with the screws getting it up for me. And one of the prisoners was constantly joining in when the screws were willing to let him, which was any time the P.O. was not there to spoil the fun.

His name was Shaw. A shrivelled-up seldom-fed bastard that had stolen money from under his dead mother's body and then put his hand on her and sworn he hadn't. He was about twenty but looked as if he had never been that young in his life. Like a little man, he was. I could have beaten him up about three times as easily as I had done James, but I was afraid, not of him, but of the whole lot of them.

Again they were muttering, and I had to sit every day beside the wall at the back when I could, where I could not be attacked from all four sides at once. Charlie sat beside me or behind me and walked in front or behind me at exercise, and Ginger still saluted me.

Callan, thank Christ, was working in the carpenter's shop with the convicted prisoners, and I didn't know, at that, whether to be glad or sorry he was on a different labour to me. Looking at it one way, I was glad, because he'd start them off by answering them, screw or prisoner, and looking at it the other way, if a mill did start, he'd be there to make two of us anyway. I was hoping Charlie wouldn't join in, if there was a heave, and whispered that to him, on the way to the baths, on the Monday.

"I'm your china, Paddy," was all he said, and went on down the passage.

On Tuesday I heard that Callan had nearly started a riot in the carpenter's shop. They'd started at him over the executions on the next morning, and he'd gone for someone with a wood chisel, and when we were going to our cells that evening, I noticed that his cell which was on the ground floor and under me was locked, so that he must have been there before the others. Going up to my cell I hoped that he would keep easy till morning, and then in my cell and I drinking my cocoa, I was ashamed of myself for hoping that, but it didn't change me from hoping that Callan would keep quiet. It only made me ashamed as well as being afraid.

They were two innocent men and one of them was arrested in London within half an hour of the explosion which happened in Coventry.

They were brave men. One of them before he was sentenced to death said that he would walk out smiling, thinking of all the other men that had died for Ireland.

And when he was sentenced to death, he'd said as good a thing.

The judge said, "May the Lord have mercy on your soul," and he replied, "You too."

The humour of that would be appreciated in his part of Ireland, where it was reply to such commonplace greetings as "Hello," or "Good health."

Still and all, I was here, on my own in this place, thinking of them, and even thinking of them having to face the rope in the morning didn't inspire me. It would inspire the crowds at home and in Madison Square Garden, where they would burn Union Jacks and curse the British Empire into hell and out of it back into it and think with pride and the blood surging though their veins of these brave men. The song of the Manchester Martyrs to the air of the American Civil War song, "Tramp, tramp, tramp, the boys are marching," would roar from ten thousand throats:

"God save Ireland," cried the heroes,
"God save Ireland," cry we all,
"Whether on the scaffold high or the battlefield we die,
Sure, no matter when for Ireland dear we fall."

It didn't inspire me. I thought it better to survive my sentence and come out and strike a blow in vengeance for them, than be kicked to death or insanity here.

And even that was not the truth. I only wanted to survive the night. I sat with my legs in my mailbag sewing my cell task, and thinking of sadness and sorrow and shame, and hoping that my demeanour was a peaceable one, and that the book I was going to read was a very meek one. Not that that would count with the screws. Most of them couldn't read anyway. Well, not books. My book was *Cranford* by Mrs. Gaskell.

I got into bed when the bell rang, thankful that Callan had let the night go past without starting a heave, and comfortable and warm opened my book.

It was a very comfortable class of a book. I'd never heard of it before, and when I saw it lying on my table with my other library book, I didn't think much of the look of it. It was in a heavy old cover, from the times of Queen Victoria, and I only knew of one class of book like that that was worth a God's curse, and they were by Charles Dickens. When I didn't see his name on it, I thought it wouldn't be worth opening and when I saw it was written by "Mrs." Someone, I said good night, Joe Doyle, this is a dead loss.

All that class of book was about little sweeps' boys that saved up money to buy their mothers' cloaks or little girls going out to put on the light in the lighthouse when their fathers were not able to do it. They were probably lying some place pissed drunk, I thought to myself, but that wasn't in those books of course.

So I took no heed of this *Cranford* other than to read it in bits, for a throwaway, like, in the middle of the day, after dinner, when I would be going out again out of the cell and only wanted to look at something besides the bare whitewashed walls of the cell for a while. I reserved any good or readable books for the night, when I would want something to read at my real read in bed. I could read when I was four years old, well in a kind of a way, and was always very fond of reading, but every one of the prisoners was the same with regard to their books, which were the principal and only thing we enjoyed, well the only thing we enjoyed with official permission. They could hardly stop us dreaming or thinking bad thoughts. We all kept our best book for the night, and read or looked at the worst rubbish at dinner-time.

I started this *Cranford* in the dinner-time, but after I got into it a bit, I promoted it to the night time, and even had to ration myself to twenty pages a night, which would leave forty each for Saturday and Sunday.

This night, I decided, I could lawfully allow myself a few pages extra, as a matter of that, and as much as I could read before I went asleep, and forgot everything.

> For Miss Barker had ordered (nay, I doubt not, prepared, although she did say, "Why, Peggy, what hev you brought us?" and looked pleasantly surprised at the unexpected pleasure) all sorts of good things for supper—scalloped oysters, potted lobsters, jelly, a dish called "little Cupids" (which was in great favour with the Cranford ladies,

although too expensive to be given except on solemn and state occasions—macaroons sopped in brandy, I should have called it, if I had not known its more refined and classical name). In short we were to be feasted with all that was sweetest and best; and we thought it better to submit graciously, even at the cost of our gentility—which never ate suppers in general, but which, like most non-supper-eaters, was particularly hungry on all special occasions.

Miss Barker, in her former sphere, had, I dare say, been made acquainted with the beverage they call cherry-brandy. We none of us had ever seen such a thing, and rather shrank back when she proffered it us: "Just a leetle, leetle glass, ladies; after the oysters and lobsters, you know." We all shook our heads like female mandarins; but at last, Mrs. Jamieson suffered herself to be persuaded, and—

There was an unmerciful roar from a cell beneath me: "U—u-u-u-up the Rep—u-u-u-u-ub—lic!" roared Callan.

That the devil may choke you and the Republic, I snarled to myself, and why the fughing hell isn't he satisfied with his own exclusive martyrdom without dragging me into it. You're not much good alone and unarmed, are you? I said to myself and answered, No, by Jesus, I am not, not worth a light. But maybe with the help of the Holy Mother of God, he'll carry on his Plan of Campaign by himself, all honour to him, of course, I'll never deny it to him, but tell them at home how all alone he stood and shouted for the cause all on his own. If he only leaves me out of it.

"Be—eee-han. Bren—daaaaaaaaan Be-ee-haaan!"

You lousebound bastard, said I to myself, putting down *Cranford*.

"Uu—uuuuu—up the Rep—uuuuuuub—lic!"

Answer you better, you whore's melt, to give the man back his overcoat and leave the Republic to look after itself.

"Breeeeeeeeeeeennnnnn—daaaaaaaaaaannnn Beeeeeeeee—hann! Get up and give a shout—a sh-ooooooouuuuuuuuut!"

A kick up in the ballocks is what I'd like to give you, said I resentfully, getting out of the bed. I stood for a moment in my shirt, wondering what to do. May God direct me, said I to myself.

"Uuuuu—uuu—uup the Rep—uuuub—lic, Beeee—haaaaan!"

All right, all right. I gave a discreet shout down the ventilator of "Up the Republic."

"I caaaaaaaa—n't heeeeeeeer youuuuuuu riiiiiightly," answered Callan.

"I'm shouting," I said in a low tone down the ventilator, "the walls here are three feet thick."

"All right. Gooooood maaaaaaan. Up the Reeeeee—puuuuub—liiic!"

"Up the Republic," I said, but in a lower tone down the ventilator. "We defy you. To hell with the British Empire," I added in a hurried whisper, for I'd heard voices down below, and the noise of keys at Callan's door.

I jumped back into bed. Callan was getting done. They'd burst open his door and were on top of him. They'd be round to my door in a few seconds, for a look in the spy-hole. And where was I, when they did come round? In bed reading *Cranford*.

"What are you doing there, Behan?" they shouted in from the spy-hole.

I put down my book and looked up at the door. "I'm reading, sir."

He snuffled something of a threatening nature, and went off. I heard Callan's door being opened and heard moaning. They were after finishing with him, and were carrying him down to the chokey cells.

I went back to *Cranford*.

> ". . . It's very strong," said Miss Pole, as she put down her empty glass; "I do believe there is spirit in it."
>
> "Only a little drop—just necessary to make it keep," said Miss Barker. "You know we put brandy-paper over preserves to make them keep. I often feel tipsy myself from eating damson-tart."
>
> I question whether damson-tart would have opened Mrs. Jamieson's heart as much as the cherry-brandy did; but she told us of a coming event, respecting which she had been quite silent until that moment.
>
> "My sister-in-law, Lady Glenmire, is coming to stay with me."

Lady Glenmire—Glenmire, that was the name of the Cork City railway station, I remembered, before I fell asleep.

"Cahm on, cahm aht of it," I heard a voice shout in at me.

I jumped out of bed remembering it was the morning of the executions at Birmingham, and then about Callan last night, and I was a bit alarmed, but it wasn't that at all. I was going to court.

I got dressed quickly and emptied my slops down at the recess, went back and collected my kit. The screw hurried me down the stairs and through the prison to the Reception. I looked at the clock there, and it was a quarter to eight. They were going to be hanged at nine, I knew.

When I was bathed and dressed in my own clothes, I was told to stand in line with some prisoners. They were all grown-up men and I did not know any of them. I had been there only a few minutes when I was brought by two screws in civilian clothing to the yard, where they told me to stand a minute.

A car came into the yard and I was handcuffed to the two screws and put into it. As we drove down the road from the prison, I saw a newspaper placard, "Irish Murderers to Die."

A church bell rang out a little later. They are beginning to die now, said I to myself.

As it chimed the hour, I bent my forehead to my handcuffed right hand and made the Sign of the Cross by moving my head and chest along my outstretched fingers. It was the best I could do.

The screw who was handcuffed to me on my right looked at me and I looked back at him. If he was going to say anything, he changed his mind, and we both looked ahead of us again, towards the windscreen.

I was the first to be tried. The proceedings were short and sweet like an ass's gallop.

The stuff had been caught with me, and as a soldier of the Irish Republican Army I refused to recognize the court. This made the clerk enter a plea of "Not Guilty," after it had been established that I was not a deaf mute, but mute of malice.

The judge asked me had I anything to say. I delivered my speech which I had off by heart.

After I had said, My lord and gentlemen, it is my privilege and honour and all that effect, he very rudely interrupted me to say, as casually as he could, though he was a ham actor, and in a temper, that he and the jury did not wish to listen to a political speech.

I waited on him to finish and went on with my speech, in a louder voice. I have a sense of humour that would nearly cause me to burst out laughing at a funeral, providing it was not my own, and solemn speeches are not easily made by me. I can't keep it up. But when I'm speaking to ignorant people I will use any and every means to needle them as best I can according to their particular brand of insolence. For instance, I was at the races one day, and a very wealthy citizen made some indulgently funny remark to me. I pretended to think that he was touching me for money, and handed him a shilling, and said, "Excuse me now, my good man, I've a bet in this race." Another time I was singing double-meaning songs in a public house in the country and a lady was shocked and complained to her husband who complained to the management. My friends and I pretended to believe that she was a prostitute, and convinced the publican that she was, and that she was doing business on his premises, and we had her thrown out.

So as this judge was in a vicious and not very judicial temper, I decided to put him in a worse one.

"...and this to a proud and intelligent people, who had a language, a literature, when the barbarian woad-painted Briton was first learning to walk upright.

"By plantation, famine, and massacre you have striven to drive the people of Ireland from off the soil of Ireland, but in seven centuries you have not succeeded.

"Many times you have announced that you had stamped out the rebels, that 'you had terrorism by the throat,' that you had settled the 'Irish Question.'

"But there is but the one settlement to the Irish Question, and until the thirty-two-county Republic of Ireland is once more functioning, Ireland unfree shall never be at peace.

"God save Ireland. No surrender."

The two screws looked at me, and the judge had given up his pretence of boredom, and settled himself to sentence me.

He stated, which was a lie, that I had taken advantage of the mildness of British law in regard to the punishment of persons under eighteen. He also expressed regret that he had to give me the benefit of this mildness, and that he could not sentence me to fourteen years' penal servitude, which he would have, if I had been eighteen years of age. He also said that he thought that the law should make allowances for people like myself, who though young in age were mature of purpose. He could only sentence me to three years' Borstal Detention.

I shouted "Up the Republic!" across the court and right into his face, and went down the stairs in good humour, because I had needled the ill-mannered judge into admitting that he was nearly cutting his throat that he couldn't give me fourteen years, and also because I had only got three years.

I did not know enough about Borstal to be glad that it was Borstal Detention I was sentenced to, and if he had given me the choice of three years' Borstal Detention or two years imprisonment, I'd have taken the imprisonment.

I got down the stairs, well satisfied with myself that I had given the judge as good as I'd got, and also that the world would know that my two comrades now lying in the clay these two hours past were not so soon forgotten.

Thousands had marched in mourning all over Ireland and in the United States, but I was the only one privileged to stand up for the cause ennobled by these humble men openly and defiantly in the midst of our enemies—great as they were, with their money, their Army, Navy, and Air Force, their lions, unicorns, and ermine robes to hide their hangman's overalls.

I got down to the door of my cell and waited for the screws to open it.

"Hey, you," a woman's voice shouted at me. I looked round and it was a policewoman or wardress with a young weeping girl. "Dry your tears, dear, and 'ave a look at the 'ero. 'Ere's a poor girl got in trouble, and is up over doing away with 'er baby, though of course it will only mean she'll be bound over," she put in quickly, "and you young pup 'ave nothing better to do than coming over 'ere making trouble for everyone and your poor Dad and Mum worried to death, I'm sure, over in Ireland, and, you young pup, give you three years' Borstal, did he? I know what I'd have done, tan your backside for you, that's what I'd have done, taken down your pants and given you a good tanning and sent you back on the boat tonight. And this poor girl 'ere—" She glared at me, and I didn't know what to say to the old bitch. I only wished the screws would open the cell and let me get to hell away from her.

But under the court the cells are not like prison cells of solid wood and steel, but gates with bars, the same as you see on the pictures, so there would be no escape from her there. At least she could have the decency to go away and let me have a piss.

"'Ere," she came over to me and handed me a package, "you don't deserve them, but Elsie 'ere can't eat them. We'll be 'aving a cup of tea afterwards."

I looked at the screws. One fellow was standing smoking a pipe and said, "Go on, take them, they're sandwiches."

Well, to get rid of the old whore, I took them, and muttered thanks. Elsie was called then , so I shouted "good luck" after them as they went up the stairs to the dock. After all, it wasn't Elsie's fault that old one had given out to me, and I ate the sandwiches and also Sessions Pie, which the screws gave me with tea. They were very good sandwiches, and after the humiliation I had undergone from that old screwess I might as well eat them. The tea was very good, too, and so was the Sessions Pie. It is a kind of pastry stuffed with bully beef.

When I finished eating, I looked round for something to put my mark up on the wall.

It is surprising what people will find to do this with. There were inscriptions all over the walls. Even from men sentenced to death. One had a man's name, and then the words, "sentenced to death" and a date, and then "for killing my dear wife, with a hammer I am innocent of as a new born baby."

Others read: "Six months for larceny ladies watch I only took to keep it safe." "Jesus and dear God help a wicked sinner. Oh, if I get out I will go straight."

There were defiant ones that read: "—— 'em all—bar one—he can —— himself." "The Preston Jacks are all bastards and perjurers." "To h—— with everyone and —— the rest." The "h——" was spelt like that but the "——" was spelt in full.

There were a few from Irishmen, and three from the Irishmen sentenced at the last Assizes. I decided to stick mine up there between a Corkman's name and a Dublinman's:

> Breandán Ó Beacháin, Óglach,
> 2adh Cath, Briogaíd Atha Chliath,
> I.R.A. An Phoblacht abu!

which means,

> Brendan Behan, Volunteer,
> 2nd Battalion, Dublin Brigade,
> I.R.A. The Republic forever!

I wrote "I.R.A." in English so as they would understand it that read it.

When I was sitting down, having a smoke, they brought another kid into the cell. He was a Liverpool-Irish boy called Patrick George Hartigan. His father was a Catholic from the West of Ireland, he told me, and his mother. They had given him his two Christian names to give the Catholic Church and the Protestant religion fair play. He was a very hungry-faced boy with puffed eyes and white jaws stretched on his peaky face, and though he said he was twenty he was smaller and much lighter than I. I never seen anyone so young rely so much on a cigarette which he hung on to, and drew smoke out of, and carried it down into his guts, and kept it there before he blew it out as if he was doing it for a bet.

"I didn't like my old man," said he, "because he used to bash my Mum, but I'm half-Irish just the same, Paddy, and you and me will be chinas, getting sentenced and all the same day, what?"

"Yes, sure we will," said I, though I didn't want the poor bastard for a china. Besides, what would Charlie say? We were chinas first.

"We might get sent to the same Borstal, Paddy, and do our bird together."

May God forbid, said I, treacherously, to myself. "Yes, we might, on account of being sentenced the same day, what?"

"They call me 'Harty,' Paddy, that's what all my mates calls me outside, like."

"And a good name, too, Harty," said I, and we laughed together.

"'Ere you are, Paddy, 'ave a Senior Service. They'll be taking them off us up above, in the nick. A bastard 'ole."

"What part of it were you in up there?"

"What part was I in? What wing, do you mean? I was in the Y.P. wing same as you. But I went out a couple a days before you was picked up. I saw your case in the papers. It said you was going to blow up Cammell Lairds' shipyard over in Birken'ead."

"They said that," said I, "and they'd say Mass if they knew the Latin."

"Well, I was let out on bail—to get married."

"To get married?"

"Yes, my Judy's 'aving a nipper, that's why they let me out."

"Oh, I see, good man, yourself." I didn't know whether to say congratulations or what. Harty didn't seem that pleased about it.

"She was in court, and all, and pleaded and all. But 'e wasn't 'aving any." Harty got indignant. "'E said Borstal would make a man of me and I'd be a better 'usband when I came out. I'd too much form anyway. Remand 'ome, approved school, six months up 'ere with the Y.P.s I been screwing since I was ten year old. I 'ad to. I wouldn't 'ave eaten if I didn't. 'Course it's different now, a bit more work starting. Funny thing, I didn't mean it any other time when I said I'd go straight, and they believed me a couple of times. Now I do mean it, they won't bleedin' well believe me. I'd go to work I would, if I was out. Always would, if I could have got any other job but shoving a bleedin' messenger boy's bicycle about with two 'undredweight of stuff on it for ten bob a week." He drew on his cigarette, shook his head, sighed and blew out a lot of used smoke.

"That's the way with the world, Harty," said I.

"And I 'ate the nick, I do, lot of bleedin' sex maniacs, most of them." He spat with genuine disgust. "Filthy bleeders. You keep yourself to yourself, Paddy, and don't listen to them, because I can tell you, their talk is mostly filth, and in those Borstals I believe they're a bleedin' sight worse."

"I can imagine it," said I.

Up in the Reception they changed me into blue convicted clothes, but the same shape, jacket, shirt, and shorts. Harty looked miserable in his shorts, and shook his head when we were going up to our cells.

He looked down at his bare knees when we were going up the stairs. "Like a bleedin' Boy Scout," he muttered. "Ah, well, Paddy, that's one day of it up 'is arse. Only one thousand and ninety-four to go. Roll on death."

We stopped at my door, while the screw unlocked it and put on the light, and Harty wished me "good night" and said he'd see me in the morning during the slop out.

The next day I didn't see Charlie or Ginger because they were gone down to the Assizes, but the day after we were all on the convicted exercise together, and though we didn't get our smoke any more we looked with condescension and pity on the remands that did. To us they were new kids. Another thing they brought a few of us, Charlie and Ginger and me included, out to shovel coke into heaps for the prison boilers, and it was out in the open air. Though there was still snow on the ground we weren't perished with the cold like we were on the exercise yard but as warm as toast, and sweating because we were shovelling and using our muscles. Harty wasn't allowed on it because he wasn't allowed on that labour. The doctor had marked him "No. 2" labour.

He let on he didn't mind, and laughed at us, going out like bleedin' 'alf-pay navvies, he said, but I think he was disappointed.

His jaw dropped a bit when I fell in with Charlie and Ginger on the day after they were sentenced. I had gone round with him on the first day because they were down at the court and Harty fell in beside me and seemed to think I'd be with him.

I was sorry for him but then there was nothing I could do about it since he seemed used to being miserable, and just went round with anyone that was handy, at exercise.

Charlie and Ginger and I were in great humour, waiting to go to Borstal, though we were a bit impatient, wondering when we were going to be sent there.

THE
YELLOW BERET

Hapless Dublin parents Mag and Don react badly to news that two murders have occurred nearby in this 1960 story by Mary Lavin.

"MAYBE IT'S THE SAME ONE," said Mag.

"*How* could it be the same?" cried Don. "Wasn't the other one down at the docks? Do you never look at the papers?"

"But two murders in the one night!" Mag knew the note of doubt in her voice would annoy him, but she couldn't help it.

To please him, she peered across the breakfast table at the paper in his hand, but without her glasses the sun made one of everything on the table—plates, napery, and newsprint. And waywardly too her mind swayed away from it all, and went back to her own concerns. She'd soon have to call Donny. She glanced to see if his entrance card for his examination was still propped in front of the clock, so he couldn't possibly forget it when he was going out. She looked around the room to make sure there was nothing else he was likely to forget—his fountain pen, or the key of his locker in College.

But all the time, however, she felt Don was critical of her lack of attention.

"I hope we're not going to have a wave of crime!" she said.

Exactly the wrong thing to say. She had only revealed the full extent of her heedlessness.

"Wave of crime!" he scoffed. "I told you there was no connection between the two crimes. You're as bad as the newspapers," he said, irritated. But as he read on he became more amiable. "I admit it's a disturbing business," he conceded. "It will have a very upsetting effect on people, I'm afraid!"

Well, here was something Mag could discuss with a genuine interest and liveliness.

"I don't see why!" she cried. "I don't see why anyone should be upset—ordinary people, I mean—there's always a reason for these murders! Don't tell me they come out of a clear sky! I see no reason why people should be concerned at all about them—beyond feeling sorry for those involved, of course! Take that girl at the docks. I'm sure what happened to her was only the end of a long story!"

"Not necessarily," said Don curtly. "As a matter of fact they're looking for a Dutch sailor who only went ashore a few hours before the murder—"

"—but he knew her from another time, I suppose, and—"

"Not necessarily," said Don again.

Mag reddened. She hadn't understood that it might all have happened in that doorway, not only the murder, but . . . well . . . it all.

"Oh!" she said slowly, repulsed, and then her voice quickened. "Oh, Don," she cried, "let's not talk about it. Let's not even think about it. You know how I feel about that kind of thing."

It was not so much a feeling as an attitude. She had always made it a point to draw a circle, as it were, around the home, and keep out all talk of such things. She had always tried to let the boys feel they lived in a totally different world from the world where such things happened. Don't talk about it. Don't think about it. That was her counsel to herself as well as to them.

It wasn't as easy to practise as to preach, though. Last night she had only caught a word or two about that girl who was strangled on the docks, and yet she could not get the thing out of her mind all night. Although she had never been out to the Pigeon House where it happened, and had only seen the long sea wall from the deck of the B.&I. Boat—seen it sliding past as the steamship pulled out into the Alexandra Basin—yet her mind kept picturing the scene as if it were a place she knew well.

Through the cranes and ships' rigging, she had seen the wide wharf narrow into a place with no human habitations; nothing but coal-yards, and warehouse yards, and the Power Station of Pigeon House itself, its windows lit by day as well as night with a cold inimical light. Then it narrowed again until it seemed only a promenade for birds, bollarded here and there, and splattered with glaring white droppings. The steps that led down from it into the water seemed senseless, more than half of them always under water, wobbly-looking and pale, while sometimes a wash of water, thin as ice, lay over the top step.

It was there she pictured it happening. Not at the edge near the sea-steps, but where, in an abortive bit of wall, an iron gate stood giving entrance or egress to nowhere. She saw the gate distinctly. It was reinforced top and bottom with rusty corrugated iron that had been cut in jags along the top as if with giant pinking shears.

How could a place she had never been be so vivid in her mind? Even then, in the sunny breakfast-room, with terror she felt the picture forming once more in her mind. But this time there was a man in the picture. It was him: the murderer. Who else could it be?

Bending downward, in the gateway, but with his back to her she saw him, too, as clearly as she saw the place he stood. His clothes—a faded blue shirt—his hair —a carroty red—were as plain as if he were in front of her in the flesh. A feeling of gratefulness that she could not see his face had hardly passed over her till it was followed by the knowledge that in a minute he would straighten up and turn around. He would have to turn. For him—if it was him—and who else could it be—that Dutch sailor—there was no going further down the sea wall. He would have to get back to peopled places. And she would be forced to see him face to face. And when she saw his face—ah, this was the terror—it would be, she felt certain, a face that was known to her.

What was the meaning of it? There was never anything psychic about her.

Desperately she closed her eyes to blot it all out—the gateway, the figure, but against her closed lids they formed again; more clearly. And then—as she knew he must—the man turned, or half-turned rather, because only his eyes turned towards her; his face and head remained partly averted. His head indeed, seemed fixed in an implacable pose as if it had no power to move, and yet in another sense it was all movement. Within itself as it were there was a terrible motion. Every cell of skin and hair and membrane seemed to vibrate. The coarse orange hair quivered, and the fibrous beard, while the enormous white whorl of the one ear visible seemed as if evolving still from its first convolution. And not only the face but the very air seemed to whirl and spin until it, too, became all spirals and oscil-lations. She was rigid with tension.

But the white whorl of that ear brought her suddenly to her senses. Van Gogh! The self-portrait! Relief left her so limp she slumped down in her chair. She glanced at Don. What a fool she was!

Why *did* Van Gogh come into her mind? Could there be any reason? And what did he look like—the real murderer?

To think that he might at that moment be walking the streets of Dublin! Again—she saw him. This time he was standing on Butt Bridge, leaning over the parapet and staring down the river. Another wave of terror swept over her.

"Did you say the other murder was in Dublin too, Don?" she asked sharply.

"Still trying to connect the two? I tell you, there was no connection between them, Mag. This other poor creature—" and he nodded down at the paper—"this other poor creature was the soul of respectability—"

"—it was a woman too?"

"An elderly spinster," said Don, as if not altogether corroborating her state-ment. "A school-teacher, I think it said." He bent and looked for verity to the paper. "Yes, a school-teacher living in Sandford Road. Respectable enough address! Over fifty, too!"

But Mag rushed over and grabbed the paper out of his hand.

"Over fifty? Oh, no, Don! No! Why didn't you tell me? That's terribly sad. I didn't realize. I thought it was another of those ugly businesses. Why didn't you tell me it was so sad? The poor creature!"

Don stared at her.

"What's sadder about it than the girl on the docks?" he asked.

But Mag had got her glasses and was gathering up the pages of the paper. "Where is the front page? Was there a picture of the poor thing?"

"I don't think so," said Don. "There was a picture of that girl, though! She was only seventeen. A lovely-looking girl. Now that was what you might call sad! Oh, I know the sort she was, and all that, but she was so young. She had her whole life ahead of her. There is no knowing but she might somehow have been influenced for good before it was too late. And anyhow," he said limply, "the other poor thing"—he shrugged his shoulders, "she can't have had much of a life. She can't have had much to look forward to in the future. Lived alone, kept herself to herself, an odd sort apparently. Say what you like—it wasn't the same as being seventeen!"

"Oh, stop it, Don. I can't bear it. You don't understand. To come to such an end after a lifetime of service." Mag was poring over the paper. "Yes! she was a teacher. To make it worse she was a kindergarten teacher—oh, the poor thing. I can't bear to think of it. The head was battered in—with a stone, they think—and bruises on the neck and back."

"Not a sex crime, anyway," said Don.

"Oh, Don, how can you? There's no question of anything like that! She was over fifty! Fifty-four. And several people have already come forward, voluntarily, to testify to her character. She led the most normal, regular . . ."

"Nothing very normal or regular about wandering the streets in the small hours!"

"Oh, you didn't read it properly." Mag consulted the paper again. "She was *found* in the small hours, but it was *done* before midnight. They haven't given the pathologist's report yet, but the police put the time between eleven and twelve. She wasn't found earlier because the body was dragged into someone's front garden."

"Nice for those people!" said Don.

"Oh, Don, how can you joke about it! Do you realize that if she had been left in the street, there might have been a spark of life in her when she was found, although it seems she wouldn't have been found at all until daylight only a couple coming home from a dance happened to step inside the garden gate."

"Nice for them too!" said Don irrepressibly. "Sorry, Mag, sorry! I feel as bad as you do about it, but you never take any interest in murders, and to hear you carrying on about these women——"

She pulled him up short.

"Don't speak of them in the same breath!" she said coldly.

But he was looking down at the paper again.

"Oh, look, there's more about it in the late-news column. They're looking for any information that may lead to the recovery of a yellow beret believed to have been worn by the victim earlier in the evening."

Mag pressed her lips together.

"Poor unfortunate girl! She little thought when she was putting on that beret——"

"It wasn't the girl! It was the other woman."

"The elderly woman? Are you sure? A yellow beret! It sounds more like what a young girl would wear, surely?"

"The old girl must have fancied herself a bit, it seems."

"Oh, Don, don't take that tone again, please. I'm certain it was simply a case of some fellow attacking her in the hope that she might have money on her. He probably didn't intend anything more than to stun her, but maybe she screamed, the poor thing, and he got frightened and hit her again to keep her quiet. Maybe he didn't realize he'd killed her at all."

"Then why did he drag her into that garden?"

"Oh, I forgot about that."

"You forgot about calling Donny too," said Don. He had got his hat and coat in the hall and was putting them on.

"Oh, he has plenty of time yet," said Mag. "All the same, I'll go right up now and call him before I do anything else." But at the door she turned back. "Don't go till I come down," she said, quite without reason.

Or was it, she thought afterwards, that even then, at the foot of the stairs, a vague uneasiness had already taken possession of her? Had she, all morning, been unconsciously aware of a sort of absolute silence upstairs, different altogether from the merely relative silence when the boy was up there, but asleep? Certainly half-way up the stairs she looked into his room through the banister rail and she was outrageously relieved to see that his bed had been slept in, although he was not in it.

"Oh, you're up?" she cried, talking to him, although she wasn't sure whether he was in the room, behind the door, perhaps, taking down his clothes from the clothes hooks, or in the bathroom—or where? "Where are you?" she asked, when he wasn't in the room. "Are you in there, Donny?" she asked, outside the bathroom door. "Where are you, Donny?" She asked sharply, still addressing herself to him. But when she leaned over the banisters to know if he was downstairs, it was to Don she called. "Is he down there, Don?"

"Why would he be down here?" Don had come to the foot of the stairs. She thought there was an uneasy note in his voice. He started up the stairs.

"Why are you coming up?" she cried.

Then she must have begun to cry, because Don shouted at her.

"Stop that noise, for God's sake, Mag! The boy probably stayed out last night. But what of it? If I had a pound note for every time I stayed out all night when I was his age! He has you spoiled; that's all! There's some perfectly reasonable explanation for his staying out!"

"But he didn't stay out! Wasn't he in bed when I brought up his hot jar last night?"

"He's gone out somewhere then, I expect," said Don, "that's all."

"Where? And when? I was down early. There wasn't a stir in the house. I didn't hear a stir till I heard you!"

Together they stood stupidly, one above the other, in the middle of the stairs.

"He must have gone out during the night then," said Don.

"But why? And why didn't he tell us?" said Mag. "He knows I'm a light sleeper. He knows I never mind being wakened. Many a night, before his other exams, he came into my room and sat on the end of the bed to talk for a while when he couldn't sleep."

"Well, come downstairs anyway," said Don, more gently. "There's no use standing up here in the cold. He hasn't done this before, has he? No! You'd have told me, of course. And he didn't have a sign of drink on him last night, I suppose?"

"Has he ever had?" she flashed.

In spite of anxiety that was creeping over him too, Don was irritated by her righteous tone.

"Look here, Mag," he said, "it wouldn't be the end of the world, you know, if he *did* take a drink! we can't expect to keep him off it for ever. Moderation is all we can demand from him at his age."

But Mag set her face tight.

"I'd never believe it of him," she said. "Not Donny!"

"Well, how else are you going to account for his behaviour now?"

"Maybe he thought of something he wanted to find out before the exam. You know Donny! If it was anything important—anything except for his exam—he'd think nothing of getting up and dressing again and going out to ask some of his pals about it. Not like other fellows that would be too lazy and would leave it to the morning! Donny would never chance leaving anything to the morning!"

"Yes, but in that case he'd have been back in an hour or so."

"Unless he stayed talking, wherever he went!"

"He would have telephoned!"

"In the middle of the night?"

They looked at each other dully.

"You don't suppose . . . that he might have met with an accident or something?"

"Funny, I never thought of that," said Don.

Yet, now, it seemed such an obvious thought.

"Hadn't we better do something?" said Mag.

"Like ring the hospitals?"

He went over to the hall table where the phone stood. There, he hesitated.

"Which hospital ought I to ring? Street accidents are usually brought to Jervis Street Hospital, I think, but I don't suppose they are brought there from all parts of the city. I suppose all the hospitals have casualty wards. I wonder where I ought to try first?" Suddenly his hesitancy left him, and confidently he put out his hand to take up the receiver. "I know what I'll do, I'll ring the police. That's the thing. They must get reports from all the hospitals." He turned to her. "Did he have his name on him, I wonder? Or any form of identification?"

When she didn't answer he looked up. She had gone very white in the face. He put down the phone.

"Don't look like that, Mag," he said. "I'm sure he's all right. It was only to reassure you that I was phoning at all. We've got a bit hysterical, if you ask me. I think we should wait a bit longer before doing anything. He'll breeze in here any minute, I bet. Wait till you see. And look here, Mag, let me give you a bit of advice. When he does come back . . ."

But he saw that she was in no condition for taking advice.

"Don't ring the police anyway," she said.

It was the way she said it, dully and flatly, that made him feel suddenly that whatever had come into her mind to trouble her, was out of all proportion to his own vague fears.

"You're not keeping anything from me, are you?" he asked, sharply.

"Oh no," she cried. "It's just that I don't think we ought to draw attention to him in case——"

"——In case he got himself into some scrape or other, is that it? What scrape could he get into?" he asked, stupidly.

"Oh, I don't know," she said, "but it seems a bad time to draw attention to him—with all this going on. . . ."

It could not have been a more formless reference to what they had been discussing at breakfast, but he got her meaning at once, and his face flushed angrily.

"You can't mean that! You just don't know what you're saying!" he said. "Your own son!"

"Oh, don't go on that way," she cried. "You didn't listen to me. You didn't wait for me to finish."

But he wasn't listening then, either. He was just staring at her.

"Oh, please! Please!" said Mag, wearily. "I only meant that he might be innocently involved, drawn into something against his will, or even accidentally, and afterwards perhaps been afraid of the consequences. That was all I meant!" Then she looked up at him sharply. "What did you think I meant?"

In enmity each probed the other's eyes for a fear worse than his own.

"Might I ask one thing?" said Don, bitterly. "Which of these killings is the one in which you think my son—our son—is involved? Battering in the head of an old woman? Or the other one?"

"You know right well the one I mean!" Mag snapped. "How could he be involved in the other? Nothing on earth could justify killing that poor old creature."

Don gave a kind of laugh.

"Well! You women are unbelievable. So you consider the poor girl on the docks was fair game for any kind of treatment! Bad luck if it should end as it did—bad luck for the *man*, that is to say!" He turned away as if in disgust, but the next minute he swung back vindictively. "Tell me this," he said. "Just how did you think that anyone could be innocently implicated in a business like that? Your son, for instance!"

"I don't know," cried Mag. "It's not fair to take me up like that. I didn't say I thought anything of the kind. I was only frightened, that's all! Any woman would be the same. Many a time when we were first married, I waited up for you when you were late coming home, watching the clock, and imagining all kinds of things!"

"About *me*?"

"Oh, you don't understand! What comes into one's mind at a time like this has nothing to do with the other person. It doesn't mean one thinks any the less of him. It's as if all the badness of the world, all the badness in *oneself*, rushes into one's mind, and starts up a terrible reasonless fear. I *know* Donny is a good boy. And I know he wouldn't do harm to anyone, but he might have been passing that doorway——"

"Down at the docks, on a dark night—it was raining too, the paper said——"

"Well, how do we know what might have brought him down there? How do we know where he is any night he's out, if it comes to that? He could have been passing that way just at the wrong moment, and maybe seen something. Then, who knows what might have happened!"

"But you forget he came home last night! We saw him! You went up and said good night like you always do!"

She said nothing for a minute.

"I didn't tell you because it seemed silly, but it wasn't quite like always," she said then, slowly. "His light went out as I went up the stairs. He had put it out although he heard me coming. I didn't notice it at the time—well, hardly—I tried not to be a bit hurt—but I thought his eyes might be giving him trouble after so much studying all the week. He put out his hand and took the hot bottle. It wasn't *quite* like always."

"Oh, you're splitting hairs," said Don, impatiently. Yet he seemed to be considering her words. "I think there's something you ought to get straight in your mind though, Mag," he said then, slowly, "even if he were to walk right in the door this minute. You've got the thing wrong. It's just possible that a young fellow like our Donny might on occasion have some truck with a girl like that poor girl who was strangled, without it being necessarily taken that he be mixed up in her murder, but he couldn't be mixed up in her murder without it necessarily being taken that he had some sort of truck with her! Get your mind clear on that!"

Mag's mind, however, had unexpectedly cleared itself not only of that, but of all fear.

"Oh, I'm sure we are being ridiculous," she cried. "I'm sure there is some simple explanation." She put her hand gently on Don's arm. "If it makes you feel better, dear, go ahead and ring the police, though." But when he said nothing, she spoke still more gently. "What do you really think?" she asked.

"I don't know what to think now!" he said, roughly. "You've succeeded in getting me into a fine state." He moved over and stood at the window. "Well, well," he said. "They didn't hang him yet anyway; he's coming down the road!"

"Oh, thank God. Let me look. Where is he?"

She ran to the window, and then, when she had seen him with her own two eyes, she ran towards the door.

"Mag!" Don's voice was so strident she turned back, but instantly, as their eyes met, they were at one again and could seek counsel from each other.

"What will I say to him?" she asked.

"Let him speak first," he said, authoritatively.

What they didn't realize, either of them, was that Donny with his smile would speak first to them: his smile that was always so open, and with a peculiar sweetness in it.

"I suppose I'm in for it!" he said. "Or did you miss me? I thought I'd be back before you were awake." When they didn't answer, he reddened slightly. "I meant you to come down and find me as fresh as a lark instead of like most mornings, trying to get my eyes unstuck." He turned to Mag. "Were you worried, Mother? I'm sorry. I'll tell you how it happened, but I hope you weren't worried."

Mag felt flustered.

"Well, it was mostly on account of your exam, Donny—" she said vaguely, glancing at the pink card. If it was an ordinary morning . . ."

Donny glanced at the card too, and also at the clock. He went over and took the card and put it in his pocket. "I mustn't forget this. It's a good job I came home. I'd have forgotten it. I wasn't going to come home at all, but go right on to the College, only for thinking about you and how you might worry."

"It was a bit late in the day to begin worrying about us then," said Don

"I know," cried Donny. "But I ought to have been home hours ago, only I got a darned blister on my heel. It hurts like hell still. I ought to bathe my foot, but I don't suppose I've time. If it wasn't for knowing you'd have been in a state about me, I could have bathed my foot in the lavatory down at the examination hall. But then I'd have had nothing to eat, and I'm starving." Seeing some unbuttered toast, he picked it up and rammed it into his mouth.

817

"Oh, that toast is cold," cried Mag. "Let me make some more."

But Don brought his fist down on the table.

"Toast be damned," he said. "Where the hell was he! that's what we want to know. Where were you? You don't seem to realize—your mother was nearly out of her mind."

"Oh, Don, what does it matter now!" cried Mag—"as long as he's back, and everything is all right."

For, of course, everything was all right now. Only the absent son had been unknowable, capable of—well—anything. The real Donny, standing in their midst, was once more enclosed within the limits of their loving concept of him.

But Don could be so stubborn. "How are we so sure everything is all right?" he snapped. "My God, Mag, but you have a short memory!" He turned to Donny. "It's a queer thing to find a person has got up out of his bed in the middle of the night, and taken himself off somewhere—God knows where—without so much as a word of explanation. Why didn't you tell your mother where you were going? You know she's a light sleeper, and you knew you needn't have been afraid of waking me: I'd never have heard you. Why didn't you do that? Why didn't you tell her what was going on?"

"Oh Don, don't upset him," cried Mag. "Look at the clock. He can tell us at supper tonight, and——"

"There's nothing to tell!" cried Donny. "It'll sound foolish now. It would have been so different if I'd got back before you were awake. I only meant to go out for a few minutes in the first place, but the night was so fine——"

"Are you trying to tell us you just went out for a nice little walk?" said Don. "In the middle of the night?"

Missing the ironic note in his father's voice, Donny turned round eagerly.

"Not a walk—I didn't even mean to do that! I only intended getting a breath of air." He turned back to Mag. "I couldn't sleep after I went to bed. You know how it is before an exam! Well, after I was a while tossing about, I knew I'd never sleep. I knew the state I'd be in for the exam, so I got up and dressed. I thought I'd look over the books again for a bit, but then I thought I'd step outside the door and get a breath of air first. I had no idea of going for a walk. That hour of night! I only meant to stand at the door, or take a few steps down the road. But it was such a night! You've no idea. I just kept walking on and on, till I found myself nearly in Goatstown! I was actually standing on Milltown Bridge before I realized how far I'd walked! And there were the hills across from me when I leant over the bridge—and somehow they seemed so near and——"

"You didn't go up the hills?" cried Mag.

"Well, as far as the Lamb Doyle's," said Donny. "I'd have liked to go on further, up by Ticknock, but it was beginning to get bright—not that it was really dark at all, but day was breaking—you should have seen the sky—I'd like to have stayed up there. But I had the old exam to think about, so I had to start coming down again. Oh, but it was great up there; I felt wonderful. I'd been going a bit hard at the work in the last few weeks and everything was sort of bunged up in my brain. Up there, though, I could feel my mind clearing and everything falling into place. But I don't suppose you understand?" he said, suddenly aware of their lack of comment.

"If only you'd come to my door, son," said Mag.

"As if you'd have let me go, Mother! You know you'd have got up and come downstairs, and it would be cups of tea, and re-heating jars and re-making beds. You'd never have let me out! But that breath of air, and the exercise, was just what I needed. I felt great! The good is well taken out of it now though by all this fuss!" he cried, looking accusingly from one to the other of them.

Mag turned to Don.

"Now! What did I tell you! He could have explained everything at supper."

"Let's have no more of it so," said Don, and he took up his brief-case. "All I'll say is, it's a pity he didn't cut short his capers by an hour or so, and save us all this commotion."

"I told you I got a blister on my heel," said Donny, indignantly. "I would have been back home hours ago only for that."

"Oh! Let me look at it!" cried Mag. "The dye of your sock might get into it. You could get an infection. We'll have to see that it's clean and put a bit of bandage on it. Sit down, son," she said, and as he sat down, she sank down on her knees in front of him like when she used to tie his shoe-laces for school.

"Wait till you see the bandage that's on it now," said Donny. "I came down part way in my bare feet—as far as Sandyford, where the bungalows begin—but people were stirring, milkmen, bus conductors, and that class of person, going to work, and I had put on the shoes, but I wouldn't have got far in them only I found something to pad my heel. This!" he cried, and he rolled down his sock and pulled it up—a bit of sweat-stained blood-soaked yellow felt. "What's the matter?" he cried, as he saw Mag's face. Then he saw Don's. "What's the matter?"

Was it the texture of the cloth? Was it the colour? What was it that made them know, instantly, that it had once been part of a woman's beret?

"Why are you staring at me?" he cried. He looked down at the bit of stuff. At the same time he shoved his hand into his pocket and brought up the rest of the beret. "I felt bad about cutting it up," he said, "it looked brand new, but I told myself that somebody's loss was my gain."

Mag and Don were staring stupidly at him.

"I suppose it wasn't all a yarn you were spinning us, was it?" asked Don at last. But he answered his own question. "I suppose it wasn't," he said, dejectedly. And he walked over and took up the paper. "There's something you'd better know, boy," he said, quietly. "You evidently didn't see the morning paper." He held it out to him, pointing to one paragraph only.

Donny read quickly—a line or two.

"Is this it, do you think?" he asked then, with a dazed look at the bit of yellow felt.

"That's what we want to know," said Don. "Where did you get it?"

"I told you! I picked it up in the gutter, somewhere about Sandford Road. Oh, do you think it's it?" he cried again, and letting the pieces fall, he ran his hands down the sides of his trouser legs, over and over again, as if wiping them. "Why didn't you tell me when I came in first?" he said, looking pathetically young and stupid. But Mag began to laugh with odd gulping laughs.

"Don't mind me, son," she said, between the gulps. "I can't help it." She didn't see the warning look Don gave her. "It's from relief," she said.

Donny looked at her. He had not missed his father's look. Ignoring her, he turned to Don.

"What did she mean?"

"Nothing, boy, nothing," said Don. "We were a bit alarmed, you must realize that. You wouldn't understand, I suppose. Some day you may. Parenthood isn't easy—it induces all kinds of hysterical states in people at times—men as well as women!" he added, staunchly, taking Mag's arm and linking them together for a minute. "I mean—" he said, but suddenly irritation got the better of him. "Anyway you've only yourself to blame," he snapped. "We were beside ourselves with anxiety—almost out of our minds. We were ready to think anything."

Donny said nothing for a moment.

"You were ready to think anything!" he repeated, slowly. "But not anything bad?" He turned to Mag. "Not you, Mother? You didn't think anything bad about me? Why, you know me all through, Mother, don't you, like—like as if I were made of glass. How could you think anything bad about me?"

"Oh, of course I couldn't," cried Mag, and she longed to deny everything: words, thoughts, feelings, everything, but all she could do was show contrition— "I was nearly crazy, Donny," she cried. "You don't understand."

"You're right there! I don't understand," said Donny. He slumped down on a chair. After a minute, apathetically he began to pull on his sock over his grimy foot. "I'd better go to my exam," he said.

"Your exam!" shouted Don. "Are you joking? Well, let me tell you, you can kiss good-bye to your exam. Don't you know you'll have to account for that beret being in your possession, you young fool? You don't think you can walk into the house with a thing like that—like a dog'd drag in a bone—and when you've dropped it at our feet, walk off unconcerned about your business?" Suddenly Don, too, slumped down on a chair. "Oh, weren't you the fool to get us into this mess! You and your rambles! If you were safe in your bed where you belonged we'd have been spared all this shame and humiliation."

"Shame! Humiliation!"

Mag thought all that was over at least. Don gave her a withering look.

"We'll be a nice laughing-stock!" he said. " I can just see them reading about this in the office. There'll be queer guffaws." He looked at Donny. "And I'd say your pals in the University will have many a good snigger at you too. To say nothing of what view the University authorities may take of it. And they might be nearer the mark. It's not such a laughing matter at all. It's no joke being implicated in a thing like this. There's no end to the echoes a thing like this could have—all through your life! People have queer, twisted memories. They'll never remember that you were innocent: they'll only remember that you had something to do with it. I'd take my oath that from this day you're liable to be pointed out as the fellow that had something to do with the murder of a woman." In malice he turned to Mag. "They'll probably get things mixed up, seeing they were both the same night, and think it was in the other murder he was involved!"

Donny didn't catch the last reference. He was thinking over what Don had first said.

"God help innocence if everyone is as good at distorting things as you!" he said, angrily.

"Well, it's no harm for you to be shown what can be done in that line," said Don, a bit shamefaced, but still stubborn. "I'd be prepared to swear you'll want your wits about you when you're telling the police about it. They'll need a lot of convincing before they believe in your innocence—or your foolishness, as I'd be more inclined to call it—it isn't as if you only saw the thing, or picked it up and hung it on the spike of a railing, as many a one would have done—as I'd have done, if it was me! It isn't even as if you picked it up and put it in your pocket and forgot about it, as maybe another might have done. But oh no! You had to cut it up in pieces! How will *that* appear in the eyes of the police? And I must say I wouldn't like to be you when it comes to telling them about the blister on your heel!—As if you were a young girl with feet as tender as a flower! Those fellows have feet of cast iron. You couldn't blister them with a firing iron! I tell you, you'll wear out the tongue in your head before you'll satisfy those fellows about this. Oh, how did it happen to us!"

Mag ran over to him.

"Don! I can't understand you!" she cried. "You didn't take on this bad when we thought—"

Don glared at her. "It wasn't me thought it but you," he cried. "And if it was now, I'd know better what to think. He's only a fool—that's clear."

But Donny stood up.

"I may be a fool," he said, "but I'm not one all the way through," he said quietly, calmly. "How is anyone to know—about this? It was hardly light when I picked it up. There wasn't a soul in sight. And if no one knows, why should I go out of my way to tell about it? It was up to the police to find it anyway. Isn't that what they're paid for—paid for by us and people like us? Whose fault is it if they don't do their job properly? There must have been any number of them in that vicinity last night, with flashlights and car lights and the rest of it. If the beret was so important, why didn't they make it their business to find it! Why was it left for me? And why should I neglect my business because they don't do their business right? Here—I'm going out to my exam!"

"Oh, but son," cried Mag, "you could call at the station—or phone them—yes, that would be quicker—phone them—and tell them you found the beret, but that you had to go to your exam."

Donny sneered.

"A lot they'd care about my exam. They'd keep me half the day questioning me, like Dad said."

"Not if you explained, son. You could say you'd be available in the afternoon."

"As if they'd wait till then for their information, Mother! And if you think they would be prepared to wait till then, what's the point in my rushing to them now? No—I'm going to the exam."

"Oh, son! Time might be of the greatest importance!" She ran over to him. "Oh Donny! You don't understand," cried Mag. "Even if you were to miss your exam—think of what this might mean—it might lead to their finding whoever did it!"

Don had said nothing for some minutes.

"It could lead them astray as easily," he said, then, very quietly. "I know them—they could lose more time probing Donny than would find twenty murderers in another country. It might not be as bad as it seemed at first, Mag, for him to do as he says: keep his mouth shut!" He stooped and picked up the two pieces of felt and stared at them.

Donny put out his hand.

"Give them to me anyway," he said. "I've got to go." Almost absently, he fitted the two pieces together for a minute till they made a whole. "I'll see later what I'll do," he said. Then he looked Don in the face. "But I think I know already," he said.

Hastily, Don took up his brief-case again.

"I'll be down the street with you, son," he said. "We have to consider this from every angle." At the door he turned. "Are you all right, Mag?" he asked.

Mag wasn't looking at him. She was looking at Donny.

"Don't look at me like that, Mother!" cried Donny. "Nobody's made of glass, anyway. Nobody!"

THE DOGS IN THE GREAT GLEN

An American professor seeks his Irish roots in a story that bursts with nature. "The Dogs in the Great Glen" first appeared in the October 8, 1960, issue of The New Yorker.

T HE PROFESSOR HAD COME over from America to search out his origins and I met him in Dublin on the way to Kerry where his grandfather had come from and where he had relations, including a grand-uncle, still living.

—But the trouble is, he said, that I've lost the address my mother gave me. She wrote to tell them I was coming to Europe. That's all they know. All I remember is a name out of my dear father's memories: the great Glen of Kanareen.

—You could write to your mother.

—That would take time. She'd be slow to answer. And I feel impelled right away to find the place my grandfather told my father about.

—You wouldn't understand, he said. Your origins are all around you.

—You can say that again, professor. My origins crop up like the bones of rock in thin sour soil. They come unwanted like the mushroom of Merulius Lacrimans on the walls of a decaying house.

—It's no laughing matter, he said.

—It isn't for me. This island's too small to afford a place in which to hide from one's origins. Or from anything else. During the war a young fellow in Dublin said to me: Mister, even if I ran away to sea I wouldn't get beyond the three-mile limit.

He said: But it's large enough to lose a valley in. I couldn't find the valley of Kanareen marked on any map or mentioned in any directory.

—I have a middling knowledge of the Kerry mountains, I said. I could join you in the search.

—It's not marked on the half-inch Ordnance Survey map.

—There are more things in Kerry than were ever dreamt of by the Ordnance

Survey. The place could have another official name. At the back of my head I feel that once in the town of Kenmare in Kerry I heard a man mention the name of Kanareen.

We set off two days later in a battered, rattly Ford Prefect. Haste, he said, would be dangerous because Kanareen might not be there at all, but if we idled from place to place in the lackadaisical Irish summer we might, when the sentries were sleeping and the glen unguarded, slip secretly as thieves into the land whose legends were part of his rearing.

—Until I met you, the professor said, I was afraid the valley might have been a dream world my grandfather imagined to dull the edge of the first nights in a new land. I could see how he might have come to believe in it himself and told my father—and then, of course, my father told me.

One of his grandfather's relatives had been a Cistercian monk in Mount Melleray, and we went there hoping to see the evidence of a name in a book and to kneel, perhaps, under the high arched roof of the chapel close to where that monk had knelt. But, when we had traversed the corkscrew road over the purple Knockmealdowns and gone up to the mountain monastery through the forest the monks had made in the wilderness, it was late evening and the doors were closed. The birds sang vespers. The great silence affected us with something between awe and a painful, intolerable shyness. We hadn't the heart to ring a doorbell or to promise ourselves to return in the morning. Not speaking to each other we retreated, the rattle of the Ford Prefect as irreverent as dicing on the altar-steps. Half a mile down the road the mute, single-file procession of a group of women exercitants walking back to the female guest-house underlined the holy, unreal, unanswering stillness that had closed us out. It could easily have been that his grandfather never had a relative a monk in Mount Melleray.

A cousin of his mother's mother had, he had been told, been a cooper in Lady Gregory's Gort in the county Galway. But when we crossed the country westwards to Gort, it produced nothing except the information that apart from the big breweries, where they survived like birds or bison in a sanctuary, the coopers had gone, leaving behind them not a hoop or a stave. So we visited the woods of Coole, close to Gort, where Lady Gregory's house had once stood, and on the brimming lake-water among the stones, we saw by a happy poetic accident the number of swans the poet had seen.

Afterwards in Galway city there was, as there always is in Galway City, a night's hard drinking that was like a fit of jovial hysteria, and a giggling ninny of a woman in the bar who kept saying: You're the nicest American I ever met. You don't look like an American. You don't even carry a camera. You look like a Kerryman.

And in the end, we came to Kenmare in Kerry, and in another bar we met a talkative Kerryman who could tell us all about the prowess of the Kerry team, about the heroic feats of John Joe Sheehy or Paddy Bawn Brosnan. He knew so much, that man, yet he couldn't tell us where in the wilderness of mountains we might find the Glen of Kanareen. Nor could anybody else in the bar be of the least help to us, not even the postman who could only say that wherever it was, that is if it was at all, it wasn't in his district.

—It could of course, he said, be east over the mountain.

Murmuring sympathetically, the entire bar assented. The rest of the world was east over the mountain.

With the resigned air of men washing their hands of a helpless, hopeless case the postman and the football savant directed us to a roadside post-office twelve miles away where, in a high-hedged garden before an old grey-stone house with latticed windows and an incongruous, green, official post-office sign there was a child, quite naked, playing with a coloured, musical spinning-top as big as itself, and an old half-deaf man sunning himself and swaying in a rocking-chair, a straw hat tilted forwards to shade his eyes. Like Oisin remembering the Fenians, he told us he had known once of a young woman who married a man from a place called Kanareen, but there had been contention about the match and her people had kept up no correspondence with her. But the day she left home with her husband that was the way she went. He pointed. The way went inland and up and up. We followed it.

—That young woman could have been a relation of mine, the professor said

On a rock-strewn slope, and silhouetted on a saw-toothed ridge where you'd think only a chamois could get by without broken legs, small black cows, accurate and active as goats, rasped good milk from the grass between the stones. His grandfather had told his father about those athletic, legendary cows and about the proverb that said: Kerry cows know Sunday. For in famine times, a century since, mountain people bled the cows once a week to mix the blood into yellow maize meal and provide a meat dish, a special Sunday dinner.

The road twisted on across moorland that on our left sloped dizzily to the sea, as if the solid ground might easily slip and slide into the depths. Mountain shadows melted like purple dust into a green bay. Across a ravine and quite alone on a long, slanting, brown knife blade of a mountain was a white house with a red door. The rattle of our pathetic little car affronted the vast stillness. We were free to moralise on the extent of all space in relation to the trivial area that limited our ordinary daily lives.

The two old druids of men resting from work on the leeward side of a turf-bank listened to our enquiry with the same attentive, half-conscious patience they gave to bird-cries or the sound of wind in the heather. Then they waved us ahead towards a narrow cleft in the distant wall of mountains as if they doubted the ability of ourselves and our conveyance to negotiate the gap and find the glen. They offered us strong tea and a drop out of a bottle. They watched us with kind irony as we drove away. Until the gap swallowed us and the hazardous, twisting track absorbed all our attention we could look back and still see them, motionless, waiting with indifference for the landslide that would end it all.

By a roadside pool where water-beetles lived their vicious secretive lives, we sat and rested, with the pass and the cliffs, overhung with heather, behind us and another ridge ahead. Brazenly the sheer rocks reflected the sun and semaphored at us. Below us, in the dry summer, the bed of a stream held only a trickle of water twisting painfully around piles of round black stones. Touch a beetle with a stalk of dry grass and the creature either dived like a shot or, angry at invasion, savagely grappled with the stalk.

—That silly woman in Galway, the professor said.

He dropped a stone into the pool and the beetles submerged to weather the storm.

—That day by the lake at Lady Gregory's Coole. The exact number of swans Yeats saw when the poem came to him. Upon the brimming water among the stones are nine and fifty swans. Since I don't carry a camera nobody will ever believe me. But you saw them. You counted them.

—Now that I am so far, he said, I'm half-afraid to finish the journey. What will they be like? What will they think of me? Will I go over that ridge there to find my grandfather's brother living in a cave?

Poking at and tormenting the beetles on the black mirror of the pool, I told him: Once I went from Dublin to near Shannon Pot, where the river rises, to help an American woman find the house where her dead woman friend had been reared. On her deathbed the friend had written it all out on a sheet of notepaper: Cross the river at Battle Bridge. Go straight through the village with the ruined castle on the right. Go on a mile to the crossroads and the labourer's cottage with lovely snapdragons in the flower garden. Take the road to the right there, and then the second boreen on the left beyond the schoolhouse. Then stop at the third house on that boreen. You can see the river from the flagstone at the door.

—Apart from the snapdragons it was exactly as she had written it down. The dead woman had walked that boreen as a barefooted schoolgirl. Not able to revisit it herself she entrusted the mission as her dying wish to her dearest friend. We found the house. Her people were long gone from it but the new tenants remembered them. They welcomed us with melodeon and fiddle and all the neighbours came in and collated the long memories of the townland. They feasted us with cold ham and chicken, porter and whiskey, until I had cramps for a week.

—My only grip on identity, he said, is that a silly woman told me I looked like a Kerryman. My grandfather was a Kerryman. What do Kerrymen look like?

—Big, I said.

And this is the heart of Kerry. And what my grandfather said about the black cows was true. With a camera I could have taken a picture of those climbing cows. And up that hill trail and over that ridge is Kanareen.

—We hope, I said.

The tired cooling engine coughed apologetically when we abandoned it and put city-shod feet to the last ascent.

—If that was the mountain my grandfather walked over in the naked dawn coming home from an all-night card-playing then, by God, he was a better man than me, said the professor.

He folded his arms and looked hard at the razor-cut edges of stone on the side of the mountain.

—Short of too much drink and the danger of mugging, he said, getting home at night in New York is a simpler operation than crawling over that hunk of miniature Mount Everest. Like walking up the side of a house.

He was as proud as Punch of the climbing prowess of his grandfather.

—My father told me, he said, that one night coming home from the card-playing my grandfather slipped down fifteen feet of rock and the only damage done was the ruin of one of two bottles of whiskey he had in the tail-pockets of his greatcoat. The second bottle was unharmed.

The men who surfaced the track we were walking on had been catering for horses and narrow iron-hooped wheels. After five minutes of agonised slipping and sliding, wisdom came to us and we took to the cushioned grass and heather. As we ascended the professor told me what his grandfather had told his father about the market town he used to go to when he was a boy. It was a small town where even on market days the dogs would sit nowhere except exactly in the middle of the street. They were lazy town dogs, not active, loyal and intelligent like the dogs the grandfather had known in the great glen. The way the old man had described it, the town's five streets grasped the ground of Ireland as the hand of a strong swimmer might grasp a ledge of rock to hoist himself out of the water. On one side was the sea. On the other side a shoulder of mountain rose so steeply that the Gaelic name of it meant the gable of the house.

When the old man went as a boy to the town on a market day it was his custom to climb that mountain, up through furze and following goat tracks, leaving his shiny boots, that he only put on, anyway, when he entered the town, securely in hiding behind a furze bush. The way he remembered that mountain it would seem that twenty minutes of active climbing brought him halfways to heaven. The little town was far below him, and the bay and the islands. The unkempt coastline tumbled and sprawled to left and right, and westwards the ocean went on for ever. The sounds of market day, voices, carts, dogs barking, musicians on the streets, came up to him as faint, silvery whispers. On the tip of one island two tall aerials marked the place where, he was told, messages went down into the sea to travel all the way to America by cable. That was a great marvel for a boy from the mountains to hear about: the ghostly shrill, undersea voices; the words of people in every tongue of Europe far down among the monstrous fish and shapeless sea-serpents that never saw the light of the sun. He closed his eyes one day and it seemed to him that the sounds of the little town were the voices of Europe setting out on their submarine travels. That was the time he knew that when he was old enough he would leave the Glen of Kanareen and go with the voices westwards to America.

—Or so he said. Or so he told my father, said the professor.

Another fifty yards and we would be on top of the ridge. We kept our eyes on the ground, fearful of the moment of vision and, for good or ill, revelation. Beyond the ridge there might be nothing but a void to prove that his grandfather had been a dreamer or a liar. Rapidly, nervously, he tried to talk down his fears.

—He would tell stories for ever, my father said, about ghosts and the good people. There was one case of an old woman whose people buried her—when she died, of course—against her will, across the water, which meant on the far side of the lake in the glen. Her dying wish was to be buried in another graveyard, nearer home. And there she was, sitting in her own chair in the chimney corner, waiting for them, when they came home from the funeral. To ease her spirit they replanted her.

To ease the nervous moment I said: There was a poltergeist once in a farmhouse in these mountains, and the police decided to investigate the queer happenings, and didn't an ass's collar come flying across the room to settle around the sergeant's neck. Due to subsequent ridicule the poor man had to be transferred to Dublin.

Laughing, we looked at the brown infant runnel that went parallel to the path. It flowed with us: we were over the water-shed. So we raised our heads slowly and saw the great Glen of Kanareen. It was what Cortez saw, and all the rest of it. It was a discovery. It was a new world. It gathered the sunshine into a gigantic coloured bowl. We accepted it detail by detail.

—It was there all the time, he said. It was no dream. It was no lie.

The first thing we realised was the lake. The runnel leaped down to join the lake, and we looked down on it through ash trees regularly spaced on a steep, smooth, green slope. Grasping from tree to tree you could descend to the pebbled, lapping edge of the water.

—That was the way, the professor said, the boys in his time climbed down to fish or swim. Black, bull-headed mountain trout. Cannibal trout. There was one place where they could dive off sheer rock into seventy feet of water. Rolling like a gentle sea: that was how he described it. They gathered kindling, too, on the slopes under the ash trees.

Then, after the lake, we realised the guardian mountain; not rigidly chiselled into ridges of rock like the mountain behind us but soft and gently curving, protective and, above all, noble, a monarch of mountains, an antlered stag holding a proud horned head up to the highest point of the blue sky. Green fields swathed its base. Sharp lines of stone walls, dividing wide areas of moorland sheep-grazing, marked man's grip for a thousand feet or so above sea-level then gave up the struggle and left the mountain alone and untainted. Halfways up one snow-white cloud rested as if it had hooked itself on a snagged rock and there it stayed, motionless, as step by step we went down into the glen. Below the cloud a long cataract made a thin, white, forked-lightning line, and, in the heart of the glen, the river that the cataract became, sprawled on a brown and green and golden patchwork bed.

—It must be some one of those houses, he said, pointing ahead and down to the white houses of Kanareen.

—Take a blind pick, I said. I see at least fifty.

They were scattered over the glen in five or six clusters.

—From what I heard it should be over in that direction, he said.

Small rich fields were ripe in the sun. This was a glen of plenty, a gold-field in the middle of a desert, a happy laughing mockery of the arid surrounding moors and mountains. Five hundred yards away a dozen people were working at the hay. They didn't look up or give any sign that they had seen two strangers cross the high threshold of their kingdom but, as we went down, stepping like grenadier guards, the black-and-white sheepdogs detached themselves from the haymaking and moved silently across to intercept our path. Five of them I counted. My step faltered.

—This could be it, I suggested with hollow joviality. I feel a little like an early Christian.

The professor said nothing. We went on down, deserting the comfort of the grass and heather at the side of the track. It seemed to me that our feet on the loose pebbles made a tearing, crackling, grinding noise that shook echoes even out of the imperturbable mountain. The white cloud had not moved. The haymakers had not honoured us with a glance.

—We could, I said, make ourselves known to them in a civil fashion. We could ask the way to your grand-uncle's house. We could have a formal intro-duction to those slinking beasts.

—No, let me, he said. Give me my head. Let me try to remember what I was told.

—The hearts of these highland people, I've heard, are made of pure gold, I said. But they're inclined to be the tiniest bit suspicious of town-dressed strangers. As sure as God made smells and shotguns they think we're inspectors from some government department: weeds, or warble-fly or horror of horrors, rates and taxes. With equanimity they'd see us eaten.

He laughed. His stride had a new elasticity in it. He was another man. The melancholy of the monastic summer dusk at Mount Melleray was gone. He was somebody else coming home. The white cloud had not moved. The silent dogs came closer. The unheeding people went on with their work.

—The office of rates collector is not sought after in these parts, I said. Shotguns are still used to settle vexed questions of land title. Only a general threat of excommunication can settle a major feud.

—This was the way he'd come home from the gambling cabin, the professor said, his pockets clinking with winnings. That night he fell he'd won the two bottles of whiskey. He was only eighteen when he went away. But he was the tallest man in the glen. So he said. And lucky at cards.

The dogs were twenty yards away, silent, fanning out like soldiers cautiously circling a point of attack

—He was an infant prodigy, I said. He was a peerless grandfather for a man to have. He also had one great advantage over us—he knew the names of these taciturn dogs and they knew his smell.

He took off his white hat and waved at the workers. One man at a haycock raised a pitchfork—in salute or in threat? Nobody else paid the least attention. The dogs were now at our heels, suiting their pace politely to ours. They didn't even sniff. They had impeccable manners.

—This sure is the right glen, he said. The old man was never done talking about the dogs. They were all black-and-white in his day, too.

He stopped to look at them. They stopped. They didn't look up at us. They didn't snarl. They had broad shaggy backs. Even for their breed they were big dogs. Their long tails were rigid. Fixing my eyes on the white cloud I walked on.

—Let's establish contact, I said, before we're casually eaten. All I ever heard about the dogs in these mountains is that their family tree is as old as the Red Branch Knights. That they're the best sheepdogs in Ireland and better than anything in the Highlands of Scotland. They also savage you first and bark afterwards.

Noses down, they padded along behind us. Their quiet breath was hot on my calves. High up and far away the nesting white cloud had the security of heaven.

—Only strangers who act suspiciously, the professor said.

—What else are we? I'd say we smell bad to them.

—Not me, he said. Not me. The old man told a story about a stranger who came to Kanareen when most of the people were away at the market. The house he came to visit was empty except for two dogs. So he sat all day at the door of the house and the dogs lay and watched him and said and did nothing. Only once, he felt thirsty and went into the kitchen of the house and lifted a bowl to go to the well for water. Then there was a low duet of a snarl that froze his blood. So he went thirsty and the dogs lay quiet.

—Hospitable people.

—The secret is touch nothing, lay no hand on property and you're safe.

—So help me God, I said, I wouldn't deprive them of a bone or a blade of grass.

Twice in my life I had been bitten by dogs. Once, walking to school along a sidestreet on a sunny morning and simultaneously reading in *The Boy's Magazine* about a soccer centre forward, the flower of the flock, called Fiery Cross the Shooting Star—he was redheaded and his surname was Cross—I had stepped on a sleeping Irish terrier. In retaliation, the startled brute had bitten me. Nor could I find it in my heart to blame him, so that, in my subconscious, dogs took on the awful heaven-appointed dignity of avenging angels. The other time—and this was an even more disquieting experience—a mongrel dog had come up softly behind me while I was walking on the fairgreen in the town I was reared in and bitten the calf of my leg so as to draw spurts of blood. I kicked him but not resenting the kick, he had walked away as if it was the most natural, legitimate thing in heaven and earth for a dog to bite me and be kicked in return. Third time, I thought, it will be rabies. So as we walked and the silent watchers of the valley padded at our heels, I enlivened the way with brave and trivial chatter. I recited my story of the four wild brothers of Adrigole.

—Once upon a time, I said, there lived four brothers in a rocky corner of Adrigole in West Cork, under the mountain called Hungry Hill. Daphne du Maurier wrote a book called after the mountain, but divil a word in it about the four brothers of Adrigole. They lived, I heard tell, according to instinct and never laced their boots and came out only once a year to visit the nearest town which was Castletownberehaven on the side of Bantry Bay. They'd stand there, backs to the wall, smoking, saying nothing, contemplating the giddy market-day throng. One day they ran out of tobacco and went into the local branch of the Bank of Ireland to buy it and raised havoc because the teller refused to satisfy their needs. To pacify them the manager and the teller had to disgorge their own supplies. So they went back to Adrigole to live happily without lacing their boots, and ever after they thought that in towns and cities the bank was the place where you bought tobacco.

—That, said I with a hollow laugh, is my moral tale about the four brothers of Adrigole.

On a level with the stream that came from the lake and went down to join the valley's main river, we walked towards a group of four whitewashed, thatched farmhouses that were shining and scrupulously clean. The track looped to the left. Through a small triangular meadow a short-cut went straight towards the houses. In the heart of the meadow, by the side of the short-cut, there was a spring well of clear water, the stones that lined its sides and the roof cupped over it all white and cleansed with lime. He went down three stone steps and looked at the water. For good luck there was a tiny brown trout imprisoned in the well. He said quietly: That was the way my grandfather described it. But it could hardly be the self-same fish.

He stooped to the clear water. He filled his cupped hands and drank. He stooped again, and again filled his cupped hands and slowly, carefully, not spilling a drop, came up the moist, cool steps. Then, with the air of a priest, scattering hyssop, he sprinkled the five dogs with the spring-water. They backed away from him, thoughtfully. They didn't snarl or show teeth. He had them puzzled. He laughed with warm good nature at their obvious perplexity. He was making his own of them. He licked his wet hands. Like good pupils attentively studying a teacher, the dogs watched him.

—Elixir, he said. He told my father that the sweetest drink he ever had was out of this well when he was on his way back from a drag hunt in the next glen. He was a great hunter.

—He was Nimrod, I said. He was everything. He was the universal Kerryman.

No kidding, he said. Through a thorn hedge six feet thick and down a precipice and across a stream to make sure of a wounded bird. Or all night long waist deep in an icy swamp waiting for the wild geese. And the day of this drag hunt. What he most remembered about it was the way they sold the porter to the hunting crowd in the pub at the crossroads. To meet the huntsmen halfways they moved the bar out to the farmyard. With hounds and cows and geese and chickens it was like having a drink in Noah's Ark. The pint tumblers were set on doors lifted off their hinges and laid flat on hurdles. The beer was in wooden tubs and all the barmaids had to do was dip and there was the pint. They didn't bother to rinse the tumblers. He said it was the quickest-served and the flattest pint of porter he ever saw or tasted. Bitter and black as bog water. Completely devoid of the creamy clerical collar that should grace a good pint. On the way home he spent an hour here rinsing his mouth and the well-water tasted as sweet, he said, as silver.

The white cloud was gone from the mountain.

—Where did it go, I said. Where could it vanish to?

In all the wide sky there wasn't a speck of cloud. The mountain was changing colour, deepening to purple with the approaching evening.

He grasped me by the elbow, urging me forwards. He said: Step on it. We're almost home.

We crossed a crude wooden stile and followed the short-cut through a walled garden of bright-green heads of cabbage and black and red currant bushes. Startled, fruit-thieving birds rustled away from us and on a rowan tree a sated, impudent blackbird opened his throat and sang.

—Don't touch a currant, I said, or a head of cabbage. Don't ride your luck too hard.

He laughed like a boy half hysterical with happiness. He said: Luck. Me and these dogs, we know each other. We've been formally introduced.

—Glad to know you dogs, he said to them over his shoulder.

They trotted behind us. We crossed a second stile and followed the short-cut through a haggard, and underfoot the ground was velvety with chipped straw. We opened a five-barred iron gate, and to me it seemed that the noise of its creaking hinges must be audible from end to end of the glen. While I paused to rebolt it he and the dogs had gone on, the dogs trotting in the lead. I ran after them. I was the stranger who had once been the guide. We passed three houses as if they didn't exist. They were empty. The people who lived in them were above at the hay. Towards the fourth thatched house of the group we walked along a green boreen, lined with hazels and an occasional mountain ash. The guardian mountain was by now so purple that the sky behind it seemed, by contrast, as silvery as the scales of a fish. From unknown lands behind the lines of hazels two more black-and-white dogs ran, barking with excitement, to join our escort. Where the hazels ended there was a house fronted by a low stone wall and a profusion of fuchsia. An old man sat on the wall and around him clustered the children of the four houses. He was a tall, broad-shouldered old man with copious white hair and dark side whiskers and a clear prominent profile. He was dressed in good grey with long, old-fashioned skirts to his coat—formally dressed as if for some formal event—and his wide-brimmed black hat rested on the wall beside him, and his joined hands rested on the curved handle of a strong ash plant. He stood up as we approached. The stick fell to the ground. He stepped over it and came towards us. He was as tall or, without the slight stoop of age, taller than the professor. He put out his two hands and rested them on the professor's shoulders. It wasn't an embrace. It was an appraisal, a salute, a sign of recognition.

He said: Kevin, well and truly we knew you'd come if you were in the neighborhood at all. I watched you walking down. I knew you from the top of the glen. You have the same gait my brother had, the heavens be his bed. My brother that was your grandfather.

—They say a grandson often walks like the grandfather, said the professor.

His voice was shaken and there were tears on his face. So, a stranger in the place myself, I walked away a bit and looked back up at the glen. The sunlight was slanting now and shadows were lengthening on mountain slopes and across the small fields. From where I stood the lake was invisible, but the ashwood on the slope above it was dark as ink. Through sunlight and shadow the happy haymakers came running down towards us; and barking, playing, frisking over each other, ran to meet them. The great glen, all happy echoes, was opening out and singing to welcome its true son.

Under the hazels, as I watched the running haymakers, the children came shyly around me to show me that I also was welcome. Beyond the high ridge, the hard mountain the card-players used to cross to the cabin of the gambling stood up gaunt and arrogant and leaned over towards us as if it were listening.

It was moonlight, I thought, not sunlight, over the great glen. From house to house, the dogs were barking, not baying the moon, but to welcome home the young men from the card-playing over the mountain. The edges of rock glistened like quartz. The tall young gambler came laughing down the glen, greatcoat swinging open, waving in his hand the one bottle of whiskey that hadn't been broken when he tumbled down the spink. The ghosts of his own dogs laughed and leaped and frolicked at his heels.

FROM
THE COUNTRY GIRLS

*Caithleen and Barbara, the country girls of Edna O'Brien's first novel
(1960), share a sweet and lasting friendship, although that's not readily
apparent in this selection from the beginning of the book. Caithleen is
brilliant but comes from a troubled family, while "Baba" has attitude
and a father with money. The excerpt starts as Caithleen walks to school
accompanied by her mother's shady friend, Jack Holland. (Hickey, who
is mentioned several times, is a man who works for Caithleen's family.)*

I SHALL CONVEY YOU, CAITHLEEN, over the wet winding roads."

"It's not wet, Jack, and for God's sake, don't talk of rain; it's as fatal as
opening umbrellas in the house. It just reminds it to rain."

He smiled and touched my elbow with his hand. "Caithleen, you must know
that poem of Colum's—'wet winding roads, brown bogs and black water, and my
thoughts on white ships and the King of Spain's daughter.' Except of course," said
he, grinning to himself, "my thoughts are nearer home."

We were passing Mr. Gentleman's gate, and the padlock was on it.

"Is Mr. Gentleman away?" I asked.

"Indubitably. Odd fish, Caithleen. Odd fish." I said that I didn't think so. Mr.
Gentleman was a beautiful man who lived in the white house on the hill. It had
turret windows and an oak door that was like a church door, and Mr. Gentleman
played chess in the evenings. He worked as a solicitor in Dublin, but he came
home at the weekends, and in the summertime he sailed a boat on the Shannon.
Mr. Gentleman was not his real name, of course, but everyone called him that. He
was French, and his real name was Mr. de Maurier, but no one could pronounce
it properly, and anyhow, he was such a distinguished man with his gray hair and
his satin waistcoats that the local people christened him Mr. Gentleman. He seemed
to like the name very well, and signed his letters J. W. Gentleman. J.W. were the

initials of his Christian names and they stood for Jacques and something else.

I remembered the day I went up to his house. It was only a few weeks before that Dada had sent me with a note—it was to borrow money, I think. Just at the top of the tarmac avenue, two red setters shot around the side of the house and jumped on me. I screamed and Mr. Gentleman came out the conservatory door and smiled. He led the dogs away and locked them in the garage.

He brought me into the front hall and smiled again. He had a sad face, but his smile was beautiful, remote; and very condescending. There was a trout in a glass case that rested on the hall table, and it had a printed sign which read: CAUGHT BY J.W. GENTLEMAN AT LOUGH DERG. WEIGHT 20 LB.

From the kitchen came the smell and sizzle of a roast. Mrs. Gentleman, who was reputed to be a marvelous cook, must have been basting the dinner.

He opened Dada's envelope with a paper knife and frowned while he was reading it.

"Tell him that I will look the matter over," Mr. Gentleman said to me. He spoke as if there were a damson stone in his throat. He had never lost his French accent, but Jack Holland said this was an affectation.

"Have an orange?" he said, taking two out of the cut-glass bowl on the dining-room table. He smiled and saw me to the door. There was a certain slyness about his smile, and as he shook my hand I had an odd sensation, as if someone were tickling my stomach from the inside. I crossed over the smooth lawn, under the cherry trees, and out onto the tarmac path. He stayed in the doorway. When I looked back the sun was shining on him and on the white Snowcemmed house, and the upstairs windows were all on fire. He waved when I was closing the gate and then went inside. To drink elegant glasses of sherry; to play chess, to eat soufflés and roast venison, I thought, and I was just on the point of thinking about tall eccentric Mrs. Gentleman when Jack Holland asked me another question.

"You know something, Caithleen?"

"What, Jack?"

At least he would protect me if we met my father.

"You know many Irish people are royalty and unaware of it. There are kings and queens walking the roads of Ireland, riding bicycles, imbibing tea, plowing the humble earth, totally unaware of their great heredity. Your mother, now, has the ways and the walk of a queen."

I sighed. Jack's infatuation with the English language bored me.

He went on: "'My thoughts on white ships and the King of Spain's daughter'—except that my thoughts are much nearer home." He smiled happily to himself. He was composing a paragraph for his column in the local paper—"Walking in the crystal-clear morning with a juvenile lady friend, exchanging snatches of Goldsmith and Colum, the thought flashed through my mind that I was moving amid . . ."

The towpath petered out just there and we went onto the road. It was dry and dusty where we walked, and we met the carts going over to the creamery and the milk tanks rattled and the owners beat their donkeys with the reins and said, "Gee-up there." Passing Baba's house I walked faster. Her new Pink-Witch bicycle was gleaming against the side wall of their house. Their house was like a doll's house on the outside, pebble-dashed, with two bow windows downstairs and circular flower beds in the front garden. Baba was the veterinary surgeon's daughter. Coy, pretty, malicious Baba was my friend and the person whom I feared most after my father.

"Your mam at home?" Jack finally asked. He hummed some tune to himself.

He tried to sound casual, but I knew perfectly well that this was why he had waited for me under the ivy wall. He had brought over his cow to the paddock he hired from one of our neighbors and then he had waited for me at the wicker gate. He didn't dare come up. Not since the night Dada had ordered him out of the kitchen. They were playing cards and Jack had his hand on Mama's knee under the table. Mama didn't protest, because Jack was decent to her, with presents of candied peel and chocolate and samples of jam that he got from commercial travelers. Then Dada let a card fall and bent down to get it; and next thing the table was turned over sideways and the china lamp got broken. My father shouted and pulled up his sleeves, and Mama told me to go to bed. The shouting, high and fierce, came up through the ceiling because my room was directly over the kitchen. Such shouting! It was rough and crushing. Like the noise of a steam-roller. Mama cried and pleaded, and her cry was hopeless and plaintive.

"There's trouble brewing," said Jack, bringing me from one world of it more abruptly to another. He spoke as if it were the end of the world for me.

We were walking in the middle of the road and from behind came the impudent ring of a bicycle bell. It was Baba, looking glorious on her new puce bicycle. She passed with her head in the air and one hand in her pocket. Her black hair was plaited that day and tied at the tips with blue ribbons that matched her ankle socks exactly. I noticed with envy that her legs were delicately tanned.

She passed us and then slowed down, dragging her left toe along the blue tarred road, and when we caught up with her, she grabbed the lilac out of my arms and said, "I'll carry that for you." She laid it into the basket on the front of her bicycle and rode off singing, "I will and I must get married," out loud to herself. So she would give Miss Moriarty the lilac and get all the praise for bringing it.

"You don't deserve this, Caithleen," he said.

"No, Jack. She shouldn't have taken it. She's a bully." But he meant something quite different, something to do with my father and with our farm.

We passed the Greyhound Hotel, where Mrs. O'Shea was polishing the knocker. She had a hairnet on and pipe cleaners so tight in her head that you could see her scalp. Her bedroom slippers looked as if the greyhounds had chewed them. More than likely they had. The hotel was occupied chiefly by greyhounds. Mr. O'Shea thought he would get rich that way. He went to the dogs in Limerick every night and Mrs. O'Shea drank port wine up at the dressmaker's. The dressmaker was a gossip.

"Good morning, Jack; good morning, Caithleen," she said overaffably. Jack replied coldly; her business interfered with his. He had a grocery and bar up the street, but Mrs. O'Shea got a lot of drinkers at night because she kept good fires. The men drank there after hours and she had bribed the police not to raid her. I almost walked over two hounds that were asleep on the mat outside the shop door. Their noses, black and moist, were jutting out on the pavement.

"Hello," I said. My mother warned me not to be too free with her, as she had given my father so much credit that ten of their cows were gazing on our land for life.

We passed the hotel, the gray, damp ruin that it was, with window frames rotting and doors scratched all over from the claws of young and nervous greyhounds.

"Did I tell you, Caithleen, that her ladyship has never given a commercial traveler anything other than fried egg or tinned salmon for lunch?"

"Yes, Jack, you told me." He had told me fifty times, it was one of his ways of ridiculing her; by lowering her he hoped to lower the name of the hotel. But the locals liked it, because it was friendly drinking in the kitchen late at night.

We stood for a minute to look over the bridge, at the black-green water that flowed by the window of the hotel basement. It was green water and the willows along the bank made it more green. I was looking to see if there were any fish, because Hickey liked to do a bit of fishing in the evenings, while I waited for Jack to stop hedging and finally tell me whatever it was that he wanted to say.

The bus passed and scattered dust on either side. Something had leaped down below; it might have been a fish. I didn't see it, I was waving to the bus. I always waved. Circles of water were running into one another and when the last circle had dissolved he said, "Your place is mortgaged; the bank owns it."

But, like the dark water underneath, his words did not disturb me. They had nothing to do with me, neither the words nor the water; or so I thought as I said goodbye to him and climbed the hill toward the school. Mortgage, I thought, now what does that mean? and puzzling it over, I decided to ask Miss Moriarty, or better still to look it up in the big black dictionary. It was kept in the school press.

The classroom was in a muddle. Miss Moriarty was bent over a book and Baba was arranging the lilac (my lilac) on the little May altar at the top of the classroom. The smaller children were sitting on the floor mixing all the separate colors of plasticine together, and the big girls were chatting in groups of three or four.

Delia Sheehy was taking cobwebs out of the corners of the ceiling. She had a cloth tied to the end of the window pole, and as she moved from one corner to another, she dragged the pole along the whitewashed walls and the dusty, faded, gray maps. Maps of Ireland and Europe and America. Delia was a poor girl who lived in a cottage with her grandmother. She got all the dirty jobs at school. In winter she lit the fire and cleaned the ashes every morning before the rest of us came in, and every Friday she cleaned the closets with a yard brush and a bucket of Jeyes Fluid water. She had two summer dresses and she washed one every second evening, so that she was always clean and neat and scrubbed-looking. She told me that she would be a nun when she grew up.

"You're late, you're going to be killed, murdered, slaughtered," Baba said to me as I came in. So I went over to apologize to Miss Moriarty.

"What? What's this?" she asked impatiently, as she lifted her head from her book. It was an Italian book. She learned Italian by post and went to Rome in the summertime. She had seen the Pope and she was a very clever woman. She told me to go to my seat; she was annoyed that I had found her reading an Italian book. On my way down Delia Sheehy whispered to me, "She never missed you."

So Baba had sent me to apologize for nothing. I could have gone to my desk unnoticed. I took out an English book and read Thoreau's "A Winter Morning"—"Silently we unlatch the door, letting the drift fall in, and step abroad to face the cutting air. Already the stars have lost some of their sparkle, and a dull leaden mist skirts the horizon"—and I was just there when Miss Moriarty called for silence.

"We have great news today," she said, and she was looking at me. Her eyes were small and blue and piercing. You would think she was cross, but it was just that she had bad sight from overreading.

"Our school is honored," she said, and I felt myself beginning to blush.

"You, Caithleen," she said, looking directly at me, "have won a scholarship." I stood up and thanked her, and all the girls clapped. She said that we wouldn't do much work that day as a celebration.

"Where will she be going?" Baba asked. She had put all the lilac in jam jars and placed them in a dreary half circle around the statue of the Blessed Virgin. The teacher said the name of the convent. It was at the other end of the county and there was no bus to it.

Delia Sheehy asked me to write in her autograph album and I wrote something soppy. Then a little fold of paper was thrown up from behind, onto my desk. I opened it. It was from Baba. It read:

> I'm going there too in September. My father has it all
> fixed. I have my uniform got. Of course we're paying.
> It's nicer when you pay. You're a right-looking eejit.
> Baba

My heart sank. I knew at once that I'd be getting a lift in their car and that Baba would tell everyone in the convent about my father. I wanted to cry.

The day passed slowly. I was wondering about Mama. She'd be pleased to hear about the scholarship. My education worried her. At three o'clock we were let out, and though I didn't know it, that was my last day at school. I would never again sit at my desk and smell that smell of chalk and mice and swept dust. I would have cried if I had known, or written my name with the corner of a set square on my desk.

I forgot about the word "mortgage."

⤵

I was wrapping myself up in the cloakroom when Baba came out. She said "Cheerio" to Miss Moriarty. She was Miss Moriarty's pet, even though she was the school dunce. She wore a white cardigan like a cloak over her shoulders so that the sleeves dangled idly. She was full of herself.

"And what in the hell do you want a bloody coat and hat and scarf for? It's the month of May. You're like a bloody Eskimo."

"What's a bloody Eskimo?"

"Mind your own business." She didn't know.

She stood in front of me, peering at my skin as if it were full of blackheads or spots. I could smell her soap. It was a wonderful smell, half perfume, half disinfectant.

"What soap is that you're using?" I asked.

"Mind your own bloody business and use carbolic. Anyhow, you're a country mope and you don't even wash in the bathroom, for God's sake. Bowls of water in the scullery and a facecloth that your mother made out of an old rag. What do you use the bathroom for, anyhow?" she said.

"We have a guest room," I said, getting hysterical with temper.

"Jesus, ye have, and there's oats in it. The place is like a bloody barn with chickens in a box in the window; did ye fix the lavatory chain yet?"

It was surprising that she could talk so fast, and yet she wasn't able to write a composition but bullied me to do it for her.

"Where is your bicycle?" I asked jealously, as we came out the door. She had cut such a dash with her new bicycle early in the morning that I didn't want to be with her while she cycled slowly and I walked in a half-run alongside her.

"Left it at home at lunchtime. The wireless said there'd be rain. How's your upstairs model?" She was referring to an old-fashioned bicycle of Mama's that I sometimes used.

The two of us went down the towpath toward the village. I could smell her soap. The soap and the neat bands of sticking plaster, and the cute, cute smile; and the face dimpled and soft and just the right plumpness—for these things I could have killed her. The sticking plaster was an affectation. It drew attention to her round, soft knees. She didn't kneel as much as the rest of us, because she was the best singer in the choir and no one seemed to mind if she sat on the piano stool all through Mass and fiddled with the half-moons of her nails: except during the Consecration. She wore narrow bands of sticking plaster across her knees. She got it for nothing from her father's surgery, and people were always asking her if her knees were cut. Grown-ups liked Baba and gave her a lot of attention.

"Any news?" she said suddenly. When she said this I always felt obliged to entertain her, even if I had to tell lies.

"We got a candlewick bedspread from America," I said, and regretted it at once. Baba could boast and when she did everybody listened, but when I boasted everybody laughed and nudged; that was since the day I told them we used our drawing room for drawing. Not a day passed but Baba said, "My mammy saw Big Ben on her honeymoon," and all the girls at school looked at Baba in wonder, as if her mother was the only person ever to have seen Big Ben. Though, indeed, she may have been the only person in our village to have seen it.

Jack Holland rapped his knuckles against the window and beckoned me to come in. Baba followed, and sniffed as soon as we got inside. There was a smell of dust and stale porter and old tobacco smoke. We went in behind the counter. Jack took off his rimless spectacles and laid them on an open sack of sugar. He took both my hands in his.

"Your mam is gone on a little journey," he said.

"Gone where?" I asked, with panic in my voice.

"Now, don't be excited. Jack is in charge, so have no fears."

In charge! Jack had been in charge the night of the concert when the town hall went on fire; Jack was in charge of the lorry that De Valera nearly fell through during an election speech. I began to cry.

"Oh, now, now," Jack said, as he went down to the far end of the shop, where the bottles of wine were. Baba nudged me.

"Go on crying," she said. She knew we'd get something. He took down a dusty bottle of ciderette and filled two glasses. I didn't see why she should benefit from my miseries.

"To your health," he said as he handed us the drinks. My glass was dirty. It had been washed in portery water and dried with a dirty towel.

"Why do you keep the blind drawn?" Baba said, smiling up at him sweetly.

"It's all a matter of judgment," he said seriously, as he put on his glasses.

"These," he said, pointing to the jars of sweets and the two-pound pots of jam, "these would suffer from the sunshine."

The blue blind was faded and was bleached to a dull gray. The cord had come off and the blind was itself torn across the bottom slat, and as he talked to us Jack went over and adjusted it slightly. The shop was cold and sunless and the counter was stained all over with circles of brown.

"Will Mama be long?" I asked, and soon as I mentioned her name he smiled to himself.

"Hickey could tell you that. If he's not snoring in the hay shed, he could enlighten you," Jack said. He was jealous of Hickey because Mama relied on Hickey so utterly.

Baba finished her drink and handed him the glass. He sloshed it in a basin of cold water and put it to drain on a metal tray that had GUINNESS IS GOOD FOR YOU painted on it. Then he dried his hands most carefully on a filthy, worn, frayed towel, and he winked at me.

"I am going to beg for a favor," he said to both of us. I knew what it would be.

"What about a kiss each?" he asked. I looked down at a box that was full of white candles.

"Tra la la la, Mr. Holland," Baba said airily, as she ran out of the shop. I followed her, but unfortunately I tripped over a mousetrap that he had set inside the door. The trap clicked on my shoe and turned upside down. A piece of fatty bacon got stuck to the sole of my shoe.

"These little beastly rodents," he said, as he took the bacon off my shoe and set the trap again. Hickey said that the shop was full of mice. Hickey said that they tumbled around in the sack of sugar at night, and we had bought flour there ourselves that had two dead mice in it. We bought flour in the Protestant shop down the street after that. Mama said that Protestants were cleaner and more honest.

"That little favor," Jack said earnestly to me.

"I'm too young, Jack," I said helplessly, and anyhow, I was too sad.

"Touching, most touching. You have a lyrical trend," he said, as he stroked my pink cheek with his damp hand, and then he held the door as I went out. Just then his mother called him from the kitchen and he ran in to her. I clicked the latch tight, and came out to find Baba waiting.

"Bloody clown, what did you fall over?" She was sitting on an empty porter barrel outside the door, swinging her legs.

"Your dress will get all pink paint from that barrel," I said.

"It's a pink dress, you eejit. I'm going home with you, I might feck a few rings."

"No, you're not," I said firmly. My voice was shaky.

"Yes, I am. I'm going over to get a bunch of flowers. Mammy sent over word at lunchtime to ask your mother could I. Mammy's having tea with the archbishop tomorrow, so we want bluebells for the table."

"Who's the archbishop?" I asked, as we had only a bishop in our diocese.

"Who's the archbishop! Are you a bloody Protestant or what?" she asked.

I was walking very quickly. I hoped she might get tired of me and go into the paper shop for a free read of adventure books. The woman in the paper shop was half blind, and Baba stole a lot of books from there.

I was breathing so nervously that the wings of my nose got wide.

"My nose is getting wider. Will it go back again to normal?" I asked.

"Your nose," she said, "is always wide. You've a nose like a bloody petrol pump."

842

FROM
AN ANSWER FROM LIMBO

Brendan Tierney, an unhappy magazine writer from Ireland who has lived in the United States for seven years, is the protagonist of Brian Moore's fourth novel, An Answer from Limbo *(1962). When he decides to quit his job and finish his novel, he brings his mother over from Ireland to help watch his children while his wife returns to work. In the scenes that follow, Tierney, on the way to the airport to pick up his mother, examines his fading connection to Ireland. The second passage, written from his mother's point of view, describes her arrival in New York City.*

W HEN I SAW THAT ROOM, Japanned by Jane, I began to feel afraid. Anyone who can conceive of that Zen shrine as suitable for my mother will never understand my mother's world. Will I myself understand it?

These worries came at dawn this morning as I journeyed alone to meet my mother at the airport. Her world. It once was mine. But when did my world become an island? The answer: when my island was no longer the world. That was Ireland in the summer of my twenty-second year, that year in which I got my B.A. and, planning escape, began to work as a clerk at the American air base near my home.

Escape to what? To write, I thought. But was it really that?

A six-year-old boy says he will be a fireman when he grows up. His parents smile. They know he will not be a fireman, not if they can help it. It is a stage all children go through. At fourteen he says he wants to be a writer. His parents smile. It is a stage some children go through. At seventeen he says he wants to be a writer. His suits are permanently too small for him; he is shaving twice a week. It is time to have a serious talk. He says he wants to be a writer. An adolescent phase, no doubt, but still it's a hint that perhaps he is not cut out to be a doctor or an engineer. At eighteen he is writing poems for the undergraduate magazines.

Everyone is worried. Professor O'Neill is asked to have a talk with him. He says he wants to be a writer. It is now a family joke. Good evening, Shakespeare, Mother says. Don't disturb the Muse, says Sister to her Boy Friend as they come into a room where letters are being written. Why don't you write something for the films? says Mary Meenan, black-eyed and beautiful but Oh so dumb. Writer, writer, Father says, why don't you grow up, teaching jobs aren't to be sneezed at, let me tell you. Do you think I spent good money so that you could get a perfectly good Arts degree and wind up clerking for some American air base? Look at your cousins, both doing well, making something of themselves, I want you to do at least as well, is that unreasonable?

Yet I loved my family, yes, I loved them all. I said I was saving to become a writer. But now, looking back, perhaps it was not the need to write which made me leave home so much as the need to run. Wasn't it simply that I was twenty-two, that fifteen and seven made twenty-two, seven years of telling lies to keep the religious peace, seven years of observance without belief, seven years of secret rage at each mention of my "immortal soul"? Wasn't it the need to run which made me save every penny I earned that summer and, in November, when the money was in the bank, book my one-way passage out?

The night boat sailed for Heysham at nine. I ordered the taxi for eight. My sisters ran down the path to put the bags in. My father (he had written me off as a failure) frowned and shook hands, advising me to drink no tap water. My mother, my pious, quick-tempered mother, wept; warned that Mass must be attended; offered to pray for a success she knew would never come, for, in two months, this foolishness out of me at last, she was sure I would come back up the avenue, tail between my legs. Wave a last good-bye, see her wave blurrily at the departing taxi lights, then turn blind from the evening darkness, back into her bright-lit hall. Blind to my smile of rage and triumph as I settled back on the taxi seat. Blind: not knowing I had gone forever.

The night boat's hooter echoed up the lough: fog closing in. In third class amid the returning poor who work on English roads and in English kitchens, who live in slums and send their postal orders home. Old hands had bagged the benches: the rest of us sat on our suitcases. Bottles of stout went around and a pale girl in black (home for a death in the family?) sang in a choir-loft contralto: "Come back to Erin, mavourneen, mavourneen." Faces drugged with sleep and whiskey farewells turned to listen. The last channel buoys slipped past the porthole. Ireland invisible. At sea. Voices took up the girl's wistful chorus until three young laboring men, ruddy and primed with porter, countered with "The Long and the Short and the Tall," and the passengers, finding this more to their taste, cheerfully blessed all the sergeants and double-you-oh-ones. I did not sing. A war song, Rory's war and Rory dead, a war I was too young for, a war I hated just for that. Beside me a man in a greasy suit took out a Baby Power, drank, then passed it on.

"This your first time across the water, lad?"

"Yes."

"What line of work are you in?"

"A writer. I'm going to be a writer."

"Ship's writer?"

"No, just a writer."

"Would that be good wages?"

"I don't know."

I did not know. Next morning it rained, it rained at Crewe, it rained all down the midlands and was still raining as the boat train met the trailing entrails of London and slowed into Euston station, the journey over, the emigrants out in a banging of carriage doors, an embrace of welcoming pals on the platform. They ran off: I was alone with my suitcase, alone in my choice, a writer, I had said, but was I? Ahead lay the channel boat, the Spanish border and, at Barcelona, another boat bound for Ibiza where, for three pounds a week all found, I would have time to find out. Ibiza, Ted's suggestion, where, my eyeballs still bright with the after-image of my father's frown, my mother's tears, my schoolmates' uneasy jokes, I would write. Write them all wrong.

Rage and revenge. But was it really a rage to write? Eight months later, shivering in a steerage deck chair on the night boat to Mallorca, I offered a light to an American girl. A week later I lay beside her on the damp sands below the city of Palma watching dawn dilute the floodlights on the cathedral across the bay. I told her I loved her. Her name was Jane Melville, and in September she must go back to a job in New York. And what did that do to my rage to write?

Back at home, Ted Ormsby sent my stories out, got them back, sent them out. The temperature of my hopes fell with each rejection, the symptom of my fear remained constant—return to Ireland, loss of Jane. I was down to my last five pounds and uneasily debating the ethics of living off her American traveler's checks on that morning when she ran under the Moorish archway of the Plaza Mayor, a letter in her hand. I can remember my sudden and shocking tears, yes, tears of vindication and relief as I read that letter . . . happy to publish your story . . . payment enclosed . . . promise . . . high hopes . . . see more of your work.

There, in that long-ago Spanish square, I was freed. With that letter I believed that I had paid back my ducking at the fountain, erased my father's frown, my mother's angry words. With that letter I was baptized in a new communion. With that letter, I left my parents' world forever.

Yet now, seven years later, have I really been freed? Am I not still waiting to prove that the world has been wrong about Brendan Tierney? Did I come to America because of my need to write, my need of Jane, or simply my old need to run? I do not know. But this morning, as I got off the bus at the airport, as I went through a door which opened by electric eye, and rode up on a moving staircase to the observation lounge, I knew that it is this world I care about, this world of moving staircases, electric eyes, efficient loudspeakers. Exile now means exile from this. My island is no longer home.

As I stepped off the moving staircase, numbers changed on the electrically operated arrival board. A voice announced that BOAC Flight Five-three-nine had just landed. "Passengers will shortly pass through immigration and customs." I went to the windows of the observation lounge and looked down into the sealed-off customs area below. I looked at a young couple carrying a baby in a plastic basket, at a British bowler and duffel coat, a schoolboy in a too-short blue blazer, an irascible German, a Slavic blonde, a dumpy little woman, a Negro clergyman, a Kensington matron, an American student and then—shock of recognition sudden as a floodlit mask veering up in the darkness of a funhouse—I looked back at the dumpy little woman who stared about her, lost (as a child, lost in a park once, I had wept for her)—my mother.

I did not wave. I could not. I stood rooted in the sight of her as a stranger. Small and old, gray hair under her hat, wearing a badly fitting suit of green tweed, carrying a scuffed leather traveling case. I watched her hand her customs declaration to the officer and then look up, lost—saw her faded prettiness, dark circles under her large, sad eyes. She looked up at me, did not know me. She said something to the customs officer and then moved toward the customs gate. I turned away, ran down the staircase to catch her. Was I, to her, equally a stranger?

↓

Mrs. Tierney, worried that she had come out the wrong door, looked around the terminal but could not see Brendan or—but, was it—

Is it—

Ah, no, it isn't—yes, it is?

Brendan?

But, in those dark glasses, is he blind or what? His nose, that lock of hair, it *is* him—

Sees me? He's smiling—he's coming over—

Brendy!

He was older, not a boy any more, a man, what was he doing wearing dark glasses, looking like some Dago Dan you wouldn't trust your girls with?

"Brendan," she said, "Is it you?"

"Didn't you know me, Mamma?"

His arms held her. His lips (he had not shaved) touched her cheek and, close to tears, no man had held her since Grattan's death, she held this, her last man, half laughing, half crying. "How would I know you?" she said. "Is it a tin cup you're earning your living with?"

"The glasses," he said, "I forgot I had them on."

He took them off. She smiled at him, then remembered the black man who had taken her luggage, where was he, had he run off? She was glad of Brendan: this place was foreign from the first go-off, what with niggers in red caps asking for your bags. She had never before in her life spoken to a black man.

"Listen, Brendan, there's a porter took my suitcase, a nigger, could you find him? He had a red cap on him, number forty-seven it was."

"I'll find him," Brendan said. "But look, Mamma, don't go calling him a nigger around here. People wouldn't like it."

"What should I call him?"

"A Negro. Or colored, that's the polite word."

"Colored, then," she said. Why was it the first word he said to her had to be telling her she was in the wrong? "I'm colored myself," she said, trying to make light of it. "I'm red as a lobster."

He smiled: she had won him back. He patted her shoulder and told her to stay put; he would check. Check, that was a Yankee word. She looked around the great terminal, dazed, tired, excited. She had dozed a little on the plane but had not really slept, her feet were killing her, but never mind, where was Brendan's wife? Not here. Ah, she probably couldn't leave the children. Did they have a maid? She had never thought to ask.

There he was with the porter. Waving to her, telling her to come.

She went. It was good to be down. Sacred Heart of Jesus, I give Thee thanks.

Her knee was a bit stiff, getting into the taxi. She knew Brendan noticed it, for he asked at once, "How are you feeling, Mamma?"

"I have a wee touch of arthritis in my left knee. It stiffens up sometimes."

"But otherwise you're all right?"

"Oh, I'm grand."

The taxi moved out under lights suspended from long aluminum stalks, past vistas of glass, poured concrete and steel, past a file of airport buses, past a modern chapel with an airplane propeller on its wall, past a glass and concrete heating plant which revealed intestines of huge, multicolored machines, past aircraft in long parade rows, past a confusion of signs, into the swirling patterns of traffic circles and a highway's several lanes. She was reminded of an H. G. Wells film she had seen years ago, a film in which men in white togas directed the world from sterile operating theaters. But this was the future made present and real: nothing sterile about it. There was a rim of dirt on the taxi driver's collar, and the taxi itself was dirty, its cheap plastic seat covers cracked.

"Jane couldn't come," Brendan said. "She had to take the children to kindergarten. She should be home by the time we get there."

"Brendan," she said, "I hope I'm not going to be a bother to you."

"Why would you be? You'll be a great help to us."

"With the children, do you mean?"

"Right."

"Do you have a maid?"

"No," he said. "Maids cost a fortune here. Besides, now that Jane's going back to work, she wouldn't want to trust the kids to a stranger."

(Work? Why was she going back to work?)

"So you see, you'll be a great help, Mamma. We'll talk about it."

She might as well say it to him now, say it and get it over with.

"Brendan. Now, listen, I just want to mention something while we're by ourselves. Now, listen, if it becomes too much, I mean, if you ever feel you need the space—you know what I mean—I want you to promise you'll tell me."

"Why would I want the space?"

"Well, there are all sorts of reasons. Besides, Jane might not be happy with this arrangement, having me living with you. So Brendy, if ever I wanted to go home to Ireland, you wouldn't be angry, would you?"

"Of course not. But don't tell me you're homesick already?"

Homesick? Easy to see he doesn't know Dromore Estates; how could anyone be homesick for that wee misery of a place?

"Ah," she said, "when you're my age, it's the past you're homesick for."

"Yes, but I suppose you'll miss your friends?"

"I have a first cousin living here," she said. "Here in New York."

"A cousin?"

"Frank Finnerty, a first cousin on my mother's side. He left Ireland when he was about your age. I have his address, I must look him up."

"That would be the Donegal side of the family?"

"Yes," she said. "Would you remember Donegal at all?"

He was so far away from her now, a grown man with an American accent, wearing a funny shirt with buttons on the collar, the kind she remembered were in style at home thirty years ago. Hard to think of him as that wee Brendy who, aping his country cousins, ran barefoot in the fields each summer on his uncle's farm, hard to see in this man in dark glasses that Brendy who collected hard chestnuts and British Empire stamps and who came to her once (informed by a classmate called Jim McTurk) to ask if it was true that babies were born through the belly button in a lady's tummy. What kin was that boy to this stranger? But then, she thought, who's talking, what does he see when he looks at me? I must seem like Methuselah to him. "I suppose I look a lot older since you last saw me?"

"No. You look fine."

Fine, that's a Yankee way of putting it. But he *is* a Yank now. And anyway, wasn't he always different from the rest of us, even as a wee boy, his nose always stuck in a book, afraid of his own shadow, but with a terrible stubbornness about him? Wanting to be a writer. She remembered when he first said that. He couldn't have been more than twelve at the time.

"How is the writing coming along?" she asked him.

"Fine."

"I always read your articles in the magazine."

He looked out the taxi window.

"Wasn't it lucky, the way you got the job with that magazine, and you just an immigrant here."

"I'm thinking of quitting the job."

Gracious God, what did he mean, was he sacked or what? Was that why Jane was going back to work?

"You see, Mamma, I want to finish my book."

"A book?"

"A novel."

"Oh. And would you be well paid for that?"

"Pay has nothing to do with it. I'm sick and tired of writing magazine junk."

"But won't you miss the salary it pays you?"

"Of course. However, Jane's job will take up most of the slack. We'll make out."

"But when you've finished the book I suppose you could always get your job back, couldn't you?"

"I never want to see that place again. When I think of the years I've wasted there, I feel sick."

Was his wife going to support him forever, was that what he meant?

"You can't serve art and mammon," he said. "I'm tired of being a Sunday writer. I need to devote all my time to it. Having a family to support is one thing. But there are more important things."

Important, what could be more important than looking after your wife and children? Oh, you haven't changed, my boy, you're the same stuck-up wee fellow, thinking yourself a cut above the rest of the world around you. Is it any wonder I've worried about the way you're living, a fellow who can say the like of that?

"Brendan? Do you still go to Mass?"

"No."

"And your children?"

"Look, Mamma, we might as well get this straight once and for all. My children are not being brought up as Catholics."

Suspicion was one thing: knowledge was another.

"Well," she said, "are they Protestants, then?"

"Of course not. As Joyce once said, I'll not forsake a logical absurdity for an illogical one."

Joyce, who's Joyce, some girl? Never mind. Control yourself.

"As a matter of fact," he said, "the children are not anything. They're not baptized."

My grandchildren.

"Mamma, are you all right?"

Dizzy. She could not see. She lowered her head for a second and the blackness cleared. She pretended to look out of the window. "What's this we're coming to?" she asked. "A tunnel?"

It was the Midtown Tunnel, he said. He went on to talk about it, but she hardly heard him. To chase her thoughts she looked out at the cars: she had never seen so many cars in her life and now, roaring in the long lavatory-tiled tunnel with the policeman on the wall looking down, a whine of tires, *ruump, ruump, ruump,* until they came up and out into the air again, cars in front of them, cars behind them, cars coming to sudden jouncy stops before the traffic signals, their back lights starting up like mad red eyes. It was as though this city were made for cars, not people. Even the buildings seemed built to car scale and she had a sudden silly vision of cars roaring up the skyscrapers' stairs, running into rooms where there were beds for cars, nurseries for the little cars to play in—

Pagans. Not baptized.

Everything was so high, so tall. Even London was human compared with this huddle of great upended cartons, a man was like a fly beside them—

My grandchildren are heathens.

Dirt. Gray grime over so much of it, wastes of paper blowing about in the gutters and yet the people passing were clean, their clothes pressed—

Not baptized.

Glimpsed for a moment, an old boozer lying in a doorway, the only poor man in all this crowd, but only for a moment, for the taxi swung up onto a ramp and onto a bridge, a high road running along the river, and she saw big ships—the *Queen Elizabeth*, Brendan said—and then off that high road into a very grand avenue with great buildings like the side of Buckingham Palace. This was his neighborhood, he told her, and she was impressed, for surely it must be one of the best parts of New York. Canopies, and even doormen in uniform. Why did they not have a maid if they lived in a place like this, how would Jane earn enough to support all of them, including her?

Jane, what sort of person is she?

"Here we are," he said. "Home."

As she stepped out of the taxi she looked up and there was the number 468 over the entrance transom: *468 Riverside Drive*, an address she had written a thousand times, familiar to her as any prayer. Yet now it was not words on an envelope, it was a real place, a place where his wife waited upstairs, a place with a dark lobby, bald plush reception benches, a smell of strong disinfectant and, when they got out of the lift, overfilled bags of refuse outside each door. Brendan went ahead, put down her suitcases and took out his keys. Behind that door his wife waited. Behind that door.

She was not as tall as Mrs. Tierney had thought from her photo; she was like a pretty little gypsy, her dark hair drawn up in a bun, wearing a loose purple smock and black trousers which were so tight around her hips you could see the ridge of her panties underneath. She had a large smiling mouth which was very wet as it kissed your cheek. She seemed shy, not sure of herself, younger than Sheila and even Moira. How could you be afraid of her? Jane.

"Let me take your coat, Mrs. Tierney, did you have a good flight? Will I take your hat too? Oh, it's so great to see you. And how do you find Brendan? Is he very changed?"

"Sure, I didn't know him at all, when he met me," she said, smiling. "With those dark glasses on him I took him for some Jew man."

What was wrong? Jane was looking at Brendan as though somebody had hit her. What were they both looking so funny about?

"Mamma, Jane's mother is part Jewish."

"Oh." She felt the blood rise to her cheeks. "Oh, I'm very sorry, Jane. I didn't mean any harm. It was just . . ." But just what was it, how could you explain a boner like that?

"Come on," Brendan said. "Let's have some coffee."

Which was *not* the way to deal with it. Furious with herself for saying such a tactless thing, she was twice furious with Brendan for not having warned her.

"This way," he said. "In here."

Here meant the kitchen, they ate in the kitchen, who would have thought it? But something must be said—something—anything—to hurdle this awful start. "Isn't this nice," she heard herself say. "How nice and bright. I noticed the sky as we were coming in. So clear, such a change after home."

Jane smiled at her, a heroine refusing a blindfold. Brendan said something harmless. The talk staggered up on its feet and went on in weary pilgrimage, talk about the flight, talk about the children, talk about New York, talk that was like the meeting of three strangers in a dentist's waiting room, talk to pass the time until they could decently get free of each other.

And so, having swallowed a cup of coffee and eaten a small piece of toast, she said she would like to change. It had been so hot on the airplane. Jane rose, still trying not to show what showed so very plain, and led her down to the far end of the flat to open a door into a small room, white as a hospital ward, with a single bed, a teetery wee dressing table, an old stuffed armchair, no proper curtains on the window and this, said Jane, "is yours. I hope you like it."

Brendan carried in her suitcases and Jane gave her a set of clean towels. Then amid thanks from her and their reassurances that they would see her soon, the door closed and she was alone, listening to their footsteps going away. She heard them whispering: she could not catch what they said.

PATRICK KAVANAGH

POEMS

There is a clarity and directness to the poems of Patrick Kavanagh, per-
haps a product of his rural upbringing (he labored on a farm until mov-
ing to Dublin at the age of thirty-five to work as a writer). His poetry
is not in any way naïve, however, but rather displays sophistication and
a rich variety in rhyme, meter, and subject matter. The three poems
below are taken from Kavanagh's Collected Poems *(1964).*

LINES WRITTEN ON A SEAT ON THE
GRAND CANAL, DUBLIN

Erected to the memory of Mrs. Dermot O'Brien

O commemorate me where there is water,
Canal water preferably, so stilly
Greeny at the heart of summer. Brother
Commemorate me thus beautifully.
Where by a lock niagarously roars
The falls for those who sit in the tremendous silence
Of mid-July. No one will speak in prose
Who finds his way to these Parnassian islands.
A swan goes by head low with many apologies,
Fantastic light looks through the eyes of bridges—
And look! a barge comes bringing from Athy
And other far-flung towns mythologies.
O commemorate me with no hero-courageous
Tomb—just a canal-bank seat for the passer-by.

TO HELL WITH COMMONSENSE

More kicks than pence
We get from commonsense
Above its door is writ
All hope abandon. It
Is a bank will refuse a post
Dated cheque of the Holy Ghost.
Therefore I say to hell
With all reasonable
Poems in particular
We want no secular
Wisdom plodded together
By concerned fools. Gather
No moss you rolling stones
Nothing thought out atones
For no flight
In the light.
Let them wear out nerve and bone
Those who would have it that way
But in the end nothing that they
Have achieved will be in the shake up
In the final Wake Up
And I have a feeling
That through the hole in reason's ceiling
We can fly to knowledge
Without ever going to college.

IN MEMORY OF MY MOTHER

I do not think of you lying in the wet clay
Of a Monaghan graveyard; I see
You walking down a lane among the poplars
On your way to the station, or happily

Going to second Mass on a summer Sunday—
You meet me and you say:
"Don't forget to see about the cattle—"
Among your earthiest words the angels stray.

And I think of you walking along a headland
Of green oats in June,
So full of repose, so rich with life—
And I see us meeting at the end of a town

On a fair day by accident, after
The bargains are all made and we can walk
Together through the shops and stalls and markets
Free in the oriental streets of thought.

O you are not lying in the wet clay,
For it is a harvest evening now and we
Are piling up the ricks against the moonlight
And you smile up at us—eternally.

AUSTIN CLARKE

POEMS

The poems of Austin Clarke are notable not only for pointed political statements but for exuberant alliteration and wordplay reminiscent of Gerard Manley Hopkins and James Joyce. His poem on Jonathan Swift commemorates the 300th anniversary of the great satirist's birth. Ostensibly in the form of a sermon, these acerbic yet playful verses evoke numerous scatological images to be found in Swift's poems and prose, while also recalling his acidly witty social commentary. All three poems here date from the late 1960s.

THE PILL

Must delicate women die in vain
While age confabulates? Not long
Ago, I knew and wept such wrong.
My favourite cousin, Ethelind,
Bewildered, shaking a head of curls,
Was gone at twenty-two, her babe
Unmothered—she had so little breath.
Now prelates in the Vatican
Are whispering from pillar to pillar
Examining in Latin the Pill,
Pessary, letter, cap. What can
We do until they have decreed
Their will, changing the ancient creed,
But lie awake on a separate pillow?

Now in a sky-tormented world,
These nightly watchers of the womb,
May bind archangels by the pinion,
As though they had dragged them down to marble
And bronze, dire figures of the past
That veil a young girl in her tomb.

THE SUBJECTION OF WOMEN

Over the hills the loose clouds rambled
From rock to gully where goat or ram
Might shelter. Below, the battering-ram
Broke in more cottages. Hope was gone
Until the legendary Maud Gonne,
For whom a poet lingered, sighed,
Drove out of mist upon a side-car,
Led back the homeless to broken fence,
Potato plot, their one defence,
And there, despite the threat of Peelers,
With risky shovel, barrow, peeling
Their coats off, eager young men
Jumped over bog-drain, stone, to mend or
Restore the walls of clay; the police
Taking down names without a lease.
O she confronted the evictors
In Donegal, our victory.
When she was old and I was quickened
By syllables, I met her. Quickens
Stirred leafily in Glenmalure
Where story of Tudor battle had lured me.
I looked with wonder at the sheen
Of her golden eyes as though the Sidhe
Had sent a flame-woman up from ground
Where danger went, carbines were grounded.

Old now by luck, I try to count
Those years. I never saw the Countess
Markievicz in her green uniform,
Cock-feathered slouch hat, her Fianna form

Fours. From the railings of Dublin slums,
On the ricketty stairs the ragged slumped
At night. She knew what their poverty meant
In dirty laneway, tenement,
And fought for new conditions, welfare
When all was cruel, all unfair.
With speeches, raging as strong liquor,
Our big employers, bad Catholics,
Incited by Martin Murphy, waged
War on the poorest and unwaged them.
Hundreds of earners were batoned, benighted,
When power and capital united.
Soon Connolly founded the Citizen Army
And taught the workers to drill, to arm.
Half-starving children were brought by ship
To Liverpool from lock-out, hardship.
"Innocent souls are seized by kidnappers,
And proselytisers. Send back our kids!"
Religion guffed.
           The Countess colled
With death at sandbags in the College
Of Surgeons. How many did she shoot
When she kicked off her satin shoes?

Women rose out after the Rebellion
When smoke of buildings hid the churchbells,
Helena Maloney, Louie Bennett
Unioned the women workers bent
At sewing machines in the by-rooms
Of Dublin, with little money to buy
A meal, dress-makers, milliners.
Tired hands in factories.

           Mill-girls
In Lancashire were organized,
Employers forced to recognize them:
This was the cause of Eva Gore-Booth,
Who spoke on platform, at polling-booth,
In the campaign for Women's Suffrage,
That put our double beds in a rage,
Disturbed the candle-lighted tonsure.

Here Mrs. Sheehy-Skeffington
And others marched. On a May day
In the Phoenix Park, I watched, amazed,
A lovely woman speak in public
While crowding fellows from office, public
House, jeered. I heard that sweet voice ring
And saw the gleam of wedding ring
As she denounced political craft,
Tall, proud as Mary Wollstonecraft.
Still discontented, our country prays
To private enterprise. Few praise
Now Dr. Kathleen Lynn, who founded
A hospital for sick babes, foundlings,
Saved them with lay hands. How could we
Look down on infants, prattling, cooing,
When wealth had emptied so many cradles?
Better than ours, her simple Credo.

Women, who cast off all we want,
Are now despised, their names unwanted,
For patriots in party statement
And act make worse our Ill-fare State.
The soul is profit. Money claims us.
Heroes are valuable clay.

A SERMON ON SWIFT
Friday, 11:30 A.M. April 28th, 1967

Gentle of hand, the Dean of St. Patrick's guided
My silence up the steps of the pulpit, put around
My neck the lesser microphone.
                                        "I feel
That you are blessing me, Mr. Dean."
                                        Murmur
Was smile.
              In this first lay sermon, must I
Not speak the truth? Known scholars, specialists,
From far and near, were celebrating the third
Centenary of our great satirist.
They spoke of the churchman who kept his solemn gown,

860

Full-bottom, for Sunday and the Evening Lesson,
But hid from lectern the chuckling rhymster who went,
Bald-headed, into the night when modesty
Wantoned with beau and belle, his pen in hand.
Dull morning clapped his oldest wig on. He looked from
The Deanery window, spied the washerwomen
Bundling along, the hay carts swaying from
The Coombe, dropping their country smells, the hackney—
Clatter on cobbles—ready to share a quip
Or rebus with Sheridan and Tom Delaney,
Read an unfinished chapter to Vanessa
Or Stella, then rid his mind of plaguey curling—
Tongs, farthingales and fal-de-lals. A pox on
Night-hours when wainscot, walls, were dizziness,
Tympana, maddened by inner terror, celled
A man who did not know himself from Cain.
A Tale of a Tub, *Gulliver's Travels*, fables
And scatological poems, I pennied them on
The Quays, in second-hand book-stalls, when I was young,
Soon learned that humour, unlike the wit o' the Coffee
House, the Club, lengthens the features, smile hid by
A frown.
        Scarce had I uttered the words,
                "Dear Friends,
Dear Swiftians"—
        when from the eastern window
The pure clear ray, that Swift had known, entered the
Shady church and touched my brow. So blessed
Again, I gathered 'em up, four-letter words,
Street-cries, from the Liberties.
              Ascend,
Our Lady of Filth, Cloacina, soiled goddess
Of paven sewers. Let Roman fountains, a-spay
With themselves, scatter again the imperious gift
Of self-in-sight.
        Celia on a close-stool
Stirs, ready to relace her ribs. Corinna,
Taking herself to pieces at midnight, slips from
The bed at noon, putting together soilures
And soft sores. Strephon half rouses from a dream
Of the flooding Tiber on his marriage-night,

When Chloe stoops out unable to contain her
Twelve cups of tea. Women are unsweet at times,
No doubt, yet how can willynilly resist
The pleasures of defaulting flesh?
                              My Sermon
Waits in the plethora of Rabelais, since
March veered with the rusty vane of Faith. I had reached
The house of Aries. Soon in the pure ray,
I am aware of my ancestor, Archbishop
Browne, hastily come from Christ Church, to dispel
Error and Popish superstition. He supped
Last night with Bishop Bale of Ossory,
Robustious as his plays, and, over the talk
And malmsey, forgot the confiscated wealth
Of abbeys.

    In prose, plain as pike, pillory.
In octosyllabic verse turning the two-way
Corner of rhyme, Swift wrote of privy matters
That have to be my text. The Lilliputian
March-by of the crack regiments saluting
On high the double pendulosity
Of Gulliver, glimpsed through a rent in his breeches;
The city square in admiration below. But who
Could blame the Queen when that almighty
Man hosed the private apartments of her palace,
Hissed down the flames of carelessness, leaving
The royal stables unfit for Houynhnms, or tell (in
A coarse aside) what the gigantic maidens
Of Brobdignab did in their playfulness with
The tiny Lemuel when they put him astride
A pap, broader than the mizzen mast of his
Wrecked ship, or hid him in the tangle below?

Reasonable century of Bolingbroke,
Hume, hundred-quilled Voltaire. Satyr and nymph
Disported in the bosk, prim avenues
Let in the classical sky. The ancient temples
Had been restored. Sculptures replaced the painted
Images of the saints. Altars were fuming,
And every capital was amaranthed.
Abstraction ruled the decumana of verse,

Careful caesura kept the middle silence
No syllable dared to cross.
                                    Swift gave his savings
To mumbling hand, to tatters. Bare kibes ran after
Hoof as he rode beside the Liffey to sup
At Celbridge, brood with Vanessa in a star-bloomed
Bower on Tory politics, forget
Queen Anne, stride from a coffee-house in Whitehall
And with his pamphlets furrow the battle-fields
Of Europe once more, tear up the blood-signed contracts
Of Marlborough, Victualler of Victories;
While in St. Patrick's Cathedral the candling clerk
Shifted the shadows from pillar to pillar, shuffling
His years along the aisles with iron key.
Last gift of an unwilling patriot, Swift willed
To us a mansion of forgetfulness. I lodged
There for a year until Erato led me
Beyond the high-walled garden of Memory,
The Fountain of Hope, to the rewarding Gate,
Reviled but no longer defiled by harpies. And there
In Thomas Street, night to the busy stalls,
Divine Abstraction smiled.
                                    My hour, above.
Myself, draws to an end. Satiric rhymes
Are safe in the Deanery. So I must find
A moral, search among my wits.
                                    I have

It.
    In his sudden poem *The Day of Judgment*
Swift borrowed the allegoric bolt of Jove,
Damned and forgave the human race, dismissed
The jest of life. Here is his secret belief
For sure: the doctrine of Erigena,
Scribing his way from West to East, from bang
Of monastery door, click o' the latch,
His sandals worn out, unsoled, a voice proclaiming
The World's mad business—Eternal Absolution.

BEYOND
THE PALE

"Beyond the Pale," the title story of a collection published in 1981,
examines the twisted lengths to which people will go in order to keep up
an appearance of calm on the surface. In the hands of William Trevor,
a true master of the short story, the events herein resonate well beyond
the small lives of the characters.

WE ALWAYS WENT TO Ireland in June.
    Ever since the four of us began to go on holidays together, in 1965
it must have been, we had spent the first fortnight of the month at
Glencorn Lodge in Co. Antrim. Perfection, as Dekko put it once, and none of us
disagreed. It's a Georgian house by the sea, not far from the village of Ardbeag.
It's quite majestic in its rather elegant way, a garden running to the very edge of
a cliff, a long rhododendron drive—or avenue, as they say in Ireland. The
English couple who bought the house in the early sixties, the Malseeds, have had
to build on quite a bit but it's all been discreetly done, the Georgian style preserved
throughout. Figs grow in the sheltered gardens, and apricots, and peaches in the
greenhouses which old Mr. Saxton presides over. He's Mrs. Malseed's father actually. They brought him with them from Surrey, and their Dalmatians, Charger
and Snooze.
    It was Strafe who found Glencorn for us. He'd come across an advertisement
in the *Lady* in the days when the Malseeds still felt the need to advertise. "How
about this?" he said one evening at the end of the second rubber, and then read
out the details. We had gone away together the summer before, to a hotel that had
been recommended on the Costa del Sol, but it hadn't been a success because the
food was so appalling. "We could try this Irish one," Dekko suggested cautiously,
which is what eventually we did.
    The four of us have been playing bridge together for ages, Dekko, Strafe,

Cynthia and myself. They call me Milly, though strictly speaking my name is Dorothy Milson. Dekko picked up his nickname at school, Dekko Deakin sounding rather good, I dare say. He and Strafe were in fact at school together, which must be why we all call Strafe by his surname: Major R. B. Strafe he is, the initials standing for Robert Buchanan. We're of an age, the four of us, all in the early fifties: the prime of life, so Dekko insists. We live quite close to Leatherhead, where the Malseeds were before they decided to make the change from Surrey to Co. Antrim. Quite a coincidence, we always think.

"How *very* nice," Mrs. Malseed said, smiling her welcome again this year. Some instinct seems to tell her when guests are about to arrive, for she's rarely not waiting in the large, low-ceilinged hall that always smells of flowers. She dresses beautifully, differently every day, and changing of course in the evening. Her blouse on this occasion was scarlet and silver, in stripes, her skirt black. This choice gave her a brisk look, which was fitting because being so busy she often has to be a little on the brisk side. She has smooth grey hair which she once told me she entirely looks after herself, and she almost always wears a black velvet band in it. Her face is well made up, and for one who arranges so many vases of flowers and otherwise has to use her hands she manages to keep them marvellously in condition. Her fingernails are varnished a soft pink, and a small gold bangle always adorns her right wrist, a wedding present from her husband.

"Arthur, take the party's luggage," she commanded the old porter, who doubles as odd-job man. "Rose, Geranium, Hydrangea, Fuchsia." She referred to the titles of the rooms reserved for us: in winter, when no one much comes to Glencorn Lodge, pleasant little details like that are seen to. Mrs. Malseed herself painted the flower-plaques that are attached to the doors of the hotel instead of numbers; her husband sees to redecoration and repairs.

"Well, well, well," Mr. Malseed said now, entering the hall through the door that leads to the kitchen regions. "A hundred thousand welcomes," he greeted us in the Irish manner. He's rather shorter than Mrs. Malseed, who's handsomely tall. He wears Donegal tweed suits and is brown as a berry, including his head, which is bald. His dark brown eyes twinkle at you, making you feel rather more than just another hotel guest. They run the place like a country house, really.

"Good trip?" Mr. Malseed inquired.

"Super," Dekko said. "Not a worry all the way."

"Splendid."

"The wretched boat sailed an hour early one day last week," Mrs. Malseed said. "Quite a little band were left stranded at Stranraer."

Strafe laughed. Typical of that steamship company, he said. "Catching the tide, I dare say?"

"They caught a rocket from me," Mrs. Malseed replied good-humouredly. "A couple of old dears were due with us on Tuesday and had to spend the night in

866

some awful Scottish lodging-house. It nearly finished them."

Everyone laughed, and I could feel the others thinking that our holiday had truly begun. Nothing had changed at Glencorn Lodge, all was well with its Irish world. Kitty from the dining-room came out to greet us, spotless in her uniform. "Ach, you're looking younger," she said, paying the compliment to all four of us, causing everyone in the hall to laugh again. Kitty's a bit of a card.

Arthur led the way to the rooms called Rose, Geranium, Hydrangea and Fuchsia, carrying as much of our luggage as he could manage and returning for the remainder. Arthur has a beaten, fisherman's face and short grey hair. He wears a green baize apron, and a white shirt with an imitation-silk scarf tucked into it at the neck. The scarf, in different swirling greens which blend nicely with the green of his apron, is an idea of Mrs. Malseed's and one appreciates the effort, if not at a uniform, at least at tidiness.

"Thank you very much," I said to Arthur in my room, smiling and finding him a coin.

We played a couple of rubbers after dinner as usual, but not of course going on for as long as we might have because we were still quite tired after the journey. In the lounge there was a French family, two girls and their parents, and a honeymoon couple—or so we had speculated during dinner—and a man on his own. There had been other people at dinner of course, because in June Glencorn Lodge is always full: from where we sat in the window we could see some of them strolling about the lawns, a few taking the cliff path down to the seashore. In the morning we'd do the same: we'd walk along the sands to Ardbeag and have coffee in the hotel there, back in time for lunch. In the afternoon we'd drive somewhere.

I knew all that because over the years this kind of pattern had developed. We had our walks and our drives, tweed to buy in Cushendall, Strafe's and Dekko's fishing day when Cynthia and I just sat on the beach, our visit to the Giant's Causeway and one to Donegal perhaps, though that meant an early start and taking pot-luck for dinner somewhere. We'd come to adore Co. Antrim, its glens and coastline, Rathlin Island and Tievebulliagh. Since first we got to know it, in 1965, we'd all four fallen hopelessly in love with every variation of this remarkable landscape. People in England thought us mad of course: they see so much of the troubles on television that it's naturally difficult for them to realize that most places are just as they've always been. Yet coming as we did, taking the road along the coast, dawdling through Ballygally, it was impossible to believe that somewhere else the unpleasantness was going on. We'd never seen a thing, nor even heard people talking about incidents that might have taken place. It's true that after a particularly nasty carry-on a few winters ago we did consider finding somewhere else, in Scotland perhaps, or Wales. But as Strafe put it at the time, we felt we owed a certain loyalty to the Malseeds and indeed to everyone we'd come to know round about, people who'd always been glad to welcome us back. It seemed silly to lose our heads, and when we returned the following summer we knew immediately we'd been right. Dekko said nothing could be further away from all the violence than Glencorn Lodge, and though his remark could hardly be taken literally I think we all knew what he meant.

"Cynthia's tired," I said because she'd been stifling yawns. "I think we should call it a day."

"Oh, not at all," Cynthia protested. "No, please."

But Dekko agreed with me that she was tired, and Strafe said he didn't mind stopping now. He suggested a nightcap, as he always does, and as we always do also, Cynthia and I declined. Dekko said he'd like a Cointreau.

The conversation drifted about. Dekko told us an Irish joke about a drunk who couldn't find his way out of a telephone box, and then Strafe remembered an incident at school concerning his and Dekko's housemaster, A. D. Cowley-Stubbs, and the house wag, Thrive Major. A. D. Cowley-Stubbs had been known as Cows and often featured in our after-bridge reminiscing. So did Thrive Major.

"Perhaps I *am* sleepy," Cynthia said. "I don't think I closed my eyes once last night."

She never does on a sea crossing. Personally I'm out like a light the moment my head touches the pillow; I often think it must be the salt in the air because normally I'm an uneasy sleeper at the best of times.

"You run along, old girl," Strafe advised.

"Brekky at nine," Dekko said.

Cynthia said good-night and went, and we didn't remark on her tiredness because as a kind of unwritten rule we never comment on one another. We're four people who play bridge. The companionship it offers, and the holidays we have together, are all part of that. We share everything: the cost of petrol, the cups of coffee or drinks we have; we even each make a contribution towards the use of Strafe's car because it's always his we go on holiday in, a Rover it was on this occasion.

"Funny, being here on your own," Strafe said, glancing across what the Malseeds call the After-Dinner Lounge at the man who didn't have a companion. He was a red-haired man of about thirty, not wearing a tie, his collar open at the neck and folded back over the jacket of his blue serge suit. He was uncouth-looking, though it's a hard thing to say, not at all the kind of person one usually sees at Glencorn Lodge. He sat in the After-Dinner Lounge as he had in the dining-room, lost in some concentration of his own, as if calculating sums in his mind. There had been a folded newspaper on his table in the dining-room. It now reposed tidily on the arm of his chair, still unopened.

"Commercial gent," Dekko said. "Fertilizers."

"Good heavens, never. You wouldn't get a rep in here."

I took no part in the argument. The lone man didn't much interest me, but I felt that Strafe was probably right: if there was anything dubious about the man's credentials he might have found it difficult to secure a room. In the hall of Glencorn Lodge there's a notice which reads: *We prefer not to feature in hotel guides, and we would be grateful to our guests if they did not seek to include Glencorn Lodge in the Good Food Guide, the Good Hotel Guide, the Michelin, Egon Ronay or any others. We have not advertised Glencorn since our early days, and prefer our rec-ommendations to be by word of mouth.*

"Ah, thank you," Strafe said when Kitty brought his whiskey and Dekko's Cointreau. "Sure you won't have something?" he said to me, although he knew I never did.

Strafe is on the stout side, I suppose you could say, with a gingery moustache and gingery hair, hardly touched at all by grey. He left the Army years ago, I sup-pose because of me in a sense, because he didn't want to be posted abroad again. He's in the Ministry of Defense now.

I'm still quite pretty in my way, though nothing like as striking as Mrs. Malseed, for I've never been that kind of woman. I've put on weight, and wouldn't have allowed myself to do so if Strafe hadn't kept saying he can't stand a bag of bones. I'm careful about my hair, and unlike Mrs. Malseed, I have it regularly seen to because if I don't it gets a salt-and-pepper look, which I hate. My husband, Terence, who died of food-poisoning when we were still quite young, used to say I wouldn't lose a single look in middle age, and to some extent that's true. We were still putting off having children when he died, which is why I haven't any. Then I met Strafe, which meant I didn't marry again.

Strafe is married himself, to Cynthia. She's small and ineffectual, I suppose you'd say without being untruthful or unkind. Not that Cynthia and I don't get on or anything like that, in fact we get on extremely well. It's Strafe and Cynthia who don't seem quite to hit it off, and I often think how much happier all round it would have been if Cynthia had married someone completely different, some-one like Dekko in a way, except that that mightn't quite have worked out either. The Strafes have two sons, both very like their father, both them in the Army. And the very sad thing is they think nothing of poor Cynthia.

"Who's that chap?" Dekko asked Mr. Malseed, who'd come over to wish us good-night.

"Awfully sorry about that, Mr. Deakin. My fault entirely, a booking that came over the phone."

"Good heavens, not at all," Strafe protested, and Dekko looked horrified in case it should be thought he was objecting to the locals. "Splendid-looking fellow," he said, overdoing it.

Mr. Malseed murmured that the man had only booked in for a single night, and I smiled the whole thing away, reassuring him with a nod. It's one of the pleasantest of the traditions at Glencorn Lodge that every evening Mr. Malseed makes the rounds of his guests just to say good-night. It's because of little touches like that that I, too, wished Dekko hadn't questioned Mr. Malseed about the man because it's the kind of thing one doesn't do at Glencorn Lodge. But Dekko is a law unto himself, very tall and gangling, always immaculately suited, a beaky face beneath mousy hair in which flecks of grey add a certain distinction. Dekko has money of his own and though he takes out girls who are half his age he has never managed to get around to marriage. The uncharitable might say he has a rather gormless laugh; certainly it's sometimes on the loud side.

We watched while Mr. Malseed bade the lone man good-night. The man didn't respond, but just sat gazing. It was ill-mannered, but this lack of courtesy didn't appear to be intentional: the man was clearly in a mood of some kind, miles away.

"Well, I'll go up," I said. "Good-night, you two."

"Cheery-bye, Milly," Dekko said. "Brekky at nine, remember."

"Good-night, Milly," Strafe said.

The Strafes always occupy different rooms on holidays, and at home also. This time he was in Geranium and she in Fuchsia. I was in Rose, and in a little while Strafe would come to see me. He stays with her out of kindness, because he fears for her on her own. He's a sentimental, good-hearted man, easily moved to tears: he simply cannot bear the thought of Cynthia with no one to talk to in the evenings, with no one to make her life around. "And besides," he often says when he's being jocular, "it would break up our bridge four." Naturally we never discuss her shortcomings or in any way analyse the marriage. The unwritten rule that exists among the four of us seems to extend as far as that.

He slipped into my room after he'd had another drink or two, and I was waiting for him as he likes me to wait, in bed but not quite undressed. He has never said so, but I know that that is something that Cynthia would not understand in him, or ever attempt to comply with. Terence, of course, would not have understood either; poor old Terence would have been shocked. Actually it's all rather sweet, Strafe and his little ways.

"I love you, dear," I whispered to him in the darkness, but just then he didn't wish to speak of love and referred instead to my body.

If Cynthia hadn't decided to remain in the hotel the next morning instead of accompanying us on our walk to Ardbeag everything might have been different. As it happened, when she said at breakfast she thought she'd just potter about the garden and sit with her book out of the wind, I can't say I was displeased. For a moment I hoped Dekko might say he'd stay with her, allowing Strafe and myself to go off on our own, but Dekko—who doesn't go in for saying what you want him to say—didn't. "Poor old sausage," he said instead, examining Cynthia with a solicitude that suggested she was close to the grave, rather than just a little lowered by the change of life or whatever it was.

"I'll be perfectly all right," Cynthia assured him. "Honestly."

"Cynthia likes to mooch, you know," Strafe pointed out, which of course is only the truth. She reads too much, I always think. You often see her putting down a book with the most melancholy look in her eyes, which can't be good for her. She's an imaginative woman, I suppose you would say, and of course her habit of reading so much is often useful on our holidays: over the years she has read her way through dozens of Irish guidebooks. "That's where the garrison pushed the natives over the cliffs," she once remarked on a drive. "Those rocks are known as the Maidens," she remarked on another occasion. She has led us to places of interest which we had no idea existed: Garron Tower on Garron Point, the mausoleum at Bonamargy, the Devil's Backbone. As well as which, Cynthia is extremely knowledgeable about all matters relating to Irish history. Again she has read endlessly: biographies and autobiographies, long accounts of the centuries of battling and politics there've been. There's hardly a town or village we ever pass through that hasn't some significance for Cynthia, although I'm afraid her impressive fund of information doesn't always receive the attention it deserves. Not that Cynthia ever minds; it doesn't seem to worry her when no one listens. My own opinion is that she'd have made a much better job of her relationship with Strafe and her sons if she could have somehow developed a bit more character.

We left her in the garden and proceeded down the cliff path to the shingle beneath. I was wearing slacks and a blouse, with the arms of a cardigan looped round my neck in case it turned chilly: the outfit was new, specially bought for the holiday, in shades of tangerine. Strafe never cares how he dresses and of course she doesn't keep him up to the mark: that morning, as far as I remember, he wore rather shapeless corduroy trousers, the kind men sometimes garden in, and a navy-blue fisherman's jersey. Dekko as usual was a fashion plate: a pale-green linen suit with pleated jacket pockets, a maroon shirt open at the neck, revealing a medallion on a fine gold chain. We didn't converse as we crossed the rather difficult shingle, but when we reached the sand Dekko began to talk about some girl or other, someone called Juliet who had apparently proposed marriage to him just before we'd left Surrey. He'd told her, so he said, that he'd think about it while on holiday and he wondered now about dispatching a telegram from Ardbeag saying, *Still thinking*. Strafe, who has a simple sense of humor, considered this hugely funny and spent most of the walk persuading Dekko that the telegram must certainly be sent, and other telegrams later on, all with the same message. Dekko kept laughing, throwing his head back in a way that always reminds me of an Australian bird I once saw in a nature film on television. I could see this was going to become one of those jokes that would accompany us all through the holiday, a man's thing really, but of course I didn't mind. The girl called Juliet was nearly thirty years younger than Dekko. I supposed she knew what she was doing.

Since the subject of telegrams had come up, Strafe recalled the occasion when

Thrive Major had sent one to A. D. Cowley-Stubbs: *Darling regret three months gone love Beulah*. Carefully timed, it had arrived during one of Cow's Thursday evening coffee sessions. Beulah was a maid who had been sacked the previous term, and old Cows had something of a reputation as a misogynist. When he read the message he apparently went white and collapsed into an armchair. Warrington P. J. managed to read it too, and after that the fat was in the fire. The consequences went on rather, but I never minded listening when Strafe and Dekko drifted back to their school-days. I just wish I'd known Strafe then, before either of us had gone and got married.

We had our coffee at Ardbeag, the telegram was sent off, and then Strafe and Dekko wanted to see a man called Henry O'Reilly whom we'd met on previous holidays, who organizes mackerel-fishing trips. I waited on my own, picking out postcards in the village shop that sells almost everything, and then I wandered down towards the shore. I knew that they would be having a drink with the boat-man because a year had passed since they'd seen him last. They joined me after about twenty minutes, Dekko apologizing but Strafe not seeming to be aware that I'd had to wait because Strafe is not a man who notices little things. It was almost one o'clock when we reached Glencorn Lodge and were told by Mrs. Malseed that Cynthia needed looking after.

The hotel, in fact, was in a turmoil. I have never seen anyone as ashen-faced as Mr. Malseed; his wife, in a forget-me-not dress, was limp. It wasn't explained to us immediately what had happened, because in the middle of telling us that Cynthia needed looking after Mr. Malseed was summoned to the telephone. I could see through the half-open door of their little office a glass of whiskey or brandy on the desk and Mrs. Malseed's bangled arm reaching out for it. Not for ages did we realize that it all had to do with the lone man whom we'd speculated about the night before.

"He just wanted to talk to me," Cynthia kept repeating hysterically in the hall. "He sat with me by the magnolias."

I made her lie down. Strafe and I stood on either side of her bed as she lay there with her shoes off, her rather unattractively cut plain pink dress crumpled and actually damp from her tears. I wanted to make her take it off and to slip under the bedclothes in her petticoat but somehow it seemed all wrong, in the cir-cumstances, for Strafe's wife to do anything so intimate in my presence.

"I couldn't stop him," Cynthia said, the rims of her eyes crimson by now, her nose beginning to run again. "From half past ten till well after twelve. He had to talk to someone, he said."

I could sense that Strafe was thinking precisely the same as I was: that the red-haired man had insinuated himself into Cynthia's company by talking about him-self and had then put a hand on her knee. Instead of simply standing up and going away, Cynthia would have stayed where she was, embarrassed or tongue-tied, at any rate unable to cope. And when the moment came she would have turned hysterical. I could picture her screaming in the garden, running across the lawn to the hotel, and then the pandemonium in the hall. I could sense Strafe picturing that also.

"My God, it's terrible," Cynthia said.

"I think she should sleep," I said quietly to Strafe. "Try to sleep, dear," I said to her, but she shook her head, tossing her jumble of hair about on the pillow.

"Milly's right," Strafe urged. "You'll feel much better after a little rest. We'll bring you a cup of tea later on."

"My God!" she cried again. "My God, how could I sleep?"

I went away to borrow a couple of mild sleeping pills from Dekko, who is never without them, relying on the things too much in my opinion. He was tidying himself in his room, but found the pills immediately. Strangely enough, Dekko's always sound in a crisis.

I gave them to her with water and she took them without asking what they were. She was in a kind of daze, one moment making a fuss and weeping, the next just peering ahead of her, as if frightened. In a way she was like someone who'd just had a bad nightmare and hadn't yet completely returned to reality. I remarked as much to Strafe while we made our way down to lunch, and he said he quite agreed.

"Poor old Cynth!" Dekko said when we'd all ordered lobster bisque and entrecôte béarnaise. "Poor old sausage."

You could see that the little waitress, a new girl this year, was bubbling over with excitement; but Kitty, serving the other half of the dining-room, was grim, which was most unusual. Everyone was talking in hushed tones and when Dekko said, "Poor old Cynth!" a couple of heads were turned in our direction because he can never keep his voice down. The little vases of roses with which Mrs. Malseed must have decorated each table before the fracas had occurred seemed strangely out of place in the atmosphere which had developed.

The waitress had just taken away our soup plates when Mr. Malseed hurried into the dining-room and came straight to our table. The lobster bisque surprisingly hadn't been quite up to scratch, and in passing I couldn't help wondering if the fuss had caused the kitchen to go to pieces also.

"I wonder if I might have a word, Major Strafe," Mr. Malseed said, and Strafe rose at once and accompanied him from the dining-room. A total silence had fallen, everyone in the dining-room pretending to be intent on eating. I had an odd feeling that we had perhaps got it all wrong, that because we'd been out for our walk when it had happened, all the other guests knew more of the details than Strafe and Dekko and I did. I began to wonder if poor Cynthia had been raped.

Afterwards Strafe told us what occurred in the Malseeds' office, how Mrs. Malseed had been sitting there, slumped, as he put it, and how two policemen had questioned him. "Look, what on earth's all this about?" he had demanded rather sharply.

"It concerns this incident that's taken place, sir," one of the policemen explained in an unhurried voice. "On account of your wife—"

"My wife's lying down. She must not be questioned or in any way disturbed."

"Ach, we'd never do that, sir."

Strafe does a good Co. Antrim brogue and in relating all this to us he couldn't resist making full use of it. The two policemen were in uniform and their natural slowness of intellect was rendered more noticeable by the lugubrious air the tragedy had inspired in the hotel. For tragedy was what it was: after talking to Cynthia for nearly two hours the lone man had walked down to the rocks and been drowned.

When Strafe finished speaking, I placed my knife and fork together on my plate, unable to eat another mouthful. The facts appeared to be that the man, having left Cynthia by the magnolias, had clambered down the cliff to a place no one ever went to, on the other side of the hotel from the sands we had walked along to Ardbeag. No one had seen him except Cynthia, who from the cliff-top had apparently witnessed his battering by the treacherous waves. The tide had been coming in, but by the time old Arthur and Mr. Malseed reached the rocks it had begun to turn, leaving behind it the fully dressed corpse. Mr. Malseed's impression was that the man had lost his footing on the seaweed and accidentally stumbled into the depths, for the rocks were so slippery it was difficult to carry the corpse more than a matter of yards. But at least it had been placed out of view, while Mr. Malseed hurried back to the hotel to telephone for assistance. He told Strafe that Cynthia had been most confused, insisting that the man had walked out among the rocks and then into the sea, knowing what he was doing.

Listening to it all, I no longer felt sorry for Cynthia. It was typical of her that she should so sillily have involved us in all this. Why on earth had she sat in the garden with a man of that kind instead of standing up and making a fuss the moment he'd begun to paw her? If she'd acted intelligently the whole unfortunate episode could clearly have been avoided. Since it hadn't, there was no point whatsoever in insisting that the man had committed suicide when at that distance no one could possibly be sure.

"It really does astonish me," I said at the lunch table, unable to prevent myself from breaking our unwritten rule. "Whatever came over her?"

"It can't be good for the hotel," Dekko commented, and I was glad to see Strafe giving him a little glance of irritation.

"It's hardly the point," I said coolly.

"What I meant was, hotels occasionally hush things like this up."

"Well, they haven't this time." It seemed an age since I had waited for them in

Ardbeag, since we had been so happily laughing over the effect of Dekko's telegram. He'd included his address in it so that the girl could send a message back, and as we'd returned to the hotel along the seashore there'd been much speculation between the two men about the form this would take.

"I suppose what Cynthia's thinking," Strafe said, "is that after he'd tried something on with her he became depressed."

"Oh, but he could just as easily have lost his footing. He'd have been on edge anyway, worried in case she reported him."

"Dreadful kind of death," Dekko said. His tone suggested that that was that, that the subject should now be closed, and so it was.

After lunch we went to our rooms, as we always do at Glencorn Lodge, to rest for an hour. I took my slacks and blouse off, hoping that Strafe would knock on my door, but he didn't and of course that was understandable. Oddly enough I found myself thinking of Dekko, picturing his long form stretched out in the room called Hydrangea, his beaky face in profile on his pillow. The precise nature of Dekko's relationship with these girls he picks up has always privately intrigued me: was it really possible that somewhere in London there was a girl called Juliet who was prepared to marry him for his not inconsiderable money?

I slept and briefly dreamed. Thrive Major and Warrington P. J. were running the post office in Ardbeag, sending telegrams to everyone they could think of, including Dekko's friend Juliet. Cynthia had been found dead beside the magnolias and people were waiting for Hercule Poirot to arrive. "Promise me you didn't do it," I whispered to Strafe, but when Strafe replied it was to say that Cynthia's body reminded him of a bag of old chicken bones.

Strafe and Dekko and I met for tea in the tea-lounge. Strafe had looked in to see if Cynthia had woken, but apparently she hadn't. The police officers had left the hotel, Dekko said, because he'd noticed their car wasn't parked at the front any more. None of the three of us said, but I think we presumed, that the man's body had been removed from the rocks during the quietness of the afternoon. From where we sat I caught a glimpse of Mrs. Malseed passing quite briskly through the hall, seeming almost herself again. Certainly our holiday would be affected, but it might not be totally ruined. All that remained to hope for was Cynthia's recovery, and then everyone could set about forgetting the unpleasantness. The nicest thing would be if a jolly young couple turned up and occupied the man's room, exorcising the incident, as newcomers would.

The family from France—the two little girls and their parents—were chattering away in the tea-lounge, and an elderly trio who'd arrived that morning were speaking in American accents. The honeymoon couple appeared, looking rather shy, and began to whisper and giggle in a corner. People who occupied the table next to ours in the dining-room, a Wing-Commander Orfell and his wife, from Guildford, nodded and smiled as they passed. Everyone was making an effort, and I knew it would help matters further if Cynthia felt up to a rubber or two before dinner. That life should continue as normally as possible was essential for Glencorn Lodge, the example already set by Mrs. Malseed.

Because of our interrupted lunch I felt quite hungry, and the Malseeds pride themselves on their teas. The chef, Mr. McBride, whom of course we've met, has the lightest touch I know with sponge-cakes and little curranty scones. I was, in fact, buttering a scone when Strafe said:

"Here she is."

And there indeed she was. By the look of her, she had simply pushed herself off her bed and come straight down. Her pink dress was even more crumpled than it had been. She hadn't so much as run a comb through her hair, her face was puffy and unpowdered. For a moment I really thought she was walking in her sleep.

Strafe and Dekko stood up. "Feeling better, dear?" Strafe said, but she didn't answer.

"Sit down, Cynth," Dekko urged, pushing back a chair to make room for her.

"He told me a story I can never forget. I've dreamed about it all over again." Cynthia swayed in front of us, not even attempting to sit down. To tell the truth, she sounded inane.

"Story, dear?" Strafe inquired, humoring her.

She said it was the story of two children who had apparently ridden bicycles through the streets of Belfast, out into Co. Antrim. The bicycles were dilapidated, she said; she didn't know if they were stolen or not. She didn't know about the children's homes because the man hadn't spoken of them, but she claimed to know instinctively that they had ridden away from poverty and unhappiness. "From the clatter and the quarreling," Cynthia said. "Two children who later fell in love."

"Horrid old dream," Strafe said. "Horrid for you, dear."

She shook her head, and then sat down. I poured another cup of tea. "I had the oddest dream myself," I said. "Thrive Major was running the post office in Ardbeag."

Strafe smiled and Dekko gave his laugh, but Cynthia didn't in any way acknowledge what I'd said.

"A fragile thing the girl was, with depths of mystery in her wide brown eyes. Red-haired of course he was himself, thin as a rake in those days. Glencorn Lodge was a derelict then."

"You've had a bit of a shock, old thing," Dekko said.

Strafe agreed, kindly adding, "Look, dear, if the chap actually interfered with you—"

"Why on earth should he do that?" Her voice was shrill in the tea-lounge, edged with a note of hysteria. I glanced at Strafe, who was frowning into his teacup. Dekko began to say something, but broke off before his meaning emerged. Rather more calmly Cynthia said:

"It was summer when they came here. Honeysuckle he described. And mother of thyme. He didn't know the name of either."

No one attempted any kind of reply, not that it was necessary, for Cynthia just continued.

"At school there were the facts of geography and arithmetic. And the legends of scholars and of heroes, of Queen Maeve and Finn MacCool. There was the coming of St. Patrick to a heathen people. History was full of kings and high-kings, and Silken Thomas and Wolfe Tone, the Flight of the Earls, the Siege of Limerick."

When Cynthia said that, it was impossible not to believe that the unfortunate events of the morning had touched her with some kind of madness. It seemed astonishing that she had walked into the tea-lounge without having combed her hair, and that she'd stood there swaying before sitting down, that out of the blue she had started on about two children. None of it made an iota of sense, and surely she could see that the nasty experience she'd suffered should not be dwelt upon? I offered her the plate of scones, hoping that if she began to eat she would stop talking, but she took no notice of my gesture.

"Look, dear," Strafe said, "there's not one of us who knows what you're talking about."

"I'm talking about a children's story, I'm talking about a girl and a boy who visited this place we visit also. He hadn't been here for years, but he returned last night, making one final effort to understand. And then he walked out into the sea."

She had taken a piece of her dress and was agitatedly crumpling it between the finger and thumb of her left hand. It was dreadful really, having her so grubby-looking. For some odd reason I suddenly thought of her cooking, how she wasn't in the least interested in it or in anything about the house. She certainly hadn't succeeded in making a home for Strafe.

"They rode those worn-out bicycles through a hot afternoon. Can you feel all that? A newly surfaced road, the snap of chippings beneath their tyres, the smell of tar? Dust from a passing car, the city they left behind?"

"Cynthia dear," I said, "drink your tea, and why not have a scone?"

"They swam and sunbathed on the beach you walked along today. They went to a spring for water. There were no magnolias then. There was no garden, no neat little cliff paths to the beach. Surely you can see it clearly?"

"No," Strafe said. "No, we really cannot, dear."

"This place that is an idyll for us was an idyll for them too: the trees, the ferns, the wild roses near the water spring, the very sea and sun they shared. There was a cottage lost in the middle of the woods: they sometimes looked for that. They played a game, a kind of hide-and-seek. People in a white farmhouse gave them milk."

For the second time, I offered Cynthia the plate of scones and for the second time, she pointedly ignored me. Her cup of tea hadn't been touched. Dekko took a scone and cheerfully said:

"All's well that's over."

But Cynthia appeared to have drifted back into a daze, and I wondered again if it could really be possible that the experience had unhinged her. Unable to help myself, I saw her being led away from the hotel, helped into the back of a blue van, something like an ambulance. She was talking about the children again, how they had planned to marry and keep a sweet-shop.

"Take it easy, dear," Strafe said, which I followed up by suggesting for the second time that she should make an effort to drink her tea.

"Has it to do with the streets they came from? Or the history they learnt, he from his Christian Brothers, she from her nuns? History is unfinished in this island; long since it has come to a stop in Surrey."

Dekko said, and I really had to hand it to him:

"Cynth, we have to put it behind us."

It didn't do any good. Cynthia just went rambling on, speaking again of the girl being taught by nuns, and the boy by Christian Brothers. She began to recite the history they might have learnt, the way she sometimes did when we were driving through an area that had historical connections. "Can you imagine," she embarrassingly asked, "our favorite places bitter with disaffection, with plotting and revenge? Can you imagine the treacherous murder of Shane O'Neill the Proud?"

Dekko made a little sideways gesture of his head, politely marvelling. Strafe seemed about to say something, but changed his mind. Confusion ran through Irish history, Cynthia said, like convolvulus in a hedgerow. On 24 May 1487, a boy of ten called Lambert Simnel, brought to Dublin by a priest from Oxford, was declared Edward VI of all England and Ireland, crowned with a golden circlet taken from a statue of the Virgin Mary. On 24 May 1798, here in Antrim, Presbyterian farmers fought for a common cause with their Catholic laborers. She paused and looked at Strafe. Chaos and contradiction, she informed him, were hidden everywhere beneath nice-sounding names. "The Battle of the Yellow Ford," she suddenly chanted in a singsong way that sounded thoroughly peculiar, "the Statutes of Kilkenny. The Battle of Glenmama, the Convention of Drumceat. The Act of Settlement, the Renunciation Act. The Act of Union, the Toleration Act. Just so much history it sounds like now, yet people starved or died while other people watched. A language was lost, a faith forbidden. Famine followed revolt, plantation followed that. But it was people who were struck into the soil of other people's land, not forests of new trees; and it was greed and treachery that spread as a disease among them all. No wonder unease clings to these shreds of history and shots ring out in answer to the mockery of drums. No wonder the air is nervy with suspicion."

There was an extremely awkward silence when she ceased to speak.

Dekko nodded, doing his best to be companionable. Strafe nodded also. I simply examined the pattern of roses on our teatime china, not knowing what else to do. Eventually Dekko said: "What an awful lot you know, Cynth!"

"Cynthia's always been interested," Strafe said. "Always had a first-rate memory."

"Those children of the streets are part of the battles and the Acts," she went on, seeming quite unaware that her talk was literally almost crazy. "They're part of the blood that flowed around those nice-sounding names." She paused, and for a moment seemed disinclined to continue. Then she said:

"The second time they came here the house was being rebuilt. There were concrete-mixers, and lorries drawn up on the grass, noise and scaffolding everywhere. They watched all through another afternoon and then they went their different ways: their childhood was over, lost with their idyll. He became a dockyard clerk. She went to London, to work in a betting shop."

"My dear," Strafe said very gently, "it's interesting, everything you say, but it really hardly concerns us."

"No, of course not." Quite emphatically Cynthia shook her head, appearing wholly to agree. "They were degenerate, awful creatures. They must have been."

"No one's saying that, my dear."

"Their story should have ended there, he in the docklands of Belfast, she recording bets. Their complicated childhood love should just have dissipated, as such love often does. But somehow nothing was as neat as that."

Dekko, in an effort to lighten the conversation, mentioned a boy called Gollsol who'd been at school with Strafe and himself, who'd formed a romantic attachment for the daughter of one of the groundsmen and had later actually married her. There was a silence for a moment, then Cynthia, without emotion, said:

"You none of you care. You sit there not caring that two people are dead."

"Two people, Cynthia?" I said.

"For God's sake, I'm telling you!" she cried. "That girl was murdered in a room in Maida Vale."

Although there is something between Strafe and myself, I do try my best to be at peace about it. I go to church and take communion, and I know Strafe occasionally does too, though not as often as perhaps he might. Cynthia has no interest in that side of life, and it rankled with me now to hear her blaspheming so casually, and so casually speaking about death in Maida Vale on top of all this stuff about history and children. Strafe was shaking his head, clearly believing that Cynthia didn't know what she was talking about.

"Cynthia, dear," I began, "are you sure you're not muddling something up here? You've been upset, you've had a nightmare: don't you think your imagination, or something you've been reading—"

"Bombs don't go off on their own. Death doesn't just happen to occur in Derry and Belfast, in London and Amsterdam and Dublin, in Berlin and Jerusalem. There are people who are murderers: that is what this children's story is about."

A silence fell, no one knowing what to say. It didn't matter of course because without any prompting Cynthia continued.

"We drink our gin with Angostura bitters, there's lamb or chicken Kiev. Old Kitty's kind to us in the dining-room and old Arthur in the hall. Flowers are everywhere, we have our special table."

"Please let us take you to your room now," Strafe begged, and as he spoke I reached out a hand in friendship and placed it on her arm. "Come on, old thing," Dekko said.

"The limbless are left on the streets, blood spatters the car-parks. *Brits Out* it says on a rockface, but we know it doesn't mean us."

I spoke quietly then, measuring my words, measuring the pause between each so that its effect might be registered. I felt the statement had to be made, whether it was my place to make it or not. I said:

"You are very confused, Cynthia."

The French family left the tea-lounge. The two Dalmatians, Charger and Snooze, ambled in and sniffed and went away again. Kitty came to clear the French family's tea things. I could hear her speaking to the honeymoon couple, saying that the weather forecast was good.

"Cynthia," Strafe said, standing up, "we've been very patient with you but this is now becoming silly."

I nodded just a little. "I really think," I softly said, but Cynthia didn't permit me to go on.

"Someone told him about her. Someone mentioned her name, and he couldn't believe it. She sat alone in Maida Vale, putting together the mechanisms of her bombs: this girl who had laughed on the seashore, whom he had loved."

"Cynthia," Strafe began, but he wasn't permitted to continue either. Hopelessly he just sat down again.

"Whenever he heard of bombs exploding he thought of her, and couldn't understand. He wept when he said that; her violence haunted him, he said. He couldn't work, he couldn't sleep at night. His mind filled up with images of her, their awkward childhood kisses, her fingers working neatly now. He saw her with a carrier-bag, hurrying it through a crowd, leaving it where it could cause most death. In front of the mouldering old house that had once been Glencorn Lodge they'd made a fire and cooked their food. They'd lain for ages on the grass. They'd cycled home to their city streets."

It suddenly dawned on me that Cynthia was knitting this whole fantasy out of nothing. It all worked backwards from the moment when she'd had the misfortune to witness the man's death in the sea. A few minutes before he'd been chatting quite normally to her, he'd probably even mentioned a holiday in his childhood and some girl there'd been: all of it would have been natural in the circumstances, possibly even the holiday had taken place at Glencorn. He'd said goodbye and then unfortunately he'd had his accident. Watching from the cliff edge, something had cracked in poor Cynthia's brain, she having always been a prey to melancholy. I suppose it must be hard having two sons who don't think much of you, and a marriage not offering you a great deal, bridge and holidays probably the best part of it. For some odd reason of her own she'd created her fantasy about a child turning into a terrorist. The violence of the man's death had clearly filled her imagination with Irish violence, so regularly seen on television. If we'd been on holiday in Suffolk I wondered how it would have seemed to the poor creature.

I could feel Strafe and Dekko beginning to put all that together also, beginning to realize that the whole story of the red-haired man and the girl was clearly Cynthia's invention. "Poor creature," I wanted to say, but did not do so.

"For months he searched for her, pushing his way among the people of London, the people who were her victims. When he found her she just looked at him, as if the past hadn't even existed. She didn't smile, as if incapable of smiling. He wanted to take her away, back to where they came from, but she didn't reply when he suggested that. Bitterness was like a disease in her, and when he left her he felt the bitterness in himself."

Again Strafe and Dekko nodded, and I could feel Strafe thinking that there really was no point in protesting further. All we could hope for was that the end of the saga was in sight.

"He remained in London, working on the railways. But in the same way as before he was haunted by the person she'd become, and the haunting was more awful now. He bought a gun from a man he'd been told about and kept it hidden in a shoe-box in his rented room. Now and again he took it out and looked at it, then put it back. He hated the violence that possessed her, yet he was full of it himself: he knew he couldn't betray her with anything but death. Humanity had left both of them when he visited her again in Maida Vale."

To my enormous relief and, I could feel, to Strafe's and Dekko's too, Mr. and Mrs. Malseed appeared beside us. Like his wife, Mr. Malseed had considerably recovered. He spoke in an even voice, clearly wishing to dispose of the matter. It was just the diversion we needed.

"I must apologize, Mrs. Strafe," he said. "I cannot say how sorry we are that you were bothered by that man."

"My wife is still a little dicky," Strafe explained, "but after a decent night's rest I think she'll be as right as rain again."

"I only wish, Mrs. Strafe, you had made contact with my wife or myself when he first approached you." There was a spark of irritation in Mr. Malseed's eyes, but his voice was still controlled. "I mean, the unpleasantness you suffered might just have been averted."

"Nothing would have been averted, Mr. Malseed, and certainly not the horror we are left with. Can you see her as the girl she became, seated at a chipped white table, her wires and fuses spread around her? What were her thoughts in that room, Mr. Malseed? What happens in the mind of anyone who wishes to destroy? In a back street he bought his gun for too much money. When did it first occur to him to kill her?"

"We really are a bit at sea," Mr. Malseed replied without the slightest hesitation. He humoured Cynthia by displaying no surprise, by speaking very quietly.

"All I am saying, Mr. Malseed, is that we should root our heads out of the sand and wonder about two people who are beyond the pale."

"My dear," Strafe said, "Mr. Malseed is a busy man."

Still quietly, still perfectly in control of every intonation, without a single glance around the tea-lounge to ascertain where his guests' attention was, Mr. Malseed said:

"There is unrest here, Mrs. Strafe, but we do our best to live with it."

"All I am saying is that perhaps there can be regret when two children end like this."

Mr. Malseed did not reply. His wife did her best to smile away the awkwardness. Strafe murmured privately to Cynthia, no doubt beseeching her to come to her senses. Again I imagined a blue van drawn up in front of Glencorn Lodge, for it was quite understandable now that an imaginative woman should go mad, affected by the ugliness of death. The garbled speculation about the man and the girl, the jumble in the poor thing's mind—a children's story as she called it—all somehow hung together when you realized they didn't have to make any sense whatsoever.

"Murderers are beyond the pale, Mr. Malseed, and England has always had its pales. The one in Ireland began in 1395."

"Dear," I said, "what has happened has nothing whatsoever to do with calling people murderers and placing them beyond some pale or other. You witnessed a most unpleasant accident, dear, and it's only to be expected that you've become a little lost. The man had a chat with you when you were sitting by the magnolias and then the shock of seeing him slip on the seaweed—"

"He didn't slip on the seaweed," she suddenly screamed. "My God, he didn't slip on the seaweed."

Strafe closed his eyes. The other guests in the tea-lounge had fallen silent ages ago, openly listening. Arthur was standing near the door and was listening also. Kitty was waiting to clear away our tea things, but didn't like to because of what was happening.

"I must request that you take Mrs. Strafe to her room, Major," Mr. Malseed said. "And I must make it clear that we cannot tolerate further upset in Glencorn Lodge."

Strafe reached for her arm, but Cynthia took no notice.

"An Irish joke," she said, and then she stared at Mr. and Mrs. Malseed, her eyes passing over each feature of their faces. She stared at Dekko and Strafe, and last of all at me. She said eventually:

"An Irish joke, an unbecoming tale: of course it can't be true. Ridiculous, that a man returned here. Ridiculous, that he walked again by the seashore and through the woods, hoping to understand where a woman's cruelty had come from."

"This talk is most offensive," Mr. Malseed protested, his calmness slipping just a little. The ashen look that had earlier been in his face returned. I could see he was beside himself with rage. "You are trying to bring something to our doorstep which most certainly does not belong there."

"On your doorstep they talked about a sweetshop: Cadbury's bars and different-flavoured creams, nut-milk toffee, Aero and Crunchie."

"For God's sake pull yourself together," I clearly heard Strafe whispering, and Mrs. Malseed attempted to smile. "Come along now, Mrs. Strafe," she said, making a gesture. "Just to please us, dear. Kitty wants to clear away the dishes. Kitty!" she called out, endeavouring to bring matters down to earth.

Kitty crossed the lounge with her tray and gathered up the cups and saucers. The Malseeds, naturally still anxious, hovered. No one was surprised when Cynthia began all over again, by crazily asking Kitty what she thought of us.

"I think, dear," Mrs. Malseed began, "Kitty's quite busy really."

"Stop this at once," Strafe quietly ordered.

"For fourteen years, Kitty, you've served us with food and cleared away the teacups we've drunk from. For fourteen years we've played our bridge and walked about the garden. We've gone for drives, we've bought our tweed, we've bathed as those children did."

"Stop it," Strafe said again, a little louder. Bewildered and getting red in the face, Kitty hastily bundled china on to her tray. I made a sign at Strafe because for some reason I felt that the end was really in sight. I wanted him to retain his patience, but what Cynthia said next was almost unbelievable.

"In Surrey we while away the time, we clip our hedges. On a bridge night there's coffee at nine o'clock, with macaroons or *petits fours*. Last thing of all we watch the late-night News, packing away our cards and scoring-pads, our sharpened pencils. There's been an incident in Armagh, one soldier's had his head shot off, another's run amok. Our lovely Glens of Antrim, we all four think, our coastal drives: we hope that nothing disturbs the peace. We think of Mr. Malseed, still busy in Glencorn Lodge, and Mrs. Malseed, finishing her flower-plaques for the rooms of the completed annexe."

"Will you for God's sake shut up?" Strafe suddenly shouted. I could see him struggling with himself, but it didn't do any good. He called Cynthia a bloody spectacle, sitting there talking rubbish. I don't believe she even heard him.

"Through honey-tinted glasses we love you and we love your island, Kitty. We love the lilt of your racy history, we love your earls and heroes. Yet we made a sensible pale here once, as civilized people create a garden, pretty as a picture."

Strafe's outburst had been quite noisy and I could sense him being ashamed of it. He muttered that he was sorry, but Cynthia simply took advantage of his generosity, continuing about a pale.

"Beyond it lie the bleak untouchables, best kept as dots on the horizon, too terrible to contemplate. How can we be blamed if we make neither head nor tail of anything, Kitty, your past and your present, those battles and Acts of Parliament? We people of Surrey: how can we know? Yet I stupidly thought, you see, that the tragedy of two children could at least be understood. He didn't discover where her cruelty had come from because perhaps you never can: evil breeds evil in a mysterious way. That's the story the red-haired stranger passed on to me, the story you huddle away from."

Poor Strafe was pulling at Cynthia, pleading with her, still saying he was sorry.

"Mrs. Strafe," Mr. Malseed tried to say, but got no further. To my horror Cynthia abruptly pointed at me.

"That woman," she said, "is my husband's mistress, a fact I am supposed to be unaware of, Kitty."

"My God!" Strafe said.

"My husband is perverted in his sexual desires. His friend, who shared his schooldays, has never quite recovered from that time. I myself am a pathetic creature who has closed her eyes to a husband's infidelity and his mistress's viciousness. I am dragged into the days of Thrive Major and A. D. Cowley-Stubbs: mechanically I smile. I hardly exist, Kitty."

There was a most unpleasant silence, and then Strafe said:

"None of that's true. For God's sake, Cynthia," he suddenly shouted, "go and lie down."

Cynthia shook her head and continued to address the waitress. She'd had a rest, she told her. "But it didn't do any good, Kitty, because hell has invaded the paradise of Glencorn, as so often it has invaded your island. And we, who have so often brought it, pretend it isn't there. Who cares about children made into murderers?"

Strafe shouted again. "You fleshless ugly bitch!" he cried. "You bloody old fool!" He was on his feet, trying to get her on to hers. The blood was thumping in his bronzed face, his eyes had a fury in them I'd never seen before. "Fleshless!" he shouted at her, not caring that so many people were listening. He closed his eyes in misery and in shame again, and I wanted to reach out and take his hand but of course I could not. You could see the Malseeds didn't blame him, you could see them thinking that everything was ruined for us. I wanted to shout at Cynthia too, to batter the silliness out of her, but of course I could not do that. I could feel the tears behind my eyes, and I couldn't help noticing that Dekko's hands were shaking. He's quite sensitive behind his joky manner, and had quite obviously taken to heart her statement that he had never recovered from his schooldays. Nor had it been pleasant, hearing myself described as vicious.

"No one cares," Cynthia said in the same unbalanced way, as if she hadn't just been called ugly and a bitch. "No one cares, and on our journey home we shall all four be silent. Yet is the truth about ourselves at least a beginning? Will we wonder in the end about the hell that frightens us?"

Strafe still looked wretched, his face deliberately turned away from us. Mrs. Malseed gave a little sigh and raised the fingers of her left hand to her cheek, as if something tickled it. Her husband breathed heavily. Dekko seemed on the point of tears.

Cynthia stumbled off, leaving a silence behind her. Before it was broken I knew she was right when she said we would just go home, away from this country we had come to love. And I knew as well that neither here nor at home would she be led to a blue van that was not quite an ambulance. Strafe would stay with her because Strafe is made like that, honourable in his own particular way. I felt a pain where perhaps my heart is, and again I wanted to cry. Why couldn't it have been she who had gone down to the rocks and slipped on the seaweed or just walked into the sea, it didn't matter which? Her awful rigmarole hung about us as the last of the tea things were gathered up—the earls who'd fled, the famine and the people planted. The children were there too, grown up into murdering riff-raff.

POEMS

Nobel Prize-winner Seamus Heaney is the poet of the Irish soil. His subjects key on Irish places, people, and events in which the realities of the external world are mirrored in profound and direct personal experience. His ability to find the perfect pitch—just the right words, rhythms, symbols, tones—whether he's recasting a medieval Irish poem, chronicling a skirmish in Northern Ireland, or meditating on the love he feels for his wife—sets him on a par with W. B. Yeats. The poems selected here span Heaney's entire career and demonstrate his rich interweaving of elements of classical poetical craftsmanship and very human contemporary ethical themes.

"Digging," Heaney's early ars poetica, offers a tender look at his family's potato-farming legacy, and marks his place in that tradition—a poet who unearths his sustenance from the land of his forebears, by "digging" with not a spade, but a pen.

Heaney unearths other truths by resurrecting history and myth in "The Tollund Man" and "Bog Queen," likening rituals of contemporary political murder with ritual sacrifice in the former, and crafting an original take on the Celtic mermaid tale in the latter. Both are based on the discovery of human remains preserved in the mud of bogs (the "Bog People" find their way into several of Heaney's poems) and thereby metaphor and reality merge as the land is shown again and again to remember its violent past.

"In Gallarus Oratory" takes us on a subterranean tour for another effect. Here the most mystical of transformations occurs after being submerged in an ancient underground sacred space, when a people found favor not from God but "in the eye of their King," and coming aboveground see the world aflame with the glorious light of expanded, *renewed, forever-enriched perception.*

"The Skunk" portrays altered perception and renewed glory on a very personal level, as the speaker misses his absent wife with heightened pangs of love and yearning—triggered unexpectedly by nightly visitations of a skunk. Fresh and unexpected are the metaphors, as well, which Heaney uses to describe "An Artist." How he manages to get at the very nature of a mountain or an apple mystifies, shows utter obstinacy, fortitude, and even vulgarity. The ineffable in both poems (love and the creative impulse, respectively) is made tangible through inventive figurative language and deft turns of emotion. And "Postscript" depicts a contemporary paean to Yeats's wild swans, and their power "to catch the heart off guard and blow it open," a wonderful phrase that also captures one of the supreme pleasures of reading any of Heaney's poems.

DIGGING

Between my finger and my thumb
The squat pen rests; snug as a gun.

Under my window, a clean rasping sound
When the spade sinks into gravelly ground:
My father, digging. I look down

Till his straining rump among the flowerbeds
Bends low, comes up twenty years away
Stooping in rhythm through potato drills
Where he was digging.

The coarse boot nestled on the lug, the shaft
Against the inside knee was levered firmly.
He rooted out tall tops, buried the bright edge deep
To scatter new potatoes that we picked
Loving their cool hardness in our hands.

By God, the old man could handle a spade.
Just like his old man.

My grandfather cut more turf in a day
Than any other man on Toner's bog.
Once I carried him milk in a bottle
Corked sloppily with paper. He straightened up
To drink it, then fell to right away
Nicking and slicing neatly, heaving sods
Over his shoulder, going down and down
For the good turf. Digging.

The cold smell of potato mould, the squelch and slap
Of soggy peat, the curt cuts of an edge
Through living roots awaken in my head.
But I've no spade to follow men like them.

Between my finger and my thumb
The squat pen rests.
I'll dig with it.

[1966]

IN GALLARUS ORATORY

You can still feel the community pack
This place: it's like going into a turfstack,
A core of old dark walled up with stone
A yard thick. When you're in it alone
You might have dropped, a reduced creature
To the heart of the globe. No worshipper
Would leap up to his God off this floor.

Founded there like heroes in a barrow
They sought themselves in the eye of their King
Under the black weight of their own breathing.
And how he smiled on them as out they came,
The sea a censer, and the grass a flame.

[1969]

THE TOLLUND MAN

I

Some day I will go to Aarhus
To see his peat-brown head,
The mild pods of his eye-lids,
His pointed skin cap.

In the flat country nearby
Where they dug him out,
His last gruel of winter seeds
Caked in his stomach,

Naked except for
The cap, noose and girdle,
I will stand a long time.
Bridegroom to the goddess,

She tightened her torc on him
And opened her fen,
Those dark juices working
Him to a saint's kept body,

Trove of the turfcutters'
Honeycombed workings.
Now his stained face
Reposes at Aarhus.

II

I could risk blasphemy,
Consecrate the cauldron bog
Our holy ground and pray
Him to make germinate

The scattered, ambushed
Flesh of labourers,
Stockinged corpses
Laid out in the farmyards,

Tell-tale skin and teeth
Flecking the sleepers
Of four young brothers, trailed
For miles along the lines.

III

Something of his sad freedom
As he rode the tumbril
Should come to me, driving,
Saying the names

Tollund, Grauballe, Nebelgard,
Watching the pointing hands
Of country people,
Not knowing their tongue.

Out there in Jutland
In the old man-killing parishes
I will feel lost,
Unhappy and at home.

[1972]

BOG QUEEN

I lay waiting
between turf-face and demesne wall,
between heathery levels
and glass-toothed stone.

My body was braille
for the creeping influences:
dawn suns groped over my head
and cooled at my feet,

through my fabrics and skins
the seeps of winter
digested me,
the illiterate roots

pondered and died
in the cavings
of stomach and socket.
I lay waiting

on the gravel bottom,
my brain darkening,
a jar of spawn
fermenting underground

dreams of Baltic amber.
Bruised berries under my nails,
the vital hoard reducing
in the crock of the pelvis.

My diadem grew carious,
gemstones dropped
in the peat floe
like the bearings of history.

My sash was a black glacier
wrinkling, dyed weaves
and Phoenician stitchwork
retted on my breasts'

soft moraines.
I knew winter cold
like the nuzzle of fjords
at my thighs—

the soaked fledge, the heavy
swaddle of hides.
My skull hibernated
in the wet nest of my hair.

Which they robbed.
I was barbered
and stripped
by a turfcutter's spade

who veiled me again
and packed coomb softly
between the stone jambs
at my head and my feet.

Till a peer's wife bribed him.
The plait of my hair,
a slimy birth-cord
of bog, had been cut

and I rose from the dark,
hacked bone, skull-ware,
frayed stitches, tufts,
small gleams on the bank.

[1975]

THE SKUNK

Up, black, striped and damasked like the chasuble
At a funeral Mass, the skunk's tail
Paraded the skunk. Night after night
I expected her like a visitor.

The refrigerator whinnied into silence.
My desk light softened beyond the verandah.
Small oranges loomed in the orange tree.
I began to be tense as a voyeur.

After eleven years I was composing
Love-letters again, broaching the word "wife"
Like a stored cask, as if its slender vowel
Had mutated into the night earth and air

Of California. The beautiful, useless
Tang of eucalyptus spelt your absence.
The aftermath of a mouthful of wine
Was like inhaling you off a cold pillow.

And there she was, the intent and glamorous,
Ordinary, mysterious skunk,
Mythologized, demythologized,
Snuffing the boards five feet beyond me.

It all came back to me last night, stirred
By the sootfall of your things at bedtime,
Your head-down, tail-up hunt in a bottom drawer
For the black plunge-line nightdress.

[1979]

AN ARTIST

I love the thought of his anger.
His obstinacy against the rock, his coercion
of the substance from green apples.

The way he was a dog barking
at the image of himself barking.
And his hatred of his own embrace
of working as the only thing that worked—
the vulgarity of expecting ever
gratitude or admiration, which
would mean a stealing from him.

The way his fortitude held and hardened
because he did what he knew.
His forehead like a hurled *boule*
travelling unpainted space
behind the apple and behind the mountain.

[1984]

POSTSCRIPT

And some time make the time to drive out west
Into County Clare, along the Flaggy Shore,
In September or October, when the wind
And the light are working off each other
So that the ocean on one side is wild
With foam and glitter, and inland among stones
The surface of a slate-grey lake is lit
By the earthed lightning of a flock of swans,
Their feathers roughed and ruffling, white on white,
Their fully grown headstrong-looking heads
Tucked or cresting or busy underwater.
Useless to think you'll park and capture it
More thoroughly. You are neither here nor there,
A hurry through which known and strange things pass
As big soft buffetings come at the car sideways
And catch the heart off guard and blow it open.

[1996]

PATRICK McCABE

FROM
THE BUTCHER BOY

Young Francie Brady of The Butcher Boy *(1992) has an alcoholic
father and a suicidal mother and to escape from all this he immerses
himself in comics and television. But things have become even worse at
home and when Mrs. Nugent, a local busybody, refers to Francie's family as "pigs" he can no longer control his rage. Here, after his precious
TV breaks down, Francie encounters the self-satisfied Mrs. Nugent on
the street and attempts to get back at her.*

IT WAS ALL GOING WELL UNTIL the telly went. Phut!
That was that then, a blank grey screen looking back at you. I fiddled with
it but all I got was a blizzard of snow so I sat there looking at that in the hope
that something would come on but it didn't and there was still nothing when da
came home. How did it happen he says and I told him. I was just sitting there the
next thing—out like a light. He pulled off his greatcoat and it fell on the floor.
Right, he says, all business, let's have a look at this now. He was humming away
to himself happy as Larry about it all. Then he says you know there's not as much
into these televisions as the likes of Mickey Traynor makes out. He had bought it
off Mickey Traynor the holy telly man that was because he sold holy pictures on
the side. He fiddled about with it for a while but nothing happened then he shifted
it over by the window and said it could be the aerial but it only got worse there.
He hit it a thump and then what happened even the snow went. After that he
started to rant and rave about Mickey. He said he might have known better than
to trust the likes of Traynor, him and his holy pictures don't fool me. He'll not sell
me a dud television and get away with it. He'll not pull any of his foxy stunts on
Benny Brady. I'm up to the likes of Mickey Traynor make no mistake. He
smacked it with his hand. *Work*! he shouted. Look at it—I should have known
it'd be no good. Work! How long have we got? Six months that's how long we

897

THE BUTCHER BOY

have it, bought and paid for with my hard-earned money. But I'll tell you this—
Traynor will give me back every cent I paid him every cent by Christ he will!

He drew out and put his boot through it, the glass went everywhere. I'll fix it,
he said, I'll fix it good and fucking proper.

Then he fell asleep on the sofa with one shoe hanging off.

There wasn't much I could do then I got fed up watching the birds hop along the
garden wall so I went off up the street. I said to myself well that's the end of John
Wayne I knew it'd lie there glass and all and nobody would ever bother coming
to fix it. Ah well, I said sure Joe can always tell me what happens and it was when
I was thinking that I saw Philip and Mrs. Nugent coming. I knew she thought I
was going to turn back when I saw them. She leaned over and said something to
Philip. I knew what she was saying but I don't think she knew I knew. She crin-
kled up her nose and said in a dead whisper: *Just stands there on the landing and lets
the father do what he likes to her. You'd never do the like of that would you Philip?
You'd always stand by me wouldn't you?*

Philip nodded and smiled. She smiled happily and then it twisted a bit and the
hand went up again as she said: *Of course you know what she was doing with the fuse
wire don't you Philip?*

She thought I was going to turn back all red when she said that but I didn't. I
just kept on walking. Ah there you are Mrs. Nugent I says with a big grin, and
Philip. She looked right through me and it was one of those looks that is supposed
to make you shrivel up and die but it only made me grin even more. I was standing in the middle of the footpath. Mrs. Nugent held on her hat with one hand and
took Philip with the other would you let me by please she says.

Oh no I can't do that I said, you have to pay to get past. She had all these broken
nerve ends on her nose and her eyebrows went away up nearly meeting her hair
what do you mean what on earth do you mean she said and I could see Philip
frowning with his Mr. Professor face wondering was it serious maybe, maybe
something he could investigate or do a project on. Well he could if he wanted I
didn't care as long as he paid. It was called the Pig Toll Tax. Yes, Mrs. Nugent I
said, the pig toll tax it is and every time you want to get past it costs a shilling. Her
lips got so thin you really would think they were drawn with a pencil and the skin
on her forehead was so tight I thought maybe the bones were going to burst out.
But they didn't and I says to Philip I'll tell you what Philip you can have half. So
what's that then one shilling for Mrs. Nooge, I said and twopence halfpenny for
Philip. I don't know why I called her Mrs. Nooge, it just came into my head. I
thought it was a good thing to call her but she didn't. She got as red as a beetroot
then. Yup, I said again, ya gotta pay the old tax Mrs. Nooge, and I stood there

with my thumbs hooked in my braces like a Western old timer. She got all heated up then oh yes hot and bothered. Philip didn't know what to do he had given up the idea of investigating the pig toll tax I think he just wanted to get away altogether but I couldn't allow that until the pig toll tax was paid, that was the rules of pig land I told them. I'm sorry I said like they always do when they're asking you for money, if you ask me its far too much but that's the way it is I'm afraid. It has to be collected *someone has to do it ha ha*. She tried to push her way past then but I got a grip of her by the sleeve of her coat and it made it all awkward for her she couldn't see what was holding her back. Her hat had tilted sideways and there was a lemon hanging down over the brim. She tried to pull away but I had a good tight hold of the sleeve and she couldn't manage it.

Durn taxes, I said, ain't fair on folks. When I looked again there was a tear in her eye but she wouldn't please me to let it out. When I saw that I let go of her sleeve and smiled. Right, I says I'll tell you what, I'll let you by this time folks but remember now in future—make sure and have the pig toll tax ready. I stood there staring after them, she was walking faster than Philip trying to fix the lemon at the same time telling him to come on. When they were passing the cinema I shouted I ain't foolin' Mrs. Nooge but I don't know if she heard me or not. The last thing I saw was Philip turning to look back but she pulled him on ahead.

↓

A fellow went by and I says to him do you know what its a bad state of affairs when people won't pay a tax to get by. Who are you he says. Brady I said.

He was wheeling a black bike with a coat thrown over the handlebars. He stopped and rested it against a pole then dug deep in the pocket of his trousers and produced a pipe and a tin of tobacco. Brady? he says, would that be Brady of the Terrace? That's right I says. O, he says, I see. You see what, I said. Your father was a great man one time, he says. He was one of the best musicians ever was in this town. He went to see Eddie Calvert, he says then. I said I wanted to hear no more about Eddie Calvert. You don't like music, he says, do you think the town will win again Saturday? I told him I wanted to hear nothing about football either. You don't think its a great thing the town won the cup? he says. No, I says. I said it was a pity they didn't lose. I see, he says, well what's this tax you're talking about, you seem to care about that. He was all on for a discussion about the government and the way things had gone. There was a smell of turf fires and buttermilk off him. He tapped the bowl of his pipe against his thigh and he says which tax would this be now.

He thought it was some outrageous tax the government had brought in and he was about to say its time this quit or they have the country destroyed when I said ah no its not the government at all. It was invented by me, and its only the people I say.

And who are you, he says.

Francie Pig the Toll Tax Man, I says and he shook his head and tapped the pipe again, that's a good laugh he says.

Laugh, I said, I don't know where you get the idea its a good laugh. Then he said tsk tsk and you're an awful man altogether. He puffed on the pipe. Pig Toll Tax, he says, that's the first time I ever heard that now. He kept opening and closing his mouth over the brown stem like a fish smoking. Oh you needn't worry your head about it I said, it has nothing to do with you. What it really should have been called was The Mrs. Nugent and Nobody Else At All Tax but I didn't tell him that. I see he says well in that case I'll be on my way.

His index finger jumped off his forehead *gluck now* he said and away off up the town with the bike sideways and the wheels ticking.

I went into the shop. The whine of the bacon slicer and the shopgirl licking a pencil stub racing up and down a wobbly tower of numbers on the back of a paper bag. The women were standing over by the cornflakes saying things have got very dear. Its very hard to manage now oh it is indeed do you know how much I paid for Peter's shoes above in the shop. When they seen me coming they all stopped talking. One of them moved back and bumped against the display case. There you are ladies I said and they all went right back on their heels at the same time. What's this? I says, the woman with three heads? When I said that they weren't so bad. Flick—back come the smiles. Ah Francie, they said, there you are. Here I am I said. They leaned right over to me and in a soft top secret voice said how's your mother Francie? Oh I says she's flying she's above in the garage and it won't be long now before she's home. They're going to give her a service I says, hand me down the spanner Mike! Ha, ha, they laughed, that was a good one. Yup, says I, she has to come home shortly now to get the baking done for Uncle Alo's party. So your Uncle Alo's coming home! they said. Christmas Eve I said, all the way from London. Would you credit that now says Mrs. Connolly with a warm little shiver, and will he be staying long? Two weeks says I. Two weeks she says and smiled I was going to say do you not believe me or something Mrs. Connolly but I didn't I had enough on my plate with Mrs. Nugent without Connolly starting. He did well in London, Francie, your Uncle Alo, says the other woman. Then they all started it. Oh he did well surely he did indeed, a great big job and more luck to him its not easy in these big places like London. It is not! Mrs. Connolly'd say and then someone else would say the same thing over again. It was like The History of Alo programme. But I didn't mind. I said now you're talking and all this. Mrs. Connolly said: I saw him the last time he was home with a lovely red hankie in his breast pocket and a beautiful blue suit.

I seen him too, he was like someone in the government or something.

He was indeed. It takes the Bradys, they said.

Every time, I said.

Good man Francie, said the women.

I'll tell Alo to call down and see you when he comes home, I said, you can have a chat with him about London and all.

Do that Francie, they said. I will indeed, I said. Then I said well ladies I'm afraid I can't stay here I have to be off on my travels.

Dear dear aren't you a ticket Francie? they said.

I'm away off up the town on business to do with the toll tax.

Toll tax? I never heard tell of that now Francie. What would that be?

Oh it's invented by me, I told them. But of course Nugent won't pay it. You might as well be trying to get blood out of a stone.

Nugent? says Mrs. Connolly, *Mrs.* Nugent?

Yes I said. Well, be it on her own head. She won't be getting by so handy the next time.

They were all ears when they heard it was to do with her.

Getting by? But getting by *where*, Francie, they kept saying.

On the footpath I said where do you think, where else would you want to get past?

The footpath? they said.

Yes, I said again, *the footpath*. You'd think the three of them had gone handicapped all of a sudden the way they were staring at me.

I could see Mrs. Connolly fiddling with her brooch and saying something out of the side of her mouth.

Then she said: There's no denying it Francie, you're a rare character!

The other two were hiding behind her now I think they must have thought I was going to stick them for a few bob tax as well.

Oh now I said and off I went out the door as I went by the window I could see Mrs. Connolly saying something and the other women nodding then raising their eyes to heaven.

COLUM McCANN

A WORD IN EDGEWISE

One sister speaks to another in this poignant—and very Irish—story from Colum McCann's 1993 collection, Fishing the Sloe-Black River.

LOOK AT YOU AND A SMILE on you like the cracked vase that Mammy kept in the kitchen cupboard. The flowery one. With the downward chink, like a upturned smile. Daisies, I think they were, with little yellow figurines leaping all the way through them. A poet one time wrote about a vase, or an urn, and something about beauty and truth. A damnsight we were away from truth those nights, hai? You jumping around the dancehall like a prayer in an air raid, your hair running wild and frothy all around your shoulders. Weren't we a sight? You, sneaking off down to the town square with Francis Hogan, the only lad in town with a motorcar, done up to the nines, your mascara on, your ginger hair flying. Him with his elbow hung out the window, smoking, his curls all slicked back with oil. What a sight! Me sitting sidesaddle on Tommy Coyne's red tractor, chugging our way out to the fields behind the elderberry forest, going to make hay, as we say. Wasn't that the time of it? A tube of lipstick was a precious thing in those days.

The young ones nowadays, they don't think we were up to it at all. Here we are, getting letters from the grandkids, all over the globe, and I'll be bowled arse-over-backward if they think we ever misbehaved. Did I tell you about the letter I got a few days ago from young Fiachra in Amsterdam? Tells me the tulips look lovely in spring. I ask you, eighteen years old and he wants me to think he's looking at the tulips! Not only making hay, but he's probably threshing the damn stuff as well. They do that sort of thing in Amsterdam. It's a long way from Tipperary. Or a long way to tip her hairy, as Tommy Coyne was once heard to sing, outside the dancehall, sitting on the back of his tractor. Holy God! I don't mean to be rude, Moira, but I kid you not. Sitting on the back of his tractor with the blackberry juice on his teeth and his hair in a cowlick: *It's a long way to tip her hairy, it's a long way to go, it's a long way to tip the hairy of the sweetest gal I know, Godblessher.* God bless us and save us! It's the years, Moira. I'm wont to ramble, as you well know.

Lipstick. Cleanser. Mascara. A touch of rouge. Eyeliner. The whole nine yards. We'll have you smiling yet. Come off it now, of course we will. Anyway, didn't Da get into awful conniptions over me knocking the kitchen teapot over the night we came in from the dancehall? Smashed on the kitchen tiles, it did, with an awful racket. Ricocheting through the house. Us standing there, the smell of drink on our breaths, in those blue dresses sent from Paris by Aunt Orla. Him as big as the Rathcannon elk, roaring: "Weren't you two supposed to be home by ten?" And both of us stealing out again and sitting in the vegetable patch near the barn, laughing our heads off until the sun was just about up. And us just smearing the makeup all over each other's faces! We must have looked awful stupid— sitting in a straggle of turnips, wearing fancy blue dresses.

Funny thing is, these days we're always asleep by ten, let alone home. Time has a curious way. But that's how it goes isn't it? Da away and beyond, God rest his soul. Mammy too. And Aunt Orla with her. Sure, who knows where even Tommy Coyne is these days? Up and left for Australia long before it was the fashionable place to go. Remember all those jokes about Tommy Coyne and sheep! Me oh my. Hold on a minute now, Moira, and the first thing I'm going to do is put on a little cleanser. New stuff I got from Max Factor. Lovely clean smell to it, isn't there?

Good God Almighty! But haven't we been doing this since the Lord knows when? Remember the times when we were toddlers and Mammy would be on the way out to the pub with Da? He'd be there, all big-boned, at the end of the stairs, in his blue suit, shouting at her to hurry on. And Mammy always so meticulous with the lipstick, wasn't she? Forever licking her tongue over her teeth, head cocked sideways, staring at herself. I suppose that's where we got it from. Us glued wide-eyed on either side of her. Then us sneaking out of bed when they were gone, to sit in front of the big oak mirror and smear it all over our lips, trying her hats on, and making curtseys in the middle of the room. Damn it, anyway, but weren't we the holy terrors! Remember that night when we took what's-her-name, the cat, you know, oh, whatsit? Luna! That's it. Luna. Remember we took her and covered her with rouge, put mascara on the whiskers, perfumed behind the poor thing's ears and dressed her in a rag of old satin? That little wag of a tail coming out the back. That poor cat hissing around the house, like something possessed. Hiding under the bed. The hat you made for her with Da's cigarette packs. The things we remember.

Anyway, talking of teapots, strange the way things change, isn't it? Used to be a teapot was a teapot. Nothing more and nothing less. Just teapots. But I was up and beyond in Dublin last week, baby-sitting little Kieran, his mammy and daddy away in London for an advertising conference. So, anyway, I took him for a walk down by the canal—the water's filthy these days, floating with Styrofoam cups, all that smog and neon along the banks, even a couple of condoms, floating on the water. I kid you not! Who would use those things anyway, Moira? Like your Sean says, it must be like washing your feet with your socks on! But, like I was saying, we were throwing some bread to the ducks, and all of a sudden little Kieran says to me, he says: "Look at those teapots over there, Granny." And him pointing to a couple of boys wrapped together like slices of bread underneath the Leeson Street Bridge, kissing in broad daylight. Teapots. I ask you, Moira. Apparently something to do with the way the spout curves.

We'll give that cleanser a moment to settle now, Moira, then we'll get started with the foundation. Sad to say, anyway, Larry and Paula look like they're emigrating too. Paula got offered a job with that crowd, Saatchi and Saatchi. They're going to enroll little Kieran in some private school on the outskirts of London. There's another one will grow up with an English accent. Dropping h's all over the place. A terrible shame. And he'll see more than his fair share of teapots over there, I'll tell you. That sort of thing goes on all the time in London. It's as bad as Amsterdam. Before you know it there'll be none of us McAllisters left in Ireland at all. Sure, don't you remember the time we almost went ourselves? 1947, wasn't it? Anniversary of D-Day, if I'm not mistaken.

Don't you remember us walking down the main street and those two Yankee soldiers sauntering by O'Connor's butcher shop with the big red awning? Decked out in the full regalia, handsome as Sunday. Recovering from the war, of course. The lads in town didn't like them at all. Overpaid, oversexed, and over here. A wee bit of jealousy, I'd say, because aren't those Americans awful good-looking people? Great teeth and all. Anyway. Remember? You in your ochre blouse and your linen skirt and me myself in my favorite green cardigan, the one with the flowers crocheted on the side. Both of us after making our faces up lovely. And up come the two Yankee boys, asking us what was it a fella could do of an evening in a town like this? And, before you know it, we're out there driving down the Cork road with the windows open and them singing all sorts of curious songs. *Heidy-deighty, Christ Almighty, who the hell are we? Wham bam thank you ma'am we're the infantry!* And us covering our ears, pretending like we were shocked. Out into the countryside, under those huge stars, and them saying that the car was broken down so they could walk us back to town in the dark. Talk about conniving. And us pretending like we were scared, so we could lean into them. A summer night, wasn't it?

But we were tempted. Let it be said, here and now, we were tempted. Now, of course, my Eoin and your Sean wouldn't need to hear that, but we were tempted to be sure. Oh yes. On we go now, anyway. A bit of foundation. Just a dab here. I brought my finest, of course. We'll just get in there under your chin a little bit. Skim off the surplus here now, with my old camel's hair brush. You're looking really great now. Ah, it's a sad world sometimes, but it gives you such funny stories.

Who knows, but we could have been married to some Yanks! Funny thing that, when you think about it. At least for you it was love at first sight with Sean, and isn't that what makes the world go around? *Love and marriage, love and marriage, go together like a horse and carriage, ladeedadeedada, ladeedadeedadee, you can't have one without the other.* Me oh my. Can hardly remember the words now. Between yourself and myself and the walls, sometimes I almost regret putting the cart before the horse, so to speak, marrying Eoin like I did. He was never exactly— well, he was a quiet man. But, well, damn it all anyway, there's enough bad-mouthing done in this world without me adding to it. Isn't that right? Too many bickerers and begrudgers all over the place. My Eoin gave me a good home, God bless his soul, treated me right, even if now and then I got a little uppity with him. Enough said now. He was always very fond of you as well Moira. Always said nice things about you. Loved your pot roast, and I'm not just saying that. He was heard to say, more than once, that he'd run to Dublin and back if he knew one of your pot roasts was waiting for him.

And talking of men who are quick on their feet now, Moira! That time you met your Sean. That was so funny, wasn't it? At that dance in Greenore, you wearing that red velvet dress just a little bit off the shoulder. Daring for the times. 1951. October, if I'm not mistaken. Or was it November? Getting a bit on the cold side, if I remember correctly, and you wouldn't wear a cardigan over your dress. Partial to showing off, you were, and why not? You have a body on you that the rest of us have always envied, that's for sure. Anyway, remember that night? That drafty old hall with the grimy windows? Us sitting there, me with my Eoin, newly married and cuddling, and you beside us, the gooseberry just waiting for a man. Indeed you were! Don't be codding me now. Hackling for a man you were. But you were beautiful that night. You were too. With the red dress, face all done, and those fancy new stockings. And up he comes, your Sean, skipping over the floor, from the other side of the hall, his hat sideways, smelling of Brylcreem, that chip in his teeth showing, over to you, saying, "Excuse me, any chance of a dance before I get carpet burns on me tongue?" I almost wet myself laughing! Carpet burns on his tongue! And then both of you out there, dancing and laughing. You always said it was love at first sight, and why not? He's the nicest man. Him always talking you up a storm. Anyway, here I am, rambling away as usual. He gave me your note today, your Sean did. Said to me: "Do her face up good now, Eileen. It's a big journey."

And a big journey it is too. The foundation now, Moira, is on like a dream. Trust me. And, as you say, you want to be traveling like a princess. And that you will be. We got so handy with the makeup, didn't we? Even when the kids were born, and the beauty parlor was shut down, we'd always find some time for it. Trying out the lemon to get rid of the freckles. And those oatmeal face packs, Lord, they were great!

But, and let me say it, here and now, I'll never ever ever forget the time you messed up my hair. I was a crotchety old bear for months afterward, and I'm sorry for it. But you have to think about it in the light of the time. Not two months after Matthew was born. You saying I'd look great if I got a bit of the stray gray out of the hair. Pushing the auburn look. Auburn this. Auburn that. Auburn the other thing. My head was down there in the sink in your bungalow saying, "Moira, are you sure about this?" "Sure, I'm sure," you said. Not a bother on you. And for five weeks afterward my head was a fluorescent orange. Like a nuclear carrot, I was! Luminous! A tourist attraction! Everyone thought it very funny when July twelfth rolled around. All of them saying: "Oh, we can send Eileen up to Belfast for Orangeman's Day."

I was fuming, and I'm really sorry about what I did with your sunflowers. I know I never told you. But it was me. I'm very sorry. Lopped their heads off with a scissors, I was so mad. But the hair was really awful, you must admit. Come off it now! It was! Don't be fooling me. Eoin wouldn't touch me for weeks. Not that he was a mad passionate man anyway. He kept calling me a left footer. The kids all thought I'd gone barmy. Me, having to wear that awful scarf, the one with the pictures of the pound notes on it, all around town for God knows how long. Rinsing my hair every day, trying to get the dye out. But, that's said and done, and we can laugh about it now.

But we were pretty handy all the same, weren't we? Even when it was rationed, we could always find some. Sure, remember when we got those red stones that when you licked them, they'd give off a bit of paint? Down by the river when we were kids. And using the sugar water to keep the hair up. And the berry juice we'd smear on our cheeks when we had nothing else. The fun we had with those. Speaking of, Moira, here we go with the rouge now. Yardley. That rose perle tint you've always been fond of.

Strange that. Never really thought of it that way. Those stones we'd find, down by the river, us little girls, in exactly the same place where your Sean and young Liam wanted to build your bungalow. Moira, those lettuce-and-tomato sandwiches! Those flasks of tea! Weren't those the times? Your Liam there working on the house. Up we'd go with his lunch and he'd say, him hanging out of the rafters: "Mam, Auntie Eileen, are you sure yez put enough salad cream on these things today?" Always mad keen on the lettuce and tomato. And then us down to the town with another flask and a few brown bags for the men. Us meeting in the park and spreading out the big white tablecloth. Your Sean forever leaving all those dirty thumbprints on the tablecloth. Terrible. And don't you remember the day I took the driving test! Sean leaving that dirty great spanner in the middle of the passenger seat by mistake. Me so nervous that I forgot about it and along comes the driving inspector and sits on the damn thing. Moira, it must be said that he was a bit of a poofter, wearing those cream pants, don't you think? Him so snotty and dignified and stupid that he didn't say a thing. Him failing me and all. And me not even hitting the curb on the three-point turn. Livid, I was. But it was worth the price of admission, that was. That big slobber of oil on his arse pants. Him waddling off. A teapot, as your Kieran would say.

This rouge is fabulous stuff. Blending in wonderfully. Amazing what they can do nowadays. Listen to me ramble and me making a mess with the makeup! God! Your sunflowers. I'm still thinking about your sunflowers. And the way you were going to enter them in the flower competition. Sorry now. I really am. Along I came and snippety-snip, they were gone.

Well, it'll be family now, the next few days, us all back together again. The children never understand at times like these, and it's just as well that they have a bit of fun. We'll get little Orla and Fiona and Michelle and we'll teach them how to put on some makeup. Maybe even see if some of the young girls at the beauty parlor will allow me to take up a chair and teach the kids some tricks of the trade. Oh me, oh my, wouldn't that be a racket! We'll take the boys and bring them down to the bridge, lash together some fishing poles and maybe even go for a plunge, what with the hot weather we've been having. Give the rest of us time. All of us adults together. I know I said some bad things about my Eoin, but I really wish he was here. But. Well! I'm happy enough. I really am. The letters from the kids and all, keeping up the house, and baking the odd bit of bread. Up to Dublin occasionally to baby-sit. And just walking about the town. The river's bad, though, as you know. That chemical factory has been sending men down here with all their Geiger counters or whatever it is they call them. Soon we'll all be walking around glowing. Another go-around with the orange hair for me, I suppose. Just a little extra rouge here. Don't be worrying. Moira, you have the most gorgeous cheekbones! I've always envied those cheekbones.

Now let me just have a minute here now and we'll start on the eyes. A dab with the pencil first, I think. The moss-colored one. Up above the lashes here. Ah-ha. Anyway. Umm. Just a touch here. Isn't it terrible, though? There they were, promising a hundred jobs and all we get is a river we can hardly swim in anymore. But, my God, I was down there the other day and you should see some of the bathing suits the young girls are wearing! Little thongs thin as twigs. Pieces of cloth no thicker than thread. Down there flossing, Moira! I ask you. Leaving not a thing to the imagination. But why not? When you have it, flaunt it, I suppose. To hell with God and country. Now, I don't really meant that, Moira, but you know what I mean. It's not as if we were the purest things since snow or sliced bread. I mean, we were given to a bit of wiggling too, weren't we, when we had it? Not that we ever wore swimsuits like that. Let me stand back a minute and size you up.

A sight for sore eyes, you are. What do you think? Some more? All right so. Here we go. Marvelous. Jiminy cricket, but you're looking great. Then we'll see what we can do with the eye shadow and the mascara. We'll give you that green, a bit of light color under the eyebrows. Those eyes of yours always so green. Ah, Moira. You made me happy with that note of yours, strange as it may seem. Your Sean woke up this morning and the first thing he did was he phoned me, told me the news, saying that he had this envelope that he had tucked away for years in the bottom drawer of his dresser. Drove over to the house and handed it to me. Both of us crying. No airs about you. There's never been an air about you. That's how I'd like to do it myself. No fuss or bother.

It was a lovely note all the same. Such a lovely idea. When in the world did you write it? Sean said he had it for years and that many's the time he wanted to open it. Anyway, we went down to McCartan's in the rain to arrange the arrangements, and old man McCartan saying: "That's a very strange request, I'm not sure if we can do it." And your Sean—he loves you so much, he really does—taking him aside and saying that he'd give McCartan a few extra bob if he'd let me do your face. McCartan's a bit of a rat for the money sometimes. Hemmed and hawed for a moment. Sean slipped him another fiver and McCartan got every-thing ready for me—fixed you up in a way of peace and all. But him still trying to tell me that it might overwhelm me. Overwhelm me! I ask you! After all the times I've done this self-same thing. Go away out of that, Mister McCartan, I said to him. There's nobody better for the job. I'll do her up right. Sure we'll have a little natter and we'll talk about old times.

Liam's huge bicycle with the purple mudguards! Orla winning the footrace at the County Fair! You burning the pot roast the day Haughey resigned! The hol-iday in Bray, and Eoin walking the promenade and his hat blowing off and the seagull leaving a dollop on his head! Me oh my. Haven't we had the life of it? And the things we remember! Him ranting and raving and effing and blinding all over the place, what with that seagull stuff all over his handkerchief! Moira, I could talk all night, but look at me here, and I still haven't finished your eyes, not to mention the lipstick and everyone due to see you shortly. I better get cracking.

Seems like half the town went to the airport today to pick up people flying in. Shannon and Dublin. They'll be in later today to say hello. Even young Fiachra. Him and his tulips from Amsterdam. What a scoundrel he is. Okay, now, this color is just perfect. Coal green fading out gently. Perfect. It really is. Makes you look like a million dollars. You recall Fiachra, and him hardly having a hair on his head until he was three years old? Just never grew, did it? You taking him down to the super-market on Main Street when Ciara was down sick with the flu in seventy-six. And that old bat, Mrs. Roche, coming up to you and asking why in the world you'd allow your grandson to have all his hair shaved off. And then her whispering in your ear: "Was it your sister Eileen who gave him that awful haircut?" And you smacking her in the jaw with a cauliflower for the implication! Ah Lord, how I would have loved to have been a fly on the wall. Serves her right. Anyway, I know it's rude to whisper, but did you know that her youngest is up the pole, as they say?

A WORD IN EDGEWISE

True as God, Moira. Six months gone. What do you make of that?

Here we go, and we'll get the extra smudge off the eyelashes. We'll be done awful soon. Just let me get the lipstick absolutely right. That's the most important thing, I always say. Get the lips right and you've the battle won. Launch a thousand ships, you will. Here we go. Yes. Ah-ha. Pencil first, of course. You and Sean at your wedding, that's the funniest photograph. Him standing outside the church, all that confetti over his shoulders, a smile on him to beat the band, the lily in his breast pocket, all the people milling around and right there—smack dab in the middle of his cheek—that huge lipstick mark. Spent half the morning getting the lipstick just right and then you went and smeared it all over his cheek. Lord, woman! Those were the days! Listen to me ramble, and a hundred people waiting to see you. Mrs. Burden made the sandwiches and Tommy Farrell got a ton of whiskey for the evening, Father Colligan's the one to say mass, and Miss Bennet, from the school, is putting together some lovely flowers. This lipstick is really something special, let me tell you, makes your lips full and really compliments you. Estée Lauder, if you don't mind! Pale rose.

Talking like a runaway train, I am. Ah, but you were never able to get a word in edgewise, were you, Moira? Always me rattling away, no matter what. From day one on. And, sure, I'll visit you every week. Sean has got a lovely quiet spot, not too far from where your young Liam is. The only thing is that the old factory's going to belch up the odd bit of smoke in your way, otherwise you'd probably have a clear vision almost all the way to Dublin. A few yards away from that huge old chestnut tree you'll be. And never lonely, what with the boys out gathering conkers and me, myself, I'll come out there and run my mouth off as usual. Yes indeed. Now, I better get a grip of myself, because I promised myself I wasn't going to cry. And you know when I make a promise to myself. But I'll tell you, and here's another promise now.

You know what I'm going to do next week? Here's what I'm going to do. I'm going to buy a packet of sunflower seeds. That's what I'm going to do. To hell with everything else. Down in McKenna's. Going to go to McKenna's, buy myself a little trowel and some fertilizer. That's what I'm going to do. Wear my old clogs and my big hat. Walk out to the chestnut tree. Plant the seeds, away from the shade. Then sit back and watch them grow. Every day. And if anybody comes along with a snippety-snip, I'll knock them arse-over-backwards into the middle of next week. And that's a promise. From me to you. Water them every day. Now let me just take a step back here and have a look at you. Just going to step back. Water them every day. Ah-ha. Just going to stand here. Just a moment now. That's what I'm going to do.

Moira, let me tell you something. Let me tell you. You look smashing. You really do. You really, really do. Absolutely smashing. A lovely peaceful smile on you. My God, you look smashing. Really, really smashing.

EMER MARTIN

FROM
BREAKFAST
IN BABYLON

These excerpts from Emer Martin's 1995 novel trace the experiences of Isolt, a twenty-year-old Irish woman who has fled her home in Dublin to wander Europe, and her dark relationship with Christopher, a misogynistic American drug dealer who has spent most of his adult life in France.

ISOLT HAD NEVER BEGGED SO hard. Five hours sitting in four different locations—the last in a Metro tunnel during rush hour. She bought a pair of black leggings, a three-pack of knickers, a towel, shampoo and conditioner and some make-up in the Tati at Montparnasse. Tonight could be her big date. She felt good sitting with her plastic bags full of unopened and unworn items on the Metro, like a normal commuter. Soon she wouldn't look or smell so much like a beggar.

From the bridge she could see the Eiffel Tower. She was attracted to Christopher. She was attracted to the idea of being very, very old. At this very moment on the bridge she felt compelled to dive into the Seine. To throw life off course. Walk down one street or walk down another.

Isolt felt herself being drawn towards Christopher just as she had been drawn to the gash in Jim's face; she had carried his scabs in her fingernails unawares. Her friend Becky had hated Christopher because he was cruel. She had sensed Isolt's initial infatuation towards him and didn't like it. Becky had heard the death beat running through their lives. Her death had been a warning to Isolt to go look for shelter but she was not sure how.

She left the tower and hurried on to the American church on the quays.

↓

The American church had a small college attached to it. Isolt walked down the steps, through the hall and ducked into the showers without catching anyone's

911

eye. As she shampooed her hair she wished she had remembered to buy a razor for she felt monstrously hairy compared to all these young American girls. They were rich and she was poor. All those hairless First-Worlders laughing and talking shit. They came across as naive, patronizing and phoney.

Christopher had none of these traits; he was the only poor American she had ever met. She rinsed the conditioner from her hair and stood for a blissful moment under the thumping hot water. She had not had a shower in two months.

Stepping out naked, she caught an unwanted glimpse of her lumpy body in the full-length mirror; red patches from the scalding water splotched all over her fish-white flesh. She shut this out of her mind and vigorously dried herself with the towel. These Americans were so super-confident; the world was their oyster and their parents' credit cards were their pearls. They had huge brightly-coloured soft towels and a million and one products in their designer make-up bags, they knew each other and chatted merrily like birds. Isolt was jealous of their camaraderie and their ease with the world. She put on her new knickers and leggings, all the time holding in her stomach. She sniffed her bra; it smelt of smoke, but she had to put it on anyway as she had no other. She wished she had a new jumper that didn't smell of sweat; she almost cried putting on her filthy black jacket, she felt so alone. The girls were looking at her discreetly. She had meant to ask them for a lend of a hairbrush but now that they had spotted her sniffing her bra she was ashamed to ask.

She combed her shoulder-length hair roughly with her fingers. The confidence she had obtained earlier from her rampant consuming was ebbing away. Covering her face in foundation she immediately perked up; it was an improvement. Her red nose and the tiny broken veins on her cheeks were smoothed over. There had always been something about her face that had stubbornly defied prettiness. Her gray eyes were slanty and her cheeks were too big; vast expanses of cheek on either side of the nose, they were great plains, herds of wildebeest could graze on her cheeks. If she had a child with cheeks like that she would mercifully drown it.

There was nothing seriously physically wrong with her—too chubby perhaps but not fat like poor Melonie—yet she still felt deformed, handicapped, especially when she saw the beautiful women in the advertisements everywhere. Isolt was plain though the make-up was making her look pretty. She put eyeliner on the pink little rim of her socket, blinking a little as her eye watered; she put some brown eye-shadow over the whole eyelid, putting an extra shimmer green stripe in the middle. Then with the satisfaction of opening a virginal mascara she brushed her eyelashes until they were thick and black, sticking the brush back into the tube, imagining the hymen breaking, screwed the lid on. She coated her lips in slut-red lipstick, pouting involuntarily in the mirror.

Presentable and blemish-free, she avoided the full-length mirror on her way out. An American girl was using a giant can of hairspray. Sealing in your rotten thoughts with poison, Isolt thought unfairly as she stomped out, not quite a new woman but a refurbished specimen for the time being.

The pavements were wet with drizzle, their colour a damp, dark brown under the yellow street lights. Cars and trucks passed on towards oblivion. She felt oppressed by the traffic and the city at night. The sight of the Eiffel Tower failed to elate her wizened spirit. Europe was going home for the night desensitized by the day's labours. Everyone was scurrying for shelter huddled under ominous black umbrellas.

↓

Christopher said that birds were baggage. Isolt ruffled her feathers and tagged along.

If anything of real significance happened in the weeks that followed it was contained in their conversations. Christopher talking and Isolt content to listen. They formed a routine very quickly. Christopher relied on routines and took great pleasure in seeing every small detail through. They got up and both went on errands to steal whiskey. They went begging. They scoured the city for chemists who would sell them codeine cough syrup. They had coffee somewhere and drank the medicine. Washing the mess down as it clung to their throats like glue. Isolt would change her clothes, wash up and put on make-up in the Air France terminal near Invalides where they had big toilets and wash basins. Sometimes she took a shower in the American church and he sold whiskey to the Spanish caretaker who tried to buy Isolt from him too. Christopher laughed at his pathos. "He asked me how much you were but I said I didn't have the change." Jim and Rory were not back from the South yet. She wondered where her allegiance would lie then. Now and then she would meet the lads for breakfast in Babylon. Christopher never came, he would stay out begging. She made much more money than he did. He tried to punish her but she was always happy and proud to make money and didn't care. Most nights they ate indoors on the little one-ring camping stove. They shopped in the big late night supermarket by the Pompidou Centre, stealing some things and buying others. Potatoes, peanuts in their shells, broccoli, carrots, tomatoes, cucumbers, avocadoes, onions, garlic, apples, oranges, bananas, honey, and six litres of Perrier a day. Christopher made her drink water to clear up her skin. She was always back and forth to the Turkish toilet at the end of the nightmarish green hall. The wooden floor was so creaky. She stumbled against the mental-hospital coloured walls, stoned and paranoid every night.

↓

913

Isolt left Christopher fretting in his corner over the image of the neglected corpse of the dead Giant. She was not a nurturer. She did not take Christopher on hand so that she might reform or help him. Isolt was not an earth mother. If she thought of motherhood at all it was as if her womb was a raindrop, falling through time itself, ready to hit a surface and explode forming other small raindrops which would fall in turn and on and on . . . The huge falling ocean dissipating into a tiny, evaporating moist particle.

She turned a corner into a tabac to buy tobacco and papers. Looking at all the men in the cafés she wondered what all the women were doing at home. God has had a hysterectomy. We are all homeless until the stolen womb is reinstated.

Christopher had followed her. He was frantic.

"I've no drugs at all. How much money did you make today?"

"One hundred and thirty, but I have two whiskeys I'm off to sell now."

"I need some heroin."

"Look, I'll buy you a bottle of codeine. I'll even go into the chemist and get it for you. I haven't eaten yet. Let's go sell the bottles and eat in the Chinese on Rue Saint Denis."

"I'd really like some heroin. I feel suicidal. I want something to knock me out."

"Have a bottle of whiskey."

"You know I don't drink no more. You don't want to see me drunk, El Ribbo, I'll beat the shit out of you. Now give me the money. I'm sick of you sucking my brain dry for chit-chat and stories. You owe me. I'm giving you that green card, the key to the U.S. What do I get in return?"

"Europe. Just like you wanted. It was all your idea. If you want something to knock you out and you can't drink, why don't I hit you over the head with the bottle? I want something to eat, that's thirty francs, then some hash, that's one hundred francs, a few beers with the lads, that's fifty francs at least. So I need two hundred francs including this tobacco. I can give you maybe fifty francs."

"Fifty francs!!!"

"Look, if you come with me you can eat. I'll give you fifty francs for your codeine. I'll score the hash, meet you and give you half. Jesus, Christopher, that's reasonable. You're not my pimp."

"OK, done." He walked beside her, keeping a tight grip on her elbow.

Later that evening, after Isolt had scored hash from the Scottish dealers, she met Christopher hiding out in the café. He looked terrible. He stood reading *The Telegraph,* his tiny coffee cup empty on the counter. He kept his little finger entwined in the white delft handle in case the waiter took it away and he would lose his right to stand there.

"I need a little company. I think I'm cracking up." He choked back a sob.

Isolt said, "All right, let's go smoke a joint."

They took the Saint-Michel Metro one stop to Musée d'Orsay and sat at the end of that platform, smoking in relative silence. Isolt was in the mood for a few beers and some joking around. Christopher was a burden. They stepped up onto the next train. When the doors opened in Saint-Michel there was a blind dwarf with heavy glasses and a white stick; his clothes were soiled and crumpled and he clutched a plastic shopping bag. Isolt stepped off beside him and observed his hobbled step onto the train. She said to Christopher, "At least we are not as badly off as that."

Christopher snorted. "Girl. There are three hundred people on the platform who all look as if they're doing all right. This is a lesson. Why do you have to compare yourself to the most miserable motherfucker in the entire place to feel good about yourself?"

Isolt laughed. "OK. I'll see you later."

"We're going home now, Isolt."

"I need some beers and light company."

"Where is your heart? Your loyalty? I have just seen and smelt my best friend's two-week-old rat-eaten corpse. Any time now I need to grieve for Freddie by thinking about him, I have to overcome that stinking spectacle. He cried for my troubles and all I can associate him with is a carcass. Something I don't want to think about. I don't even want to catch anybody's eyes in case I see their corpse. I can't be alone. I'm scared of what I might do. No lips, no eyes. That touch of death. My fingers are still cold with it. I knew automatically that this was my next real step. My own death. Maybe your death too. Christ, I hope I don't kill anyone. Just to wake me up from this frame of mind . . ."

"You're going to be a barrel of laughs tonight. OK, I'll come back to the hotel on one condition, that I can drink my beer without a lecture on the evils of alcohol."

"Thank you, Isolt. You will not go unrewarded for this. I love you."

"No, you don't."

"No, I don't."

In the Arab shop as Isolt stocked up on bottles of beer, Christopher hovered around her. "If you drink all that beer you'll be getting up and down all night having to piss. That would drive me crazy if I was you."

When they got back to the hotel Isolt drank her beers, went up and down the stairs to the toilet and listened to Christopher rant and rave. They smoked the hash and finally lay down on their respective beds. To Isolt's surprise Christopher came to her and instead of a blow job he wanted to have sex.

"I'll plug you good like an old pork pig, you frog leg, puff-ball girl." He laughed recklessly as he climbed on top.

↓

Christopher was unhappy at the prospect of a new city to conquer. He concentrated on Isolt's explanation of the underground system. As she talked, she saw names that conjured up images of the banality that she associated with this city: Ealing, Islington, Mile End, Swiss Cottage, Stockwell, Hampstead Heath. They took the yellow Circle line to the Embankment and shuffled down white-tiled corridors through grim-faced rush hour crowds, heavily burdened with Christopher's luggage. The brown Bakerloo line was less packed. Isolt stared past her reflection to the blackened brick tunnel walls. She listened to the robotic announcement at Waterloo: MIND THE GAP, it resounded soullessly, STAND CLEAR OF THE DOORS PLEASE. MIND THE GAP. They got out at Elephant and Castle, the end of the line. She had done this many times before.

Christopher was twisting and turning, avidly taking in his new environment.

"How come we're the only white people getting off here? What kind of place are you bringing me to? A fucking jungle?"

She looked at Christopher—a black raincoat down to his feet; black, baggy, ill-fitting trousers; wrecked running shoes; a navy sweater with wool balls hanging like dingle berries from the fabric; out of his filthy shirt-collar his yellow, dirt-ringed neck protruded, the skin texture between his collar bone and neck similar to a tiny loose triangle of testicle, as wrinkled and criss-crossed as elephant skin. His eyes were so deeply brown the dilated black pupil and the iris seemed one. His skin was yellow, his nose had blackheads and even the whites of his eyes looked red and grey. His mustache glistened with snot and sweat and his face was small, encircled as it was by his abundance of curly, jet-black hair—small and poverty-stricken, unenlightened and mean. Isolt surveyed this tiny Hispanic man from the North American Third World.

"The end of the line. Elephant and Castle. We're now at the mercy of the British. This is the empire that the sun never sets on. It never rises either. In fact you never see the sun here. This is an empire on its last legs; beware of that, it is as dangerous as a dying wasp at the end of summer. We are going to live with the poor, the immigrants, refugees, exiles. The Brits have a strong caste system here. They adhere rigidly to their own class and they despise outsiders. Xenophobia; anybody past the very white cliffs of Dover is a wog. We are no longer beggars, we are scavengers. You are a kind of dirty yellow and I'm just another poor Paddy and my color is green."

"All right, Paddy, I don't need a tour guide. I travel the world to get high." Christopher mounted the flight of steps, grunting. "Let's find these feeble friends of yours and abuse their hospitality."

↓

Oliver lived with a Rastafarian man called Caesar. He held court as the dealer while Caesar preferred to keep a low profile. The squat was in good condition, wallpapered and carpeted with a kitchen kept clean by Caesar who was fastidiously tidy. Oliver had a permanent leer. He finished every muddled pronouncement with the leer, as if it were an explanation in itself. He had a huge stomach, a red bulbous nose, a bald head with thin black hair hanging over big crooked ears, sunken slitty eyes, the diseased leer and ten fat warty fingers that rolled joint after joint in front of the TV.

"Who sent you?" he asked the first time at the door.

"Niki the Greek with one arm," Isolt said.

There were couches against each wall facing the TV. They sat on one and Oliver collapsed into another.

"You know, come to think of it," Isolt said, "I think I might have been here before a year or two ago. I came with Vinnie, the Irish dealer who lived in Innis House. I used to hang out with him a lot."

"Yeah, he was a good geezer all right," Oliver nodded. "But I think you must have been upstairs where Sam Steal the painter lives with Desperate Dave. I used to live up there with him but moved down here when this place was vacated. So you met Sam?"

"I must have. Only very briefly."

There was a knock on the door and Caesar got up and went into the hall. He returned trailed by a miserable-looking human being who reminded Isolt of Payman, enthralled by some ineffable anguish.

"This is Desperate Dave from upstairs," Oliver courteously introduced everyone. "This is . . ."

"Isolt and Christopher," Isolt said.

"Christopher is from America," Oliver said proudly.

Desperate Dave sat down. He wrung his hands.

"Sam's a lazy bastard, he won't go out and get any booze no more. Won't even walk down the bleeding steps and get some fags. Been lying in bed for a day now without budging. I'm fed up with him so I came down here."

Oliver said: "Oh yeah? Not like Sam Steal, he's always pacing and roaring and going into terrible conniptions up there. I've never seen him off the grog but mind you it's probably for the best, he hasn't had a dry spell for years."

A few days later they sat in the pub across the road. It was truly English in its peculiar dreariness and sense of strong inviolable working-class traditions. Oliver treated Christopher to a coke and Isolt to a warm pint of lager. Desperate Dave came in too and sat with them.

"Sam's a boring bastard. He hasn't even cashed his dole check, first time that's happened. He won't talk to me neither. I'm fed up with sitting up there drinking with him."

"Oh leave off it, will you?" Oliver said, getting irritated. "Forget about Sam a while. He's a fucking artist, mate. They're broody, you know what I mean? It's not easy to live with genius, Dave, you have to let him have his sulks and tantrums, all geniuses are like that." He nodded towards Christopher whom he always addressed over Isolt.

"I never met a genius," Christopher said, taking his straw out of his glass and wiping the rim with a napkin before he drank.

"Are you on the dry, mate?" Oliver asked him sympathetically.

"I haven't had a drink in six years or so. I wasn't an alcoholic but I prefer drugs," Christopher said softly. "Drinking makes people stupid."

"Sure it does, mate. Good for you." Oliver slurped his pint with ulcerous lips.

"I'll drink to that," Isolt said, and they all clinked glasses. "We should get our check in the afternoon post. It's about time."

"You don't seem American," Oliver said to Christopher.

Christopher laughed ironically. "No? Well, I'm not from New York or L.A. I'm from Detroit. Motor City. You can't get more Detroit than me. Europeans have a kind of naive concept of what an American is."

"Yeah," Oliver agreed. "We think Yanks are dumb but I guess they can't be, seeing as they kick everybody's ass who gets in their way. I can respect that."

"Let's say we have a grudging admiration that thinly disguises a deep loathing." Isolt tried to rile Christopher.

"Listen to Paddy here. Don't let your old lady get away with that." Oliver winked at Christopher.

"The Irish," Christopher snorted. "The fucking super-race. How come so many of the super-race are over here then? London has the highest concentration of Paddies in the world. I know that for a fact."

Isolt shrugged. "The super-race has an unemployment problem at the moment."

"I'm not prejudiced or nothing," Oliver said, and ordered four more pints with all the indulgence of a grand old colonist. "Some of me best mates have been Micks and I loved each and every one of them, but in all fairness, the Irish aren't exactly famed for their intelligence neither, eh?"

Isolt took a deep breath: "The Irish are stupid, French are snobs, Caribbean people are lazy, Italians are slobs, Spanish are loud, Scandinavians are bland, Germans are violent, Swiss are elitist, Austrians are Germans in disguise, Greeks are greasy and the Turks are torturers, Belgian people are nondescript, Americans are phoney, Australians are vulgar, New Zealanders are envious, Nigerians smell, Canadians are just marginally better adjusted Americans, Japanese are ants, there are far too many Chinese, South Americans are thieves, Pakistanis are greedy, Indians are pagans, Arabs are molesters, Israelis are rude, Filipinos are born to be domestics, Welsh are losers, East Europeans are dowdy, Albanians are invisible, Sicilians are thugs, the Scots are as mean as the Jews, Iranians are fanatics, Koreans are the Irish of Asia, the Asians are all the same, the Irish are the blacks of Europe, Africans are savages. So where exactly does that leave the English?"

"Lords and masters!" Oliver said confidently. "You're the first normal Yank I've met. All the others lacked cop-on. That's what it is."

"How many have you met?" Christopher asked, perplexed.

"You're the first in the Elephant, that's for sure, you poor bastard."

"America is tough," Christopher said carefully. "Those TV programmes—deliberately misleading, over-sentimentalized because we are so hard-hearted. Remember this is the Devil's Workshop we are talking about, you'll see. Wait till you get there. It's the belly of the beast. Don't think you know anything about the U.S. It's bigger than you and more ruthless. It will hook you in and eat you alive and you will love it. You'll never want to come back. It's the dream-machine, baby."

"Then why are you in exile?" Oliver asked.

"I had enough. I was weary. But this young child here is just out of the cradle and wide-eyed, she's craving it all."

Desperate Dave, who had gone off to check up on Sam, came shuffling back as they were debating whether to buy another round.

"There's something the matter with Sam," Dave pleaded desperately.

Oliver pulled his huge body out of the chair and waddled off after him, puffing and panting up all the cement steps. Isolt and Christopher followed. Oliver went in alone and came out after a few minutes.

"Yeah, there's something the matter with Sam all right, you pillock," Oliver almost gloated. "He's dead."

Desperate Dave quivered weakly as Christopher held on to his arm to support him.

"Sam's brown bread, mate!" Oliver leered. "Brown bread!"

The huge body of the fifty-five-year-old Sam Steal the painter was carried down in a coffin and cremated somewhere in London by his estranged upper-class family. Desperate Dave never recovered from the discovery that he had been partying with a corpse for seven days. He could not stay there any longer and moved in with two Kurdish brothers down the street.

Isolt and Christopher had at last found a home.

NIALL WILLIAMS

FROM
FOUR LETTERS OF LOVE

One of the most accomplished and deservedly acclaimed debut novels in recent memory is Niall Williams's Four Letters of Love *(1997), a beautifully orchestrated fable about star-crossed lovers, faith in God, and the unexpected but ultimately inevitable vicissitudes of destiny. The gorgeously-Irish landscape (both real and imagined) is so well wrought it becomes another character in the book.*

    Four Letters of Love *is also a heart-wrenching tale of the love between a father and son, which the following excerpt exquisitely highlights. Nicholas's father is called by God to become an artist. His mother has died, and his father's newfound vocation has already taken him away for extended periods. Whether or not he has any real talent remains to be seen, and so for now, must be taken on faith.*

IN THE MORNING MY FATHER outlined his itinerary. He was going to Clare, to the sea. He would take the train as far as Ennis and make his way from there to the coastline. I had enough food in the house, and for milk or anything else I was to use the ten-pound note that was rolled in the jam jar of bills on the kitchen windowsill. He had gotten ready before I woke and a bundle of canvases was tied together in the hall. There was a tang of oil and spirits, smells of adventure. The front-hall door was opened on the morning and the delicate balance of the day, caught between sunlight and showers, trembled like my faith. My father in his shirt-sleeves was a silver of energy, a thin quickness moving up and down the stairs and in and out of the studio in a bustle of preparation. When he looked at me I looked at his wrinkles. "You'll be back in a week," I said, standing by my mother in the hallway. "Right," he said, reaching his hand to my shoulder and giving a short warm squeeze, letting the wrinkles unfurrow for a moment and his eyes smile.

When it was time for him to go, he stood in the doorway, loaded with canvases, brushes, and paint, and held out his hand. I held out mine and he grabbed it, sending a shock of love through my arm so forcefully that tears shot into my eyes.

"A week," he said.

"A week," I said, and felt the coolness of the air rush against the palm of the hand he had let go. He headed out the driveway and, with a flying wave of the great flag of his hand, was gone.

It took me two minutes to decide. And another ten to take the money from the jam jar, put it with what I had saved, take my coat, a small carrier bag with a jumper, socks, and underpants, and head for the train station. My father was walking, hitching an improbable lift from any car whose driver was bemused or curious enough to pull over for him. I took the bus, reasoning the expense against the necessity of catching the same train as he. I sat upstairs in the front seat and peered down into the slow morning traffic for any sight of the long, thin figure carrying his bundle like a ragman along the paths that led into the city. But there was no sign of him. At the quays the bus pulled over and I stepped out into the tremendous flux of colour and noise that was Dublin in the summertime. High clouds sailed across the sun, moving green shadows along the river. My heart was racing. What if he was already ahead of me, already in his seat on the train watching the platform going slowly backwards? I stood off the crowded path and began running.

The train left at ten to ten. I sat in the back carriage on the side farthest from the platform and watched the last stragglers flapping awkwardly past with plastic bags, rucksacks, and small cases. By ten to ten my father had not passed the window. There was an announcement: This was the train for Nenagh, Limerick, and Ennis. And then the shutting of doors all along the train, a call, a whistling, a ticket collector joking to someone out the open window of the door, and the first three jolts, the quick stiff shudders that were the releasing of the brakes and the kicking of the engine as we shook then rattled then rolled past the end of the platform out of the station and away on a curving rhythmic beating into the countryside. We slid into country I had never seen, past old trackside houses with their washing lines and small gardens, places printed with the noise and life of trains, the clockwork regularity of the whoosh throughout their days and nights. Children didn't look up or wave. Beyond them, the newer suburbs of the city, the white blocks of life neither villages nor towns, just rows upon rows of houses, attached, detached, and semi-detached. It was half an hour before we were past them, before the green outmeasured the grey and the banks beyond the windows ran up into the tangled briars and ditches of the fields of Kildare, then Laois. The ticket collector came through the carriages, swaying over the punching of paper holes and telling Spanish students to take their feet off seats. There was no smoking, he said, pacing through wafting screens of smoke and banging the flat of his fist against a back window to let in the louder rush of the wind and the tracks and the smells of woodbine and hay. It was all new to me. I sat beside a small woman in a big coat who kept her hand on her handbag at all times, nodding into the drumming rhythms to dream of thieves, suddenly jolting upright with a cry until she looked down and found the bag was safe in the sweat of her hands and she could close her eyes and be robbed in peace again. She said nothing to me. I was too excited to sleep. I was too afraid that my father was not on the train, and too afraid that he was. What I intended to do in either case I am not certain. The magic of the train would resolve it, I imagined, the newness and innocence of arrival, the fresh beginning, all that. I sat back and stared out the window. We moved into the middle of the country, a great green immensity rolling into hills and mountains that wore the shadows of the sky. Cows were still shapes in the landscape. The sense of space was incredible, the largeness, the openness of it all, the distance that stretched across the fields drawing me out, longing to be there, running or sitting or lying down into the infinitesimal sweetness of the summer grass. As the train sped on, ever farther westwards, the landscape became more extravagantly remote, the sky bigger. The rattle of the tracks was a trance, and after a while the flashing of the countryside past the window slowed into a steady rolling, a sweeping panorama that ten carriages ahead, on a southside window, I could imagine my father staring into. For two hours we moved in the same dream. Then, at Limerick, we changed for Ennis. "Change here," boomed the ticket collector, big-footing his way down through the smoke and banging open the window two cold priests had closed.

Delaying, peering from the doorway the length of the platform, I was last off the train. Clutching my bag I hurried down and stood beside a pillar that cried out in alarm as the small woman in the big coat popped out from its other side and held her handbag to her chest. I apologised and hid myself.

There were fewer than forty passengers for Ennis, a little clustering of country people standing expectantly. I looked for my father and couldn't see him. Then, slowly, from the far end of the station came an old engine pulling three wooden carriages. It heaved and squealed and soured the air with the smell of oil. From the engine window the begrimed and toothy face of the driver grinned out at us as he performed his miracle and brought the train to a stop. "He looks a hundred and ninety," muttered the handbag lady, raising her belongings chest-high and sweeping forward for her seat. I moved out from the pillar and was on the step into the carriage when I saw him, a flash of white hair, a tall figure with the underarm bundle of his things as he came out of the waiting room and climbed onto the train. He was there. My father. He was so intent on not missing the connection that he didn't look once to his right or left. He got on the train, moved into the first carriage, and sat down. A moment later and we were rattling in a new rhythm into the west.

✴

My father was on the train; I stood in the corridor between cars and felt the slopping of an oily sickness in the barrel of my stomach. My feet were rising and falling softly. I couldn't think, or couldn't think just one thing at a time, rushing instead through the myriad runaway thoughts of panic. What was I going to do? What would he do, what would he say? Would I go up to him once we arrived? Would he send me straight back? And what was he thinking now, sitting not forty steps in front of me in a train travelling the full width of the island from where he imagined he had left alone his only child in a house with his mother's ghost? I slid down against the door until I was sitting. Was he not thinking back at all? Had he already crossed over, left all thoughts of that other life and now sat anticipating only the week he had given himself to cover the canvases in the images of the west? I didn't know, but for two hours sat there on the floor of the train and let the tides of doubt and nausea wash first one way and then the other across my insides until the engine whistled when I looked up and at last we had come to Clare.

The station was small. A train arrived there only once a week, clanking nervously in next to the rings and pens of the cattle mart. The passengers got off with some relief, hastening away to cars or buses and the bustle of the country town down the road. From the rear of the train I watched my father stepping down. He crossed the small platform in the gusting of a summer breeze, a lift to the air that made him pause and steady his canvases, before heading away along the back road behind the town. I waited three minutes and then followed him. He seemed to know exactly where he was going and marched away with that same certain purposefulness that had carried him in and out of the several crises of his life.

The road ran along by a row of houses and then past a high wall that offered no shelter and caused me to let a half-mile open up between us. He was the flicker of white hair in the distance, a ruffle of coattail. The afternoon was quick and breezy, clouds flew past, the very air was different. We were still miles from the sea, but already I could feel it, out there, somewhere ahead of us, the ocean I had never seen. From time to time my father put out his thumb to the cars going past, but none took the chance of stopping for him and he never broke the steady beat of his stride to look out at them in hope. He walked out of Ennis, and I followed. He walked on the side of the road that went northwards to the sea, moving always a bend or so ahead of me until I realised he was not going to get lifts and could let him pull away by as much as a mile as long as I made it up before the next town. Throughout that afternoon, then, we paced towards the coast. He stopped once. At a low garden wall where the bushes grew at frantic angles inland away from the burning of winter storms he took off his boots and rubbed the soles of his feet. Little bits of cardboard stuffing fell out on the ground, and he tore and shaped a new insole from more he carried in his sack and then walked on. I gained ground on him then, stopped at the same place, and ate the first three biscuits of a pack I had bought at a shop along the road. It was on a rise looking west, and only as I sat there gazing down the road at the thin figure of my father moving away did I realise that on the rim of the horizon, there beyond a little curve of grass dotted with white caravans, was the sea.

It was another two hours before we had reached it. By then the afternoon sky had surrendered to the evening clouds; the wind was blustering, cracking the sheets on washing lines behind the caravans. The sea was in the wind, my sweat tasted salt. As I walked my eyes kept leaving my father and swimming out into the waves and the islands in the distance. I like to think there was something already drawing me then, something that was nothing to do with him, but a feeling the hours of walking, the sea air, and sounds themselves had already instilled in me, touching me with a sense of the freshening wildness of those western places that was not to leave me for the rest of my life. I like to think I loved it as soon as I saw it, that I knew the end of our journey was in sight the moment I looked up from that rise in the road. Whatever the case, when my father stepped in over two lines of barbed wire and made his way down to a small strand in the dimming evening, I came carefully behind and did the same, sneaking down across the tufted grass of the sand hills.

By the time I had come to the edge my father was already naked. And even in the moments I watched him walking that high thin walk of his into the thunderous crashing of the first waves, taking them across his midriff in white embraces of chill spray, yelling out in what might have been elation or anger and shaking his hair, I was already stripping and running down, screaming and shouting, leaping the waves to save him from drowning himself in the sea.

✣

My father was neither happy nor angry to see me. At least not in any way I can describe. Later I told myself he may have been both, for although a thin man he was capable of the broadest range of emotions. Over the roaring of the waves and his own shouting he didn't hear me calling, and turned as I reached him only to stagger sideways into the foam, both of us going down into the broken surge of the chest-high waters with the same gasp in our mouths and amazement in our eyes. We came up spitting. As we did, grimacing the water out of our eyes, the tide sucked at my legs, pulling with such swift undertow that I was lifted off the sand and swept at once ten feet from him out to sea. I kicked and thrashed, remembering as a second wave lowered itself into my screams that I couldn't quite swim. I was thirty feet from him in an instant, sailing and sinking away on the amazement of the swift sea, my foot and ankle poking up ridiculously into the sky, falling back, plunging down like some tremendous anchor until the water ran across the bridge of my nose and I breathed horror through my screaming eyes. My father appeared and disappeared in the scene. I saw him. He saw me, or the naked white body of what he took at first to be certainly my ghost. At first I think he imagined that as such I didn't need rescuing, I needed wrestling. He put his hands together and dived like a prayer. He vanished and I went under. The world bubbled out of me. I felt hands grappling me and my body glistening and slipping through them. He couldn't hold me, my legs were up, my head was down. The sky rolled round and round in my eyes in the last-gasp moments of my life, and then I sank a final time, plummeting through the swirling foam down down beyond the frantic waters to the still clear cold sea floor, where at last my father's fingers found my hair and jerked me up.

I burst into daylight, lifted, wild-eyed, into the air and spewing the sea back into itself. We were far out in the tide now, ebbing away so that for the first time I saw the marvel of the little strand, how perfectly cupped and secluded it was back there across the combs of the breakers, how tiny and sad the little tossed bundles of our separate clothes. My father's arms were about me. I kicked my legs and they flopped uselessly, making a small splashing that the waves carried away. I think I shouted or screamed, gulping more water, gasping and sucking at the air for it to fill me, falling out of my father's arms once more, going down, coming up, thrashing and flailing until a hand crashed into my jaw and for just a moment the sea stopped. Silver stars flew up out of the water, sound was switched off, and then my chin was cupped in the great vice of my father's hand as he swam dragging me out. When he was within his depth he stood and carried me, our two naked figures emerging into the suddenly chill air with the sea running from both of us. On the sand he laid me down. I was still coughing and spluttering, my eyes rolling, when he stood the full width of the sky over me and looking down said:

"Well, God wants you to live, Nicholas."

⤋

It was the beginning of a week of surprises. If I had surprised my father in suddenly appearing naked alongside him in mid-tide when he expected me to be on the other side of the country, that was nothing compared to what lay ahead in that week in the west of Clare. It began quietly. My father, it seemed, had had no intention of drowning himself. It had instead been a kind of western baptism, a dousing in renewal.

At first I hardly noticed that he was a different man, that he was released now from the prisons of his life into doing what he sometimes believed without doubt was the Will of God. He dried me with his shirt until the chattering of my teeth stopped and I could put on my clothes and tell how I had followed him. He looked down into the sand and laughed. Then he got up and wandered off, leaving me sitting by the canvases and bags, hugging my knees and staring out at the extraordinary seductive power of the crashing ocean. How could the fierce collapse of its thunderous waves, time after time on the dark-sand shore, seem so full of softness and ease? How could such force seem so peaceful? The very waters that had frightened the life all but out of me were in the slowly fading evening like the invitations of dreams. I might have walked down into them, so fabulous and wild did they seem, but for the sounds of my father's footsteps as he came back, armed with rubbish and sticks for the small and brief fire he lit in the shelter of the dunes. It was our first evening's camp. We ate biscuits and dry bread and cheese. My father had milk he shared. We grew hungry and cold again, of course, but to me at least it didn't matter. Wrapped in every piece of clothing I had brought, I huddled down in the hollow of the dune. It was a boy's dream, a night under the summer stars with his father, within the ever-falling sighing of the night sea and the marvelous knowledge that life was real and that God didn't want me to die just yet.

The following morning I woke at five and found my father gone. The tide had come in and the waves grown louder. Gulls were screaming in the blue sky, and the sea wind blew in the cove with a soft whispering emptiness, running round the sand hills and out again, smoothing out footprints until the morning strand looked again like the first place in the world. I got up quickly. My father's bags were still where he had left them, and imagining that somehow in nightmare we had changed places and he was the one now being swept out to sea, I hurried to the high tideline, peering out into the waves. For a while I thought he was certainly drowned. I paced up and down along the wet sand, sinking and staring outwards, shouting out his name as the water rushed in joyously across my shoes and the sound of my voice was made small by the sea. Where was he? Was he drowned? Was that dark half-shape in the distant waves his body, that flash of white his head? I squinted and stared, was sure it was, was certain it wasn't, and might have stripped again and dived in, tempting God to save me once more, were it not for the chance flight of a low gull catching my eye and turning me round to see where, forty feet above the dunes in the sloping grass, my father had set up his folding easel and was busily painting.

I sank onto the sand. He must have seen me, must have heard me calling, I thought. Why hadn't he let me know? For five minutes I sat there on the wet sand. No wave of his hand, no call, no acknowledgement of any kind, just his long figure stooped crazily to the canvas and his hand moving with the brush in quick, sudden movements. I went back up to the camp and lay down. It was five o'clock in the morning, my feet were wet, my eyes stung, and I had just learned the first lesson of that week's education in art: once you begin, nothing else matters, not love, not grief, not anything.

When my father painted, the world beyond his view vanished into nothing. Day after day, wherever we were all along that beautiful coastline, he established the same pattern, rising while I slept, setting up his canvas in view of the sea, painting for four hours in mixed tones of yellow and red and blue and green, turbulent images of spilled colour that on the third day I realised in a sudden flash were in fact nothing more than the sea itself. Everything he painted was the sea; but it was never blue or green. The sky was never the soft and limpid overhanging I saw when I looked west. For him, in his paintings, sea and sky were the expressions of something else, they were the constant and yet ever-changing monologue of God Himself, the swirling language of creation, the closest thing to the beginning of life itself. He painted for four hours and came back to where I was waking, his face drawn and exhausted, the crazy long hairs of his eyebrows flying out at the edges like wings and his eyes puffy and small and streaming tears from the wind. He lay down when I got up. He gave me money to walk to the shops to buy the day's food, and when I was gone he slept. Later, by midday, he was awake again. And if the field we were in was close enough, he stripped and went down to swim, taking me with him sometimes to teach me how to breathe in water. The days were full of uncertain weather. Rain kept threatening but never falling, holding off in huge pale continents of cloud, slow-moving shapes that above my lying-down head joined one onto the next, sliding together all afternoon until the sky itself was one immensity of whiteness and the fragments of blue were tiny gaps unreachable and high as heaven. After bread and biscuits, or cheese, or sometimes ham, and the shared pint of milk, if we were not moving on, he went back to work, starting the day's second painting, never touching the morning canvas until the following dawn, by which time, if the wind had been blowing, myriad grains of sand would have found their way onto the paint and the brush would work them deeper into the picture's texture.

While my father worked I went off walking, moving down to the popular beach or into the holiday town, where everything was hopeful and bright. There were families everywhere, loose loud chains of them wandering down the streets, in and out of shops, young children with rings of ice cream round their mouths and saddles of freckles across their noses. Sometimes I tailed along behind them, the unknown brother, the last of the family, for a while just on the edge of ordinary life.

When I got back my father would still be painting. The afternoon canvases were different from those of the morning. At first I thought it was his tiredness and the pressure into which he had stoked his brain that made the second paintings of every day seem so much more desperate and urgent. A flat grey ribboned into black in all of them, the tones of everything deepened, the yellows and blues that sparkled and raced into the morning works were here half-hidden, disappearing flickers of light into the churning swirl of darker shades. After he had painted four or five of them, I relaxed, realising that they were not the works of personal anger or grief but simply the pictures of what my father saw, God's changing humour in the afternoons and early evenings, the sky in the sea like a face aging.

Most days he painted through until eight o'clock. I watched him from a distance, looking up from whatever seashore we had stopped at to see his tall figure perched and stooping over a canvas that was buffeted like a sail in the sea breeze. There were stones around its base, anchoring him for the day at whatever site he had chosen, keeping him there under broad western skies whose swift majesty and change seemed to mock all effort to capture or tame it. Sometimes a car stopped on the road behind and tourists, Germans or Americans, made their way slowly down across the tufted grass to see. They approached uncertainly, not quite sure if this man with the long white hair was someone they ought to know or run from. When my father never turned or looked at them, mixing the colours and applying them without the slightest show of recognition, they walked away as uncertain as before, driving along the high road and out of my childish dream that they might see the paintings and be astonished, offer great sums of money, and herald my father a genius.

Our evenings were cold and quiet. Even the warmest day became a chill night. The sea wind forced us back into the sand hills. I had no books, no radio, and sat hunched on the sand staring out at the humped shapes of the islands for hours at a time. Generally, my father fell asleep early. But sometimes after we ate and before he curled into his coat on the sand, he sang a piece of a song, or rather spoke the words in the verse rhythm. I had never heard him sing and felt ever more strongly the realisation that this was a different man from the one at home in the sitting room. Here everything about him seemed released, and I could only imagine how silently he had rattled for so long in the jails of his office career. On one of the first nights he asked me, offhandedly, what I knew to sing or say, and in a faltering half-whisper that mixed into the whoosh of the night waves, I said some school poems I had learned by heart, and then, without thinking, began the slow intricate fabulations of a learned passage of Ovid, then Virgil.

"Dine hunc ardorem mentibus addunt, Euryale, an sua cuique deus fit dira cupido."

They were sounds so soft and full in my mouth that the very saying of them was a kind of magic, a kind of disappearing, upwards and outwards beyond the breaking of the surf and the distant shining of the lights on the islands. I sounded the Latin and the words floated on the wind. I said a remembered line, and another. My father's eyes were closed, but he was listening too, as if it were a fine music that the wind played off the stars.

When I finished, he slept. The sea pounded on the ancient shore.

↓

I said the Latin every night after that. He sang something poorly, stopped, and then I started, skipping the school poems and beginning, following a silent accord such as two lovers might share and conjuring magic with sounds of Latin. I was as surprised by it as he was, and found myself anticipating the nights as I wandered through the seaside towns. Looking back, I realise that I had found the beginnings of my own identity, the first quivering emergence of my own shape out of the great shadow cast by my father. In the Latin I had something. That it seemed at once absolutely foreign and at the same time strangely fitting to the wild open night spaces of the west made it all the better. We lay holed up in the corner of a dune with the wind rushing over our heads, and I said words in Latin. Of course it didn't strike me then that there was any other reason for my having turned to the Virgil or Ovid after the school poems ran out. I wasn't thinking of anything other than the flash of panic I had felt to have something to say for my father as he had asked. I didn't know then that the sounds seemed a symbol to him, that they came that first night like heraldic angels trumpeting in his ears, and through his own son's mouth, the confirmation if any was needed that God had come to the west coast of Clare and that in the sudden sweetness of the holy language was the revelatory message that yes, those paintings of the sea were the very things that He Himself had brought William Coughlan there to paint.

↓

On the last day of the week we walked south and east again in the direction of the train station. Every canvas my father had brought with him had now been worked on. Seen all together they were remarkable; there was a style running through all of them, the same underlying vision of mornings and evenings, light struggling to spread out or stay against the onrush of dark, the shimmering and answering reflections of air and water that seemed in these paintings to have aspired to the condition of fire. The two latest pictures, not yet dry, I carried back-to-back and separate from the others in a kind of drawstring carrier that seemed ready-made to fit them. They were, like all the others, slivers of the sea we were leaving behind.

There was a sadness in returning as well as a sense of victory. My father had done what he came to do and was eager now to be back in his studio. But even as we tramped quietly along the road homeward, I could feel the memories of the summer sea already shifting and sighing inside both of us. There was something that was impossible to leave about that western coast, and moving as we were with our backs to the blue horizon and the stacked canvases flapping a little in the wind, every footstep was a triumph over the temptation to stop and go back.

In the pie café my father had said it wouldn't rain for six days. It was the first time I had known him to make any prediction and had at first taken it only as some rash expression of hope not fact. It was the kind of thing you might say setting off, I told myself later, he meant nothing more by it. The skies we slept under were too uncertain for forecasts. They came and went on the moody gusts of the Atlantic, bringing half a dozen different weathers in an afternoon and playing all four movements of a wind symphony, allegro, andante, scherzo, and adagio, on the broken backs of the white waves. Clouds, thumping bass notes or brilliant wild arpeggios, were never long in coming. It had seemed it was going to rain all the time, but never did. My father did not look concerned, and on the fifth day as I woke and found myself instinctively searching the sky for the weather note, I realised that to him his prediction had not been hope but fact. It wasn't going to rain for six days, it was as simple as that. Our trip, though, was seven, and on the morning of the day we were to walk back towards the station my father drew out of his bag sheets of clear plastic with which we carefully wrapped the paintings. The two in the drawstring carrier he handled separately. "When it rains, Nicholas," he said, "we'll have to mind these two carefully. I'll give you my coat for over them as well."

The sky under which we set off that morning was pale and unremarkable. The air had a coolish lift to it, a freshness that was the forebreeze of another month, the quivering note of September. We marched out of the field, stepped over three lines of barbed wire, and headed up the softly rising hill away from the sea. Cars slipped past us. My father took no notice of them and kept his eyes straight ahead, slowing his stride sometimes to let me catch up or standing on a small crest to pause and look back, measuring in the long ribboning grey of the road how far we had come. The train was not until early the following morning, we had one more night to camp inland somewhere near the station, and it was to there we were heading, the pictures hung on our backs like the huge strange stamps of a far-off country and the rising wind pressing us forward. By noon we had left our last glimpse of the sea. By early afternoon in a place called Kilnamona it began to rain.

My father took off his coat for the two most recent paintings, bundling them tightly as the landscape all around us closed in, its colours fading into the drizzle. How quickly everything changed. The clouds sat down, the light left the day, and the pastoral greenness of all the stone-walled fields surrendered to a grey and desolate emptiness. For miles it was raining. At the edges of the sky you could see the fraying of clouds and the water spilling, like so many downstrokes of a sable brush. The lift and energy of the day were washed away. We tramped on without talking and the holiday cars swept by. My right shoe was holed and took in water, the legs of my trousers thickened and weighed, but after a while I grew used to it, for there was a kind of calmness and peace in walking through that rain. You imagined you were heading for the other side of it and moved one foot after the other in a kind of silent trance, the miles disappearing beneath you and the rain still falling into your face. My father didn't say a word. He had a soft hat in his coat pocket and wore it as his only protection, the long strands of his hair gathering and releasing little streamlets down the back of his shirt. I could see the tips of his shoulder blades pressing out through the wet fabric, their high angles jutting into the air as if at any moment they might stretch and expand, feather into wings, and take him flying off down the road ahead of me. Such things I imagined walking behind him in the rain. Everything about him had come to seem almost mythical to me, his long bent-forward figure, his great forehead, the eyes that blinked away the beating weather and gazed relentlessly forward down the road. I loved him now in a way I hadn't before, and bore the increasing water-logged weight of the coated and wrapped paintings on my shoulders as evidence or proof. Whenever my father stopped for me to catch up and come alongside him was a moment of such satisfaction and happiness, a swelling instant of love and pride that I had come with him, that he had let me, that I had seen the other side of him and was now helping him bring home the greatest paintings he had ever done, that I wanted to laugh there on the roadside. He put his hand on my shoulder, straightened the straps of the bag.

"Do you want to rest?" he asked.

"I'm fine."

"We'll go beyond the next rise, all right?"

"All right."

And on again, the rain still falling, the road winding down through a closed vil-lage of quietness, my father pacing a few yards in front of me, unable to keep his stride short or his eyes off the horizon. By mid-afternoon he looked like he had gone swimming in the sky. The clouds had thickened and lowered. Potholes in the rough road filled into grey pools which cars plashed through on their way away, anywhere out of the rain. Under the dripping of a great green chestnut tree we stopped to eat. Our biscuits and bread were damp. The trunk of the tree had a thick sweet smell of autumn, and we sat upon the base of it looking out at the dark trail our footsteps had brushed out of the silvered grass. It was a thing I remembered, years later, going back to try and find the same tree. That brief marking of our joint trail off the road and under the chestnut, that place where everything was momen-tarily perfect, where we sat under the light pattering of the leaves, father and son, and ate quietly, where my father put his face down into the paint-stained cup of his two palms, rubbing away the rain before lifting those eyes free to look across the little space at me and say: "You're a great help to me, Nicholas. I'm glad you came."

As simple as that, that moment at the end of the trail through the grass and under the dripping boughs of the chestnut tree. If we could have been lifted up, gathered into cloud then, I would have been happy forever. If we could have lain down there or burrowed like animals into the sweet brown smell of the tree itself, screened from the world in veils of rain and the scents of autumn, everything would have stayed the way it was. There could have been peace.

BIOGRAPHICAL NOTES

✧

AE (pseudonym of George William Russell) was born April 10, 1867, in Lurgan, County Armagh. A poet and mystic, Russell befriended W. B. Yeats while studying at Dublin's Metropolitan School of Art. The first of Russell's numerous verse collections, *Homeward: Songs by the Way*, was published in 1894; other works include *The Earth Breath* (1897), *Divine Vision* (1904), and *House of the Titans* (1934). The Irish National Theatre Society at the Abbey Theatre chose Russell's verse play, *Deirdre* (1906), to be one of its first productions. He also edited *The Irish Homestead* for nearly 20 years and *The Irish Statesman* for another seven. Russell took his pseudonym from the word "Aeon." He died July 17, 1935, in Bournemouth, England.

SAMUEL BECKETT was born April 13?, 1906, in Foxrock, County Dublin. Novelist, playwright, critic, and poet, Beckett graduated from Dublin's Trinity College in 1927 and relocated to Paris in 1928; there he met James Joyce, the subject of his first published piece, "Dante . . . Bruno . Vico . . Joyce" (1929; included in this book). (He also helped Joyce translate a section of *Finnegans Wake* into French.) Among Beckett's other early works are a collection of short fiction, *More Pricks Than Kicks* (1934); a novel, *Murphy* (1938); and two books of verse. In 1941 he joined the French Resistance, then was forced into hiding the following year, returning to Paris in 1945. Between 1947 and 1957 Beckett published his most enduring works, all originally written in French—the interrelated novels *Molloy* (1951), *Malone Dies* (1951), and *The Unnamable* (1953); the novel *Watt* (1953); and the plays *Waiting for Godot* (1952) and *Endgame* (1957). Beckett was awarded the Nobel Prize in literature in 1969. He died December 22, 1989, in Paris.

BRENDAN BEHAN was born February 9, 1923, into an activist family with close ties to the Irish Republican Army. He was arrested in England at 16 for terrorism and spent two years in a reform school, an experience recounted in his wry memoir *Borstal Boy* (1958). Behan later served two more prison terms—one related to the shooting of a police officer—and was released from the second under a general amnesty in 1946. He wrote his first play, *The Quare Fellow*, in 1954; his second, *The Hostage*, was produced four years later. In *Brendan Behan's Island* (1962) and *Confessions of an Irish Rebel* (1965) he drew on a lifetime of anecdotes and adventures. Behan was hospitalized many times for drinking-related ailments that finally caused his death on March 20, 1964.

CAROLINE BLACKWOOD was born July 16, 1931, in London and grew up at her family's County Down mansion, Clandeboye. The great-great-great-great-granddaughter of Richard Brinsley Sheridan, she is known for her witty, macabre fiction. Blackwood's first book, *For All I Found There*, combines fiction and nonfiction and was published in 1973. Subsequent works include the novels *The Stepdaughter* (1976), *Great Granny Webster* (1977), and *Corrigan* (1984), as well as *The Last of the Duchess* (1995), an account of her futile, sometimes obsessive quest to interview the Duchess of Windsor. Blackwood was married to the painter Lucian Freud, the composer Israel Citkowitz, and the poet Robert Lowell. She died February 14, 1996, in New York City.

ELIZABETH BOWEN was born June 7, 1899, and spent her childhood in Dublin and at her family's ancestral County Cork home (whose history she recounts in *Bowen's Court* [1942]). She started writing fiction at 20 and published her first book of stories, *Encounters*, in 1923. Later works include the novels *The Hotel* (1927), *The Last September* (1929), *The House in Paris* (1935), *Death of the Heart* (1938), *A World of Love* (1955), and *Eva Trout* (1969), as well as the story collections *The Cat Jumps* (1934), *Look at All the Roses* (1941), and *The Demon Lover* (1945; titled *Ivy Gripped the Steps* in the U.S., 1946). Wartime England provides the backdrop for some of Bowen's best short fiction, as well as her celebrated novel *The Heat of the Day* (1949). She died February 22, 1973, in London.

AUSTIN CLARKE was born May 9, 1896, in Dublin. Poet, novelist, and dramatist, Clarke attended the Jesuit Belvedere College and University College, Dublin. After moving to England, he worked for many years as a journalist and book reviewer. *The Vengeance of Fionn*, his first poetry collection, appeared in 1917; though his early work was often compared to W. B. Yeats's, Clarke eventually found his own satiric, politically aware, and reflective voice, publishing almost 20 books of verse. In 1932, on the recommendation of Yeats and George Bernard Shaw, Clarke was chosen as one of the first members of the Irish Academy of Letters. Returning to Ireland in 1937, he founded the Dublin Verse Speaking Society, which later became the highly regarded Lyric Theatre Company. For some 20 years Clarke published nothing, devoting himself in part to the creation of his greatest work, "Mnemosyne Lay in Dust" (1966), a long poem about his nightmarish experiences as a psychiatric patient. He died March 20, 1974, in Dublin.

T[HOMAS] CROFTON CROKER was born January 15, 1798, in Cork. An antiquary who was perhaps the first collector to regard Irish folktales as literature, Croker created anthologies that inspired and sustained many writers of the Irish Literary Renaissance. His indispensable works include *Fairy Legends and Traditions of the South of Ireland* (1825-28), which the Brothers Grimm later translated into German; *Legends of the Lakes* (1829); and *Popular Songs of Ireland* (1839). Croker died August 8, 1854, in London.

LORD DUNSANY (Edward John Moreton Drax Plunkett Dunsany) was born July 24, 1878, in London. Of Anglo-Irish parentage, he graduated from Eton and became known for his fascination with fantasy, as well as his association with the Irish Literary Renaissance. After service in the Boer War and World War I, Dunsany published his first book of mythological tales, *The Gods of Pegana*, in 1905. His first play, *The Glittering Gates*, was produced by W. B. Yeats at the Abbey Theatre in 1909 to much acclaim. Subsequent plays include *The Gods of the Mountain* (1911), *A Night at an Inn* (1916), and *If* (1922). Among his prose works are *The Book of Wonder* (1912), *My Talks with Dean Spanley* (1936), *The Story of Mona Sheehy* (1937), and *A Glimpse from a Watch Tower* (1946). Dunsany died October 25, 1957, in Dublin.

LADY GREGORY (Isabella Augusta Persse Gregory) was born March 15, 1852, in Roxborough, County Galway. After the death in 1882 of her husband—a member of Parliament—she grew interested in Irish literature and history and became a vital force in the Irish Literary Renaissance. She was W. B. Yeats's lifelong friend and patron and co-founded the Irish National Theatre (later the Abbey Theatre), for which she also wrote short plays and served as director. (Her history of the INT, *Our Irish Theatre*, was published in 1914.) Gregory's often comic stage works—such as *Cathleen ni Houlihan* (1902; co-written with Yeats), *Spreading the News* (1904), and *The Gaol Gate* (1906)—focus on

Irish peasant life. She also created public interest in Irish legends and folklore through her acclaimed translations, including *Cuchulain of Muirthemne* (1902) and *Poets and Dreamers* (1903). Gregory died May 22, 1932, at Coole in western Ireland.

SEAMUS HEANEY was born April 13, 1939, in Castledawson, Londonderry. Educated at St. Columb's College, Derry; and Queen's University, Belfast; Heaney (like his poetry) is deeply connected to Irish rural life, as well as the lore and history of his homeland. His early verse—collected in volumes such as *Death of a Naturalist* (1966), *Door into the Dark* (1969), and *Wintering Out* (1972)—was highly praised and focused largely on the natural world. Later volumes reflect Heaney's increasing social awareness—*North* (1975), *Field Work* (1979), *Station Island* (1984), *The Haw Lantern* (1987), *Seeing Things* (1991), and *The Spirit Level* (1996). He has also written extensively on poets and their craft (*Preoccupations* [1980] and *The Government of the Tongue* [1990]). Heaney was awarded the Nobel Prize in literature in 1995; *Opened Ground*—bringing together 30 years of his poetry—appeared in 1998. He currently lives in Dublin.

DOUGLAS HYDE was born January 17, 1860, in Frenchpark, County Roscommon. Scholar, statesman, and cultural nationalist, he was fiercely dedicated to the preservation of the Irish language. He became the first professor of modern Irish at University College, Dublin, holding the job for more than 20 years. He also served as the first president of the Republic of Ireland, from 1938 to 1944. Hyde published many influential books on Irish history, literature, and folklore, including *A Literary History of Ireland* (1892) and the anthology *Love Songs of Connacht* (1893). He died July 12, 1949, in Dublin.

JAMES JOYCE was born February 2, 1882, in Dublin. One of the most influential writers of the 20th century, he was the eldest of ten children and attended the Jesuit schools Clongowes Wood College and Belvedere College, then graduated from University College, Dublin. Rejecting the restrictive Catholic lifestyle of his childhood, Joyce left Ireland in 1902, returning only infrequently and briefly. His first published work was a collection of poems, *Chamber Music*, which appeared in 1907. A prospective Irish publisher turned down his seminal short story collection, *Dubliners* (1914), to avoid prosecution for obscenity and libel. (The book was first published in England.) His brilliant novels also faced disheartening opposition: the first edition of *A Portrait of the Artist as a Young Man* (1916) was printed in America; and *Ulysses*, which Sylvia Beach published in Paris on Joyce's 40th birthday, was banned in the United States and England for years. Joyce's final and most complex work, *Finnegans Wake*, appeared in 1939. His adult life was marred by eye ailments (he underwent 25 operations in 13 years), concerns over his daughter's deteriorating mental health, and the lack of recognition for his work. He died January 13, 1941, in Zurich.

PATRICK KAVANAGH was born October 21, 1904, near Inniskeen, County Monaghan. The son of a farmer and shoemaker, Kavanagh was self-educated and worked the fields until 1939, when he moved to Dublin to focus full-time on journalism and poetry. He detested the quaint depictions of peasant life favored by writers of the Irish Literary Renaissance; in his most significant poem, *The Great Hunger* (1942), Kavanagh creates an unsentimental portrait of the rural world's pleasures and harsh demands. His other works include *Ploughman and Other Poems* (1936), *A Soul for Sale* (1947), *Tarry Flynn* (1948), *Come Dance with Kitty Stobling* (1960), and *Collected Poems* (1964). Kavanagh died November 30, 1967, in Dublin.

BIOGRAPHICAL NOTES

BENEDICT KIELY was born August 15, 1919, near Dromore. After joining the Jesuit novitiate, he decided against a clerical life and graduated from National University, Dublin, in 1943. His writing ranges from groundbreaking criticism (*Modern Irish Fiction: A Critique*, 1950) to murder mysteries (*Honey Seems Bitter*, 1952), but Kiely will likely be remembered for his short stories, many of which first appeared in *The New Yorker*. Among his story collections are *A Journey to the Seven Streams* (1963), *A Ball of Malt and Madame Butterfly* (1973), and *The State of Ireland* (1980). Kiely lives in Dublin.

MARY LAVIN was born June 11, 1912, in East Walpole, Massachusetts, of Irish parents and returned to Ireland with her family when she was ten. Her first book, *Tales from Bective Bridge* (1942), won the James Tait Black Memorial Prize, and she later became a regular contributor to *The New Yorker*. Overall Lavin published 19 books of stories, among them *The Great Wave* (1961) and *A Family Likeness* (1985), as well as two novels— *The House in Clewe Street* (1945) and *Mary O'Grady* (1950). Among her Irish homes were a farm in County Meath and a Dublin mews; she raised three daughters after being widowed at a young age. Lavin died March 25, 1996, in Dublin.

SHERIDAN LE FANU was born August 28, 1814, to a well-educated Dublin family. The great-nephew of Richard Brinsley Sheridan, he graduated from Trinity College, Dublin, but abandoned a law career in favor of writing. Often compared to Poe, Le Fanu spiced his ghost stories and mysteries with dark humor; his best-known books include *Uncle Silas* (1864), *The House by the Churchyard* (1863), and *In a Glass Darkly* (1871). Though he became reclusive after the death of his wife in 1858, the prolific Le Fanu was a best-selling author of his day. He died February 7, 1873, in Dublin.

FRANCIS MacMANUS was born March 8, 1909, in Kilkenny. He taught for nearly 20 years, then became an editor at Radio Éireann. The first three of his 11 novels form a trilogy focusing on 18th-century peasant life: *Stand and Give Challenge* (1934), *Candle for the Proud* (1936), and *Men Withering* (1939). For his next trilogy—*This House Was Mine* (1937), *Flow On, Lovely River* (1941), and *Watergate* (1942)—MacManus turned to modern rural life. His other notable works include the novels *The Wild Garden* (1940), *The Greatest of These* (1943), and *The Fire in the Dust* (1950), and two biographies. MacManus died of a heart attack in Dublin on November 27, 1965.

LOUIS MacNEICE was born September 12, 1907, in Belfast. The son of a rector, he attended Sherborne preparatory school, Marlborough, and Oxford University. In the 1930s he was associated with a group of poets whose topical, leftist verse was known as the "new poetry"; the group was led by W. H. Auden and also included Cecil Day-Lewis and Stephen Spender—all of whom MacNeice had met as an undergraduate. Among his poetry collections are *Blind Fireworks* (1929), *Collected Poems* (1949), *Autumn Sequel* (1954), *Eighty-five Poems* (1961), and *Solstices* (1961). He also won praise as a writer and producer of radio documentaries and dramas; *The Dark Tower*, his verse play, is often cited as one of his finest works and was published in 1947. In addition, MacNeice was a classical scholar who translated Aeschylus' *Agamemnon* (1936) and Goethe's *Faust* (1951). He died September 3, 1963, in London.

EMER MARTIN was born in Dublin in 1968. Her first novel, *Breakfast in Babylon*, was named Ireland's Best Book of 1996 and nominated for the *Irish Times* Literature Prize. Her follow-up, *More Bread Or I'll Appear*, is scheduled for publication in 1999, and also forthcoming is a collection of novellas, *The Rover's Return*. Martin, who "escaped" Ireland at 17, has lived in Paris and London and now makes her home in New York.

PATRICK McCABE was born March 27, 1955, in Clones, County Monaghan. He worked as a teacher in Dublin and London for many years, writing only in his spare time. His first two novels—*Music on Clinton Street* (1986) and *Carn* (1989; U.S., 1997)—were largely ignored when first published, but *The Butcher Boy* (1992) was shortlisted for the Booker Prize and won McCabe the recognition he deserves. *The Dead School* (1995) and *Breakfast on Pluto* (1998; also a Booker finalist) complete a trilogy begun with *Butcher Boy*. McCabe lives in Sligo.

COLUM McCANN was born in 1965 in Dublin and attended Clonkeen College; Dublin Institute of Technology, Rathmines; and the University of Texas, Austin. He has worked as a journalist, teacher, rancher, bartender, bicycle mechanic, and wilderness guide. His first short story, "Tresses," won the 1991 Hennessey Award for Best First Fiction. *Fishing the Sloe-Black River* (1993), a story collection, received the Rooney Award for Irish Literature, and McCann's debut novel, *Songdogs* (1995), was greeted with worldwide acclaim. In 1998 he published his second novel, *This Side of Brightness*, also to high praise. McCann divides his time between Dublin and New York.

THOMAS D'ARCY McGEE was born April 13, 1825, in Carlingford, County Louth. At age 17 he emigrated to the U.S., where he earned a reputation as a compelling public speaker and, at 19, was appointed editor of Boston's *The Pilot*. Upon returning to Ireland he became immersed in the Nationalist cause and worked on *The Nation*, the publication of the Young Ireland movement. After the uprising of 1848 he returned to the United States to avoid possible prosecution, and he later renounced revolutionary politics altogether. In 1857 he moved to Canada and quickly became prominent there, serving in the Legislative Assembly. His notable works include *Gallery of Irish Writers: The Irish Writers of the 17th Century* (1846), *A Popular History of Ireland* (1862), and, posthumously, *The Poems of Thomas D'Arcy McGee* (1869). McGee was assassinated, probably by Irish revolutionaries, in Ottawa on April 7, 1868.

JOHN MITCHEL was born November 3, 1815, near Dungiven, County Londonderry. An Irish revolutionary and journalist, he was the son of a Presbyterian minister and educated at Trinity College, Dublin. He began writing for *The Nation* in 1845; but, finding that journal too tame for his tastes, started his own, *The United Irishman*, which advocated aggressive rebellion. In May 1848 he was convicted of sedition and sentenced to 14 years' transportation; after confinement in Bermuda and South Africa, he was sent to Tasmania, where he lived in relative comfort until escaping to the United States in 1853. In America Mitchel embarked on a second turbulent career—as an editor of proslavery journals. Two of his sons died as Confederate soldiers, and after the war Mitchel himself was jailed for publishing pro-Confederacy articles. He later edited the *Irish Citizen* and, after returning to Ireland, was elected to Parliament. Today Mitchel is best known for *Jail Journal* (1854), an account of his time in captivity. He died on March 20, 1875, in Newry.

BRIAN MOORE was born August 25, 1921, in Belfast. He graduated from St. Malachy's College in 1939 and nine years later moved to Canada, where he became a reporter and, eventually, a Canadian citizen. (He later settled in California.) Moore's first book, *The Lonely Passion of Judith Hearne* (1955), established his reputation, and three of his novels—

The Doctor's Wife (1976), *The Color of Blood* (1987), and *Lies of Silence* (1990)—were short-listed for the Booker Prize. Moore also wrote for television and film, including the screenplay for Alfred Hitchcock's *Torn Curtain* (1966) and adaptations of three of his own works. He died in Malibu, California, on January 11, 1999.

THOMAS MOORE was born May 28, 1779, in Dublin. The son of a grocer, he is best remembered for *Irish Melodies* (1808-34), a group of lyrics set to traditional music. Many of Moore's songs have endured, including "'T Is the Last Rose of Summer" and "Believe Me, If All Those Endearing Young Charms." During his life he was considered the country's "national poet," his fame nearly equaling that of Byron or Sir Walter Scott. His satires *Intercepted Letters; or, The Two-Penny Post Bag* (1813) and *The Fudge Family in Paris* (1818) were hugely popular, and his long poem *Lalla Rookh* (1817) was among the most frequently translated poems of its era. In one of the most notorious episodes of the Romantic period, Moore burned the memoirs left to him by Lord Byron, who had been his close friend. (Moore's well-received biography, *Letters and Journals of Lord Byron, with Notices of His Life* [1830], does quote from the destroyed materials.) Moore died February 25, 1852, in Wiltshire, England.

EDNA O'BRIEN was born December 15, 1932, at Tuamgraney, County Clare. Novelist and short story writer, she is best known for her Country Girls trilogy—*The Country Girls* (1960), *The Lonely Girl* (1962), and *Girls in Their Married Bliss* (1964)—which follows the lives of two Irish women and was later published as one volume. O'Brien's uninhibited representations of female sensuality led the Irish censors to ban some of her works. Her collections of short stories include *The Love Object* (1968), *A Scandalous Woman and Other Stories* (1974), *A Fanatic Heart* (1984), and *Lantern Slides* (1990).

FITZ-JAMES O'BRIEN was born in 1828 in County Cork. His writing career began at 16, when his poem on the famine, "Oh, Give a Desert Life to Me," appeared in *The Nation*. In 1849 O'Brien inherited his family's fortune and left Ireland for London, where he adopted an extravagant lifestyle and continued to write and publish (including, some say, a poem in Charles Dickens' *Household Words*). After using up his inheritance in just two years, O'Brien sailed to the United States in search of a new life. He became a jack-of-all-trades writer while leading a hand-to-mouth bohemian existence in New York. Three of his stories—"The Diamond Lens" (1858), "What Was It?" (1859), and "The Wondersmith" (1859)—are classics of the form, and his tales of speculative science and the uncanny are considered forerunners of science fiction. When the Civil War broke out O'Brien joined the Union Army; he died April 6, 1862, after being wounded in Cumberland, Maryland.

FLANN O'BRIEN (pseudonym of Brian O'Nolan) was born October 5, 1911, at Strabane, County Tyrone. Educated at University College, Dublin, O'Brien worked for the Irish Civil Service from 1937 until his retirement in 1953. For 30 years he published brilliant satirical columns in the *Irish Times* under another pseudonym, Myles na Gopaleen. His first and best-known novel, *At-Swim-Two-Birds* (1939), was a failure until its republication in 1960; his second, *An Béal Bocht* (1941), was written in Gaelic and not translated into English until 1973, when it appeared as *The Poor Mouth*. Among O'Brien's other well-known works are *The Hard Life* (1961), *The Dalkey Archive* (1964), and *The Third Policeman* (1967). He died April 1, 1966, in Dublin.

SEAN O'CASEY was born John Casey on March 30, 1880, in Dublin. A poor Protestant who grew up on the streets of Dublin, he attended school for just three years but was a voracious reader (despite poor eyesight). While still a youth he became caught up in the Nationalist movement, joining the Irish Citizens Army and converting his name to its Irish form. After losing faith in politics, O'Casey turned to drama and began a pivotal relationship with the Abbey Theatre. His first effort, *The Shadow of a Gunman*, was staged there in 1923, followed the next year by his most popular work, *Juno and the Paycock*. The Abbey's production of *The Plough and the Stars* (1926) touched off Nationalist riots; and when the theatre rejected his more experimental *The Silver Tassie* in 1928, O'Casey moved to London, where *Tassie* was successfully staged soon after. His later works, which never achieved the success of his first plays, include *Within the Gates* (1934) and *The Bishop's Bonfire* (1955). In 1963 his six volumes of memoirs were published in the U.S. as one book, *Autobiographies*. O'Casey died September 18, 1964, in Devon, England.

FRANK O'CONNOR (pseudonym of Michael O'Donovan) was born in 1903 in Cork. With minimal schooling, he became a biographer (of Michael Collins), critic, and gifted translator—but he is best known for his short fiction. He was writing stories in Gaelic when AE asked him to submit pieces in English to *The Irish Statesman*. O'Connor became especially popular in the United States; his work appeared regularly in *The New Yorker* for more than 15 years, and his *Collected Stories* was published to acclaim in 1981. He was also a director of the Abbey Theatre in the 1930s. O'Connor died March 10, 1966, in Dublin.

JULIA O'FAOLAIN was born June 6, 1932, in London. The daughter of Sean O'Faolain, she worked as a translator and teacher before turning to writing. She has also traveled extensively—to France, Italy and the United States—and has used these locales as backdrops for her fiction. O'Faolain's story collections include *We Might See Sights!* (1968), *Man in the Cellar* (1974), *Melancholy Baby* (1978), and *Daughters of Passion* (1982). Among her novels are the Booker Prize nominee *No Country for Young Men* (1980), as well as *Three Lovers* (1971), *Women in the Wall* (1975), *The Obedient Wife* (1982), and *The Judas Cloth* (1992). She has also translated works from Italian under her married name, Julia Martines.

SEAN O'FAOLAIN (original name John Whelan) was born February 22, 1900, in Cork. The son of a police constable, he joined the Irish Republican Army (and Gaelicized his name) while in his twenties. He attended Harvard from 1926 to 1929, then returned to Ireland at about the time his first book of stories, *Midsummer Night Madness and Other Stories* (1932), became a success. His debut novel, *A Nest of Simple Folk* (1933), was also highly praised; later works include *Bird Alone* (1936) and *Come Back to Erin* (1940)—both novels—and the story collections *The Man Who Invented Sin* (1947), *The Heat of the Sun* (1966), and *The Talking Trees* (1979). His three-volume *Collected Stories* was published from 1980 to 1982. O'Faolain was also the founding editor of *The Bell*, an influential Irish literary magazine, and wrote biographies of Constance Markievicz, Daniel O'Connell, Eamon de Valera, and Hugh O'Neill, as well as an autobiography, *Vive moi!* (1964). He died April 20, 1991, in Dublin.

LIAM O'FLAHERTY was born August 28, 1896, in the Aran Islands, County Galway. His teachers recognized his intelligence early on, and he was sent to a Tipperary boarding school that specialized in preparing boys for the priesthood. But O'Flaherty decided against a clerical life and enrolled in University College, Dublin. Soon after, he left to fight with the Irish Guards in France during World War I, suffered shellshock, and spent a year in treatment. He then traveled extensively in South America, Canada, the United States, and the Middle East, arriving back in Dublin in 1921. That year he led a group of ragtag rebels who seized the Dublin Rotunda; was forced to leave the country in 1922; and, while in England, met Edward and Constance Garnett, who encouraged his writing. O'Flaherty's first novel, *Thy Neighbor's Wife* (1923), sold well, and *The Informer*—considered to be his finest work—was published two years later. He is also known for his moving, sometimes bleak short stories, especially those set on the Aran Islands. His other novels include *The Black Soul* (1924), *Skerrett* (1932), *Famine* (1937), and *Insurrection* (1950); among his story collections are *Two Lovely Beasts* (1948), *The Wounded Cormorant* (1973), and *The Pedlar's Revenge* (1976). O'Flaherty also published three memoirs recounting his travels. He died September 7, 1984, in Dublin.

AOGÁN Ó RATHAILLE, born c. 1675, recorded the turbulent Ireland he knew; his poems deal with the Gaelic dispossession and suppression of Catholics that marred the late 17th and early 18th centuries. He died in 1729.

MAURICE O'SULLIVAN was born in 1904 and grew up in the Blasket Islands off the southwest coast of Ireland. With little schooling and no literary ambitions, he wrote a collection of stories for his own pleasure. The manuscript came into the hands of an Oxford student, and in 1933 it was published as *Twenty Years A-Growing*, with a foreword by E. M. Forster. O'Sullivan, who later worked as a policeman in Dublin, never published another book. He died in 1950.

T. W. ROLLESTON was born in 1857. A versatile man of letters who was well known in his day, Rolleston wrote on the ancient philosophers, translated the works of Richard Wagner, popularized legendary tales of Irish heroes, and composed his own poetry. He died in 1920.

GEORGE BERNARD SHAW was born July 26, 1856, in Dublin. He moved to London in 1876 and seemed destined for an unremarkable literary career, publishing five novels to little or no acclaim. He began writing reviews in 1885 and gained his first notoriety as the *Saturday Review's* theatre critic, brilliantly campaigning for greater realism in drama. He also started to create his own plays and proved prolific in this, as in all other genres, completing more than 50 stage works in his long career. Among his most famous: *Candida* (1898), *Mrs. Warren's Profession* (1898), *Caesar and Cleopatra* (1901), *Man and Superman* (1903), *Major Barbara* (1907), *Androcles and the Lion* (1912), *Pygmalion* (1913), and *Saint Joan* (1924). In his plays (and his life) Shaw practiced the principles he advocated as a critic, bringing both humor and honesty to important social issues. In 1925 he was awarded the Nobel Prize in literature; he accepted the prize but declined the money. Shaw died November 2, 1950, in Hertfordshire, England.

FRANCES CHAMBERLAINE SHERIDAN was born in 1724 in Dublin. The mother of Richard Brinsley Sheridan, she was also a novelist and dramatist in her own right. In 1761 she published *The Memoirs of Miss Sidney Bidulph*, which is modeled on Samuel Richardson's *Pamela*. (Richardson was Sheridan's ardent supporter.) The following year her play *The Discovery* was staged in London with her husband, Thomas Sheridan, in the cast. (Aldous Huxley created an updated version of *Discovery* in 1924.) Sheridan also wrote a sequel to *Sidney Bidulph* called *Continuation of the Memoirs* (1767) and a highly praised novel, *The History of Nourjahad* (1767), set in the Orient. Frances Sheridan died September 26, 1766, in Blois, France, where she and her family had moved to escape creditors.

RICHARD BRINSLEY SHERIDAN was born November 4, 1751, in Dublin. Member of a well-known theatre family, he was raised in England and educated at Whyte's School and Harrow. He eloped to France with the singer Eliza Linley, over whom he fought two duels; the couple married in 1773. He wrote his first play, *The Rivals*, in a matter of weeks and quickly followed it with *St. Patrick's Day* and *The Duenna*—all produced in 1775. In 1776 he became manager of the Drury Lane Theatre, where his mother's plays had been staged and his father had acted. The next year *The School for Scandal* was produced and became a hit; *The Critic*, Sheridan's last original play, was staged in 1779. He then turned to politics, serving in Parliament from 1780 to 1811 and seemed destined for a Cabinet post. But he had earned a reputation as a hard drinker and a poor manager, compiling astonishing personal debt that eventually led to his arrest in 1813. He died penniless on July 7, 1816, in London, though his well-connected friends provided him with an elaborate funeral. He is buried in Poets' Corner at Westminster Abbey.

SOMERVILLE AND ROSS (Edith Somerville and Violet Martin) were born, respectively, May 2, 1858, in Corfu, Greece, and June 11, 1862, in County Galway. These second cousins enjoyed a literary partnership that endured for nearly 30 years, producing fiction that has been compared to the novels of Jane Austen, E. M. Forster, and George Sand. Their first book, *An Irish Cousin* (1889), was well received, but *The Real Charlotte* (1894) is considered their finest work. They are also remembered for their popular story collection *Some Experiences of an Irish R.M.* (1899) and its numerous sequels. Martin died December 21, 1915, in Cork, but Somerville continued to publish under their joint pen name, claiming that they still communicated. Somerville died October 8, 1949, in Castlehaven, County Cork.

EDMUND SPENSER was born c. 1552 in London. Recognized as one of England's foremost poets, he is included here because of his close association with Ireland, where he lived, worked, and wrote for years. Spenser was educated at Pembroke Hall, Cambridge, where he first met Sir Walter Raleigh. In 1579 he published his first major work, *The Shepheardes Calender*, which has also been called the first work of the English literary Renaissance. In 1580 Spenser became secretary to Lord Grey of Wilton, lord deputy of Ireland, and around this time probably began writing his epic poem, *The Faerie Queene*. In 1589 he traveled to London under Raleigh's sponsorship to see the first three books of the poem published. He also was given an audience with the Queen and eventually received a lifetime stipend from her. He returned in 1591 to Kilcolman, his Irish castle, and recorded his journey abroad in *Colin Clouts Come Home Againe* (1591). When Kilcolman burned in the Irish uprising of 1598, Spenser traveled back to London in despair and died there on January 13, 1599.

JONATHAN SWIFT was born November 30, 1667, in Dublin. He was educated at Trinity College, Dublin, where he was punished for lack of discipline but still graduated. In 1689 he moved to England, where he served as secretary to Sir William Temple at Moor Park, Surrey. It was there that he met and tutored young Esther Johnson, later immortalized as Stella in his famous *Journal to Stella* (1710-13). (The two were apparently intimate and may have been married.) In 1694 Swift returned to Ireland and was ordained as an Anglican priest; shuttling back and forth between his two homes, he became active in politics, first as a Whig, then as a Tory, eventually editing the Tory journal *The Examiner*. *Gulliver's Travels*, Swift's greatest satire (and the only piece of writing he ever received payment for), appeared in 1726. He was lionized in Ireland for his *Drapier Letters* (1724) and the satire *A Modest Proposal* (1729). Afflicted for much of his life with what some believe was Ménière's disease (a brain illness), he died October 19, 1745, in Dublin.

JOHN MILLINGTON SYNGE was born April 16, 1871, in Rathfarnham, near Dublin. Educated at Trinity College, Dublin, he has been called the preeminent playwright of the Irish Literary Renaissance. While studying music in Paris, Synge met W. B. Yeats, who encouraged him to visit Ireland's Aran Islands and be inspired by the poetic language of the peasant inhabitants. Synge spent each summer from 1898 to 1902 on the islands and drew on his experiences to write *The Aran Islands* (1907) and his early plays *In the Shadow of the Glen* (1903) and *Riders to the Sea* (1904). He became a director of the Abbey Theatre in 1906, where *The Playboy of the Western World* was first performed in 1907; though audiences of the day resented its portrayal of Irish foibles, *Playboy* is now considered Synge's best work. His career was cut short by Hodgkin's disease on March 24, 1909, in Dublin. Synge's last play, *Deirdre of the Sorrows*, was performed posthumously in 1910.

WILLIAM TREVOR (pseudonym of William Trevor Cox) was born May 24, 1928, in Mitchelstown, County Cork. Though he first set out to become a sculptor, Trevor switched to writing as a more direct form of expression. A winner of two Whitbread prizes, he found success with his second book, *The Old Boys* (1964), and has since published more than 15 novels, including *The Children of Dynmouth* (1976), *Fools of Fortune* (1983), *The Silence in the Garden* (1988), *Two Lives* (1991; Booker Prize shortlist), *Felicia's Journey* (1994), and *After Rain* (1998). Trevor is perhaps best known, however, for his short stories, which have appeared in *The New Yorker* and in collections such as *The Day We Got Drunk on Cake* (1967), *Lovers of Their Time* (1978), and *Beyond the Pale* (1981). His *Collected Stories* was published to great acclaim in 1992. Trevor lives in Devon, England.

LADY WILDE (Jane Francesca Elgee) was born c. 1824 in Wexford. Using the pseudonym "Speranza," she regularly contributed Nationalist verse to *The Nation*. After marrying William Wilde in 1851, she played host to an almost endless stream of writers and artists, among them George Bernard Shaw and W. B. Yeats. And after her husband's death, in 1876, she moved to London and established a more bohemian salon. Though she is most often remembered as the mother of her famous second son, Oscar, Lady Wilde authored many works of her own, including poetry, translations, essays, and accomplished renderings of Irish folklore. Her books include *Ancient Legends, Mystic Charms and Superstitions of Ireland* (1887), *Ancient Cures, Charms and Usages of Ireland* (1890), and *Notes of Men, Women, and Books* (1891). She died February 3, 1896, in London.

OSCAR WILDE was born October 16, 1854, in Dublin. Educated at Trinity College, Dublin, and Magdalen College, Oxford, he married Constance Lloyd, a barrister's daughter, in 1884 and had two children by her. As a lecturer and critic, Wilde advocated "art for art's sake"; his dandified dress and manner were both celebrated and belittled in his day. His only novel, *The Picture of Dorian Gray*, appeared in 1891, but his greatest successes were his comic plays about Victorian society: *Lady Windermere's Fan* (1892), *A Woman of*

No Importance (1893), *An Ideal Husband* (1895), and *The Importance of Being Earnest* (1895). In 1895 Wilde was sentenced to hard labor for having a homosexual relationship with Lord Alfred Douglas, son of the Marquess of Queensberry. After his release in 1897, bankrupt and in ill health, Wilde changed his name to Sebastian Melmoth and moved to France, where he wrote *The Ballad of Reading Gaol* (1898). He died November 30, 1900, in Paris. A letter Wilde wrote to Lord Alfred from prison was published as *De Profundis* in 1905.

WILLIAM WILDE was born in the village of Kilkeevin, near Castlerea, in 1815. Husband of Lady Wilde and father to Oscar, he was a respected eye and ear surgeon as well as an antiquary, archaeologist, and occultist. His most popular works were nature and travel guides, among them *The Beauties of the Boyne and Blackwater* (1849) and *Lough Corrib* (1867). He also wrote medical texts and a collection of folklore, *Irish Popular Superstitions* (1852). In a high-profile 1864 case, Wilde was arrested on suspicion of administering chloroform to a patient and then seducing her. He had five children altogether, three of them illegitimate. Wilde died in 1876.

NIALL WILLIAMS was born in Dublin in 1958. He studied French and English at University College, Dublin, then moved to America. In 1985 he abandoned a promising Manhattan publishing career for life in a small West Clare cottage. In 1997 he published his first novel, *Four Letters of Love*, to high acclaim. He has also collaborated with his wife, Christine Breen, on four books, including *O Come Ye Back to Ireland: Our First Year in County Clare* (1989) and *The Luck of the Irish: Our Life in County Clare* (1995). His second novel, *As It Is in Heaven*, is scheduled for 1999 publication.

WILLIAM BUTLER YEATS was born June 13, 1865, at Sandymount, Dublin. The son of painter John Butler Yeats, William studied at the Metropolitan School of Art in Dublin for three years but gave up painting for literature at age 21. Mystical religion and the Irish land and people are central themes in his work, and he is generally regarded as the foremost writer of the Irish Literary Renaissance. He helped found the Irish Literary Theatre (later the Abbey) and wrote the first play it staged, *The Countess Cathleen* (1899). His first book of poems, *The Wanderings of Oisin and Other Poems*, was published in 1889—the same year Yeats met Maud Gonne, the Irish patriot who became the great unrequited love of his life and a recurring figure in his writings. His greatest works are his mature poems, in volumes such as *The Green Helmet and Other Poems* (1910), *The Tower* (1928), and *The Winding Stair* (1929). He received the Nobel Prize in literature in 1923 and served as a senator of the Irish Free State from 1922 to 1928. Yeats died January 28, 1939, in Roquebrune-Cap-Martin, France.

ACKNOWLEDGMENTS

"The Man Who Invented Sin" by Sean O'Faolain. Copyright © 1983 by Sean O'Faolain. First appeared in *The Collected Stories of Sean O'Faolain* published by Atlantic-Little, Brown Books. Reprinted by permission of Curtis Brown, Ltd.

"A Pot of Soothing Herbs" from *We Might See Sights!* by Julia O'Faolain. Copyright © 1968 by Julia O'Faolain. Reproduced by permission of the Author c/o Rogers, Coleridge & White, 20 Powis Mews, London W11 1JN, UK.

Excerpt from *The Fire in the Dust* by Francis MacManus. Copyright 1951 by Francis MacManus. Reprinted by permission of Harcourt Brace & Company.

"Dante . . . Bruno . Vico . . Joyce" from *Disjecta* by Samuel Beckett. Copyright © 1928 by Samuel Beckett. Used by permission of Grove/Atlantic, Inc.

"Dante and the Lobster" from *More Pricks Than Kicks* by Samuel Beckett. Copyright © 1934 by Samuel Beckett. Used by permission of Grove/Atlantic, Inc.

Excerpt from *Waiting for Godot* by Samuel Beckett. Copyright © 1954 by Samuel Beckett. Used by permission of Grove/Atlantic, Inc.

"James Joyce's World & Letters of James Joyce" from *Literary Criticism of Louis MacNeice*, edited by Alan Heuser. Copyright © 1987 by The Estate of Louis MacNeice. Reprinted by permission of Oxford University Press.

Excerpt from *Borstal Boy* by Brendan Behan. Copyright © 1958, 1959 by Brendan Behan. Reprinted by permission of Alfred A. Knopf, Inc.

"The Yellow Beret" by Mary Lavin. Reprinted with the permission of Simon & Schuster from *The Great Waves and Other Stories* by Mary Lavin. Copyright © 1961 by Mary Lavin. Originally appeared in *The New Yorker*.

"The Dogs in the Great Glen" from *The State of Ireland* by Benedict Kiely. Reprinted by permission of David R. Godine, Publisher, Inc. Copyright © 1980 by Benedict Kiely.

Excerpt from "The Country Girls" from *The Country Girls Trilogy* by Edna O'Brien. Copyright © 1986 by Edna O'Brien. Reprinted by permission of Farrar, Straus & Giroux, Inc.

Excerpt from *An Answer from Limbo* by Brian Moore. Copyright © 1962 by Brian Moore. Reprinted by permission of the Estate of Brian Moore and Curtis Brown, Ltd.

"Lines Written on a Seat on the Grand Canal, Dublin," "To Hell with Commonsense," and "In Memory of My Mother" from *Collected Poems* by Patrick Kavanagh. Copyright © 1964 by Patrick Kavanagh. Reprinted by permission of Devin-Adair Publishers, Inc.

"The Pill," "The Subjection of Women," and "A Sermon on Swift" from *Selected Poems* by Austin Clarke. Copyright © 1991 by Dardis Clarke.

ACKNOWLEDGMENTS